CONTENTS

Legal and management

CONTENTS

Health and safety law

Supporting INFORMATION

GT700 Toolbox talks / supporting checklists and forms

Toolbox talks on some of these topics are available in the GT700 publication. Supporting checklists and forms covering some of these topics are available on our companion website.

HEALTH AND SAFETY LAW

Overview

The purpose of health and safety legislation is to protect the wellbeing of those at work and others, such as the general public, by ensuring work is carried out in a manner that is safe and free of risks to health for everyone who may be affected.

There are a number of different legislative requirements that must be followed to ensure this is achieved. This chapter outlines the main Act and regulations that apply.

1.1   Introduction

There has always been a risk of accidents or ill health associated with work activities. Society no longer accepts this as being part of the job. In recent years, the number of accidents and incidences of work-related ill health has dramatically reduced but accidents still happen and people's health continues to be damaged. The construction industry has a disproportionately high rate of both occurrences compared to other industries.

Everyone who goes to work has a right to return home uninjured and in a good state of health. Similarly, visitors to sites and members of the public have the same right to the protection of their health and safety.

Health and safety legislation sets out to protect people's right not to suffer injury or have their health damaged. It is a criminal offence to breach health and safety legislation. Punishments are related to the potential severity of the breach – a person does not need to be killed or injured for severe penalties to be imposed.

Minor breaches may result in the enforcing authority initiating corrective actions on the wrongdoer, either by offering advice or issuing an improvement or prohibition notice. For more serious offences, the punishment available to the courts includes unlimited fines and/or imprisonment.

Whilst health and safety legislation is embedded in criminal law, in some circumstances legislation gives a person who has been injured or made ill through work the right to take legal action against the employer for compensation, through the civil courts.

 You can insure against civil liabilities but you cannot insure against criminal liabilities.

1.2   Important points

● The primary focus of health and safety legislation is to put legal duties on employers (and the self-employed, who in many cases have the same legal duties as employers) to ensure that work is carried out safely and without risks to health.

● It should be noted that some legislation places legal duties upon employees (for example, to take reasonable care of their own health and safety and the safety of others who may be affected by their acts or omissions).

● In specific situations legal duties are also placed upon *duty holders* (for example, clients, designers and contractors), as defined in the relevant legislation.

● In many situations site-based staff (such as supervisors, site managers or project managers) will be nominated by the employer to ensure that the employer's legal duties are complied with at site level.

● The overall legal duties lie with the employer, who must be confident in the ability and competence of their supervisors, managers and others who manage health and safety on their behalf.

The actions that must be taken to fulfil these duties are explained in the appropriate chapters of this book.

1.3   History of health and safety law

Since the introduction of the Health and Safety at Work etc. Act 1974 (HSWA), Britain has achieved one of the best health and safety records in the world. In 1974, there were 651 fatalities to employees.

Figures for 2021–22 show that across all industries there were 123 workers killed in work-related accidents, and 80 members of the public killed due to work-related accidents (excluding deaths to patients and service users in the healthcare and adult social care sectors in England). There were 30 fatal injuries to workers in the construction sector, and five fatalities to members of the public involving construction work.

(Sources: Construction statistics in Great Britain, 2022 and Work-related fatal injuries in Great Britain, published by the Health and Safety Executive (HSE) in November 2022.)

The graph below shows the number of fatal injuries per 100,000 workers.

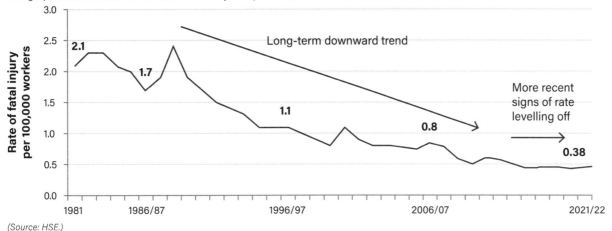

(Source: HSE.)

These figures are still too high and the industry remains a high risk for injuries, but the significant improvements are evident. Over the long-term, the rate of fatal injury to workers showed a downward trend, though in the recent years prior to the Covid-19 pandemic, the rate had been broadly flat. The current rate is broadly in line with pre-Covid levels.

Before the introduction of the 1974 Act there were a number of different regulations or, in some areas, there were no regulations at all. HSWA became an enabling Act and since its introduction it has allowed for a number of regulations to be implemented and subsequently revised and/or revoked where necessary. Nearly 50 years on, HSWA has demonstrated it can be applied to new responsibilities and demands, creating the framework for people to come home safe and well from a day's work in any sector of the economy. *(For further information on HSWA refer to 1.6.)*

For over 200 years, the UK has had a continually evolving legal framework in place for the protection of workers' safety and health. A brief overview of key legislation is listed below.

● The first Act of Parliament directly concerned with safety was the Factories Act, passed in 1802, which dealt with the morals of apprentices.

● From 1812 onwards, a succession of Acts regulated working conditions in factories, with particular reference to women and children.

● In 1833, the first four factory inspectors were appointed. Children aged nine were being sent up chimneys as chimney sweeps, where they could work a 48-hour week. They were supposed to spend two hours a day at school. People as young as 13 sometimes worked a 69-hour week.

● The first two female factory inspectors were appointed in 1893 and the first medical inspector in 1898.

● In 1901, a comprehensive Factories and Workshops Act was passed. It lasted until the Factories Act of 1937 replaced it. This, in turn, was repealed by the Factories Act of 1961.

● HSWA, the basis for modern legislation, came into force in 1974, bringing with it protection for virtually everyone at work and consolidating much of the earlier industry-specific legislation under a single Act.

● In 1994, the Construction (Design and Management) Regulations (CDM) were drafted to address the continuing unacceptably high rate of accidents and ill health befalling construction workers.

● In 2005, the Work at Height Regulations were introduced to address the continuing, unacceptably high rate of death and injury caused by falls from height. The regulations require employers and those in control of any work at height to ensure that work is properly planned, supervised and carried out by competent workers.

● The CDM Regulations were revised in 2007. As the cornerstone legislation for the construction industry, they reinforced the requirements for competence, co-operation and co-ordination, with a focus on 'the right information, to the right people, at the right time'.

● The coming into force of the Corporate Manslaughter and Corporate Homicide Act (2007) and the Health and Safety (Offences) Act (2008) demonstrated a hardening of Government's attitude towards serious breaches of health and safety legislation.

● The Löfstedt report *Reclaiming health and safety for all: an independent review of health and safety legislation* was published in 2011 as part of the Government's plan to overhaul the health and safety system in Britain. The report considers how legislation can be combined and simplified, aiming to reduce the burden on British businesses, which has resulted in a review of current legislation, including CDM.

● In 2012, the Control of Asbestos Regulations came into force. This updated the earlier asbestos regulations and made changes around some types of non-licensed work with asbestos, including medical surveillance, record keeping and notification of work.

● The Health and Safety (Fees) Regulations (introduced in 2012) administer the HSE cost recovery scheme. The HSE recoups its costs against those who contravene health and safety laws.

HEALTH AND SAFETY LAW

- In 2015, the CDM Regulations were amended to implement the requirements of Directive 92/57/EEC, which lays down minimum safety and health requirements for temporary or mobile construction sites. This covers any construction site at which building or civil engineering works are carried out and intends to prevent risks by establishing a chain of responsibility linking all the parties involved. The main changes were to make the regulations easier to understand, replace the CDM co-ordinator role with a principal designer, replace the detailed and prescriptive requirements for individual and corporate competence with a more generic requirement, and align notification requirements with the Directive and apply the regulations to domestic clients in a proportionate way.

- In March 2015, the Legal Aid, Sentencing and Punishment of Offenders Act was amended. Magistrates' Courts were previously limited to fines of a maximum of £20,000 under Sections 2 to 6 of HSWA but this has now been amended to allow Magistrates' Courts to issue unlimited fines.

- In November 2018, new sentencing guidelines for health and safety, corporate manslaughter and food safety and hygiene offences came into force. These provide judges with a starting point for fines for companies that commit health and safety offences.

- In April 2022, the Personal Protective Equipment at Work (Amendment) Regulations 2022 came into force. They amend the 1992 regulations, and extend employers' and employees' duties regarding personal protective equipment to limb (b) workers.

- In June 2022, the Building Safety Act 2022 was introduced after the Grenfell Tower fire in 2017, and contains provisions intended to secure the safety of people in or about buildings, and to improve building standards. The new, stricter regulatory regime will govern the design, construction and maintenance of the built environment. Central to this is the creation of a national Building Safety Regulator (BSR), sitting within the HSE, which will become operational over the next few years. The BSR will have three main functions:

1. overseeing the safety and standards of all buildings

2. helping and encouraging the built environment industry and building control professionals to improve their competence

3. leading implementation of the new regulatory framework for high-rise buildings.

1.4   Summary of health and safety law

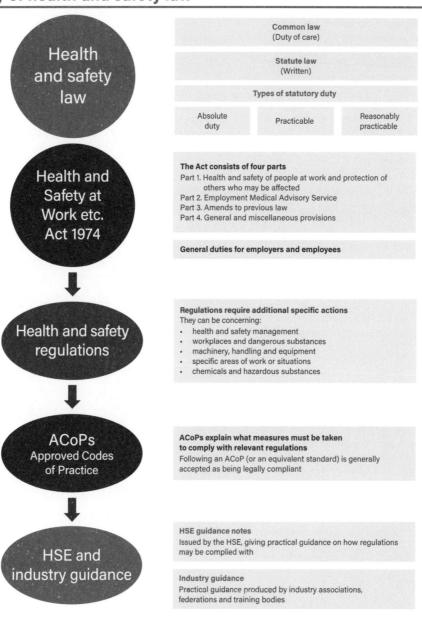

Health and safety law

Common law (Duty of care)		
Statute law (Written)		
Types of statutory duty		
Absolute duty	Practicable	Reasonably practicable

Health and Safety at Work etc. Act 1974

The Act consists of four parts
Part 1. Health and safety of people at work and protection of others who may be affected
Part 2. Employment Medical Advisory Service
Part 3. Amends to previous law
Part 4. General and miscellaneous provisions

General duties for employers and employees

Health and safety regulations

Regulations require additional specific actions
They can be concerning:
- health and safety management
- workplaces and dangerous substances
- machinery, handling and equipment
- specific areas of work or situations
- chemicals and hazardous substances

ACoPs Approved Codes of Practice

ACoPs explain what measures must be taken to comply with relevant regulations
Following an ACoP (or an equivalent standard) is generally accepted as being legally compliant

HSE and industry guidance

HSE guidance notes
Issued by the HSE, giving practical guidance on how regulations may be complied with

Industry guidance
Practical guidance produced by industry associations, federations and training bodies

1.5 Contract, common and statute law

All employers, principal contractors, contractors and the self-employed, as well as employees, can have responsibilities in three distinct areas of law.

1.5.1 Contract law

● Requires agreement by two parties.

● Both parties must intend to form a legally binding agreement and must have the authority to enter into the contract.

● Under the Contracts (Right of Third Parties) Act the contract can include or exclude the rights of a third person.

1.5.2 Common law

● Evolved over centuries with judicial judgements creating legally binding precedents.

● Decisions made in higher courts are binding on all lower courts.

● Where parties disagree on the law, a common law court looks to past precedential decisions of relevant courts. If a similar dispute has been resolved in the past, the court is bound to follow the reasoning used in the prior decision.

● If the current dispute is fundamentally distinct from all previous cases judges have the authority and duty to make law by creating a new precedent.

● An individual has the right to protection from harm and the right to sue for compensation when they suffer loss, ill health or injury through the negligence of another.

1.5.3 Statute law

● Acts of Parliament, regulations and EU Directives.

● Laws made by the government.

● HSWA is an enabling Act, which permits the Secretary of State or other ministers to replace legislation with regulations requiring a higher standard of health and safety.

● Regulations are referred to as statutory instruments that are made under the enabling Act.

● If there is a conflict between common law and statute law, statute law takes precedence.

1.6 Health and Safety at Work etc. Act 1974

HSWA is the primary piece of health and safety legislation in the United Kingdom. The Act is termed as an enabling Act, which allows the Government to make health and safety regulations that become part of the law. The requirements of the Act are general and wide-ranging, such as:

 It shall be the duty of every employer to ensure, so far as is reasonably practicable, the health, safety and welfare at work of all their employees.

This typical requirement does not specify any technical requirements or set any minimum standards of behaviour that can be measured, but it does clearly outline the requirement for safe places of work.

Health and safety regulations expand upon the legal requirements of the Act with regard to specific occupational work and include specific and technical requirements. Health and safety regulations are often supported by guidance notes or Approved Codes of Practice (ACoPs), which explain in plain language how compliance with the law can be achieved.

 For further information on HSWA refer to Chapter A02 The Health and Safety at Work etc. Act.

The legal duties of employers and employees, as specified in HSWA, are shown below.

1.6.1 Employers' responsibilities

Under HSWA, an employer must, so far as is reasonably practicable:

● protect the health, safety and welfare at work of all their employees

● provide and maintain plant and systems of work that are safe and without risk to health

● have arrangements for ensuring safety and absence of risk to health in connection with the use, handling, storage and transport of articles and substances

● provide such information, instruction, training and supervision as is necessary to ensure the health and safety at work of employees

- maintain any place of work under their control in a condition that is safe and without risks to health, and with access to and egress from it that are safe and without such risks

- provide and maintain a working environment that is safe, without risks to health and adequate as regards facilities and arrangements for the welfare of employees.

1.6.2   Employees' duties

Employees also have the following duties under health and safety law.

- Take reasonable care for the health and safety of themselves or others who may be affected by their acts or omissions.

- Co-operate with their employer in all matters relating to health and safety.

- Not intentionally or recklessly interfere with or misuse anything provided in the interests of health, safety and welfare.

- Use anything provided by the employer in accordance with instructions.

- Report anything that is thought to be dangerous.

The requirement, on the employer, to do what is reasonably practicable to ensure the health, safety and welfare of employees at work is balanced by a requirement, on the employees, to comply with any necessary rules or instructions and to take reasonable care of themselves and others.

1.7   Health and safety regulations

Many sets of regulations have been developed and introduced as a means of incorporating European Union legislation into the UK domestic legal framework. There are many sets of health and safety regulations in existence that are relevant to the work carried out by the construction industry. Some sets of regulations apply to construction work only.

The UK's departure from the European Union has no impact on the Health and Safety at Work etc. Act 1974. Equally, UK regulations that were implemented to align with EU Directives, both generally and in relation to the construction industry exclusively, still apply, as they have been transposed almost entirely into UK law. Nevertheless, changes to legislation do occur from time to time, and CITB strongly urges you to remain alert to possible future changes.

Health and safety regulations are a part of UK law that place duties on employers and employees. It is a criminal offence to contravene them. Legislation that affects the building and construction industry includes the following examples.

1.7.1   Construction (Design and Management) Regulations

The main aim of the Construction (Design and Management) Regulations 2015 (CDM) is to ensure that health and safety risks are considered and addressed, from concept through to completion of the project. The guidance identifies the main elements to securing construction health and safety, as shown below.

- **Appointing** the right people and organisations at the right time.

- Applying the **general principles of prevention**.

- Ensuring that everyone has the **information, instruction, training and supervision** necessary to enable them to carry out their jobs in a way that secures health and safety.

- Duty holders **co-operating and communicating** with each other and **co-ordinating** their work.

- **Consulting workers and engaging** with them to promote and develop effective measures to secure health, safety and welfare.

1.7.2   Control of Asbestos Regulations

These regulations state the minimum standards for protecting workers and the general population from risks associated with exposure to asbestos, and require the identification of asbestos and asbestos-containing materials (ACMs) before any work is carried out.

1.7.3   Electricity at Work Regulations

The necessary level of competency must be established, and all necessary information, instruction, training and supervision must be given. Formal written safe systems of work should be employed including, where necessary, the use of a 'permit to work' procedure.

1.7.4   Health and Safety (Display Screen Equipment) Regulations

These regulations aim to protect the health of people who work with display screen equipment (DSE), including PCs, laptops and notepads. These regulations were introduced because DSE has become one of the most common forms of work equipment.

Incorrect use of DSE can result in upper limb disorders and other conditions, such as repetitive strain injury (RSI).

The following legal duties are placed on employers but do not apply to workers who use DSE equipment infrequently or for short periods.

- Analyse the workstation to assess or reduce risk.
- Make sure controls are in place.
- Provide information and training.
- Provide eyesight tests, on request.
- Review the DSE assessment when the user or DSE changes.

1.7.5   Management of Health and Safety at Work Regulations

These regulations make employers' duties more explicit and explain what they need to do to manage health and safety. The main requirement is for employers to carry out a suitable and sufficient risk assessment. (The duty to risk assess includes the duty to identify specific risks to young people and new and expectant mothers.) Employers with five or more employees must record significant findings of the risk assessment.

1.7.6   Provision and Use of Work Equipment Regulations

This details the specific duties on organisations that own, operate or have control over work equipment. These regulations require that all information, instruction, training and supervision must include:

- conditions and methods in which the equipment will be used
- any foreseeable abnormal conditions and appropriate action
- any conclusions drawn from experience when using equipment
- safe working methods
- possible risks and precautions to be taken.

It is important that equipment is used for the purposes for which it was designed, ensuring that consideration is given to the working conditions and the health and safety of the person(s) where the equipment is to be used and that all equipment is maintained and inspected as appropriate.

Employers must always consider:

- the nature and condition of the equipment
- the place where it is to be used
- the purpose for which it is to be used
- its suitability for the workplace and the task to be completed.

1.7.7   Reporting of Injuries, Diseases and Dangerous Occurrences Regulations (RIDDOR)

A legal duty is placed on employers, the self-employed and those in control of premises to report:

- work-related deaths or specified injuries
- injuries resulting in an employee being unable to perform their normal work duties for more than seven days
- reportable diseases
- dangerous occurrences.

1.7.8   Work at Height Regulations

Duty holders are required to ensure the following:

- All work at height is properly planned and organised.
- All work at height takes account of weather conditions that could endanger health and safety.
- Those involved in work at height are trained and competent.
- The place where work at height is carried out is safe.
- All equipment used for work at height is appropriately inspected.
- The risks from fragile surfaces are properly controlled, as are the risks from falling objects.

1.7.9   Working Time Regulations

These regulations implement the European Working Time Directive and govern the hours most workers can work. The following are specified in the regulations.

- Set limits on the average working week – up to 48 hours per week over a 17-week period.
- Statutory entitlement to paid leave for most workers.
- Limit the normal hours of night work to an average of eight hours in any 24-hour period, and an entitlement for night workers to receive regular health assessments.
- Limit the working time of young people to not exceed eight hours per day, or 40 hours per week.
- Allow a daily rest period of 11 hours between each working day, and a weekly rest period of not less than 24 hours in each seven day period, but this may be averaged over two weeks.
- Entitle an adult worker to a rest break of not less than 20 minutes, within a daily working time of more than six hours.
- Entitle a young person to a rest break of at least 30 minutes, when they are working more than four and a half hours.

1.7.10 Lifting Operations and Lifting Equipment Regulations

These regulations place duties on people and companies who own, operate or have control over lifting equipment, and are required to ensure that:

- All lifting operations involving lifting equipment are properly planned by a competent person, appropriately supervised and carried out in a safe manner.

- All equipment used for lifting is fit for purpose, appropriate for the task, suitably marked and in many cases subject to statutory periodic 'thorough examination'.

- Records are retained of all thorough examinations, and that any defects are reported to both the person responsible for the equipment and the relevant enforcing authority.

1.7.11 Control of Substances Hazardous to Health Regulations

Employers must control substances that are hazardous to health by identifying what the health hazards are; deciding how to prevent harm to health; providing control measures to reduce harm to health and ensure that they are followed; keeping all control measures in good working order; providing information, instruction and training for employees and others; providing monitoring and health surveillance in appropriate cases; and planning for emergencies.

1.8 Approved Codes of Practice

HSWA makes provision for the production of Approved Codes of Practice (often referred to as ACoPs), where appropriate, in support of some health and safety regulations. ACoPs are prepared and issued by the HSE.

Although they are not strictly a part of the law, ACoPs have special legal status in that failure to comply with the guidance contained in an ACoP may be cited in court as a failure to comply with the law and may form part of the evidence in a health and safety prosecution. ACoPs give practical advice on how to comply with the law in respect of those specific matters on which the Code gives advice.

Where an employer is accused of failing to comply with the requirements of an ACoP it is a valid defence for the employer if it can be shown that alternative measures, which were equally or more effective, were implemented. ACoPs are issued after wide public consultation with stakeholders, the involvement of other Government bodies and with the consent of the Secretary of State.

1.9 Guidance notes

These are issued by the HSE, and give practical advice on how regulations may be complied with. While they are not legally enforceable, they do provide practical guidance on how employers and employees may comply with health and safety legislation.

1.10 Standards of compliance

Within health and safety legislation specific words or phrases are used to qualify or describe the standard of compliance that must be achieved with regard to some legal (statutory) duties, such as the words 'absolute', 'practicable' (or 'best practicable means') or 'reasonably practicable'. The meanings of these types of statutory duty are explained below.

1.10.1 It shall be the duty of an employer to...

This means that the employer **must** comply with the legal duty being described, regardless of time, effort and cost. The word 'shall' (if not qualified by the phrase 'so far as reasonably practicable' or the word 'practicable') leaves no scope for not complying with the duty.

Duties referred to using the terms 'shall', 'must', 'will' (or 'shall not', 'must not', 'will not') are referred to as **absolute** duties, in that there is no choice but to comply. Non-compliance is a breach of the duty and, as such, is an offence.

1.10.2 It shall be the duty of an employer to... so far as is practicable

'Practicable' means that there is no scope for taking cost and convenience into account; the duty must be complied with if it is possible to carry it out within the current state of knowledge and technology (if it is technically possible, then the duty must be complied with).

> **e.g. Practicable**
>
> It was necessary for a worker to use a disc cutter to cut paving slabs to the required size.
>
> The legal duty requires that the rotating blade of the machine be guarded to the extent that it is practicable to do so. This acknowledges that total guarding of the blade is not possible because the machine could not then be used for the job for which it was designed.
>
> The law requires that the guard be adjusted to expose enough blade to enable the job to be carried out safely whilst providing the maximum degree of protection for the operator. Not to use a guard at all is not an option, even if it causes cost or inconvenience.

1.10.3   It shall be the duty of an employer to... so far as is reasonably practicable

Where a requirement to carry out a specific legal duty is qualified by the phrase 'so far as is reasonably practicable', employers are allowed to exercise their judgement on the extent of the measures that need to be taken to ensure the health and safety of the person(s) carrying out the job and anyone else who may be affected by it.

Deciding what are reasonably practicable measures to take should be based upon the findings of a risk assessment.

 Reasonably practicable **means that the risks involved in carrying out the work may be balanced against the cost in terms of money, inconvenience and time.**

Where the risks to health and safety in carrying out a job are found to be low in comparison to what would be disproportionately high costs to totally overcome the risks, the employer need only take the measures that are considered to be reasonably practicable.

 Reasonably practicable

It was necessary to provide access to working platforms of a scaffold at four different levels for a 12-week period, the higher level being a narrow lift between two structures. A decision had to be made on the best means of access.

Legislation on working at height requires 'every employer to ensure that work at height is carried out in a manner which is, so far as reasonably practicable, safe'.

In planning the job, the risk assessment showed the following.

- It would be necessary for tools and materials for various trades to be carried up to and down from the main working platform but not from the higher level lift. The ground was firm and level and there was plenty of space at the bottom of the scaffold.

- If a ladder was used, it could be securely tied to the scaffold and suitable handholds could be provided at the stepping-off point. The tools and materials could be hoisted up using a small electric hoist fixed to the scaffold.

- Various trades could be working together on the working platforms and at the same time a means of access only was required to the higher level lift, not for a place of work on the higher level lift. There were no weather considerations that would make the use of a ladder unduly unsafe.

Given the circumstances, it was decided that a ladder was not a reasonably practicable measure to prevent a fall with regard to access to the main working platforms where tools and materials were required and, therefore, a stair tower was used.

The stair tower also offered quicker, safer and easier access. For access to the higher level lift, a ladder was considered to be suitable, complete with a ladder safety gate.

1.10.4   Burden of proof

Many of the duties on employers are qualified with the phrases 'so far as is practicable' or 'so far as is reasonably practicable'.

Generally, in a court of law a defendant is innocent until proven guilty. However, with regard to these phrases, the burden of proof is reversed and so the defendant must prove that it was not reasonably practicable, or practicable, as the case may be, to do more than was done to mitigate the risks.

In effect, the defendant is guilty until they prove their innocence.

1.11   Consultation

HSWA made provisions for the appointment of a safety representative from a recognised trade union. As a result, the **Safety Representatives and Safety Committees Regulations** were introduced. These regulations apply on sites where an employee is a member of a recognised trade union.

Regulation 14 of CDM requires the principal contractor to consult and engage with workers. Their duties include making arrangements to ensure workers co-operate, consulting with workers or representatives in good time on matters relating to health and safety and ensuring workers or their representatives can inspect or take copies of any information that may affect health, safety and welfare on site.

 For examples of how the principal contractor could consult with workers refer to the CDM industry guidance for workers.

The aim of all applicable regulations is to promote effective two-way dialogue between employers and employees, or their representatives.

On sites where there is no recognised trade union member representation, the **Health and Safety (Consultation with Employees) Regulations** will apply. These regulations were introduced as HSWA only covers union-appointed safety representatives. These regulations give all employees, whether union members or not, the right to have consultation with their employers and to be provided with information. There are many similarities with the Safety Representatives and Safety Committee Regulations.

HEALTH AND SAFETY LAW

The following areas are covered by the regulations.

- Duty of the employer to consult.
- Persons to be consulted.
- Provision of information.
- Functions of the representative of employee safety.
- Training, time off and the provision of facilities.

1.11.1 Duty of the employer to consult

It is the duty of the employer to consult with their employees in good time on the following types of health and safety measures.

- The introduction of any measures that will affect the health and safety of employees.
- The arrangements for appointing or nominating the person(s) to assist the employer in complying with health and safety legislation.
- The provision of relevant information as required under health and safety legislation.
- Any planning or organisation of training required by relevant health and safety legislation.
- The health and safety implications of the introduction of new technologies into the employer's workplace.

1.11.2 Persons to be consulted

Employers may consult directly with all their employees or through representatives of employee safety, elected by a group of employees to represent them in health and safety consultation with their employer.

The employer must provide employees with a list of names of representatives of employee safety and the group they are representing in the workplace. The employer must inform employees of any changes in the form of consultation, such as a move from dealing with representatives to directly consulting with each employee. The employee representatives must also inform the employer when they no longer represent a group or groups of employees.

1.11.3 Provision of information

The employer must provide any information that the employees may require in order for them to participate fully in the consultation procedure. This will either be directly with all employees or with the elected representatives of employee safety.

The following are issues that the employer must consult on.

- Introduction of measures at the workplace that may substantially affect the health and safety of employees.
- Arrangements for obtaining or appointing the competent person to assist the employer to interpret and comply with health and safety requirements.
- Information on risks to employees' health and safety and the measures taken to remove or minimise them.

1.11.4 Functions of the representatives of employee safety

The functions of the representatives of employee safety are similar to those of the trade union safety representative appointed under the Safety Representatives and Safety Committee Regulations. They may make representations on hazards, risks, dangerous occurrences, ill health and general health and safety matters.

1.11.5 Training, time off and provision of facilities

The employer must provide the employee representative with appropriate and reasonable training time and reasonable facilities to enable them to perform their functions. This includes the employer meeting reasonable costs associated with training and time off to perform the function. The employee is protected from unfair dismissal when participating in consultation with employers on matters.

1.12 Occupiers' Liability Act

Legal duties are placed on the occupiers of premises to ensure the health and safety of anyone entering those premises, whether authorised to be there or not.

- The Occupiers' Liability Act covers civil law duties that an occupier of any land or premises has towards other people in general.
- It applies irrespective of whether the owner is the occupier or whether the premises are rented or occupied under any terms.
- Where premises, or part of the premises, are handed over to the contractor, it would be likely that the contractor would be regarded as the occupier.
- Premises include the grounds surrounding a building (for example, an unfenced excavation outside a construction site).
- A visitor can be anyone who is not an employee. Therefore a visitor may be any person who is a lawful visitor with genuine reason to visit the premises, or a trespasser.
- The occupier must expect children and young persons to be inquisitive to trespass. Therefore greater measures may be required where the risk is foreseeable.

- Control measures (such as immobilising plant and machinery, isolating sources of ignition, locking away substances hazardous to health, providing lighting and correct stacking of materials) should be implemented, where applicable.

One area of particular concern is house building or repairs and maintenance, when property may remain in occupation at the time of work being undertaken. Additional control measures may be required if work areas cannot be fully segregated from other persons in the premises.

1.13   Corporate Manslaughter and Corporate Homicide Act

Since 6 April 2008, companies whose gross negligence leads to the death of individuals can face prosecution for manslaughter (homicide in Scotland) under the Corporate Manslaughter and Corporate Homicide Act. Under this legislation companies, organisations and, for the first time, Government bodies face an unlimited fine if they are found to have caused death due to their gross corporate health and safety failures.

The legislation primarily came about as a result of the failure to identify 'the controlling mind' in companies with complex management structures during court cases, which followed several high profile disasters.

However, presentations by authoritative legal professionals have indicated that the legislation might have much wider ranging implications (such as prosecutions following at-work-related road deaths and fatalities). The Act offers employees of companies, consumers and other individuals greater protection against corporate negligence. It will also help to focus the minds of those in companies and other organisations by ensuring that they take their health and safety obligations seriously.

1.13.1   Corporate Manslaughter Act

The Act applies to the whole of the United Kingdom, with the term *corporate homicide* applying to Scotland only. The Corporate Manslaughter and Corporate Homicide Act:

- makes it easier to prosecute companies and other large organisations, when gross failures in the management of health and safety lead to death, by delivering a new, more effective basis for corporate liability

- has reformed the law so that an important obstacle to successful prosecutions has now been removed. It means that both small and large companies can be held liable for manslaughter where gross failures in the management of health and safety cause death, not just health and safety violations

- complements the current law under which individuals can be prosecuted for gross negligence manslaughter and health and safety offences, where there is direct evidence of their culpability. The Act builds on existing health and safety legislation – so the new offence does not impose new regulations on business

- lifts Crown immunity to prosecution. Crown bodies – such as Government departments – will be liable to prosecution for the first time. So the Act will apply to companies and other corporate bodies, in the public and private sector, Government departments, police forces and certain unincorporated bodies, such as partnerships, where these are employers.

(The above text is an extract reproduced from a Ministry of Justice press release under licence from His Majesty's Stationery Office.)

An organisation will be guilty of the offence if someone has been killed as a result of the gross failure of senior managers (for example, failure to ensure safe working practices for their employees, such as ensuring that staff are properly trained and equipment is in a safe condition, or to maintain the safety of their premises, such as ensuring that lifts are properly maintained and fire precautions taken).

The Act covers organisations providing goods and services to members of the public, the construction, use or maintenance of infrastructure or vehicles, or when operating commercially. Crown bodies and other public sector organisations, including police forces, will be on an equal footing with the private sector when carrying out similar work.

The offence is clearly linked to the standards required under other health and safety laws. It does not apply to circumstances where an organisation does not owe a duty of care, or to certain public and government functions whose management involves wider questions of public policy and is already subject to other forms of accountability. For example, it does not apply to strategic decisions about the spending of public money or activities like statutory inspection, holding prisoners in detention, emergency service response, policing or child protection.

If a company is found guilty of corporate manslaughter the penalty is an unlimited fine. The Act also gives the courts power to impose a remedial order, which can already be imposed for health and safety offences, and requires the company to address the cause of the fatality.

1.14   Sentencing guidelines

In November 2018, new sentencing guidelines for health and safety, corporate manslaughter and food safety and hygiene offences came into force. Sentencing guidelines help judges and magistrates to decide on the appropriate sentence for a criminal offence. They direct the courts to consider the sentencing of offending organisations by way of a step-by-step approach, primarily examining culpability, the likelihood of harm and the seriousness of the harm.

These categories are then divided into different levels to reflect the scale within each category. The guidelines require an assessment of turnover in order to set a starting point for a fine. The majority of the other sentencing steps relate to the consideration of increasing or decreasing the level of fine according to a range of factors. There are similar guidelines for sentencing individuals for health and safety offences, with a stronger focus on the risk of a custodial sentence for those found guilty of serious breaches.

 For more information on the sentencing guidelines visit the Sentencing Council website.

1.15 Health and Safety (Offences) Act

This legislation, which came into force in January 2009, amends Section 33 of HSWA, and in doing so it:

- increased the maximum fine that can be awarded by the courts for breaches of health and safety regulations, from £5,000 to £20,000 (now superseded by the Legal Aid, Sentencing and Punishment of Offenders Act *(refer to 1.16)*)

- increased the number of health and safety offences for which a guilty person can be imprisoned

- enables certain offences, which could previously only be tried in Magistrates' Courts, to be tried in either Magistrates' Courts or Crown Courts.

1.16 Legal Aid, Sentencing and Punishment of Offenders Act

This amends the table at Schedule 3A to HSWA, by removing the limits that could be awarded in a lower court in England and Wales. However, the limits remain the same in Scotland.

The maximum penalty for an offence depends on the date of the commission of the offence and the type of court (lower (Magistrates') court or upper (Crown) court) dealing with the case. For offences committed before 16 January 2009, the maximum was £20,000 in the lower court, and an unlimited fine in the higher court.

Between 16 January 2009 and 12 March 2015, the maximum penalty was £20,000 and/or imprisonment for up to six months in the lower court, and an unlimited fine and/or imprisonment up to two years in the higher court. The maximum penalties for offences committed on or after 12 March 2015 are shown in the table below. Those found guilty of a health and safety offence can now be sentenced by a Magistrates' Court in all cases.

The table summarises amends to Schedule 3A to HSWA, and sets out offences and maximum penalties under health and safety legislation.

Offence	Court	Maximum penalty
A breach of Sections 2–6, which set out the general duties of employers, self-employed persons, persons who have control of premises, employees, manufacturers and suppliers to safeguard the health and safety of employees and members of the public who may be affected by work activities.	Lower court maximum	Unlimited fine (£20,000 in Scotland) and/or 12 months' imprisonment*
	Higher court maximum	Unlimited fine and/or two years' imprisonment
A breach of Section 7, which is the failure of an individual to take reasonable care of their own health and safety or that of someone else who is affected by their acts or omissions, or failure to co-operate with the employer in matters of health and safety.	Lower court maximum	Unlimited fine (£5,000 in Scotland) and/or 12 months' imprisonment*
	Higher court maximum	Unlimited fine and/or two years' imprisonment
A breach of Section 8, which imposes a duty on all persons not to intentionally or recklessly interfere with anything provided in the interests of health, safety or welfare.	Lower court maximum	Unlimited fine (£20,000 in Scotland) and/or 12 months' imprisonment*
	Higher court maximum	Unlimited fine and/or two years' imprisonment
A breach of Section 9, which imposes a duty on employers not to make a charge for anything provided in the interests of health or safety.	Lower court maximum	Unlimited fine (£20,000 in Scotland)
	Higher court maximum	Unlimited fine
A breach of Section 33(1)(c), which is to contravene any health and safety regulation.	Lower court maximum	Unlimited fine (£20,000 in Scotland) and/or 12 months' imprisonment*
	Higher court maximum	Unlimited fine and/or two years' imprisonment
A breach of Sections 33(1) (e), (f) or (g), which are concerned with: ▪ contravening any requirement of an inspector when exercising their enforcement powers ▪ preventing anyone appearing before an inspector, or ▪ contravening any requirement imposed by an improvement or prohibition notice.	Lower court maximum	Unlimited fine (£20,000 in Scotland) and/or 12 months' imprisonment*
	Higher court maximum	Unlimited fine and/or two years' imprisonment
A breach of Section 33(1)(h), which is to intentionally obstruct an inspector in exercising their powers or duties.	Lower court maximum	Unlimited fine and/or 12 months' imprisonment** (one year in Scotland)
	Higher court maximum	Not applicable
A breach of Sections 33(1)(k), (l) or (m), which are concerned with making false statements, false entries in a register or book or forging or using a document to deceive an inspector.	Lower court maximum	Unlimited fine (£20,000 in Scotland) and/or 12 months' imprisonment*
	Higher court maximum	Unlimited fine and/or two years' imprisonment

Offence	Court	Maximum penalty
A breach of Section 33(1)(o), which is to fail to comply with a court remedy order under Section 42.	Lower court maximum	Unlimited fine (£20,000 in Scotland) and/or 12 months' imprisonment*
	Higher court maximum	Unlimited fine and/or two years' imprisonment
A breach of Sections 36 or 37 of HSWA, which relate to offences committed by corporate bodies due to the personal failings of directors, senior managers, company secretaries, and so on. *See also Note 4 below.*	Lower court maximum	Five years' disqualification
	Higher court maximum	15 years' disqualification

Notes

1. *A lower court is a Magistrates' Court (or Sheriff Court in Scotland).*

2. *A higher court is a Crown Court (or High Court of Judiciary in Scotland).*

3. **The maximum term of imprisonment that may be imposed by a Magistrates' Court is currently six months. When s154(1) of the Criminal Justice Act 2003 is brought into force the maximum term will be increased to 12 months.*
   **The maximum term of imprisonment that may be imposed by a Magistrates' Court is currently six months. When s281(5) of the Criminal Justice Act 2003 is brought into force the maximum term will be increased to 51 weeks in England and Wales or 12 months in Scotland.

4. *On conviction of directors for indictable offences in connection with the management of a company, the courts may also make a disqualification order (Company Directors Disqualification Act 1986, Sections 1 and 2). The courts have exercised this power following health and safety convictions and health and safety inspectors draw this power to the court's attention whenever appropriate.*

Appendix A – Prosecution under the Corporate Manslaughter and Corporate Homicide Act

 Company fined £2.4 million following two corporate manslaughter charges

A construction company director has been jailed after two workers fell from a first-floor balcony at a luxury flat in Knightsbridge, West London. The 44-year-old director of the renovation firm was found guilty of breaching Section 2(1) of the Health and Safety at Work etc. Act (HSWA) and received a 14-month prison sentence for each death, to run concurrently. He was also barred from being a company director for four years.

The company, which has gone into liquidation since the incident, despite previously having an annual turnover of around £9.7 million, was found guilty of two counts of corporate manslaughter and two breaches of Section 2(1) of the HSWA. The company was fined £1.2 million for each death and £650,000 for HSWA breaches, all of which apply concurrently. It also had to pay £72,000 costs.

The court heard that in November 2014 two Polish nationals, aged 22 and 29 years, fell from the balcony of a flat in London's Cadogan Square, which was being refurbished by the director's renovation company. The men were part of a group of five workers who were using ropes to haul a 115 kg sofa up 6 m, over a balustrade and onto a balcony, with only the Victorian iron railings of the balcony acting as a barrier. The 130-year-old railings gave way and the two men fell from the balcony to the ground. The 22-year-old was pronounced dead at the scene, while the 29-year-old was taken to a central London hospital in a critical condition, where he later died of his injuries.

The sofa delivery company had recommended that an external furniture lift should be hired for the lift and had emailed the director of the renovation company with an estimated budget of £848 to hire an external lift. The director responded with a message saying: 'Unfortunately, we do not have time for all that. Please deliver the sofa and we will get it up to the flat'.

By autumn 2014, work on the flat was over budget and behind schedule. The renovation budget had increased from around £650,000 to as much as £920,000. The court heard that on the day of the accident there was a failure to identify who was supervising the site.

The prosecution told the court that none of the training documents provided were in Polish, despite the workers not speaking English, suggesting that the documents were 'just for show'. The men were also not provided with a plan, method statement or risk assessment before the task started.

The judge stated that the director's motive for ignoring the warnings about the furniture lift 'must have been in one way or another to benefit his business. The word has got to get out that health and safety on building sites is not a boring technicality. It is vital to the safety of employees and others in what is inherently a dangerous environment. Those who are wilfully blind to the risks, despite warnings – as you were – have got to expect to go immediately to prison'.

(Source: HSE.)

Appendix B – Prosecution under common and criminal law

 Safety fall-arrest netting would have saved the life of workman; contracts manager handed two year prison term

Manchester Crown Court has heard how a 54-year-old construction worker died from severe head injuries when he fell through the fragile roof on which he was working in 2015. The circumstances surrounding the death were investigated jointly by Greater Manchester Police and the Health and Safety Executive (HSE). The investigators found: 'there had been fundamental breaches of duty on the part of those who organised the work to the roof'.

Practicable steps that could and should have been taken to ensure the safety of those working on the site had not been taken, thereby exposing the workforce to risks that they should never have been exposed to, and which led directly to the death. The practical steps required included providing netting to arrest any fall. Experts assessed the site after the fall and advised that such netting was necessary. A further expert stated that it was not difficult to provide safety netting and, if it had been installed, it would have caught the man. Experts told investigators that netting would have cost approximately £1,250 to safely install.

During the investigation the police examined the computer of a contracts manager for one of the companies involved in the project, and found that he had altered the records 'in order to mislead the investigation'. He presented a risk assessment document containing the forged signature of the deceased worker, in order to mislead and attempt to justify his actions.

The 50-year-old contracts manager from Warrington was sentenced to two years in prison after pleading guilty to failing to take reasonable care of other persons, pursuant to Section 7 of the Health and Safety at Work etc. Act 1974, contrary to Section 33(1)(a) (a failure to discharge a duty to which a person is subject by virtue of Sections 2 to 6). He also pleaded guilty to the common law charge of perverting the course of justice.

The employer of the deceased person and the contracts manager were fined £100,000 and ordered to pay £30,000 in prosecution costs after pleading guilty to Section 2(1) of the Health and Safety at Work etc. Act 1974. The other roofing contractor involved in the project and incident was fined £12,000 and ordered to pay £33,000 in prosecution costs after being found guilty of Regulation 15(2) of the Construction (Design and Management) Regulations 2015 following a trial.

A detective chief inspector from Greater Manchester Police's major incident team said: 'Today's result should serve as a stark reminder to those who employ people and have a responsibility to look after them in the workplace – cutting corners in this way is dangerous and can ultimately rip families apart, because it was these actions that had absolutely cataclysmic consequences and led to an unnecessary and preventable death. The fact that the manager went on to forge the deceased man's signature demonstrates that rather than thinking about the deceased man and his loved ones in the aftermath of his death, the sole thought of the contracts manager was to cover his tracks and prevent the investigation from establishing what had occurred.'

A HSE principal inspector said: 'This was an entirely foreseeable and preventable incident, which resulted in a tragic and needless loss of life. Falls from height remain the biggest cause of workplace fatalities in the UK construction industry. It is vital that those involved in planning, managing and carrying out work at height understand the risks and identify and implement suitable control measures to prevent injury. Had such steps been taken in this case, this incident would not have occurred.'

(Source: HSE.)

The Health and Safety at Work etc. Act

02

Supporting
INFORMATION

GT700 Toolbox talks / supporting checklists and forms

Toolbox talks on some of these topics are available in the GT700 publication. Supporting checklists and forms covering some of these topics are available on our companion website.

THE HEALTH AND SAFETY AT WORK ETC. ACT

Overview

The Health and Safety at Work etc. Act 1974 (HSWA), also referred to as 'the Act' within this chapter, is the primary legislation covering health and safety in England, Scotland and Wales.

The Act mainly places legal duties on employers, the self-employed, and other designated persons such as manufacturers, designers and, to a lesser extent, employees. The aim is to promote health and safety awareness and effective standards of health and safety management for all.

This chapter outlines what the Act is about and what is required.

2.1   Introduction

The Act sets out the general duties that employers and the self-employed have towards their employees and other persons, as well as the duties that employees have towards themselves, their employer and to other persons, including fellow employees.

These duties are qualified in the Act by the principle of 'so far as is reasonably practicable'. In other words, an employer does not have to take additional measures to avoid or reduce the risk if such measures are technically impossible or if the time, trouble or cost of the measures would be grossly disproportionate to the risk.

 It shall be the duty of every employer to ensure, so far as is reasonably practicable, the health, safety and welfare at work of all their employees.

 For an explanation of *absolute*, *practicable* and *reasonably practicable* refer to Chapter A01 Health and safety law.

Occupational health and safety

Occupational health refers to all health problems in the work environment. The term covers health problems workers bring to the workplace, as well as health issues caused or made worse by work.

It covers serious and fatal diseases, physical effects on skin, breathing, hearing, mobility and functioning, and psychological effects on mental wellbeing.

Effects may be immediate and visible, but are more often unseen and take a long time to develop, so vigilance and monitoring can be key to identifying problems.

Some effects can be cured if diagnosed early; many can only be prevented from getting worse, and some diseases are terminal.

Safety is the protection of people from physical injury. It refers to a workplace having an acceptable degree of freedom from risk.
(Sources: CONIAC and NEBOSH.)

2.2   Important points

- The Act is statute law and breaches of the Act are a criminal offence.
- The HSE and Local Authorities are responsible for enforcing the Act.
- What the law requires is what good management and common sense would lead prudent employers to do anyway: that is, to look at what the risks are and take sensible and proportionate measures to tackle them.
- The ultimate aim of the Act is to promote health and safety awareness and effective standards of health and safety management by every employer.

2.3   Aims and scope of the Act

The Act provides for a comprehensive, legislative framework to promote, stimulate and encourage high standards of health, safety and welfare in the workplace, and to improve the way work is planned, performed and executed.

One of the main aims of the Act is to **involve everyone** in matters of health and safety.

- Management.
- Employees.
- Self-employed.

- Employees' representatives.
- Controllers of premises.
- Manufacturers of plant, equipment and materials.

The Act also requires that adequate measures are taken to protect others (such as members of the public) where their health or safety would be at risk from a business undertaking or the way a business performs its activities.

All persons at work are covered by the Act, with the exception of domestic and service staff in private households. This is an enabling Act that allows the Secretary of State to make further laws without the need to pass another Act of Parliament. Regulations are laws, approved by Parliament. These are usually made under the Act following proposals from the HSE.

2.4   Relevant statutory provisions

The Act requires compliance with the relevant statutory provisions.

● The Act itself.

● Other health and safety legislation, as listed in Schedule 1 of the Act.

● All the legislation made under Section 15 of the Act. (This covers all health and safety regulations made since 1974.)

2.5   Main parts of the Act

The Act consists of four parts, shown below.

Part 1	Health, safety and welfare in the workplace.
Part 2	Employment Medical Advisory Service (EMAS) – functions and responsibilities.
Part 3	Building Regulations and relating amendments to the law.
Part 4	Miscellaneous and general provisions.

Employers and their representatives, managers, supervisors, safety supervisors, safety representatives and others with a responsibility for ensuring legal compliance will be mainly concerned with Part 1 of the Act.

2.5.1   Part 1. Health, safety and welfare in the workplace

The main provisions of Part 1 of the Act are shown below.

● Securing the health, safety and welfare of persons at work.

● Protecting persons, other than persons at work, against risks to health and safety, arising out of, or in connection with, the activities of persons at work.

● Duties of employees.

● Establishing the Health and Safety Commission (HSC) and the HSE, which are generally responsible for enforcing and administering the Act, or any of the regulations made under it. The HSC has since been abolished, and its role and duties have been passed over to the HSE.

● The power of the Secretary of State to make regulations, the provision of regulations and repeal and modification of existing statutory provisions.

● Approval by the HSE of Approved Codes of Practice in accordance with the Legislative Reform (Health and Safety Executive) Order 2008.

● Using Approved Codes of Practice in criminal proceedings, in accordance with Section 17 of the Act.

● The powers of the HSE to make adequate arrangements for the enforcement of relevant statutory provisions, both in relation to this and other health and safety legislation, whether by appointing its own inspectors or transferring its powers to other Local Authorities.

● The appointment of inspectors in writing, specifying their powers and means for the enforcement of the Act.

● Improvement notices.

● Prohibition notices.

● Appeals procedures against improvement or prohibition notices.

● The provision for criminal offences and punishments.

2.5.2   Part 2. Employment Medical Advisory Service

The main provision of Part 2 of the Act is the continuation of the Employment Medical Advisory Service (EMAS).

The responsibility for maintaining this service has been delegated by the Secretary of State to the HSE.

2.5.3   Part 3. Building Regulations

The main provision of Part 3 of the Act is the extension of the scope and coverage of the Building Regulations.

2.5.4   Part 4. Miscellaneous and general

The main provision of Part 4 of the Act concerns amendments, repeals and modifications to other Acts or instruments.

These amendments affect (among other matters) general fire precautions, including means of escape in most factories, offices and shops. These can now be dealt with by the fire authorities, under the provisions of the Regulatory Reform (Fire Safety) Order 2005.

The HSE remains responsible for control over 'process risks' (that is, risk of outbreak of fire associated with particular processes or particular substances).

In future, regulations may be made so that company reports will have to include information on health, safety, welfare and environmental performance.

The HSE recommends that companies give information about health and safety performance in their shareholders' or annual report.

2.6   Duty holders under the Act

The Act **mainly** places legal duties on employers, the self-employed and employees, but there are some exceptions.

- Section 4 places duties on the persons who control premises with regard to the health and safety of other persons who are not their employees.

- Section 6 places duties on the manufacturers, designers, importers and suppliers of equipment.

- Section 8 places a duty on all people to not intentionally or recklessly interfere with or misuse anything provided in the interests of health, safety or welfare.

2.6.1   Duties of employers

Part 1 of the Act places a general duty on every employer (Section 2) to ensure, so far as is **reasonably practicable**, the health, safety and welfare at work of all their employees.

The Act goes on to state that, so far as is reasonably practicable, the employer must meet the following requirements.

- Protect the health, safety and welfare at work of all their employees – Section 2(1).

- Provide and maintain plant and systems of work that are safe and without risk to health – Section 2(2)(a).

- Ensure safety and absence of risks in the use, handling, storage and transport of articles and substances – Section 2(2)(b).

- Provide adequate information, instruction, training and supervision, as is necessary, to ensure the health and safety of their employees – Section 2(2)(c).

- Provide and maintain a working environment that is safe, without risks to health and with safe access and egress – Section 2(2)(d).

- Provide and maintain a working environment that is safe, without risks to health and with adequate welfare and facilities arrangements – Section 2(2)(e).

Certain additional duties have been placed on the employer.

- Where five or more persons are employed, to prepare, publicise and revise, as often as may be appropriate, a written statement of the employer's health and safety policy and the organisation and arrangements in force for implementing the policy – Section 2(3).

- To ensure, as far as is reasonably practicable, that the conduct of their work does not endanger persons not in their employment who may be affected by operations under their control (for example, sub-contractors or the public) – Section 3(1).

In certain circumstances, employers must provide information to others about those aspects of their undertaking that might affect health and safety.

This duty is explicit in the Construction (Design and Management) Regulations 2015 (CDM).

Trade unions recognised by the management at the workplace have the right to appoint safety representatives from within the workforce.

Section 2(4), (6) and (7) state that employers must achieve the following.

- Provide for the appointment, by recognised trade unions, of safety representatives from the employees, in order to consult with, as appropriate.

- Establish safety committees, when requested in writing by at least two safety representatives.

For further details of the employers' duty to consult with employees, refer to Chapter A01 Health and safety law.

2.6.2   Duties of employees

The Act places two general duties on employees (Section 7).

● To exercise reasonable care for the health and safety of themselves or others who may be affected by their acts or omissions at work – Section 7(a).

● To co-operate with the employer, as far as is necessary, to enable them (the employer) to comply with their legal duties in health and safety matters – Section 7(b).

Employees also have duties under various other regulations that expand on these general duties (for example, Regulation 14 of the Management of Health and Safety at Work Regulations).

2.6.3   Duties of the self-employed

A general duty is placed on the self-employed to conduct their undertaking in such a way as to ensure, so far as is reasonably practicable, that they and other persons are not exposed to risks to health and safety. In many ways, the self-employed person has similar duties to an employer, including giving information to persons other than their employees about those aspects of their undertaking that might affect their health and safety – Section 3(2) and (3).

 Self-employed builders fined for illegal asbestos removal

Two self-employed builders were sentenced for exposing householders, as well as themselves, to asbestos. The builders were prosecuted after they illegally removed and broke up asbestos panels from a home.

Samples were taken to test for asbestos and the results revealed that asbestos was present. However, the HSE's investigation concluded that by the time the test results were known, the builders had already broken up the asbestos insulating boards (AIBs) with a hammer and removed them. Neither of the builders held the necessary licence to remove the asbestos boards. Nor did they carry out, or ask to see, an asbestos survey, which is required by law before any demolition or refurbishment work is undertaken.

In failing to take adequate steps to prevent both the exposure to and spread of asbestos fibres generated by their work, they put the householders, themselves and others at risk of inhaling the potentially harmful airborne fibres. The subsequent clean-up of the site cost more than £6,500.

Both builders pleaded guilty to a breach of the Health and Safety at Work etc. Act 1974. They were individually fined a total of £2,000 and ordered to pay costs of £1,200.

Speaking after the prosecution, an HSE inspector said: 'An estimated 70% of properties contain asbestos. It is illegal to undertake any work which will disturb the fabric of the building without carrying out and obtaining the results of an asbestos survey. The type of work being undertaken should have been carried out by a builder who holds the necessary licence, in a safe manner and with the necessary control measures. Instead (the builders) exposed the householders and others – including themselves – to potentially harmful airborne asbestos fibres. They also demonstrated a complete disregard for the law'.

 Section 3(2) of the Health and Safety at Work etc. Act 1974 states: it shall be the duty of every self-employed person to conduct their undertaking in such a way as to ensure, so far as is reasonably practicable, that they and other persons (not being their employees) who may be affected thereby are not exposed to risks to their health or safety.

 For further information on duties of the self-employed visit the HSE website.

2.6.4   Duties of those in control of premises

Duties are imposed on anyone who is in control of non-domestic premises to ensure the health and safety of anyone, who is not an employee, who enters those premises to carry out work. The duties also apply to premises where machinery, equipment or substances are provided for the use of others. The person in control of non-domestic premises is generally the owner, occupier or other person who has specific obligations for maintenance or repair of those premises by virtue of a contract or tenancy agreement – Section 4.

2.6.5   Duties of manufacturers, designers, importers and suppliers

A general duty is placed on any person who manufactures, designs, imports or supplies any article, material or substance for use at work to ensure, so far as is reasonably practicable, that articles and substances are, by design and construction, safe and without risks to health when being used, set, cleaned or maintained by persons at work – Section 6.

 Information on design noise levels under normal working conditions should be supplied if noise levels may be a risk to health, or exceed the lower exposure action value specified in the Control of Noise at Work Regulations. Similarly, manufacturers of tools that may be a source of hand-arm vibration must provide details of the levels of vibration generated.

More specifically, a duty exists to ensure that arrangements are made to carry out the necessary testing, examination and research of any article, material or substance, and that steps are taken to provide adequate information about any conditions necessary to ensure that it will be safe when used.

A general duty is placed on installers or erectors of any article for use at work to ensure, so far as is reasonably practicable, that it is safe and without risk to health when used by persons at work – Section 6(3).

2.6.6 Duties of all people

This section of the Act places a duty on all persons to not intentionally or recklessly interfere with or misuse anything provided in the interests of health, safety and welfare – Section 8.

This can apply to all persons, regardless of employment status.

2.6.7 Duty not to charge employees

Employers must not charge, or permit any employee to be charged, for anything that must be provided to meet any of the relevant statutory provisions – Section 9.

2.7 Health and Safety Executive (HSE)

The HSE has certain powers and duties under the Act. The powers may also be exercised by Local Authority environmental health officers on certain smaller sites and in offices.

The enforcement of all health and safety law is carried out under the provisions of the Act. This means that methods of enforcement are the same throughout the country.

The HSE is responsible for maintaining a force of health and safety inspectors, and has a construction division with their own construction inspectors. It plays an active role in collaborating with industry and key stakeholders, and focuses on policy initiatives and new construction legislation.

HSE and Local Authority inspectors have a range of tools at their disposal in seeking to secure compliance with the law and ensure a proportionate response to offences.

For more serious offences, inspectors may serve improvement or prohibition notices and they may prosecute or, in Scotland, report to the Crown Office and Procurator Fiscal Service (COPFS) with a view to prosecution.

 Prosecution and enforcement figures for 2020–21

- HSE prosecuted 185 cases, or referred cases to COPFS for prosecution in Scotland, where a conviction was achieved.

- Across all enforcing bodies there were 2,929 notices issued.

- A total of £26.9 million in fines resulted from prosecutions taken, or referred to COPFS for prosecution in Scotland, by HSE where a conviction was achieved, compared to £54.5 million in fines in 2018–19.

 The restrictions imposed by the Covid-19 pandemic have had an impact on the number of prosecutions and notices issued. 2021 saw a substantial fall in the number of cases prosecuted. The number of notices issued by HSE bodies showed a substantial decrease compared to the previous year. Though the total value of all fines has decreased, the average fine per case has increased from £107,000 to £145,000.

(Source: HSE.)

Health and safety inspectors have wide-ranging powers, vested in them by the Act. They also have enforcement powers under the Regulatory Reform (Fire Safety) Order (RR(FS)O). Below and on the next page is a summary of the main powers that inspectors and offices from Local Authority possess. Officers of the local fire and rescue service also have enforcement powers when dealing with matters under the RR(FS)O, which falls under the Building Safety Act (2022) England.

- Prosecute a company or individual for a breach of health and safety law.

- Visit or carry out an inspection of a workplace, at a reasonable time, without giving prior notice.

- Issue a prohibition or improvement notice.

- Stop the further use of equipment that is considered to be a serious risk to health or safety.

- Investigate accidents or dangerous occurrences.

- Require that any designated part of a premises remains undisturbed for as long as is deemed necessary.

- Investigate a particular work activity or any plant or equipment following a complaint or accident.

- Take measurements or photographs as necessary.

- Inspect or take copies of any books or records.

- Demand the full co-operation of any persons to assist them in their duties.

- Demand information from employers or employees and require them to sign a statement of their answers.

- Remove or make safe any article or substance considered to be a source of danger or serious personal injury.

- Require additional fire precautions work to be carried out on a construction site.

- Provide information for employers and employees about hazards that may affect their health and safety at work.

- Act as a source of information on health, safety and welfare at work.

 The HSE offers a range of services to assist employers and employees. Many publications are produced each year – with some at no charge or downloadable from its website.

2.7.1   Investigation

Inspectors are given a general right to examine and investigate as necessary – Section 20. They may:

- enter premises (accompanied by a police officer or other authorised person if necessary), taking with them any equipment or material required by them for the purposes of the examination

- direct that anything shall be left undisturbed if required for examination or investigation

- take measurements, samples, photographs and such recordings as may be necessary

- have dismantled or tested any article or substance considered dangerous, or take possession of any article for examination and evidence.

Inspectors may inspect or take copies of record books or documents. They may demand from an employee or other person any information they think necessary and can ask an employee or other person to sign a declaration of the truth of their answers.

In general, they can demand the full co-operation of any person to provide them with such facilities and assistance as they may deem necessary.

2.7.2   Advisory

Inspectors also act as a source of information and advice. It is their duty to tell employee representatives (safety representatives or trade union-appointed safety representatives) or the employees about anything that may affect their health and safety at work.

This information should be similar to that given to the employer.

2.7.3   Enforcement options

Inspectors can use any of the powers listed in the following table against any person taking part in, or in control of, any work activity or piece of equipment.

Any person means an employer, self-employed person, a supplier or an employee.

1. Informal	Inspectors may give advice on compliance in the case of minor breaches.
2. Formal letter	A formal letter may contain details of breaches and the action needed to comply with the legislation. It may also contain more detailed and formalised advice. Whilst visiting a site, an inspector can prepare an instant visit report with a date agreed for work to be completed.
3. Improvement notice	Where a breach is more serious, the inspector may issue an improvement notice, which will outline the work required and the date for completion. This will be at least 21 days from the date of receipt. *(Refer to Appendix A for an example of an improvement notice.)*
4. Prohibition notice	If an activity involves, or is likely to involve, a serious risk of personal injury, the inspector may serve a prohibition notice to stop that activity either immediately or at the end of the period specified. *(Refer to Appendix B for an example of a prohibition notice.)*
5. Prosecution	In addition to the enforcement outlined above, the inspector may consider that it is also necessary to prosecute. This can be either in a Magistrates' Court or Crown Court.

Failure to comply with an improvement notice

A building company was found guilty of breaching the Health and Safety at Work etc. Act by failing to comply with an improvement notice, and also found guilty of breaching CDM.

During three months the company had been served with three prohibition notices and two improvement notices. The site manager was also issued with a prohibition notice because the operation of the site was far below minimum legal safety standards.

The company was fined a total of £40,000 and ordered to pay costs of £10,035.

After the hearing the HSE inspector said: 'If the HSE visits a construction site and has to issue prohibition notices preventing further work, that in itself shows that there is a very real and immediate risk to workers there, and possibly to members of the public.

'The company failed on several fronts to safeguard the workforce from risks that are well known in the construction industry. They either did not identify those risks or neglected to manage them effectively.

'Proper management of work
activities and competent site supervision are essential, but the company fell well below the required standards'.

 Section 33(1)(g) of the Health and Safety at Work etc. Act states: it is an offence for a person to contravene any requirement or prohibition imposed by an improvement notice or a prohibition notice (including any such notice as modified on appeal).

Contravention of certain requirements of the Act can lead to summary prosecution in a Magistrates' Court (or Sheriff Court in Scotland).

In October 1992, under the provisions of the Criminal Justice Act, the maximum fine that could be imposed by a Magistrates' Court or Sheriff Court was raised from £2,000 to £5,000.

This was subsequently raised to £20,000 by the Health and Safety (Offences) Act and this has now been superseded by the Legal Aid, Sentencing and Punishment of Offenders Act. From 12 March 2015 the cap on fines, for offences committed on or after that date, has been removed in England and Wales.

Contravention of other provisions can result in either summary prosecution or an indictment in the Crown Court (High Court in Scotland). The maximum penalty, on summary conviction, in a Magistrates' Court is an unlimited fine for each offence, or six months' imprisonment, or both.

For offences that are dealt with at a Crown Court, there is no limit to the fine and prison sentences of up to two years can be imposed.

 ## Breach of the Health and Safety at Work etc. Act

A company director pleaded guilty to breaching Section 37 of the Health and Safety at Work etc. Act, after consenting to a worker working at height in an excavator bucket.

He was sentenced to eight months in prison (suspended for two years), disqualified from acting as company director for three years, and fined £32,000 with £11,000 costs (the director was driving the excavator at the time of the offence).

2.7.4 Appeals

Anyone served with an improvement or prohibition notice has the right to appeal to an employment tribunal.

This must be done within 21 days of the issue of the notice.

The tribunal may cancel, confirm or modify the notice on appeal, following the issue of either of the following notices.

- An improvement notice: the notice will be suspended until the tribunal meets and decides the issue.

- A prohibition notice: the notice will stand until the appeal has been decided, or the tribunal orders it to be suspended.

Offences under the Act can be committed by individuals as well as by corporate bodies, such as limited companies.

When an offence has been committed, with the help or knowledge of a director, manager, company secretary or other company official, that individual person may be prosecuted as well as the company.

The same duty is placed on the Crown (for example, Government departments and the armed forces) except that the employer cannot be prosecuted. However, individual members of that organisation can be prosecuted for offences they commit, but not for those committed by their employer – Section 37.

Where a person has been prosecuted for failing to comply with a duty or requirement of the Act, and is claiming that it was not reasonably practicable for them to carry out that duty or requirement, it is the responsibility of that person to prove that it was not reasonably practicable to comply, and that there was no reasonably practicable alternative way in which they could have carried out that duty or requirement – Section 40.

2.8   Fees for intervention

The HSE introduced a fee for intervention (FFI) cost recovery scheme from October 2012, under the Health and Safety (Fees) Regulations.

The regulations apply to businesses and individuals who are regulated by the HSE.

These regulations place a duty on the HSE to recover its costs for carrying out its regulatory functions from those found to be in material breach of health and safety law (such as investigations, inspections and enforcement action).

A material breach is when, in the opinion of the HSE inspector, there has been a contravention of health and safety law that is serious enough to require them to notify the person in material breach of that opinion by issuing a notification of contravention (NoC) after their visit.

The HSE will charge an hourly rate for all the time spent by the inspector in identifying the breach, including visits, letter writing, telephone conversations, drafting notices, their help to put it right, and so on, and subsequently ensuring corrective actions have been taken.

The HSE will actively inspect those businesses that are known to be high risk – construction businesses are one of these. The HSE will also visit businesses and individuals if they have information that people may be at unnecessary risk, irrespective of the business sector, or if there has been a reported incident.

Businesses and organisations are advised that if the HSE identifies a material breach of health and safety law corrective action should be taken promptly, so minimal time is spent by the investigating inspector and hence the fee will be less than if corrective action is delayed.

The HSE and Government believe it is right that businesses and organisations that break health and safety laws should pay for the HSE's time in putting matters right, investigating and taking enforcement action. Without FFI this would be paid for from the public purse.

In 2014, an independent report concluded that during the first 18 months of implementation the FFI scheme was working effectively and should be retained.

2.9   Employment Medical Advisory Service

The Employment Medical Advisory Service (EMAS) is an integral part of the HSE, and provides expert medical advice to them, as well as giving advice to a wide range of organisations and individuals.

 For further information on EMAS visit the HSE website.

2.10   Health and Safety (Enforcing Authority) Regulations

The responsibility for enforcing health and safety is broadly split between the HSE and the Local Authority.

These regulations provide for the transfer of the responsibility for the enforcement of health and safety legislation between the HSE and the Local Authority (and vice versa) in certain circumstances.

Local Authorities are responsible for regulating health and safety in lower-risk workplaces.

2.10.1   Local Authority enforcement

Schedule 1 of the regulations lists the main activities for which the Local Authority will be responsible. These include offices, shops, warehouses and consumer services.

For further main activities allocated to Local Authorities, refer to Schedule 1 of the Health and Safety (Enforcing Authority) Regulations.

2.10.2   HSE enforcement

If a main activity is not specified in Schedule 1, the HSE will be the enforcing authority. Some examples of activities reserved to the HSE are shown below.

- Construction work.
- Mines and quarries.
- Manufacturing industry.
- Fairgrounds.

- Hospitals.
- Educational establishments.
- Agricultural activities.

2.10.2.1   Transfer of responsibility for enforcement

Where construction work is carried out on premises for which the Local Authority is normally the enforcing authority, and the work is to be carried out by persons who do not normally work at those premises, the HSE will become the enforcing authority for the duration of the work in the following circumstances.

- When the work is notifiable to the HSE by virtue of CDM.
- If, in whole or part, it involves work to the external fabric or other external parts of the structure.

- Where work is carried out in a physically segregated area of the premises and work activities normally carried out in that area are suspended.
- When work involves the installation, maintenance or repair of gas or electrical systems.
- If work involves the use of ionising radiation (in some cases only).

2.11   Examples of health and safety court cases

The following examples summarise the outcomes of two court cases that arose out of failings in the management of health and safety.

 Regina -v- Swan Hunter Shipbuilders Ltd and Telemeter Installations Ltd

This important Court of Appeal case, resulting from a prosecution under Sections 2 and 3 of the Health and Safety at Work etc. Act 1974, demonstrated that an employer (the main contractor) has a duty to inform, instruct and supervise not only its own employees but also other workers (sub-contractors) who might, by their behaviour, endanger the main contractor's employees.

 Regina -v- Associated Octel Company Ltd

This equally important Court of Appeal case demonstrates that under Section 3 of the Health and Safety at Work etc. Act 1974 an employer can be prosecuted for failing to secure the safety of an independent contractor's employees, whether or not it has been involved with that third party's work. If an employer asks an independent contractor to do work that forms part of the overall job being carried out by the employer, the employer must stipulate the conditions needed to avoid risks to health and safety and that are reasonably practicable to protect that contractor's workforce.

The HSE website breaks down regulations into easy to follow topic areas, industry sectors (such as construction) and different levels of guidance aimed at company owners through to employees. It also contains ACoPs and guidance, which are available as free downloads.

 Copies of all acts and regulations can be downloaded from the Government's legislation website.

2.12   Prosecutions under HSWA, the Company Directors Disqualification Act and the Fraud Act

 ## Two directors prosecuted following fatal incident

A businessman, who was disqualified from being a company director, was jailed for serious fraud and safety offences. A second businessman was given a suspended prison sentence for similar offences. The two were sentenced following joint proceedings brought by the Department for Business, Innovation and Skills (BIS) and the HSE. The safety offence related to the tragic death of a 40-year-old worker.

The first director was jailed for a total of 26 months; 16 months for a breach of Section 2(1) of the Health and Safety at Work etc. Act 1974 (HSWA); 10 months for a breach of Section 2 of the Fraud Act 2006; and a total of eight months concurrent for four breaches of Section 13 of the Company Directors Disqualification Act 1986. He was also disqualified from being a company director for a maximum of 15 years.

The second director was given a 12 month prison sentence, suspended for two years, after admitting the same breach of the HSWA, and a concurrent six months, also suspended, after pleading guilty to aiding and abetting the first director in his disqualification. He was disqualified as a director for seven years, ordered to pay £8,000 toward prosecution costs and given 150 hours community service.

The safety offences related to the directors' running of their now insolvent company, and became apparent following a fatal incident where a worker was crushed by a two tonne metal sand moulding box. The box fell from the lifting chains of a crane the worker was using to manoeuvre it. Colleagues scrambled to free him, but he was pronounced dead at the scene by paramedics.

The HSE investigated the death and identified serious concerns with the systems of work in place at the time, and with the lifting equipment. They became aware of the Companies Act offences and a joint investigation with BIS was undertaken.

The HSE found that the crane at the centre of the incident had not been checked and tested as the law requires, and there were inadequate provisions in place covering competency, supervision and training. The court heard the incident could have been prevented, had the system of work been reviewed and properly assessed.

HSE inspectors also identified problems with lead exposure at the company. The control and health surveillance measures were insufficient, meaning workers were being exposed to potentially harmful levels of lead without realising it.

The court was told that at the time of the worker's death the company was the subject of three improvement notices served by the HSE following earlier visits.

A number of important safety improvements were required, but few had been satisfactorily implemented, largely, claimed the management team, because of financial constraints. The HSE argued the fatal incident could have been avoided had the necessary changes in the relevant enforcement notices taken place.

The company was also sentenced for a breach of Section 2(1) of the HSWA, after a guilty plea was submitted on behalf of the insolvent firm by its administrators. The court imposed a fine of £100,000.

The court was told how the first director had previously been disqualified from acting as a company director for 12 years. However, he had contravened two orders by acting in that capacity in no fewer than four separate companies over a five year period, including at The Company.

He was also responsible for the cross-firing of cheques, which were written from the bank account of one of the companies, which was no longer trading, to provide funds to The Company. BIS investigators established that The Company drew almost £92,500 in this way, taking advantage of a short window after cheques were presented but before they bounced.

The investigators also established that the second director aided and abetted the first director as the registered director of The Company, performing tasks, such as writing blank cheques for the first director to use, but not fulfilling the responsibilities of being the director of the company, allowing the first director to run the business.

In his sentencing comments the judge said that the defendant had behaved in a disgraceful way and had been culpable of extremely shoddy business practice.

After reading a statement from the worker's father, the judge said the impact of the incident had been devastating: 'It was harrowing, and underlines the personal tragedy that could have been avoided'.

After sentencing the HSE director of operations said: 'The safety standards at The Company fell well short of those required, as the directors were only too aware. They knew improvements were needed to protect workers like the deceased and they had clear responsibilities as senior management to ensure the necessary changes were implemented.

'Sadly, one of the many areas that was seemingly overlooked was the system of work surrounding the overhead crane. Had this been properly assessed then the deceased's tragic death could have been prevented'.

The worker's father commented: 'I brought my son up since he was an infant and cared for him all his life until his death.

'His passing has left a huge empty void in my life, a devastating loss that I will never recover from'.

The deputy chief investigation officer from BIS said: 'Individuals are disqualified from being company directors for good reason, usually because of conduct which shows them to be unfit to operate a business.

'This case shows the tragic consequences of the defendant ignoring his disqualification'.

(Source: HSE.)

 ## Company fined £2.6 million after worker is fatally crushed in trench

A construction company was fined £2.6 million with £54,000 costs after an employee was killed when the trench he was working in collapsed on him.

The 32-year-old worker was in a trench, laying ducting for new cable for an offshore wind farm. The trench had been dug to a depth of 2.4 m, without any shoring.

The worker became trapped in the trench after it collapsed on him. He died in hospital 10 days later.

After an investigation by the HSE, the Crown Court heard that the company failed to adequately risk assess the works or control the way in which the excavation took place.

The company pleaded guilty to breaching Section 3(1) of the Health and Safety at Work etc. Act 1974, Regulation 31(1) of the Construction (Design and Management Regulations) 2007 and Regulation 3(1)(a) of the Management of Health and Safety at Work Regulations 1999.

A HSE inspector said after the hearing: 'The level of this fine should serve as a warning to industry not to ignore health and safety matters.

'The company failed to adequately assess, plan and supervise the work being undertaken.

'Trench collapses are easy to prevent, and it is disappointing that this young man's life was lost in such a tragic way.

'The family has shown great patience and support throughout this investigation, which is a credit to both them and their son's memory'.

The deceased worker's mother said after the hearing that: 'no amount of money can bring my son back, but we hope it will help to stop anything like this happening again and stop other parents having to go through what we have been through'.

(Source: HSE.)

CONTENTS

Construction (Design and Management) Regulations

03

Supporting
INFORMATION

GT700 Toolbox talks / supporting checklists and forms

Toolbox talks on some of these topics are available in the GT700 publication. Supporting checklists and forms covering some of these topics are available on our companion website.

CONSTRUCTION (DESIGN AND MANAGEMENT) REGULATIONS

Overview

The Construction (Design and Management) Regulations (CDM) are the main regulations that cover the management of health, safety and welfare on construction projects. The regulations apply to all construction projects, regardless of size, duration and nature of the work. The current regulations (in force from 6 April 2015) replaced the 2007 CDM Regulations.

This chapter outlines what the regulations are about, what they require, what needs to be done and by whom.

3.1 Introduction

The CDM Regulations were first introduced in 1994, with revisions in 2007 and 2015. While some requirements have been adjusted and developed, the overall aim remains improving health and safety within the construction industry.

 Where CDM is mentioned in this chapter, it should be read as the Construction (Design and Management) Regulations 2015.

CDM focus attention on effective planning and management of all construction work, from the design concept onwards. The aim is for health and safety considerations to be treated as a normal part of a project's development, not an afterthought.

The object of CDM is to reduce the risk of harm to those that have to build, use, maintain and demolish structures.

The main aims of the regulations are listed below.

● Encourage everyone to work together to make health and safety integral to the design, construction and management of projects.

● Improve planning and management from day one to identify hazards so that they can be eliminated or properly managed.

● Have the right people, for the right job, at the right time to manage the risks on site.

● Encourage co-operation and co-ordination throughout the project.

While CDM cover most of the construction-specific risks, it is important to ensure compliance with other relevant regulations, such as the Work at Height Regulations and the Control of Substances Hazardous to Health Regulations.

 Every construction project or building job, no matter how small, is a CDM job. The requirements of CDM apply regardless of whether the project is notifiable or not.

 CITB has produced a short video which explains the basics of CDM.

3.2 Important points

● CDM apply to all building and construction work, including new build, demolition, refurbishment, extensions, conversions, repair and maintenance.

● Designers and contractors should be appointed at the earliest opportunity to help them prepare for, and plan, the project.

● Everyone controlling construction work has health and safety responsibilities.

● Employers need to provide information, instruction, training and supervision, with workers having their needs assessed against the needs of the job. Employers are required to meet the gap in workers' skills and knowledge through provision of appropriate training.

● CDM apply to domestic client projects.

● On a project where there is more than one contractor, a principal contractor and principal designer will need to be appointed.

● Checking that working conditions are healthy and safe before work begins, and ensuring that the proposed work is not going to put others at risk, requires planning and organisation.

● A project is notifiable if construction work on a site is scheduled to: last longer than 30 working days and have more than 20 workers working simultaneously at any point in the project; or exceed 500 person days.

● CDM are supported by a regulatory package, which includes CDM, HSE CDM legal (L) series guidance and industry guidance.

● A legal series guidance (L153) supports the regulations and details the legal requirements for CDM. It should be used to help anyone who has duties to comply with the regulations.

 The legal series guidance (L153 CDM) is available on the HSE website.

A series of industry guidance documents for main duty holders sets out in practical terms what actions are required to deliver a safe and healthy project. These have been written by the Construction Industry Advisory Committee (CONIAC) with small businesses in mind.

The **main duty holders** under CDM are listed below.

- Clients (including domestic clients).
- Principal designers.
- Designers.

- Principal contractors.
- Contractors.
- Workers.

 Industry guidance for each duty holder is available on the CITB website.

 For a summary of the duty holders' main responsibilities refer to Appendix B.

3.3 Main elements to securing construction health and safety

The incorporation of the following elements into all projects is key to securing construction health and safety.

- Managing the risks to health and safety by applying the **general principles of prevention** (the Management of Health and Safety at Work Regulations (MHSWR)).
- **Appointing** the right people and organisations at the right time.
- Ensuring everyone has the **information, instruction, training and supervision** they need to carry out their jobs in a way that secures health and safety.
- Duty holders **co-operating and communicating** with each other and co-ordinating their work to promote and develop effective measures to secure health, safety and welfare.
- **Consulting** workers and engaging with them to promote and develop effective measures to secure health, safety and welfare.

3.3.1 General principles of prevention

Principal designers, designers, principal contractors and contractors must apply the general principles of prevention when carrying out their duties and use these to identify control measures required to control the risks identified on the project.

The general principles of prevention are specified in Schedule 1 to the MHSWR and referred to in CDM. They are shown below.

- Avoiding risks.
- Evaluating the risks that cannot be avoided.
- Combating the risks at source.
- Adapting the work to the individual, especially regarding the design of workplaces, the choice of work equipment and the choice of working and production methods, with a view, in particular, to alleviating monotonous work and work at a predetermined work rate and reducing their effect on health.
- Adapting to technical progress.

- Replacing the dangerous with the non-dangerous or the less dangerous.

- Developing a coherent overall prevention policy that covers technology, organisation of work, working conditions, social relationships and the influence of factors relating to the working environment.

- Giving collective protective measures priority over individual protective measures.

- Giving appropriate instructions to employees.

3.3.2 Appointing the right people and organisations at the right time

Anyone involved in the project must ensure they have the skills, knowledge, training and experience (and if they are an organisation, the organisational capability) to carry out the work. This applies to those making the appointment, as well as those accepting the appointment.

Appointments for the project must be made as soon as practicable (for example, the principal designer should be appointed as early as possible). Failure by the client to make this appointment means that the client must fulfil the duties of the principal designer until such an appointment is made. Therefore, if the appointment is made late this could have a negative impact on the collation of data for the pre-construction information pack and design considerations may be overlooked, which could have an impact on the safety of the construction and residual maintenance requirements.

When appointing a designer or contractor, reasonable steps should be made to ensure they understand how to identify the significant risks likely to arise during either design or construction. They should also be able to prevent those risks, or manage or control them to an acceptable level.

Pre-qualification questionnaires can be a useful tool. For example, the free, publicly available PAS 91 standard: *Construction related procurement – pre-qualification questionnaire* (PAS 91) for procuring supply chain specialists includes health and safety questions, along with other matters (such as financial information). There is also the free, publicly available *Specification for collaborative sharing and use of structured health and safety information using BIM* (PAS 1192-6:2018). BIM is an intelligent 3D model-based process that gives architecture, engineering and construction professionals the insight and tools to more efficiently plan, design, construct and manage buildings and infrastructure.

PAS 1192-6 specifies requirements for the collaborative sharing of structured health and safety information throughout the project and asset life cycles. It supports the development of structured health and safety information for all construction projects progressively from the outset. The PAS provides guidance on how health and safety information is produced, flows and can be used throughout the project and asset life cycle. The principles and requirements of this PAS can be applied equally to non-BIM projects.

For further information refer to Regulation 8 *General duties*. This regulation applies to anyone working on a project and includes workers, as well as those with specific duties.

 Failure to appoint the right people at the right time could have an impact on the health and safety performance and success of the project.

3.3.3 Supervision, instruction and information

Contractors and principal contractors must make sure that the supervision provided is effective and the required information is provided.

An assessment of the workforce's skills, knowledge, training and experience, plus the health and safety risks involved in the project, needs to be made to ensure the correct level of supervision, instruction and information is provided. Other factors to consider to determine the correct level of supervision to be provided are the individual's age, agility, level of safety awareness, literacy and attitude.

Anyone with a duty under CDM to provide health and safety information or instructions must ensure they are easy to understand. For example, the information should be in clear English, or other languages, as appropriate for the people using it. The use of diagrams and pictures should also be considered and information should be proportionate to the scale and complexity of the risks.

Information about hazards is essential to all project workers and managers to ensure they understand the risks involved.

Instructions are actions that must be followed to prevent or minimise those risks.

3.3.4 Co-operating, communicating and co-ordinating

The regulations stipulate that all duty holders must co-operate with other duty holders involved in the project or any project adjoining the site (Regulation 8(4)) and co-ordinate their work to ensure effective health and safety. They must also communicate with each other to ensure that everyone understands the risks and the measures that need to be put into place to control those risks.

 Regulation 4 requires that the client takes reasonable steps to ensure that the principal designer and principal contractor comply with their duties, which include the requirement to plan, manage, monitor and co-ordinate their work.

There are many examples of where the various contractors involved in a project can co-operate, communicate and co-ordinate their work, agreeing who works where and when so that construction work runs smoothly and without the risks created by one set of workers endangering the health and safety of other workers.

Daily briefings and project meetings are also good examples of achieving this.

3.3.5 Consulting and engaging with workers

Regulation 14 places a legal duty on principal contractors to consult and engage with workers.

Additionally, the **Safety Representatives and Safety Committee Regulations** and the **Health and Safety (Consultation with Employees) Regulations** require employers to consult their workforce about health and safety.

Worker consultation and engagement is basically effective two-way communication between an employer and its workforce. It can help workers spot workplace risks and know what to do about them, ensure that controls are effective and increase workers' commitment to working in a safe and healthy way.

The following are requirements for the principal contractor.

● Make and maintain arrangements that will enable the principal contractor and the workers engaged in construction work to co-operate effectively in developing, promoting and checking the effectiveness of measures to ensure the health, safety and welfare of the workers.

● Consult with workers or their representatives in good time on matters connected with the project, which may affect their health, safety or welfare.

● Ensure that workers or their representatives can inspect and take copies of any information that the principal contractor has, or which these regulations require to be provided to the principal contractor, which relate to the health, safety or welfare of workings at the site. There are a number of exceptions to this requirement, which are detailed in Regulation 14(c)(i-v).

Encouragement and ample opportunity must be given for all members of the workforce to feed back to management any concerns that they might have regarding health and safety. It is the workforce that has first-hand experience of actually carrying out the job and may, therefore, be more knowledgeable about the risks involved.

Depending upon the circumstances, consultation might be carried out directly with a single worker, groups of workers or through health and safety representatives, whether trade union-appointed or not.

 The HSE website hosts the leadership and worker involvement toolkit (LWIT), which aims to help contractors and managers learn how to make health and safety improvements in their business.

3.4 The regulations

CDM place responsibility for managing the health and safety of a construction project on the many duty holders.

The **client** must ensure that suitable arrangements are made, reviewed and maintained to manage the health and safety risks involved in the project.

For projects involving more than one contractor the regulations require the client to appoint a principal designer and principal contractor and to make sure they carry out their duties.

The **principal designer** is required to plan, manage, monitor and co-ordinate the work during the pre-construction phase.

They must also liaise with the principal contractor to provide them with the relevant information for planning, management and monitoring during the construction phase.

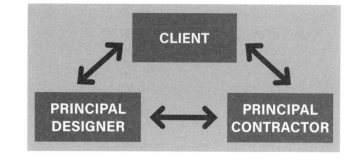

The main duty of the **principal contractor** is to plan, manage, monitor and co-ordinate the work during the construction phase. They must also liaise with the client and principal designer throughout the project, including during the pre-construction phase.

Depending on the nature of the project the principal designer and principal contractor may be supported by **designers, contractors** and **workers**.

There are three important phases of the project, known as the pre-construction phase, the construction phase and the post-construction phase.

The **pre-construction phase** covers the inception, design and planning stage of a project (before the construction or building work starts), although it is acknowledged that design and planning continues into the construction phase.

Data for the *pre-construction information* will be collated during this stage.

The **construction phase** runs from start to finish of the construction or building work.

The *construction phase plan* will be followed during this stage.

The **post-construction phase** is the practical completion of the construction or building work, including handover.

The *health and safety file* will be completed and handed over during this stage.

 A project is notifiable if the construction work is scheduled to take more than 30 working days and have more than 20 workers working simultaneously or exceed 500 person days.

CONSTRUCTION (DESIGN AND MANAGEMENT) REGULATIONS

The following parts of the regulations apply to the whole construction process on all projects, from concept to completion.

Part 1	Introduction.	Part 5	General.
Part 2	Client duties.	Schedule 1	Particulars to be notified under Regulation 6.
Part 3	Health and safety duties and roles.	Schedule 2	Welfare facilities.
Part 4	General requirements for all construction sites.	Schedule 3	Work involving particular risks.

Parts 1, 2, 3 and 5 of CDM cover the whole construction project, from concept to completion.

Part 4 sets out a number of provisions that apply to work carried out on the construction *site*.

Where there is more than one contractor, or it is reasonably foreseeable that more than one contractor will be working on the project at any time, the client needs to appoint, in writing, a principal designer and principal contractor and ensure that a construction phase plan is prepared. **These appointments must be made regardless of whether a project is notifiable or not.**

The requirement for duty holders to have the skills, knowledge, training and experience (or where they are an organisation, the organisational capability) and the arrangements for the co-ordination of work and co-operation between all those working on the project **applies to all projects.**

For definitions, in accordance with CDM, refer to Appendix A.

For Schedule 2 Welfare facilities, refer to Appendix D.

3.5 Notification (Form F10)

A project is notifiable by the client when it is scheduled to last longer than 30 working days and have more than 20 workers working simultaneously at any point in the project or exceed 500 person days.

A day is taken as being eight hours' work and a working day is where work is planned. **If there is a major change that will result in a significant delay or change to the project itself, the work could become notifiable at a later date.**

Holidays and weekends do not count if construction work is not carried out at those times.

A *person day* is the number of hours worked by an individual and includes any shift work. In any one working day, where shift work takes place, there will be more than one person day in the working day. A person day also includes any other length of time worked that is less than one full day.

The responsibility of the designers and contractors to ensure that the client is aware of their CDM duties is vitally important. As construction professionals they are in the best place to advise on the planned timescales.

Clients must ensure an up-to-date copy of the notice is displayed on the construction site and that it can be easily understood, taking into consideration workers whose first language may not be English. The client can do this themselves or ask the principal contractor or contractor to do so.

The notice to the relevant enforcing authority must be in writing. The enforcing authority could be the **HSE**, the **Office of Rail and Road**, or the **Office for Nuclear Regulation**.

Details of the information required for the notification are given in Schedule 1 of CDM and include details such as the planned start date, contact details of the duty holders and the planned number of contractors on the site.

The easiest way to notify any project is using the online F10 form. The online system also allows the retrieval, amendment and re-submission of previously completed F10 forms.

The F10 form is located in the CDM section of the HSE website.

The notification must be sent as soon as practicable before the construction phase begins. If not all of the details are known at that time, as much detail as possible must be sent and the remaining details forwarded as soon as they become known.

Where the client is a domestic client the duty to notify can be carried out by either the contractor (if there is only one contractor), the principal contractor (where there is more than one contractor) or the principal designer (where there is a written agreement that the principal designer will fulfil the client's duties).

The F10 form is a living document that may need updating throughout the project.

3.6   Duty holders

3.6.1   Client

 Clients

A *client* is any person for whom a project is carried out.

A *commercial client* is an organisation or individual for whom a construction project is being carried out in connection with a business, whether the business operates for profit or not.

A *domestic client* is a client for whom a project is being carried out, which is not in the course or furtherance of a business of that client.

03

The term *client* includes both domestic clients and commercial clients. However, Regulation 7 limits the way in which CDM apply to a domestic client.

Clients have an important role in the construction process. The regulations make them accountable for the impact that their decisions and approach have on the health, safety and welfare of those working on the project, plus anyone who may be affected by those project activities. The client has contractual control, makes appointments and determines the money, time and resources available for the project.

Where it is not clear who the client is, due to the number of individuals and organisations involved, Regulation 4(8) allows all the possible clients to elect one or more person(s) to be treated as the client. When deciding who this could be consideration should be given to who:

- decides what is constructed where, when and by whom
- commissions the design and construction work
- initiates the work
- is at the head of the procurement chain
- appoints contractors (including the principal contractor) and designers (including the principal designer).

> **!**   **If a commercial client fails to appoint either a principal designer or a principal contractor they must fulfil those duties themselves, until an appointment has been made.**

Further details of client duties can be found in the legal series and industry guidance (L153), and are summarised below.

Summary of client duties	
Commercial client	**Domestic client**
▪ Make arrangements to manage the project without risk to health and safety. ▪ Ensure welfare arrangements are provided, as detailed in Schedule 2. ▪ Allow sufficient time and resources for all stages. ▪ Provide pre-construction information to designers and contractors as soon as possible. ▪ Ensure, before the construction phase begins, a construction phase plan is drawn up by the principal contractor, or the contractor if there is only one contractor. ▪ Ensure the principal designer prepares the health and safety file for the project. ▪ Take reasonable steps to ensure the principal designer and principal contractor comply with their duties. ▪ If the client's interest in the structure changes, they must pass the health and safety file onto their successor, making sure they are aware of the contents of the file. ▪ Ensure those they appoint have the skills, knowledge, training, experience and capabilities to carry out those roles.	▪ Where there is one contractor the client's duties must be carried out by the contractor. ▪ Where there is more than one contractor the client's duties must be carried out by the principal contractor. ▪ Domestic clients can have a written agreement to transfer their client duties to the principal designer. In this case, the principal designer must fulfil the duties of the client as well as their own duties, and the principal contractor will work to the principal designer as the client. ▪ Where there is more than one contractor a principal contractor and principal designer should be appointed. ▪ If the domestic client fails to appoint a designer, the designer in control of the pre-construction phase becomes the principal designer. ▪ If the domestic client fails to appoint a contractor, the contractor in control of the construction phase is the principal contractor.

>   **For further information on working for a domestic client refer to Appendix 6 of the legal series guidance (L153), or refer to the industry guidance for clients.**

3.6.2 Principal designer

 Principal designer

The *principal designer* is the designer with control over the pre-construction phase of the project. They are appointed by the client.

Principal designers are designers appointed by the client, and are responsible for influencing how the health and safety risks should be controlled and incorporated into the project's delivery.

They must plan, manage, monitor and co-ordinate matters relating to health and safety during the pre-construction phase to ensure that the project is carried out without risks to health or safety, taking into account the principles of prevention.

They must consider their own skills, knowledge, training, experience and, where they are an organisation, they must also consider their organisational capabilities and seek advice where required. They may also have separate duties as a designer.

Further details of principal designers' duties can be found in the legal series (L153) and industry guidance, summarised below.

Summary of principal designer duties

- Plan, manage, monitor and co-ordinate the pre-construction phase.
- Co-ordinate matters relating to health and safety during the pre-construction phase.
- Estimate the period of time required to complete work stages.
- Take account of the general principles of prevention.
- Identify, eliminate or control foreseeable risks to health and safety of any person carrying out construction work, maintaining or cleaning a structure and/or using a structure designed as a workplace.
- Ensure designers comply with their duties.
- Ensure all persons co-operate with the client, principal designer and each other.
- Assist the client in the provision of the pre-construction information.
- Provide pre-construction information promptly and in a convenient form to every designer or contractor.
- Liaise with the principal contractor and share information relevant to the planning, management and monitoring of the construction phase and the co-ordination of health and safety during construction.
- Review, update and complete the health and safety file and pass to the client upon completion.
- Hand over the health and safety file to the principal contractor if their appointment finishes before the end of the project.

 For further information refer to the industry guidance for principal designers.

3.6.3 Designer

 Designer

A *designer* is an organisation or individual who prepares or modifies a design for a construction project (including the design of temporary works) or arranges for or instructs someone else to do so.

Designers include architects, consulting engineers, quantity surveyors, interior designers and contractors, and may include individual tradespeople on smaller domestic projects.

Designers are in a unique position at an early stage of a project to reduce the potential risks to health and safety that could arise during the construction phase or at a later stage (such as during maintenance of the completed structure).

Therefore, designers should address health and safety issues from the outset. If designers fail to consider health and safety at an early stage this could result in delays to the project and could cause problems during the construction phase, as contractors will need to identify ways to undertake the work safely.

Further details of designers' duties can be found in the legal series (L153) and industry guidance, and are summarised below. These duties become applicable as soon as a design has been prepared, which may be used for construction work. It is irrelevant if planning permission and funds have not yet been secured.

The duties of a designer are outlined on the table on the next page.

 Designers have the same duties when working for a domestic client as they do when working for a commercial client.

Summary of designer duties

- Must not commence work unless they are satisfied that the client is aware of their duties.
- Eliminate hazards and reduce risks during design.
- Provide information about remaining risks to the principal designer and ensure information is in the health and safety file.
- Take into account the principles of prevention when preparing or modifying a design.
- Eliminate health and safety risks that may affect those carrying out future construction work, maintaining or cleaning a structure or using a structure designed as a workplace.
- Take steps to reduce any residual risks through the design process.
- Supply information to the client, other designers and contractors, so they can comply with their duties.
- The same duties apply to designers for designs that are prepared or modified outside of Great Britain.

 For further information refer to the industry guidance for designers.

 For an example of CDM RAG lists (practical aids for designers on what to eliminate or avoid and what to encourage) refer to Appendix C.

3.6.4 Principal contractor

Aa Principal contractor

A *principal contractor* is the organisation or person who co-ordinates the work of the construction phase of the project involving more than one contractor, so that it is carried out in a way that secures health and safety.

A principal contractor is appointed by the client and they, and anyone they appoint, must have the skills, knowledge, training and experience (and where they are an organisation, the organisational capability) to carry out their work in a way that secures health and safety. The principal contractor must ensure the principles of prevention are taken into account. They must plan, manage, monitor and co-ordinate the construction phase to ensure that construction work is carried out without risks to health and safety.

Plan

- Take into account risks to workers, members of the public and clients' employees.
- Consider risks likely to arise during construction.
- Provide the right level of supervision, necessary information, instruction and training.

Manage

- Ensure those engaged to carry out the work are capable.
- Put preventative and protective measures in place.
- Provide the right plant, equipment and tools.
- Demonstrate good leadership.
- Ensure workers understand the risks and control measures, and who has responsibility for health and safety.
- Investigate incidents so that lessons can be learnt.

 Good supervision is part of showing good leadership in health and safety.

Monitor

- Check standards regularly, taking into account the rapidly changing construction environment, and allocate sufficient time and effort for this.
- Treat health and safety in the same way as other important business aspects.
- Take prompt action.
- Use both active and reactive monitoring.

 Active monitoring includes routine checks of areas, plant and equipment, or health risk management to prevent harm.

Reactive monitoring includes investigating near-miss incidents, injuries and monitoring ill health cases.

CONSTRUCTION (DESIGN AND MANAGEMENT) REGULATIONS

Co-ordinate

- Ensure contractors co-operate with each other.
- Apply the general principles of prevention.
- Follow the construction phase plan.
- Liaise with those on site so they understand the health and safety standards expected and gain their co-operation.
- Work with the client to ensure co-ordination of contractors on neighbouring sites.

 There should only be one principal contractor for a project at any one time. Their role, when working on a project for a domestic client, is no different to the role undertaken for a commercial client.

Summary of principal contractor duties
▪ Plan, manage, monitor and co-ordinate the construction phase plan.
▪ Estimate the time required to complete the work.
▪ Take into account the general principles of prevention.
▪ Organise co-operation between contractors.
▪ Comply with the health and safety legal requirements.
▪ Ensure the construction phase plan is followed.
▪ Provide suitable site induction.
▪ Prevent unauthorised access to the site.
▪ Provide welfare facilities.
▪ Liaise with the principal designer.
▪ Consult and engage with workers.
▪ Review, update and complete the health and safety file, if the principal designer's appointment finishes before the end of the project.

 Principal contractor fined for safety failings during property development

A principal contractor was fined £50,000 and ordered to pay £5,478 costs after the company failed to effectively plan and manage works at a property development. This included failing to ensure that appropriate measures were in place to control risks on site, including falls from height, exposure to asbestos and risk of fire.

The principal contractor pleaded guilty to breaching Regulation 13(1) of CDM and Section 33(1) of the Health and Safety at Work etc. Act 1974.

 For further information refer to the industry guidance for principal contractors.

3.6.5 Contractor

 Contractor

A *contractor* is anyone who directly employs or engages construction workers or manages construction. A contractor can be an individual, sole trader, self-employed worker or a business that carries out, manages or controls construction work as part of their business.

A contractor must plan, manage and monitor how the construction work is carried out, either by the contractor or by the workers under the contractor's control. If a contractor gets involved in any design work (such as temporary work or design of a hot air system) they could also have duties as designers.

 The duties on contractors apply whether the workers under their control are employees, self-employed or agency workers.

All contractors, including, for example, utility companies, specialist contractors and the self-employed, have a part to play in ensuring health and safety on site, via the proper co-ordination of their work, underpinned by effective communication and co-operation.

The main duties of contractors are outlined on the table on the next page.

Summary of contractor duties

- Check that the client is aware of their duties.

- Plan, manage and monitor construction work.

- If there is only one contractor on site, that contractor must take into account the principles of prevention, estimate the time required to complete the project and draw up the construction phase plan.

- Comply with directions given by the principal designer or principal contractor.

- Comply with the construction phase plan.

- Consult workers who are their employees.

- Appoint workers who have, or are in the process of obtaining, the necessary skills, knowledge, training and experience to carry out the tasks that have been allocated.

- Provide supervision, as required, depending on the hazards, risks, skills, knowledge, training and experience of the individuals.

- Provide information and instruction.

- Provide a site induction (if not already provided by the principal contractor).

- Prevent unauthorised access to site.

- Provide welfare facilities for their own employees who are working on the site or anyone else working under their control.

- Contractors appointed by the client (such as those on term contracts) are under the control of the principal contractor for the purposes of planning, managing and monitoring the construction work.

 Contractors have the same duties when working for a domestic client as they do when working for a commercial client.

 For further information refer to the industry guidance for contractors.

3.7   Workers

CDM recognise the importance of workers.

They help managers and workers to work together to improve health and safety, which will result in fewer construction workers suffering fatal injuries, becoming injured and/or suffering from ill health.

Employers, contractors and principal contractors should provide workers with the following.

- Health and safety information.

- Site induction, which covers site familiarisation and orientation (not just training).

- The necessary health and safety training, relevant to the work activities being carried out, and consultation and engagement on health and safety matters.

- A respected and trusted workplace health and safety culture.

- Appropriate supervision, relevant to the work activities being carried out, and the skills, knowledge and training of the workers involved.

- A safe place to work by managing hazards and communicating those control measures to workers.

- An explanation of the arrangements for co-operation and co-ordination.

- Adequate clean and accessible welfare facilities for men and women.

Where English is not the worker's first language, in order for contractors to fulfil their duties they could consider translating the site rules, using interpreters for inductions and task briefings, or supplementing written notices with symbols or diagrams.

 For further information refer to the industry guidance for workers.

3.8   Project documents

With regard to project documentation, CDM require the creation of a construction phase plan for all projects and, in some cases, a health and safety file.

Furthermore, the regulations require that relevant pre-construction information is gathered and compiled to form the basis of the construction phase plan for all projects.

This must include all the project-specific information that is relevant to health and safety during construction.

CONSTRUCTION (DESIGN AND MANAGEMENT) REGULATIONS

3.8.1   Pre-construction information

Pre-construction information provides health and safety information needed by designers and contractors, who are bidding for work on the project or who have already been appointed, to enable them to carry out their duties. It also provides information to the principal designers and principal contractors in planning, managing, monitoring and co-ordinating the work of the project, and it will form the basis of the construction phase plan.

It is the client's duty to provide pre-construction information. For projects where there is more than one contractor the client should expect the principal designer to help them bring the pre-construction information together, help them identify what must be obtained and provide it to the designers and contractors.

The client or principal designer may have to approach other organisations (such as utility companies or asbestos surveyors) to gather some of the information required.

Information for the file must:

- be relevant to the project
- have the appropriate level of detail
- be proportionate given the health and safety risks involved.

Where the client has created a useful pack of information, the tendering contractors' responses to questions asked can be used as part of the client checks to ensure that people and organisations appointed have the necessary skills, knowledge, training and experience (and, if an organisation, the organisational capability) to manage the health and safety risks.

3.8.2   Construction phase plan

The construction phase plan must record the following information.

- Health and safety arrangements for the construction phase.
- Site rules.
- Specific control measures where a worker could be put at risk, as detailed in Section 3.10 **(Schedule 3 of CDM)**.

Information included in the plan must:

- be relevant to the project
- have sufficient detail to set out the arrangements, site rules and special measures needed to manage the construction phase
- be proportionate to the scale and complexity of the project and risks involved.

The client must ensure the construction phase plan is drawn up **before** the construction phase begins. For projects involving more than one contractor the principal contractor is responsible for drawing up the plan.

For single contractor projects the contractor is responsible. The principal designer must help the principal contractor to prepare the plan by providing any relevant information that they hold. As the project develops it is likely that the construction phase plan will be amended and further developed in the light of emerging issues and situations.

It is a live working document that is the basis for the effective health and safety management of the project.

The principal contractor or contractor is responsible for the following.

- Preparing a construction phase plan, before the start of the construction phase, which is sufficient to ensure that the construction phase is planned, managed and monitored in such a way that construction work can be carried out without risk to health or safety, so far as is reasonably practicable, paying adequate regard to the pre-construction information provided by the designers.
- Throughout the project, reviewing, revising and refining the plan as often as is appropriate, so that it continues to be sufficient to fulfil the above requirement.
- Arranging for the plan to be implemented in such a way as to ensure, so far as is reasonably practicable, the health and safety of all persons carrying out construction work and other persons who may be affected by it.

Generally, during the construction phase, the construction phase plan will be expanded to outline the following.

- Details of the arrangements for protecting the health and safety of all persons who may be affected in any way by the construction work.
- Arrangements for the monitoring of the health and safety performance of persons involved in construction work to ensure they are complying with relevant statutory provisions and the construction phase plan.
- Information concerning the welfare arrangements that have been made.

> **Relevant parts of the information contained in the construction phase plan must be made available to, or be made known to, contractors before construction commences, so that they may be aware of risks to health and safety that may arise for their employees.**

With this knowledge they will be able to meet the requirements that are imposed on them under the construction phase plan. They obviously also have to meet the requirements that are imposed on them by the relevant statutory provisions.

CITB has designed a free CDM Wizard tool, which is available to download as an app or desktop version. The tool is intended for use on small-scale jobs, such as domestic client work (for example, installing a kitchen, building an extension, structural refurbishment and roofing work).

It is quick to use and produces a simple construction phase plan.

 For further information on the CDM Wizard visit the CITB website.

 Construction phase plans are required for all construction work under CDM. They do not replace risk assessments and method statements. They are a plan to show how the work will be managed and to identify significant hazards associated with the work.

CDM Wizard app

3.8.3 Health and safety file

The purpose of the health and safety file is to ensure that, at the end of the project, the client has information about the health and safety risks that anyone carrying out subsequent construction work on the building will need to know about.

The client must ensure that the principal designer prepares the health and safety file and that it is revised, as appropriate, and kept available for inspection by any person who may need to refer to it to obtain necessary information to undertake the work safely.

This means that the role involves selecting relevant information to include, and possibly rejecting other material that is submitted.

For example, putting the construction phase method statements about groundworks in the file is unlikely to be useful in the future, whereas identifying the position and size of the crane used for lifting in steelwork or air-conditioning units may be of use.

If the role of the principal designer finishes before the end of the project, the client should ensure that the file is handed to the principal contractor. The emphasis is on information that has a relevance to the future.

At the completion of the project, the file is given to the client and, unless further changes to the structure are made, it then remains as a permanent record of how the project was designed and built.

3.9 General requirements for all construction sites

Part 4 of the regulations sets out a number of provisions (listed below) that relate specifically to the construction site.

● Applies only to a construction site.

● Requires a contractor to comply with the requirements of this part.

● Requires a domestic client, who controls the way in which construction work is carried out, to comply with the requirements of this part, so far as they relate to matters within the client's control.

 The duties in the following table apply to all construction sites, regardless of size, nature or duration.

Regulation number and title	Details of duties and requirements
16. Application of Regulations 17 to 35.	This regulation states that every contractor carrying out construction work must comply.
17. Safe places of work.	Every place of work must be safe to access, egress and to work at. Unauthorised access must be prevented and sufficient working space must be provided.
18. Good order and site security.	Sites must be tidy, secure (to prevent unauthorised access), have their perimeter identified by suitable signs and have no projecting sharp objects.
19. Stability of structures.	Buildings and structures must not be allowed to become unstable during work and any supports provided must be adequate for the job.
20. Demolition or dismantling.	This work must be carried out so as to prevent any danger and there must be a written plan (for example, method statement) in place before work starts.
21. Explosives.	Explosives must be stored, transported and used safely. Steps must be taken to ensure persons are not exposed to risk of injury from the explosion or the projected or flying material.

CONSTRUCTION (DESIGN AND MANAGEMENT) REGULATIONS

Regulation number and title	Details of duties and requirements
22. Excavations.	Work in excavations must be properly planned. They must not be allowed to collapse or have materials falling or slipping into them. No-one should become trapped because of inadequate shoring. Excavations must be inspected and reports written as appropriate. Work in an excavation must not start where an inspection has revealed that it is not safe to do so.
23. Cofferdams and caissons.	Cofferdams and caissons must be suitably designed, constructed, maintained and inspected. They must be appropriately equipped so that workers can gain shelter or escape if water or materials enter them. Cofferdams and caissons must be inspected by a competent person at the start of every shift or if the strength or stability has been affected. If the inspection reveals it is not safe then work must not start until this has been rectified.
24. Reports of inspections.	The duty to carry out inspections refers to Regulations 22 and 23 and requires inspections to be made at the start of every shift and after any event likely to affect the safety of the excavation, cofferdam or caisson. The person carrying out the inspection must inform the person on whose behalf the inspection was carried out, before the end of the shift, of any health and safety risks identified. A written record of an inspection must be made at intervals not exceeding seven days. It must be retained until completion of the project and then for a further three months.
25. Energy distribution installations.	Energy distribution installations must be located, checked and indicated. Overhead power cables must be protected against being damaged or causing injury or damage. Work must not take place where there is a risk of damage to, or accidental disturbance of, energy distribution systems, unless suitable control measures have been taken.
26. Prevention of drowning.	Where there is risk of a person drowning because of falling into water or other liquid, suitable measures must be put in place to prevent falls and, where a risk remains, minimise the risk of drowning and ensure there is a rescue plan and maintained equipment in place. Where workers are transported over water, to and from their place of work, the vessel must not be overcrowded or overloaded.
27. Traffic routes.	Traffic routes must be organised to protect people from injury from vehicles and be suitable for the number of vehicles and persons using them. Traffic routes must be properly maintained, suitably signed and regularly inspected. Where it is unsafe for pedestrians to use gates intended for use by vehicles, separate pedestrian gates must be provided, marked and kept free of obstruction.
28. Vehicles.	Arrangements must be made to prevent unintended movement of any vehicle. Vehicles must be used safely, not overloaded, and be prevented from falling into any excavation. No-one must be allowed to ride on any vehicle unless it is designed to carry passenger(s) and it is safe to do so. No-one must remain on any vehicle that is being loaded unless a safe place is provided and maintained on the vehicle.
29. Prevention of risk from fire, flooding, and so on.	Steps must be taken to avoid the risk of fire, explosion, flooding and asphyxiation from any substance.
30. Emergency procedures.	A plan must be in place for the safe evacuation of all people on site in situations where there is a foreseeable risk of an emergency. Everyone on site must be made aware of the emergency plan and it must be practised at suitable intervals.
31. Emergency routes and exits.	Adequate means of evacuation (emergency escape routes) to a safe place must be established. Routes must be kept clear of obstruction and be adequately signed.
32. Fire detection and fire-fighting.	Suitable fire-fighting equipment, fire detection equipment and alarms must be provided, examined and tested at suitable intervals and be suitably located. Manual fire-fighting equipment (such as hand-held extinguishers) must be easy to access and indicated by appropriate signs. An appropriate number of on-site staff must be trained in the selection and use of fire-fighting equipment.
33. Fresh air.	Places of construction work or on the approach to construction work must have adequate fresh or purified air available. Where fresh or purified air is provided by plant, it must be equipped with suitable audible or visible warnings to indicate any inadequacy in the supply or machine failure.
34. Temperature and weather protection.	Steps must be taken to ensure that indoor temperatures are reasonable. Outdoor workplaces must be arranged to provide adequate protection against adverse weather, taking into account usage and protective clothing or equipment provided.
35. Lighting.	Every place of work, its access and egress routes and any traffic route must be adequately lit, preferably by natural light. Where lighting is by artificial means, a back-up system must be in place where failure of the primary system would result in risks to health or safety. Artificial light must not adversely affect or change the perception of any health and safety sign or signal.

3.10   Work involving particular risks (Schedule 3)

A construction phase plan, where applicable, must include specific measures concerning work that falls within one or more of the categories set out in Schedule 3, listed below.

- Work that puts workers at risk of burial under earthfalls, engulfment in swampland or falling from a height, where the risk is particularly aggravated by the nature of the work or processes used or by the environment at the place of work or site.

- Work that puts workers at risk from chemical or biological substances constituting a particular danger to the health or safety of workers or involving a legal requirement for health monitoring.

- Work with ionising radiation requiring the designation of controlled or supervised areas under Regulation 16 of the Ionising Radiations Regulations.

- Work near high-voltage power lines.

- Work exposing workers to the risk of drowning.

- Work on wells, underground earthworks and tunnels.

- Work carried out by divers having a system of air supply.

- Work carried out by workers in caissons with a compressed air atmosphere.

- Work involving the use of explosives.

- Work involving the assembly or dismantling of heavy, prefabricated components.

Details of the assembly of heavy, prefabricated components (such as this truss lift) must be included in the construction phase plan

Appendix A – Definitions (Regulation 2)

Design. Includes drawings, design details, specifications, bills of quantities (including specification of articles or substances) relating to a structure, and calculations prepared for the purpose of a design.

Construction work. Carrying out any building, civil engineering or engineering construction work, such as those listed below.

- Construction, alteration, conversion, fitting out, commissioning, renovation, repair, upkeep, redecoration or other maintenance (including cleaning that involves using water or an abrasive at high pressure), cleaning (using corrosive or toxic substances), decommissioning, demolition or dismantling of a structure.

- Preparatory works for an intended structure, including site clearance, exploration, investigation (but not site survey) and excavation (but not pre-construction archaeological investigations), and clearance for preparation of the site or structure for use of occupation at its conclusion.

- Assembly on site of prefabricated elements to form a structure or the disassembly on site of the prefabricated elements, which immediately before disassembly formed such a structure.

- Removal of a structure or of any product or waste resulting from demolition or dismantling of a structure from disassembly or prefabricated elements, which immediately before such disassembly formed such a structure.

- Installation, commissioning, maintenance, repair or removal of mechanical, electrical, gas, compressed air, hydraulic, telecommunications, computer or similar services, which are normally fixed within or to a structure.

Structure. This means any building, timber, masonry, metal or reinforced concrete structure, railway line or siding, tramway line, dock, harbour, inland navigation, tunnel, shaft, bridge, viaduct, waterworks, reservoir, pipe or pipeline, cable, aqueduct, sewer, sewerage works, gas holder, road, airfield, sea defence work, river work, drainage work, earthwork, lagoon, dam, wall, caisson, mast, tower, pylon, underground tank, earth retaining structure or structure designed to preserve or alter any natural feature, fixed plant and any structure similar to those listed, or formwork, falsework, scaffold or other structure designed or used to provide support or means of access during construction work. *(Note: any reference to a structure includes part of a structure.)*

Project. A project which includes or is intended to include construction work, including planning, design, management or other work involved in a project until the end of the construction phase.

Notifiable project. Specific details of the project have to be notified to the relevant enforcing authority, the HSE (or Office of Rail and Road, or Office of Nuclear Regulation) by the client as soon as practicable before the construction phase begins. A project is notifiable if the construction work on a construction site is scheduled to last longer than 30 working days and have more than 20 workers working simultaneously at any point in the project or exceed 500 person days.

The **construction phase** starts when construction work on the project commences, and ends when construction work on that project is completed.

Client. A client may be a single person or an organisation. They are the people for whom the work is being carried out. They have duties under CDM when a project is commissioned in connection with a business activity, even if it is commissioned by a not-for-profit organisation. Whether or not the client's duties apply will be obvious on many occasions, but may require some delicate questioning of the client by the designer, contractor or others.

Domestic client. A person who has construction work carried out in their own home, or the home of a family member, which is not done as part of a business, whether for profit or not. A domestic client can transfer their duties to a contractor, principal contractor or principal designer. Regulation 7 limits the way in which the regulations apply to domestic clients.

Principal designer. The person appointed by the client on projects that have more than one contractor. This can be an individual or an organisation with sufficient knowledge, skills, training and experience (and if an organisation, the organisational capability) to carry out the role for the construction project.

Designer. Any person who whilst at work (whether they are paid or not) carries out any design work, including modification, or arranges for someone under their control to do design work.

Principal contractor. The contractor appointed by the client. Their most important duties are to co-ordinate and manage the construction phase of the project, and ensure the health and safety of everyone involved in the construction work or anyone who may be affected by it.

Contractor. Can be an individual or a company who are completing the actual construction work.

03

Appendix B – Summary of duty holders' roles and duties under CDM

CDM duty holders	Who are they?	Summary of role/main duty
Clients	Organisations or individuals for whom a construction project is carried out.	Make suitable arrangements for managing a project. This includes making sure: ■ other duty holders are appointed ■ sufficient time and resources are allocated ■ relevant information is prepared and provided to other duty holders ■ the principal designer and principal contractor carry out their duties ■ welfare facilities are provided.
Domestic clients	People who have construction work carried out on their own home, or the home of a family member, that is not done as part of a business, whether for profit or not.	Their duties as a client are normally transferred to either: ■ the contractor on a single contractor project, or ■ the principal contractor, on a project involving more than one contractor. However, the domestic client can choose to have a written agreement with the principal designer to carry out the client duties.
Designers	Those who, as part of a business, prepare or modify designs for a building, product or system relating to construction work.	When preparing or modifying designs, to eliminate, reduce or control foreseeable risks that may arise during: ■ construction, and ■ the maintenance and use of a building once it is built. Provide information to other members of the project team to help them fulfil their duties.
Principal designers	Designers appointed by the client in projects involving more than one contractor. They can be an organisation or an individual with sufficient knowledge, experience and ability to carry out the role.	Plan, manage, monitor and co-ordinate health and safety in the pre-construction phase of a project. This includes: ■ identifying, eliminating and controlling foreseeable risks ■ ensuring designers carry out their duties. Prepare and provide relevant information to other duty holders. Liaise with the principal contractor to help in the planning, management, monitoring and co-ordination of the construction phase.
Principal contractors	Contractors appointed by the client to co-ordinate the construction phase of a project where it involves more than one contractor.	Plan, manage, monitor and co-ordinate the construction phase of a project. This includes: ■ liaising with the client and principal designer ■ preparing the construction phase plan ■ organising co-operation between contractors and co-ordinating their work. Ensure the following. ■ Suitable site inductions are provided. ■ Reasonable steps are taken to prevent unauthorised access. ■ Workers are consulted and engaged in securing their health and safety. ■ Welfare facilities are provided.

03

CONSTRUCTION (DESIGN AND MANAGEMENT) REGULATIONS – APPENDIX B

CDM duty holders	Who are they?	Summary of role/main duty
Contractors	Those who do the actual construction work and can be either an individual or a company.	Plan, manage and monitor construction work under their control so that it is carried out without risks to health and safety. For projects involving more than one contractor, co-ordinate their activities with others in the project team – in particular, comply with directions given to them by the principal designer or principal contractor. For single contractor projects, prepare a construction phase plan.
Workers	The people who work for, or under, the control of contractors on a construction site.	They must: ■ be consulted about matters that affect their health, safety and welfare ■ take care of their own health and safety and that of others who may be affected by their actions ■ report anything they see that is likely to endanger their own or others' health and safety ■ co-operate with their employer, fellow workers, contractors and other duty holders.

(Reproduced from the Construction (Design and Management) Regulations 2015 legal series (L153 series) guidance book.)

! **All duty holders must co-operate with each other and co-ordinate their work to ensure health and safety on site.**

Appendix C – Schedule 2 Welfare facilities

Regulations 4(2)(b), 13(4)(c) and 15(11).

1. Sanitary conveniences

(1) Suitable and sufficient sanitary conveniences must be provided or made available at readily accessible places.

(2) So far as is reasonably practicable, rooms containing sanitary conveniences must be adequately ventilated and lit.

(3) So far as is reasonably practicable, sanitary conveniences and the rooms containing them must be kept in a clean and orderly condition.

(4) Separate rooms containing sanitary conveniences must be provided for men and women, except where and so far as each convenience is in a separate room, the door of which is capable of being secured from the inside.

2. Washing facilities

(1) Suitable and sufficient washing facilities, including showers if required by the nature of the work or for health reasons, must so far as is reasonably practicable, be provided or made available at readily accessible places.

(2) Washing facilities must be provided:

   (a)   in the immediate vicinity of every sanitary convenience, whether or not also provided elsewhere; and

   (b)   in the vicinity of any changing rooms required by paragraph 4, whether or not provided elsewhere.

(3) Washing facilities must include:

   (a)   a supply of clean hot and cold, or warm, water (which must be running water so far as is reasonably practicable)

   (b)   soap or other suitable means of cleaning; and

   (c)   towels or other suitable means of drying.

(4) Rooms containing washing facilities must be sufficiently ventilated and lit.

(5) Washing facilities and the rooms containing them must be kept in a clean and orderly condition.

(6) Subject to paragraph (7), separate washing facilities must be provided for men and women, except where they are provided in a room the door of which is capable of being secured from inside and the facilities in each room are intended to be used by only one person at a time.

(7) Sub-paragraph (6) does not apply to facilities which are provided for washing hands, forearms and the face only.

3. Drinking water

(1) An adequate supply of wholesome drinking water must be provided or made available at readily accessible and suitable places.

(2) Where necessary for reasons of health and safety, every supply of drinking water must be conspicuously marked by an appropriate sign.

(3) Where a supply of drinking water is provided a sufficient number of suitable cups or other drinking vessels must also be provided, unless the supply of drinking water is in a jet from which persons can drink easily.

4. Changing rooms and lockers

(1) Suitable and sufficient changing rooms must be provided or made available at readily accessible places if a worker:

   (a)   has to wear special clothing for the purposes of construction work; and

   (b)   cannot, for reasons of health or propriety, be expected to change elsewhere.

(2) Where necessary for reasons of propriety, there must be separate changing rooms for, or separate use of rooms by, men and women.

(3) Changing rooms must:

   (a)   be provided with seating; and

   (b)   include, where necessary, facilities to enable a person to dry any special clothing and any personal clothing or effects.

(4) Suitable and sufficient facilities must, where necessary, be provided or made available at readily accessible places to enable persons to lock away:

   (a)   any special clothing which is not taken home

   (b)   their own clothing which is not worn during working hours; and

   (c)   their personal effects.

5. Facilities for rest

(1) Suitable and sufficient rest rooms or rest areas must be provided or made available at readily accessible places.

(2) Rest rooms and rest areas must:

  (a) be equipped with an adequate number of tables and adequate seating with backs for the number of persons at work likely to use them at any one time

  (b) where necessary, include suitable facilities for any woman at work who is pregnant or who is a nursing mother to rest lying down

  (c) include suitable arrangements to ensure that meals can be prepared and eaten

  (d) include the means for boiling water; and

  (e) be maintained at an appropriate temperature.

(Reproduced under licence from The Controller of His Majesty's Stationery Office)

03

CONTENTS

Health and safety management systems

04

Supporting
INFORMATION

GT700 Toolbox talks / supporting checklists and forms

Toolbox talks on some of these topics are available in the GT700 publication. Supporting checklists and forms covering some of these topics are available on our companion website.

HEALTH AND SAFETY MANAGEMENT SYSTEMS

Overview

Organisations have a legal duty to put in place suitable arrangements to manage health and safety. By law, if a company employs five or more people, they must have a written health and safety policy.

The health and safety policy and associated documents are the basis of the company's health and safety management system. The management system should be specific to the business and detail how the health and safety of employees will be protected whilst at work.

This chapter explains the benefits of a health and safety management system, what it should contain and how it should be used.

4.1   Introduction

The production and implementation of a health and safety management system will be specific to individual companies, based on the level of risk of their operational activities and the environment where the work takes place.

 The Health and Safety Executive (HSE) provides a guide to health and safety management systems for leaders, owners and line managers in the free guidance document *Managing for health and safety* (HSG65).

Other health and safety management systems and guidance are available, including ISO 45001:2018. This is an international standard that is intended to be applicable to any organisation, regardless of its size, type and nature; the standard can be used by small, low-risk operations or equally by high-risk and large, complex organisations.

ISO 45001:2018 specifies requirements for an occupational health and safety (OH&S) management system, with guidance for its use, to enable an organisation to proactively improve its OH&S performance in preventing injury and ill health.

The first step to a health and safety management system is to produce the required health and safety policy.

Health and safety policy

A *health and safety policy* is a statement of how a company will, within its overall business, manage health, safety and welfare for the benefit of its employees and all other persons who may be affected by the company's operations.

There is no such thing as a standard health and safety policy, as a company's policy must be clearly and directly related to its own operations. Therefore, the policy will vary from one company to another.

It is common for companies to obtain policies via the internet or purchase them from third parties. These are generic and, although they may cover general health and safety issues, they rarely reflect the type of work that is carried out and may lead a company into a false sense of security. The content of the organisation and arrangements sections of the policy should be specific to each company. If a generic policy is used, and the contents are not further scrutinised and reviewed to suit the company's needs, it is likely that there will be serious omissions in its content and therefore in the way that health and safety is managed.

Each company's policy must be based upon its own work, management and organisational structure, and staff competencies.

The act of compiling a health and safety policy will focus the employer, or senior member of staff to whom the job is delegated, on the day-to-day management of health and safety issues. This will help them to become aware of shortcomings, duplications of effort and requirements for certain competencies, which can then be rectified.

Evidence shows that companies with a well-structured and properly implemented health and safety policy, together with the organisation and arrangements for putting the policy into effect, have much better overall health and safety performance. Clients and pre-tender documentation now regularly require a company not only to have a health and safety policy but also to demonstrate its implementation from the most senior management level downwards.

HSE construction accident statistics show that the main causes of accidents have been the same for the last 20 years. The main types of accident on site remain slips, trips or falls on the same level; injuries while handling, lifting or carrying; falls from height; and being struck by moving objects, including flying or falling objects. In addition work-related ill health statistics are alarmingly high due to lack of awareness and insufficient control measures; further, because symptoms can take years to develop, work-related health issues aren't seen as requiring immediate action. It is through the ongoing development of a company's health and safety policy that shortcomings can be identified and procedures put in place to help eliminate common causes of accidents and reverse this unenviable record.

The HSE's Accident Prevention Advisory Unit has shown that human error is a major contributor in 90% of accidents, 70% of which could have been prevented by management action. A comprehensive and accurate policy is the basis of an effective management system. A small company working on a small site has the same general health and safety responsibilities as a large company working on a large site.

Being on a small site does not mean that workers are any less likely to fall from height or fragile roofs, breathe in dust, be trapped in collapsed excavations, or be struck by falling material or reversing vehicles. There is no difference in the standard of protection required during a house extension compared to that for a major construction project; what is likely to differ is the complexity of the management system.

Health and safety, and the provision of proper welfare facilities, are crucial to the proper running of any building, construction or civil engineering project. They are not an add-on, an extra or an afterthought, but are a basic requirement and important control measure against illness, should be integrated with the normal day-by-day work of project planning, tendering and management, and are a shared duty from client to end user.

4.2   Important points

- The Health and Safety at Work etc. Act 1974 (HSWA) requires every employer to have a policy on how health and safety will be managed within the company.

- Organisations have a legal duty to put in place suitable arrangements to manage health and safety.

- The health and safety management system should explain how matters of health and safety will be organised within the company and the arrangements that the company has put in place for implementation.

- The health and safety management system and policy should be periodically reviewed to ensure that they are still current, and amended when necessary, with the content and changes made available to all employees.

- Before issuing contracts, clients and principal contractors will often make it a contractual requirement to see a written copy of each contractor's health and safety policy so that an assessment of their health and safety competency can be made, even if the contractor has fewer than five employees and there is no legal need to have one. Contractors will have to comply if they want the work.

- The health and safety policy should be based on a recognised health and safety management system (such as that outlined in HSG65 or similar).

- The health and safety policy needs to be company specific and should be written in consultation with the company's employees.

- If there are five or more employees, the policy must be written down.

- 'Off the shelf' health and safety policies, obtained from third parties, are unlikely to contain sufficient company-specific content.

- The health and safety management system and policy will have little value unless they are communicated to relevant employees.

Whether working as a principal contractor or as a contractor, companies must be able to demonstrate how they effectively manage health and safety. If the company cannot demonstrate competence in health and safety issues, it will impact on winning work and repeat business. It is no longer acceptable to simply state that the company has been in the industry for many years without experiencing an accident.

4.2.1   Competent person

A competent person is someone who has sufficient training and experience or knowledge, in addition to other qualities, that allows them to properly assist. The level of competence will depend on the complexity of the situation and the particular help required.

Health and safety law requires that every employer has access to competent health and safety advice, which in practical terms means that the employer must:

- be competent to manage relevant health and safety issues themselves, and/or

- have an employee who is, or (if there isn't anyone within the organisation)

- bring in external expertise.

Competence can be described as a combination of skills, knowledge, attitude (which includes the positive behaviours of individuals), training and experience that a person has, and their ability to use them.

Skills	The ability to perform a specific task to a desired standard, time after time.
Knowledge	Understanding how to do the job, to the extent it can be explained to others.
Attitude	Having the right approach and behaviours.
Training	Gained knowledge, instruction and information.
Experience	Gained over a period of time in the workplace (not just theoretical).

This can be referred to as **SKATE**. (Physical attributes and mental attitudes can also affect someone's competence.)

A **principal contractor** will have to satisfy the client and the principal designer that they are competent as an organisation to carry out their legal duties. This will include taking into account the competence of their employees, contractors and self-employed persons who will be carrying out the work.

HEALTH AND SAFETY MANAGEMENT SYSTEMS

A **contractor working for a principal contractor** will have to satisfy the principal contractor that they themselves, their employees and any other people they bring onto site (such as sub-contractors) are competent to do the work they have been contracted to do, as well as provide specific evidence of this.

Contractors have to satisfy themselves of their own competence, that of their employees and any other people they bring onto site (such as sub-contractors).

4.3   The business case

In addition to the legal considerations (for example, compliance with the law) there are strong economic and social drivers for a robust health and safety management system and policy.

The economic argument is that if there are fewer accidents on site and no occupational ill health, more employees will be at work rather than off sick. This means improved business continuity with a greater prospect of completing projects on time, to budget and to the satisfaction of the client.

The social argument is similar. Clients and customers are far more likely to place business with a company who they see is behaving with integrity, and taking proper care of the health, safety and welfare of their employees and others who might be affected by the work of the company.

Clients, in particular Local Authority clients, assessing the competence of small companies that are seeking entry onto approved lists will be looking for evidence of effective health and safety management. Some Local Authorities use a standard questionnaire, which asks companies to provide comprehensive details of the following.

● The competent person who provides health and safety advice.

● Its general policy on health and safety, its organisation and arrangements for implementing the policy.

● Training provision and training providers.

● Accident statistics.

● Arrangements for distributing new health and safety information.

● Examples of risk assessments.

● Arrangements for liaison with clients.

● Management arrangements (such as audits and inspection reports).

● Health surveillance (where applicable).

● Arrangements for assessing contractors.

● Where applicable, the ability to undertake roles under the Construction (Design and Management) Regulations 2015 (CDM).

A well-structured health and safety management system and policy will provide a great deal of this information, and any additional information needed can easily be incorporated as an annexe to the policy.

If a company is successful in gaining entry onto an approved list for one Local Authority, it will then be much easier to seek similar approval from other authorities.

4.4   Health and safety management systems

Effective health and safety management systems have been developed over a number of years within many industries. The methodology and language used in these systems may seem very different, as they can suit a wide range of industries, but the key actions in all systems are based on the principles of *Plan, Do, Check, Act*.

Two of the common systems in use, **ISO 45001:2018** and **HSG65**, are outlined below.

4.4.1   ISO 45001:2018

The international standard that is now recognised by all major clients and contractors is ISO 45001:2018 (published on 12 March 2018). With this release, OHSAS 18001 was withdrawn.

This is an internationally applied standard for OH&S management systems and its implementation demonstrates sound occupational health and safety performance. It has been developed by international collaborative groups comprising representatives from national standards bodies, academic bodies, accreditation bodies, certification bodies and occupational safety and health institutions, with the international standards body (ISO – the International Organization for Standardization) providing the administration of the standard. ISO is an independent, non-governmental international organisation with a membership of 167 national standards bodies.

Through its industry or sector-based standards organisations, it brings together experts to share knowledge and develop voluntary, consensus-based, market relevant international standards that support innovation and provide solutions to global challenges.

ISO 45001:2018 OH&S management system is the world's first OH&S international standard that is intended to help thousands of organisations to provide a safe and healthy workplace for their workers and other people, to prevent deaths, work-related injuries and ill health, and to continually improve its OH&S performance. The standard is applicable to any organisation, regardless of its size, type and activities. It is applicable to the OH&S risks under the organisation's control, taking into account factors such as the context in which the organisation operates and the needs and expectations of its workers and other interested parties.

ISO 45001:2018 specifies requirements for an OH&S management system, and gives guidance for its use, to enable organisations to provide safe and healthy workplaces, by prevention of work-related injury and ill health, as well as proactively improving OH&S performance. The standard enables an organisation, through its OH&S management system, to integrate other aspects of health and safety, such as worker wellness or wellbeing. However, it should be noted that organisations may be required by applicable legal requirements to also address such issues.

ISO 45001:2018 can be integrated with other management systems within the company, including quality standard BS ISO 9001 and environmental management standard BS ISO 14001.

4.4.2 Managing for health and safety (HSG65)

The HSE has developed and revised guidance on health and safety management systems, a document commonly known as HSG65.

Organisations have a legal duty to put in place suitable arrangements to manage health and safety. This guidance provides a framework to help organisations do that effectively, in a way that every organisation can tailor to its own circumstances. The latest version is behavioural based and should be an integral part of a company's management system.

The current HSG65, *Managing for health and safety*, is the first action for delivering effective health and safety arrangements for the company health and safety policy and is based on the Plan, Do, Check, Act model.

HSG65 will assist owners, trustees and line managers in putting the right measures in place to manage the real risks to health and safety in an organisation. It can help you achieve a balance between the systems and behavioural aspects of management. It also treats health and safety management as an integral part of good management generally, rather than as a standalone system.

HSG65

Part 1 gives the core elements of managing health and safety and how they can fit into running the business.

Part 2 suggests what to look for when deciding what needs to be included.

Part 3 gives advice on delivering effective arrangements. It is particularly useful for those who put in place or oversee their organisation's arrangements for health and safety (for example, health and safety managers).

Part 4 signposts resources from the HSE and other organisations. Short *Find out more* lists provide relevant sources of advice throughout the guidance.

There is sufficient significant detail in the document to produce a company-specific health and safety management system, and to know how to include relevant content and arrangements for controls, how to carry out checks and measure performance, how to review performance and how to take action on lessons learned.

HSG65 guidance provides a framework for meeting the legal requirements, based on the following key elements.

Plan. To implement your policy, an effective health and safety management system will need to be established and maintained.

Do. Delivery depends on an effective management system to ensure, so far as is reasonably practicable, the health and safety of employees and other people affected by work activities.

Check. To monitor and report on health and safety arrangements and the performance of the health and safety policy.

Act. To review health and safety management systems, to ensure they are effective in managing risk and protecting people.

Details of these elements are covered in the following pages.

 For a free guidance document for leaders, owners and line managers on health and safety management systems, *Managing for health and safety* (HSG65), visit the HSE's website.

4.5 Plan (Setting standards)

In order to develop or implement plans, or set standards, companies should be sufficiently competent in health and safety to know what the law requires, and how to interpret those requirements into safe and healthy working practices.

The aim of any health and safety management system must be to prevent injuries, occupational disease and near misses from occurring and to improve health and safety engagement and worker consultation. To achieve this, employers must take the following actions (*listed overleaf*).

- Commit themselves to proactively managing the health and safety aspects of their work activities.

- Actively involve employees in the health and safety decision making process and maintain their interest.

- Recognise areas of health and safety weakness.

- Select appropriate actions to overcome those weaknesses.

- Ensure that sufficient resources (time, competent people and money) are in place to implement the actions.

- Implement the actions and make sure they are complied with.

- Monitor the results to establish if improvements can be made.

- Review the plan at least annually, or as a result of an incident or a worker bringing something to the employer's attention.

- Investigate when things go wrong to prevent them from happening again.

Ultimately, the effectiveness of the plans will depend upon the assessment and control of the risks to health and safety that arise from the employer's work activities. Health and safety must be proactively managed, in the same way that good supervisors and managers will manage people, quality and productivity.

 Clearly define and set the direction for effective health and safety management within your company.

A health and safety policy that sets a clear direction will help to communicate health and safety duties and responsibilities throughout the organisation, and highlight the benefits of effective health and safety management.

4.5.1 Determining and setting the policy

HSWA states that all employers who employ five or more people to have a written statement of their general health and safety policy. This will include details of the necessary organisation, arrangements for implementing the health and safety policy and arrangements for controlling the organisation's day-to-day health and safety risks. The five employees include any person who is directly affected by the activities of the company (for example, trainees, apprentices, office staff and some self-employed people who are contracted for paid work under the management of the employer).

Even if someone is self-employed or employs fewer than five people, the law still requires them to:

- **have a health and safety policy, even if it is not written down**

- **manage their work in such a way as to protect the health and safety of themselves, those working for them, and anyone else who may be affected by their work.**

The starting point for all health and safety must be a clear policy statement. This will inform employees of the company's intentions towards the health, safety and welfare of the workforce and the standards to which they aspire.

Managing health and safety at work is a **legal requirement** and must always be an integral part of any business activity.

Section 2(3) of HSWA states that a health and safety policy should cover three distinct aspects.

1. A **general statement of health and safety policy**, specific to the company's business needs, setting the company's intentions and commitment to managing health and safety, and highlighting the intent of the employer to have high standards of health and safety in the company, including what they intend to achieve and how they will achieve it.

2. The **organisation** within the company for the effective implementation and maintenance of the health and safety management system; an organisational structure that shows the responsibility tree (some larger companies may have one for each site).

3. The **arrangements** for the effective implementation and ongoing monitoring of the health and safety management system; the arrangements will explain the duties of each position on the responsibility tree. For many companies, the arrangements section will evolve over time and with the needs of the business.

4.5.1.1 Safety policy (organisation and arrangements)

Every employer with five or more employees must have a written statement of their general policy on health and safety at work, together with details of the organisation ('the who') and arrangements necessary to put the commitment into practice ('the how'). Employers must ensure the policy is clearly displayed or give a copy of it to each employee and ensure that it is fully understood. Employers with fewer than five employees must formulate how they will proactively manage health and safety as an integral part of their work activities. (There is no reason why a company with fewer than five employees should not have a written health and safety policy.)

A policy should describe the following in full.

- The known and foreseeable risks (as stated in the organisation's risk profile).

- How the company is going to set up and maintain a safe and healthy working environment.

- What health and safety responsibilities already exist.

- Who is responsible and for what.
- The arrangements for developing safe systems of work.
- The arrangements for reviewing and updating the policy as necessary.

 Policy requirements

- To be written by someone within the organisation – those who know the organisation best and how it operates, rather than someone from outside. If companies cannot write the policy in house, it is common to seek external assistance and advice but, essentially, the policy should be appropriate to the specific needs of the business.
- It must reflect the organisation's values, beliefs and commitment to providing a safe and healthy environment.
- Companies must consult their workforce when developing the policy. As well as benefiting from workers' day-to-day experience of the job, consultation increases the likelihood that the workforce will commit to carrying out the policy's aims.
- It must be signed and dated by the person with ultimate responsibility for health and safety (for example, the owner or a managing director). Most importantly, you should make sure your actions, and those of your workers, mirror the statements you have made.
- The policy should be periodically reviewed, updated as necessary, and re-signed and dated.

A copy of a company's health and safety policy is often requested when companies are tendering for work, and when they want to get onto approved supply chain lists. For a sole trader or very small firm, all health and safety duties are likely to be the responsibility of one person.

It is important to remember that once this information is written down, if there is a serious accident, it will be used in court, either by the HSE or lawyers in a civil claim. This means people need to be aware of their responsibilities.

Appendix B contains a suggested layout of a health and safety policy for a medium-sized company carrying out small building works.

Not all of it will be relevant to some companies and, conversely, it may not contain specific content that some companies require.

- For most companies, the general statement of health and safety policy should fit onto one side of A4 paper.
- The organisation and arrangements sections will be longer depending on the size of the company and the type of work that is carried out.
- Overall, the final document should be a clear indication to clients, employees and other interested parties (such as the HSE) that the company is honestly, openly and totally committed to the proper and effective management of all aspects of health, safety and welfare.

 For guidance on the preparation of health and safety policy documents visit the HSE website.

4.5.2   Planning for implementation

Effective planning is essential for the implementation of health and safety management systems.

Adequate control of the risks to the organisation can only be achieved through effective **communication**, **co-operation** and **co-ordinated action** by all members of the organisation.

Effective planning is concerned with prevention of accidents and ill health through identifying and controlling risks. This is especially important when dealing with health risks that may only become apparent after a long period of time.

In addition to setting your policy, planning should include steps to ensure legal compliance and procedures for dealing with emergency situations. It should involve people throughout the organisation.

Basic principles for consideration in effective policy development and planning are outlined below.

4.5.2.1   Competence

When developing plans and policies, consider the level of competence necessary to comply with the law.

4.5.2.2   Directors, leaders and managers

Make a statement of intention. Say what you will do to keep a safe and healthy environment for your workers and anyone else who could be affected by your work activities.

Clearly set out everyone's roles and responsibilities and highlight those with particular roles (for example, directors, supervisors and managers, safety representatives, workers, fire wardens, first-aiders and the competent person).

Say how things will be done and what resources will be allocated to make things happen.

Include details of the systems and procedures that will be in place to help to meet your legal obligations (*see overleaf*).

- How risk assessments will be carried out.

- Plans for staff and worker training and safe use of equipment.

- Controls to ensure specifiers and buyers are competent in assessing the risks in procurement (for example, that they know the requirements for purchasing suitable personal protective equipment (PPE)).

- Plans and procedures for accident and incident investigation.

- Plans and methods for consulting with workers.

- Procedures for equipment and plant maintenance.

Consider how you will measure health and safety performance. Will there be achievable targets (such as reductions in accidents or absences, or increases in reporting issues or near misses)?

Think about management of contractors when developing a policy, if this is relevant to your work.

Identify when you will revisit your policy and plans, for example, in the following circumstances.

- When changes have been made to work methods or processes.

- When changes to staffing have taken place.

- Following accident or incident investigations, both within the organisation and where lessons have been learned from others.

- Following consultation with employees' representatives.

- If you receive new information (for example, from regulators (HSE), manufacturers or others in the same sector or industry).

- After discussing safety arrangements with other occupants not employed or managed by you, but who share the same premises.

4.5.2.3   Worker consultation and involvement

Discuss your plans with workers or their representatives and communicate the plan so that everyone knows what is required.

4.6   Do (Delivering)

Delivery depends on an effective management system to ensure the health and safety of all employees and other people affected by the organisation's work.

Organisations should aim to protect people by introducing management systems and practices that ensure risks are dealt with sensibly, responsibly and proportionately.

4.6.1   Profiling your organisation's health and safety risks

Effective leaders and line managers should know the risks their organisations face on a daily and longer-term basis. They should rank these risks in order of importance and take effective action to control them.

- Assess the risks, identify what could cause harm in the workplace, who it could harm and how, and what you will do to manage the risk.

- Decide what the priorities are and identify the biggest risks.

The range of risks goes beyond health and safety risks to include quality, environmental and asset damage risks. Issues in one area could have an impact in another. For example, unsafe forklift truck driving may create service or quality problems as a result of damage to goods and materials.

A **risk profile** examines the nature and levels of threats faced by an organisation. It examines the likelihood of adverse effects occurring, the level of disruption, the costs associated with each type of risk and the effectiveness of the control measures in place.

The basic foundations of a risk profile should cover the following.

- The nature and level of the risks faced by your organisation.

- The likelihood of adverse effects occurring and the level of disruption.

- The costs associated with each type of risk.

- The effectiveness of the controls that are in place to manage those risks.

4.6.1.1   Assessing the risks

In some organisations and industries (such as construction), the health and safety risks will be tangible, immediately recognisable safety issues (for example, work at height, confined spaces, plant and machinery) whereas in other industries the risks may be health-related and it may be a long time before an illness becomes apparent.

Poorly maintained plant and degrading plant integrity could also lead to later-emerging risks.

Health and safety risks range from things that happen infrequently but with catastrophic effects (high-hazard, low-frequency events, such as an oil refinery explosion) to things that happen much more frequently but with less severe consequences (low-hazard, high-frequency events). Clearly, the high-hazard, low-frequency example could destroy the business and would be high-priority in a risk profile.

A risk assessment should be completed by someone with knowledge of the activity, process or material that is being assessed. Workers and their safety representatives are a valuable source of information.

If an adviser or consultant assists in completing the risk assessment, managers and workers should still be involved. Risk assessments should consider all your activities, taking account of possible harm to the following people.

- Employees.
- Contractors.
- Members of the public.
- Those using products and services.
- Anyone else affected by the activity (such as neighbours).

 For detailed information on risk assessments refer to Chapter A05 Risk assessments, method statements and permits to work.

4.6.1.2　Effective risk profiling

Effective risk profiling should involve members of the whole workforce, as a broad knowledge of the entire organisation will be needed to draw up its risk profile. In high-hazard organisations, establish what specialist advice may be necessary to identify hazards and analyse risks. Make sure workers are trained and have information about risk controls. Identify who takes ownership of risks. This person might be the owner or chief executive; in larger organisations there may be a risk committee or a senior board champion for health and safety.

 What may be the consequences of the worst possible occurrence for your organisation?

How confident are you that plans are in place to control the effects?

Maintain an overview of the risk-profiling process and make sure you are aware of the major risks within your organisation. Check that minor risks have not been given too much priority and that major risks have not been overlooked. Identify who is responsible for implementing controls and over what timescale. Make sure you consider the following points.

- Assess the effects of changing technology.
- Think about issues related to changes in asset ownership. (These may increase the risk if design information and knowledge isn't passed on.)
- Plant and equipment will deteriorate with age, so you may need to change inspection regimes to reflect this.
- Think about everyone who might be affected by your work activities.
- Remember that certain groups may be at increased risk (for example, young or inexperienced workers, pregnant workers, workers with a disability, migrant workers or ageing workers).

4.6.1.3　Control measures, reporting and consultation

Control measures. Consider whether any control measures are already in place or if further action is needed. Recognise that full implementation of control measures may take time, and implement interim measures to minimise the risks.

Report, record and review. Report risk control performance regularly. Make sure any paperwork generated is kept to the minimum level necessary, to avoid overload or miscommunication. Review the organisation's risk profile regularly. Change within the organisation can affect the risk profile (for example, during economic cycles such as recession and recovery, when there is an increase in workload, or when experience levels drop).

Worker consultation and involvement. Consult with workers and their representatives in all parts of the organisation to ensure that all areas of risk have been identified.

 Do workers understand the organisation's risk profile and their responsibilities?

Do they have the necessary information, instruction and training to deal with the risks that have been identified?

4.6.2　Organising for health and safety

Organising for health and safety is the collective label given to activities in four key areas that together promote positive health and safety outcomes. This section of the management system should clearly show the specific arrangements that a company has put in place to manage health and safety across its normal work activities.

Controls within the organisation – the role of managers and supervisors: leadership, management, supervision, performance standards, instruction, motivation, accountability, rewards and sanctions.

Co-operation between workers, their representatives and managers through active consultation and involvement.

Communication across the whole organisation, through visible behaviours, written material and face-to-face discussion.

Competence of individuals through recruitment, selection, training, coaching, specialist advice and avoiding complacency. Capability training helps people gain the skills, knowledge and, ultimately, the competence to carry out their work safely and without risk to their health. You may also need to engage specialist help if your business has hazardous or complex processes.

Some of the site-wide elements that might need to be addressed with control, co-operation, communication and competence are shown below.

Site activities		Administration procedures
■ Hot works	■ Vehicle movements	■ Emergency procedures
■ Production of dust or fumes	■ Manual handling	■ First aid
■ Noise and vibration	■ Use of access equipment	■ Fire
■ Work at height	■ Scaffolding	■ Means of escape
■ Confined space entry	■ Use of ladders and stepladders	■ Accident reporting
■ Protection of the public	■ Mobile elevating work platforms (MEWPs)	■ Welfare facilities
■ Authorisation for the use of plant and equipment	■ Excavations	■ Employee consultation
■ Lone working	■ Hazardous substances	■ Monitoring for the effectiveness of health and safety procedures
■ Machine guarding	■ Working in occupied premises	■ Health surveillance
■ Loading and unloading		■ Driving at work/Use of company vehicles
■ Lifting equipment and lifting operations		■ Young persons

4.6.2.1   Controls within the organisation – the role of managers and supervisors

Anyone engaging contractors has health and safety responsibilities both for the contractors and for anyone else who could be affected by their activities.

Due to their regular contact with workers, managers and supervisors can make an important contribution to risk control by:

● making sure everyone knows how to work safely and without risk to their health, and

● making sure all workers follow the organisation's rules.

Managers' and supervisors' roles and responsibilities should be clearly defined.

Managers and supervisors should be suitably trained and competent in carrying out their roles, recognising the importance of supervision as a part of active risk control. The supervisor or team leader should have sufficient resources to deal with health and safety issues as part of getting the job done. Ask yourself: does everybody know their specific responsibilities and roles with regard to maintaining safe places of work?

❓ Responsibilities

Who is responsible for the following roles?

● Developing and implementing safe systems of work.

● Consultation with the workforce and worker engagement.

● Issuing instructions on how work is to be carried out safely.

● Supervising or managing day-to-day health and safety issues.

● Making sure that everyone is competent to do what is required of them.

● Developing risk assessments and method statements that include the persons responsible for managing each risk.

● Carrying out periodic health and safety inspections.

● Dealing with maintenance matters.

● Measuring health and safety performance and reviewing or updating procedures as necessary.

● Ensuring that sub-contractors have a satisfactory health and safety management system and follow safe working practices on site.

4.6.2.2 Co-operation – Consultation and engagement with employees

An essential part of health and safety management is the two-way communication process between employers (or their representatives) and employees. There are legal duties on both parties with the intent that communication takes place in both directions. Employers and their managers must talk to, and listen to, the people who actually do the work.

The **Safety Representatives and Safety Committees Regulations** and the **Health and Safety (Consultation with Employees) Regulations** *(refer to Chapter A01 Health and safety law)* outline the requirements of the employer to consult with employees. The **Construction (Design and Management) Regulations** *(refer to Chapter A03)* also have a requirement for consultation with workers.

To gain co-operation, **worker involvement** is essential. This means involving the workforce beyond the legal minimum requirements and in more than a basic consultation. Such an approach can help develop a genuine management and workforce partnership, based on mutual trust, respect and co-operation, where problems can be jointly explored and solved and workers' thoughts and ideas freely shared, valued and acted upon.

Beyond the required legal minimum standard, worker involvement means the full participation of the workforce in the management of health and safety.

At its most effective, full involvement creates a culture where relationships between employers and employees are based on collaboration, trust and joint problem solving. Employees are involved in assessing workplace risks and in the development and review of workplace health and safety policies in partnership with the employer.

 For guidance on leadership and worker engagement refer to Chapter A09.

4.6.2.3 Communication

Employers are legally required to bring their health and safety policy and management system, and any subsequent revisions, to the notice of all employees. CDM emphasise the need for consultation and engagement with workers. Communicating the health and safety policy is a good way of achieving this.

Often the reality of workplace conditions and the practices that have developed escape the notice of senior management. This may be because pressures, techniques, environments and expectations change over time.

The only way to find out if the requirements of the policy and management system are realistic and workable is to talk to the people who have to comply with them in the workplace.

Think about what needs to be communicated and to whom. How will your health and safety policy, risk assessment findings and safe systems of work be shared? Sufficient time should be allocated for communications to take place.

Consider the arrangements for receiving and distributing information and formulate plans that explain how information will be distributed and communicated throughout the organisation.

Plans should consider and identify how you will communicate effectively with the following people.

- Employees.
- Contractors.
- Anyone with low levels of literacy.
- Workers whose first language is not English.

Delegation of health and safety duties and procedures for safety-critical tasks should also be clearly communicated.

Suitable arrangements for enabling anyone to report suspected or actual failings in health and safety management to someone in authority must be in place. These arrangements must be communicated to workers along with the reassurance that their concerns will be listened to and feedback provided.

Emergency procedures for first aid, fire, and the reporting and recording of near misses, incidents, accidents and dangerous occurrences will also need to be communicated, and confirmation given by recipients that they have clearly understood the information.

 For detailed information on methods of communication refer to Chapter A08 Behavioural safety.

 ## Larger sites

The system of communication on larger sites (where there may be many companies on site and several tiers of sub-contractor) must allow for the health and safety concerns of individuals to be considered by someone with the authority to rectify the situation.

- The person on the tools and their supervisor might be more aware than others on site of an unsafe situation developing at the workplace.

- All workers should have clear lines of communication and the opportunity to feed any health, safety or welfare concerns directly to a site-based manager or supervisor who has the authority to take the appropriate action.

4.6.2.4 Competence

Under health and safety law, employers must appoint one or more competent persons to help carry out the measures needed to comply with the law. It is important for organisations to decide the level of competence necessary to comply with the law. The preference would be for the nominated person to be someone from within the organisation who has the appropriate skills, knowledge and training, together with experience of the business.

In deciding who to appoint to the role, a judgement can be made using the organisation's risk profile. The role could be allocated to the owner or to someone else in the organisation who does not necessarily have a qualification but does have knowledge and experience of the business.

 The nominated person should be able to recognise issues outside their competence, so that more experienced advice can be sought where necessary.

Where relevant expertise is not present within the organisation, companies may choose to procure the services of suitable consultants and advisers.

4.6.3 Training

HSWA requires that employers provide all necessary information, instruction, supervision and training to enable their workforce to carry out their tasks safely and without risks to their health.

The law also requires that you make sure workers understand the information, instruction and training you are giving them, taking account of any language difficulties or disabilities. You may need to provide information in a language other than English.

Consider workers' individual capability before allocating work. Will they have the capacity to react safely to changing circumstances? If they are unable to do so, what might the consequences be?

 Questions that should be asked

- Is there provision for training now, and for the future?
- Who identifies the gaps between *skills needed* and *skills held*, and establishes the training needs of individuals?
- Who is responsible for making sure training is carried out?

Training may take many forms, in addition to conventional training room sessions. For example:

- site inductions
- toolbox talks
- safety leaflets, books and informational posters explaining the company's health and safety policy and procedures
- on-the-job training and instruction on plant, tools or equipment, explaining risk assessments and method statements.

Procedures should be in place to:

- track the type of training given and who has received it
- assess the training and provide feedback that the training was appropriate and has been understood; and, if not,
- make arrangements for additional training.

 For detailed information on competence and training refer to Chapter A06 Induction and training.

4.6.4 Appointing and managing contractors

Anyone engaging contractors has health and safety responsibilities, both for the contractors and for anyone else who could be affected by their activities. Contractors themselves also have legal health and safety responsibilities. Make sure everyone understands the part they need to play in ensuring health and safety.

 Use of contractors in itself does not result in poor health and safety standards, but poor management can lead to injuries, ill health, additional costs and delays.

Working closely with the contractor will reduce the risks to your own employees and the contractors themselves. Contractors may be at particular risk; they may be strangers to your workplace and therefore unfamiliar with your organisation's procedures, rules, hazards and risks. Even regular contractors may need reminding. The level of control needed will be proportionate to the complexity of the task.

On sites with major accident hazards, consider shut downs, turnarounds and span of control over the contractor – given the potentially high numbers of contractors on site (compared with the numbers in routine operations).

When contractors are engaged, the contract documents should clearly explain the work you expect the contractor to do and the standards of competence that will be required. Demonstrate the importance your organisation places on health and safety in the selection of safe contractors, and ensure you allocate sufficient time and resources to the task – in planning, preparing and carrying it out. Suitable arrangements for monitoring and supervision should be allocated to ensure shortcuts are not taken to reduce costs and that there is no conflict of performance versus safety. Directors should support management decisions to stop work if there are serious health and safety concerns raised about contractors' actions or performance, and they should be ready to address health and safety failings by engaging directly with the leader of the contracting organisation. Similarly, directors should acknowledge any successes. Contingencies and procedures should be in place if things don't go to plan.

 Further details of the requirements for assessing and appointing contractors can be found in the third-party contractor assessment in Appendix A, and in Chapter A03 Construction (Design and Management) Regulations.

 Visit the HSE website for *Using contractors: A brief guide* (INDG368).

4.6.5 Implementing your plan

4.6.5.1 Risk control plans

Leaders should take positive steps to address issues arising from human factors and to encourage safe behaviour. They will need to recognise that the prevailing health and safety culture is a major influence in shaping people's safety-related behaviour. The necessary resources should be made available to successfully implement the plan. Resources include the following.

- Human resources and specialised skills.
- Organisational infrastructure.
- Technology.
- Financial resources.

To effectively implement workplace precautions, the risk control systems and management arrangements should be designed to recognise the existing risks, practices, human capabilities and limitations present within the organisation. It will then be possible to decide on the preventative and protective measures needed and put them in place.

- Provide the right tools and equipment to do the job, and keep them maintained.
- Provide training and instruction to ensure everyone is competent to carry out their work.
- Provide supervision, to make sure that arrangements are followed.

The control of **relatively minor risks** affecting all employees (such as ensuring passages and gangways remain free from obstruction) can be dealt with by a number of simply stated general site rules and housekeeping procedures.

The control of **more hazardous activities** may require the use of more detailed risk control systems.

The control of **high-hazard activities** may demand detailed workplace precautions and a risk control system that needs to be strictly followed (such as a permit-to-work system).

Maintenance activities can introduce additional risks. The type, frequency and depth of maintenance activities should reflect the extent and nature of the hazards and risks revealed by a risk assessment.

The balance of resources devoted to the various risk control systems will also reflect your risk profile.

4.6.5.2 Documentation

Any risk control documentation produced should be **functional** and **concise**, with the emphasis on its effectiveness rather than on a sheer volume of paperwork.

 Focusing too much on the formal documentation of a health and safety management system will distract from addressing the human elements of its implementation – the focus becomes the process of the system itself, rather than actually controlling risks.

4.6.5.3 Principles for effective implementation

- Responsibilities and accountabilities should be clearly defined, communicated and understood by all involved in the process.
- Realistic timescales for meeting objectives should be clearly agreed with the workforce.
- Documentation should be proportionate to the complexity of the risks concerned. Keep it to the minimum needed for effectiveness and efficiency.
- Demonstrate your commitment to delivery at all levels within the organisation, through visible behaviour and by using a variety of communication channels to engage your workforce (for example, written material and face-to-face discussions).
- Keep people informed of progress and maintain a focus on the main risks and issues.

- Use review meetings (or make use of existing internal forums) as a basis for identifying further improvements.

- Measure progress of implementation against clear milestones or performance indicators and make adjustments if there is early evidence that requirements are not being met.

- Recognise contributions and safe behaviours that help to create or reinforce positive attitudes and behaviours.

- Monitor arrangements to give you the assurance that workers and contractors are following workplace precautions and risk controls.

- Involve and consult workers and representatives throughout any implementation.

- Ensure you have systems in place that allow workers to raise concerns and make suggestions (for example, staff suggestion schemes, online communities, safety forums or committees, and so on).

- Make sure you consider all feedback, take action and provide prompt responses to concerns or questions raised.

4.7 Check (Measuring performance)

Checking that you are managing risks in your organisation is a vital, sometimes overlooked step. Taking this step, however, will give organisations the confidence that you are keeping on top of health and safety. It may also identify improvements for the future. Organisations need to make sure plans are implemented and risks are being controlled.

Checking involves setting up an effective monitoring system, backed up by sensible performance measures and, in some circumstances, by formal audits.

4.7.1 Types of monitoring

There are many different types of monitoring but they can generally be categorised as either **active** or **reactive**.

- Active monitoring methods monitor the design, development, installation and operation of management arrangements. These tend to be preventative in nature, as follows.
  - Routine inspections of premises, plant and equipment by staff.
  - Health surveillance to prevent harm to health.
  - Planned function check regimes for important pieces of plant.

- Reactive monitoring methods monitor evidence of poor health and safety practice but can also identify better practices that may be transferred to other parts of a business. For example:
  - investigating accidents and incidents
  - monitoring cases of ill health and sickness absence records.

Most organisations use performance measures as part of their monitoring. Checking performance against a range of predetermined measures is one of the most frequently used monitoring techniques. Selecting the right measures to use is critical. Using the wrong measures will cause unnecessary and unproductive effort, with little benefit for the organisation.

 For detailed information on measuring performance refer to Chapter A10 Inspections and audits.

4.7.2 Investigating accidents and incidents

In any organisation, things don't always go to plan. You need to prepare to deal with unexpected events in order to reduce their consequences. Workers and managers will be more competent in dealing with the effects of an accident or emergency if there are effective and regularly tested plans in place.

Investigating and analysing incidents will also make a big contribution to understanding health and safety in your business. You should monitor and review any measures that are in place to help control risk and prevent accidents and incidents from happening. Findings from investigations can form the basis of the following actions.

- Preventing the accident or incident from happening again.

- Improving overall risk management.

- Pointing to areas of risk assessment that need to be reviewed.

An effective investigation requires a methodical, structured approach to information gathering, collation and analysis. Investigation findings will also provide essential information that may be required in the event of a civil claim, or HSE enforcements or prosecutions.

 For detailed information on investigation refer to Chapter A13 Accident reporting and investigation.

4.8   Act (Reviewing and learning lessons)

Reviewing health and safety performance is an important part of business and the process of continual improvement in health and safety management. It will help organisations establish whether their health and safety principles are embedded as a natural part of day-to-day operations.

A health and safety performance review will tell you if your systems are effective in protecting your people.

4.8.1   Reviewing performance

Carrying out reviews will confirm whether the organisation's current health and safety arrangements still make sense. A review also does the following.

- Enables the company to check the validity of its health and safety policy and ensure that the systems in place for managing health and safety are effective.

- Identifies how the health and safety environment in the business has changed.

- Enables leaders to highlight and to stop doing things that are no longer necessary, while allowing the business to respond to new risks.

- Gives the opportunity to celebrate and promote health and safety successes.

Increasingly, third parties are requiring partner organisations to report health and safety performance publicly.

The most important aspect of reviewing is that it closes the loop. The outcomes of a review become the next steps in the plan for health and safety.

4.8.2   Learning lessons

Learning lessons involves acting on the findings of accident investigations and near-miss reports and resolving organisational vulnerabilities identified during monitoring, audit and review processes.

As is common with management arrangements, it is an ongoing challenge to ensure that all health and safety requirements are complied with consistently. All too often, many organisations find out after an accident or case of ill health that they already had systems, rules, procedures or instructions that would have prevented the event but which were not known about, considered or complied with.

The underlying causes often lie in arrangements which have been designed without taking proper account of human factors, or where inappropriate actions are condoned implicitly or explicitly by management action or neglect.

 For detailed information on audits and reviews refer to Chapter A10 Inspections and audits.

4.8.3   Updating management systems and policies

The law requires that employers revise their management systems and policies as often as may be appropriate. This means they should be updated in light of any new legislation, HSE or industry guidance and British or European Standards, as well as take into account actual experience in using the policy on a day-to-day basis (for example, by evaluating whether the policy is effective).

Changes in the type of work carried out, changes in staff and changes made as a result of any accidents or incidents will also give rise to the need for a policy review. In addition, the policy should be regularly reviewed to ensure that it stays relevant to the company's overall operations.

 It is recommended that the policy is reviewed annually, with the policy being re-signed, dated and any changes communicated to the workforce. Even if there are no required changes, it should still be re-signed and dated in order for the company to demonstrate a review has taken place. This is important for companies that have to provide copies of their policy for a third-party assessment scheme or to prospective clients.

Appendix A – Third-party contractor assessment

Being able to prove health and safety competence in the construction industry is a crucial element to securing contracts. Clients will always seek highly competent principal contractors who then, in turn, will look for the same in the sub-contractors that they employ.

CDM state that both contractors and sub-contractors must be able to demonstrate the necessary skills, knowledge, training and experience to fulfil their role.

There are many different ways that this is achieved; a common method is through a pre-qualification questionnaire, where health and safety documentation is submitted for review and assessment. The information includes, amongst other things, the requirements for contractors to have a health and safety policy, to have access to competent health and safety advice and to ensure that employees are appropriately trained.

Assessing health and safety competence can be a complicated and time-consuming process. There are two levels that need to be considered.

Stage 1 – The primary level. This is the ability of an organisation to prove that their arrangements for managing health and safety are sufficient to allow them to carry out work safely and without risk to the health of their workers.

Stage 2 – The second level assesses competence in relation to experience and the needs of the particular job. It looks at an individual's track record of working on similar types of project to those being tendered for.

Several schemes have been developed to help clients and contractors alike to meet their obligation to only appoint competent contractors.

The schemes are a pre-qualification assessment designed around the requirements of CDM. Competence is assessed against the criteria set out in Stage 1 including, amongst others, the requirements for contractors to have a health and safety policy, access to competent health and safety advice and to ensure employees are appropriately trained.

By satisfying the scheme assessment, the contractor is able to demonstrate Stage 1 competence to future employers, avoiding the need to repeat the process for every client or contractor worked for. This also helps those buying services from contractors, as they need only worry about Stage 2 type assessments (for example, matching the experience of the contractor to the work being undertaken).

Safety schemes in procurement

Safety schemes in procurement (SSIP) was founded in May 2009 following a government report called *Accelerating the SME economic engine: through transparent, simple and strategic procurement*. Supported by the HSE, SSIP aims to streamline pre-qualification and encourage straightforward mutual recognition between its member schemes.

The aim of SSIP is to actively reduce health and safety assessment costs and bureaucracy in the supply chain by standardising the contents of requested information and through accreditation of a single scheme. This should make cross-recognition between member schemes as effective as possible, and highlight the savings to buyers and suppliers. Bodies such as the Contractors Health and Safety Assessment Scheme (CHAS), Constructionline, Exor and the National House-building Council (NHBC) are SSIP members.

SSIP forum founder members agreed and signed up to achieve the following.

- Act as an umbrella organisation to facilitate mutual recognition between health and safety pre-qualification schemes wherever it is practicable to do so.

- Actively advise and influence clients about acceptable interpretation and appropriateness of health and safety competence standards in UK schemes.

- Embrace the core guidance on skills, knowledge, training and experience of CDM.

 SSIP forum members are committed to avoiding duplication within pre-qualification. If contractors have already been assessed by another SSIP member they can apply for registration for another SSIP recognised scheme, usually by downloading and completing the 'Deem to satisfy' application form.

 More information about the scheme can be found on the SSIP website.

Contractors Health and Safety Assessment Scheme

The Contractors Health and Safety Assessment Scheme (CHAS) is a pre-qualification scheme, widely used to identify companies that have demonstrated, through the CHAS assessment process, that they have a robust approach to health and safety management.

CHAS assesses applicants in the following areas.

- Health and safety policy statements.

- The health and safety arrangements of their organisation.

- Their specific health and safety arrangements to a standard acceptable to buyers and others.

The scheme is a private limited company owned by the London Borough of Merton and concentrates on what it refers to as *fundamental health and safety management and compliance issues* related to the type of work the applicant has indicated they do.

 More information about the scheme can be found on the CHAS website.

Constructionline

Constructionline is the Government's national register and is the UK's largest register for pre-qualified contractors and consultants. It is a public-private partnership between Capita and the Department for Business, Innovation and Skills. Like CHAS, Constructionline provides a pre-qualification tool for use in financial standing, technical references and other areas. The CHAS management group supports the principles of a single register and so works jointly with Constructionline.

CHAS and Constructionline have formed a mutual working agreement. This sets out how they will work together to provide an improved service for the industry's clients. CHAS and Constructionline are independent bodies but their databases are linked. It is therefore possible that not having an acceptable health and safety policy could be detrimental to company assessment by Constructionline.

 More information about the scheme can be found on the Constructionline website.

Safecontractor

Safecontractor is a health and safety assessment scheme with more than 350 major clients and over 27,000 contractor members.

Registered members with the Safecontractor scheme include clients and contractors from a wide range of professional disciplines working within a number of industry sectors. The Safecontractor scheme is now used by many large organisations as a way of obtaining competent contractors.

 More information about the scheme can be found on the Safecontractor website.

Safemark

Safemark is the health and safety competence assessment scheme of NHBC. It is the only scheme designed by house-building specialists for house builders. It is recognised by SSIP.

 More information about the scheme can be found on the NHBC website.

Appendix B – Example of a health and safety policy

HSE **Example health and safety policy**

Health and Safety
Executive

Example policy for an alarm installation company

Setting the scene

Daly Response Alarm Systems supply and install intruder alarms to residential and business premises. Manager and founder John Daly employs a total of 22 staff, consisting of an assistant manager, a receptionist, three customer service support advisers, four sales representatives, two accounts assistants, a head engineer and ten site engineers.

The office is open Monday to Friday 9.00-5.30 and Saturday morning 9.00-12.00 and cleaning is shared by the office-based staff, who have a rota.

John Daly prepared his own health and safety policy statement, using the combined template available on the HSE website at www.hse.gov.uk/simple-health-safety/policy/policy-statement-template.pdf He genuinely cares for his staff and wants to portray this in his health and safety policy.

John downloaded the template and referred to the example policy statement and other guidance available on the HSE website at www.hse.gov.uk/risk. This helped him to think about the things that should be documented and built into his own health and safety policy, such as remote working, personal protective equipment, staff consultation and training etc. He decided that he and his assistant manager would be the most competent (experienced and capable) people to take responsibility for health and safety issues.

John presented the policy statement at the staff meeting and decided to review and update the document every year or straightaway if there are any major changes in the workplace.

Employers with less than five employees don't have to write down their health and safety policy.
For further information and to view our example risk assessments, see www.hse.gov.uk/risk.
Example health and safety policy published by the Health and Safety Executive 08/14

HSE **Example health and safety policy**

Health and Safety
Executive

This is the statement of general policy and arrangements for:	**Daly Response Alarm Systems**	
John Daly – Manager	**has overall and final responsibility for health and safety**	
	has day-to-day responsibility for ensuring this policy is put into practice	
Paul Phillips – Assistant Manager		
Statement of general policy	Responsibility of: Name/Title	Action/Arrangements (What are you going to do?)
Prevent accidents and cases of work-related ill health by managing the health and safety risks in the workplace	John Daly Manager	Relevant risk assessments completed and actions arising out of those assessments implemented. (Risk assessments reviewed when working habits or conditions change.)
Provide clear instructions and information, and adequate training, to ensure employees are competent to do their work	Paul Phillips Assistant Manager	Staff and subcontractors given necessary health and safety induction and provided with appropriate training (including working at height, asbestos awareness and electrical safety) and personal protective equipment. We will ensure that suitable arrangements are in place to cover employees engaged in work remote from the main company site.
Engage and consult with employees on day-to-day health and safety conditions	John Daly (Manager) Paul Phillips (Assistant Manager) All staff	Staff routinely consulted on health and safety matters as they arise but also formally consulted at regular health and safety performance review meetings or sooner if required.
Implement emergency procedures – evacuation in case of fire or other significant incident. You can find help with your fire risk assessment at: https://www.gov.uk/workplace-fire-safety-your-responsibilities	John Daly Manager	Escape routes well signed and kept clear at all times. Evacuation plans are tested from time to time and updated as necessary.
Maintain safe and healthy working conditions, provide and maintain plant, equipment and machinery, and ensure safe storage/use of substances	Paul Phillips Assistant Manager	Toilets, washing facilities and drinking water provided. System in place for routine inspections and testing of equipment and machinery and for ensuring that action is promptly taken to address any defects.
Signed: * (Employer)	*J Daly*	Date:	*21st December 2022*

You should review your policy if you think it might no longer be valid, eg if circumstances change. If you have fewer than five employees, you don't have to write down your policy.

Health and safety law poster is displayed at (location)	Reception
First-aid box is located:	Staff room
Accident book is located:	Reception

Accidents and ill health at work reported under RIDDOR (Reporting of Injuries, Diseases and Dangerous Occurrences Regulations) http://www.hse.gov.uk/riddor

(Dates updated by CITB)

04

CONTENTS

Risk assessments, method statements and permits to work

05

Supporting INFORMATION

GT700 Toolbox talks / supporting checklists and forms

Toolbox talks on some of these topics are available in the GT700 publication. Supporting checklists and forms covering some of these topics are available on our companion website.

RISK ASSESSMENTS, METHOD STATEMENTS AND PERMITS TO WORK

Overview

The assessment of risk is the fundamental principle behind the drive for a reduction of workplace accidents and work-related ill health.

Risk assessments and method statements (RAMS) need to be suitable and proportionate to the risks, specific to the site, tasks and activities, and fully understood and appreciated by the workforce.

Assessing risk is not a difficult process, but many companies rely on generic risk assessments and method statements that bear little resemblance to how their workers actually carry out the work.

5.1 Introduction

The principle of risk assessment is fundamental to the management of health and safety in the workplace. Legislation places a legal duty on employers to assess the risks, to the health and safety of their employees and others, that arise out of their work.

There is also a requirement in other sets of regulations for employers to carry out risk assessments in relation to specific threats to health or safety in the workplace, such as those shown below.

- The use of hazardous substances.
- Noise.
- Manual handling.

- The presence of asbestos.
- Work at height.
- Work with vibrating tools and equipment.

However, this does not put an obligation on employers to carry out two risk assessments for the same hazard.

If the general risk assessment covers the specified hazards, that risk assessment alone will be sufficient.

 Risk assessment

There is no legal definition of a risk assessment, but in practice it is a careful and structured examination of a work activity so as to identify:

- what could cause harm (the hazards) to people (employees or others)
- how, by the use of appropriate control measures, the risks (the chance that the hazard will cause harm) arising from the hazards may be eliminated or controlled.

The amount of effort that needs to be put into carrying out a risk assessment should be appropriate and proportional to the nature of the hazard and the perceived level of risk.

 It is essential that all high risks are assessed and controlled first, before looking at the medium risks. Only look at the low risks once all high and medium risks have been either eliminated or adequately controlled.

Simple work activities with few hazards, which present a low risk, should need only simple assessments. If a risk assessment is to be effective, it is essential that the person who carries it out is competent in all aspects of the task that is being assessed.

 Risk assessment is not about creating huge amounts of paperwork - it is about identifying sensible measures to control the risks in your workplace.

Risk assessments do not necessarily need to be carried out by a health and safety professional. When the task being assessed is often repeated or is otherwise familiar, simple or routine, managers and supervisors will often be sufficiently skilled, knowledgeable and have the training and experience to carry out a risk assessment.

However, where a task presents complex, unusual or technical issues it may be necessary to seek the advice of a competent person, or to seek advice from other sources, such as the Health and Safety Executive (HSE) or a relevant trade organisation.

Digitalisation of risk assessments should be considered, as investing in technology gives a business the competitive edge over others. It will aid collaboration, as it gives a business the tools to get everyone involved in the process.

It will also enhance and improve health and safety, as it ensures that everyone is involved.

5.2   Important points

- The assessment of risk is the fundamental principle behind the drive for a reduction of workplace accidents and work-related ill health.

- Employers with five or more employees are required by law to record the significant findings of their risk assessments.

- Main (or principal) contractors may wish to see written risk assessments from any contractor they intend to employ, regardless of the number of employees.

- Risk assessments must consider the potential risks to the health and/or safety of anyone who may be adversely affected, which may include employees, the employees of other contractors, site visitors, members of the public, and so on.

- Carrying out risk assessments need not be difficult or unduly time-consuming; the effort should be proportionate to the degree of perceived risk.

- There is no official content or way of structuring a risk assessment; it is for each employer to decide what works best for their organisation.

- It is vital that written risk assessments, method statements and permits to work are presented in an easy to understand format for those that are actually doing the work.

- Method statements are a way of integrating the information gained during the risk assessment process into a structured sequence of work for completing a job.

- Permit to work systems are often used to regulate how activities with the potential to be high risk can be carried out in a healthy and safe manner (for example, entry into a confined space or hot works). As such, they support the risk assessment from which they are derived.

5.3   Terms used in risk assessment

Anyone carrying out risk assessments must be familiar with the meaning of the following terms that are used in the process.

Hazard: anything that has the potential to cause harm (ill health, injury or damage).

Risk: the likelihood of an event occurring from a hazard coupled with the severity of harm.

Likelihood: the chance (probability) that an accident will occur (certain, likely, possible, unlikely or rare).

Severity: the severity (consequences) of any incident that arises.

Danger: a person is in danger when they are exposed to a risk.

Accident: an unplanned event that results in damage, injury or ill health.

Near miss: (including dangerous occurrence) an event that, while not causing harm, has the potential to cause injury or ill health.

Competence: having practical and theoretical knowledge, training and actual experience of the work involved.

e.g. Severity

- At one extreme, someone who is buried in a collapsed excavation could be killed, whereas, at the other end of the scale, the consequences of someone not using a hand tool correctly might only be grazed skin or a cut.

- When assessing risk to health, severity can be misunderstood or underestimated. Someone breathing in silica dust for a day or two will not seemingly be harmed, but continual exposure over many months or years could lead to a fatal lung disease.

5.4   Legislative requirements

5.4.1   Principles of risk assessment

All recent health and safety legislation is structured around a goal-setting or risk-based approach to managing health and safety in the workplace. Employers are required to establish systems that identify hazards, assess the associated risks, develop and implement suitable control measures, and monitor the adequacy and effectiveness of such risk control systems. Employer responsibilities are shown below.

Identify the hazards (things with the potential to cause harm) that arise out of the work activity being assessed.

Assess the risks to the health and safety of any person(s) who is likely to be affected by the hazards.

Identify the individuals or groups of people who are at risk.

Eliminate the hazards (where possible) thereby removing the risk of injury.

Identify and implement appropriate measures to control the remaining risks.

Effectively monitor and review control measures for the work activity and amend them if they are no longer valid or become ineffective.

5.4.2 Management of Health and Safety at Work Regulations

The regulations require employers to carry out a suitable and sufficient assessment of the risks to health and safety for all work activities.

When carrying out risk assessments, employers must consider not only the wellbeing of their own employees but also anyone else who may be affected by that work activity.

This includes, but is not restricted to, the following.

- The employees of other contractors or the self-employed.

- Site visitors (such as delivery drivers).

- Members of the public, including children.

- The client, customers or other occupiers of the property.

Particular provision is made in the regulations for the protection of young persons in the workplace.

Although not mentioned in the regulations, it is implicit that any risk assessment must, where appropriate, take into account the requirements of anyone on site who may suffer from a disability (for example, someone who is partially or totally deaf).

The duty to undertake risk assessments is placed on all employers irrespective of the number of persons they employ but, where five or more persons are employed, the significant findings of the assessment must be recorded (either in writing or electronically).

However, clients may, if they choose, require contractors to produce recorded risk assessments even when fewer than five persons are employed by them. The self-employed have a similar duty to undertake risk assessments for the work that they do, to identify the risks to the health and safety of both themselves and others who may be affected by the work that they carry out.

Once the risk assessment has been carried out, employers must then implement the control measures that are necessary to protect those at risk. It is then important to ensure that the significant findings of the risk assessment are made known to all persons who are likely to be involved in the work or be affected by it.

In order to understand the principles of risk assessment, it is necessary to first understand the meaning of the terms used, as defined by the HSE in its publication *Risk assessment: A brief guide to controlling risks in the workplace*.

A *hazard* is anything with the **potential** to cause harm. Examples are electricity, noise, vibration, chemicals, asbestos, working at height, working over water, excavations, confined spaces, manual handling, falling materials, and the use of tools, plant and vehicles.

A *risk* is the **likelihood** that the **hazard** will actually cause harm.

e.g. Risks of working at height

If working from a ladder the likelihood of the person falling (the risk) could be regarded as high when compared with doing the same job from a scaffold platform fitted with guard-rails. A control measure (the scaffold) has been introduced and so the likelihood of a fall occurring is significantly reduced.

The regulations require that all risk assessments are **suitable** and **sufficient**. For a risk assessment to comply with this requirement it must achieve the following.

- Establish the risks arising from the work activity.

- Be appropriate, given the nature of the work, such that it remains valid for a reasonable period of time.

- Be proportionate to the level of risk and the nature of the work.

- Identify and prioritise the control measures required to protect the health and safety of the employees and others who may be affected.

Furthermore, to be suitable and sufficient each risk assessment must take account of any factors that could change during the course of the job, thereby introducing additional hazards or increasing the level of risk arising from existing hazards.

Examples of this are variable labour levels, being asked at short notice to do something a different way to accommodate others, and work or hired equipment having to be returned if the job overruns.

The law does not expect you to eliminate all risk, but you are required to protect people as far as is reasonably practicable.

5.4.3 Young persons and children

Regulation 19 of the Management of Health and Safety at Work Regulations contains specific provisions in respect of the health and safety of children and young persons.

Employers are required to specifically assess and review the risks to the health and safety of children and young persons on construction sites due to their lack of maturity, experience or knowledge of potential risks.

Young persons and children

A *young person* is anyone under the age of 18.

A *child* is anyone who has not yet reached the official minimum school-leaving age. Pupils reach the minimum school-leaving age in the school year in which they turn 16.

Children under 13 years cannot be employed at all. At the age of 13 they can work part time, with restrictions, and can start full-time work (40 hours per week) when they reach the minimum school leaving age.

If someone starts work at the age of 16 they are paid through PAYE. At the age of 18 adult employment rights and rules apply.

Children between 13 and the minimum school leaving age may, in accordance with local byelaws, with the permission of the Local Authority and after significant risks have been explained to the parents or carers, attend a construction site for site visits and organised work experience.

If a child is employed on work experience the employers' liability insurance policy will cover the work placement, as long as the insurer is a member of the Association of British Insurers or Lloyds.

Furthermore, there will be occasions when 14- to 16-year-old children are on site under an apprenticeship training scheme.

A young apprentice receiving training on site

If children will be doing or observing work on a construction site the employer must consider the risk involved and they must be satisfied that the instruction, training and supervisory arrangements have been properly thought through and work in practice.

Where children are employed either for work experience or work in offices then the employer must, before commencing the employment of the child, provide that child's parents or guardians with details of any risk assessment that has been carried out. This information must contain details of any risk and a description of any preventative or protective measures, whether the risk arises from the employer's own activity or the work of others at the workplace.

Before a young person or child is employed, the employer must ensure that any risk assessments relating to the job take account of the following factors in relation to the young person.

- Their inexperience.
- Their immaturity and lack of awareness of risks.
- The tools and equipment that they may have to use as part of their training.
- The layout of the workplace and the environment in which they may have to work.
- Any hazardous substances with which they may come into contact.
- Exposure to physical, chemical or biological hazards.
- The organisation of work and work processes.
- The extent of health and safety training that is to be provided.

 Careful consideration must be given to the way in which information is conveyed to young persons to ensure that it is fully and readily understood.

Employers are further required to consider the special nature of young persons due to their lack of experience, reduced knowledge of risks and the fact that they are not fully mature. To that end, young people must not be employed in any of the following work.

- That which they cannot physically or psychologically cope with.
- That which exposes them to a range of hazardous substances, including any carcinogen, toxic substance or radiation.
- Where they might not recognise the risk of accidents due to their inexperience or lack of training.
- Where their health would be at risk from excessive cold, heat, noise or vibration.

The prohibition above does not apply when a young person is undergoing recognised training, or when they are being properly supervised by a competent person, or when any risks identified in a risk assessment have been reduced to the lowest level that is reasonably practicable.

For the training provision to apply, the training must be necessary within a trade or occupation, and be part of an identified unit of NVQ, SVQ or other similar work-related qualification.

 For further information on employing young people and children visit the HSE website.

Builder sentenced after young worker seriously injured

Magistrates ordered a builder from Cornwall to pay out nearly £10,000 after an employee sustained serious, life-changing hand injuries whilst operating a hand-held circular saw. Bodmin Magistrates' Court heard how the building services company was refurbishing a barn in Callington. A young worker, who had just turned 17, was using a circular saw to cut wooden flooring sheets when the blade made contact with his hand. It severed his index finger, cut three quarters of the way through his middle finger and half way through his ring finger.

An investigation by the HSE found that the builder had no record of any information, instruction or training that he had provided to his employee in the safe use of the circular saw, and nor had he ensured that safe working practices were followed when the employee was cutting the flooring sheet. The investigation also found that, at the time of the incident, the circular saw blade had not been properly adjusted for the size of material being cut and that the flooring sheet was not appropriately supported while being cut.

The accused builder pleaded guilty to breaching Section 2(1) of the Health and Safety at Work etc. Act 1974 and Regulation 3(4) of the Management of Health and Safety at Work Regulations 1999. He was fined £1,120 and ordered to pay costs of £8,489.48. A HSE inspector said after the hearing: 'This injury was easily preventable and the risk associated with the task should have been identified. Employers should make sure they properly assess and apply effective control measures to minimise the risk of contact with dangerous parts of machinery to ensure that the risks are given careful attention to ensure they are properly controlled.'

5.4.4 Expectant and nursing mothers

In accordance with regulations 16-18 of the Management of Health and Safety at Work Regulations, once an employee has notified her employer in writing that she is a new or expectant mother, employers have certain obligations towards the employee, where the nature of the work may put the mother or unborn child at risk.

When an employee provides written notification to her employer stating that she is pregnant, or that she has given birth within the past six months or that she is breastfeeding, the employer should immediately take into account any risks identified in their workplace risk assessment.

The assessment may identify the need to temporarily alter the work environment, work pattern, work activity or working hours and provide additional facilities or support.

If this is not possible, the employee should be offered suitable alternative work (at the same rate of pay). If this is not available or feasible then the employee will need to be suspended from work on paid leave for as long as necessary in order to protect her child's health and safety.

 For further information refer to *Guidance for new and expectant mothers at work*, available from the HSE website.

5.5 General principles of prevention

Preventative and **protective** (control measures) must be taken to address the hazards and to eliminate or reduce the risks to an acceptable level. These measures must be based upon the general principles of prevention, which are listed in Schedule 1 of the Management of Health and Safety at Work Regulations as follows.

- Avoiding risks where possible.
- Evaluating risks that cannot be avoided.
- Combating risks at source.
- Adapting the work of an individual, especially regarding the:
  - design of the workplace
  - choice of work equipment
  - choice of working and production methods.
- Adapting to technical progress.
- Replacing the dangerous with the safe or less dangerous.
- Developing a coherent prevention policy that covers:
  - technology
  - working conditions
  - organisation of work
  - social relationships.
- Giving collective measures priority over measures that protect the individual.
- Giving appropriate instructions to employees.

Using a remote controlled trench compactor eliminated the need for a person to be in the excavation

5.6   Steps to risk assessment

The HSE has a step-by-step process for controlling health and safety risks caused by hazards in the workplace. The steps needed to manage risk are as follows.

Step 1. Identify the hazards.

Step 2. Assess the risks.

Step 3. Control the risks.

Step 4. Record your significant findings.

Step 5. Review the controls.

5.6.1   Step 1. Identify the hazards

Some typical examples of hazards found on construction sites are shown below.

- An untidy site with lots of slipping and tripping hazards.
- The use of equipment with rotating blades (like disc cutters).
- The use of power tools creating dust.
- The risk of fire from spark-emitting tools (like angle grinders).
- Manual handling work or working in cramped conditions.

- Work at height with the potential for falls (such as roofing work).
- The operation of construction plant near to people on foot.
- The presence of contaminated ground.
- The use of chemicals, solvents, paints, and so on.
- What safe or unsafe work practices exist.

5.6.2   Step 2. Assess the risks

Having established the hazards, identify the individuals or groups of people who could be harmed and how serious it could be, such as those shown below.

- Yourself.
- Other employees (particularly the young and inexperienced).
- Employees who need special consideration (for example, someone who is deaf or who is not fluent in English).
- Employees who are pregnant, or nursing mothers.

- Employees of other contractors.
- Visitors (such as delivery drivers, maintenance staff and clients).
- Members of the public or trespassers (particularly children).
- Anyone else who might be affected by your work (for example, neighbouring businesses).

5.6.3   Step 3. Control the risks

Having identified the hazards, now consider what risk-control measures are necessary to ensure the health and safety of the people who have been identified as being at risk.

Consider if a hazard can be removed altogether. If not, consider how to control the risks so that harm is unlikely, for example by: redesigning the job; replacing material, machinery or process; organising and planning work to reduce exposure; identifying and implementing practical measures for safe working; or, as a last resort, providing personal protective equipment and ensuring that it is worn.

Even when control measures have been put in place there will usually be a remaining (residual) risk. You will have to exercise your judgement as to whether, in your opinion, the residual risk is high, medium or low.

 Ask yourself: *What have I done to control the risks and what more do I need to do?*

 Considerations when establishing controls

When establishing appropriate control measures, consideration should be given to the following techniques.

Combat risks at source – for example, use a safer method (such as using a block splitter instead of a petrol cut-off saw).

Take advantage of technical progress and adopt new, safer methods of working – for example, use a modern trestle system, complete with guard-rails and toe-boards.

Replace the dangerous with the non-dangerous or less dangerous – for example, prohibit the use of all 230 V power tools, allowing only battery-powered or 110 V tools.

Adopt measures that protect the greatest number of individuals – for example, safety nets protect everyone working above them, whereas a safety harness only protects the wearer.

Give appropriate information, instructions and training to employees and others – assess the need for training.

Provide personal protective equipment (PPE) – always the very last resort.

5.6.4 Step 4. Record your significant findings

Health and safety law requires that all employers carry out risk assessments for their work, although legally only employers with five or more employees need to record the significant findings of their risk assessments. However, in practice, many of the larger contractors will not accept any sub-contractor on site, even those with fewer than five employees, if they do not have written risk assessments. Risk assessments may be recorded electronically providing that they can be easily retrieved for scrutiny if required.

In the interests of clarity, risk assessments may identify where relevant supporting information can be found (such as the company health and safety policy), rather than including masses of information in the risk assessment itself. However, if this approach is taken, the supporting documents may also have to be supplied to whoever needs to refer to the risk assessment. The law does not specify how risk should be measured but three common methods have evolved over time.

Qualitative risk assessment – outlines hazards present and risk control measures needed; no attempt is made to quantify the level of risk.

Semi-quantitative risk assessment – the process is the same but the level of risk is quantified by categorising it as high, medium or low, to enable corrective actions to be prioritised.

Quantitative risk assessment – numerical scores rather than a grade are assigned to the likelihood and severity of the risk.

Examples of these approaches to risk assessment are included later in this chapter *(refer to 5.7)*.

 What to identify in a risk assessment

Irrespective of how a risk assessment is laid out, it is considered good practice for it to identify the following.

- Person(s) who will manage the residual risks.
- Review date.
- Date(s) by which any essential actions must be taken, in the interests of health or safety.

5.6.5 Step 5. Review the controls

Risk assessments should be reviewed from time to time to ensure the control measures are still appropriate and effective. If there is a change to any aspect of the way the job has to be carried out that might affect health and safety (for example, having to use a different item of equipment part way through the job, the arrival of a new operative who is inexperienced, unexpected deteriorating weather or the late arrival of materials) the assessment must be reviewed and the risks re-evaluated.

 The HSE has produced *A brief guide to controlling risks in the workplace.*

5.7 Types of risk assessment

The risk of something going wrong is considered in terms of likelihood (probability) and severity (consequences).

5.7.1 Generic risk assessments

- A generic risk assessment is an assessment that may be used more than once because the job to which it relates is being repeated and it can be guaranteed that the hazards and level of risk are the same on each occasion that the job is carried out.
- When an employer intends to rely on a generic risk assessment, great care must be taken to ensure that there are no factors that could introduce additional hazards or increase the level of risk.
- In many cases, generic risk assessments are not acceptable within the construction industry because each site is different and conditions change as construction work progresses.

5.7.2 HSE risk assessments (Qualitative)

The HSE has produced a simple qualitative template that does not use ratings, but instead uses the headings listed below. Some prefer this method as it follows logical risk assessment steps. It can also be easier for the workforce to understand.

What are the hazards?	Who might be harmed and how?	What are you already doing?	Do you need to do anything else to control the risk?	Action by whom?	Action by when?	Done

 The HSE has made this free-to-download template available in Word format and produced a series of example risk assessments, which can be found on its website.

5.7.3 Semi-quantitative assessments

The **likelihood** of a hazard actually causing harm or an accident is rated as being high, medium or low in accordance with the following.

High: it will happen regularly, or it could be a usual or a common occurrence.

Medium: it is less regular, but is still recognised as being likely to happen.

Low: it has not happened for a long time, is known to be infrequent and is not likely to happen.

The **severity** of the event, should it happen, can then be categorised as follows.

High: the result could be a fatal accident or multiple injuries, major property damage, substantial pollution or environmental impact.

Medium: it would probably cause serious injuries (or persons would be off work for over seven days due to their injuries), substantial property damage or there may be some pollution.

Low: there would be minor injuries to persons or some slight damage to property.

Probability and consequences can then be shown on a matrix as follows.

Likelihood	High			
	Medium			
	Low			
		Low	Medium	High
			Severity	

Probability and consequences can then be assessed and the highest outcome of the two entered in the matrix as follows.

Likelihood	High	High	High	High
	Medium	Medium	Medium	High
	Low	Low	Medium	High
		Low	Medium	High
			Severity	

- A combined risk of **high** should be totally unacceptable and the work should not be undertaken until the risk has been reduced.

- When there is a combined risk of **medium**, action must be taken and work stopped if necessary to reduce the risk level.

- If the combined risk is **low**, start the work as long as everything reasonably practicable has been done in order to reduce the risk, and review the assessment at regular intervals.

Using this information, decisions can now be made on whether an activity is safe to continue, or whether control measures are necessary, either to completely change the way that the job is done or to put measures in place to bring the risks down to an acceptable level. In the ideal situation, both probability and consequences should be **low**.

5.7.4 Quantitative assessments

These are generally used for higher-risk situations or environments. The principle is the same as for semi-quantitative assessments, but numerical scores are assigned to likelihood (probability) and severity, generally rated on a scale of one to five, as shown below.

5 **Certain** to happen.

4 **Very likely** to happen, and would not be at all unusual.

3 **Likely** to happen, and would not be totally unexpected.

2 **Unlikely** to happen, but not by any means impossible.

1 **Very unlikely** to happen.

The severity (consequences) of the event, should it happen, are also then rated using the same scale, as shown below.

1 No injury, ill health or damage. It would be a near miss.

2 Minor injury or minor ill health complaint, no time lost. Minor property damage or minor environmental incident.

3 Lost time injury, up to and including reportable injury to the HSE with over seven days' time lost, but not a specified injury. Some risk of immediate or long-term health issues. Significant property damage or local environmental damage.

4 Specified injury, long-term absence or significant risk that could lead to immediate or long-term health illness, including reportable disease. Substantial property damage and/or serious environmental impact.

5 Fatal accident or multiple specified injuries. Catastrophic event or environmental disaster. Public or others could be involved as well.

A matrix can then be constructed using these numbers, as follows.

Likelihood	5					
	4					
	3					
	2					
	1					
		1	2	3	4	5
				Severity		

All possible resulting numbers are calculated by multiplying all the likelihood figures by all the severity figures. These are included in the matrix, as shown below. This means that once a risk assessment has been made on a particular activity, and the likelihood factor is multiplied by the severity factor, the number produced indicates where the assessment places the risk associated with the activity on the matrix.

Likelihood	5	5	10	15	20	25
	4	4	8	12	16	20
	3	3	6	9	12	15
	2	2	4	6	8	10
	1	1	2	3	4	5
		1	2	3	4	5
				Severity		

Risk rating	Colour	Risk description
Above 15		Totally unacceptable and the work will not be undertaken until the risk has been significantly reduced.
Between 9 and 14		Immediate action must be taken, including a stoppage of work, if necessary, to reduce the risk level to acceptable.
Between 5 and 8		Acceptable, provided that everything reasonably practicable has been done to reduce the risk.
4 or less		Acceptable, provided that the assessment is reviewed at regular intervals and further reduced if possible.

Clearly, the higher the resulting number the less acceptable the level of risk. The matrix shows where actions need to be taken to reduce either the likelihood or the severity in order to reduce the risks to an acceptable level. Employers can use these numbers to set in-house criteria, if desired, along the following lines, and as indicated by the shaded areas in the above matrix.

 It is for individual companies or managers to decide where the boundaries between what is and what is not acceptable lie, and the numerical score at which certain actions should be taken. The above matrix is only an indication of what can be done.

If either the qualitative or semi-quantitative methods are used in conjunction with a simple form, then the employer will have a straightforward, basic risk assessment procedure.

 The HSE research report *RR151 - Good practice and pitfalls in risk assessment* can be found on its website.

5.8   Risk assessment in practice

If the task to be assessed is substantial, difficult or complex then, in all probability, it will not be practical or effective to carry out a single risk assessment to cover the whole of the work. The job will need to be broken down into separate elements or work, each of which will have to be assessed separately. Alternatively, it should be possible to cover the whole of a relatively straightforward job (such as retiling the roof of a house) with a single risk assessment. The process of practical risk assessment has no fixed rules for how it should be undertaken, or how risk assessments should be structured or laid out. Each company will decide upon what suits its needs.

The process for developing risk assessments should not be over-complicated. The simpler the process, the less likely that anything will be overlooked. It may need input from both management and employees, and should address the points below.

● What is going to be done? (This should include plant, equipment, people, materials and the working environment.)

● How exactly is the activity to be carried out (for example, what plant and competences are required)?

● Where and when is the work to be done?

● How could this work affect employees and other people?

● What risk control measures are already in place?

● Is the level of risk to health or safety acceptable?

● What additional risk control measures are necessary?

The above approach to the identification of all relevant hazards associated with the work will address the following.

● The likelihood of injury or harm arising to employees and others who may be affected by the work.

● Any other specific legal requirements.

● All of the risks.

● The necessary control measures to eliminate or reduce health and safety risks associated with the work, based on the hierarchy of preventative and protective measures.

● The information needed for those involved or affected by the work.

5.8.1   Actions for employers

Once you have created a risk assessment, you will need to do the following.

● Put into effect the measures that you have decided will adequately control the risks.

● Communicate the findings of your risk assessments, particularly details of the hazards identified and what control measures are in place, to anyone who needs to know (for example, the main (or principal) contractor, your employees and sub-contractors).

 It is extremely important that the findings of risk assessments are communicated to anyone whose health and/or safety is likely to be affected by the job.

5.8.2   Actions for supervisors

Once you have received the risk assessment, you will need to do the following.

● Speak to the site manager on a regular basis.

● Check that the risk control measures to be put in place are right for the work situation.

● Seek clarification of uncertainties and make your manager aware of any findings of a point of work risk assessment so that control measures are corrected and recorded.

● Before briefing your work team ensure the risk assessments and method statements are correct for the site specifics.

● Explain the risk assessments and method statements to your work team, ensure understanding (by asking questions) and record the names of those briefed (and when).

5.9   Communication

 Those people physically carrying out the task should be consulted in the assessment process as they can have valuable knowledge and experience. By being involved, they have effectively bought into and better appreciate the risks and the control measures needed, and thus are more likely to follow them.

5.9.1   Documentation

In many cases the person completing the risk assessment is not the person doing or directly supervising the work. There are many types of documentation with varying levels of complexity. Whilst a risk assessment or method statement is technically correct, it may be that it is in a format that is too complicated or long for workers to take in.

 Asking the workforce to read lots of text and to obtain a signature to say they have read and understood the content before they start work is not helpful in achieving a safe and healthy workplace.

RISK ASSESSMENTS, METHOD STATEMENTS AND PERMITS TO WORK

If the workforce do not read or cannot understand everything provided, they will not appreciate the risks involved in the activity. In turn, they will not appreciate the consequences of failing to incorporate the required control measures, or understand why they are required, therefore continuing to work as they always have.

It may, therefore, be necessary to convert the findings of a risk assessment into a simpler document, both in terms of terminology and layout, which relates to what the workforce must do. Consideration should be given to the use of images or sketches of what is needed (such as a slinging arrangement or pictures of respiratory protective equipment (RPE) being used correctly).

Involving the workforce in the risk assessment process is vital in developing a safe system of work that they feel comfortable with. It may well be that their preferred or alternative method of working is quicker and easier, but it has (or may have) additional risks. This can then be assessed and any necessary working practices amended and agreed, so that the workforce and their supervisors know they are following the risk assessment or method statement.

5.9.2 Language difficulties

The needs of any site workers who have poor, or no, understanding of either written or spoken English must be taken into account when compiling and communicating risk assessments. Consideration also needs to be given to how workers will be communicated with to ensure they are suitably engaged with and consulted.

Effective communication is an essential element of controlling risk; how such communication can be established must be a priority where there is the potential for language difficulties on site. Control measures can be put into place to ensure that the supervisor is able to communicate effectively with the workers, or to ensure that workers who do not understand English work with someone who can speak their language and interpret for them.

 For further information refer to Chapter A07 Communication with non-English speaking workers.

5.9.3 Worker engagement in practice

 The construction section of the HSE website contains a series of worker engagement case studies, which outline how businesses have introduced safe working practice and how they have used the HSE website to assist them in doing so.

5.10 Method statements

A method statement is a document prepared by an organisation that describes in a logical sequence exactly how a work activity is to be carried out in a manner which is safe and without risk to health.

To a large extent, the way that the job will be undertaken, and therefore detailed in the method statement, will reflect the findings of the risk assessment(s) for the same job. The methods identified for controlling risk will influence the way a job is carried out. In most cases, extensive reference to the risk assessment(s) will be necessary during the drafting of a method statement. Well-written method statements provide an ideal way of communicating vital health and safety information to those who will be doing the work, and others (such as contractors) who have an interest in how the job will be carried out.

For routine and repetitive activities (work that is carried out many times where the hazards and risk are the same) a previous method statement may be applied, again provided it has been reviewed at point of work (by the supervisor or person carrying out the work) to ensure that it is still relevant. This is known as a **generic method statement**.

Where the work is new, more complicated or unusual then a **specific method statement** will need to be produced. This can be a generic method statement updated to take the new situation into account. It should then be used to ensure that the work is carried out safely, properly and in the correct order.

 For method statement guidance refer to Appendix A.

5.11   Permit to work

Whilst there is no requirement in law to use a permit to work system, they are often used to regulate how potentially high-risk activities are to be carried out in a healthy and safe manner. As such, they support the risk assessment from which they are derived. Permits to work are often, but not exclusively, required in the following situations.

- If the activity involves entry into a confined space.

- When the activity depends upon the isolation of high-voltage electrical equipment.

- If the activity involves the disturbance of any system carrying a fluid or gas under pressure.

- If the activity involves hot works.

- If the activity involves excavation work where services may be present.

A permit to work is a formal, dated and time-limited certificate signed by a properly authorised and competent person. Receipt of a permit is acknowledged by the signature of the person in charge of the work, who will retain a copy; another copy will be retained by the person issuing the permit to work.

Other signatures on the permit will certify that any control measures necessary for the job to start have been implemented (for example, using the lock-out, tag-out, try-out (LOTOTO) procedure on an electrical supply, or checking the atmosphere in a confined space). A permit will indicate the time and date at which it expires. If the work is not completed at that time, depending upon the circumstances:

- it is usually necessary to make everything safe, for everyone to leave the work area before the permit expires and for the permit to be cancelled

- it may be safe for the authorised person who issued the permit to extend the expiry time and for the work area to be reoccupied.

When the work is completed, or the expiry time has passed, the person in charge of the work must return their copy of the permit to the person who issued it and the permit is cancelled or extended.

 More information on the permit to work can be found in GE700C 3.6.4.

 To find examples of completed (qualitative) risk assessments, visit the HSE website.

05

Appendix A – Method statement guidance

Method statements should be written clearly to enable those doing the work to fully understand the details of the job and its health and safety requirements. The suggested content for a method statement is outlined below.

If the work is of a simple or minor nature, a simplified form of method statement may be more appropriate. Alternatively, it may be preferable to use the format below, but to state 'Not applicable' in the inappropriate sections.

Validity	Insert the issue number of the method statement and brief details of the changes associated with each new issue. Identify the intended start and finish dates.
Hazards	List the known hazards associated with the work, as identified by the risk assessment.
Means of access and egress	Identify: ■ locations of work (for example, at height or in excavations) ■ access equipment required ■ specialist contractors involved.
Work details	Outline: ■ the limits of the work covered by this method statement ■ in a logical order, the list of work that makes up the whole job, indicating how health and safety issues will be addressed for identified hazards, including the protection of other trades.
Permits to work	Describe: ■ which tasks will be controlled by a permit to work (for example, hot works, excavation or breaking ground and work in confined spaces) ■ who will issue and co-ordinate the permits.
Supervision	Identify who will supervise the job and, if necessary, who will supervise different parts of the job. Identify contact details for all supervisors.
Workforce details	Identify: ■ the specific labour required to carry out the job in a safe and healthy manner ■ any special training or skills required ■ details of competence cards held.
Health and safety monitoring	Specify how day-to-day standards of health and safety will be monitored and controlled.
Plant inspection and operator training	Identify: ■ what items of plant and equipment will be used ■ operators' experience/qualifications ■ thorough examination and maintenance details.
Disconnection/reconnection of services	Identify: ■ which services must be isolated/reconnected ■ who will carry out the work ■ methods of locating underground services ■ who will certify that the services have been isolated/reconnected ■ method of isolation.
Hazardous substances	Identify: ■ the hazardous substances that will be used or disturbed ■ how those affected will be informed of the health hazards ■ the protective measures to be used ■ details of any sampling that may be required.
Occupational health assessments	Identify: ■ which works will require health surveillance for the operatives carrying them out ■ which operatives are affected ■ who will arrange for the health surveillance ■ who will carry out the health surveillance.

05

Personal protective equipment/ respiratory protective equipment	Identify: ■ which items of PPE/RPE will be used, for which training will be required ■ who is responsible for arranging the training ■ who will carry out the training.
Emergency procedures	Identify: ■ possible causes of emergency or site evacuation ■ how emergency procedures will be communicated ■ who is responsible for calling the emergency services ■ contact details for out-of-hours emergencies ■ location map and contact details of nearest accident and emergency hospital.
Environmental controls	Describe: ■ threats to the environment arising from the work ■ which environmental protection measures will be put in place ■ how different types of waste will be managed, stored and disposed of.
Safety of the public and occupiers	Identify who will ensure that the health and safety of the public and other occupiers will be protected. Describe how the health and safety of the public, including, if necessary, the occupiers of the building, will be protected.
Public nuisance	Identify: ■ possible sources of nuisance for neighbouring people/properties ■ who will be responsible for neighbourhood liaison, and their contact details.
Briefing register	List by name those people to whom the method statement has been explained and consider including a signature block to indicate that the content has been understood.

05

 For more information on risk assessment, method statement and permit to work templates, visit the HSE website.

05

CONTENTS

Induction and training

06

GT700 Toolbox talks / supporting checklists and forms

Toolbox talks on some of these topics are available in the GT700 publication. Supporting checklists and forms covering some of these topics are available on our companion website.

Supporting
INFORMATION

INDUCTION AND TRAINING

Overview

Construction sites are dangerous places to work, even for experienced workers. It is a legal requirement to give everyone on site, whether new to the industry, experienced or even a temporary visitor, basic information about the site so they can remain safe and healthy. This is usually done in the form of a site induction and can vary in style, delivery method and length depending upon factors such as company induction procedures, location and size of site, type of work and client requirements.

Whatever the content, it is important that those attending understand it and that it is specific to the site.

This chapter explains why site inductions and training are important and offers some suggested content and strategy.

6.1 Introduction

It is a requirement of health and safety law that employees are provided with health and safety training whenever they are exposed to new or increased risks.

When employees first arrive in the company or at a new site, this training takes the form of an induction. It is a legal requirement under the **Construction (Design and Management) Regulations 2015** (CDM) that principal contractors and, where applicable, contractors must ensure a suitable site induction is provided. It is accepted that providing proper and effective health and safety induction training can have a significant impact on the likelihood of accidents and injuries during a person's first few days, weeks or months with a company or on a particular site.

Given that every accident occurring to an employee can be seen as an eventual financial cost to the employer, then anything that can be done to reduce accidents is of direct financial benefit to the employer. The costs of giving proper and effective health and safety induction training are relatively minor when viewed as one of the cost benefits that can accrue from accident avoidance and prevention. This also applies to the prevention of long-term ill health and the avoidance of dangerous occurrences.

6.2 Important points

- Everyone arriving on a new site, whether new to the industry, experienced or a visitor, should be given a site induction.
- Accident statistics show that the chances of accidents happening to people are increased during their first few days on site.
- The threats to health and safety will vary from site to site and even on the same site as work progresses and the hazards change.
- An effective induction process is an essential part of on-site health and safety management.
- The content of the induction must:
    - be understandable, comprehensive and relevant to the hazards present on site at that time
    - anticipate and inform inductees of forthcoming changes to the hazards on site
    - allow for the effective induction of inductees who do not speak English as their first language or may otherwise have difficulty in understanding what is being said.
- CDM place a specific duty on contractors and/or principal contractors (where appointed) to provide all of their workers with a site induction.

6.3 Induction requirements

Two types of induction are covered in this chapter: induction training and site inductions.

6.3.1 Induction training

Induction training is for new employees or for training existing employees in new topics or risks.

The Management of Health and Safety at Work Regulations require every employer to ensure that employees are provided with adequate health and safety training in the following situations.

- During recruitment into the employer's undertaking.
- When exposed to new or increased risks because:
    - they have been transferred or given a change of responsibilities within the employer's undertaking
    - new work equipment or a change regarding work equipment already in use within the employer's undertaking has been introduced
    - new technology has been introduced into the employer's undertaking
    - a new system of work or a change regarding a system of work already in use within the employer's undertaking has been introduced.

6.3.2 Site inductions

CDM specifically require the following.

● That the principal contractor must ensure a suitable site induction is provided to every site worker.

● That contractors provide all of their workers with the information and training that is necessary for their health and safety, including a suitable site induction, where it is not provided by a principal contractor.

The above requirement on contractors to provide site inductions means that inductions must be carried out on any type, size and duration of a project. The requirements of other regulations, which in themselves indicate a need for competence in certain work situations, when viewed against the type of work to be carried out, might indicate additional topics that need to be covered during site induction.

6.3.3 Responsibilities of employers and employees

To assist in preparation and delivery of induction training, an aide-memoire of the responsibilities of employers and employees can be found in Appendices B and C. This could also help training providers with any questions that may arise during or after an induction training programme.

It will be for the employer to decide when and where the training takes place. Induction training should take place before anyone starts work and when they are new to the site.

It is important that the induction training is seen as a formal company procedure, which the company provides for the benefit of the inductee, so that the employer can be seen to be meeting both the letter and the spirit of the law.
If it is seen as 'something that is just necessary, we have to do it anyway' then it will fail to have the desired long-term effects.

The style and content of the induction will vary between company and site. However, the person facilitating it needs to have both the necessary skills and knowledge, together with the ability and presence to deliver it effectively and in a meaningful manner.

6.4 Types of inductees

The words *induction* or *inductee* may suggest that a person is totally new to the company or to working on site. Whilst this is the case for some people, there will be a significant number of people who do not fall into this category. In wider terms, the following could also be referred to as inductees.

● Young people joining the industry for the first time (this will generally be persons joining a company as trainees or apprentices).

● Persons arriving at a new site even though they have been in the industry for some time.

● Persons transferring between companies within the industry.

● Persons who have been promoted (for example, from tradesperson to chargehand).

● Employees who have been given different responsibilities (for example, employees who have successfully gained competence cards for specific items of plant and will now be driving plant on site as opposed to their former occupation).

● Those who do not regularly work on the site but visit occasionally (for example, architects or students).

 The inductions should be proportionate to the nature of the visit.

It must be appreciated that different types of inductee will probably require different levels or styles of induction training because of their varying levels of knowledge, experience and competence within the industry.

It is only after induction, when they have all the appropriate information about company policy and site rules (including the principal contractor's site rules, where applicable), that they will be able to integrate into the workforce and work without risks to their own health and safety or to others who may be affected.

Escorted visitors only need to be made aware of the main hazards and control measures.

6.5 Induction difficulties

It is essential that the health and safety messages put across during site induction are fully understood by everyone. Possible barriers to learning will depend largely upon the training methods used. For example, reliance on written training materials will disadvantage those with reading difficulties.

Similarly, for workers where English is not their first language, the induction could be of limited value.

The person responsible for the training should establish the limitations of those undertaking induction, remembering that some inductees may be embarrassed about their limitations and reluctant to admit them.

To successfully induct those whose first language is not English, but who have some understanding, you will probably need to modify the delivery style, timescales and the aids used. Induction aids may need to be more visual, with less reliance upon the written word.

Where there are inductees who do not speak English at all, it is likely that specialist help, such as interpreters, will be required.

There may also be scope for training someone on the site who speaks both languages to carry out bilingual induction sessions for specific groups. Encouragement should be given to those who have reading, writing or language difficulties to seek help from appropriate sources.

Whatever the reason for any inductee experiencing difficulty in understanding what they have been told, all inductees must be given the opportunity to ask for any point to be rephrased in a different way.

 For further information refer to Chapter A07 Communication with non-English speaking workers.

6.6   Induction content

Different companies will have different issues to include in the induction training. The requirements will vary as work on the site progresses. In the early days there may be demolition, excavations and other activities at ground level.

As the site and above-ground works progress, the hazards will change and it will be necessary for the emphasis in the health and safety training to change.

As the site develops, temporary or permanent traffic routes may be introduced, or the circulation of traffic on site may need to change (for example, due to the repositioning of a crane or the installation of services).

All these issues should be reflected in the induction training that will be provided for people arriving on site or as the project progresses. It is quite possible, or even likely, that the induction session delivered on day one of the project will not be valid after three months.

Part of the induction process must be to find out what the audience already knows, to identify the most important areas that must be covered and to use plain language, illustrating with diagrams, drawings and pictures to ensure that inductees can easily take in information.

At the end of the induction, an assessment of knowledge should take place, and written confirmation of attendance should be recorded.

 Check that all inductees fully understand the induction content. Ask direct questions or check understanding by issuing a written test.

The induction should be site specific and highlight risks and control measures. The following should be considered.

- Outline of the project.
- Management of the project.
- First-aid arrangements.
- Accident and incident reporting arrangements.
- Arrangements for briefing workers on an ongoing basis (such as noticeboards and toolbox talks).
- Individuals' responsibility for health and safety.

This chapter contains some of the suggested topics and other examples that should be considered when induction training is to be given. It is not suggested that all are relevant to all sites or that issues relevant to more than one site should be given the same weighting.

They are given as an indication of subject areas that need to be covered – the depth to which they are covered will depend upon site conditions.

There will undoubtedly be other issues that are specific to a company or site and these will need to be considered and developed by the company concerned.

Appendix A contains a list of topics that should be considered for site induction content, together with a brief explanation of each.

In turn, some additional items not covered may be of particular importance to your company, and these should be included.

The comments made are of a general nature and do not attempt to explain the specific requirements of legislation.

 Refer to the HSE website for an induction presentation template aimed at smaller construction companies.

6.7   Competency and card schemes

6.7.1   Competence

In 2011, following consultation with industry, research report RR877 was produced for the HSE, which addressed the construction industry routes to competence, including all the different competency card schemes.

 The report can be downloaded from the HSE website.

6.7.2   Behavioural competence

The report supported a need for a broader definition of competence to include not only job competence and (above-basic) health and safety awareness, but a third strand of behavioural competence. This behavioural competence includes self-awareness, risk awareness and situational awareness.

 Behavioural competence

Behavioural awareness comprises those individual behaviours, attitudes, self-awareness and limitations that impact upon performance and safety at work.

It covers the interaction between people and the environment in which they work, the equipment they use, and the procedures and techniques they use.

The objectives of behavioural competence are enhanced effectiveness and safety.

This expanded definition of competence is made up of three parts, and should include the following.

- **Occupational skills.**

- Deep and relevant **knowledge and understanding**.

- Ongoing evidence of **appropriate behaviours and attitudes**, to be embedded at all levels.

6.7.3   Supervisor and management competence

The report went on to say that qualifications should be enhanced to include mentoring and coaching skills in behavioural competence.

Over the years, many of the recommendations from the report have been incorporated into qualifications, training courses and development programmes for supervisors and management, such as those listed below.

- Alignment to new definitions of competence, behaviours and attitudes.

- A greater focus on **taught** qualifications whereby the basis of the input of knowledge is on risk, causation, person-management skills and situational awareness.

- Continued professional development (CPD) (a necessary aspect and a fundamental component).

- Opportunity to train people in roles to be effective assessors of staff.

 For details of courses, training programmes or further information on competency visit the CITB website.

6.7.4   Card schemes

Access to construction sites may require a relevant scheme card. Different schemes have different requirements, such as an up-to-date *Health, safety and environment test*. The Construction Skills Certificate Scheme (CSCS) recently announced changes to the requirements, and how they are issued.

While all construction workers should hold the relevant CSCS card to access a construction site, people attending site to perform a non-construction related occupation should not be expected to carry a card. It will be the responsibility of site managers to induct non-construction related workers, and those on short-term work experience, before escorting them where appropriate so that they remain safe on site. Examples of various card schemes are highlighted in the table below.

General	CSCS	Construction Skills Certification Scheme.
Plant operatives	CPCS	Construction Plant Competence Scheme.
Demolition operatives	CCDO	Certificate of Competence for Demolition Operatives.
Scaffolders	CISRS	Construction Industry Scaffolders Record Scheme.
HVACR operatives	ESS	Engineering Services SKILLcard.
Plumbers	JIB-PMES	Joint Industry Board for Plumbing and Mechanical Engineering Services.
	SNIJIB	Scottish and Northern Ireland Joint Industry Board.

 For more information, visit the CSCS website.

6.7.5 Health, safety and environment test

The CITB *Health, safety and environment test* helps contribute towards a qualified workforce with the right skills, knowledge and training. For everyone working on UK construction sites the test helps to:

● raise health, safety and environmental standards

● support the prevention of incidents related to health, safety and the environment

● establish consistent standards.

Different tests have been developed to meet the demands of different trades and professions.

www **Visit the CITB website for more information about the tests and how to prepare for them.**

6.8 Records

It is extremely important that records are kept showing which workers have attended site induction, together with details of the training they have received and the date it was carried out.

This will enable employers to demonstrate to the HSE, the client, the principal contractor and other interested parties that they have complied with the requirements of legislation and that they are committed to ensuring the health and safety of their employees and any others who may be affected.

Such records could help prove that health and safety induction training was given, should there be a legal challenge.

6.9 Ongoing training

Once the employee has been inducted to the site, and/or into the organisation, the company should ensure a training programme is implemented to help employees develop their knowledge, skills and attitudes, to ensure they are competent in health and safety aspects of their work.

A company could choose to implement a training cycle, which has six phases.

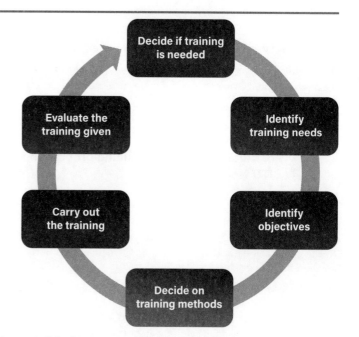

6.9.1 Phase 1. Deciding if training is needed

● Use information from job specifications, known abilities, experience and previous training records.

● Compare data against what the organisation requires the individual to know and to be able to do.

● Any variation between the two identifies a potential training requirement.

6.9.2 Phase 2. Identifying training needs

● Look at accident and health records and determine training requirements linked to causes and preventative means.

● Discuss procedures, materials and use of tools and equipment with employees to establish their understanding and highlight any skills gap.

● Observe and question employees whilst they are performing their roles and responsibilities.

6.9.3 Phase 3. Identifying objectives

● Does the law require you to carry out specific training (for example, first-aid training)?

● Clarify what the targeted employees should learn through their training.

● Priorities should include:

   - those where lack of information and/or training might result in serious harm

   - those that benefit the largest numbers of staff

   - new recruits or people new to the working environment

   - people changing jobs, working practices or taking on new responsibilities

   - people using new equipment.

- Consult employees, or their representatives, for their views.

- You must provide training during working hours and not at the expense of your employees.

- Special arrangements may be needed for part-timers or shift workers.

6.9.4   Phase 4. Deciding on training methods

- Organise training either internally or through external training providers.

- Ensure trainers are qualified and competent in their subject field.

6.9.5   Phase 5. Carrying out the training

- Trainers should encourage full engagement from the trainees.

- On-the-job training can generate new risks. Therefore, in some instances, off-site training may need to be completed.

- Use internal resources or external organisations.

6.9.6   Phase 6. Evaluating the training given

- Evaluate the effectiveness of the training programme.

- Determine if the training has achieved the objectives.

- Establish whether the training has been worth the money and time spent on delivery and attendance.

- The training plan, structure, content and methods may be subject to revision, following evaluation.

6.10   Promoting health and safety training

Health and safety training is sometimes viewed with suspicion, and those identified as requiring training can feel they are being picked on, or that their performance is thought to be substandard. Incentives (such as promotion or increased pay), applicable to some forms of training, do not generally result from health and safety training. Managers should encourage their employees to engage willingly and positively in such training. This task can be even more difficult in organisations with limited training history.

The following points may help in the initial planning stage of training.

- Encourage employees' genuine participation.

- Raise their awareness of the employer and employee responsibilities.

- Use relevant sector examples to illustrate the consequences of inadequate health and safety training.

- Inform employees about the organisation's training policy, including how individuals are chosen for training.

- Make arrangements for payment of wages or salaries during training, or reimbursements of expenses or fees paid.

- Support and reassure those who may lack confidence, especially those who have not attended training since leaving education.

- Make arrangements for knowledge checking during and after the delivery of training.

- Emphasise the value to everyone concerned of the short and long-term benefits of a working life free from injury and ill health.

 Visit the CITB website for advice on a range of health and safety training courses.

 ## Worker loses sight in one eye because of insufficient training

A company was fined after a worker lost his sight in one eye when a compressed air hose whipped him in the face while he was carrying out maintenance work to clean a paint fume filter. When he had finished, he isolated the compressed air supply at the connection point and went to disconnect the equipment. However, he was unaware the pressure from the flexible hose needed venting before disconnection and, as a result, the hose whipped and struck him in the face, hitting his eye and breaking his cheekbone. The 49-year-old permanently lost the sight in his right eye, but he has been able to return to work.

The HSE investigation found the company had failed to provide the worker with sufficient information, instruction or training on the equipment he was using when the incident happened. The company pleaded guilty to breaching Section 2(1) of the Health and Safety at Work etc. Act 1974. They were fined £20,000 and ordered to pay £7,813.70 in costs.

After the hearing, an HSE inspector said: 'This was an entirely preventable incident that has resulted in a worker losing his sight in one eye – an injury which will affect him permanently. The sudden release of compressed air is a known hazard in industry. The company should have ensured that there was a safe system of work in place and that anyone working with compressed air had been given sufficient information, instruction and training to keep themselves and others safe from air blasts and whipping or snaking hoses.'

Appendix A – Site induction topics

Access and egress

Explain the rules regarding access to, and egress from, the workplace. Are there any one-way systems? Are there any prohibited areas? Are there any special rules or conditions applying to the site or workplace?

Accident reporting

Participants should be in no doubt of the requirements for reporting accidents, incidents and near misses. Explain when, where and to whom these must be reported and, in general, how they will be investigated. Procedures may go beyond those required by legislation as a company policy decision. Explain the importance of reporting all unsafe conditions and near misses and any site reporting scheme in operation. These can then be investigated, and appropriate remedial measures put in place, so that the next near miss does not become an accident.

Alcohol and drugs

Explain the rules or company policy about arriving or being on site under the influence of alcohol or drugs, or consuming or dealing them during the hours of employment, including action that will be taken. There may be a policy of random testing and/or post-incident testing, and this should also be explained. The issue of prescribed drugs and use of some over-the-counter medicines should also be covered, as some can have side effects, such as drowsiness. If the user is authorised to operate plant or drive vehicles, this needs to be addressed and resolved with the supervisor or management. The support provided to individuals who disclose that they have a drugs or alcohol problem must be made clear, as well as the prescribed limits of both alcohol and drugs, and the consequences of a negative result.

Asbestos

If the project is a new build on a greenfield site, the probability of finding asbestos is remote. However, if it is on a brownfield site, there may be asbestos in the ground, and if carrying out a refurbishment or renovation on a building/grounds built before 2000, there is a significant chance of discovering asbestos within the existing structure or surrounding grounds. If asbestos-containing materials are potentially present, it is a legal requirement to provide asbestos awareness training, including details of any prohibited areas, to reflect the site conditions. You should have a company policy for dealing with any material suspected of being asbestos, and staff should be informed of this policy.

Assembly points

See also **emergency procedures**. Explain where the assembly points are for site evacuation in the event of an emergency.

Boundaries

Explain the boundaries of the site if there is no perimeter fence. Include the prevention of trespass.

CDM

Explain any appropriate on-site rules, the provisions the principal contractor has made for consultation with the workforce and where the F10 form (if the project is notifiable) is displayed.

Competence

You may need to advise staff and others of the levels of competence required for operating certain types of plant or carrying out certain activities. See also **registration schemes**.

Confidential issues

Explain the provision for 'whistle blowing'. Also how staff can raise confidential (including medical) issues if the need arises.

Confined spaces

Explain the rules that apply on site. Many staff will fail to recognise that a confined space can be above ground, or be as innocuous as a sub-basement boiler room. Unfortunately, confined spaces have been responsible for a number of deaths in the industry, all of which could have been avoided by compliance with proper health and safety procedures.

Consultation with employees

It is a legal requirement to consult with staff, which should be two-way. Key points to communicate during induction should include:

- the mechanism for workers to bring any health and safety concerns to the attention of site management
- whether there is a health and safety committee on site and, if so, who the members are
- whether there are any trade union-appointed representatives and, if so, who they are.

If there is a suggestion box or scheme, explain how staff can put forward ideas for improvements in health, safety and welfare, waste minimisation and so on, on a day-by-day basis.

06

Contamination

Raised environmental awareness makes the prevention of ground contamination increasingly important. Explain how staff can prevent spillage of diesel fuel, paint, oil, thinners, cement, concrete or any other substance that could lead to contamination.

Control of Substances Hazardous to Health (COSHH)

Explain on-site procedures relating to hazardous substances. Are there any additional substances to the usual cement, oils, paints, and so on?

Competency card schemes

Explain the requirements for competency cards. See also registration schemes.

Dangerous occurrences

Explain the reporting policy for dangerous occurrences. It is thought that many go unreported as staff regard them as an accident where nobody was injured. Given this could lead to company prosecutions, it is important that appropriate instructions are given at inductions.

Dermatitis

Explain that contact dermatitis can be caused by relatively common substances (such as diesel and mould release oil, paints, thinners and cement). When appropriate, gloves should be worn and barrier creams should be properly used, with situations identified by risk assessments.

Discipline

Explain the company policy regarding breaches of health and safety legislation, site or company rules.

Dress code

Explain the effects of sun exposure and the importance of preventing skin cancer. Explain company or site rules on whether shorts or sleeveless vests are permissible on site.

Drones

If drones are being used on site for surveying or other purposes, the protocols and risks presented during drone operations must be explained.

Drying rooms

Explain the location and use of drying rooms, and who is responsible for maintaining cleanliness, tidiness and disposal of discarded or abandoned clothing and equipment.

Edge protection

Explain the standard that is used and the safe system of work for persons working on or near open or leading edges.

Electricity

Explain the site or company rules concerning:

- temporary or permanent repairs by competent persons on site
- use of 230 V equipment
- use of RCDs or circuit breakers
- use of transformers and 110 V equipment
- testing, inspection and maintenance of portable electrical equipment (PAT testing).

Emergency procedures

Explain site or company procedures. What is the siren or alarm? Where are the emergency evacuation assembly points? Explain procedures to be followed in the event of an emergency other than fire. This may be civil disturbance, a bomb scare, structural collapse or other eventuality.

Environment

Environmental pollution can affect air, ground or water. Explain specific issues of protection and control concerning the company or site; procedures to be followed in the event of an incident (for example, spills); and how everyone is expected to positively contribute. Also explain how everyone on the site can positively contribute to the environmental agenda and encourage these behaviours.

Escape routes

Explain recognised routes on site and from buildings in the event of emergency, and that access/egress routes must be well-defined and kept clear. How are they marked? How will they be lit when dark, or during winter? How will changes be shared as construction progresses?

06

Excavations

Explain the policy regarding:

- permit to dig systems
- excavation support and inspections
- proper entry and exit from an excavation, and edge protection around an excavation.

Eye protection

Explain if there are any specific eye protection issues, or rules applicable to the site or any particular work that is taking place. See also **personal protective equipment**.

Fall arrest

You may wish to comment on the use of safety nets, safety decking, air bags and other similar systems. See also **safety harnesses**.

Fall prevention

Explain hierarchy of control measures used to prevent falls or safely catch those who fall. This will vary depending on the type of site and work.

Fire

In the induction session you should at least cover the following.

- Fire precautions, fire prevention and good housekeeping.
- Who will be responsible for calling the emergency services.
- Location of fire points and fire extinguishers.
- Training and competence in the use of fire-fighting equipment.
- Testing of the fire alarm, fire drills and practice evacuations.
- Policy for hot works, including permits.

First aid

Clearly explain the arrangements for first-aid provision.

- The location of the first-aid kit(s).
- The details of the first aider(s), emergency first aider(s) or appointed persons (and mental health first aiders, if on site), and how they can be identified and contacted in the event of an emergency.
- Location of the first-aid room (where provided).
- Emergency procedures that should be taken in the event of an injury.
- Location of the nearest accident and emergency hospital (with map, address and contact details).

Flammable liquids

If flammable liquids (such as paint thinners, solvents, spirit-based paints and others) are kept and used on site, explain the rules for:

- storage
- withdrawal from storage
- use and return to storage.

Health and safety committee

See also **consultation with employees**. If there is a site health and safety committee, explain the terms of reference for:

- the committee, membership and how often the committee meets
- agenda items and how the outcomes of meetings are made known to staff on site.

Health surveillance and screening

If mandatory surveillance is a legal requirement due to the associated health risks of site activities, then the process needs to be discussed. This must also include awareness of general health screening programmes that are aligned to the occupational health and wellbeing strategy.

Hearing protection zones

See also **noise**. Are there any mandatory hearing protection zones on site? How are they marked? Explain the supply and issue of hearing protectors and when they should be worn.

High-visibility clothing

Explain the site or company rules for when this clothing should be worn and clearly define the appropriate locations. Also clearly define the standard for high-visibility clothing.

Hoists

Explain the site or company rules for passenger hoists.

- Who is the competent person to operate the hoist?
- If anyone can operate it, do they need training prior to being authorised as competent?
- What is the maximum number of people permitted in the hoist?

Explain the site or company rules for goods hoists.

- Explain that passengers cannot be carried
- Who is the authorised competent person to operate it? Can any other persons be authorised?

- Which rules apply regarding goods carried in the hoist?
- If controls are seen as so simple that the hoist may almost be regarded a public lift, is there any danger of control override?

- What are the rules for closing the gates and what is the rated capacity (safe working load)?

Ladders/stepladders

Explain the company standards and site rules for:

- any restrictions on use of ladders/stepladders (permits)
- where used, the securing or tying of ladders/stepladders

- use of ladders/stepladders for light work of short duration or for gaining access.

Lasers

If lasers are to be used on site, explain what class of laser is to be used and what, if any, hazards could be caused. Levelling lasers (used, for example, by suspended ceiling fixers) are not normally regarded as hazardous as long as appropriate health and safety rules are followed.

Legal issues

Discuss any particular points of law that apply to the company/site. Explain that different projects/clients have different rules, and that staff should understand the need for rules and how they are enforced. Give the location of the health and safety law poster that must be displayed.

Lifting equipment

Explain the site or company rules for:

- who has authority to use lifting equipment of various sizes/types
- the duties of slingers and signallers

- testing and inspection of equipment, and current colour coding, if such a system is used.

Lighting

Explain the site or company rules for provision of work lighting and emergency lighting, including:

- the placing of luminaires

- extra lighting during winter or for work outside normal hours.

Liquefied petroleum gas

Explain the rules for:

- use, storage and separation of full and empty cylinders
- separation from oxygen and acetylene, as appropriate

- use of hose check valves and flashback arresters
- emergency procedures and use of fire extinguishers.

Manual handling

Explain the site or company rules for:

- the avoidance of manual handling wherever possible
- the use of mechanical devices to aid manual handling

- safe systems of work.

Method statements

Explain the importance of supervisors discussing the method statement to be used for particular tasks, and the benefits to be gained from staff input. Method statements must be specific to the site, task and persons carrying out the work.

Mobile elevating work platforms (MEWPs)

Explain who is competent to operate or use MEWPs, and the evidence required to prove competence and training. Where can MEWPs be used, and under what ground conditions? Where are they not allowed? Explain safety harness use when working from platforms; actions and procedures for emergency lowering controls; and any rescue plans for entrapment and requirements for using anti-crush protection systems.

Needles and syringes

Staff should be warned to be vigilant, particularly regarding the discovery of used hypodermic syringes (needles and risk of needlestick injury) and other drug-taking equipment. Explain actions to be taken on finding discarded needles or receiving a needlestick injury. Explain who is responsible for safely removing any sharps, and how this person can be identified and contacted in the event of any being found. It should be noted that most gloves in common use on site do not offer any protection against a needlestick injury. Suitable training should be provided to nominated individuals for safe handling and disposal of any discovered sharps, and use of specialist gloves and equipment.

Noise

See also hearing protection zones. Explain the site or company rules concerning the use of equipment that produces excessive noise. Does the Local Authority impose any restrictions? Explain the use of hearing protection and noise control zones.

Occupational health

Stress the importance of reporting any cases of ill health to supervisors, as it may be potentially work-related. This is particularly important if staff are working where there may be rats, or if the area has been used for illegal drug taking and related materials may be found. In the case of refurbishment and renovation works, there may be residual materials from previous occupants likely to cause ill health.

> **Construction dusts are the biggest cause of construction-related ill health, with over 5,000 people a year dying from respiratory diseases. Risk assessments and method statements must identify dust produced in any activity as a hazard, and control measures put in place to minimise exposure.**

Overhead electricity cables

Explain the site or company rules on:

- location and marking
- allowable proximity for vehicles
- working nearby and precautions.

Permits to work

Explain company or site procedures regarding issuing, working with and the cancellation of permits to work. Where lock-off systems are used, explain the rules regarding padlock keys.

Personal protective equipment (PPE)

Explain the site or company rules regarding:

- minimum PPE (for example, safety helmets, safety footwear, high-visibility clothing, light eye protection and gloves)
- respiratory protective equipment (RPE) and task-specific PPE
- storage and maintenance of PPE (for example, light eye protection cleaning stations)
- any other issues (such as dress code).

Remind staff that PPE generally, and RPE particularly, should be a last resort when all other control measures have been considered and found unworkable. Other than mandatory PPE, the need for PPE should be covered in the risk assessment and method statement.

> **Where task-specific PPE has been identified, the type or grade must be stated (for example, rather than just specifying 'dust mask' the type must be stated, such as 'FFP3-rated half-mask respirator').**

Plant and equipment

Explain the site rules regarding:

- the authority to operate plant and equipment, including the requirement for competence cards, where necessary
- any type of plant or equipment that is prohibited (for example, mains-powered hand tools)
- the need for noise control where appropriate
- the requirement for permits to work where appropriate.

Registration schemes

Explain the site or company rules regarding registration schemes.

Reporting defects

Explain the importance of reporting all defects in plant and equipment, scaffolding, excavation supports, and so on. Early reporting will allow swift remedial measures, and help prevent accidents. Possible consequences of not doing so may be accidents or disciplinary procedures.

Restricted or prohibited areas

Explain whether there are any areas on site that are restricted to all people, or a specific class of people. Include what identifies a restricted area – typical examples are areas where demolition, impact cleaning, water jetting, or asbestos removal are taking place.

Risk assessments

Explain the significant findings of risk assessments, as they will affect staff on site as a whole, or those working on a particular activity. It may be useful to explain the risk assessment process and the health and safety benefits that can be gained. See also **method statements**.

Safe systems of work

The crucial need arising out of risk assessments and method statements is for safe systems of work. Explain that site rules require staff to work in accordance with any safe systems of work that have been developed by the employer.

Safety harnesses

Explain the company or site requirements for inspecting, wearing, using and maintaining safety harnesses and lanyards. See also **fall arrest**.

Safety policy

Explain any relevant areas of the company's health and safety policy, together with the organisation and arrangements for the implementation of the policy. If relevant, explain where a copy of the policy is displayed on site.

Safety signs and notices

Remind all staff that they must comply with all safety signs and notices at all times. Explain the whereabouts of any site noticeboard, hazard board and how changes and modifications to site rules will be made known to the workforce.

Scaffolding (including mobile access towers)

Explain the site rules regarding:

- who is allowed to erect, alter and dismantle tube and fitting/ system-built scaffolds
- the implications (safety/disciplinary) of unauthorised dismantling or alteration
- the safe use of mobile access towers
- safe access to and egress from scaffolds
- assessing competency to erect proprietary mobile access towers.

Explain any other company or site-specific rules about the use of scaffolding as either a working place or as access to the working place.

Site layout

Explain whether any specific rules apply to pedestrian and traffic movement. This will depend on the size and complexity of the site. You may also include where contractors may lay down materials and which areas they may use for the prefabrication of components.

Site security

Security is very much allied to health and safety in that a breach of security can lead to trespassers on site and possible exposure to a risk of injury. Open a discussion if you have any particular company or on-site rules concerning security. Also consider the issue of health and safety awareness of site security staff, whether they are staff or a sub-contracted security company.

Skin protection

It may be appropriate to discuss the need for skin protection, both in terms of gloves and barrier creams. If barrier creams and rehydrating lotions are used, where are they dispensed? Also explain that the types of gloves used must be the most suitable for the levels of protection needed. If likely to be a significant hazard, you should also include details of the risk of skin cancer associated with excessive sun exposure.

Smoking

Explain the policy on smoking and vaping in the workplace and the welfare areas, clearly identifying areas where smoking is not allowed.

Sustainability

Explain the policy on sustainability in terms of suppliers, materials and procedures.

Tidiness (housekeeping)

Explain the importance of maintaining a tidy site in order to eliminate many of the slip, trip and fall hazards. Include:

- materials storage and delivery arrangements
- how materials are to be distributed and returned
- how and when to remove rubbish and excess materials
- who is responsible for organising delivery and removal of skips
- good housekeeping, sweeping up, vacuuming and dust extraction (general tidiness)
- maintaining tidy workplaces, access routes, staircases and cable management.

Toilets

See also **welfare facilities**. Explain site/company rules on cleanliness, abuse of facilities/graffiti, and consequences. Include defect reporting.

Traffic routes

These are dependent on the size and complexity of the site. Explain:

- one-way systems and the need to minimise or avoid reversing
- duties of the vehicle marshaller
- segregation of pedestrians from vehicles and plant and machinery (pedestrian walkways).

Training

What training will be given to persons on site? Explain the need for all contractors to ensure that staff are trained and competent.

Underground services

Explain site/company procedures if underground services (gas, electricity, telecommunications, fibre optics, water, sewerage) are discovered.

Vehicles

Explain the rules for the presence and operation of vehicles on site. Include:

- the parking of private vehicles
- deliveries (access constraints, timings, restrictions, off-loading methods (tower crane/telehandler), HIABs and fall prevention)
- keeping clear of site (working) vehicles
- the security of vehicle keys when not in use
- who is allowed to operate plant on site (proof of competence)
- security measures to make vehicles unavailable to trespassers and children during non-working hours
- traffic routes, speed limits and noise (for example, time limitations imposed by the Local Authority).

Vibration

Explain the potential severity of hand-arm vibration syndrome (HAVS), the risks of whole-body vibration (WBV), and company/site policy on:

- hand-held vibrating equipment and maximum trigger use times
- plant/vehicle operator training, smooth operation and job rotation
- the use and limitations of PPE
- the design and selection of tools and equipment
- rest breaks and the rotation of work
- the symptoms of HAVS and WBV
- the arrangements for health surveillance
- the need for staff to seek medical advice if they have symptoms.

Waste disposal

Give skip/waste container locations. Explain segregation; responsibility for removal; and site/company policy if contractors don't remove waste.

Waste minimisation

Explain that this is a financial as well as environmental matter, closely linked with site tidiness, pollution control, housekeeping and accident prevention. There are company and national benefits, and projects are more likely to finish on time and to budget. See also **environment**.

Welfare facilities

Explain:

- location of facilities and (if appropriate) canteen opening hours
- responsibilities for cleaning and maintenance of the facilities
- the provision of barrier creams and rehydrating lotions
- the need for good personal hygiene.

Working at height

This is allied to fall prevention, safe systems of work and PPE. Explain the company or site rules for:

- working at height, including safe systems of work
- competence of employees
- protection of those below, including the public
- prevention of materials falling (containment and debris nets).

Working near, on or over water

Explain the site or company rules for working near, on or over water, including:

- wearing of lifejackets, buoyancy aids or other flotation devices
- prevention of falls into water
- the rescue of anyone who has fallen into water, plus lookouts and alarms.

Appendix B – Employer responsibilities

The following information is provided as an aide-memoire, for any questions that may arise during or after an induction training programme.

Set out below, in an abbreviated form, are the principal responsibilities of employers, managers and supervisors. For ease of presentation, the reader is assumed to be an employer (this list is not exhaustive).

- Ensure, so far as is reasonably practicable, the health, safety and welfare of employees.
- Display an employer's liability compulsory insurance certificate.
- Have a general statement of health and safety policy.
- Prepare and display a written health and safety policy, if you employ five or more persons.
- Make employees aware of your company health and safety policy.
- Display an approved poster (such as the health and safety law poster) or give each employee a copy of an approved leaflet to comply with the Health and Safety (Information for Employees) Regulations.
- Carry out risk assessments of your work and record the significant findings, if you employ five or more persons.
- Implement any control measures identified by your risk assessment.
- Regularly review risk assessments and any associated control measures.
- Ensure that scaffolding is only erected, altered or dismantled under the supervision of a competent person.
- Appoint a competent person to assist the company with health and safety requirements, where necessary.
- Establish a safety committee, if requested by two union-appointed safety representatives.
- Assess manual handling operations in the workplace and take appropriate steps to reduce the risk of injury to employees.
- Ensure all accidents that result in injury, however slight, are entered in the accident book and investigated.
- Report to the HSE all reportable accidents, dangerous occurrences and notifiable diseases.
- Provide employees with PPE, as necessary.
- Avoid entry into confined spaces, wherever possible.
- Protect employees and others who may be exposed to asbestos as a result of any work that may cause exposure.
- Ensure that all excavations are safe and that work in excavations is carried out safely.
- Provide sufficient and suitable welfare facilities on construction sites, including sanitary conveniences, washing facilities, drinking water and changing facilities.
- Provide information, instruction, training and supervision to ensure the health and safety of all employees.
- Appoint trained and competent persons for the purpose of selecting and mounting abrasive wheels.
- Examine, test and properly maintain plant, equipment, cranes, lifting appliances and associated working gear (lifting accessories) at regular intervals, and record the findings.
- Provide adequate first-aid facilities with sufficiently trained first aiders and appointed persons.
- Consult with your employees on health and safety matters.
- Authorise only competent persons to carry out work on electrical installations and appliances.
- Take measures to prevent or adequately control employees' exposure to harmful dusts and fumes.
- Prepare and maintain a construction phase plan appropriate to your operations.
- Ensure that the workplace is safe and without risk to the health of employees.
- Take the necessary steps to ensure that the health and safety of the public is not put at risk by works being carried out.

06

Appendix C – Employee responsibilities

Below, in an abbreviated form, are the main responsibilities of employees (this list is not exhaustive). The reader is assumed to be an employee.

- Co-operate with your employer and follow any information, instructions and training given to you.
- Do not interfere with or misuse anything that has been provided in the interests of health, safety and welfare.
- Take reasonable care at all times and make sure that you do not endanger yourself or any other person.
- Use all tools and equipment safely and in accordance with instructions given or training received.
- Report any defects or potential hazards in equipment to your supervisor as soon as possible.
- Make proper use of any safe system of work or mechanical means provided by your employer in connection with manual handling.
- Only operate the plant and equipment you have been trained and authorised to use.
- Use the PPE supplied by your employer correctly, take care of it and report any loss or defects in the equipment.
- Report to your employer any work situation that might present a danger.
- Do not erect, alter or dismantle scaffolding unless competent to do so or under the supervision of a competent person.
- When operating goods hoists, keep the gates closed except when loading. Do not override any controls. Do not allow any passengers.
- Use only the proper safe means provided for entering and leaving an excavation.
- Do not block or obstruct any access or escape route.
- Make full use of any control measures provided to prevent or limit exposure to substances hazardous to health, and wear the PPE provided.
- Observe safe use and handling instructions for hazardous substances, and return unused quantities to the designated store.
- Do not use a MEWP for any use other than as a work platform.
- Co-operate with health and safety inspectors, as required.
- Do not remove safety guards or stop any safety device fitted to any plant or equipment from working.
- Do not ride on plant or vehicles in unauthorised and insecure places.
- Recognise the importance of personal cleanliness, especially when working with substances harmful to the skin.
- Never exceed the rated capacity (safe working load) of any equipment.
- Report to your supervisor all accidents that cause any injury to you.
- Understand and comply with all signs that are displayed.
- Wear hearing protection in designated areas where mandatory warning signs are displayed.
- Follow all company and site health and safety rules.

06

CONTENTS

Communication with non-English speaking workers

Supporting **INFORMATION**

GT700 Toolbox talks / supporting checklists and forms

Toolbox talks on some of these topics are available in the GT700 publication. Supporting checklists and forms covering some of these topics are available on our companion website.

COMMUNICATION WITH NON-ENGLISH SPEAKING WORKERS

Overview

Good communication is essential for the management of health and safety on construction sites.

Communication problems can occur where workers have limited or no understanding of English, particularly during site induction.

This chapter offers advice to those who may not have company communication policies, and offers some suggested approaches.

7.1   Introduction

The number of workers whose first language is not English has increased on UK sites over recent years. Some of these workers have excellent skills in spoken and written English, but there are others for whom understanding English is a problem. This can be a barrier to effective communication of health and safety information.

However, failure to engage with non-English speaking workers for this reason will be in breach of the provisions of health, safety and equality-based legislation. The Health and Safety Executive (HSE) legal (L) series guidance on the Construction (Design and Management) Regulations 2015 (CDM) states:

> **Anyone with a duty under CDM to provide health and safety information or instructions to anyone else must ensure that it is easy to understand.**
>
> **Any information or instruction provided should be in simple, clear English (and/or other languages, where appropriate). It should also be set out in a logical order and have illustrations where appropriate.**

7.2   Important points

- Employers are legally required to provide information that is comprehensible – in other words, provided in a format that can be understood by the worker.

- This requirement can result in problems where the recipients of the information have limited or no understanding of English, particularly during site induction.

- Communicating using images has the potential to overcome these problems, regardless of the mix of languages spoken on site.

- It may be necessary to hold separate training sessions to assess the understanding of safety critical words and phrases by workers with English language problems.

- Confirming that the workers being assessed can associate each image with a spoken short phrase in plain English will give supervisors and managers confidence that the workers have an understanding of safety critical words in English.

- The simplicity of these phrases aids translation into other languages, if needed.

- Before using any images, workers' competence, training and language skills must be assessed. This will also indicate the level of supervision required generally.

- The images can be used to support site inductions, toolbox talks or other training, or superimposed on site plans to identify the location of welfare facilities, fire-fighting equipment, and so on.

- The images also help to fill gaps in translation, as well as improving memory recall of site rules.

- If appropriate, the images can enhance and complement existing procedures (for example, using interpreters) rather than replace them.

- An understanding of the images should not be solely relied upon to ensure that work of a higher risk nature can be carried out safely.

7.3   Managing the language situation

Contractors who employ workers who cannot speak and/or understand English have several options when deciding how to manage communications. These include hiring a bilingual supervisor who can give information, instruction and training to workers. Alternatively, English speaking co-workers are often used on site to communicate with non-English speaking workers. However, their competence (both technically in construction and as a translator) must be assessed first.

Another option is for training materials to be translated or to be represented in a pictorial form (images) *(refer to 7.5)*. The effectiveness of images to overcome language barriers has been confirmed through research. The images were developed from British Standard safety signs, HSE guidance documents and other picture-based guidance. These were tested for comprehension on live sites with foreign workers and refined to help contractors to carry out effective health and safety training and, in so doing, discharge their legal duties.

They were developed for a generic site induction and targeted at the most critical health, safety and welfare issues relevant to construction workers. However, these are only examples of a larger database of images.

7.4 Pre-start assessments

Before any worker starts on site the following facts must be established.

- The worker's competence and training.
- The worker's understanding of English.
- Supervision required.

The type of work to be done by the worker will dictate the required level of competence and identify any training needed. Regardless of language issues foreign workers must meet the level of competence and training expected of **any** worker asked to do the task(s). Therefore, contractors should apply the same criteria for non/low-English speaking workers as they do for English speakers, which will require some form of competency assessment. It is possible that some foreign workers will have trade qualifications gained in their home countries.

 UK ENIC – the UK National Information Centre for the recognition and evaluation of international qualifications and skills – offers a service to compare overseas qualifications with UK ones. Although not comprehensive, it is a useful resource.

With regard to training undertaken in the United Kingdom, holding a valid CSCS, CPCS or similar card will indicate that an acceptable level of training has been undertaken and a minimum level of health and safety knowledge is held. Failure to prove an acceptable level of competence will indicate that further training is required before considering the other pre-start factors. (Such training is beyond the scope of this chapter.)

Assuming that the worker meets the contractor's competence criteria, the next thing to consider is the worker's language skills. NARIC can also provide assistance in this respect. There are a number of methods for assessing a worker's English language skills, which use simple self-assessment criteria. One of these is the Association of Language Testers in Europe (ALTE) 'can do' statements. These can be objectively described and assessed by non-specialists. Therefore, a worker's language skills can be easily determined by site managers and supervisors by following the guidance provided in the ALTE work statements summary (see table below and overleaf).

Workers below ALTE breakthrough level are those with no English language skills whatsoever, who need an interpreter or written translation for all communications. Furthermore, it may be unwise to assume these workers can read in their own language. To prove their competence these workers will have to demonstrate their understanding of the images without the benefit of reference to the phrases. Most workers who have lived and worked in the UK for at least one year may have picked up a basic level of understanding of English at listening breakthrough level or Level 1. Workers at this level will find the images and phrases to be useful learning aids.

Co-workers, who can interpret for their colleagues, will need to be at least ALTE Level 3 for listening and speaking. The presence of an interpreter does not make the images redundant as they can still fill gaps that may be lost in translation. The combination of competence, training and language skills will dictate the level of supervision required. Another factor, as with any worker, will be the result of the employer's risk assessment for the task(s).

However, where there is a language barrier to communication, the level of supervision will also have to consider an appropriate ratio of workers to each bilingual supervisor. This can vary from as much as 1:20 to 1:1 depending on the circumstances. Where workers are grouped close together in the same area and undertaking low-risk work the ratio can be high. But, if the workers are dispersed around the site and/or undertaking higher risk work, the ratio may need to be as low as 1:1. Lone working for workers with no/low English language skills is not recommended.

ALTE work statements summary table			
ALTE level	**Listening or speaking**	**Reading**	**Writing**
ALTE breakthrough level	CAN take and pass on simple messages of a routine kind, such as 'Friday meeting 10 a.m.'.	CAN understand short reports or product descriptions on familiar matters, if these are expressed in simple language and the contents are predictable.	CAN write a simple routine request to a colleague, such as 'Can I have 20X please?'
ALTE Level 1	CAN state simple requirements within own job area, such as 'I want to order 25 of...'.	CAN understand most short reports or manuals of a predictable nature within their area of expertise, provided enough time is given.	CAN write a short, comprehensible note of request to a colleague or a known contact in another company.
ALTE Level 2	CAN offer advice to clients within own job area on simple matters.	CAN understand the general meaning of non-routine letters and theoretical articles within own work area.	CAN make reasonably accurate notes at a meeting or seminar where the subject matter is familiar and predictable.
ALTE Level 3	CAN take and pass on most messages that are likely to require attention during a normal working day.	CAN understand most correspondence, reports and factual product literature they are likely to come across.	CAN deal with all routine requests for goods or services.

ALTE Level 4	CAN contribute effectively to meetings and seminars within own area of work and argue for or against a case.	CAN understand correspondence expressed in non-standard language.	CAN handle a wide range of routine and non-routine situations in which professional services are requested from colleagues or external contacts.
ALTE Level 5	CAN advise on/handle complex, delicate or contentious issues, such as legal or financial matters, to the extent that they have the necessary specialist knowledge.	CAN understand reports and articles likely to be encountered during their work, including complex ideas expressed in complex language.	CAN make full and accurate notes and continue to participate in a meeting or seminar.

(Reproduced with permission from ALTE.)

 For further information on the ALTE Can Do project visit the ALTE website.

7.5   Critical health, safety and welfare images

Each image is set out in a similar format, as shown to the right and below on this page.

The **reference number** at the top of each image is for ease of identification. The next element is a **short phrase or sentence**. These have been developed, with help from language experts, to:

- communicate, in plain English, the particular health and safety issue depicted by the graphical symbol

- aid translation into other languages.

The phrase or sentence will remind the person delivering the training of the response required from the person being assessed during the induction. Depending on circumstances, a decision will have to be made as to whether it is more beneficial to reveal or hide the phrase or sentence during the assessment. Having sight of the phrase or sentence may have the potential to help workers with a limited understanding of written English to associate the written words with the message of the graphical symbol.

The **graphical symbol** is the main element in each image. Most are self-explanatory. Some enable the person delivering the training to add site-specific information (for example, the postal address or telephone number).

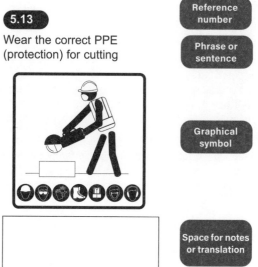

As demonstrated in the figures below, it is recommended that some images are regarded as linked, and are shown sequentially to convey the correct meaning.

If image 3.7 is shown to a worker who cannot understand the written phrase, it could be misinterpreted as 'the site is closed' or 'keep out'. However, by showing image 3.6 and 3.7 in sequence, a visual link is created and the chance of misinterpretation is reduced.

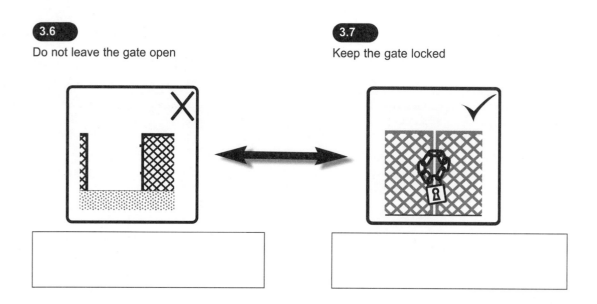

7.6 Delivering a safety-critical communication toolbox talk

1. Find the hazard in the contents list.

2. Turn to the appropriate page (yellow image).

3. View the risk to health or safety on the opposing red page (see below left).

4. Fold out the red page to reveal the necessary control measures on the green page(s) (see below right).

5. Deliver the toolbox talk.

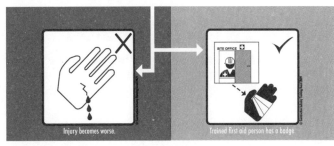

7.6.1 Explanation of the elements on each coloured page

Explains the hazard that the toolbox talk is covering

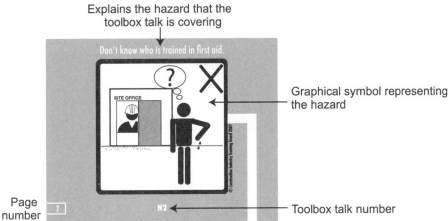

Graphical symbol representing the hazard

Page number

Toolbox talk number

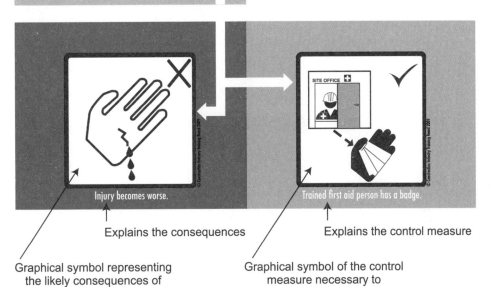

Explains the consequences

Explains the control measure

Graphical symbol representing the likely consequences of ignoring the hazard

Graphical symbol of the control measure necessary to overcome the hazard

7.7 Using the images

7.7.1 Site induction

The critical health, safety and welfare images are examples of a wider resource for use by site managers or supervisors. It is envisaged that the primary use will be during the induction training of foreign workers.

The images can also be used to support other forms of training (such as during the delivery of toolbox talks to foreign workers). However, they have their limitations as described later.

The images are intended to enhance the induction procedures for non/low-English speaking workers. However, in future it may be possible to import the images directly into existing induction presentations.

With careful forethought, this may enable foreign workers to be successfully inducted during the same presentation as other workers. If this approach is taken it is likely that additional effort will be required to confirm the retained level of understanding of the foreign workers, possibly including subsequent follow-up checks.

Existing induction training procedures for foreign workers who do not understand English may involve the use of an interpreter. However, problems can occur during translation and the use of the images may help to fill any gaps in worker understanding.

7.7.2 Site plans

Some of the images (such as those showing the location of welfare facilities, fire-fighting equipment and assembly points) lend themselves to being overlaid (physically or electronically) on site layout plans.

Depending on the size of the plans, it may be feasible for copies of the images to be electronically superimposed directly onto the plans in the appropriate location, or placed in the margin with arrows pointing to the actual location. These can be displayed during site inductions and kept in a suitable place for future reference.

7.7.3 Site inspections

The images can be used during site walkabout. For example, a worker not wearing essential personal protective equipment (PPE) can be informed using images starting with the number '5', which show items of PPE required on construction sites.

Furthermore, the images in the CITB database are presented in the sequence Hazard-Risk-Control(s) and can be used to educate the worker by showing them a hazard, which may be an unsafe act or condition, followed by the potential risk (consequences) and the necessary control(s).

Management controls are beyond the worker's direct authority but can be dealt with using an image containing a 'report to supervisor' message.

Workers can be tested for comprehension by asking them to consider whether an image is good or bad practice, or by showing the first sequence of images (hazard/risk) and asking the worker to identify the correct control image.

In addition, observation of workers after instruction has been given will confirm whether they have implemented the necessary controls/safe system of work.

7.7.4 Limitations of using pictorial images

Whilst pictorial images are useful aids for communicating health and safety information, they have their limitations. For example, some of the critical health, safety and welfare images contain some work that needs a permit to work. However, the rationale for introducing a particular type of permit or the procedures for obtaining one must be taught through detailed instruction, not easily covered solely by pictorial images.

Images should not be seen as a complete alternative to using interpreters but rather as tools to enhance existing practices; the law requires this should include interpreters, where appropriate.

CONTENTS

Behavioural safety

GT700 Toolbox talks / supporting checklists and forms

Toolbox talks on some of these topics are available in the GT700 publication. Supporting checklists and forms covering some of these topics are available on our companion website.

BEHAVIOURAL SAFETY

Overview

The chapter explores behavioural safety and the elements of working practice that can have an impact, both positive and negative, on this area. It offers information and models that can inform good practice in this significant area of focus for health and safety.

Studies have shown that up to 90% of accidents are attributable in some extent to human failure. Human factors are understandably an important focus for many accident investigations. The importance and relevance of these to preventing incidents, injuries, deaths and ill health within the workplace, as identified through case study research, therefore warrant the attention of all organisations, managers and employees.

8.1   Introduction

Promoting a behavioural safety culture is the responsibility of the whole organisation, including its supply chain, and this drives the way it operates on a daily basis.

There are rules, regulations, systems, procedures, codes of practice, standards and training requirements in place to support and govern health and safety in the workplace, but these can only be effective if there is a top-to-bottom and bottom-to-top culture of commitment to safe behaviour at all times.

Having good systems in place is not always enough. All individuals need to hold safety as a value, not just a priority. They need to demonstrate this commitment through their behaviour in taking responsibility for their own safety, as well as the safety of their co-workers and any other organisations or individuals that may be affected by the work they are undertaking.

The level of success is defined by how organisations 'live' their systems day-to-day – the behavioural culture of the organisation.

The HSE identifies behavioural safety as one important area within the overarching title of human factors that:

 refer to environmental, organisational and job factors, and human and individual characteristics, which influence behaviour at work in a way which can affect health and safety.

Creating a culture of behavioural safety in any organisation provides a focus for understanding and influencing the way managers and individuals act in relation to work and decision making. It is based on the following process.

- Identifying and making evident safe and unsafe practices.

- Observing and intervening, where appropriate, to encourage safe practice or to amend unsafe practice.

- Feeding back vital information to inform decision making.

- Training, process, material and environmental change, as appropriate.

- Recognising safe working practices and supporting good practices.

Behavioural safety represents a proactive rather than a reactive process, engaging all managers and workers within a culture of continuous improvement and safety awareness.

For this reason, communication at and across all levels of an organisation is vital to the development of a successful and influential strategy.

 Useful HSE publications are available from the HSE website.

A significant factor in reducing the number of accidents is to raise awareness, at all organisational levels and within the supply chain, to ensure that behavioural safety change is part of the culture.

8.2   Important points

- Historically, improvements in health and safety standards have been achieved through **engineering technology/controls** (plant and equipment) and **safety management systems** (risk assessments, permits to work and so on).

- These improvements will not fully eradicate incidents and accidents.

- Understanding how people make decisions and **why people act** as a consequence is the vital third element.

- The biggest gain in improving health and safety performance comes from integrating and understanding the human element of risk management.

- Companies that incorporate behavioural safety programmes into the day-to-day running of their business see dramatic drops in accident rates.

08

- In order for a behavioural safety approach to work, consistently high standards of engineering technology/controls and safety management systems need to be established.

- Behavioural safety is not a quick-win initiative – it takes time and commitment from all levels of a company or organisation. It is not an alternative to applying sound, basic principles of health and safety management.

- Effective leadership, management and workforce support is crucial for the success of any programme.

- People may generally think they are working safely, or that the risk of something happening is minimal, due to their knowledge and past experience. Those observing can often see that the risk is greater than first thought and thus intervention techniques play an important role in developing a positive safety culture.

- Workers respond more positively to co-worker/peer intervention.

- Worker engagement is a fundamental component of any behavioural safety programme.

8.3   Reasons for using a behavioural safety approach

Over recent years, significant improvements have been achieved in health, safety and environmental performance. These have been gained largely through technological advances and improved focus through the use of management controls and systems.

However, this successful downward trend is levelling off. Increased focus on human elements associated with health and safety practice, awareness, commitment and decision-making in the form of a behavioural safety approach will contribute to more improvements over time in construction and other industries.

Evidence and support for this has come from HSE case study investigations and research into major reportable accidents.

The case studies identify actions and strategies that have been implemented within the example organisations in order to improve specific health and safety practice.

From this work, the HSE and contributing partners have identified a list of human factors. These include the following.

- Introducing human factors.

- Competence.

- Humans and risk (integration of human factors into risk assessments and accident investigation).

- Written procedures.

- Emergency response.

- Maintenance.

- Safety culture.

Commitment by the team is vital

- Safety critical communications.

- Alarm handling and control room design.

- Fatigue.

- Organisational change and transition management.

- Human factors and the major accident prevention policy (MAPP).

The HSE also notes other problems (such as those listed below) found from inspection and assessment.

- Too much emphasis being placed on reducing personal accidents (slips, trips and falls), without an equal focus on preventing major accidents.

- Failing to realise that safety culture is about everyone in the organisation, including managers, employees and the supply chain.

- Not being clear about how the safety management system will prevent or reduce human errors, which may lead to major accidents.

To be effective, a behaviour-based approach to health and safety requires the following.

- Commitment and a proactive approach from the senior management team to improving behavioural safety. This commitment should be demonstrated by how they fund, lead and support it.

- Effective, open top-down and bottom-up communication and engagement on all aspects of safety in the workplace and the ability to influence and implement good practice.

- A procedure for individuals or groups, including the supply chain, to raise issues or concerns to inform decision making and take remedial action without fear.

- A focus on people, often incorporating formal and informal one-to-one or group observations of workers performing work tasks. This includes setting goals carefully and giving timely feedback on safety-related behaviour through coaching and mentoring.

- Recognition of good practice and sharing it at all levels.

- Creation of a learning culture for people to continuously improve through formal and informal training, coaching and mentoring.

- An effective response and solution to unsafe behaviour, incidents and near-misses.

- Transparent and fair leadership.

- Awareness amongst individuals or groups, including the supply chain, of different ways to consider or query human factors – how we do what we do and why.

- Solid principles about engaging, motivating, assisting, reinforcing and sustaining safe behaviours.

- A systematic approach, examining the motivation and underlying behaviours, in order to increase safe behaviour.

- Continuous rather than a one-off approach to deliver sustainable and positive results.

- Allowing time to achieve measurable results. However, results can be achieved immediately through observation and action where appropriate.

- Emphasising an increase in safe behaviours rather than focusing on length of time without injury.

- A proactive, preventative approach as well as learning from incidents.

- Integration with existing practices.

www **For a human factors checklist visit the HSE website.**

8.4 Preparing to implement a behavioural approach

The HSE's core guidance defines human factors as the interaction between three main areas affecting human performance at work.

These consist of the following.

- The job.

- The individual.

- The organisation.

8.4.1 The job

Tasks should be designed in accordance with ergonomic principles to take into account limitations in human performance. Matching the job to the person will ensure that they are not overloaded and that the most effective contribution to the business results.

INDIVIDUAL
Competence, skills, personality, attitudes, risk perception...

JOB
Task, workload, work environment, procedures, display and controls...

ORGANISATION
Culture, leadership, resources, work patterns, communications...

Physical match includes the design of the whole workplace and working environment. Mental match involves the individual's information and decision-making requirements, as well as their perception of the tasks.

Mismatches between job requirements and workers' capabilities create the potential for human error.

Job design will have a focus on the following.

- Areas of work and the environment in which it is carried out.

- Materials and tools.

- Control and display panels and devices.

- Communication and management systems.

- All job-related written guidance and information.

8.4.2 The individual

People bring to a job their attitudes, skills, habits and personality, which can be strengths or weaknesses depending on the demands of the task. Individual characteristics influence behaviour in complex and significant ways. Their effects on task performance may be negative and may not always be mitigated by job design. Some characteristics, such as personality, are fixed and cannot be changed. Others, such as skills and attitudes, may be changed or enhanced. Personnel selection policies and procedures to select appropriate individuals for the job specifications should consider the following:

- age, physique and capabilities matched to job requirements

- aptitude, intelligence and personality

- competence (the right skills, knowledge, experience and training)

- fitness for work and health surveillance, where this is needed

- the needs of special groups of employees

- monitoring of personal performance on safety for safety critical staff.

8.4.3 The organisation

Organisational factors have a major influence on individuals and group behaviour, yet it is not uncommon for this to be overlooked during the design of work and in the investigation of accidents and incidents. Organisations need to establish their own positive health and safety culture. The climate needs to promote employee involvement and commitment at all levels, emphasising that deviation from established safety standards is not acceptable.

The organisation will ensure that it supports managers to:

- take responsibility for all aspects of work and work design
- devise and maintain a good safety management system
- encourage a good safety culture by showing commitment
- consult the workforce on important decisions
- commit to learning from the latest thinking on good practice in safety
- openly encourage identification and shared learning from accidents and near misses.

Together, these areas constitute the solid foundations on which behavioural safety programmes can be addressed and developed.

 Good practice and case studies indicate that prior to commencing any behavioural safety change programme, intervention, factors relating to the job, the individual and the organisation will all need to be considered.

Before sites embark on a behavioural safety programme, it is recommended that the following preparation has taken place.

- All hazards have been identified.
- Human performance issues have been identified and managed (particularly in relation to safety critical roles and activities).
- The hierarchy of control has been applied to prevent the occurrence of identified hazards/minimise their consequences should they occur.
- The site has the required engineering, operating and maintenance capability and experience (including appropriate staffing levels).
- Accurate operating procedures are available for all eventualities, including emergencies.
- Individuals (operators) are fully prepared to deal with all conditions. This will include identification of training needs, training, assessment, rehearsal and reassessment.
- Training should include underlying knowledge of the process, so that operators can troubleshoot (identify and respond to abnormal situations as they develop). It should not just provide the minimum knowledge required to operate the plant. This approach will help to manage residual risk arising from hazards that were not identified or effectively addressed.
- Lessons have been learnt from site, company and industry experience.
- Succession planning ensures that corporate knowledge is retained.
- Safety management arrangements and risk control measures have been reviewed to ensure that they remain usable and relevant.

It is recommended that only when these technical and systems issues have been addressed can the timing and appropriateness of a behavioural programme be addressed. The guidance also goes on to highlight the following for consideration.

- Do not underestimate the resources required – it is not a one-off exercise, but a new way of working that must be maintained for any positive results to be sustained.
- Do not be over-optimistic – not all interventions are completely successful in their main aim. High expectations may lead to disappointment later.
- Be clear about what you want to achieve and how you will know that you have achieved it.
- Pilot the intervention (for example, to ensure that the approach is workable, that the facilitators or observers understand what is required and that the appropriate data is being recorded).
- Talk to similar companies and trade associations about their interventions and experiences.
- As with all interventions, listen toemployees and use the process to improve dialogue – involve them early in the choice of programme.
- Make the language and style of the package your own, as off-the-shelf packages may not be appropriate for your site's needs.
- Use strong site facilitators – the success of such interventions is greatly helped by using personable, experienced and respected site personnel as facilitators.
- Ensure that the focus is on the root causes of behaviours.
- On major hazard sites, don't neglect process safety. Beware of 'what gets measured gets done' – that is, while regular measurement and reporting keeps you focused on improvement, placing too much emphasis on reducing personal accidents (such as slips, trips and falls) could mean neglecting the prevention of major accidents.

8.5   Factors influencing a behavioural approach

The practicalities involved in successfully implementing a behavioural approach to health and safety are listed below and overleaf.

- Preparation – knowing what you are doing and why.
- Establishing an effective system of two-way communication to develop mutual trust between management and workers.
- Engaging the right people in the decision making.
- Observing people at work.
- Assessing safe and unsafe behaviours (being non-judgemental).
- Making timely and appropriate interventions.
- Establishing why unsafe behaviours take place.

08

- Influencing those behaving unsafely not to do so in the future.
- Recognising safe behaviour and, if appropriate, rewarding it.
- Continuing assessment and research whilst looking for improvements in safe behaviour.

The overall and wider benefits to this implementation can include the following.

- More effective communication regarding safety between management and frontline workers.
- Greater management visibility and engagement.
- Increased efficiency.
- Greater flexibility and effectiveness of workers.
- A reduction in the number of workplace injuries.
- Improvement in the standards of health and safety.
- Reduced physical and financial losses for the individual and the employer.
- The extension of safe working practices into home life.

The following elements, on the pages following this one, are all factors that are relevant and require consideration when implementing a behavioural safety programme.

8.5.1 Psychology of behaviour

Behavioural safety applies tried and tested psychological principles in order to mediate the way people and organisations do things, particularly how people act or behave in respect of their own health and safety and that of others. Among many other factors, the behavioural approach takes into account how people think, act, behave and respond to certain situations. It also considers how people's immediate surroundings can influence their thoughts and actions.

8.5.1.1 Thought processes

Contrary to previous belief, the conscious or alert state of mind can only be actively engaged in one activity or thought process at any one time. Neuroscience research has identified that distractions from a single task can, at best, result in less efficient working and, at worst, can contribute to a stress response. This is particularly so if someone tries to finish a task but cannot complete it as time goes on.

The human brain is strongly programmed to avoid perceived threats and generally (but less strongly) programmed for reward from tasks achieved. This latter results in the small, so-called 'dopamine spike', which drives us to continue with reward-based behaviour. In practical terms, if a distraction disturbs a person's thought processes or task, they may, for example, trip over a toolbox they have placed on some steps or fall into a hole they have recently dug. Other thoughts have entered their conscious mind and the hazardn is momentarily forgotten.

At the most basic level, good workplace practice (such as avoiding distractions and removing hazards immediately) can support the wider behavioural safety programme. Often the ability to increase safety awareness by the individual doing a mental risk assessment (that is, asking 'What is going to put me at risk while I do this job?') is not improved or encouraged once relevant training has been undertaken. Practising this type of self-awareness has safety benefits, especially if it is recorded.

People at work benefit from being able to discuss and take responsibility for the day-to-day aspects of their job and from feeling competent to do so. The human side of the working environment is a highly significant factor in determining the success of a behavioural safety environment and this warrants a focus on management training and commitment. By helping people understand the implications of how they work and engaging their knowledge, we can identify the process that integrates human factors into the core management system of the business. Effort should be targeted at encouraging positive, open and real communication that resolves issues when they arise, rather than keeping them hidden until an incident occurs.

8.5.1.2 Habitual behaviours

Habits are subconscious ways of thinking, both positive and negative. They are formed when a task or behaviour is repeated over time. This enables the thinking part of the brain (the pre-frontal cortex) to conserve energy through reducing its need for active attention and processing. Effectively, the brain is saying 'I have done this before – no need to pay conscious attention to this then!'

The more repetitions an action has, the stronger the habit, until very little, if any, conscious thought is given to the task. This is termed being *unconsciously competent*, and an example would be driving a car after much experience. An example of a habit that can have negative consequences is not wearing eye protection when using a disc cutter because the past is used to justify present actions. The worker has not been injured before so argues that they will not be injured now. Similar arguments are often put forward to dismiss many self-protective and safety-focused equipment and practices.

Similarly, a positive habit can be formed by communicating the benefits and consciously ensuring that eye protection is worn. This could be achieved through raising awareness via posters or stickers on the disc cutter, ensuring suitable eye protection is available with the disc cutter, or spoken reminders from work colleagues and managers. When encouraged and reinforced, through these or similar measures, wearing eye protection becomes a comfortable habit and the expected norm.

8.5.1.3 Values, beliefs, expectations, attitudes and behaviour

We all have our own values and beliefs (attitudes) that underlie how we think, and which then drive the way we act and behave. Being able to influence these is a significant management responsibility, which can be achieved through day-to-day working practice, the level and manner of communication and the delivery of any structured programme to address health and safety interventions.

Whilst the commitment of managers can send a powerful positive message regarding behavioural culture, a lack of commitment can be equally but negatively powerful. Case studies suggest that low expectations and poor leadership from management can create negative attitudes and a lack of trust from employees. This in turn can result in poor methods of working resulting in poor health and safety performance.

8.5.2   The challenge

Some **potential barriers to progress** that have been identified from existing behavioural safety programmes are shown below.

- Management promoting a negative or passive message, making the workforce believe that it is collecting unnecessary data or that the information will never provide solutions.

- Overreliance on off the shelf solutions and thereby not fully owning the ongoing development of the programme.

- Middle managers either excluded from communication or not understanding the programme.

- Processes not reaching their potential because they are time-consuming and seen as stopping people from getting on with the job without consideration of the huge potential benefits.

- Processes that generate committees, create databases and induce an overload that the majority of small and medium businesses find difficult to resource.

- Organisations fully understanding that behavioural safety approaches are not short-term solutions but may be 'a change in the way we do things round here' that will need an effective investment of time, resources and commitment.

- A lack of trust leading workers to feel that they will be blamed in some way.

- An existing environment of poor industrial relationships or grievance procedures.

Some **enablers to progress** are shown below.

- Commitment of executives, directors and management to the programme implementation.

- Middle managers' involvement in, and understanding of, the behavioural safety programme objectives.

- Sufficient resources at all levels with which to support work, materials and training.

- A good level of trust between managers and frontline workers.

- The absence of industrial relations issues.

- Existing workforce involvement in health and safety practice.

- Innovative and new practice features to the programme on a regular (for example, annual) basis.

Induction for all: enabling progress on a behavioural safety programme

8.6   Key stages in a behavioural safety programme

08

Following research, the Keil Centre* produced a report for the HSE, *Strategies to promote safe behaviour as part of a health and safety management system*. This offers the following model of how programmes may be implemented within organisations. Not all elements need to be included in all programmes; this is for guidance and adaptation as appropriate.

* The Keil Centre is a company of chartered psychologists and registered ergonomists offering professional services to industry, government and private individuals.

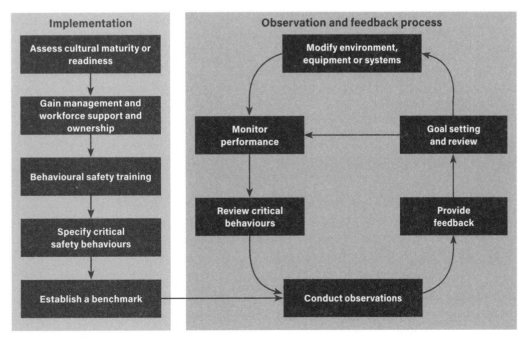

Overview of a behavioural safety programme

BEHAVIOURAL SAFETY

 For further information on behavioural safety, visit the HSE website.

 Recognising the importance of management commitment to a behavioural safety programme is vital to determine the successful implementation of that programme.

8.6.1 Implementation

8.6.1.1 Assess cultural maturity or readiness

At this first stage, the organisation would assess whether it is ready to commit to the implementation of a behavioural safety programme.

This is the stage where potential challenges to success are identified and addressed. This could include an organisational restructure or relocation.

It could also highlight and benchmark management commitment and communication processes, by holding workshops, issuing questionnaires or simply through one-to-one interviews.

8.6.1.2 Management and workforce support and ownership

Management and workforce support is crucial for the success of the programme. It defines the culture within which the behavioural safety work occurs and can be encouraged through early involvement of all individuals.

Involvement is generally an emotional response and depends on both the commitment of the individual and the organisation's support and appreciation of their input, views and opinions. People will need to see that they carry influence and can positively transform the style and content of the programme to be implemented.

Success of the programme will also depend on the opportunities for individuals involved in managing the programme, or in acting as behavioural safety champions. Not everyone can fulfil these roles and so the organisation may create a process for recruiting employees to a steering group or to co-ordinator roles. Volunteers can be requested and consideration given to representatives from the entire workforce

 Many programmes require that observations are made of colleagues carrying out tasks. These observations are generally carried out by frontline workers and identify issues relevant to behavioural safety practice and the overall programme. Training is required for these observers to record information, deliver feedback and focus on the objectives that are critical for continuous improvement.

8.6.1.3 Behavioural safety training

Training managers and workers to understand behavioural safety tools and objectives is crucial to programme success. At the most basic level, this can be awareness training, whilst co-ordinators, managers and those carrying out the main responsibilities will require more comprehensive information and training. Some programmes train all staff, whereas others train a minority of employees. Decisions regarding who to train are taken on the basis of internal knowledge and resources (people, financial and material) and the depth of the programme itself.

8.6.1.4 Specify critical safety behaviours

Behavioural safety programmes focus on developing a checklist of critical safety behaviours that is completed by the trained observers. Critical health and safety behaviours are identified through a number of different means. These include, but are not solely based on, the analysis of previous accident and incident reports. Additional information can be gained from other sources.

These can include reviewing previous risk assessments (such as COSHH) and audits, in addition to formal and informal input from frontline staff and managers. Near-miss or dangerous occurrence reports are equally valid sources of critical safety behaviours. Preparation that focuses solely on formal reporting is important but limited in scope. This will exclude critically unsafe behaviours that have not yet resulted in serious consequences but which hide latent risk. It is vital that critical safety behaviours and their measures are sufficiently well defined to enable meaningful observations to be made and recorded.

 Formal and informal reporting are significant areas of research when defining the critical safety behaviours to be addressed by the programme. Important contributions to this process can be made from a number of levels within an organisation.

8.6.1.5 Establish a benchmark

The final preparatory element involves identifying a baseline, or benchmarking the organisation's current situation, in relation to the selected critical safety behaviours. This is established through conducting observations of these areas in practice.

A benchmark will enable review and evaluation of the programme's effectiveness to be more clearly defined.

8.6.2 Continuous process of observation and feedback

After the implementation phase, this next continuous stage of observation, feedback, goal setting and review commences.

8.6.2.1   Conduct observations

The next stage in the process is conducting observations. This is generally peer-to-peer, but can be done by managers. It is usual for the observer to be provided with a checklist (the critical behaviours identified previously). The observer indicates on the list whether the individual is safe, unsafe or if the behaviour was not observed.

 Defining critical safety behaviours clearly at the pre-observation stage and through the benchmarking process will increase quality and meaning during the programme.

8.6.2.2 Provide feedback

The provision of feedback is an imperative process within the behavioural safety programme, which can survive or flounder depending on the skills of observers, their style and credibility. For this reason, feedback must be considered a critical skill and individuals should be trained accordingly. It most effectively reinforces safe behaviour when it is positive and delivered by someone perceived as credible and knowledgeable by the individual receiving the feedback. Feedback can have a greater or lesser impact depending on the following factors.

- When it is delivered. (Generally, the closer and more relevant to the observation the more meaningful the feedback.)

- The focus of the feedback. (This should be on the observed behaviour, not on the individual practising the behaviour.)

- Relevance. (The feedback should fit the expectations of the person receiving the feedback and with the behaviour under observation.)

There are two main types of feedback.

1. **Summative feedback** offers more general comment on an individual's overall performance.

2. **Formative feedback** provides more detailed information on how they might improve their performance in the future.

 **The quality of feedback and its style of delivery is critical to the success of a behavioural safety programme. Observers will need to be trained in positive feedback skills in order to contribute as effectively as possible to the behaviour improvement cycle.**

8.6.2.3 Goal setting and review

Goals are crucial to any system of managing performance as they can have an important influence in terms of encouraging and supporting behavioural change.

- They describe the desired result.

- They give a sense of direction and purpose.

- They provide a yardstick for assessment.

- They enable people to prioritise.

- They link activities to the overall direction of the organisation.

Goals describe something to be accomplished by individuals, teams and organisations over a period of time. They can be expressed as targets to be met, such as tasks to be completed, or changes in behaviour by specified dates. Goals need to be defined and agreed. They will relate to the overall purpose of the job and define performance areas – all the aspects of the job that contribute to achieving its overall purpose.

Defining goals

- Agreeing the job aim establishes **why** a job is done.

- Identifying key result areas or criteria establishes **what** has to be done.

- Setting goals establishes **what** specifically has to be done.

- Setting measurable goals identifies the **degree** to which something has to be done and by **when**.

- Agreeing actions shows **how** measurable goals are to be achieved.

Skilful goal setting focuses attention on the important targets to be achieved. They enable the cascading of the organisation's objectives to individual level so that everyone, at every level, is aware of how they contribute to teams, divisions and the organisation as a whole. Goals need to be **SMART**.

Specific – unambiguous, concrete. Teams and individuals know exactly what is expected of them.

Measurable – quantified either by a statistical result or a behaviour that can be observed.

Achievable – stretching and challenging but not impossible.

Realistic – linked to the individual and to the team's and organisation's business plans.

Timely – include agreed completion dates.

Goal setting is a participative process involving the observer and either the individual or group concerned.

8.6.2.4   Monitor performance

Behavioural safety programmes are monitored over time and focused on measuring the impact of the programme on the initially identified critical safety behaviours. A good measure of success is an improved percentage of observations where behaviour is observed as safe. If there is little or no change in this measure over time for some or all observations, it will be important to review the specific behaviours with regard to barriers to change. The factors that work against safe behavioural practice could be related to people or to product or design.

8.6.2.5   Review critical behaviours

A review of critical behaviours can be carried out within a defined timescale to ensure that the programme is still addressing areas that are relevant and improving. Once these behaviours have become habitual they may be replaced by other significant critical behaviours, which are developed through the same looped cycle as detailed by this general model.

 Once implemented, the success of the programme is highly dependent upon the commitment made, particularly by managers, at each stage of the process. People will value action and communication regarding progress and assume a lack of commitment if these are not carried through as expected.

8.7   Reducing human error and influencing behaviour

People can cause or contribute to accidents by failing to do a job correctly, and by hearing but not listening to or understanding health and safety information associated with the task, thereby failing to work to expectations. People do not generally set out to make errors deliberately, but they are often set up to fail by the way the brain processes information. For example, errors may occur as a result of the following.

- Stress or fatigue.
- Working long hours without sufficient rest/erratic shift patterns.
- Slipping into autopilot mode.
- A lack of training.
- Poor design of equipment.
- Poorly maintained equipment.
- Unclear procedures, or lack of effective procedures.

- Shortcomings in the culture of the organisation.
- Poor decision making, even when aware of the risks.
- Misinterpretation of a situation or inappropriate action taken.
- Poor situational assessment leading to incident escalation.
- Bored or disheartened staff.
- Medical problems.

When confident and knowledgeable to do so, other people (such as colleagues, supervisors and managers) can intervene to prevent potential accidents or mitigate their possible effects. The severity of an accident can be reduced by the effectiveness of the immediate or emergency response. This effectiveness can be improved by planning and appropriate training. The following are some of the topics that can influence human error and behaviour.

8.7.1   Active and latent failures

The consequences of human failure can be immediate or delayed. It is important to have an understanding of active and latent failures and how they affect health and safety.

Active failures have an immediate consequence and are usually made by frontline people (such as drivers, operators or even the public). In a situation where there is no room for error, these active failures have an immediate impact on health and safety.

Latent failures are caused by actions generally involving people (such as designers, decision makers and managers) whose tasks are removed in time and space from operational works. Latent failures are typically failures in the design, implementation or monitoring of health and safety management systems.

Latent failures can provide a significant potential danger to health and safety. These can be highlighted only through positive safety discussions that utilise the experience and knowledge of the workforce. Latent failures (such as the examples on the next page) are generally hidden within an organisation until they are triggered by an event likely to have serious consequences.

- Poor design of workplaces, plant and equipment.
- Gaps in supervision.
- Undetected manufacturing defects.
- Maintenance failures.
- Unworkable procedures.
- Clumsy automation.
- Ineffective competency assurance.
- Ineffective training.
- Ineffective communications.
- Uncertainties of role and responsibility.
- Ageing assets, plant, tools and equipment.
- Poor planning (insufficient people/time).
- Poor information on health and safety incidents.

Latent error*

* The image of the latent error (right) shows graphite blocks fitted in the Hinckley Point B reactors. These blocks have small cracks within them, which has resulted in the reactors being run at 70% power output. It is believed that these cracks could be due to handling the blocks during construction. This has not affected safety but it has affected productivity. This is a perfect example of a latent error.

08

8.7.2   Impact of change

Change of any type within an organisation can create people issues and behavioural issues. For example:

- an organisation may appoint new leaders and managers
- the need to develop new skills and capabilities may increase.
- roles can change

Workers may be uncertain and resistant because of the following.

- Limited communication and explanation of changes.
- They feel that they will be disadvantaged by the change.
- People do not see the need for change.

Dealing with these issues on a reactive, case-by-case basis puts the progress of the job, workforce morale, and overall performance of the behavioural approach at risk.

Change is unsettling for people at all levels of an organisation. The manager, or management team, will need to focus on working together and understanding that change can lead to alterations in typical working practice, stressful responses and a potential need for increased communication and support. Change affects people personally; this can also be a factor in the implementation of a behavioural safety approach. Individuals (or teams of individuals) will require timely information regarding the following.

- The changes they will see as a result of a behavioural safety programme.
- How they and their behaviours will be measured.
- What will be expected of them during and after the change programme.
- What success or failure will mean for them and those around them.

8.7.3   Leading by example

The implementation of behavioural safety can pose particular problems with a fragmented and mobile workforce, such as that found in the construction industry. To be successfully implemented on site, the principles of behavioural safety will need to be embedded within the organisation's culture and understood by the workforce and management from the initiation and planning stages.

The foundations, expectations and compliance processes should be communicated, discussed and agreed from the beginning. If employees and contractors are involved, empowered to influence and are provided with the relevant induction, critical safety behavioural standards will be set for the future.

Managers are a critical element within the success or failure of programmes. Non-compliance and the breaking of basic rules (such as not wearing safety helmets or safety goggles) sends a message that a behavioural safety approach is not taken seriously, despite policies and procedures to the contrary. Similarly, when senior managers visit sites, they should receive the same induction and live by the same rules – body language and leading by example can send a powerful message.

8.7.4   Communication style and content

Communication style and content are important elements that contribute significantly to the building of trust. People feel trust when an individual's behaviour and body language is congruent with what is being said – when 'walking the talk' is evident. Our brains are particularly good at picking up on communication signals from others, whether intended or, as can sometimes be the case, unintended.

Communication is at the heart of all that we do, at work and in our own time. It takes many forms and can be transmitted via various media (for example, face-to-face, radio, telephone, email or video conferencing). It is essential, especially within our working environment, that we get it right. Barriers to effective communication may include background noise, the type of language used and sociocultural issues. The potential for confusion and misinterpretation can be high. In any communication process, it is vital to give the person receiving information the time and space to be able to think and formulate a response. In communication it is the quality, not the quantity, that matters.

8.7.4.1   Verbal and non-verbal communication

During a normal conversation, we usually transmit and receive in three ways.

- What is said (words).
- Body language (conscious or not).
- How it is said (tonality).

During periods of high workload or stress, our body language goes largely unnoticed. This is when the words we use and the way in which we say them become more important. In addition, our listening capability reduces as our workload or stress increases.

- Communication involves both a communicator and a receiver and is generally the responsibility of the communicator.
- What we say, how we say it and when we say it are perceived differently by different individuals.
- Overload of work and stress can be main factors that hinder effective communication. If the receiver is feeling overloaded, communication will need to reflect this. If the message is important then we need to lessen the workload.
- Job-critical communication requires undivided attention by both the communicator and the receiver.
- The most effective communicators will always check that the meaning they intend is the one that has been received.

There is a difference between hearing and listening. Hearing is a mechanical process involving the way sound waves are translated.

Listening is paying attention to what is being said. When we do this, we are able to evaluate the message within the correct context. An appropriate response can then be planned.

Listening is often described as taking place at different levels, from the less attentive Level 1 (conversational listening) to the more engaged Level 4 (deep listening). At this level, the listener is paying as much attention to body language and signals regarding what is not being said as they are to the words spoken. This type of listening takes skill and practice, and is the mark of a good communicator. Observers within a behavioural safety programme would find great benefit in becoming listening masters, so they have the potential to pick up on, and challenge, safety-related information that could otherwise be missed.

8.7.4.2   Questioning skills

How questions are asked can inform the overall effectiveness of a discussion in terms of information shared. There are several types of question, with those most commonly used shown on the right.

It is important to recognise that we are always communicating. Silence can imply annoyance or criticism, for example. Take time to consider and understand the effect of your personal communication style on others. Some good practices include the following.

Type	Response
Closed	A fact or YES/NO.
Open	Invites an extensive reply.
Leading	Indicates the required answer.
Limiting	Restricts options.
Multiple	Many questions in one – confusion.

- Control distractions as much as possible.
- Where possible, make visual and eye contact.
- Clearly identify the communicator and receiver.
- Be clear, precise and concise.
- Avoid the use of leading questions.
- Always confirm the intended message has been understood.

- Never assume meaning.
- Avoid ambiguous words, or words that could be misinterpreted.
- Encourage inclusive discussion and dialogue.
- Use phonetics for alphanumeric detail ('M for mother').
- Acknowledge communication from the listener (closed loop).

8.7.5   Facilitation, coaching and mentoring

Managers and team leaders should be as honest and explicit as possible about factors influencing health and safety within their workplace. This is particularly key when undergoing a change programme. Facilitation, coaching and mentoring are interventions and support mechanisms via which individuals are encouraged to take responsibility and contribute ideas to benefit safety of others and the organisation.

A facilitator is an individual who enables groups and organisations to work more effectively by collaborating to achieve results. They do not take sides or express or advocate a point of view during the meeting. They can also be a learning or dialogue guide to assist a group in thinking deeply about its assumptions, beliefs and values, and about its systemic processes and context.

Coaching is the process of enabling individuals to acquire the knowledge, skills and techniques needed to perform effectively in their occupational role by inspiring, motivating, challenging, stimulating and guiding them. Mentoring involves the long-term passing on of support, guidance and advice. It is an ongoing relationship that can last a long time and, being more informal than coaching, meetings can take place as and when individuals need guidance. Mentoring has a focus on career and personal development.

Individual commitment, ownership and accountability for safety is vital to making change happen. Everyone must be willing to accept responsibility for change in the areas they influence or control. It is important that the need to support and be supported through change is also recognised throughout the workforce, as a part of the behavioural safety culture.

Ownership of challenges is often encouraged by involving people in identifying problems and crafting solutions. It is reinforced by coaching and facilitation, incentives and, in some instances, rewards. These can be tangible (for example, financial compensation) or psychological (for example, camaraderie and a sense of shared involvement).

The most effective behavioural change programmes reinforce the core messages of safety through regular, timely engagement and communications that are both inspirational and practicable. Facilitated discussions are targeted to provide employees with the right information at the right time and to solicit their input and feedback.

8.7.6   Staffing levels

Some companies operate with the lowest possible number of people required to achieve their commercial objectives. Margins are tight, and contracts are won and lost on cost. Under these circumstances, people can be stretched beyond acceptable limits, with high workloads, long shifts and high levels of stress and fatigue. Operating without sufficient human resources can result in significant risk to the workforce.

8.7.7   Training and competency

It is likely that a workforce is more effective and efficient if it is:

- motivated and well trained
- not under unreasonable time pressure

- given correct information, instruction, training and supervision
- working with the right, well-maintained equipment.

Conversely, high workloads and tight timescales often result in training and competency assessments falling by the wayside. This can lead to ineffective decision making, poor working practices, out-of-date certification of plant, equipment and, of course, a negative effect on people's skills and behavioural safety practice.

As part of managing change, it is essential that a training and competency assessment is carried out, so that shortcomings are identified and addressed, and thus people are not put at risk. Every company is legally responsible for ensuring that people are trained and competent to carry out tasks. Greater efficiencies are achieved through correct skill levels, and further gains are made in completion times and work output.

8.7.8 Intervention

There are many recorded instances of people failing to intervene when they see an unsafe or illegal act. Whilst it is fully understandable that someone might not want to become involved in a violent confrontation in the street, in the context of work the personal risk to, say, a supervisor who intervenes to prevent someone working unsafely is generally not as great. However, the behaviour of supervisors and managers can directly affect the behaviour of operatives.

The effect of failing to intervene in an unsafe situation is to condone that activity, practice or behaviour. This in turn, sends a message to the operatives that the activity concerned is permitted, resulting in potential confusion for site teams and their working practices. Intervention by managers and supervisors is therefore crucial in every case in order to show commitment to, and support for, behavioural safety programmes. From general research and available information, the reasons for a failure to intervene appear to be split between a **lack of knowledge** that anything is wrong and a **conscious decision** not to take any action.

8.7.9 Conscious decision

The conscious decision not to intervene may possibly be based upon financial or time considerations. For example, a supervisor might ignore the unsafe use of a ladder because it saves the time and expense of hiring a mobile elevating work platform (MEWP). However, there may be other personal factors for not intervening.

- Overload, where the supervisor or manager may be suffering from a heavy workload and is simply unable to identify the unsafe situation developing. Having a lack of situational awareness due to overload (for example, being unaware and failing to take notice of what is going on around them) can lead to supervisors or managers not noticing existing hazards or bad practice taking place on site, resulting in an increase in risks and accidents.

- Actions of others, especially other managers or senior managers, can shape the decisions of the supervisor. Usually the fact that no-one else involved in the operation is concerned about it is excuse enough for not getting involved. If other managers or senior managers are not concerned about unsafe actions, it may shape the decision of supervisors or managers, who may feel unwilling or uncomfortable to speak out or raise concerns. This may be the culture of the organisation – *'this is the way we do things around here'* – or may come from peer pressure or from fear of repercussions or unfair treatment for speaking out.

- Ownership of the situation where the supervisor or manager does not actually believe or understand their duties, or where they are not directly in charge of the operation and believe they have no jurisdiction. If a supervisor or manager feels they have no clarity about taking ownership of safety issues, or no authority to intervene, it may be because they fear lack of support from others or fear being overruled or marginalised for the intervention. They may feel they should not get involved and, instead, adopt a 'not my job' mentality, believing it is not their problem and someone else should deal with it.

- Where a supervisor or manager lacks knowledge about the task or lacks the important communication skills, then they are less likely to get involved – having the skills to resolve the issue is important. If a supervisor or manager is not suitably knowledgeable about a task, or doesn't have the right communication skills, they may avoid taking responsibility and not get involved. They may feel embarrassed by a lack of knowledge, unable to effectively intervene and communicate what is required, and fear that they will be criticised if they get it wrong. Supervisors and managers should be given training in communication skills and be empowered to act if they feel a situation is becoming, or is, unsafe.

- The risk of possibly entering into a situation where they may be required to make a difficult decision that could have a significant effect on the project. The support of senior managers is critical to allow junior managers and supervisors to become involved in safety issues and empower them to take whatever action they deem necessary if an unsafe situation arises. This could even involve the cessation of work until the safety issue is investigated further.

8.7.10 Managing the risk

Making assessments about risks and reaching an informed decision requires access to the information held within the safety management system. The process of obtaining information begins with the recognition that the problem exists, and then raises questions to which answers are required.

Deciding on the level of accuracy and precision of the risk and safety assessment will depend on the sampling and measurement methods used in collating the initial risk information. In behavioural terms, this is done through identifying 'what' is happening during an observation and asking 'why'. The 'whats and whys' are analysed and tabulated to identify trends, often by interpreting the data.

Interpretation is based on the personal perception of what has been observed and so identifying trends can be difficult. Although risk can be quantified as abstract principles, health and safety cannot.

Whilst risk assessment is based on knowledge of the job and past experience, the corresponding judgement on safety is subjective and can be political. It may be possible to obtain group agreement on objective and rational measures of risk for various work. However, there will often be controversy over what are considered to be safe conditions. Attempting to define acceptable levels of risk immediately raises the question of 'to whom' or 'on what terms' is the risk acceptable?

The distinction between risk and safety is relevant to many organisations and there are a number of factors to be considered in defining the acceptability of risk (*see overleaf*).

Cost. Safety is always compromised by available budget yet it costs far more to investigate and restore safe working conditions after an accident than it does to resolve the issues in the first place.

Controls. Who has control? Those at the place of work should have control over the safety requirements of the task. Ownership of health and safety controls is critical for a safe working environment.

Customs. Many risks are taken because certain work has always been done that way.

Conditions. Many people are put at risk because conditions have changed, resulting in longer working hours, tight timescales, lack of resources, workload, fatigue, stress or an ageing workforce. This can lead to an increase in overall errors, and to more serious errors occurring.

Consequences. Managers rarely evaluate in advance the consequences of something going wrong. Often the thought process seems to be 'if it hasn't happened yet, it won't happen at all'.

Benefit. What benefits does the individual get from taking a short cut, such as an early finish when the job is done?

8.7.11   Benefits of health and safety discussions

One method of enhancing any safe system of work is through frequent and open discussions. The heart of any process is communication, with all involved recognising the value of shared ideas and knowledge. This has the potential to impact positively on bottom-line profits, with individuals and teams working more efficiently towards achieving high-quality business objectives. The company's image will also benefit if, by the actions exhibited, it is shown to be committed to a safe and healthy working environment, where no-one is injured or becomes ill as a result of coming to work.

 An example of good-practice communication is for site managers to have an informal 10-minute chat with their employees and/or contractors' supervisors at the start of every day. The manager should encourage them to tell each other where they will be working and how their activity could affect other people. This will help supervisors to plan their day, as well as improve co-ordination, consultation, production and, ultimately, safety.

The aim of a behavioural safety discussion is to identify any difficulties in completing tasks safely and to aid the supervisor, manager and individual in identifying problems and achieve a safe system of work. Participants in the discussion should be encouraged to use open questions, smooth the way forward, be clear in what they are saying, avoid any misunderstanding and proactively resolve issues through positive actions rather than reactively observing unsafe actions.

Those with more knowledge and experience can assist newer colleagues in understanding the hazards around them and stop people putting themselves at risk. Learning through a coaching and mentoring approach can be more effective and less onerous than more formal observation work.

All workers and managers can make valid contributions to discussions on behavioural safety. Do not impose your own thoughts and avoid passing judgement. Above all else, problems or issues should be resolved immediately with someone who has the authority to make the necessary changes.

CONTENTS

Leadership and worker engagement

GT700 Toolbox talks / supporting checklists and forms

Toolbox talks on some of these topics are available in the GT700 publication. Supporting checklists and forms covering some of these topics are available on our companion website.

LEADERSHIP AND WORKER ENGAGEMENT

Overview

This chapter gives a general overview of the principles of leadership and worker engagement. It looks at how these principles affect organisations within the construction industry. Additional resource information, tools and techniques are presented, which can inform workplaces and influence leadership and engagement behaviours.

9.1 Introduction

The construction industry is one of the UK's most significant economic sectors, with over 353,365 registered construction companies operating in the construction industry across Great Britain. Construction is also consistently one of the most dangerous sectors to work in, according to Health and Safety Executive (HSE) statistics.

The industry is therefore continually seeking to find innovative ways to reduce ill health and accidents by engaging with its workforce. This has a number of identifiable business benefits, including the promotion of sustainable behavioural change to ensure that health and safety is taken seriously on site.

Success depends upon the quality of leadership and management practice within organisations. Commitment and responsibility at all levels are critical to the development of a successful, innovative business and proactive worker engagement.

Definitions of leadership vary across organisations and leadership experts. Leadership is largely centred around building relationships and interpersonal skills, focusing on individuals who are:

- visionary
- motivational
- inspirational
- emotionally intelligent
- trustworthy
- natural leaders and communicators
- driven
- ambitious
- resilient – able to deal with pressure and failure.

There is a need for a range of skills and knowledge. These fall into three main areas.

1. Appropriate technical and professional skills, relevant to the organisation.
2. Commercial and financial, including a high level of business acumen and experience (both success and failure).
3. Skills in people management and development (coaching and feedback, communication and team management).

Good leadership is seen as encompassing a strong mix of all these skills, with weaknesses in one area being seen to diminish the overall capability of the leader. Research has identified various traits, differentiating good from outstanding leadership. These outstanding leaders are described as having the following abilities.

- Being able to think and act systematically.
- Understanding the whole and the connection between internal work and the external environment.
- Seeing people as the route to performance through high performing teams.
- Building relationships and providing an environment in which teams and people can shine.
- Being self-confident without being arrogant.
- Being professional.
- Having personal humility.
- Providing appropriate space and the support to allow people to think and make decisions.

A vital task facing leaders is to engage workers within the day-to-day operation of their own roles in order to achieve the wider organisational objectives. Leaders who are able to bring the full range of worker motivation, creativity, skills and knowledge to their businesses are those whose organisations succeed in an increasingly competitive and fast-moving market place.

 Leadership development, worker engagement and business performance are strongly linked. In organisations where management and leadership development are embedded, employee engagement levels are higher.

09

9.2 Understanding worker engagement

9.2.1 Work Foundation

The Work Foundation, a provider of research-based analysis, knowledge exchange and policy advice in the UK, defines employee (worker) engagement in the following way.

 Employee engagement describes employees' emotional and intellectual commitment to their organisation and its success. Engaged employees experience a compelling purpose and meaning in their work and give of their discrete effort to advance the organisation's objectives.

Effectively, engagement is about how workers behave at work and the impact this has on their own performance and that of the organisation, in particular with respect to the discretionary effort they apply within the workplace.

Within the construction industry, there is a specific focus on health and safety within worker engagement practice.

 For further information visit the Work Foundation website.

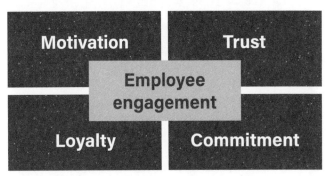

A typical representation of factors influenced by employee (worker) engagement strategies

9.2.2 Barriers to workforce engagement

Research by the HSE has identified that barriers to workforce engagement are, in many ways, similar to behavioural change barriers.

- The disparate, transient and multicultural nature of the workforce on site.
- Working style associated with a results-focused and target-driven industry.
- Disincentives to report health and safety issues that may result in future loss of projects and income.
- Lack of client motivation to adopt worker engagement practices.
- Appropriateness of off-the-shelf solutions, given the variance in industry-related organisations.
- Lack of management commitment to, or understanding of, the benefits of worker engagement practice.

The following list shows some potential solutions to **overcoming barriers**.

- Treating each engagement project as a separate strategy.
- Training relevant individuals in behavioural change and worker engagement skills.
- Focusing on the supply chain as a route for delivery of worker engagement.
- Including the supply chain and sub-contractors in behavioural change and engagement training.
- Running launch events for worker engagement and building behavioural change and worker engagement in to sub-contracts.
- Building a preferred supply chain.

In addition, there is a real focus on worker engagement tools that can be employed to aid implementation of good practice. This is particularly the case for the construction industry, where a lack of worker engagement is directly linked to the potential for health and safety incidents.

9.3 Tools and techniques, hints and tips

9.3.1 Engaging workers

- The process of engaging workers takes time; those that have done it say that while results were noticed within a year, it was nearer five years before the process was embedded. The process is **never** complete.
- Make sure the directors and senior managers visibly support a worker involvement culture. They can do this by addressing meetings, sending out messages, instructing managers, and 'talking the talk and walking the walk'.
- Explain why you want to talk to workers and what it involves.
- Run an employee opinion survey and be seen to act rapidly on suggestions or shortcomings. Employees will then start to appreciate that the employer is serious about worker engagement.
- When receiving suggestions, ensure that the person making the suggestion receives feedback, even if the answer is 'sorry, we can't, and these are the reasons why'. The fact that the views are treated seriously is usually more important than agreeing with them. Ensure that you publicise responses to employees' suggestions.

- Talk to personnel at all levels, using different tactics for different groups and even individuals. For example, email might elicit suggestions from office-based workers, but may be less appropriate on a construction site.

- Be visible. Walk around. Talk to staff. Take small numbers of staff on regular safety walk rounds.

- An anonymised system of reporting complaints or problems is helpful in the initial stages of embracing worker engagement, but appears to be rarely used once the culture is embedded.

- Ensure you take the views of shift-workers and part-time staff into account.

- Take staff to another organisation where worker engagement is working.

- Worker engagement in health and safety will not happen without a genuine no-blame culture.

- Ensure representatives have suitable training for the role (covering eliciting views, presenting a case, feeding back to colleagues) as well as in health and safety. Even in the best examples, representatives are often not trained in this role.

- As people are often reluctant to volunteer as a representative of employee safety, it may be worth speaking with employees you think would do a good job. Assertive and confident individuals facilitate better engagement than 'yes' people. Informal leaders (who workers already turn to for advice) may make good representatives themselves, or be important in lending credibility to the notion and practice of engagement. Consider also offering incentives or rewards (financial or otherwise).

- Make sure that joint health and safety committees have a fair balance of employee representatives and managers. Managers may consider absenting themselves from part of a meeting in order to ensure representatives are not intimidated from speaking. This should not undermine the case for strong leadership from the top, and the need for such absence will lessen as representatives grow in experience and confidence.

- Ensure your managers and staff are trained in soft skills as well as hard skills.

 Worker involvement in health and safety will not happen unless there is a no-blame culture in place.

 There is no doubt that the quality and effectiveness of management and leadership has a significant impact on the level to which workers are engaged within their jobs. This, in turn, has direct consequences for health and safety measures within organisations.

9.4 National Occupational Standards – Management and leadership

The National Occupational Standards (NOS) for management and leadership are statements of good practice that outline the performance criteria, related skills, knowledge and understanding required to effectively carry out various management and leadership functions. They are produced by the Management Standards Centre (MSC), the Government-recognised standards-setting body for the management and leadership areas. The MSC describes the standards as:

 the activities/functions of management and leadership at various levels of responsibility and complexity. Therefore, they are relevant to anyone for whom management and leadership is, to a greater or lesser extent, part of their work. This applies to managers and leaders in all sizes and types of organisation, and in all industries and sectors.

This information presents the suite of standards most relevant to different levels of management and leadership. These standards are generic and so equally applicable to management and leadership practice within organisations of all sizes and across all sectors.

For further information visit the NOS section of the Government's website.

9.5 Legislative requirements

The Health and Safety at Work etc. Act 2(4) allows regulations to be made for appointing safety representatives from recognised trade unions.

As a result the **Safety Representatives and Safety Committees Regulations** were introduced. These were later amended by the Management of Health and Safety at Work Regulations.

The **Health and Safety (Consultation with Employees) Regulations** widened the scope of the duties of employers to consult with employees who are not members of a trade union.

Additionally, the **Construction (Design and Management) Regulations 2015** (CDM) have placed an increased emphasis on consultation. There is also a specific duty on the principal contractor to consult and engage with workers.

 Where an employee is a member of a recognised trade union, the Safety Representatives and Safety Committees Regulations will apply, together with the Health and Safety at Work etc. Act. Where there is no recognised trade union membership representation, the Health and Safety (Consultation with Employees) Regulations apply.

9.5.1 Legal requirements for communicating with all employees

Employers must inform employees of the following points.

- The main terms and conditions of employment.
- Changes in terms and conditions of employment.
- The reason for dismissing them from their job, where applicable.
- Certain business matters (for example, when there is a significant change in the way the business operates).
- Health and safety issues and consultation with the workforce on health and safety.

These Health and Safety (Consultation with Employees) Regulations and the Safety Representatives and Safety Committees Regulations will apply to most workplaces.

 The HSE has developed easy-to-use guidance that shows the relationship between the two sets of regulations and how they may affect businesses and their workforces.

The business may benefit from consulting employees on a regular basis and making staff aware of ways they can contribute ideas and raise concerns. The business does not need to have complex structures for consultation – often ad hoc groups can work best.

For effective consultation consider the following.

- Explaining final decisions, particularly when employees' views are rejected.
- Giving credit and recognition to those who provide information that improves a decision.
- Ensuring that the issues for consultation are relevant to the group of employees discussing them.
- Avoiding minor issues and petty grievances.
- Making the outcome of the meeting available to everyone.

Good communication processes will make employee engagement easier and more effective. The main aspects of achieving that include the following.

- Involving the workforce in building a set of values by which the company will operate.
- Building dialogue with the workforce by communicating regularly and openly about matters that affect the business. This will build credibility and create an environment of trust.
- Involving the workforce in the most important employee issues as soon as possible.
- Avoiding leaks of information or rumours spreading.
- Living the values.

In the construction industry it is especially important to ensure that this communication is effective and timely, particularly in relation to health and safety. All workers have a right to be consulted on the work they do, to be given adequate information and training to carry out this work in a safe and healthy manner, and to have fit-for-purpose site facilities. Being directly involved in the process, employees often see problems as they emerge.

Recent years have seen a large increase in the number of foreign workers in all sectors. English may not be their first language and communication can become more difficult, leading to a greater risk of misunderstanding. These workers must be fully engaged and consulted on matters of health and safety at work, and employers must find adequate mechanisms to do this. Similar consideration should be given to other workers who have difficulties in communicating.

CDM place a duty on principal contractors to make and maintain arrangements to enable effective co-operation between all parties on site, and to consult with all workers on site. Consultation means not only giving information to workers, but also listening and taking account of what workers say, before making health and safety decisions. Part of the purpose of consultation is to make sure the measures taken on site to protect workers' health and safety are effective. Principal contractors are encouraged to develop a variety of methods of communication and consultation with the workforce to develop collaboration and trust. When matters of concern are raised by workers these should be taken seriously and feedback given.

Evidence that this is happening provides assurance that effective worker engagement is in place. Involving the workforce in identifying and controlling risks is crucial in preventing accidents. Whether projects are notifiable or not, contractors have a duty to inform workers of their procedures for stopping work in the event of serious and imminent danger, and to provide training where necessary. This should make sure workers are willing and able to intervene to prevent an accident from happening.

9.5.2 Safety Representatives and Safety Committees Regulations

A summary of the **role of the safety representative** is shown below.

- Representing their members' interests in matters of health, safety and welfare.
- Representing their members in consultation with the HSE or other enforcing authority.
- Carrying out the statutory functions outlined in the regulations.

Functions of the safety representative include the following.

- Consulting with the employer.

- Investigating and reporting significant hazards and dangerous occurrences.

- Investigating accidents in the workplace.

- Providing representation on general health and safety matters.

- Receiving complaints by employees.

- Providing representation in consultation with the HSE or other enforcing authority.

- Receiving information from the enforcing authority.

- Attending safety committee meetings.

- Inspecting the workplace.

 For further information on consulting workers on health and safety visit the HSE website.

9.5.3   The Equality Act

Equality and diversity are issues of rising importance that the construction industry needs to acknowledge and address. This has been brought into sharper focus following the recent changes to legislation, with the introduction of the Equality Act, which became law in October 2010. It replaces previous legislation (such as the Race Relations Act and the Disability Discrimination Act) and ensures consistency in what employers need to do to make the workplace a fair environment and to comply with the law.

The Equality Act covers the same groups that were protected by existing equality legislation – age, disability, gender reassignment, race, religion or belief, sex, sexual orientation, marriage and civil partnership, pregnancy and maternity – but extends some protections to groups not previously covered, and also strengthens particular aspects of equality law.

The Equality Act is a mixture of rights and responsibilities that have:

- stayed the same – for example, direct discrimination still occurs when someone is treated less favourably than another person because of a protected characteristic

- changed – for example, employees can now complain of harassment even if it is not directed at them, if they can demonstrate that it creates an offensive environment for them

- been extended – for example, associative discrimination (direct discrimination against someone because they associate with another person who possesses a protected characteristic) covers age, disability, gender reassignment and sex, as well as race, religion and belief and sexual orientation

- been introduced for the first time – for example, the concept of discrimination arising from disability, which occurs if a person with a disability is treated unfavourably because of something arising as a consequence of their disability.

Whilst construction sites can be hazardous places of work for anyone, employers must accept their legal duties and make reasonable adjustments within the working environment to ensure that fairness is achieved and discrimination does not occur.

e.g. Impacts of equality and diversity on the health and safety environment

Equality and diversity impact on the health and safety environment because:

- staff who are bullied or suffer harassment at work may not feel safe or act in a rational manner – bullying/harassment, including initiation ceremonies and horseplay, banter and fooling around can also involve unsafe acts

- a person may have a visual, hearing or speech impairment that could, for example, make communication of risks difficult

- a person may have restricted mobility and therefore have difficulty in walking, climbing ladders, lifting or carrying out certain aspects of work

- poorly fitting personal protective equipment (PPE) for employees can be uncomfortable, impede mobility and/or movement necessary for safe working (for example, a person's physique may mean standard-issue PPE is too small or large).

A part of making reasonable adjustments is likely to be consultation between the employer and the person(s) on how certain situations will be managed.

Employers have a responsibility to ensure their employees are supported and not discriminated against. Supervisors and managers must be aware of these responsibilities and the way to eliminate or effectively manage situations if they arise.

In addition, employers have a responsibility to ensure every employee understands safety information and messages, both in terms of language used and the workplace culture. Ensuring clear messaging can result in better working conditions and practices and a more productive team approach.

09

Inspections and audits

Supporting INFORMATION

GT700 Toolbox talks / supporting checklists and forms

Toolbox talks on some of these topics are available in the GT700 publication. Supporting checklists and forms covering some of these topics are available on our companion website.

INSPECTIONS AND AUDITS

Overview

Measurement is a vital step in the management process and forms the basis of continual improvements. If measures (such as site inspections or health and safety audits) are not carried out correctly, there is no reliable information to show if health and safety risks are being managed.

This chapter outlines the types of measurement and the benefits of monitoring health and safety.

10.1 Introduction

Employers and employees have a moral, social and legal duty to prevent accidents by every practicable means available to them.

The costs of getting it wrong, to a company, its employees and others affected, may be great and provide ample motivation to all involved to reduce the risks to health and safety.

Motivation must, however, be translated into effective action, and this can only be achieved by the commitment of management and supervisors at all levels. It is well established and documented that accidents can be prevented by:

- identifying the hazards that employees face within the workplace

- understanding how accidents are caused by unsafe acts, unsafe systems of work and unsafe conditions on site

- taking steps to control the activity of the worker, the work method and the workplace.

Employers, managers, supervisors and safety representatives all have equally important roles to play.

By obtaining and providing information through the **inspection, investigation and examination** of the workplace, they can help provide a basis for effective management action to promote safer and healthier workplaces, and induce a greater awareness of health, safety and welfare on the part of all concerned.

There are strong links between this topic content and the need to speak with employees on matters of health and safety.

10.2 Important points

- Health and safety inspections and audits can become a productive part of consultation between management and the workforce.

- They are often carried out by directors, managers or health and safety professionals, and are a key element of the site management teams role.

- The successful outcome of any inspection or audit is that remedial actions are put in place where shortcomings have been identified.

- Workplace inspections are most effective when carried out against a predetermined checklist incorporating some method of recording the findings.

- Whereas workplace inspections tend to be a 'snapshot in time', an audit is a thorough examination not only of the site conditions prevailing at any one time but also of the:
  - commitment of management to health and safety
  - procedures and systems that underpin the health and safety management system.

- The emphasis on contractors being able to demonstrate their competence in matters of health and safety management potentially puts a greater importance on them being able to show that inspections and audits are carried out and acted upon.

10.3 Measuring performance

There are several ways in which a company may measure the effectiveness of its health and safety performance.

- Evaluating the effectiveness of earlier risk assessments.

- Gathering and evaluating information on the number of accidents over a reference period, their causes and effects.

- Evaluating worker feedback on near misses and dangerous occurrences.

- Gathering information on reportable diseases.

- The results of health and safety audits.

- The results of inspections, whether regular, unannounced or specific.

- The level of health and safety awareness among employees in the form of feedback from training courses and safety committee meetings.

- Benchmarking against previous audits.

10.4　Monitoring

Employers are required to monitor performance. There are two types of monitoring used in auditing and inspecting: active and reactive.

10.4.1　Active monitoring

Active monitoring (often referred to as *proactive monitoring*) measures current levels of compliance with legislation and company procedures. Effective active monitoring will help to reduce accidents and ill health in the longer term, and can take the following forms.

- Health and safety inspections
- Pre-use checks
- Safety tours

- Hazard-spotting exercises
- Health surveillance
- Audits.

Health and safety inspections tend to be the site manager's snapshot of the health and safety standards on site at any one time. Alternatively, or in addition, a company's health and safety adviser or director may carry out these inspections. A health and safety inspection or audit may examine the big picture or concentrate on only one feature. Irrespective of who carries out an inspection, they must have the knowledge to detect unsafe situations and the authority to ensure these are rectified.

10.4.2　Reactive monitoring

This type of monitoring investigates anything that has actually happened. Accidents, incidents, near misses and illness resulting in serious injuries and fatalities, including health hazards, are too often a feature of work in the construction industry. The active management of health and safety should serve to keep such incidents to a minimum.

 It should not be forgotten that a near miss today could be a potential accident tomorrow. Everyone has an important role to play in both active and reactive monitoring.

10.5　Inspections

Formal inspections at reasonably regular intervals should add to site managers' day-to-day checks, inspections and examinations, which occur as part of any task. These should follow a properly designed checklist for the systematic inspection of the workplace.

Advantages of regular inspections include that they ensure good housekeeping is maintained within the workplace and that awareness is developed, amongst employees at all levels, of the need to promote and maintain safety, health and environmental standards. The disadvantage or danger of regular inspections is that they may become a rather mechanical routine for all concerned, and that their impact might be lessened.

Carrying out joint inspections with safety representatives, other members of the team or even nominated workers from different trades or contractors can help to identify issues that may be overlooked during a routine inspection.

Feedback and results can be jointly presented to the workforce via various communication methods in place, such as toolbox talks. Stopping and engaging in a two-way conversation with workers during inspections is vital, to understand their way of working and any issues and concerns.

This goes a long way in helping to build a positive safety culture, but it is just as important to follow through or feed back on issues. More often than not, workers will be able to help find and agree solutions. Random inspections carried out without any prior notice to the workforce, on different days of the week, at irregular intervals and at different times of the day, avoid the shortcomings of a predictable inspection and help to encourage a continuous

Inspection apps for smartphones and tablets enable instant emailing of pictures and reports

interest in health, safety and environmental matters by all personnel. In practice, a combination of both regular and random inspections is encouraged.

10.5.1　Safety representatives

In accordance with the **Safety Representatives and Safety Committees Regulations** safety representatives are entitled to inspect the workplace. An Approved Code of Practice (ACoP) and guidance notes have been issued by the HSE to support the relevant regulations. These emphasise areas where safety representatives should reach agreement with their employers.

A safety representative may consider the company's safety inspection procedure to be adequate. In such cases, the representative may only need to seek an agreement with the management that they are involved in any future inspections. However, if the company's arrangements for the inspection are thought to be inadequate, recommendations should be made in writing in order that action may be taken to remedy the situation.

10

INSPECTIONS AND AUDITS

10.6　Hazard-spotting techniques

Hazard-spotting exercises are a modified version of the safety sampling method, where a particular department, hazard or work activity is singled out for a closer and more thorough examination.

The exercises should be arranged via collaboration between management and the health and safety team, or by the training manager through line management, and should involve supervisors, safety representatives and operatives. Observers may include first line or senior managers, but there should be at least an equal number of operatives. Some managers may prefer a predominant number of operatives up to foreperson level in the team, thereby encouraging workers to take an active interest in health and safety and accident prevention in the workplace.

10.6.1　Hazard-spotting programme

A properly structured programme of inspections and sampling will ensure that all of the main activities of a company are continuously under scrutiny. Hazard-spotting exercises should be used not only where there is seen to be a need to ensure the safety and health of people at work, but also as a preventative and continuing monitoring exercise.

10.6.2　Hazard-spotting team

Members of the proposed hazard-spotting team should have had some training or experience in health and safety matters in relation to the work or hazards to be assessed and be able to recognise any unsafe acts of people at work or unsafe or potentially unsafe conditions of work or methods of work. One person should be appointed leader of each group, and their functions should include the following.

● The collection of the written findings of the members of the team.

● The study of these findings and the summary of unsafe acts and conditions that have been observed during the tour.

● The preparation of a brief report, setting out the unsafe acts and conditions that were observed during the tour and making recommendations for action by the management or their representative to rectify any situation that may have been observed.

● Noting and recording the response of the line or senior management, satisfying themselves that action will be taken by management to rectify any situations observed.

● Reporting back to members of the team what action will be taken by the line manager concerned and when the action will be taken.

10.6.3　Safety sampling

Health and safety sampling of a particular work activity, process or work area may be necessary in the following situations.

● The activity, process or work area presents particular health and safety concerns, where there have been changes to an activity, process or work area that are relevant to health and safety.

● There is a need to improve the health and safety performance in a particular area of operations.

● There are areas of high labour turnover.

Sampling should be carried out by someone familiar with the work activity, process or work area under inspection.

10.6.4　Safety tours

A variety of roles, such as directors, senior managers, site managers, engineers, supervisors and operatives, should have the opportunity to observe health and safety conditions prevailing within the workplace during normal construction work.

Production, however, will often be their first priority and this need to get the job done may adversely affect their judgement on health and safety matters. Familiarity with certain work and hazards may further cause them to overlook, fail to recognise or ignore real or potential dangers that are present at the workplace.

For these reasons, additional **health and safety tours** (general inspections of the workplace) made by competent health and safety professionals, supervisors and safety representatives should take place at regular intervals.

A site health and safety tour

 For HSE guidance aimed at directors and board members, covering the identification and management of health and safety risks at work, visit the HSE website.

10.6.5　Health and safety surveys

These are carried out at longer intervals to assess current health and safety standards and activities.

They can be compared against other departments in the same organisation or similar companies within the industry.

Surveys provide the following opportunities.

● Compare the current health and safety performance of the company against previous years.

● Review the understanding of health and safety objectives and determine future objectives and key performance indicators (KPIs).

● Establish adequate and suitable current levels of health and safety training.

● Improve procedures, records, communication and information.

● Decide if additional resources are required.

Surveys can be anonymous to encourage an open and honest response and they can also encourage worker engagement.

10.7 Inspection reports

Details of inspections and their findings should be recorded. Depending on the company, inspection checklists can be recorded and shared via electronic devices, or by using paper versions.

Whatever the type of checklist or form used, it should provide a record of any action requested to remedy conditions and working practices considered to be unsafe. The date and place of the inspection and details of any corrective action identified, subsequent action to be taken or, if no action was required, an explanation of why this was so should also be recorded.

Reports should also contain elements of positive or good practice, such as identifying that safe systems of work for high-risk activities were being followed. Good practice should also be captured and shared and opportunities made to offer recognition to individuals who are working safely.

Remedial actions identified to eliminate or lessen the risk to health and safety should always be implemented *(refer to 10.9)*.

 For further information on inspections and reports visit the HSE website.

10.8 Audit and review

A health and safety audit is a demonstration of the management's commitment to monitor and improve, where necessary, the effectiveness of the company's health and safety management system from the top down.

The process of carrying out health and safety audits, evaluating the findings and implementing remedial action, where necessary, results in a continuous cycle of improvement.

Audits tend to be formal, pre-planned, events with the findings documented for later evaluation and review.

 Audit

An *audit* is the structured process of collecting independent information on the efficiency, effectiveness and reliability of the total health and safety management system and identifying plans for corrective action.

Therefore, the main requirements of a health and safety audit include the following.

● A critical examination of the whole operation.

● An assessment of how the risks to health and safety are being managed.

● The identification of the efficient and safe performance of people.

● The detection and identification of falling standards, ineffective company procedures, and non-compliance with industry standards and legal requirements.

● The use of meaningful standards consistent with the organisation's operations.

● The identification and implementation of a corrective action plan.

Health and safety auditing should also be seen as an integral part of the overall monitoring of health and safety within an organisation.

 The aim of a health and safety audit is to identify problem areas that may exist, so that you can make improvements to your standard of health and safety. The audit should look at the interaction of all the activities of your company, as well as at the work itself.

Audits may discover health and safety failings that arise through factors that occur off site (such as design issues), which are therefore outside the direct control of site-based staff. They may also identify good practices that should be shared and incorporated into a process of improvement. By comparison, health and safety inspections are normally a less formal style of audit; the results are not necessarily recorded and they may be more appropriate for some smaller sites. Remember, however, **no record – no proof!**

10

INSPECTIONS AND AUDITS

Both health and safety audits and inspections are carried out on a pre-notified or no-notice basis, as suited to the situation at the time. If too many are pre-notified or regularly scheduled, it may tend to create a false impression, as those on site may only improve their behaviour or practices in the short-term.

Audits should be carried out by a member of management, often the company health and safety professional or a director, who may or may not be accompanied by a representative(s) of sub-contractors or the employees.

The aim is to identify problem areas, implement improvements and increase the overall standard of health and safety awareness.

It requires attention to the following.

- Work environment.
- Person carrying out the task.
- Task itself.

- Safety culture.
- Way in which each affects the others.

The important thing is that, where shortcomings are found, remedial action is promptly taken and lessons learned to prevent recurrence.

10.9   Remedial actions

A clear understanding of the remedial actions required to eliminate or lessen the risks to health and safety, and when those actions should be taken, is an essential part of health and safety management.

The following lists suggest how shortcomings that are highlighted during health and safety inspections should be prioritised for remedial action.

10.9.1   Items requiring immediate action

- Any accident or incident that is reportable to the HSE under the Reporting of Injuries, Diseases and Dangerous Occurrences Regulations (RIDDOR).
- The occurrence of accidents, incidents or near misses that produce situations of possible or immediate danger to the health and safety of employees or other people, including members of the public.
- Any activity or situation that is giving rise to conditions that could affect the short or long-term health of workers (for example, creating dust).
- The contravention of any statutory requirements or ACoP.
- The risk of financial liabilities, as a result of damage to plant and equipment, or compensation to workers or members of the public following litigation, the risks of fire, explosion or other hazards involving electricity, toxic materials or substances.
- The existence of unsafe working practices and unsafe places of work.
- Any shortages of correct and adequate personal protective clothing and equipment.
- The risk of environmental pollution.

10.9.2   Items requiring prompt action

- Any potential hazards that may exist, but which do not cause any imminent or immediate danger of injury, damage or pollution.
- Any signs of inadequate information, instruction or supervision, which should have been provided by either the management or others.
- Any first-aid facilities and training that fall short of statutory requirements.
- Occasions when new plant, new work methods, new equipment or different materials are to be introduced into the workplace.

10.9.3   Items requiring short-term action

- Where there is a lack of planning and control affecting safety, occupational health or the environment within the workplace, either directly or indirectly (for example, through the inadequate supply of materials and equipment to enable the workforce to carry out their tasks satisfactorily and safely).
- Where there are signs of inadequacies in the personal skills, knowledge and experience of the workforce, which may have an adverse effect on safety.

10.9.4   Items requiring long-term planning and action

- Where there is a lack of certain categories of safety skills and trained personnel amongst the workforce.
- Where there is a need for the training of safety advisers, supervisors and safety representatives, to keep abreast of the future needs of the company and its employees.
- Where there is a need for the improvement of standards of health, safety and welfare within the company.

10.10 Benchmarking

One of the most difficult things about auditing is deciding whether the measured performance is satisfactory. Within health and safety, experienced external auditors will typically audit against two parameters.

- Performance against internal systems.

- Performance against legal standards.

This is acceptable as it allows an organisation to self-check, but it does not indicate how a performance rates against other companies.

As a comparative measure, some companies use accident or injury numbers, or the number of prosecutions and/or enforcement notices.

Various attempts have been made within the industry to produce key performance indicators (KPIs) for health and safety, but difficulties are caused by comparing the relevance of, say, KPIs of a small plastering contractor employing four people to a Build UK member.

As a result there is no right or wrong answer, and it is a case of selecting areas of measurement most appropriate to a company. Another driver for benchmarking certain elements is that these may be a requirement of client or pre-qualification questionnaires.

Some trade associations, including the National Access and Scaffolding Confederation (NASC), compile accident statistics for their members. NASC believes that their members represent approximately half of the scaffolding industry in the UK; as a result, the accident statistics gathered may not be a true representation of accidents across the whole scaffolding industry.

In recent years active indicators are measured in addition to the traditionally reactive indicators (such as accident statistics). Active indicators can include the number of:

- toolbox talks carried out per employee

- senior management tours

- site inspections and audits

- near-miss reports.

Benchmarking can be a useful exercise but participants need to be aware that the information may need to be interpreted carefully.

Health and safety performance can be assessed in the following way.

- Relating it to the same reporting period of the previous year.

- Comparing it with similar organisations and/or departments in the same industry.

- Relating it to official national statistics.

- Making regional comparisons between sites in different parts of the country.

In a market of open communication between managers, such comparisons should be extremely useful and readily available to help identify and address trends, and take appropriate action where common hazards have been recognised.

10.11 Additional benefits to a company

As legislation increasingly requires risk assessments and other assessments, clients, principal contractors and contractors are demanding to see health and safety policies and method statements. Evidence that you have an auditing programme will help your business.

A good audit will benefit everyone from senior management to the most inexperienced employee, and should be accepted on its merits as the resultant changes bring improvements in health and safety performance.

The health and safety audit should be carried out, as far as possible, by independent auditors. This overcomes the problems faced by line managers when auditing their own area of work, or even a second line manager being critical of their peers. Auditing must be carried out objectively and with a high degree of honesty when identifying non-compliance with management systems and techniques.

The frequency of audits should ensure that the health and safety management system of the organisation does not degrade over time or through changes in the company's organisation, personnel or the work it carries out.

Several health and safety auditing systems are available commercially but, in the main, these are directed towards the larger business, which can afford either to employ its own dedicated auditing team or contract consultants to come in and carry out the audit.

The construction industry identified the need for an auditing system for the smaller and medium-sized company where the site manager or site supervisor could inspect the site and, within a couple of hours, produce an acceptable appreciation of the standard of safety on site.

10.12 Construction site safety – Health, safety and environmental auditing system

The CITB *Construction site safety – Health, safety and environmental auditing system* (SA 03 CD) is closely related to *Construction site safety* (GE700). It is a CD-ROM containing a number of ready-made auditing forms and is aimed at companies that have not yet addressed the subject or concept of safety audits. It has been designed with simplicity in mind.

The aim is to introduce companies to safety auditing and encourage them to adopt the concept as a part of their overall safety policy.

10

INSPECTIONS AND AUDITS

It represents a proactive, cost-effective method of becoming safer, rather than a reactive approach. It shows that the company and its staff are trying to ensure that everything is safe and prevent the conditions that cause accidents, instead of picking up the pieces and changing work practices after accidents have happened.

If, in due course, it is decided that the company has outgrown this auditing system and the move is made to a more complex system, the *Construction site safety – Health, safety and environmental auditing system* will have served its purpose.

If, by adopting an effective auditing system, one accident is prevented, then all the work, time and resources that a company has put into its preparation will have been worth it.

 For further information on the *Construction site safety – Health, safety and environmental auditing system*, please contact CITB Publications or visit the website.

Statutory forms, notices and registers

11

STATUTORY FORMS, NOTICES AND REGISTERS

Overview

This chapter gives a brief outline of some of the requirements for the completion and use of various statutory and non-statutory forms, notices, signs and registers used within the building and construction industry, and the keeping of records and other details.

It also includes guidance on the types of daily and weekly inspection work that should be carried out and records that must be kept.

11.1 Introduction

Record keeping is important as it is the means to ensure that inspections and examinations are carried out. It ensures that there is a history of what occurred at what point during a project, and can be referred to if necessary, for example if needing to defend and protect a company against a claim.

Some records are required by legislation and others by the employer as they are good practice and vital in preventing accidents.

11.2 Important points

- The selection of forms or notices should be appropriate or applicable to the individual site or premises, and the circumstances that exist on that site.

- The listings contained in this chapter are not intended to be a full and precise guide to all the statutory requirements that currently exist. All cases of doubt should be resolved by reference to the appropriate enforcing authority or to the legislation.

 A statutory inspection means legally it must be carried out.

11.3 Record keeping

Records are generally split into two categories.

Active (proactive) (for example, inspecting scaffolding or excavations to ensure they remain safe).

Reactive (for example, an accident investigation to establish the causes).

Records of toolbox talks are also important, as this demonstrates that (usually site-based) and on-going awareness training is being provided.

Daily site briefings are a good way of reviewing what has happened and looking at what has to be done and the associated hazards for the forthcoming day. These can be extended to discussing point of work risk assessments.

Health surveillance records must be kept for all employees under health surveillance. They must be kept for at least the period specified in the relevant regulations, from the date of last entry. For example, this would be 40 years under the Control of Substances Hazardous to Health Regulations (COSHH).

Where regulations do not specify how long they should be kept for, the health record should be kept at least while the worker is employed.

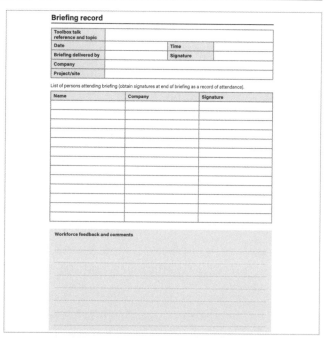

An example of a toolbox talk briefing record

Inspection records must be kept, and the duration will be specified by the regulation.

For example, the Provision and Use of Work Equipment Regulations (PUWER) state that an inspection record should be kept until the next inspection is made.

However, inspections of excavations, cofferdams and caissons, made in accordance with the Construction (Design and Management) Regulations (CDM), have to be kept on site until the works are completed, and after that for a further three months.

 An individual has three years to make a claim for neglect, act or omission where an injury or loss has been sustained.

11.4   Daily user and visual checks

Daily user and visual checks form a vital part of good health and safety site management, and reduce the risk of plant and equipment breakdown or failure, such as those listed below.

- Engine or motor seizure due to lack of lubrication.

- A low-pressure tyre being damaged, causing a vehicle to overturn.

- Missing scaffold edge protection increasing the likelihood of falling materials or persons.

- Damaged power plugs, sockets and leads, which could lead to electrocution.

Construction plant and equipment are exposed to harsh environments and they require effective maintenance regimes to prevent defects from developing. A programme of daily visual checks, regular inspections, servicing and maintenance schedules should be established according to the manufacturer's instructions and the risks associated with the use of each vehicle, piece of equipment or tool.

Plant hire companies must provide information with all plant and equipment that they supply to enable it to be used and maintained safely. Contractual arrangements between user and hirer should set out who is responsible for maintenance and inspection during the hire period and this should be made clear to all parties.

Plant and vehicles should have a maintenance log to help manage and record maintenance operations. Employers should establish procedures designed to encourage supervisors and operators to report defects or problems, and ensure that problems with plant and vehicles are put right. Planned inspection and maintenance needs to follow manufacturers' instructions.

 Records of servicing, maintenance, inspections and examination should be kept up-to-date and available on site for all construction plant and equipment in use.

11.5   List of key requirements

The following is a list of key 'reporting and recording' requirements. (*For an explanation of these requirements refer to Appendix A.*)

	Category	Brief description
1.	**Accident book BL510 (2018 edition)**	Report of an accident must comply with the General Data Protection Regulation (GDPR).
2.	**F2508***	Report of an injury or dangerous occurrence.
3.	**F2508A***	Report of a case of disease.
4.	**F2508G1***	Report of a flammable gas incident.
5.	**F2508G2***	Report of a dangerous gas fitting.
6.	**F10**	Notification of a project that falls under CDM.
7.	**F2067**	Ionising radiation health record.
8.	**F2533**	Safety representatives' report form.
9.	**F2534**	Safety representatives' inspection form.
10.	**Air receivers**	Safe working pressure and record of test.
11.	**Asbestos**	Licence, notice and records. Where appropriate, maintaining a written asbestos management plan.
12.	**Builders' skips**	On road, permits, lighting and signs.
13.	**Consultation with employees**	Rights of employees.
14.	**COSHH assessments**	Maintenance of assessment forms and other records.
15.	**Danger areas**	Identify with signs.
16.	**Dangerous substances and explosive atmospheres**	Display of notices.
17.	**Diving**	Records and registration.
18.	**Electrical equipment**	Records, certification of new installations.
19.	**Electric shock placard**	Display in workplaces.
20.	**Emergency evacuation**	Emergency evacuation route signage as necessary and assembly point sign(s).

STATUTORY FORMS, NOTICES AND REGISTERS

Category (continued)		Brief description
21.	Excavations, cofferdams and caissons	Records of inspections of places of work.
22.	Explosives	Certificate and records.
23.	Falsework	Records of design, including calculations, to be kept.
24.	Fire	Fire risk assessment and safety plan. Notices for extinguishers, fire points and other fire-fighting equipment. Fire exit signs.
25.	First aid	Notice regarding facilities and identity of first aiders.
26.	Food hygiene	Display of notices, and certificates of staff training.
27.	Fragile surfaces	Notice to be displayed. (Warning signs.)
28.	Hazardous substances	Labels on containers. Manufacturers' safety information, COSHH assessments.
29.	Health and safety policy	Display or distribute to all employees.
30.	Holes in floors and similar openings	Cover to be clearly marked. (Warning signs.)
31.	Information for employees (see also Training)	Display approved Health and Safety Executive (HSE) law poster or distribute approved leaflet to all employees.
32.	Insurance (employers' liability)	Display of current insurance certificate.
33.	Ionising radiation	Advance notification to HSE of work. Licence, records and appropriate signage/ barriers at work site.
34.	Lead	Records of inspection and thorough examination of control measures.
35.	Lifting operations	Records of inspection, examination and safe working load (SWL) indication.
36.	Management of health and safety	Risk assessments, appointments, procedures.
37.	Manual handling	Assessment, marking of loads. Training.
38.	Noise	Marking of hearing protection zones.
39.	Plant and equipment	Inspection and records.
40.	Pressure vessels	Display of working pressure, and other details.
41.	Protective clothing and equipment	Assessments, maintenance, training.
42.	Safety representatives and safety committees	Access to documents, minutes, and so on. Information on identity of trade union-appointed safety reps.
43.	Safety signs	Signs and notices as appropriate.
44.	Scaffolding	Records of inspections, display of 'incomplete' notice.
45.	Training	Records.
46.	Visual display units (VDUs) or display screens	Records of assessments, training, eyesight tests.
47.	Waste management	Completion of duty of care documentation, forms, permits and certificates.
48.	Work equipment	Suitability, maintenance, warnings.
49.	Work in compressed air	Records of equipment inspection and health surveillance.
50.	Working time	Permitted hours of work.
51.	Working at height	Records of inspection of equipment.

Only 'responsible persons' including employers, the self-employed and people in control of work premises should submit reports under the Reporting of Injuries, Diseases and Dangerous Occurrences Regulations (RIDDOR). Responsible persons should complete the appropriate online report form.

11.6 Statutory or recommended inspections and examinations

The following table sets out the recommended daily user checks, weekly inspections, statutory inspections and examinations.

Work activity plant item	Pre-use daily	Statutory or recommended					Form for statutory examination or report to comply with
		Weekly record	Monthly record	Three monthly record	Six monthly record	12 monthly record	
Excavations, cofferdams and caissons	✓ Inspect	✓ Inspect					Construction (Design and Management) Regulations
Plant and equipment (not electrical or for lifting)	✓ Inspect	✓ Inspect			✓ Examine	✓ Examine	Provision and Use of Work Equipment Regulations
Plant and equipment (electrical) including fixed RCDs and portable 110 volt equipment	✓ Inspect	✓ Inspect		✓ Examine			Maintaining portable electrical equipment (HSG107)
Cranes and plant for lifting people, MEWPs, safety harness, lifting accessories and safety nets	✓ Inspect	✓ Inspect			✓ Examine	✓ Examine	Provision and Use of Work Equipment Regulations, Lifting Operations and Lifting Equipment Regulations
Cranes and plant used for lifting	✓ Inspect	✓ Inspect				✓ Examine	Lifting Operations and Lifting Equipment Regulations
Work at height, all scaffolds, working platforms, mobile towers, ladders and steps, and similar items	✓ Inspect	✓ Inspect			✓ Examine		Work at Height Regulations, Provision and Use of Work Equipment Regulations, Construction (Design and Management) Regulations
Fire-fighting appliances			✓ Inspect			✓ Examine	Construction (Design and Management) Regulations, Regulatory Reform (Fire Safety) Order
Site offices electrical equipment and installation		✓ Inspect				✓ Examine	Construction (Design and Management) Regulations, Workplace Health, Safety and Welfare Regulations

Note: this table is to be used only as a guide. A competent health and safety professional should confirm the frequency of the checks required.

Appendix A – Brief explanation of key requirements

1.	**Accident book BL510** The keeping of an accident book is required by the Social Security (Claims and Payments) Regulations, the Social Security Administration Act and the Reporting of Injuries, Diseases and Dangerous Occurrences Regulations (RIDDOR). While there is no statutory book, the design of BL510 allows for an entry to be made without the personal details of a previous entry being seen. Any business that has its own accident book must ensure their version complies with the General Data Protection Regulation (GDPR). All accidents that cause any injury to an employee, no matter how slight, must be entered. Entry may be made either by the employee or anyone acting on their behalf. Completed book stubs and records must be kept for three years from the date of the last entry. An individual has three years to make a claim for neglect, act or omission where an injury or loss has been sustained.
2.	**F2508 Report of an injury or dangerous occurrence** Form F2508, report of an injury or dangerous occurrence, is required by the Reporting of Injuries, Diseases and Dangerous Occurrences Regulations (RIDDOR). Notification should now be made online. The form will then be submitted directly to the RIDDOR database and a copy received back for record purposes. All incidents should be reported online but a telephone service remains for reporting fatal and specified injuries only.
3.	**F2508A Report of a case of disease** A report on form F2508A is required by the Reporting of Injuries, Diseases and Dangerous Occurrences Regulations (RIDDOR). It must be completed when a registered medical practitioner has diagnosed in writing that an employee is suffering from a scheduled reportable disease and the person has been employed in a scheduled work activity by the employer.
4.	**F2508G1 Report of flammable gas incidents** A report is required online, via this form, if you are a distributor, filler, importer or supplier of flammable gas and you learn, either directly or indirectly, that someone has died or suffered a specified injury in connection with the gas that you distributed, filled, imported or supplied.
5.	**F2508G2 Report of a dangerous gas fitting** Gas installation businesses, registered with the Gas Safe register, must provide the HSE with details (using this form) of any gas appliances or fittings that they consider to be dangerous to such an extent that people could die or suffer specified injuries because the design, construction, installation, modification or servicing could result in: ■ an accidental leakage of gas ■ inadequate combustion of gas (such as increasing the proportion of carbon monoxide in appliance flue gases to a dangerously high level in normal or abnormal and adverse weather conditions) ■ inadequate removal of the gas combustion products.
6.	**F10 Notification of a project under the Construction (Design and Management) Regulations** This form is required under the above regulations and must be filled out and submitted to the HSE online before the start of any construction work on a construction site. A project is notifiable if the construction work is likely to: ■ last for more than 30 working days and have more than 20 workers working simultaneously at any point in the project, or ■ exceed 500 person days.
7.	**F2067 Ionising radiation health record** The record, or a copy of it, must be preserved until the person to whom it relates has, or would have, attained the age of 75 years, but in any event for at least 50 years from the date of the last entry.
8.	**F2533 Safety representatives' report form** The Safety Representatives and Safety Committees Regulations. This form is used by trade union-appointed safety representatives to notify the employer of any matter discovered during a workplace inspection, which is considered to be unsafe and/or unhealthy.
9.	**F2534 Safety representatives' inspection form** This form is used by trade union-appointed safety representatives to record the time, date and location of workplace health and safety inspections carried out.
10.	**Air receivers** The Pressure Systems Safety Regulations. Every air receiver must have the safe working pressure clearly displayed on it. It must be examined and tested as laid down in the regulations and records kept.

11.	**Asbestos**
	The Control of Asbestos Regulations.
	Virtually all work with asbestos requires a licence from the HSE or the giving of 14-days' notice of the intention to work with asbestos to the enforcing authority. The majority of work must only be undertaken by a licensed contractor. This work includes most asbestos removal, all work with sprayed asbestos coatings and asbestos lagging and most work with asbestos insulation and asbestos insulating board (AIB).
	Brief written records should be kept of non-licensed work, which has to be notified (for example, copy of the notification with a list of workers on the job), plus the level of likely exposure of those workers to asbestos. This does not require air monitoring on every job if an estimate of degree of exposure can be made, based on experience of similar past tasks or published guidance.
	Persons in charge of premises have a duty to manage the existence of asbestos in those premises, which will entail keeping records of surveys and possibly a register of where asbestos has been found, its condition and how its presence is being managed. This is known as an asbestos management plan.
	If an employee is exposed to asbestos above the control limit, health records of the employee must be maintained and kept for 40 years after the date of the last entry. All products containing asbestos must be properly labelled and recorded on the asbestos register. All waste must be in properly sealed and labelled containers.
12.	**Builders' skips**
	The Highways Act – Section 139.
	If a builder's skip is placed on a road, a permit must be obtained from the local highway authority and the requirements of the permit strictly followed. These will include ensuring the skip is properly lit during the hours of darkness. It must not pose a hazard to highway users and pedestrians but must be clearly and indelibly marked with the owner's name and telephone number or address.
13.	**Consultation with employees**
	The Health and Safety (Consultation with Employees) Regulations were introduced because the Health and Safety at Work etc. Act 1974 only covered union-appointed safety representatives. They now extend to all employees the right to have consultation with their employers and be provided with information. There are many similarities with the Safety Representative and Safety Committees Regulations and they also implement the consultation provisions of the European Union Framework Directive on health and safety.
14.	**Control of Substances Hazardous to Health and Approved Code of Practice**
	The Control of Substances Hazardous to Health Regulations (COSHH) and the Approved Code of Practice (ACoP) require assessments to be made of substances hazardous to health and, except in the simplest and most obvious of cases, for the assessments to be written and kept accessible for those who need to know the results. If health surveillance is appropriate, the health records of employees under health surveillance must be maintained and kept for 40 years after the date of the last entry. All mechanical control measures (such as dust extraction) must be subject to routine examination in accordance with the regulations and records kept. Substances hazardous to health must be properly labelled.
15.	**Danger areas**
	Identify with signs under the relevant regulations.
16.	**Dangerous substances and explosive atmospheres**
	Under the Dangerous Substances and Explosive Atmospheres Regulations, the following definitions and conditions apply.
	Dangerous substances
	A substance or preparation that is explosive, oxidising, extremely flammable, highly flammable or flammable, or any dust that can form an explosive mixture with air or an explosive atmosphere.
	Explosive atmosphere
	A mixture, under atmospheric conditions, of air and one or more dangerous substance in the form of gases, vapours, mists or dusts in which, after ignition has occurred, combustion spreads to the entire unburned mixture.
	Where an explosive atmosphere may occur, a specific sign is to be erected.
	In accordance with the Health and Safety (Safety Signs and Signals) Regulations, the sign must consist of black letters on a triangular yellow background with black edging.
17.	**Diving**
	The Diving Operations at Work Regulations.
	Records must be kept of the written appointment of all diving supervisors and of the qualifications and medical certificates of divers. All dives must be recorded in the diver's logbook. Diving rules have to be in writing. Diving is a specialised area, even in onshore waters. All diving contractors must be registered with the HSE.
18.	**Electrical equipment**
	The Electricity at Work Regulations.
	All electrical equipment, including portable equipment, should be inspected on a regular basis by a competent person and records kept. Portable electric tools should be PAT-tested in accordance with HSE guidance.

11

19.	**Electric shock placard**
	The Electricity at Work Regulations.
	Guidance notices or placards giving details of emergency resuscitation procedures in the event of an electric shock should be displayed in locations where people are at an enhanced risk of electric shock.
20.	**Emergency evacuation**
	The Construction (Design and Management) Regulations state there must be a sufficient number of emergency escape routes, which must lead as directly as possible to a point of safety. Escape routes must be indicated by signs and kept clear and free from obstructions.
21.	**Excavations, cofferdams and caissons**
	The Construction (Design and Management) Regulations require that excavations, cofferdams and caissons must be inspected and written reports of the inspections made.
22.	**Explosives**
	Virtually all possession of explosives requires an explosives certificate, which is issued by the local chief officer of police. Detailed records have to be kept of all movements or usages of explosives.
23.	**Falsework and temporary works**
	The Construction (Design and Management) Regulations and British Standard BS 5975 *Code of Practice for falsework*.
	These regulations include falsework under the definition of construction work and, therefore, the designer's duties apply. Temporary works require designing and can simply be defined as anything that is not part of the permanent works. It is recommended that records should be kept of all design calculations, drawings, estimated loadings and specifications for falsework, together with written permissions to pour concrete or to load falsework, and to dismantle it.
24.	**Fire**
	The Regulatory Reform (Fire Safety) Order.
	Documentary information relating to fire safety should include:
	■ a suitable and sufficient fire risk assessment to be carried out by a responsible person, or someone appointed to do so with sufficient experience and qualifications
	■ records of staff training in the use of extinguishers
	■ records of fire extinguisher servicing
	■ records of practice evacuations
	■ written fire risk assessment and a written fire safety plan
	■ display of relevant signs where flammable and highly flammable substances are stored.
25.	**First aid**
	The Health and Safety (First Aid) Regulations state:
	'An employer shall inform his employees of the arrangements that have been made in connection with the provision of first aid, including the location of equipment, facilities and personnel.'
	The guidance notes recommend that first-aid notices are displayed as an effective means of informing the workforce of the employer's arrangement for first aid.
	There is no statutory form but a range of first-aid notices are available from the suppliers of workplace safety signs.
26.	**Food hygiene**
	The Food Safety Act.
	Toilets adjacent to food rooms must be separated by a lobby. A notice stating 'Now wash your hands' must be displayed.
	Checks and inspections of equipment and staff training should be recorded.
	Certificates of staff training in food hygiene and handling must be displayed.
27.	**Fragile surfaces**
	A requirement of the Work at Height Regulations is that if people have to work near or pass close by any fragile roofing materials, the appropriate warning notices must be clearly displayed at all approaches to the area.
28.	**Hazardous substances**
	Generally, under the Control of Substances Hazardous to Health Regulations and the European Union Directive for Classification, Packaging and Labelling of Dangerous Goods, all containers containing hazardous substances should be clearly marked with their contents and the appropriate hazard warning symbol.
	Assessments must be made and, with minor exceptions, recorded. (There is no statutory form.) (*See also entries under* **Asbestos** *and* **Lead**.)

11

29.	**Health and safety policy**
	The Health and Safety at Work etc. Act 1974 requires employers to have a safety policy and arrangements to bring it into force. If five or more persons are employed, that policy must be written down. There is no statutory form but the HSE publication *Writing your health* and *safety policy statement* may be used.
	The policy must be brought to the notice of all employees.
30.	**Holes in floors and similar openings**
	The Work at Height Regulations require that holes in floors and flat roofs, where a person is liable to fall through (referred to as *danger areas* in the regulations), must be properly protected. If a cover is used over a hole it must be clearly marked to show its purpose.
31.	**Information for employees**
	The Health and Safety (Information for Employees) Regulations require every employer to display the approved health and safety law poster in a position where it can be easily read by the employees, or to give to each employee a copy of the approved leaflet entitled *Health and safety law. What you should know,* which contains the same information.
32.	**Insurance (employers' liability)**
	The Employers' Liability (Compulsory Insurance) Act requires there to be in force insurance against liability for bodily injury or disease sustained by employees. The Employers' Liability (Compulsory Insurance) Regulations require a certificate of employers' liability insurance to be displayed at the place of business in such a position that it can be easily seen and read by employees, including every construction site.
	Employers can display an online version of the certificate, providing all employees have access to it. A hard copy may still be displayed.
33.	**Ionising radiation**
	Under the provisions of the Ionising Radiation Regulations, any employer intending to use any source of ionising radiation must give 28-days' notice to the HSE. Very detailed records, including health records, have to be kept. Advice should be sought from the HSE or other competent source. The appropriate warning signs and notices for controlled areas must be displayed.
34.	**Lead**
	The Control of Lead at Work Regulations, together with the Approved Code of Practice and guidance notes, require a number of forms to be completed by employers (and in some cases medical practitioners) if the required risk assessment under the regulations carried out by the employer shows that an employee's exposure to lead is liable to be significant. Some of the types of work likely to lead to significant exposure are:
	■ high temperature work (over 500ºC), including welding and cutting
	■ abrasion of lead or lead-painted surfaces
	■ spray painting with lead paint.
	Details of all the forms are given in the Approved Code of Practice.
35.	**Lifting operations**
	Under the Lifting Operations and Lifting Equipment Regulations:
	■ all machinery and accessories used for lifting are marked to indicate their safe working load (SWL) for each configuration in which they can be used
	■ lifting equipment designed to lift persons is clearly marked as such
	■ lifting equipment not designed for lifting persons but which could be easily mistaken for such is marked appropriately
	■ all lifting equipment and accessories should be subjected to a periodic or scheme approach to thorough examination
	■ records of thorough examination are made and kept available for inspection.
36.	**Management of health and safety**
	There is no statutory or recommended style of form for risk, or any other assessments. Your own devised form or a commercially obtained form may be completed either manually or on a computer database.
	Risk assessments must be made of all work activities. **If you employ five or more people, the significant findings must be recorded and, in addition:**
	■ health surveillance – if needed, individual health records must be kept
	■ emergency procedures – must be written down.
37.	**Manual handling**
	The Manual Handling Operations Regulations.
	Assessment to be made where risks from manual handling cannot be avoided. It is recommended that all but the simplest assessments should be recorded.

11

38.	**Noise**
	The Control of Noise at Work Regulations require that all hearing protection zones are identified by means of a sign *(refer to the Health and Safety (Safety Signs and Signals) Regulations)*.
	A hearing protection zone is anywhere where an employee is likely to be exposed to a daily personal noise exposure of 85 dB(A) or a peak sound pressure of 137 dB(C).
39.	**Plant and equipment**
	If it is not otherwise provided for, it is strongly recommended that all plant, tools and equipment are subject to inspection and examination, and proper records kept. This will fulfil the employer's obligations under the Health and Safety at Work etc. Act 1974, Section 2 and the Provision and Use of Work Equipment Regulations.
	A daily inspection and a six-monthly examination may be appropriate. Insurance companies may also require such routine inspections and examinations.
40.	**Pressure vessels**
	The Simple Pressure Vessels (Safety) Regulations apply to all pressure vessels intended to contain air or nitrogen at a greater pressure than 0.5 bar. Any such vessel first used after 1 July 1992 must have (amongst other things) details of the maximum working pressure, maximum and minimum working temperatures, and cubic capacity clearly displayed on it.
41.	**Protective clothing and equipment**
	The Personal Protective Equipment at Work (Amended) Regulations 2022.
	The following must be recorded:
	■ risk assessment of the need for personal protective equipment (PPE)
	■ PPE inspection, maintenance or results of any required tests
	■ records of PPE issue and use.
42.	**Safety representatives and safety committees**
	The Safety Representatives and Safety Committees Regulations, and the Approved Code of Practice and guidance notes, give safety representatives the right to inspect and take copies of any document relevant to safety that an employer is required to keep (except health records of identifiable individuals).
	The employer must make available to them any health and safety information that would help safety representatives fulfil their functions. Where a safety committee has been established, proper minutes and records should be kept. Safety representatives may give written reports to management concerning safety in the workplace.
43.	**Safety signs**
	The Health and Safety (Safety Signs and Signals) Regulations.
	All signs giving health or safety information or instructions must comply with the relevant British Standard. A safety sign is anything that combines geometrical shape, colour and pictorial symbols to give safety information.
44.	**Scaffolding**
	■ Display of incomplete scaffold notice.
	Under the Work at Height Regulations, designated danger areas must be created where there is a risk of a person falling or being hit by a falling object. In the case of incomplete scaffolding, suitable notices must be displayed to discourage attempted access on to the scaffold.
	■ Handover certificates.
	There are no statutory provisions requiring the use or production of scaffold handover certificates. However, all reputable scaffold contractors will issue them and they can be used to demonstrate that the scaffold was properly erected by competent persons and for the purpose for which the scaffold was designed.
	■ Reports of inspections.
	To be completed and retained to comply with the Work at Height Regulations.
45.	**Training**
	Section 2 of the Health and Safety at Work etc. Act 1974, together with various other regulations made under the principal Act, require employers to provide information, instruction and training. It is most strongly recommended that all such information, instruction and training are properly and fully recorded so that employers are in a position to prove that duties under the Act or regulations have been met.
46.	**Visual display units (VDUs) or display screens**
	The Health and Safety (Display Screen Equipment) Regulations.
	Suitable and sufficient analysis of workstations for the purpose of assessing health and safety risks. All but the simplest and obvious cases must be recorded.
	Entitles employees to eyesight tests. Records of requests and results are recommended.

11

47.	**Waste management**
	All contractors that carry or collect waste should have a waste carrier's licence and all waste disposal facilities should have a waste management licence or permit unless they are exempt. All waste transfers must be supported by the correct documentation, called a controlled waste transfer note (or, in the case of hazardous waste, a consignment note).
48.	**Work equipment**
	The Provision and Use of Work Equipment Regulations.
	Records must be kept, including risk assessment for selection and use, regular and statutory inspections, maintenance, training and instructions.
	All work equipment must be marked in a clearly visible manner where necessary, in the interests of health and safety.
	Warnings, audible or visible, to be incorporated into work equipment as necessary.
49.	**Work in compressed air**
	The Work in Compressed Air Regulations.
	This is an extremely specialised area where expert knowledge is needed. Detailed records must be kept of, for example, the following areas.
	■ Clinical records by a doctor.
	■ Exposure records by a compressed air contractor.
	■ Health records by an employer.
	These must be kept and maintained for 40 years from the date of the last entry.
50.	**Working time**
	The Working Time Regulations give details of permitted work hours and special consideration that should be given to young workers. Records of agreements, which can only last up to five years, must be kept by the employer.
51.	**Working at height**
	The Work at Height Regulations.
	This regulation specifies the need for competence in all persons involved in any capacity with regard to work at height. Any training carried out to achieve competency should be recorded.
	Where any person at work may pass across or near to a fragile surface, or actually work on it, prominent signs indicating that it is a fragile surface must be fixed at every approach to that place.
	Where any person could be injured by falling or being hit by a falling object, danger areas must be created to prevent such an occurrence. Danger areas must be clearly indicated, usually by signs and/or barriers.
	Where inspections of work equipment are carried out under this regulation, a record of the inspection must be made and retained as specified.

11

STATUTORY FORMS, NOTICES AND REGISTERS

CONTENTS

Accident prevention and control

12

Supporting
INFORMATION

GT700 Toolbox talks / supporting checklists and forms

Toolbox talks on some of these topics are available in the GT700 publication. Supporting checklists and forms covering some of these topics are available on our companion website.

ACCIDENT PREVENTION AND CONTROL

Overview

There are many factors that contribute to accidents in construction, their trends and causes, the impact accidents can have and the preventative measures that are required. This chapter is designed to help managers gain an appreciation of the factors that need to be considered when developing construction phase plans and safe systems of work, assessing risk, undertaking site inspections and managing health and safety on site each day.

12.1   Introduction

Accident statistics are a reliable indicator of the health and safety performance of the construction industry. The HSE publishes an annual statistical report of key statistics covering work-related ill health (all illness) and work-related injuries (fatalities and non-fatal injuries).

 This report highlights accident and ill-health trends, and is free to download from the HSE website.

The construction industry statistics for 2021–22 are given below.

- 30 fatal injuries to workers, and also five fatal injuries sustained by members of the public.

- An estimated 78,000 workers suffering from work-related ill health (new or long-standing cases): 53% were musculoskeletal disorders.

- 4,185 non-fatal injuries to employees were reported. Of these, 1,556 (37%) were specified injuries, and 2,629 (63%) were over seven-day injuries.

- Falls from height are still the biggest cause of fatalities, with 51% of all fatal injuries in 2021–22 being caused by falling from height.

- The total economic cost in 2019-20 of injuries and new cases of ill health from current construction working conditions was estimated at £1.4 billion.

- Vibration white finger, carpal tunnel syndrome, occupational deafness and dermatitis are the most common cases of non-lung disease in the construction industry.

Around 2.2 million working days are lost each year.

- Working days lost through illness account for 1.7 million.

- Working days lost through injury account for 0.5 million.

 View the latest health and safety statistics detailing the kinds of injuries that have occurred in construction on the HSE website.

Each year the plan of work for the construction division of the HSE acknowledges that some parts of the industry have made significant steps forward over recent years; this is particularly noticeable on larger projects. However, these improvements are not mirrored to anything like the same extent on smaller sites, where many instances of unacceptable standards can still be found.

 For details of the HSE's plan of work visit the HSE website.

This diagram is a version of **Bird's triangle**. Its aim is to demonstrate the approximate relationships between the different levels of accident that occur. It shows that for each fatality there are on average 10 serious injuries, 30 accidents with injury, 600 incidents without injury (near misses or property, equipment or material damage) and thousands of unsafe acts or conditions.

Bird's research illustrates that accident prevention should not be about just concentrating on fatalities and serious injury, but on preventing unsafe acts and conditions. Near misses can be understood as an early indication that unsafe acts or conditions are happening, rather than reacting to actual accident and injury trends. This is why near-miss reporting and proactive hazard-spotting techniques (such as pre-use daily checks, workplace inspections and audits) are so important.

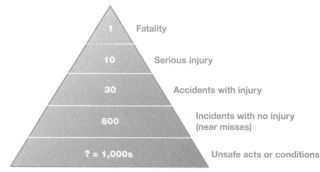

Bird's accident ratio triangle

An unsafe act or near miss under a slightly different set of circumstances could be a serious or even fatal accident. This makes prevention more difficult, particularly if incidents go unreported. Many companies have found that their accident rate has reduced as the number of reported incidents with no injury or near misses has increased, through management encouragement for such incidents to be reported.

12.2 Important points

- The construction industry remains a high-risk industry and consistently accounts for a high number of fatalities and accidents.

- The construction industry accounts for about 6% of employees in Great Britain.

- Accident prevention has to be actively managed; a good safety record will not just happen and everyone has their part to play.

- Reported details of accidents show that in the vast majority of cases the accident could easily have been prevented by taking simple precautions.

- The HSE has stated that many accidents result from decisions taken before work actually starts (planning and identifying safe systems of work).

- You may have no influence over these decisions but find that you need to challenge the health and safety implications that arise as a consequence of them.

- The true cost of an accident goes beyond the financial implications.

- Statistics show that new starters on site, and those at both ends of the age spectrum, are the most prone to accidents.

(AA) Accident prevention

- An **accident** is an unplanned, unscheduled, unwanted event or occurrence, or any undesired circumstance, that may result in injury to persons and damage to property. The injured person may not be an employee and damaged property may not belong to an employer.

- **Hazard** is the potential to cause harm, including ill health and injury; damage to property, plant products or the environment; production losses or liabilities.

- **Risk** is the likelihood that a specified, undesired event will occur due to the realisation of a hazard by or during work or by products created by work. The severity of harm is also considered when calculating the risk level.

- **Incident** is another word that is sometimes used to describe an accident. The main difference is that an incident is something that happened that may or may not have resulted in an injury or damage.

12.3 Near-miss reporting

The importance of learning from experience cannot be overstated. It is an essential element of accident prevention.

A near miss is an incident that had the potential to result in personal injury and/or damage to the structure under construction, plant and equipment or the environment.

Individual companies will decide on their criteria for categorising an incident as a near miss.

Unsafe conditions - something with the potential to cause harm.

Near misses - an incident that nearly resulted in an injury, damage or loss.

Accidents - an accident that resulted in an injury, damage or loss.

The details of all near misses must be accurately and honestly reported to enable the circumstances to be investigated and measures put in place to prevent a recurrence.

To achieve an effective near-miss reporting system, the following are required of the workforce.

- To trust that management will treat the incident fairly and objectively.

- Be encouraged to report near misses with the assurance that individuals involved will not be disadvantaged by their honesty.

- Have confidence that the issues raised will be addressed, or else 'why bother?'.

- Be provided with the means of promptly recording the details of exactly what happened and offering their opinion as to why it occurred.

Companies may find it is beneficial to provide easy to access near-miss reporting forms or cards, which can be completed in privacy and anonymously if that is the individual's choice.

However, anonymous reporting does not provide the opportunity for follow-up discussions to establish more details, and it may encourage malicious reports to be submitted.

Evidence shows that near-miss reporting linked to recognition or a reward scheme has the best chance of succeeding.

12

ACCIDENT PREVENTION AND CONTROL

12.4　Accident and incident trends

Broad categories are used to classify all accidents that are reported to the HSE.

 Reportable accident statistics for the construction industry show that the same types of accident happen frequently, year after year. Those that continue to figure prominently in the statistics include: falls from a height; being trapped by something collapsing or overturning; struck by moving (including flying or falling) objects; slips, trips or falls on the same level; and being injured while handling, lifting or carrying.

Further challenges may have been added as the competition for contracts has increased and tendered margins decreased. Commercial pressure may tempt contractors to take increased risks with their employees' health and/or safety.

The stubborn resistance of the accident statistics to significantly reduce is often attributed to the difficult working conditions experienced on construction sites, where the environment of the workplace is continually changing as work progresses.

However, in reality, it is often a lack of training or health and safety awareness among construction workers, or a lack of effective health and safety management, that prevents a reduction in accidents.

12.5　The cost of accidents and incidents

12.5.1　Cost to the victim and their family

- Pain and suffering.
- Loss of earnings.
- Extra expense.
- Continuing disability and depression.
- Incapacity for the same job.
- Incapacity for work outside the job.
- Effect on dependants and friends.

12.5.2　Cost to people directly responsible

- Worry and stress.
- Recriminations and guilt.
- Extra work (reports, training and recruitment).
- Loss of credibility.

12.5.3　Cost to the company

- Working time lost by victim.
- Time lost by other employees out of sympathy, curiosity or discussion.
- Time lost by supervisors and others investigating the accident.
- Possible damage to machines or materials.
- Idle time (replan, repair and reinstate job).
- Rise in insurance premiums and cost of prosecution or civil action.
- Damage to reputation and possible failure to obtain work.

12.5.4　Cost to the working group

- Shock, disbelief, anger and personal grief.
- Low morale and negative effects on production.

12.5.5　Cost to the nation

In social and economic terms, accidents are an unwanted expense.

- Hundreds of thousands of person-days are lost each year.
- Industrial accidents have an impact on NHS resources.
- Millions of pounds are paid in pensions and death benefits.
- Countless lives are changed for the worse.

It must be emphasised that these are all negative impacts.

Good health and safety management prevents accidents, which means fewer or no victims or affected families, no additional costs to companies, no loss of reputation and no loss of work.

12

12.6   HSE research into accident costs

 HSE Research Report No. 464 contains a number of accident case studies that highlight the cost of accidents to the victims, in the widest terms.

Several of the case studies feature accidents to construction workers.

The consequences of each accident are considered from different standpoints.

Vocational – impact on future job prospects.

Economic – significant loss of income.

Social – standard-of-life issue for victim and family.

Behavioural – reliance on medication, inability to concentrate, inability to sleep, ill-temper, and so on.

Psychological – mood swings, loss of memory, emotional instability and guilt.

Examples of the impact that the accidents had on the victims and on family members, as extracted from the construction case studies, are listed below.

- 'I had no realistic prospect of returning to work in the immediate future'.
- 'I received no support from company or colleagues upon returning to work other than "light duties" for the first two weeks'.
- 'My family was reliant on state benefits of £66 per week during three and a half months off work'.
- 'I am unable to bathe or dress myself, have problems with walking and no longer visit the gym'.
- 'I am unable to sleep due to discomfort, increased eating and inability to concentrate'.
- 'Years later I still suffer flashbacks and nightmares'.

12.7   Causes of accidents and incidents

Examining accident details will help to establish common factors and trends, revealing any weaknesses in a company's health and safety management system.

Accidents can be caused by unsafe acts and attitudes or behaviours of people at work, which result in unsafe conditions being created.

They are also caused by a lack of foresight or planning, which may be a failure to set up a safe system of work, or failure to appreciate the results of risk assessments, control of substances hazardous to health (COSHH) assessments or other similar work.

✋ **Unsafe acts can create unsafe conditions, which can cause accidents. These accidents often result in injury or damage.**

It is impossible to list all the different types of unsafe acts and unsafe conditions that can exist in the construction industry.

However, it is worth recording the most frequent known causes of accidents on construction sites, as follows.

- Lack of planning, management control and supervision.
- Lack of knowledge of good safety techniques or lack of safety awareness.
- Unsafe methods of working at height, including lack of provision for fall prevention.
- Incorrect or unauthorised use of machinery and equipment.
- Failure to segregate operating plant and pedestrians.
- Failure to inspect and maintain all types of machinery and equipment.
- Incorrect use of tools and equipment (hand tools and power tools).
- Use of faulty equipment with improvised repairs or modifications.
- Unsafe manual handling (lifting, loading, moving, stacking and storing).
- Overloading of working places (scaffolds, falsework, hoists, machines, vehicles and roofs).
- Failure to use protective safety equipment (safety helmets, eye protection, gloves, respiratory protective equipment and footwear).
- Carrying out work on moving parts with guards removed or safety devices inoperative.
- Failure to report faulty or unsafe equipment, or dangerous occurrences and incidents.
- Creating unstable structures.

ACCIDENT PREVENTION AND CONTROL

12.8   Planning for health and safety

Despite the effort made by the majority to fulfil their legal, moral and social obligations, difficulties are often encountered in human behaviour that require time and tolerance before acceptable health and safety standards are achieved. It is essential that careful consideration is given to pre-planning, communication, training, supervision and consultation with the workforce, if safe systems and safe and healthy places of work are to be developed and maintained. All of the following measures can make a significant contribution towards the prevention of accidents through the implementation of safe systems of work and procedures.

- Allowing enough resources (time and financial).

- Establishing procedures for communication and consultation with the workforce.

- Providing adequate protection and guarding of working places, platforms, machinery, tools, plant and equipment.

- Implementing an adequate system for the maintenance and repair of plant, equipment and tools.

- Bringing about and maintaining an awareness of, and compliance with, all safety legislation and information relating to systems and procedures of work.

- Providing appropriate training, instruction and information at all levels, including safety training.

- Providing adequate supervision and control.

- Planning, siting and/or stacking materials and equipment to allow safe access or egress of site plant, vehicles and equipment.

- Pre-planning and organising site layout, to provide maximum efficiency, safety and progression of the work sequences and operations.

- Providing adequate resources and equipment to protect and maintain the health and welfare of all personnel.

- Producing, declaring, maintaining and supporting a health and safety policy, and updating it as appropriate to accommodate advancement and development.

The safe segregation of construction plant and pedestrians avoids accidents

Organised site layout, to provide maximum safety

12.9   Factors to consider

Health and safety at work will be affected by human and personal factors, job factors and environmental factors.

12.9.1   Human and personal factors

Attitudes of people at work often play an important part in the prevention of accidents, and conversely, a wrong attitude can cause accidents to happen. Attitudes differ depending on the characteristics of the person.

- Age and gender.

- General health, natural dexterity, agility, physique and ability.

- Disabilities or medical conditions, if any.

- Senses of smell, sight, hearing, touch and, sometimes, taste.

- Education and qualifications, training and skills.

- Home and social life, status at home and work and position in peer group.

 Safe attitudes = safe actions = safe conditions.

 For further information refer to the HSE publication *Reducing error and influencing behaviour* (HSG48).

12.9.2 Job factors

Every work activity has a degree of inherent hazard. Building and construction sites can be particularly hazardous and demand the co-ordination of a large number of trades, skills and work at any one time.

Particular attention should be given to the following.

- The adequacy of time and resources to plan the job and to do the job.
- Provision of tools and equipment that are safe to use, inspected regularly and properly maintained.
- Implementation of safe systems of work.
- Personnel who are unfamiliar with established safe systems of work and practices.
- Personnel who are new to a specific worksite or unfamiliar with a new working environment.
- Those lacking induction training and/or experience.
- The provision of adequate training, information and supervision.
- Balanced workload, fatigue and boredom.

12.9.3 Environmental factors

The majority of people do not work in isolation.

The attitudes of others in a working group (for example, managers, supervisors, safety advisers, safety representatives and shop stewards) may help to prevent accidents, but the following should also be considered.

- The accident record of the firm, site and working group.
- The inter-relationship of people within the group.
- Information and communication processing methods.
- Weather conditions (hot, cold, wet, wind, ice or snow).
- Working at heights, in confined spaces or underground.
- Working conditions (noise, dust, light and ventilation).
- Health and welfare facilities.

12.10 Hazards

12.10.1 Obvious dangers

- Vehicles not being segregated from pedestrians.
- The presence of highly flammable material and other fire hazards.
- Work platforms or work places at height with no fall prevention.
- Insecurely stacked, slung, lifted and transported loads.
- Unsafe machinery, equipment and tools.
- Unsafe working areas due to weather conditions.
- Confined spaces or unsupported excavations.

12.10.2 Potentially dangerous situations

Below are some examples of circumstances that might result in an accident (this list is not fully exhaustive).

- Working with machinery or tools with guards or fences removed.
- Using the incorrect type of plant, tools or equipment for the work involved.
- Unauthorised removal of guard-rails, or failure to replace them following removal for access of plant or materials.
- Transport of insecure or unstable loads.
- Dropping tools and materials from a height.
- Failure to wear personal protective equipment (PPE) or respiratory protective equipment (RPE).
- Working in unstable excavations, without adequate supervision and control.
- Untidy working places or congested walkways and areas, creating a tripping/safe exit hazard.
- Working at height or over water without edge and/or personal protection.
- Inadequate, incorrect or badly placed lighting.
- Unsafe electrical equipment, underground services and overhead cables.

12

12.10.3 Operational risks

Examples of work requiring competence, careful monitoring and/or close supervision are listed below.

High risk activities	Operations creating health hazards or risk of injury
■ Demolition	■ Work producing dust or fumes
■ Working at height	■ Jobs with continual high exposure to noise or vibration
■ Excavations	■ Jobs with continuous elements of the same type of manual handling (such as block laying and kerb laying)
■ Lifting operations	
■ Work in confined spaces	■ Work with asbestos
■ Timber, concrete or steel frame erection	■ Work with hazardous substances (respiratory, eye splash and skin)
■ Roof work and cladding	
■ Work associated with live traffic	
■ Work around power lines/electricity	

12.10.4 Site security

Owners or occupiers of sites have a common law duty under the Occupiers' Liability Act to protect the health and safety of **anyone** who might enter the site, even if that entry is unlawful. This duty is also stipulated in the Construction (Design and Management) Regulations 2015 (CDM) and the contractor or, where applicable, the principal contractor must take the necessary steps to prevent unauthorised access to site.

Contractors must not commence work until reasonable steps have been taken to prevent unauthorised access. This includes unauthorised access by members of the public, particularly young children (who in some cases have been killed or injured), who may trespass on the site, either during or outside of normal working hours.

Accidents have been caused by falls into holes, being trapped by earth, drowning, accidents involving vehicles and those involving falls and falling materials. In all these cases, better site security and management might have prevented the accident. Contractors must take all reasonable and practical steps to ensure that sites are secure.

 For further information refer to the HSE publication *Protecting the public: Your next move* (HSG151).

The guidance focuses on the reality that hazardous construction work can be a fatal danger, not only for those within the industry but for the wider public too.

12.11   Implications of inexperience

12.11.1 Young persons

 A *young person* is anyone under the age of 18.

Before employing a young person, the employer must assess the risks to the young person's health and safety, arising from the work they are required to do, in accordance with the relevant regulations. This assessment must take account of a number of factors.

● The inexperience and immaturity of young persons, and their lack of awareness of risks.

● The type of any work equipment involved and the way it is used.

● The potential for exposure to physical, biological and chemical agents.

● Any health and safety training that is required for young persons.

Having carried out this assessment, employers must then determine whether the level of risk has been reduced to as low as is reasonably practicable. There is particular importance placed on avoiding work that:

● is beyond the young person's physical or psychological capacity

● involves harmful exposure to agents that are toxic or carcinogenic, causes heritable genetic damage or harm to an unborn child or which in any way chronically affects human health

● involves harmful exposure to radiation

● involves the risk of accident, which it may be reasonably assumed cannot be recognised by young people owing to their insufficient attention to safety or lack of experience or training

● involves exposure to physical agents (such as extreme cold or heat, noise and vibration).

Consideration to the level of acceptable risk may be given for young persons over the minimum school-leaving age, where the work is necessary for their training, and where they are properly supervised.

12.11.2 New starters

New starters in a company or on a site, and inexperienced persons of any age, have similar problems to those of young workers.

They are subjected to a new environment, rules, methods and procedures; they are also under different supervision, are working with new colleagues and are using a variety of tools, equipment and manual effort to produce the work required. The start of their health and safety training is usually an induction into the company.

The need for refresher and continuance training should be reviewed at intervals and carried out as necessary.

12.11.3 Older workers

There is legislation in place that makes it illegal to discriminate against older workers. It is also interesting, however, to note that the number of injuries to older workers is higher than average.

There are various reasons that have been suggested as to why.

- Overfamiliarity with the job.
- General slowing of reactions.
- General loss of strength and flexibility.
- Pre-existing damage to body and systems.
- Age-related degeneration of hearing and eyesight.

What is also noteworthy is that when an older person is injured, often the recovery time is longer, because the injury is more severe than it would be for a younger person.

12.12 Contractors and the self-employed

Problems may arise if accident prevention and reporting measures are not communicated to contractors and self-employed persons on site. Arrangements must be made to ensure that contractors and the self-employed are acquainted with, and adhere to, the principal contractor's health and safety standards and procedures, or any other policy or special instructions that may be in force, or relevant to specific operations.

The following recommendations are not exhaustive. Pre-planning at the tender stage may reveal additional requirements.

- Discussion, as necessary, should take place to ensure complete understanding or clarification of what is required.
- A listing of site personnel (who's who and details of established channels of communication).
- The availability, and validity, of certificates and documentation relating to health and safety knowledge and trade competency, including CSCS, CPCS and CISRS cards.
- Safe systems or methods and sequences of work should be established, particularly where such work may affect the health and welfare of others.
- Attention should be given to the requirements for the delivery of plant or equipment, transportation, loading and unloading of materials and provision of means of access, particularly when this work takes place out of normal working hours.

12.13 Supervision and control

The accident trend can be strongly influenced by providing adequate training and supervision to control the worker, the machine or the equipment and the working environment.

12.13.1 The worker

The following points are essential requirements for the worker.

- Be adequately trained and informed of the work they are expected to do.
- Be aware of all the hazards in any activity they are expected to do.
- Be competent to do the work or be under adequate suitably qualified supervision.
- Adopt a safe system of work and use the protection provided.
- Be aware of accident and emergency procedures.
- Be aware of the company's health and safety policy, rules and legislation **applicable to the work**.

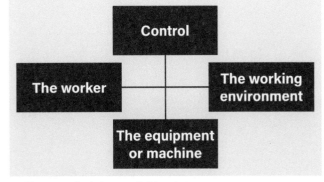

Accident prevention is the control of these factors

12

12.13.2 The working environment

This applies to all areas of the site, including the work area, stores, offices, depot and welfare facilities.

Regular checks are essential to ensure that these areas remain safe and are not a risk to health.

12.13.3 The equipment or machine

Ensure that the following procedures and practices are observed.

- Regular inspections are completed by trained and competent persons.
- No defective equipment is used.
- Defects are properly rectified.
- Adequate servicing and maintenance is carried out.
- Records and reports are maintained.
- All moving parts are adequately guarded or protected.
- Manufacturers' literature and instructions are available for operatives.
- Proper handling, lifting and slinging of equipment is conducted.
- Equipment and machines are adequately secured, both when in use and parked.
- Hand tools are inspected and maintained.

 For further guidance refer to Chapter A10 Inspections and audits.

CONTENTS

Accident reporting and investigation

13

Supporting INFORMATION

GT700 Toolbox talks / supporting checklists and forms

Toolbox talks on some of these topics are available in the GT700 publication. Supporting checklists and forms covering some of these topics are available on our companion website.

ACCIDENT REPORTING AND INVESTIGATION

Overview

The recording of incidents and accidents at work is important, to help establish what went wrong and to prevent similar incidents and accidents from recurring.

This chapter outlines why and how details of incidents and accidents should be captured, what has to be reported to the Health and Safety Executive (HSE) and how to conduct an investigation.

13.1   Introduction

It may be said that there is no such thing as an accident and without people there are no accidents. An accident can always be put down to human error but it is by no means always the fault of the injured person.

In fact, the HSE considers that a lack of safety management, or procedures, is often a contributory factor in a high percentage of accidents, particularly within construction.

The reporting of certain types of accident is a legal requirement and failure to comply is a criminal offence. The reports that are made allow the HSE to identify accident trends, and to take remedial action by producing additional health and safety guidance and legislation, where it is deemed necessary.

If you are an employer, self-employed or are in charge of work operations, you have duties under the law. You have to report deaths, specified injuries, non-fatal accidents requiring hospital treatment to non-workers and dangerous occurrences immediately – the HSE should be in receipt of a report within 10 days of the incident. Accidents resulting in injuries lasting for more than seven days have to be notified to the HSE within 15 days of the incident. Occupational diseases should be reported as soon as the employer receives the diagnosis.

13.2   Important points

- It is important that all workplace accidents, no matter how minor, are reported to the injured person's employer, site manager or supervisor as appropriate.

- There is a legal requirement for details of all accidents to be recorded.

- Once completed, the record of an accident is subject to the General Data Protection Regulation (GDPR) and is confidential.

- Certain types of accident, cases of occupational disease and some dangerous occurrences must be reported to the HSE.

- Each company or organisation should have a procedure for investigating workplace accidents.

- The investigation of accidents will enable trends to be established and preventative measures put in place.

- The level of investigation should be proportionate to the seriousness of the accident.

13.3   Reporting of Injuries, Diseases and Dangerous Occurrences Regulations

The Reporting of Injuries, Diseases and Dangerous Occurrences Regulations (RIDDOR) require the following to be reported directly to the appropriate enforcing authority (either the nearest HSE office or the Local Authority).

- Deaths and specified injuries.
- Over seven-day injuries.
- Specified occupational diseases.
- Dangerous occurrences.

The regulations place a duty on the responsible person to make reports to the enforcing authorities. In the case of injuries to employees, the responsible person will be the employer. In the case of the victim being self-employed or a member of the public, the responsible person will be the person in control of the site where the event occurred.

All sub-contractors must notify both the enforcing authority and the main/principal contractor of any reportable accidents.

Where an accident, occupational disease or dangerous occurrence takes place that requires reporting under RIDDOR, a report should be made online via the HSE website.

- F2508 Report of an injury.
- F2508 Report of a dangerous occurrence.
- F2508A Report of a case of disease.
- F2508G1 Report of a flammable gas incident.
- F2508G2 Report of a dangerous gas fitting.

The following must be reported immediately to the appropriate authority by the quickest practicable method. All incidents must be reported online but a telephone service remains for reporting fatal and specified injuries only. The completed report must be submitted on the approved form within **10 days**.

- Death of any person as a result of an accident at work.

- An accident to any person at work resulting in specified injuries or serious conditions specified in the regulations.

- Any one of the dangerous occurrences listed in Schedule 2 of the regulations.

- Non-fatal accidents requiring hospital treatment to non-workers.

Over seven-day injuries must be reported on an approved form within **15 days**.

13.3.1 Why report and record?

The report informs the enforcing authorities (the HSE, Local Authorities and Office of Rail and Road (ORR), where relevant) about deaths, injuries, occupational diseases and dangerous occurrences, so they can identify where and how risks arise and whether they need to be investigated. This allows the HSE, Local Authorities and ORR to target their work and provide advice about how to avoid work-related deaths, injuries, ill health and accidental loss.

Records of incidents covered by RIDDOR are important. They ensure that you collect the minimum amount of information to allow you to check that you are doing enough to ensure safety and prevent occupational diseases. This information is a valuable management tool that can be used as an aid to risk assessment, helping to develop solutions to potential risks.

In this way, records also help to prevent injuries and ill health, and control costs from accidental loss.

13.3.2 What must be reported?

13.3.2.1 Work-related accidents

Reportable injuries (including deaths) must be reported if they occur as the result of a work-related accident and the type of injury is reportable, as listed under types of reportable injuries. For the purposes of RIDDOR an accident is a separate, identifiable, unintended incident that causes physical injury. This specifically includes acts of non-consensual violence to people at work.

When deciding if the accident that led to the death or injury is work-related, the key issues to consider are whether the accident was related to the following.

- The way in which the work was carried out.

- Any machinery, plant, substances or equipment used for work.

- The condition of the site or premises where the accident happened.

If any of the above factors were related to the cause of the accident, then it is likely that it will need to be reported to the enforcing authority as a death or reportable injury. If none of the above factors are satisfied, it is likely that you will not be required to send a report.

 Guidance and examples of incidents that do and do not have to be reported are available on the RIDDOR section of the HSE website.

13.3.2.2 Deaths

A death to workers and non-workers must be reported if it results from a work accident or an act of physical violence to the worker.

 Where an employee, as a result of an accident at work, has suffered a reportable injury that has caused their death within one year of the date of that accident, the employer shall inform the relevant enforcing authority, in an appropriate manner, of the death as soon as it comes to their knowledge.

13.3.2.3 Injuries to people at work

RIDDOR gives two types of injury that must be reported if the person was at work – specified injuries and over seven-day injuries.

Specified injuries include the following.

- A fracture, other than to fingers, thumbs and toes.

- Amputation of an arm, hand, finger, thumb, leg, foot or toe.

- Permanent loss of sight or a reduction of sight.

- Any injury arising from working in an enclosed space leading to hypothermia, heat-induced illness, resuscitation or admittance to hospital for more than 24 hours.

- Unconsciousness caused by asphyxia or head injury.

- Crush injuries leading to internal organ damage.

- Serious burns (covering more than 10% of the body or damaging the eyes, respiratory system or other vital organs).

- Scalping (a separation of the skin from the head) requiring hospital treatment.

Over seven-day injuries are where an employee, or self-employed person, is away from work or unable to perform their normal work duties for more than seven consecutive days (not counting the day of the accident).

13

13.3.2.4 Injuries to non-workers

You must report injuries to members of the public or people who are not at work, if they are injured through a work-related accident and are taken from the scene of the accident to hospital for treatment to that injury.

Examinations and diagnostic tests do not constitute treatment in such circumstances and there is no need to report incidents where people are taken to hospital purely as a precaution when no injury is apparent.

13.3.2.5 Reportable occupational diseases

Employers and self-employed people must report diagnosis of certain occupational diseases and conditions (such as those listed below), where these are likely to have been caused or made worse by their work.

● Hand-arm vibration syndrome (HAVS) (due to operating hand-held vibrating tools and equipment).

● Occupational dermatitis, due to work substances (such as cement, solvents and epoxy resins).

● Carpal tunnel syndrome.

● Severe cramp of the hand or forearm.

● Tendonitis or tenosynovitis of the hand or forearm.

● Any occupational cancer (such as mesothelioma, asbestosis (due to work with or exposure to asbestos) and lung cancer).

● Occupational asthma, where the person's work involves significant or regular exposure to a known respiratory sensitiser.

● Any disease attributed to an occupational exposure to a biological agent.

 Occupational deafness (noise induced hearing loss) is not reportable under the list of occupational diseases, as it is hard to prove the cause of acquired hearing loss (deafness); for example, it could have been caused by any past work activity with exposure to high levels of noise, or through noisy hobbies undertaken outside of the working day.

13.3.2.6 Reportable dangerous occurrences

Dangerous occurrences are certain, listed, near-miss events. Not every near-miss event must be reported.

There are 27 categories of dangerous occurrences that are relevant to all workplaces. Some examples are shown below.

● The collapse, overturning or failure of load-bearing parts of lifts and lifting equipment.

● Plant or equipment coming into contact with overhead power lines.

● The accidental release of any substance that could cause personal injury, other than through combustion and flammable liquid or gases.

 A full list of dangerous occurrences applicable to all workplaces, and additional categories of dangerous occurrences, can be found on the RIDDOR section of the HSE website.

13.3.2.7 Reportable gas incidents

If you are a distributor, filler, importer or supplier of flammable gas and you learn, either directly or indirectly, that someone has died, lost consciousness or been taken to hospital for treatment to an injury arising in connection with the gas you distributed, filled, imported or supplied, this should be reported online using F2508G1.

In practice, the emergency service providers representing gas conveyors usually carry out reporting duties.

If you are a gas engineer, registered with the Gas Safe register, you must provide details of any gas appliances or fittings that you consider to be dangerous to the extent that people could die or suffer a specified injury (this should be done online using form F2508G2).

These dangers may be due to the design, construction, installation, modification or servicing, and could result in the following.

● An accidental leakage of gas.

● Inadequate combustion of gas.

● Inadequate removal of products of the combustion of gas.

 For an accident and incident reporting matrix refer to Appendix A.

e.g. Some examples to provide clarification

- A directly employed person breaks their arm at work. This must be reported by the employer, in their capacity as a responsible person, as a specified injury.

- A self-employed sub-contractor breaks their leg at work. The injury must be reported as a specified injury by the main/principal contractor acting in their capacity as the responsible person who was in control of the premises.

- An employee of a sub-contractor is informed by their doctor that they are suffering from work-related vibration white finger and subsequently informs their employer. The employer, in their capacity as a responsible person, must report the incident to the HSE as a reportable disease.

- An employee inadvertently hits an underground electric cable whilst operating a road-breaker. There is minor damage to the external sheath, but the conductor is not exposed. This is not reportable as there was not an electrical short circuit with fire and explosion. The incident, however, warrants significant internal investigation.

- A member of the public is knocked down by a lorry entering the site as it crosses the pavement. They are taken to hospital by ambulance and it is obvious they have suffered an injury. This would be reportable as it involves a member of the public being taken directly to hospital for treatment.

- A sub-contracted employee burns their hand and is taken to the accident and emergency department of the local hospital. The employee is back on site later that afternoon and continues to work as normal for the rest of the week. This would not be reportable. However, had the employee suffered more than 10% burns, the incident would be reportable.

- An employed delivery driver twists their ankle when they step down from their cab. They receive first aid, insist they are fit to drive and later leave the site. They subsequently take the following seven days off because of pain and swelling in their ankle. The incident should have been recorded in the site accident book, but it would seem unreasonable for the site to be aware of the consequence. The delivery driver's employer would have a responsibility to report this as an over seven-day injury.

- An employee sustains a head injury as a result of tripping over debris left on site. The accident occurred on a Friday and, because of the injury, the person is unable to return to work until a week later, on the following Monday. Although only five actual working days have been lost, the accident must be reported as an over seven-day injury because the Saturday and Sunday also count, as the injured person would have been unfit for work had these been working days.

13.3.3 How to report

 Complete the appropriate online form, available from the HSE website. All incidents must be reported online, but a phone service remains through the Incident Contact Centre for reporting fatal injuries, specified injuries and major incidents only (+44 (0) 151 922 9235).

13.3.4 Reporting out of hours

The type of circumstances where HSE may need to respond out of hours include:.

- following a work-related death

- following a serious incident where there have been multiple casualties

- following an incident which has caused major disruption, such as evacuation of people, closure of roads, or large numbers of people going to hospital.

13.4 Accident records

Employers are legally required to keep records of all accidents. These can be stored in any medium, including electronically, as long as printable copies are readily available if required. You must keep a record of the following.

- **Accident, occupational disease or dangerous occurrence** that requires reporting under RIDDOR.

- Other occupational accident causing injuries that result in a worker being away from work or **incapacitated for more than three consecutive days** (not counting the day of the accident but including any weekends or other rest days). If you are an employer, who must keep an accident book under the Social Security (Claims and Payments) Regulations 1979, that record will be enough.

You do **not** have to report over three-day injuries, unless the incapacitation period goes on to exceed seven days, but you still have to keep a record of the over three-day injury.

ACCIDENT REPORTING AND INVESTIGATION

The following details must be recorded.

- Full name, address and occupation of the injured person.
- Date and time of the accident.

- Location of the accident.
- Nature of the injury and how it was caused.

Details of an accident should be recorded by the injured person, but can be completed by any employee. However, some employers insist that records are completed by first aiders, which requires a first aider to be available at all times. This is a company operating procedure and is not strictly necessary. Completion of an accident record does not meet the employer's obligation to report specific accidents and dangerous occurrences to the HSE or Local Authority.

All accident records must comply with the General Data Protection Regulation (GDPR) to ensure the confidentiality of entries. The HSE's accident book BL510 enables each accident record to be detached and stored separately when complete, thus maintaining the confidentiality of the injured person's details. All personal information must be kept in confidence, and in a secure location, such as a lockable cabinet.

Accident books designed and produced in-house may still be used in the following circumstances.

- Where all details required by BL510 are recorded.
- If the requirements of GDPR are met.

- When information recorded electronically can be made readily available in hard copy.

13.5   Calculating the incidence and frequency rates of accidents

From company accident records and other statistics, it is possible to calculate the incidence and frequency rates for accidents at a particular place of work and for the types of injury, severity or duration.

13.5.1   Accident incidence rate (AIR)

The incidence rate is based on the number of accidents, taken over a fixed period (usually 12 months), per 100,000 employees. The formula highlighted is the one most commonly used by UK Government departments to calculate the incidence rate.

$$\text{Incidence rate} = \frac{\text{Number of reported injuries in a 12-month period} \times 100{,}000}{\text{Average number of employees in a year}}$$

If, during a 12-month period, there were six reportable accidents and during that year the company employed an average of 120 employees, the calculation would be:

$$\frac{6 \times 100{,}000}{120} = 5{,}000$$

13.5.2   Accident frequency rate (AFR)

The accident frequency rate allows a calculation to be made that balances the number of reportable accidents that occur against the number of hours worked in a fixed period (usually 12 months).

$$\text{Frequency rate} = \frac{\text{Number of accidents in a 12-month period} \times 100{,}000}{\text{Number of hours worked in that period}}$$

If a company had six reportable injuries in a period during which its 120 workers worked a total of 280,000 hours, the accident frequency rate would be:

$$\frac{6 \times 100{,}000}{280{,}000} = 2.14$$

It should be noted that the HSE uses a multiplier of 1,000,000 rather than 100,000 in its guidance on the calculation of AFR. Generally the industry uses 100,000: 100,000 working hours at 45 hours per week for 49 weeks per year represents 45 years' work for one person or 90 years' work for two persons, and so on.

13.5.3   All accident rates

Similarly, by using the above incident and frequency calculations, all accident rates (minors, lost time and reportable accidents) can be calculated. Computers are ideal for calculating the various incidence and frequency rates, moving averages, and so on.

There is a wide range of commercially-available computer software to manage accident statistics or a simple spreadsheet can be easily devised, using the known labour resources and their total working hours as a basis for calculating the statistics. Accident statistics are often displayed as bar charts, histograms and graphs to visualise trends more clearly.

The robust and effective reporting of accidents, along with their thorough investigation, can have major benefits for a company, such as:

- reduced costs by proactively implementing change and preventing accidents
- identifying training needs, which will also improve performance
- satisfying clients and principal contractors that the workforce is properly trained and safety orientated
- a possible reduction of insurance premiums following years of hard work to reduce accidents.

13

13.6 Post-accident investigation

An effective investigation will meet the following criteria.

- Be factual and without bias.
- Clearly show the sequence of events leading to the accident or incident.
- Establish the immediate cause(s) and the underlying cause(s) (for example, unsafe acts or conditions).
- Identify the root cause(s) (for example, performance-influencing factors such as lack of safety systems, poor work planning leading to workload pressures, or a poor health and safety culture).

The root cause(s) must be identified, in order to be able to learn lessons from accidents and incidents, and then take action to prevent reoccurences.

13.6.1 Accident procedure

Many companies have established procedures to be followed in the event of an accident. The procedure below is given as general guidance and outlines the steps that should be taken immediately after an accident.

1.	Identify any injured persons and assess the severity of the injuries.
2.	Make the area safe, preserve the scene and notify relevant parties (such as management, the health and safety team or HSE).
3.	Call the appropriate emergency services, and arrange first aid for the injured person(s) if safe to do so.
4.	Isolate machinery, tools or equipment if safe to do so.
5.	Do not disturb or move anything unless to release an injured person.
6.	Ensure that any remaining hazards are controlled.
7.	Take notice of anything significant and make general observations at the scene of the accident.

13.6.2 Conducting an investigation

It is not usually practical to investigate every minor accident, but those involving specified or serious injuries to persons and major damage to plant or equipment should be thoroughly investigated so that immediate action can be taken to prevent a recurrence. The following steps may be useful as a guide to the steps to be taken.

- Investigate promptly and record evidence.
- Identify types of evidence (for example, factual or corroborative).
- Interview the injured person, if possible.
- Question the person in charge and other supervisors.
- Obtain details of the injured person's job and what they usually do.
- Interview witnesses.
- Inspect plant, equipment and tools for signs of misuse or defects.
- Establish the full sequence of events.
- Ascertain the nature and extent of the injury or damage.
- Complete the accident report and the accident book.
- Notify the appropriate authorities.

13.6.3 Investigating promptly

The sooner an investigation is started, the better – provided it is safe to do so. Engineers and supervisors will be anxious to find ways to repair any damage to plant, machinery or buildings, but the **first priority** should be to establish the cause(s) of the accident. Safety specialists, managers and safety representatives should concern themselves solely with the safety implications and preventing a recurrence. It is important that the investigation is properly supervised and organised. Where the police or HSE inspectors need to investigate, any other persons responsible for, or involved in, investigating the accident must take care not to disturb possible evidence at the scene.

13.6.4 Recording evidence

Statements from witnesses should include their age and occupation. The time, date and place of interview should be indicated at the end of the statement. Witnesses' statements should always be written in their own words, even if these include slang or expletives.

The completed statement should be read to the witness and signed by them and by the person who took the statement.

13

13.6.5 Identifying the types of evidence

The following will usually be included within evidence.

- Statement of witnesses and others given orally, or in writing. 'Others' may include experts who, for example, might have been called in to examine a machine or the state of a scaffold.

- Documentation of all kinds.

- Material exhibits of all kinds.

Factual evidence comprises the facts related by persons directly involved, and by witnesses who are able to say what they felt, saw, heard, or give an expert opinion. This type of evidence is primary, direct and positive and should be written in simple language, keeping to the facts and avoiding inferences, opinions and beliefs. The facts should be recorded clearly, accurately and in sequence.

The best witnesses are those persons directly involved, who have the following qualities.

- Can listen carefully to the questions.

- Are able to answer directly, fairly, impartially and truthfully.

- Can state clearly when they do not know the answer.

- Are able to remain calm when they are being asked questions.

Material evidence includes, for example, items of plant, equipment, machines, scaffolds, ladders or hand tools, where the use of, or the state or condition of, the item has a bearing on the accident.

Corroborative evidence tends to support the truthfulness and accuracy of the evidence that has already been given. The confirming evidence may take the form of site records, plant or maintenance records, warning notices and written procedures or reports made by safety officers or safety representatives.

Opinions are not generally acceptable as evidence in a court of law, but people in the vicinity of an accident should be asked to give an opinion. In this way a full picture can be built up of the circumstances of the accident.

Experts, or specialists, who are familiar with the type of accident, or technical and other factors surrounding the accident, may be called upon to express their **expert** opinions. When there is a lack of real or factual evidence, other forms of evidence (such as circumstantial and corroborative evidence) tend to become more valuable.

Photographs taken immediately after an accident record the state of the scene and often highlight conditions that existed at the time. The position of machines, equipment and tools, obstructions, and factors such as floor conditions, space and dimensions, may show up well on photographs.

The time, date and place or subject photographed should be recorded on the photographs.

Too many photographs are far better than too few, and it is a good idea to make drawings of the area where the incident happened. Digital photography may not be accepted as primary evidence but may be suitable as supportive evidence.

Procedures should be in place to ensure that photographs have not been, or cannot be, altered in any way, as this would destroy their value as evidence.

13.6.6 Interviewing the injured person

In the event of a major incident or fatality, the police may initially take charge to investigate or rule out any criminal intent. They should be notified immediately of any intention to interview injured persons, as the nature and content of interviews may form part of their criminal investigation.

Once the police have satisfactorily ruled out any criminal intent, the HSE will then take over the investigation.

Interviewing the injured person should be an early priority. Even the briefest description of the accident should suffice initially.

The physical and mental state of the injured person will need to be considered, and tact and patience will be required during the interview. The injured person should be fit to answer questions.

The injured person should be encouraged to talk about how the accident happened and it is important they have confidence and trust in the listener. It is important to stress that the purpose of the investigation is to find the cause so that preventive action can be taken. Blame should not be apportioned.

Questioning should not take the form of an interrogation. Someone well known to the injured person is probably the best person to do this. Safety officials are more likely to receive the co-operation of an injured person if they are able to demonstrate a genuine interest in their welfare and recovery.

This may involve visiting the injured person, with the doctor's approval, in hospital or at home.

Given the nature of the industry, often with multiple layers of sub-contracting, there may be a number of interested parties. Sharing statements is one way of reducing the stress on witnesses.

However, regulators (such as the police and HSE) may be less forthcoming about such arrangements as they may see this as an employer trying to interfere in a criminal investigation.

13.6.7 Questioning the person in charge

Establish from the injured person, manager, supervisor or the person in charge, what the normal job and tasks of the injured person were. Did they include the activity that led up to the accident?

? Other questions that might be asked

- What task or type of job was being performed?
- Was it planned or part of a planned activity?
- At what stage of the work did the accident occur?
- Was the person involved trained and authorised and, if so, when?
- Was the person authorised to be where the accident occurred?
- What instructions had been given?
- Were safe and correct procedures being followed?
- Did unsafe acts cause the accident? If so, were they those of the injured person, workmates or others?
- Did any unsafe conditions contribute to the accident?
- What safety equipment or personal protection was available and in use?

13.6.8 Interviewing witnesses

Skill is required when interviewing. Witnesses should be interviewed one at a time. If they wish to say anything before notes are taken, they should be allowed to do so.

? Basic questions interviewers should seek answers to

- What did the witness actually see or hear?
- What was the witness doing at the time?
- What was the proximity of the witness to the accident or occurrence?
- What actions did the witness take?
- What actions did others take before and after the accident?
- What was the condition of the workplace at the time?
- What hazards or unsafe conditions existed and what unsafe acts were performed?
- What was the probable cause(s) of the accident or occurrence?

Skilled interviewers allow witnesses to tell things in their own way, intervening only to clear up specific points or answers where necessary. Questions should be impartial, they should not be leading, and the interviewer must be unbiased. Questions and answers given should be recorded.

It is quite acceptable to go through an incident with a witness making rough notes and then to take a statement after that. That way, the witness often has more chance to remember the facts, and sometimes provides far more detail on the second run through.

The important witnesses are those persons who were involved. Their evidence will be more valuable than evidence from witnesses who saw or heard only from a distance, although they, too, should be interviewed. Corroborative evidence and information is often required, particularly when witnesses are few or are not reliable.

As much evidence and information as possible should be collected, since the action taken to prevent a recurrence will be based on what is learned.

13.6.9 Inspecting plant for misuse or defects

Inspection of plant, equipment, tools and machinery immediately after an accident may reveal signs of misuse, or defects, which may or may not have contributed to the accident.

The scene should also be carefully examined to see if trip hazards, slippery floors, or some other defect contributed to, or caused, the accident.

Assistance from specialists and persons directly involved or familiar with the type of plant, equipment, tools or machinery in question can provide valuable information.

13

13.6.10 Establishing a sequence of events

Evidence gained from interviews and from inspection of the scene, plant, equipment, tools or machinery should give an indication of the sequence of events leading up to the accident.

13.6.11 Ascertaining the extent of injury or damage

It is not always possible to ascertain the full extent of injuries and damage resulting from an accident.

There may be complications or delayed effects from injuries. The total time off work will obviously not be known at the time of investigation.

Whilst it may be easy to identify the extent of the damage caused to plant, machinery, equipment, buildings and materials, it is far from easy to measure the overall effects of the accident in terms of lost time, lost production and, of course, the suffering of the injured person or persons.

13.6.12 Completing the accident investigation report

Accident report details will vary, depending on who produces the report and whom the report is for. To help eliminate or reduce this variation, guidance in making reports and the use of a standard form is recommended.

As far as possible, reports should be concise, based upon fact rather than speculation, be unbiased and should summarise the essential information obtained during the investigation.

It is becoming relatively common for HSE inspectors to simply ask for a copy of an accident investigation report completed by the employer. It is a criminal offence to intentionally falsify or manipulate the findings of an accident investigation report and it is therefore important to make sure that the report is unbiased and, as far as possible, accurate.

13.6.13 Lessons learnt

It is essential that, following an investigation, lessons learnt are communicated throughout relevant areas of the business, and with wider industry groups if appropriate.

Changes to controls, systems, procedures, communications and so on should be implemented to ensure the continual improvement of health and safety.

 For further information on investigating accidents and incidents visit the HSE website.

Appendix A – Accident/incident reporting matrix

Type of incident	Enter in company records and investigate	Put in accident book	Send Form 2508 to enforcing authority*	Phone enforcing authority and send Form 2508*	Send Form 2508A to the enforcing authority*
Any incident or near miss	✓				
Every injury**	✓	✓			
Over three days' time lost	✓	✓			
Over seven days' time lost ***	✓	✓	✓		
Specified injury or fatality	✓	✓	✓	✓	
Dangerous occurrence	✓		✓		
Reportable occupational disease*	✓				✓

* Refer to the accident reporting section of this chapter for the different methods of submitting accident reports to the enforcing authority.

** Note employers and others with responsibilities under RIDDOR must still keep a record of all over three-day injuries. An accident book record will be enough.

*** Note the deadline by which the over seven-day injury must be reported is 15 days from the day of the accident.

13

Index

INDEX

INDEX

B Health and welfare

Management of health

Supporting
INFORMATION

GT700 Toolbox talks / supporting checklists and forms

Toolbox talks on some of these topics are available in the GT700 publication. Supporting checklists and forms covering some of these topics are available on our companion website.

Overview

Figures from the Health and Safety Executive (HSE) show that work-related ill health increases the likelihood of early death, long-term illness and lost time. The actual costs to industry, and to the individual companies within it, are significantly greater than the costs attributed to accidents.

Good employee health is good for business, as anything else will involve extra work for the employer and extra costs somewhere along the line (for example, temporary staff costs, sick pay and prosecution).

Physical health and mental health are closely related and both must be taken into account in managing the health of employees. Work is a part of our identity and meets important social needs, and being happy and satisfied at work is good for a person's health and wellbeing.

1.1 Introduction

The prevention of ill health on site benefits the employer and the workforce. Employees will be able to work to their full capacity, rather than being off work sick or working under the limitations (physical or physiological) imposed by an illness or as a result of poor management of occupational ill health.

For many years, the focus of health and safety legislation has tended to be the issue of safety on building and construction sites, rather than on occupational health. Employers should give the same attention to occupational health as they do to preventing accidents at work.

The introduction of the **Health and Safety at Work etc. Act 1974** marked a major change in emphasis, acknowledging that ill health arising from work was a problem and giving it equal importance to safety. Section 2 of the Act places a duty on every employer to ensure, so far as is reasonably practicable, the health, safety and welfare at work of all employees.

1.1.1 Occupational health and safety

Occupational health **is promoting and maintaining the highest degree of physical, mental and social wellbeing of workers in all occupations. This means keeping workers as healthy as possible, by removing or preventing the hazards and risks that can cause harm to people at work.**

 It is also about existing health problems that workers may bring to the workplace, as well as health issues caused or made worse by work. It covers serious and fatal diseases, physical effects on skin, breathing, hearing, mobility and functioning, and psychological effects on mental wellbeing.

Safety **is freedom from physical harm; the condition of being protected from, or unlikely to cause, danger, risk or injury.**

Occupational health deals with all aspects of health and safety in the workplace. The main focus is the prevention of hazards. To make sure the health of workers is not affected, employers have to protect people from risks in the workplace.

Some work activities, and some equipment, materials and chemicals that are used in workplaces, can have risks that lead to accidents, musculoskeletal diseases (long-term spine or back problems), respiratory diseases (breathing problems, from breathing in dust or fumes), hearing loss, circulatory (blood) diseases, cancers, stress and mental health disorders, and many other conditions.

Some of these problems and conditions can cause harm inside the body for many years before the effects are known or felt. In some cases it can be up to 60 years before people are diagnosed with a disease that has no cure, which was caused by their breathing in harmful dusts or asbestos fibres whilst working as a young adult in construction.

A number of regulations, including the Control of Substances Hazardous to Health (COSHH) Regulations as well as regulations about lead, asbestos, manual handling, noise and vibration, have been introduced to further address health issues, as it is now recognised that construction is a high-risk industry for health issues, and it must be given significant attention and management.

The legal duties require employers to make provisions to safeguard the health of employees.

- It is estimated that for every fatal accident 100 construction workers die from work-related illnesses, such as cancer.
- The construction industry has the largest burden of occupational cancer. It accounts for over 40% of occupational cancer deaths and cancer registrations each year in Great Britain.
- The most significant carcinogen is still past exposure to asbestos, followed by silica, solar radiation, and coals, tars and pitches.
- There are approximately 5,000 asbestos-related deaths per year currently, including mesothelioma, lung cancer and asbestosis.
- Around 450 people every year are dying as a result of past exposure to silica dust, which causes lung cancer. Much of this exposure would result from activities such as cutting blocks, kerbs and so on.
- Annually, around 79,000 construction workers in Great Britain suffer from an illness they believe was caused or made worse by their work. Around 40% of these are new conditions that had started during the year and the remainder are long-standing conditions.

- Work-related musculoskeletal disorders are more common in the construction industry than in other industries.

- The number of people who self-report stress, depression or anxiety is lower in the construction industry than in other industries, but the impact of these issues in a high-risk environment should not be underestimated.

- Vibration white finger, carpal tunnel syndrome, noise-induced hearing loss and dermatitis are the most common non-lung diseases suffered by those in the construction industry.

- The Labour Force Survey (LFS) estimated 36.8 million working days were lost due to work-related ill health and non-fatal workplace injuries in 2021/22.

- Stress, depression or anxiety and musculoskeletal disorders accounted for the majority of days lost due to work-related ill health in 2021/22 (17 million and 7.3 million respectively).

- On average, each person suffering took around 16.5 days off work. This varies as follows.

  - 10.6 days for injuries.

  - 17.2 days for ill health cases.

  - 18.6 days for stress, depression or anxiety.

  - 15.2 days for musculoskeletal disorders.

 Whilst an injury caused by an accident is, in most cases, instantly obvious, the symptoms of occupational ill health and a person's awareness of it can take months or years to show. It could be considered to be a slow accident.

Occupational ill health can result in the sufferer having long periods of time off work or having to give up work completely. Even short-term sickness absence can have an adverse effect on business. Worker absence can cost the employer more for staff cover and may also cause low morale within the remaining team by increasing their workload and the pressure on them. In turn, this increases the likelihood of team members becoming absent from work.

The prevention of occupational ill health can be achieved if the following requirements are met.

- A suitable assessment of the risks to health is carried out and reviewed as necessary.

- Adequate control measures are identified, put in place, monitored, reviewed and adjusted as necessary.

- The persons at risk fully use the control measures provided.

Occupational health and its risks should be considered as early as possible, ideally at the design or pre-construction planning stage. The contractor should be provided with details of any residual risks, so the impact to workers can be reduced.

Risk assessments should be reviewed from time to time to ensure that control measures are still appropriate and effective. If there is a change to any aspect of the way the job has to be carried out which might affect health and safety (for example, having to use a different item of equipment part way through the job, or a new operative joins who is inexperienced), the assessment must be reviewed and risks re-evaluated.

There are no specific legal requirements that state that employers must provide occupational health services, but in some circumstances employers have a legal duty to provide health surveillance to employees. Where occupational health services are provided, clear advice and guidance should be provided to managers and human resources on individual cases.

Occupational health service providers will also work with human resources, the relevant managers and health professionals to support the individual's return to work. Advice will be provided to managers on any job or workplace modifications that are required to assist the individual in their recovery or allow them to return to work.

Raising the awareness of managers, supervisors and workers to ensure effective control measures are always put in place and followed is fundamental to help reduce these numbers.

 At any one time, far more people are off work through occupational ill health than through work-related accidents.

1.2　　Important points

- Health risks should be considered at the design and planning stage of the project.

- Delays in identifying work-related ill health can make it challenging to address, and make it more difficult to put preventative measures in place before the effects become irreversible.

- Designers play an important role in designing out occupational health risks. They must make the other duty holders aware of any residual health risks.

- Managers and supervisors play an important role in ensuring the required control measures are fully adhered to.

- Health surveillance may be required in some circumstances.

- Employers should actively encourage a healthy work-life balance.

- Employee assistance programmes and/or occupational health providers can provide staff with specialist advice, guidance and support.

- Good quality employment can contribute to a positive healthy life and a more productive workforce.

01

1.3 Legislative requirements

1.3.1 Management of Health and Safety at Work Regulations

Employers have a duty to assess the risks to health that arise out of their work and to introduce measures that control the risks to an acceptable level. In accordance with Regulation 3 a risk assessment must be undertaken.

The following information should be explained within the assessment.

● Health hazards of the job (for example, silica dust created when mechanically cutting a concrete slab or block).

● Risks (such as a person breathing in the silica dust).

● Control measures needed to minimise the health risk to a safe level (such as wet cutting the slab and wearing suitable respiratory protective equipment (RPE)).

Regulation 4 states that the general principles of prevention, as detailed in Schedule 1 of the regulations, must be applied when making decisions on appropriate risk control measures. Some examples are shown below.

● Avoiding the risk (such as ordering pre-cut slabs or using a block splitter).

● Combating risks at source (such as suppressing dust by wet techniques rather than relying solely on personal protective equipment (PPE)).

● Adapting to technical progress (such as buying new work equipment that is designed to produce a cleaner cut or which incorporates a dust extraction system).

The regulations impose the following legal duties on employers.

● Provide employees with comprehensive information of the risks identified by the assessment and the measures implemented to control those risks.

● Ensure that employees are capable in all respects of carrying out the work that they are required to do in a safe manner and without risks to health.

● Co-operate with other employers, in the interests of health and safety, where the employees of more than one employer share a workplace.

Regulation 6 requires every employer to ensure that their employees are provided with the appropriate health surveillance, having regard for the risks to their health and safety, as identified by the risk assessment. Regulation 7 requires employers to appoint a competent person to help them meet their health and safety duties. A competent person is someone with the necessary skills, knowledge and experience to manage health and safety. Self-employed employers are exempt from this requirement if they deem themselves to be competent.

 Health risk considerations

The following are examples of health risks that need to be considered when undertaking a risk assessment.

● Personal injury caused by inadequate manual handling techniques (such as carrying materials and equipment).

● Respiratory problems and diseases (such as occupational asthma), resulting from the inhalation of existing harmful substances or insulation materials in the course of insulation and cutting operations.

● Noise-induced hearing loss caused by failing to protect the ears when working in noisy environments.

● Dermatitis and other skin complaints caused by failing to protect exposed skin from contact with adhesives, cement mixes and harmful dusts, or by persistently working with wet hands.

● Asbestos-related diseases caused by exposure to harmful asbestos-containing materials.

● Hand-arm vibration syndrome caused by exposure to vibratory equipment and tools.

● Stress and fatigue, which can contribute to a range of mental health conditions, including depression and anxiety.

● Mental health - male construction workers are three times more likely to commit suicide than the average UK male. Suicide kills more construction workers than falls do.

1.3.2 Reporting of Injuries, Diseases and Dangerous Occurrences Regulations (RIDDOR)

These regulations cover fatalities and specified injuries, incapacity to work for more than seven days, occupational diseases and dangerous occurrences. The people covered are employers, employees, the self-employed, trainees, visitors and members of the public injured on the premises. Specified injuries and reportable occupational diseases are shown in the table on the next page.

Specified injuries	Occupational diseases
■ Any bone fracture diagnosed by a registered medical practitioner, other than to the fingers, thumbs and toes.	■ Carpal tunnel syndrome, where the person's work involves regular use of percussive or vibrating tools.
■ Amputation of an arm, hand, finger, thumb, leg, foot or toe. (Amputation includes both a traumatic amputation injury at the time of an accident, and surgical amputation following an accident as a consequence of the injuries sustained.)	■ Cramp of the hand or forearm, where the person's work involves prolonged periods of repetitive movement of the fingers, hand or arm.
■ Any injury diagnosed by a registered medical practitioner as being likely to cause permanent blinding or reduction in sight in one or both eyes.	■ Occupational dermatitis, where the person's work involves significant or regular exposure to a known skin sensitiser or irritant.
■ Any other injury arising from working in a confined space leading to hypothermia or heat-induced illness; or requiring resuscitation or admittance to hospital for more than 24 hours.	■ Hand-arm vibration syndrome, where the person's work involves regular use of percussive or vibrating tools or holding materials subject to percussive processes or processes causing vibration.
■ Any loss of consciousness caused by asphyxia or head injury. (Loss of consciousness means that the injured person enters a state where there is a lack of response, either vocal or physical, to people trying to communicate with them. The length of time a person remains unconscious is not significant in terms of whether an accident is reportable.)	■ Occupational asthma, where the person's work involves significant or regular exposure to a known respiratory sensitiser.
	■ Tendonitis or tenosynovitis in the hand or forearm, where the person's work is physically demanding and involves frequent, repetitive movements.
■ Burn injury (including scalds) covering more than 10% of the body's surface or where it causes significant damage to the eyes, respiratory system or other vital organs.	■ Any occupational cancer (such as mesothelioma or asbestosis (due to work with, or exposure to, asbestos) and lung cancer).
■ Crush injury to the head or torso, causing damage to the brain or internal organs in the chest or abdomen.	■ Any disease attributed to occupational exposure to a biological agent.
■ Scalping, requiring hospital treatment.	

1.3.3   Social Security (Claims and Payments) Regulations

● Employers are legally required to keep records of all accidents.

● Every accident involving personal injury to an employee must be entered in the accident book, either by the employee or someone acting on behalf of them.

● The accident book must be easily accessible. This may be a physical book or a digital system, but it needs to be secure and confidential.

● An employer must investigate all reported accidents.

 For further information on RIDDOR refer to Chapter A13 Accident reporting and investigation.

1.3.4   Control of Substances Hazardous to Health Regulations

Regulation 11 requires that, where it is appropriate for the protection of the health of their employees who are, or are liable to be, exposed to a substance hazardous to health, the employer shall ensure that such employees are under suitable health surveillance.

The regulation goes on to specify the circumstances in which health surveillance is appropriate and when health surveillance has to include medical surveillance under the supervision of an (HSE) employment medical adviser or an appointed (by HSE) doctor.

 For further information refer to Chapter B07 Control of substances hazardous to health.

1.3.5   Other relevant legislation

● Control of Lead at Work Regulations *(for further information refer to Chapter B08 Lead).*

● Control of Asbestos Regulations *(for further information refer to Chapter B09 Asbestos).*

● Control of Noise at Work Regulations *(for further information refer to Chapter B11 Noise).*

● Control of Vibration at Work Regulations *(for further information refer to Chapter B12 Vibration).*

1.4 Safety policy or *health* and safety policy?

Under the requirements of the Health and Safety at Work etc. Act 1974, all employers who have five or more employees must:

 ... prepare, and, as often as may be appropriate, revise a written statement of general policy with respect to the health and safety of employees, and the organisation and arrangements, for the time being in force, for carrying out that policy.

The requirement is for a written policy statement that sets out the employer's aims and objectives for improving work-related health as well as safety at work. It must also set out the organisation and arrangements currently in force for achieving those objectives. *Organisation* can be taken to mean people and their responsibilities; *arrangements* can be taken to mean systems and procedures.

In the past many companies considered **safety issues** within their safety policy document and devised safe working procedures to address the risks. However, as the Health and Safety at Work etc. Act makes clear, it is also important to look at the **health hazards** involved in the work that is carried out and to devise an equally efficient policy to deal with them. **Health in the construction sector can no longer be treated as the 'poor relation' of safety, and must be considered equally**.

Work-related ill health can often result in employees being unable to work as productively or as efficiently as before, and sometimes they may never work again. Having an effective health and safety policy will ensure consideration is given to managing work-related ill health issues as they are identified.

The health and safety policy should be reviewed if ill health issues are identified.

1.5 Managing health and wellbeing

The management of health and safety at work applies to work-related health risks, as well as safety, and requires employers to take the following actions.

- Identify the potential health risks (short, medium and long-term) arising from the work activities to be carried out.
- Investigate what can be done about the health risks and decide how to address and control them.
- Give staff information, instruction and training on the health risks and the control measures to be followed.
- Monitor work to make sure that the procedures are being implemented and are effective.
- Introduce health surveillance where necessary.
- Look for benefits and improvements.

One of the most difficult parts of managing health is understanding and assessing the impact an activity may have on an individual. When assessing risk it is therefore important to understand the short, medium and long-term health impacts.

 The World Health Organization defines *health* as 'a state of complete physical, mental and social wellbeing and not merely the absence of disease or infirmity'.

It is not about assessing the health risk on a given day, but the cumulative effect over time. This difficulty is compounded by the transient nature of the workforce, which can move from employer to employer and site to site. Nevertheless, the controls on any given day should minimise the risk of work-related ill health.

The HSE recommends following the common principles, below, towards effectively managing ill health and promoting wellbeing.

Ill health can be prevented. It is possible and practical to carry out construction work without causing ill health.

Treat health like safety. Managing health risks is no different to managing safety risks.

Everyone has a role to play. Everyone involved in construction has a responsibility for managing risks to health. Each person must take ownership of their part of the process.

Control the risk, not the symptoms. Monitoring and health surveillance programmes are not enough on their own. While they are an effective part of managing health risks, the first priority is to stop people being exposed to the risk in the first place.

Manage risk, not lifestyle. The law requires steps to be taken to prevent or adequately control work-related health risks. Helping workers tackle lifestyle issues (such as smoking or diet) may be beneficial but is not a substitute for risk management.

Definitions of health and wellbeing can be subjective and are often subject to individual feelings and experiences. Health, in particular, is not merely an absence of disease and wellbeing can be a poorly defined term. Wellbeing is often linked to feelings of happiness, contentment, fulfilment and life satisfaction (it includes physical, material, social and emotional happiness, and development and activity dimensions).

On occasions the meanings of health and wellbeing can clash. For example, a person can do something that makes them happy, but it could be unhealthy for them (for example, smoking).

 Wellbeing **'is a state of being with others, where human needs are met, where one can act meaningfully to pursue one's goals, and where one enjoys a satisfactory quality of life'.**

1.6   Improving health and wellbeing on construction projects

The construction industry is aware that the overall health and wellbeing of employees plays a significant part in maintaining a healthy and safe working environment.

More and more organisations are becoming committed to supporting the health and wellbeing of employees through a range of initiatives that can offer advice, support and guidance on how to deal with a variety of health issues, both in and out of the workplace, enabling people to increase control over, and to improve, their health and wellbeing.

Various campaigns have been undertaken on many large construction projects. Clients, principal contractors and contractors have successfully implemented wellbeing initiatives, many based on national campaigns (such as smoking, cancer, drinking habits, exercise and mental health awareness), to increase people's understanding of health and wellbeing and promote the benefits of a healthy lifestyle.

Some examples of this are listed below.

- Employee assistance programmes, offering confidential advice, support, guidance and counselling to employees (and, in some cases, family members) on a range of issues, including smoking, alcohol, finances, domestic factors and mental health.

- Occupational health programmes, providing access to free health checks to workers (such as blood pressure and cholesterol checks).

- Provision of information, work-based campaigns and seminars.

- Getting people involved in the development of the promotion (this can be achieved through the use of consultation and involvement mechanisms).

- Policies encouraging staff to walk to work, in conjunction with public transport if required, and the provision of cycle racks and changing facilities to encourage cycling (this may also work to support the organisation's aspirations and policies for the environment).

- Promoting healthy food options if food is provided or made available at work.

- Encouraging exercise (such as a 'use the stairs' policy).

- Well persons' clinics, providing advice and health checks (such as screening for cancers), immunisation programmes (such as the flu jab) and smoking cessation clinics.

- Subsidised gym membership or discounted bicycle purchase schemes.

- Family events and team days.

Promoting good health and wellbeing in the workplace has a direct effect by reducing work-related ill health and sickness absence, which can have an immediate reduction in the cost of sick pay (paid for by the worker's employer or the state). The reduction in short- and long-term ill health will reduce the costs of benefits that have to be paid to offset the effects of ill health.

Employers will also have an interest in making sure any sickness absence is minimised. Presenteeism, and the thought that you must go to work even if you are not well, may also be an issue. These rates are often higher than sickness absence rates.

A systematic approach to the health and wellbeing of the workforce and to improving the working environment will help to increase workers' commitment and satisfaction. Morale will be enhanced by workers knowing they are working for a caring and supportive employer.

This will result in greater efficiency and effectiveness and will contribute to reduced absenteeism and staff turnover, resulting in an increase in productivity. A healthy workplace contributes to the success and long-term survival of the organisation and contributes to the overall wellbeing of society.

 Health and wellbeing practices on a major contractor's site

The following examples of health and wellbeing practices on a major contractor's site are part of their health risk management programme.

- Toolbox talks, linked to occupational health trends.

- Exercise equipment available for use by their workers on site, including fitness challenges.

- On-site health checks and clinics.

- Free fruit available for their workers.

- Regular health and wellbeing campaigns that can also be linked to current national campaigns.

- Exercise programmes for sedentary workers with targeted challenges (for example, providing activity trackers with a target of 10,000 steps per day).

- Programmes that promote the importance of good mental health, as it is just as important as physical health.

- Participation in HSE health campaigns to raise awareness.

- Engaging staff through awareness events and education programs, such as the Mates in Mind and national health awareness days and weeks.

01

1.7   Health surveillance

Health surveillance is a system of ongoing health checks that enables occupational ill health to be identified early and allows for intervention, to stop any condition from worsening.

In accordance with Regulation 6 of the Management of Health and Safety at Work Regulations 'every employer shall ensure that their employees are provided with such health surveillance as is appropriate, having regard to the risks to their health and safety which are identified by the assessment'.

Health surveillance will help to confirm whether control measures identified in the risk assessment are sufficient, and should be considered if there is a risk from noise, vibration, asbestos, lead, dust, fumes or other COSHH substances.

There is a requirement for health surveillance in the following circumstances.

● When there is an identifiable disease or adverse health effect and evidence of a link with workplace exposure.

● If it is likely that a disease or health effect may occur.

● Where there are valid techniques for detecting early signs of the disease or health effect.

● If these techniques do not pose a risk to employees (for example, the techniques are non-invasive).

Depending on the findings of the risk assessment health surveillance could involve employees checking themselves for signs or symptoms of ill health (for example, looking for signs of dermatitis if working with cement). Employees will need to be trained on what to look out for and who to report any symptoms to. A responsible person can be trained to perform basic checks but, for more complicated risks, it is advisable to seek the guidance of an occupational health nurse or doctor.

There are some hazardous substances (such as asbestos) and other agents where the law may require that the health surveillance programme includes **statutory medical surveillance**. This involves a medical examination. It can also involve tests by a doctor (who must have been appointed by the HSE), who has the appropriate training and experience.

 ## Benefits of health surveillance

● Encourages early detection of workplace hazards and helps protect workers.

● Enables the correct preventative and control measures to be put in place to prevent the effects of exposure from getting worse.

● Allows organisations to collect data on health risks and identify trends, and assists in budget forecasting.

● Allows organisations to check the effectiveness of their control measures and collect data of employees' exposure to the hazards identified.

Regulation	Example of situation when health surveillance could be required	Suggested approach
Control of Asbestos Regulations.	For workers involved in licensable work or notifiable non-licensed asbestos work.	Medical examination and health surveillance by an appointed doctor.
Control of Lead at Work Regulations.	For significant lead exposure or as advised by a doctor.	Medical examination by an appointed doctor and blood-lead testing. Blood-lead levels are usually checked every three months.
Control of Noise at Work Regulations.	For frequent exposure above the upper exposure action value or if a worker already has damage or suffers from hearing loss.	Questionnaire, regular hearing checks and medical examination by a doctor where hearing damage is identified.
Control of Substances Hazardous to Health Regulations.	When using a substance that is associated with a disease (such as dermatitis, asthma or cancer), if it is possible to detect the disease and reduce the risk of further harm, or if the conditions on site mean that the disease could appear.	Questionnaire and visual assessment for dermatitis or, where risks are significant, lung function tests for asthma. Assessment of lung function and occupational physician input to determine likely degree of risk.
Control of Vibration at Work Regulations.	Where a risk assessment indicates a health risk to the individual, if they are likely to be exposed to vibration at or above an exposure action value or if they have a diagnosed vibration health issue.	Questionnaire, followed by a health assessment, as required.
Working Time Regulations.	For night workers, as defined.	Confidential medical questionnaire, including a risk assessment, where necessary.

1.8 Employees returning from sickness absence

The **fit note** system requires general practitioners to categorise patients as *fit for work*, or *may be fit for work*.

The purpose of the system is to encourage communication between an employee who is categorised as *may be fit for work* and their doctor and employer, to establish what work the employee might be able to do if returning to work.

Fit notes are designed to encourage a controlled return to work, with compromises being made on both sides, as necessary, particularly after prolonged periods of sickness absence. Alternative working hours, adaptations to the workplace and alternative types of work are options available to the employer.

However, ultimately it is the employer's decision regarding what course of action to take in these circumstances. If poor decisions are made and the employee's health deteriorates as a consequence, the employer may be challenged to explain why they took the decisions they did.

 For further guidance for employers and line managers visit the Government website.

In order to decide what actions to take the employer may wish to take advice from an ergonomist, an occupational nurse and/or other health care professionals (for example, a physiotherapist, occupational therapist, occupational psychologist or counsellor). A brief description of the role of these professionals is given below.

Ergonomists apply anatomy, physiology and psychology to the design, systems and the environment for human use.

Occupational health nurses are registered nurses and, depending on their level of experience, they can develop protocol and procedures, carry out statutory health surveillance (including skin inspections) and provide training and advice.

Occupational therapists work with individuals, families, companies and groups to facilitate health and wellbeing through engagement or re-engagement in employment.

Occupational psychologists provide advice and guidance on mental health problems (such as depression and stress).

Counsellors provide a confidential counselling service to employees.

1.9 Typical examples of work-related ill health

Many employees leave the industry because of ill health. Often a person's illness is not traced back to the construction industry, so the actual incidence of ill health caused by work in the industry is probably higher than the official figures tell us. The following are some typical issues and further information can be found in the relevant chapters, as indicated.

- Stress *(refer to Chapter B03 Stress and mental health at work)*.
- Skin cancers *(refer to Chapter B06 Personal protective equipment)*.
- Dermatitis *(refer to Chapter B07 Control of substances hazardous to health)*.
- Respiratory diseases *(refer to Chapter B10 Dust and fumes (Respiratory hazards))*.
- Noise-induced hearing loss/deafness *(refer to Chapter B11 Noise)*.
- Vibration white finger/hand-arm vibration syndrome (HAVS) *(refer to Chapter B12 Vibration)*.
- Spine, back and upper and lower limb disorders *(refer to Chapter B13 Manual handling)*.

A brief summary of other health risks is given below.

1.9.1 Fatigue

Fatigue can be a serious health and safety risk, especially on construction projects as workers can be required to work longer hours than in other industries. Getting a good night's sleep can help reduce the chance of human error, mistakes and accidents.

1.9.2 Bird and bat droppings (guano)

The presence of large populations of roosting birds, particularly pigeons, or a bat colony, can present significant risks to health if their droppings are disturbed. This has obvious implications for some types of construction work and preliminary work such as surveys.

The main hazard is the inhalation of dust or water droplets, containing contaminated bird droppings, that become airborne as a result of disturbance. Exposure can result in **psittacosis** (symptoms include a flu-like illness and pneumonia appearing 5 to 19 days after exposure) and **salmonella** (which can cause diarrhoea).

Skin contact with pigeon droppings has been known to cause an acne-like skin condition and ulcers.

The HSE has taken enforcement action against companies who fail to undertake an adequate risk assessment and to protect employees against the associated risks of working with bird droppings.

1.9.3 Leptospirosis (Weil's disease)

When working near to water or on sites that are otherwise wet, consideration must be given to the health implications associated with the presence of rats.

Leptospirosis is an occupational hazard for anyone working near water, damp areas or anywhere else where rats might be present. It is a disease caused by bacteria that are present mainly in the urine of infected rats and are therefore also in the water where they live. The bacteria thrive in damp conditions of riverbanks or streams, and can enter the body through unprotected cuts and scratches, by swallowing infected water and through the lining of the nose.

If anyone thinks they may have come into contact with the disease, they should be aware that the early symptoms closely resemble the symptoms of influenza, namely fever, headache and chill.

Later symptoms include the following.

- Tightening of the skin.
- Internal bleeding.
- A yellowing of the skin (similar to jaundice).

It is essential that anyone who is at risk and becomes unwell with flu-like symptoms should visit their doctor, describe where they have been working and say that they are at risk from leptospirosis. Persons regularly at risk (for example, canal or sewage workers) should carry a card explaining their occupation and the occupational hazard of leptospirosis.

The following personal precautions should be taken.

- Discourage the presence of rats on site (do not leave food lying around and do not throw away food scraps).
- Do not handle the carcasses of dead rats.
- Avoid inadvertent entry or immersion in water that could be infected. If you do come into contact with such water and you think that you may be infected, particularly if you swallowed any water, see a doctor as a matter of urgency.
- Wear appropriate PPE.
- Prior to entering the work area, wash any cuts or grazes with soap and clean running water, then cover all cuts and broken skin with suitable waterproof dressings before and during work and wear PPE as necessary.
- Upon completion of work, wash hands, forearms and all other exposed areas of skin thoroughly, and remove any wet protective clothing as soon as possible to dry it.
- Avoid rubbing your nose, mouth or eyes with your hands during work.
- Do not smoke, eat or drink without first washing your hands.

Leptospirosis can be fatal, typically within four to six weeks, if the early symptoms are not recognised and treated.

Another form of leptospirosis can be transmitted to humans from the urine of infected dairy cattle (the *Hardjo* form of leptospirosis). Anyone involved in construction work on dairy farms must be made aware of this hazard.

Further advice on leptospirosis can be obtained from the Employment Medical Advisory Service of the HSE or by contacting any local office of the HSE.

 For further information refer to Chapter B02 Welfare facilities.

1.9.4 Needlestick injuries

A needlestick injury is an accidental puncture of the skin by a hypodermic needle.

It is a sad fact that the drug culture affects the construction industry as much as other industrial sectors. The abuse of both legal and illegal drugs brings with it the risk of discovering discarded hypodermic syringes or discarded needles.

Employees in the refurbishment sector of the industry are probably at greatest risk, especially if the property is derelict or has been occupied by squatters. However, any work in occupied or previously occupied premises carries with it some risk of finding needles that have been randomly discarded or hidden away in areas where they are difficult to see, until it is too late.

If not handled in a safe manner, discarded needles can pose serious health risks to anyone whose skin is accidentally pricked. Blood on a needle could be infected with a blood borne virus (for example, hepatitis B or C or HIV).

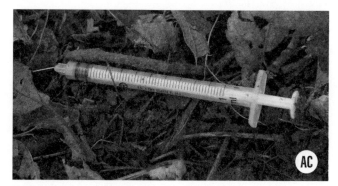

Treat discarded needles with care

Company and site procedures should ensure that the risk of needlestick injury is addressed in a risk assessment and any workers who might be at risk are identified.

Site inductions should cover the actions that employees and supervisors should take whenever discarded needles are found. In the appropriate circumstances, employees should be told to assume that any needle they find has been used by a drug user and is potentially contaminated by infected blood. The removal from site and safe disposal of such items should be properly covered. Advice may be sought from the site nurse (if there is one) or the Local Authority Environmental Health department.

Where a risk of needlestick injury is identified, training should be provided to nominated workers on how to deal with needles that have been found or reported. Training should cover the use of suitable PPE (for example, anti-sharps gloves or gauntlets, and plastic tongs or grabbers for safely picking up sharps), safe disposal of sharps using sharps bins, first-aid requirements (including access to warm water), post-exposure arrangements and incident reporting.

Generally, employees should be clearly told not to touch or move any needles or hypodermic syringes they find, but to ask a responsible person to guard it whilst reporting the matter to their supervisor.

If a needle or syringe **must** be moved then some examples of suitable instructions to employees are shown below.

- If possible, bring the sharps bin to the sharp. **Always** avoid carrying sharps to the bin.

- Suitable PPE (such as sharps gloves and suitable plastic tongs or grabbers) should be used. (Pliers or similar tools with steel jaws should be avoided.)

- Do **not** wrap it in paper or put it into a household waste bin.

- If available, place it in a sharps bin, or otherwise a clear glass bottle or jar.

- Store the sharps bin, bottle or jar in a secure location.

- Carefully follow site or company procedures regarding disposal.

- Wash hands thoroughly.

Employees should not panic if a needle punctures their skin. Encourage the wound to bleed, but **do not suck the wound**. Wash the site of the injury thoroughly with soap and water at the first opportunity and obtain medical assistance as soon as possible, from either a trained first aider, the site nurse or the nearest hospital with an Accident and Emergency department. If it is safe to do so, take the syringe or needle with you. Inform the employer so it can be recorded in the accident book and the correct action can be taken to prevent recurrence.

If dealt with properly and promptly, the risks of a resulting health problem are small.

 Needles and sharps are often hidden out of sight by the person who discarded them. Be careful: do not put your hands anywhere you cannot see into.

1.9.5 Sepsis

Sepsis is a life threatening reaction to an infection. It happens when the body's response to an infection spirals rapidly out of control, injuring its own tissues and organs. Instead of attacking just the infection, the immune system starts to attack the whole body, injuring tissues and organs. Sepsis can become very serious very quickly and therefore it needs to be treated urgently.

People should always seek medical help if they suspect sepsis as getting treatment quickly can improve outcomes and the chances of survival. Sepsis is indiscriminate – it can affect anyone regardless of age, sex or their state of health.

Five people in the UK die every hour from sepsis. It accounts for around 50,000 deaths each year. Sepsis is a bigger killer than breast, bowel and prostate cancer put together.

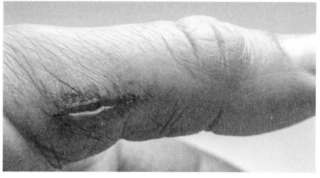
Wound providing a portal for infection

It is so important to raise awareness within the construction workforce. Everyone needs to know the signs and symptoms to look out for. The five key symptoms to look out for in adults are:

very high or low temperature

uncontrolled shivering

confusion

passing less urine than normal

blotchy or cold arms or legs

If anyone has a combination of these symptoms and they are getting noticeably worse, medical attention **must** be sought **urgently**.

The treatment of sepsis is time critical. It needs to be treated with antibiotics, oxygen and fluids in a hospital.

Due to the nature of the construction working environment, workers in the construction industry may be at higher risk from wounds or injuries. Any type of wound – a graze, cut, gash, burn or even a prick on the finger - provides a portal on the skin for entry to infection.

Most cases of infected wounds are caused by bacteria, originating either from the skin, other parts of the body or the outside environment.

It is important that a wound is washed with normal soap and water for at least 20 seconds as soon as possible after the injury as part of first aid treatment. This may temporarily cause an increase in minor bleeding which should be treated with five to 10 minutes of continuous mild-moderate pressure.

Once the bleeding has stopped, dry and cover the wound. If it is a more serious wound or any foreign material like wood, metal, or glass is retained in the tissue, seek medical advice.

A wound which has become, or is becoming, infected may:

- become more painful, instead of gradually improving.
- look red around the skin edges.
- feel warm or hot (around the red area).
- ooze a yellow material (pus).

There is no definitive timescale for when sepsis may develop following an infection, so the monitoring of any wound or injury is essential and should be done for up to a few weeks; and if there are any signs or symptoms of sepsis, it will require urgent medical attention.

Infection may result from an injury or wound at work, but it is important to know that any type of infection; bacterial, viral, or fungal, can lead to sepsis. When infection is present, the most common reaction is that the body's immune system will fight the infection in a localised way.

However, in some cases, the body's immune system will overcompensate, attacking not just the infection but everything else around it. **This is sepsis - the body's extreme response to an infection**.

It is not fully understood why this reaction happens in some people, but the GenOMICC research study undertaken by the University of Edinburgh, funded by UK charity Sepsis Research FEAT, is looking at the genetic factors that influence susceptibility to sepsis.

The aim is to identify key genes associated with severely ill sepsis patients, and use this information to develop new and more effective treatments. Other common conditions that can lead to sepsis are pneumonia, gall bladder infections, urinary tract infections or infections post-surgery.

Recognising the key symptoms and knowing what to do can make the difference between life and death. Medical attention should be sought immediately, and 'trusting your instincts' must be acted upon.

Sepsis awareness in the construction industry should be encouraged via relevant communication methods such as toolbox talks, awareness sessions, and as part of the occupational health strategy.

Everyone in the industry has a part to play to raise awareness of sepsis as not enough people know what sepsis is and what to look out for.

For general information and support regarding sepsis, and to continually improve awareness in your workplace, visit the Sepsis Research FEAT website.

1.9.6   Contaminated ground

As the drive to develop brownfield sites continues, the magnitude of the health hazard arising from the disturbance of contaminated ground is almost certain to increase.

The disturbance of contaminated ground can release hazardous fibres (such as asbestos), hazardous gases or fumes and even hazardous micro-organisms (such as anthrax spores).

Where ground that has been previously used is to be disturbed, a risk assessment must be carried out to determine whether there will be any risk to health.

The findings of a thorough assessment of the risks will determine exactly what the hazards are and how the risks can be eliminated or controlled to an acceptable level.

Given the wide range of possible contaminants, the potential for ill health may result from inhalation, ingestion or skin contact with the hazardous substance.

For further information refer to Chapter E09 Soil management and contamination control.

1.10 Occupational health support services

1.10.1 Employment Medical Advisory Service

The Employment Medical Advisory Service (EMAS) is an integral part of the HSE that is staffed by specialist occupational health professionals (both doctors and nurses). In many ways, the functions of EMAS are similar to those of the HSE. EMAS exists to offer advice to employers and employees and take enforcement action where necessary on workplace health issues. EMAS doctors are medical inspectors and EMAS nurses are occupational health inspectors. Both have the same powers as other HSE inspectors under the Health and Safety at Work etc. Act 1974, where the HSE is the enforcing authority. The functions of EMAS staff are shown below.

- Investigate complaints and concerns of ill health from employers, employees, trade unions, the public and health care professionals.
- Investigate ill health reports received from employers under RIDDOR.
- Help other HSE inspectors and Local Authorities to make sure that other people comply with health and safety law.
- Provide advice in the workplace to employers, employees and trade unions.
- Provide expert advice to doctors and nurses in general health care and occupational health.
- Provide support for the HSE's occupational health campaigns.

 EMAS staff are based in some but not all HSE offices. Check the HSE website for your local contact.

1.10.2 Scottish Centre for Healthy Working Lives

The Healthy Working Lives website offers employers and workers free confidential advice to help improve health and safety and the wellbeing of everyone at work. They offer free events throughout Scotland.

 Full details are available on the Healthy Working Lives website.

1.10.3 British Occupational Hygiene Society

The British Occupational Hygiene Society (BOHS) is one of the biggest hygiene societies in Europe and is the only professional society representing qualified occupational hygienists in the UK.

Occupational hygienists use science and engineering to prevent ill health caused by the work environment. They specialise in the assessment and control of risks to health from workplace exposure to hazards.

Hygienists help employers and employees to understand these risks and to minimise or eliminate them. Occupational hygienists can come from many backgrounds (for example, chemists, engineers, biologists, physicists, doctors, nurses and others who have chosen to apply their skills to improving working practices and conditions).

There are several publications on the BOHS website, including technical publications, position papers and newsletters. It has also

Breathe freely campaign

launched a construction-related *Breathe freely* campaign, which has a useful resource section, listing construction-related occupations and the common health risks they face.

 For further information visit the BOHS website.

1.10.4 The Strategic Forum Plant Safety Group

A good practice guide is available from the The Strategic Forum Plant Safety Group (SFPSG). The SFPSG worked in conjunction with the HSE, CBH, Build UK, occupational health providers and others in industry to draw up guidance aimed specifically at the management of medical fitness issues for persons operating plant. The guide provides clarity about the medical fitness assessment process and outlines the steps that should be taken by employers to ensure plant operators have the appropriate level of fitness.

 For further information visit the SFPSG website.

01

1.10.5 Construction Industry Advisory Committee

The Construction Industry Advisory Committee (CONIAC) advises the HSE and relevant stakeholders of emerging health and safety developments and risks in the construction industry, and sets a direction and plan for their promotion and mitigation. Its membership provides representation from key industry stakeholders, including SMEs. CONIAC's core aim is to stimulate action aimed at securing better health and safety outcomes in the construction industry.

CONIAC was set up alongside the introduction of the Health and Safety at Work etc. Act 1974 with a raft of other industry advisory committees. It is one of the remaining three cross-industry health and safety organisations. It has gone through a series of reconstitutions, and is currently organised into four working groups and a steering group.

1. Managing risk well (working group).

2. Tackling ill health (working group).

3. Keeping pace with change (working group).

4. Supporting small employers (working group).

The chairs of the groups, along with TU representatives, meet three times a year as the Acting Together Steering Group, which sets out the CONIAC work plan. The Construction Industry Advisory Network (CONIAN) provides a platform for the industry to provide information to CONIAC, and to promote information produced by HSE. Within this structure, the construction industry can promote engagement with workers to change behaviours.

 For further information visit the CONIAC website.

CONTENTS

Welfare facilities

02

Supporting
INFORMATION

GT700 Toolbox talks / supporting checklists and forms

Toolbox talks on some of these topics are available in the GT700 publication. Supporting checklists and forms covering some of these topics are available on our companion website.

Overview

The availability of welfare facilities, their location on site and how they will be maintained must be considered at the planning and preparation stages of every construction project, before any construction work (including demolition) starts.

This chapter describes the minimum welfare facilities that should be provided or made available on all types of construction project to comply with an employer's fundamental and basic legal duties as laid down in Section 2 of the Health and Safety at Work etc. Act 1974 (HSWA), and further elaborated on in Schedule 2 of the Construction (Design and Management) Regulations 2015 (CDM).

2.1   Introduction

Welfare facilities 'set the tone' of a construction project. In line with CDM, welfare starts with the client duty holder – they are responsible as they have an 'absolute duty' to ensure they have made suitable arrangements for managing a project, and these arrangements include the provision of facilities in respect of anyone carrying out construction work.

However, it should be deemed as a 'shared duty' from client all the way to end-user. Welfare facilitates are a basic requirement and an important control measure against illness. Good welfare facilities are expected throughout construction sites, regardless of their nature or size.

Construction site workers need good toilet and washing facilities, a place to warm up and eat their food and somewhere to store clothing. These basic requirements must be in place, and should not be neglected. Good facilities can have a positive benefit on health and wellbeing and can help prevent a number of occupational diseases and illnesses (such as dermatitis).

The principal contractor must ensure that suitable and sufficient welfare facilities are provided and maintained throughout the construction phase, which must take into account any changes in the nature of the work that could, in turn, change the welfare facilities that are required. What is suitable and sufficient will depend on the size and nature of the workforce involved in the project.

Contractors are required to provide welfare facilities that meet the minimum requirements. This duty only extends to the provision of welfare facilities for the contractor's own employees who are working on a construction site, or anyone else working under their control. The client must also ensure that workers are provided with suitable welfare facilities for the duration of the construction work. Facilities must be made available before any construction work starts and should be maintained until the end of the project.

 Details of the minimum welfare facilities required on all construction sites can be found within Schedule 2 of CDM. A summary has been provided at Appendix A. Also, refer to the Health and Safety Executive's (HSE's) updated Operational Guidance (OG) Construction – Welfare (2022). This guidance should be followed as a stepping stone towards welfare standards expected on sites, and is available via the HSE website.

2.2   Important points

- Suitable and sufficient sanitary conveniences (toilets) and washing facilities (including showers if required) must be provided or made available at readily accessible places.

- An adequate supply of drinking water, clearly marked with the appropriate sign, should be provided or made available at readily accessible, suitable places.

- Suitable facilities must be provided for the accommodation of clothing not worn at work and for clothing worn at work but not taken home. Such facilities shall include provisions for drying wet clothing.

- Facilities must be provided to enable people to change clothing where a person has to wear special clothing for special work and cannot change elsewhere. The facilities shall be separate for men and women, where necessary, for reasons of privacy.

- Suitable and sufficient facilities for rest (such as a site canteen) must be made available at readily accessible places, including:
  - sufficient tables and chairs (with backs)
  - suitable arrangements to protect non-smokers from discomfort caused by tobacco smoke
  - where necessary, suitable facilities for pregnant women and nursing mothers
  - a means for boiling water and suitable arrangements to ensure that meals can be prepared, heated up and eaten.

2.3   Smoking

Smoking is prohibited in nearly all enclosed workplaces and public spaces in England (such as site cabins, canteens and company premises). Similar prohibitions apply in Wales, Scotland and Northern Ireland.

Although smoking is totally prohibited on many sites employers, or the person in control of the site, may make provision for smoking in areas that are not enclosed or substantially enclosed, as long as non-smokers are not exposed to tobacco smoke.

Broadly, the differing legislation has similar aims, as follows.

Sites may make provision for smoking in designated areas

● The act of smoking in smoke-free premises is an offence.

● The act of **permitting** smoking in smoke-free premises (or a smoke-free vehicle) is an offence.

● Work vehicles that are used by more than one person must be smoke free.

● Smoke-free premises must have an official 'No smoking' sign, with the approved text prominently displayed at each entrance. In Wales these must be displayed in both Welsh and English.

● Smoke-free vehicles must have at least one official 'No smoking' sign prominently displayed.

Businesses can be fined up to £2,500 if they do not stop people smoking in the workplace.

In Scotland, this is a fixed penalty fine of £200 that can increase to £2,500 if the fine is not paid.

2.3.1   Vaping

Currently, there are no legal restrictions on vaping (or the use of e-cigarettes) in public areas, but there are local laws in force that prohibit vaping.

Many public places and establishments have applied customised rules, and the same will apply to most construction sites.

Companies and site managers should inform and indicate to workers where vaping is permitted or prohibited, and communicate the company policy clearly to everyone.

Where appropriate, this could will also include additional signage.

Employers should encourage and support workers who are trying to give up smoking and using alternatives such as vapes or e-cigarettes.

Using a vape or e-cigarette

2.4   Welfare facilities overview

Welfare facilities should be kept clean, adequately lit, ventilated as necessary and kept in a good state of repair.

Washing facilities must include the following.

● A supply of hot (or warm) and cold water, ideally from a running supply.

● Soap or other cleansers.

● Disposable (or roller) towels or another means of drying.

● Separate facilities for men and women except where they:

  – are in a separate room that can be locked from the inside

  – can only be used by one person at a time

  – are only used for washing the hands, forearms and face.

The provision of toilets must include separate facilities for men and women, except where each toilet is in a separate room that can be locked from the inside.

Details of the welfare facilities should be provided during the site induction.

These details could include the following.

- The location and details of the welfare facilities provided on site.
- If appropriate, the opening hours of site canteens.
- Responsibilities for the cleaning and maintenance of the facilities.
- The provision of barrier creams and rehydrating lotions.
- The need for good personal hygiene.
- The company policy regarding damage and graffiti.
- The arrangements (if any) made for smokers.

Separate facilities provided for men and women

Contractors, including principal contractors, must make sure that a suitable site induction, covering welfare arrangements, is provided.

2.5 Welfare facilities at fixed construction sites

The principal contractor (where appointed) or the contractor will need to provide welfare facilities for everyone.

If work is carried out in occupied premises (for example, offices, factories, and so on), it may be possible to make written arrangements with the client to use the permanent facilities at the premises.

2.5.1 Planning

- Make sure welfare arrangements are detailed in the construction phase plan.
- Consider welfare facilities, their location on site and regular maintenance during the planning and preparation stage of any project in accordance with CDM.
- Arrange for equipment to be available, provided, sited and connected to services before construction work (including demolition) starts or when additional numbers of workers start on site.
- Make sure the facilities reflect the site size, nature of the work, and numbers of people who will use them. If a large number of people are working on site or the work being carried out is particularly dirty or involves a health risk (for example, pouring concrete), you will need more washing facilities, which may include showers, toilets, and so on.

2.5.2 Toilets

- Make sure that an adequate number of toilets are provided at all times.
- Calculations for the number of persons using sanitary conveniences should reflect normal peak usage, and prevent any undue queuing. The following ratio of WCs to workers provides a good rule of thumb:

Provision for mixed workplaces		Alternative ratio for men only use		
Number of people at work	Number of cubicles	Number of people at work	Number of cubicles	Number of urinals
1 to 5	1	1 to 15	1	1
6 to 25	2	16 to 30	2	1
26 to 50	3	31 to 45	2	2
51 to 75	4	46 to 60	3	2
76 to 100	5	61 to 75	3	3
		76 to 90	4	3
		91 to 100	4	4

- Ensure that toilets are readily available. Workers should not have a significant wait when they need to use a toilet, as this can lead to distress or intensify health issues. As a 'benchmark', workers should only have to walk 150 m to a toilet regardless of their site location. On larger sites, satellite conveniences should be provided in more remote parts that are away from central compounds.
- For very remote sites or sites covering a large geographical area (such as roadworks) it may not be possible for workers to access a convenience without the use of transport. Transport should always be available, and the journey time should be aligned to the time taken to walk 150 m.
- Men and women may use the same toilet, provided it is in a lockable room and partitioned from any urinals that may also have been provided; otherwise separate toilets will be required.

- Wherever possible, connect toilets to a mains drainage system and ensure they are water flushing. If you cannot do this, use facilities with built in supply and drainage tanks.

- Only use chemical toilets as a short-term measure. When they are used, it is important that they are of robust construction, regularly emptied and maintained. Access will need to be provided and kept for emptying and maintaining chemical toilets. Suppliers of portable facilities will be able to advise you.

- Make sure that an adequate supply of toilet paper is always available.

- Consideration must be given to female workers, and sanitary waste disposal must be in place.

- Facilities should be suitably ventilated so that offensive odours do not linger. Measures should also be taken to prevent odours entering other rooms. Ventilation may be natural, e.g. windows with openings to the outside, or mechanical.

- Facilities should be well lit, ideally by natural light during daylight hours, and non day light ours by the use of electric

No matter how basic or extensive the welfare facilities, they must be properly maintained, cleaned, well-ventilated and lit

lighting to a minimum of 100 lux (200 lux for accessible toilets). Low energy lighting should be considered, but systems that respond to movement should be used with caution to ensure people are not left in the dark.

- Facilities must be kept clean and orderly and the frequency and thoroughness of cleaning should be adequate to ensure these standards.

2.5.3 Drinking water

- Ensure that an adequate supply of wholesome drinking water is provided or made available at readily accessible and suitable places. The NHS recommends individuals should drink about 1.2 litres when working in a moderate climate doing normal physical activity. In hot weather and when doing strenuous activity, this amount will need to be appropriately increased.

- Whenever possible, it should be supplied direct from the existing mains supply. If water cannot be supplied direct from the mains, then a temporary water supply should be appropriately planned and managed in accordance with BS 8551:2015: *Provision and management of temporary water supplies and distribution networks*.

- Preferably, a temporary distribution network from a public or private treated water supply would be used. If this cannot be achieved, water should only then be supplied or stored in an appropriate vessel as outlined in BS 8551:2015.

Drinking water must be supplied

- Clearly mark the drinking water supply to prevent it being confused with water that is not fit to drink or with hazardous liquids.

- Provide cups or other drinking vessels at the water tap, unless it is supplied in an upward jet that can be drunk easily (such as a drinking fountain).

- All drinking water taps/containers should not be installed or stored in locations where contamination is likely, including close to WCs.

- If a drinking fountain is required, it should be installed within the toilet facilities, but should be as far away from the WCs, urinals and other sources of contamination as possible.

- Sealed bottled drinking water should be provided as a supplementary source when required (e.g. when undertaking strenuous work). It should be stored in a cool, dark place out of direct sunlight, and away from strong odours and volatile materials that can permeate.

- While workers are able to bring drinking containers for their own personal use, this is in addition to any drinking water provided, and is not a substitute for it.

2.5.4 Washing facilities

- Washing facilities should be situated next to both toilets and changing areas. Make sure they include:
  - basin(s) or sink(s) large enough for people to wash their face, hands and forearms
  - a supply of hot (or warm) and cold running water
  - soap and towels (either cloth or paper) or dryers.

- If mains water is not available, use clean water supplied from a tank.

Washing facilities

- You may need more washing facilities, including showers, where the work is particularly dirty or when workers are exposed to especially hazardous substances (such as development of contaminated land, or demolition of old industrial buildings that are contaminated with toxic substances). These will need to be separate from the main facilities.

- Men and women can share basins used for washing their hands, face and arms.

- A shower may be used by both men and women as long as it is in a separate, lockable room that can only be used by one person at a time.

2.5.5 Storing and changing clothing

- Every site should have arrangements for storing:
  - clothing not worn on site (such as own clothing not worn during site hours)
  - protective clothing needed for site work that is not taken home (such as wellington boots, overalls and reflective jackets)
  - personal effects.

- Separate lockers might be needed. On smaller sites the site office may be a suitable storage area, provided it is kept secure.

- Where there is a risk of protective site clothing contaminating everyday clothing, store items separately.

- Men and women should be able to change separately.

- Make sure that wet site clothing can be dried.

Changing area with heating, seating and separate personal lockers

- Many fires have been caused by placing clothing to dry on electrical heaters, making the heater overheat. If electrical heaters are used, ensure they are properly ventilated and, if possible, fitted with a high temperature cut-out device.

- Changing rooms must have seating and the facility to allow workers to dry any PPE, personal clothing and effects.

2.5.6 Rest facilities

- Provide facilities for taking rest breaks and meal breaks. The facilities should provide shelter from the wind and rain, be heated as necessary and contain:
  - tables and chairs (with backs)
  - a kettle or urn for boiling water
  - a means for warming up food (for example, a microwave oven)
  - a means of keeping perishable food chilled (for example, a fridge), if appropriate.

- On small sites, the site office or hut can make a suitable rest area, especially if it is one of the common portable units.

- Do not store plant, equipment or materials in rest areas.

Site canteen area for taking breaks

2.5.7 Heating

Rest facilities will normally require heating. Using properly maintained electrical equipment can eliminate the risks associated with liquefied petroleum gas (LPG) heaters. Inadequately ventilated LPG cookers and heaters can produce carbon monoxide, with potentially fatal results. Flammable gas may escape from leaking cylinders that have not been properly turned off. If LPG is used take the following actions to reduce the risks.

- Use and store the cylinders in safe, well-ventilated places outside the accommodation (including overnight) or in purpose-built ventilated storage areas.

- Ensure that the appliances have been properly installed by a suitably qualified person. They are then checked and maintained regularly, with inspection records kept up to date.

- Provide adequate combustion ventilation (fixed grilles at high and low level).

- Check that the ventilation provided is not blocked (for example, fixed grilles blocked by newspaper or rags in cold weather to stop draughts).

- Check that cylinders are properly turned off when not in use.

- Use wall- or ceiling-mounted carbon monoxide detectors.

2.5.8 First-aid rooms

On a large building or construction site, a first-aid room, suitably staffed and equipped, should be provided. The need for such a room cannot be decided purely on the number of people employed, but should be assessed on the type of work being carried out and whether a hospital or other emergency facilities are close to hand.

The first-aid room will normally be under the control of the first aider who should be nearby or on call, with access to the room when employees are at work. The name of this person should be displayed, together with the names and locations of all other first aiders and appointed persons. On some larger sites, the first-aid room could be staffed by a qualified nurse.

The room should be clearly identified, available at all times and used only for rendering first aid. It should be large enough to hold an examination/medical couch, with enough space at each side to allow people to work, and have an access door to allow the passage of a stretcher or other carrying equipment. Pillows and blankets should be provided and be frequently cleaned.

The room itself should be cleaned each working day, have smooth-topped, impermeable working surfaces and provision for privacy and refuse disposal.

Heating, lighting and ventilation should be effective. In addition to the first-aid materials that should be stored in a suitable cabinet, the following items may also be provided.

- A sink with running hot and cold water.
- Drinking water and disposable cups.
- Soap, nail brush and paper towels.
- A store for first-aid equipment.
- A foot-operated bin or a suitable container for disposal of clinical waste (yellow bags).
- A chair.

In first-aid rooms that are supervised by the site nurse, other items may be provided on their advice. The room should have a telephone, where possible, and a siren or klaxon to alert personnel on call.

If the first-aid room cannot be reserved exclusively for first aid, employers need to make sure that the first-aid facilities can be quickly made available, if necessary. Consideration should be given as to whether:

- the furnishings and equipment can be moved easily and quickly
- activities carried out in the room can be stopped immediately
- there is a storage room for first-aid equipment.

 For further information on first-aid requirements refer to Chapter B05 First aid.

2.6 Welfare facilities at transient construction sites

A transient construction site is either where short-duration work (up to a week) is carried out at one or many locations, or is of a longer duration carried out while moving over a continuous geographical area (such as major roadworks, cable laying-contracts, and so on).

In such cases, it may be appropriate to make arrangements to use facilities provided by the owner of existing premises in which the work is being done, local public facilities or the facilities of local businesses. For mobile workers, these can be provided at a central location accessible within a reasonable distance and time.

Clear agreement should be made, preferably in writing, with the provider of the facilities; it should not be assumed that local commercial premises can be used without their agreement. Facilities must be readily accessible at the worksite, open at all relevant times, be at no cost to the workers, be of an acceptable standard in terms of cleanliness and have hand-washing facilities.

Workers need to be made aware of the arrangements to use them and be informed of their location.

When planning welfare provision, consider the following.

- The nature of the work to be carried out and the health risks associated with it. For example, consider the provision of showers if the project involves hazardous substances or dirty work (such as sewer maintenance, dusty demolition work, work with contaminated land or pouring concrete).

- The distance workers will have to travel to the welfare facilities.

- The duration of the work and number of different locations.

- The number of people who will use them.

- The cleaning and maintenance of the welfare facilities.

- Whether they need to be relocated during construction.

Toilet and welfare facilities need to be provided for transient sites

WELFARE FACILITIES

You need to plan how welfare units will be moved from delivery vehicles into position. It is preferable to mechanically move these units; if manual handling cannot be avoided then you should manage the risk effectively. Your plans should cover safe lifting practices and ensure proper protection of workers from falls from vehicles or portable units. You should locate welfare units and manage traffic effectively to ensure adequate segregation of pedestrians and vehicles.

 For further information on provision of welfare facilities at both fixed and transient construction sites visit the HSE website.

2.6.1 Use of private and public facilities

Where the construction activity is a long way from central facilities, use of facilities in private premises (such as in cafes) is not considered suitable as permanent alternative arrangements. The use of private facilities may be acceptable in limited circumstances (for example, where there is no alternative and the work is of no more than a week's duration). Permission, preferably in writing, should be obtained from the proprietor in advance of the work starting.

Use of public toilets is acceptable only where it is impractical to return to facilities provided at the main base or to use a portable installation at the worksite.

2.6.2 Toilets

So far as is reasonably practicable, you need to provide flushing toilets and running water, connected to mains water and drainage systems. If this is not possible, facilities with a built-in water supply and drainage tanks should be used.

Portable chemical toilets are acceptable only if it is not reasonably practicable to make other adequate provision.

Portable toilets have a limited capacity and will need emptying. The number of portable toilets needed depends on the number of people and the frequency of emptying.

2.6.3 Drinking water

There is no differential to the requirements for a fixed construction site. *(Refer to 2.5.3 Drinking water.)*

Toilet facility at a transient site

2.6.4 Washing facilities

There is no differential to the requirements for a fixed construction site. *(Refer to 2.5.4 Washing facilities.)*

2.6.5 Heating

There is no differential to the requirements for a fixed construction site. *(Refer to 2.5.7 Heating.)*

2.7 Food safety legislation

Food safety legislation only applies in circumstances where food is prepared, or handled, to be eaten by others. Getting food hygiene wrong can have severe implications for other people.

- Food hygiene is usually monitored by Local Authority environmental health officers (EHOs), who:
  - have similar rights of entry to site as HSE inspectors
  - can issue hygiene improvement and hygiene emergency prohibition notices and instigate prosecutions
  - can close down unsatisfactory catering facilities.

- Anyone who handles food for consumption by others:
  - must have training in basic food-handling techniques
  - must report to their supervisor details of any illness that they may be suffering from
  - may have to be suspended from work if they contract an infectious illness.

- Premises in which food is handled, prepared and served must conform to certain standards of construction and cleanliness.

- Food poisoning is caused by bacteria (germs or bugs) that have lain dormant in most uncooked or unprepared foods, whether meat, fish, poultry or some vegetables. It keeps people off work through sickness, just as accidents do.

- Complying with food safety legislation and applying appropriate hygiene standards on site are essential because of the potential for:
  - time lost through sickness absence
  - lost production
  - enforcement action (such as hygiene improvement notices, hygiene emergency prohibition notices and even prosecution by Local Authorities) when your food handling does not come up to the required standard.

2.7.1 Food Safety Act

 Food Safety Act

Food – food or drink of any description, or any of the ingredients used in the preparation of food.

Food room – any room in which a person is involved in the handling of food, including a servery or counter.

The Food Safety Act provides the framework for all food legislation in Great Britain. Similar legislation applies in Northern Ireland.

The Food Safety Act and regulations apply to all workplaces. This includes building or construction sites where food or drink is supplied, provided or sold by you or anyone else for the benefit of employees and others working on site.

Your main responsibilities under the Act are to ensure the following.

- The duty holder does not include anything in food, remove anything from food or treat food in any way that means it would be damaging to the health of the people eating it.

- The food served or sold is of the nature, substance or quality that consumers would expect.

- Food is labelled, advertised and presented in a way that is not false or misleading.

The following requirements must be met in order to comply with the legislation.

- Toilets adjacent to food rooms must be separated by a lobby. A notice stating 'Now wash your hands' must be displayed.

- Employees in food rooms must not smoke. A notice must be displayed to that effect.

- Checks and inspections of equipment and staff training should be recorded.

- Certificates of staff training in food hygiene and handling must be displayed.

- A building or construction site that has a canteen or mess room where food is stored, sold, supplied or provided (whether for profit or not) is classified as a **business** and the rooms are classified as **premises** for the purposes of the Act.

- All food businesses that prepare, cook or sell food for the benefit of others must be registered with the Local Authority. This involves completing the appropriate form available from the Environmental Health department of that authority. (Registration is only applicable if food is handled on five days in five consecutive weeks. If in doubt, contact the Local Authority.) There should be no charge for registration.

2.7.2 Food Safety and Hygiene (England) Regulations

The regulations do not apply to sites where employees only consume their own food and drink. Nevertheless, in accordance with the Health and Safety at Work etc. Act and CDM, these areas must be kept in good order and in a reasonable state of cleanliness.

Food safety legislation is enforced by the Environmental Health department of the Local Authority, and any doubt regarding the application of the regulations should be referred to the EHO. Food inspectors, usually EHOs, may visit the site, with or without prior notice, on either a one-off or regular basis. Every facility and assistance must be afforded to the inspecting officers. Obstruction in any form is an offence.

The Food Safety and Hygiene Regulations set out basic hygiene principles. They focus on how to identify and control food safety risks at each stage of the process of preparing and selling food. Controls do not have to be complex; a simple example would be the use of refrigeration to prevent the growth of harmful bacteria on perishable, ready-to-eat foods.

The regulations require all food businesses to have a written food safety management system based on the principles of Hazard Analysis and Critical Control Points (HACCP). Such a system should be proportionate to the food safety risks of the business.

The proprietor of the food business must ensure the following.

- Food is supplied or sold in a hygienic way.

- Safety controls are in place, maintained and reviewed.

- Food safety hazards are identified.

- Appropriate documentation is maintained.

- Knowledge of which steps are critical for food safety.

 Refer to the Food Standards Agency booklet *Hygiene requirements for your business* for good food hygiene practice – essential reading if you sell food.

2.7.2.1 Premises

The siting, design and construction of the premises must aim to avoid the contamination of food and harbouring of pests. Premises must be kept clean and in good repair so as to avoid food contamination.

Surfaces in contact with food must be easy to clean and, where necessary, disinfected. This will require the use of smooth, washable, non-toxic materials unless you can prove to the EHO that other materials are appropriate.

Adequate provision must be made for cleaning foodstuffs, and the cleaning and (where necessary) disinfection of utensils and equipment.

WELFARE FACILITIES

You must take all reasonable, practical steps to avoid the risk of contamination of food or ingredients. Washbasins must be designated for washing hands, have hot and cold (or appropriately mixed) running water, and be equipped with soap and suitable hand-drying facilities (such as disposable towels). Toilets must not lead directly into food rooms and they must be kept clean, maintained in good repair and ventilated.

Adequate arrangements and facilities for the hygienic storage and disposal of hazardous and inedible substances and waste (whether liquid or solid) must be available. Food waste must not be allowed to accumulate in food rooms and should be deposited in closable containers.

Adequate facilities and arrangements for maintaining and monitoring suitable food temperature conditions must be available.

2.7.2.2   Food

Stored raw materials and ingredients must be kept in appropriate conditions that will prevent harmful deterioration and protect them from contamination likely to make them unfit for human consumption.

2.7.2.3   Water

There must be an adequate supply of potable (clean, drinkable) water that must be used whenever necessary to ensure foodstuffs are not contaminated. This includes the use of ice, which must also be made, handled and stored in a way that protects it from contamination.

2.7.2.4   Temperature control

The Food Safety and Hygiene (England) Regulations state that foods intended for sale or supply, which need temperature control for safety, must be held either **hot** (at or above a minimum temperature of 63°C) or **chilled** (at or below a maximum temperature of 8°C). Rather than providing a long list of food items, the regulations apply the requirement for temperature control to all types of food that might support the growth of harmful (pathogenic) bacteria or the formation of poisons (toxins).

 Some of the requirements are different in Scotland; please contact the local Environmental Health department for details.

2.7.2.5   Food handlers

Anyone who works in a food handling area must maintain a high degree of personal cleanliness. The way in which they work must also be clean and hygienic. Food handlers must wear clean and, where appropriate, protective over-clothes. Adequate changing facilities must be provided where necessary.

Food handlers must protect food and ingredients against contamination, which is likely to render them unfit for human consumption or create a health hazard. For example, uncooked poultry should not contaminate ready-to-eat foods, either through direct contact or via work surfaces or equipment.

Anyone whose work involves handling food should adhere to the following.

- Observe good personal hygiene.
- Routinely wash their hands before handling foods.
- Never smoke in food handling areas.
- Report any illness (such as infected wounds, skin infections, diarrhoea or vomiting) to their manager or supervisor immediately.

If any employee reports that they are suffering from any condition or illness, the business may have to exclude them from food-handling areas. Such action should be taken urgently. If there is any doubt about the need to exclude, seek urgent medical advice or consult the local Environmental Health department.

Food handlers must receive adequate supervision, instruction and training in food hygiene. Each food business must decide what training or supervision their food handlers need by identifying the areas of work most likely to affect food hygiene.

Local colleges of higher and further education and private training companies provide food hygiene training courses.

? To determine whether you have complied with all legislative requirements, ask yourself the following questions

- Have you carried out a hazard analysis of food handling and production techniques?
- Are your standards of food hygiene good?
- Are your foods stored properly and kept at the correct temperatures?
- Have your staff been adequately and properly trained?
- Do you understand your food safety responsibilities?

If you can answer **yes** to each of these questions, your standards are probably satisfactory.

Appendix A – Welfare requirements

The table summarises the requirement for the client, principal contractors and contractors to ensure that adequate welfare facilities are provided, as required by Schedule 2 of CDM.

Sanitary conveniences	Suitable and sufficient sanitary conveniences must be provided or made available at readily accessible places. So far as is reasonably practicable, the rooms containing sanitary conveniences must be: ■ adequately ventilated and lit ■ kept in a clean and orderly condition. Separate rooms containing sanitary conveniences must be provided for men and women, except where each convenience is in a separate room and the door can be locked from the inside.
Welfare facilities	Suitable and sufficient washing facilities, including showers, if required by the nature of the work or for health reasons, must, so far as is reasonably practicable, be provided or made available at readily accessible places. Washing facilities must be provided adjacent to: ■ sanitary conveniences, whether or not provided elsewhere ■ changing rooms, where provided, whether or not provided elsewhere. Washing facilities must include: ■ a supply of clean cold and hot (or warm) water that, so far as is reasonably practicable, shall be running water ■ soap or other suitable means of cleaning ■ towels or other suitable means of drying. Rooms containing washing facilities must be sufficiently lit and ventilated. Washing facilities and the rooms containing them must be kept in a clean and orderly condition. Except for washing facilities that are intended for the washing of hands, forearms and face only, separate rooms must be provided for men and women except where: ■ they are in a room, the door of which can be secured from the inside ■ the room is intended to be used by one person at a time.
Drinking water	An adequate supply of wholesome drinking water, visibly marked with an appropriate sign, should be provided or made available at readily accessible, suitable places. Sufficient cups or other drinking vessels must be provided, unless the water supply is in the form of a jet (drinking fountain) from which a person can easily drink.

Changing rooms and lockers	Suitable facilities must be provided or made available at readily accessible places if:
	■ the worker has to wear special clothing for the purposes of construction work
	■ for reasons of health or personal privacy, changing cannot be carried out elsewhere.
	Where necessary, in the interests of personal privacy, separate changing rooms for men and women must be provided. Changing rooms must:
	■ contain seating
	■ include, where necessary, facilities to dry clothing and personal effects
	■ include, where necessary, facilities for locking away:
	  – special clothing that is not taken home
	  – a person's own clothing that is not worn at work
	  – personal effects (property).

Facilities for rest	Suitable and sufficient facilities for rest must be provided at readily accessible places. They must: ■ be equipped with an adequate number of tables and adequate seating with backs (not benches) ■ where necessary, include facilities for any pregnant woman and nursing mother to rest, lying down ■ include a means of boiling water and suitable arrangements to ensure that meals can be prepared and eaten ■ be maintained at an appropriate temperature.

Stress and mental health at work

03

Supporting INFORMATION

GT700 Toolbox talks / supporting checklists and forms

Toolbox talks on some of these topics are available in the GT700 publication. Supporting checklists and forms covering some of these topics are available on our companion website.

Overview

One in four British adults will experience at least one diagnosable mental health problem in any one year. Anxiety and depression are the most common forms and can be caused by many things, including issues away from the workplace or work-related problems.

Workers who experience stress, anxiety or depression are unlikely to perform as well in the workplace. This can create more general health and safety risks, which can also result in financial costs for employers in the construction industry.

Recent estimates suggest that around 700 construction workers take their own lives every year. This is more than two people each day, and more than in any other professional sector. Being able to identify the signs of mental health problems early is vital, so that the appropriate support and treatment can be accessed.

While employers have a legal duty of care for the mental health and wellbeing of their workers, it also makes good business sense. Positive management of stress can increase efficiency and productivity, improve staff retention and reduce sickness payments and other associated costs. Therefore, this is good for workers, good for teams and good for business.

3.1 Introduction

Stress is not an illness in itself, but it can lead to a reduced ability to perform at work and have an impact on the person's health and wellbeing. According to research, if not controlled, stress can lead to common mental health problems (such as anxiety and depression) and also physical chronic health conditions (such as heart disease, back pain, headaches, gastrointestinal disturbances and alcohol and drug dependency).

Work-related stress and mental health problems are closely linked. Symptoms of stress and common mental health problems are similar. Work-related stress may trigger an existing mental health problem, that the person may have previously successfully managed without letting it affect their work. For people with existing mental health problems, work-related stress may worsen those conditions.

 Stress and mental health

Work-related stress is the adverse reaction that people have to excessive pressures or other types of demands placed on them at work.

Mental health is how we think, feel and behave.

Common mental health problems are those that are most frequent, more prevalent and are successfully treated in primary health care settings (such as general practitioner (GP) surgeries), rather than through specialist treatment.

Anxiety is an unpleasant feeling when you feel worried, uneasy or distressed about something that may or may not be about to happen *(Source: NHS Direct)*.

Depression is when you have feelings of extreme sadness, despair or inadequacy that last for a long time *(Source: NHS Direct)*.

3.2 Important points

In the recent years prior to the COVID-19 pandemic, the rate of self-reported work-related stress, depression or anxiety had shown signs of increasing. The current rate is higher than the 2018/19 pre-COVID levels.

It is important to remember that it is not an employer's or a line manager's job to diagnose or treat stress, whatever its cause. If an employee is having problems, it is important that they get help as soon as possible.

The main difference between stress and common mental health problems is the way they are caused and the way they are treated. As the signs are similar a GP should make the diagnosis, then prescribe and offer the required treatment.

- Stress at work is a reaction to experiences or events at work.
- Common mental health problems can arise from factors outside of work (for example, divorce, money concerns, or a family history of mental health problems).
- People can have common mental health problems without an obvious cause.
- Employers can treat work-related stress by improving working conditions.
- Mental health problems are usually treated through specialist treatment, which may include medication.
- Managers have a role to play to help the employer manage the problem at work and make reasonable adjustments.

3.2.1 UK mental health statistics

- One in four people experience poor mental health every year.

- At any given time, one in six adults of working age have mental health symptoms.

- Poor mental health is attributable for 72 million working days lost, and costs between £74 and £99 billion each year.

- The total cost of mental health in England is estimated at around £105 billion per year.

- People with long-term mental health conditions lose their jobs every year at about double the rate of those who do not have a mental health condition.

- In Great Britain 1,752 people died in road traffic accidents in 2020. 6,479 died by suicide.

- 30 to 50% of people with severe mental health conditions also have problems with substance use. Drug and alcohol misuse increases the risk of suicide attempts and completions.

- More men die by suicide: 75% male, 25% female.

 The Health and Safety Executive (HSE) has produced a practical guide to managing and supporting people with mental health problems in the workplace. For further information visit their website.

3.3 Legislative requirements

Organisations have a legal responsibility to protect their employees from stress under the following legislation.

- Health and Safety at Work etc. Act.
- Management of Health and Safety at Work Regulations.
- Protection from Harassment Act.
- Equality Act.
- The Employment Equality Act.

- Employment Rights Act.
- Health and Safety (Consultation with Employees) Regulations.
- Safety Representatives and Safety Committee Regulations.
- Construction (Design and Management) Regulations.
- Protection of Freedoms Act.

Under health and safety legislation, employers have a duty to undertake risk assessments and manage work to reduce the incidence of stress at work. However, this is a complex area of law and there are also cases brought within civil law where individuals have successfully applied cases against employers. It is recommended that legal advice is always sought by the individual and the employer should the need arise.

3.3.1 Health and Safety at Work etc. Act

The Health and Safety at Work etc. Act imposes general duties on employers to secure the health, safety and welfare of people at work and protect others against risks arising from the work activity.

The Act makes it the duty of every employer to ensure, as far as is reasonably practicable, the health, safety and welfare at work of all employees. This includes provision and maintenance of plant and systems of work that are safe and without risks, and the provision of information, instruction and training.

3.3.2 Management of Health and Safety at Work Regulations

The Management of Health and Safety at Work Regulations place a legal requirement on employers to assess the risks to health and safety that arise out of their work and to introduce measures that control the risks to an acceptable level. The following information is explained within a risk assessment.

- The hazards of the job (for example, responsibility for the safety of others).
- The risks (such as stress).
- The control measures needed to minimise the risk of stress to a safe level (such as support through other welfare services).

The regulations specify that where an employer implements any preventative and protective measures they shall do so on the basis of the principles of prevention specified in Schedule 1 of the regulations.

3.3.3 Equality Act

Under this Act a person is classified as disabled if they have a physical or mental impairment. Anxiety, stress and depression may be sufficient to qualify a person as disabled and therefore they will be covered by the Act, as long as there is a substantial and long-term effect (for at least a year) on their ability to carry out normal day-to-day duties. Those with clinically recognised mental health diagnoses are likely to be covered by the Act. If an employee is covered by the Act, the organisation has a responsibility to make reasonable adjustments to accommodate the needs of that employee.

3.3.4 Employment Rights Act

The Employment Rights Act is relevant to issues regarding work-related stress. This may be particularly so for situations where there are challenges made by employees in relation to their rights under this Act.

3.4   Work-related stress, anxiety or depression

Figures from the HSE show that work-related stress, anxiety or depression have a larger impact on our society, UK organisations and workers than many may think.

- In 2021/22, stress, depression or anxiety accounted for 51% of all work-related ill health cases and 55% of all working days lost due to ill health.
- The total number of working days lost due to work-related stress, anxiety or depression in 2021/22 was 17 million. This equated to an average of 18.6 days lost per case.
- Approximately one in seven people say they find their work either very or extremely stressful.

Stress in the workplace is not always avoidable, and a perfect amount is acceptable as it can aid motivation, enables an individual to thrive and therefore can be considered to be healthy. However, if it becomes unmanageable, it can impact health and work performance.

Some common causes of work-related stress are listed below.

- Excessively high workloads, with unrealistic deadlines, making people feel rushed, under pressure and overwhelmed.
- Insufficient workloads, making people feel that their skills are being under-utilised.
- A lack of control over how people do their work.
- A lack of interpersonal support or poor working relationships, leading to a sense of isolation.
- People being asked to do a job for which they have insufficient experience or training.
- Difficulty settling into a new job role or promotion; meeting the new role's requirements and adapting to possible changes in relationships with colleagues.
- Concerns about job security, a lack of career opportunities, or the level of pay.
- Bullying, violence, intimidation, victimisation or harassment.
- A blame culture within your organisation, where people are afraid to get things wrong or to admit to making mistakes.
- Weak or ineffective management, leaving employees feeling they don't have a sense of direction, or over-management, leaving employees feeling undervalued and affecting their self-esteem.
- Lack of clarity about your role – multiple reporting lines for employees, with each manager asking for their work to be prioritised.
- Failure to keep employees informed about significant changes to the business, causing them uncertainty about their future.
- A poor physical working environment (for example, excessive heat, cold or noise, inadequate lighting, uncomfortable seating and poorly maintained or malfunctioning equipment).

Understanding common causes of stress in the workplace can help managers to assess what is happening in their organisation and identify solutions to reduce it to the lowest level or remove it completely. There is a clear distinction between stress and pressure. Pressure can be a motivating factor and is often a part of everyday work, but stress can have the opposite effect.

Actively managing the effects of work-related stress, along with other workplace hazards, is required in order to reduce the impact on cost, productivity and the safety, health and wellbeing of employees. Work-related stress is a management issue that managers can help to resolve and it is often a symptom of poor employee relations and lack of leadership, communication and control.

Organisations that talk regularly with their employees and have effective systems and procedures in place for dealing with issues (such as absence and discipline) are much more likely to avoid work-related stress and to be able to deal with potentially stressful situations when they arise. Developing an open and positive culture of health and wellbeing, with robust systems to support it, is good business practice.

Work can have a positive impact on our health and wellbeing and healthy, well-motivated employees can have an equally positive impact on the productivity and effectiveness of a business. Stress can cause many challenges within the workplace. Some examples are shown below.

- A fall in a manager's or worker's productivity.
- Risks to health and safety.
- Poor decision-making.
- Increased sickness absence.
- High staff turnover.
- Poor workplace relations.
- An increase in mistakes that may in turn lead to poor finishes and bad workmanship.

Stress often has a cumulative effect. If one member of staff becomes ill through stress, it places added pressure on those covering for them. Equally, a stressed manager may find it difficult to create a positive working environment and monitor stress levels in others.

The following are some possible business benefits that could be expected when encouraging a healthy workforce.

- Reduced sickness absence.
- Fewer accidents.
- Higher commitment.
- Improved brand.
- Improved staff retention.
- Improved resilience.
- Higher productivity.

Organisations must risk assess for the potential of stress at work. This will be covered in more detail later in this chapter.

HSE's work-related stress toolkit

The HSE has identified stress, depression and anxiety as the second biggest cause of work-related ill health in the construction industry, and have put together a tool kit to help small businesses with a regular workforce (employed and contracted) to start looking at this issue. It will also help site managers wanting to identify project-specific issues.

There are six main themes that the document looks at, and by using the toolkit you can hopefully start simple and practical conversations regarding stress, and look at steps to reduce pressure, manage potential stressors and limit the negative impact work might be having on staff. The toolkit outlines how workers should feel in relation to these themes, and provides a series of questions to help explore what the issue might be where this is not the case. Here are the key discussion points for employer or supervisors:

● Timing: this depends on what works best for the employer or worker. A conversation could be had once a week.

● Theme: the conversations could focus on one theme at a time.

● Setting: the conversations could be held on a one-to-one basis or with a whole team – during a tea break, for example.

● Time: make time for these discussions. They don't have to be more than 10 or 15 minutes for each theme.

● Openness: the toolkit relies on open and honest discussion around issues. Everyone needs to listen to what is being said.

● Questions: these are intended to help start a discussion, and are not prescriptive – the important thing is to have a conversation that is relevant for your work.

● Solutions then actions: these should be agreed together.

It is important to remember that the overall responsibility for managing work-related stress rests with the employer. They need to ensure that supervisors or site managers are appropriately supported when tackling this issue.

 More help and information is available on the HSE's work-related stress website.

3.5 Signs and symptoms of work-related stress

Anyone can suffer from work-related stress, no matter what work they do or what level they operate at. Men in the UK are three times more likely to die by suicide than women. However, in construction – a male-dominated industry – men are three times more likely to die by suicide than the national average for men.

● Managers.

● Road workers.

● Designers.

● Administration staff.

Some of the signs of stress are listed below. The list is by no means exhaustive and individuals will vary in terms of how their own symptoms manifest in the workplace.

3.5.1 Behaviour

If an individual displays or reports any of the following behaviours, this may indicate that they are under stress.

● Find it hard to sleep.

● Have altered eating habits, including food cravings.

● Smoke or drink more.

● Avoid friends and family.

● Are generally quiet and withdrawn.

● Have a lack of assertiveness.

● Are frequently tearful.

● Cannot show their true feelings.

● Have a disproportionate response to situations.

● Do not have a problem.

● Avoid difficult situations.

3.5.2 Physical symptoms

Symptoms of stress can vary considerably from one person to another but some examples are shown below.

● Tiredness.

● Indigestion.

● Headaches.

● Aching muscles.

● Palpitations.

● High blood pressure.

● Breathlessness.

● Chest pains.

● Nausea.

● Tendency to sweat.

● Constipation or diarrhoea.

● Restlessness.

3.5.3   Mental symptoms

People can exhibit the following tendencies.

- Be more indecisive.
- Have poor judgement.
- Find it hard to concentrate.
- Suffer loss of memory.
- Feel inadequate or have low self esteem.

- Dread the future.
- Dread failure.
- Feel isolated.
- Have a lack of interest in others.

3.5.4   Emotional symptoms

People can behave in one or more of the following ways.

- Get irritable or angry.
- Lose their sense of humour.
- Be anxious.

- Feel numb.
- Be hypersensitive.
- Feel drained and listless.

3.6   Assessing whether stress is a problem at work

Having regular conversations with the workforce can help to identify if stress is an issue within your workplace.

You can also use **questionnaires** to gather the same information. Although there is a range of commercially available questionnaires, you may be better off developing your own checklist of areas that are relevant to the needs and working conditions of your organisation.

A number of important areas you should consider are shown below.

- Work scheduling and the type and design of work.
- Working relationships with colleagues.
- The level of communication and reporting.

- The physical working environment.
- Employees' expectations of their work.

 The HSE has produced a useful checklist, designed to help organisations to clarify whether their own risk assessment approach to stress is appropriate and sufficient. This can be accessed through the HSE website.

❓ Is my risk assessment approach suitable and sufficient?

Answering **yes** to all of the questions below would indicate that your approach is likely to be considered a suitable and sufficient risk assessment for work-related stress.

- Do you include all the steps in the HSE stress risk assessment tool?
- Do you focus on prevention and organisational-level solutions?
- Do you include provision for dealing with other issues (for example, personal issues)?
- Do you ensure commitment from all parties (senior management, employees and their representatives)?
- Do you have arrangements to identify those aspects of the work, work organisation or environment that are known to be risk factors for work-related stress?
- Does your approach highlight the extent and nature of the gap, if any, between the current situation, and what is seen as good practice (such as the stakes to be achieved in the management standards), for each of the identified stress risk areas?
- Do you involve the workforce?
  - By asking about their views regarding good and bad features of workplace conditions?
  - By seeking their suggestions, advice and comments on potential solutions to problems (such as improvements to working conditions, changes in the way work is organised, and so on)?
  - By ensuring that people are empowered to contribute and feel that their views are listened to and acted upon?
  - By communicating outcomes (such as action plans)?
- Do you seek to develop and adopt solutions that are reasonably practicable?
- Do you provide documentation to show what you have done at each stage of the process and that you are implementing the recommended actions?

The HSE recommends that the process is documented, whatever the approach to carrying out a risk assessment for work-related stress. Documenting the process provides an audit trail, and allows it to be reviewed later on if something changes, as well as allowing you to demonstrate to any relevant authorities that what has been done represents a suitable and sufficient risk assessment.

3.6.1 The role of the line manager

Managers have a significant impact on the work-related stress of people with whom they work, notably their team.

- They can both prevent and cause stress simply through their behaviour towards employees.

- The manager's influence, or lack of it, can protect or expose employees to working conditions that may cause stress. This can be the case for both internal (organisational) factors and for those that are external (perhaps customer related).

- Managers can identify (or miss) the signs of stress at an early stage.

- If an employee is suffering from work-related stress, the manager would be likely to be involved in supporting and helping to deliver change that could result in a solution.

- Increasingly, managers are responsible for the uptake and delivery of risk assessments for work-related stress in relation to their team and department.

3.7 Management standards for work-related stress

Six main causes of work-related stress have been identified across all organisations and a framework of management behaviours or competencies has been created. The HSE describes the standards as follows.

 The management standards define the characteristics, or culture, of an organisation where the risks from work-related stress are being effectively managed and controlled.

The six management standards (shown below) cover the primary sources of stress at work.

1. **Demands.** Issues that should be considered include workload, work patterns and the working environment.

2. **Control.** How much control the individual has over the way they do their work.

3. **Support.** Whether workers feel that adequate encouragement and resources are provided by the company, managers and colleagues, and whether there are easy access systems to respond to individual concerns.

4. **Role.** Workers at all levels must understand their role and how they fit into the organisation, and have the skills, experience and support to deliver. There must not be any conflicting roles.

5. **Change.** People can be suspicious of the real motives behind organisational change which, whether large or small, must be well-managed and effectively communicated.

6. **Relationships.** Workers at any level must not be subjected to unacceptable behaviours by anyone at work and conflicts must be effectively dealt with. Bullying is a potentially significant factor for workplace relationships and can take many forms; what appears to be light-hearted banter to one person may be perceived as bullying by another. Personal and work-related bullying behaviours may both be evident within a workplace. Examples of these are shown in the table below.

Personal behaviours	Work-related behaviours
■ Ignoring/excluding/silent treatment/isolating.	■ Public humiliation.
■ Malicious rumours or gossip.	■ Being shouted or yelled at.
■ Belittling remarks.	■ Giving unachievable tasks/impossible deadlines/unmanageable workloads.
■ Undermining integrity.	■ Giving meaningless tasks/unpleasant jobs/belittling a person's ability.
■ Lies told about you.	■ Withholding information deliberately/concealing information/failing to return calls or pass on messages.
■ Sense of judgement questioned.	■ Undervaluing contribution/no credit where due/taking credit for work that is not their own.
■ Opinions marginalised.	■ Constant criticism.

The management standards for work-related stress, and the underpinning processes that support them, are designed to help simplify and carry out stress risk assessments, help all parties to work together to address work-related stress and provide the means by which companies can gauge their performance in tackling the main causes of stress.

In addition management competencies have been developed that describe the behaviours managers need to show in order to prevent and reduce stress in their teams. They map across to the areas identified as being the primary sources of stress at work.

The HSE describes the benefits of implementing these standards as shown below.

- Being able to demonstrate good practice through a step-by-step risk assessment approach.

- Enabling assessment of the current situation using surveys and other techniques.

- Encouraging active discussion and working in partnership with employees to help decide on practical improvements that can be made.

- Helping to simplify risk assessment for work-related stress by:
  - identifying the main risk factors
  - helping employers focus on the underlying causes and their prevention
  - providing a yardstick by which organisations can gauge their performance in tackling the main causes of stress.

> **www** **The management standards themselves revolve around a series of activities and map directly across to the main causes of work-related stress. The process of implementing the management standards is described in full on the HSE website.**

03

There are effectively five discrete processes within the standards, defined below.

1. **Identify the stress risk factors.** When assessing the risks to which your employees may be exposed, it is important to focus on organisational-level issues that have the potential to impact groups and possibly large numbers of employees, rather than individual employees.

2. **Who can be harmed and how?** The aim of the data gathering and analysis is to get a measure of where an organisation's current performance is against the management standards. Achieving this aim does not require organisations to perform extensive statistical analysis of their data. It is suggested that organisations, where possible, use existing data to identify the underlying causes. Typically, most organisations have access to data relating to sickness absence, staff surveys, turnover data, and so on.

3. **Evaluate the risks.** The primary aim of this step is to take the output from the previous step (data collection and analysis), discuss the conclusions with a representative sample of employees and work with them to explore the problems and develop solutions.

4. **Record your findings.** By now you will have consulted your employees, explored areas of concern and taken initial steps to develop some proposed solutions. It is important that you record your findings. To do this you could produce and disseminate an action plan. An action plan will:
   - help you set **goals** to work towards
   - help you **prioritise**
   - demonstrate that you are **serious** about addressing employees' concerns
   - provide you with something to **evaluate** and review against.

5. **Monitor and review.** You should review any action you take to tackle the sources of excessive workplace pressure. You need to:
   - **monitor** against your action plan to ensure the agreed actions are taking place
   - **evaluate** the effectiveness of the solutions you implement
   - **decide** what further action or data gathering, if any, is needed.

The management standards demonstrate good practice through a step-by-step risk assessment approach

3.7.1 Line manager competency indicator tool

The line manager competency indicator tool is designed to assess whether the behaviours identified as effective for preventing and reducing stress at work are part of your management repertoire or not. The aim is to help you to reflect upon your own behaviour and management style. The competencies measured by the tool fall into four main domains, with three sub-competencies in each.

Respectful and responsible	Managing and communicating existing and future work
■ Integrity. ■ Managing emotions. ■ Considerate approach.	■ Proactive work management. ■ Problem solving. ■ Participative/empowering.
Reasoning/managing difficult situations	**Managing the individual within the team**
■ Managing conflict. ■ Use of organisation resources. ■ Taking responsibility for resolving issues.	■ Personally accessible. ■ Sociable. ■ Empathetic engagement.

> **www** **The line manager competency indicator tool will enable individuals to compare their own behaviours against the management competencies relevant to the management standards. This can be accessed on the HSE website.**

3.8 Dealing with stress

Anyone can suffer from stress, in any role and at any level of an organisation. If stress is not addressed it can lead to common mental health conditions (such as anxiety and depression).

The biggest barrier to obtaining support is the stigma associated with the condition.

People who work alone or who have particular responsibilities that set them apart from their work colleagues could be particularly vulnerable.

If an individual feels that they may have the symptoms of stress, there are a number of ways they can address the challenges facing them.

- Identify and tackle the underlying causes.
- Talk to someone trusted, with whom they can share issues and challenges.
- Talk to their line manager about modifying their role, task or hours of work, and any training or development required for an early resolution.
- Practise relaxation techniques (such as meditation or mindfulness, which have been shown through research to benefit individuals suffering from stress and depression).
- Improve their diet; avoid foods high in refined sugars and cut down where appropriate on alcohol, smoking and caffeine.
- Avoid regularly working long hours if at all possible.
- Take regular breaks from the workplace and incorporate frequent moving and stretching.
- Do regular exercise.
- Take time off work for holidays.
- Seek additional support and guidance (such as human resources or occupational health) if work is impacting their health.
- If signs and symptoms of stress are impacting their health, they should seek medical advice from their GP.

3.8.1 Creating a supportive environment

Creating a supportive environment is essential to ensure mental health and stress can be openly discussed.

Support can take many forms, and can include regular one-to-ones with line managers/supervisors to talk about any problems, to encourage positive mental health through mental health awareness training, workshops and appointing mental health first 'champions' who staff can talk to.

 Signs and symptoms of stress can vary for individuals. More guidance on dealing with the symptoms of stress can be found on the Mind website.

3.9 Common mental health problems

There are many factors and causes that lead to poor mental health or diagnosable mental health conditions.

There are many 'risk factors' in everyone's life's that can sometimes contribute to poor mental health.

These include:

- Individual factors – inadequate parenting, illness, disability, genetics, drugs and alcohol, abusive or traumatic events, stress and lack of support, and imprisonment.
- Societal factors – poor education, poor housing, inequality, discrimination and stigma, poverty and unemployment.

There are also 'protective factors' that can contribute to positive mental health, such as:

- Life skills – confidence, coping skills, values and beliefs, conflict resolution, problem solving, communication.
- Community engagement and physical health – nutrition, rest, self-reflection, stable home environment, social network, physical activity.

People with mental health conditions can work to their full potential. However, they often fear prejudice from society.

Studies have shown that people with mental health problems want to be treated the same as other employees and being at work can often improve the condition.

It is a misconception that people with a mental health problem will have more sickness absence; this is not necessarily the case.

 Famous people believed to have lived with a mental health condition include Charles Dickens, Sir Isaac Newton and Sir Winston Churchill.

Mates in Mind - mental health in the UK construction industry

Construction work has a variety of pressures from tight contracts to long hours, time away from loved-ones and managing budgets, not to mention the added stresses of the pandemic and the rising costs of materials and supplies. Additionally, within construction lies a 'macho' culture which prevents many workers from seeking support and help when they may need it, putting further stress on their own mental health and wellbeing.

Research by the charity Mates in Mind and the Chartered Institute of Building has identified the following:

- Two people working in construction in the UK die by suicide very working day. This equates to over 700 a year.
- 48% have taken time off work owing to unmanageable stress.
- 91% have felt overwhelmed and 26% have experienced suicidal thoughts.
- A third of construction workers suffer with elevated levels of anxiety every day.
- 44% worry their workload is too high.
- Over two-thirds of construction workers believe there's a stigma surrounding mental health, which stops them from talking about it.
- Almost half find it hard to talk about their mental health.

A report by the Chartered Institute of Building found that 26% of construction industry professionals thought about taking their own lives in 2019, and 56% of construction professionals work for organisations with no policies on workplace mental health.

 For further information, guidance and resources on improving mental health and wellbeing across the construction industry and related sectors, visit the Mates in Mind Website.

3.9.1   Anxiety

Anxiety is a natural response that helps individuals avoid dangerous situations. It can present as uneasiness through to terrifying panic attacks. Episodes can last few minutes or many years. Statistics from the Princess Trust highlight that 49% of 16 to 24 year-olds experience some form of anxiety on a daily basis. Although episodes of anxiety and panic attacks are common, if left untreated they can cause distress to the individual. At work the individual may lose interest, lack concentration, display low morale and be irritable. Individuals with anxiety may benefit from medication, psychological therapies and self help.

 For advice about helping people with anxiety visit the Anxiety UK website.

3.9.2   Depression

Depression impacts individuals in various different ways. Depression affects thinking, behaviours, moods, emotions and physical wellbeing. In severe cases, it can stop an individual from functioning. Individuals with depression can often feel helpless, have low moods and morale and lose interest in activities they previously enjoyed. Depression can be mild, moderate or severe.

The impact on an individual's health and safety if they are suffering with depression at work can depend on the type of activities their job involves. (For example, those working in the construction industry who suffer with unmanaged depression can have serious health and safety implications to other workers on site.) When making an assessment of the worker's condition and its impact on their work, the employer should consider the type of work the individual is involved in and the treatment they are receiving. Anti-depressant medication can cause drowsiness, which may affect the individual's ability to drive or operate plant and machinery.

3.9.3   Bipolar disorder

Bipolar disorder is a severe mental health condition and affects people from all ages and from all backgrounds. It causes unusual shifts in mood, energy, activity levels, concentration and the ability to complete day-to-day tasks. Extreme mood swings range from emotional highs through to depressive lows. At each end of the mood scale, both extreme mania or deep depression can develop into psychosis where an individual loses touch with reality and can experience hallucinations, extreme paranoia and delusions. Individuals with bipolar disorder in the workplace can be managed in many ways to ensure health and safety is not compromised by:

- creating a psychologically and socially healthy spaces
- promoting flexibility (e.g. moving around during breaks)
- transparent communication

- colleague support
- encouraging treatment and keeping on top of treatment
- setting boundaries.

 For advice about helping people with bipolar disorder visit the Bipolar UK website.

3.10 Occupational health

The role of occupational health is to provide support and advice when the health of the employee is impacting their work and also if their work is having an adverse impact on their health. Referral to occupational health for work-related stress issues and other mental health issues should only be made if line management or human resources have not been able to resolve the issues causing the stress, or if there is a concern for the employee's health. The vast majority of work-related stress can be resolved within the workplace.

The following services are available to support individuals and employers on matters relating to work-related stress and mental health issues.

- Employment Medical Advisory Service (EMAS).

- Healthy Working Lives.

 For further information on these services refer to Chapter B01 Management of health.

03

3.11 Mental health first aiders and training

You should consider ways to manage mental ill health that are appropriate for your workplace and business, such as providing information or training for managers and employees, employing occupational health professionals, appointing mental-health trained first aiders and implementing employee support programmes.

Training is available on how to help a person who may be developing a problem, experiencing a worsening mental health problem or is in a mental health crisis.

Mental Health First Aid (MHFA) is the support provided to an individual who is experiencing poor mental health if professional help is not required or before professional help is accessed. An MHFA can check if someone okay, signpost to other supports or to seek immediate professional help. An MHFA is not a therapist, counsellor or diagnostician. The purpose of the role is to take a holistic approach to an individuals mental health.

 For further information visit the Mental Health First Aid website for your home nation: MHFA England, MHFA Scotland, or MHFA Wales.

03

Drugs and alcohol

04

Supporting
INFORMATION

GT700 Toolbox talks / supporting checklists and forms

Toolbox talks on some of these topics are available in the GT700 publication. Supporting checklists and forms covering some of these topics are available on our companion website.

Overview

The misuse of drugs and alcohol can have a devastating impact on individuals and employers, and can result in social problems, poor health, absenteeism and therefore loss of productivity, as well as severely compromising health and safety and contributing to workplace accidents. It is a growing problem in society and construction sites are no exception, so diligence is required to identify and support those who are affected by it.

This chapter gives a general overview of the misuse of drugs and alcohol: identification, symptoms, impact and management. It also outlines the legal framework that regulates it.

04

4.1 Introduction

Identifying, managing and supporting individuals affected by drugs and alcohol are important challenges facing society and the construction industry. The effects of drugs and alcohol can have a huge negative impact on individuals, employers, their businesses and also any occupants of property where work is being undertaken, as well as neighbouring properties.

Drug and alcohol misuse poses a threat to individuals in terms of their health, safety and welfare, as well as threatening their livelihood, now and in the future, if misuse is not controlled. These substances can cause effects (including drowsiness, trembling, lack of concentration and reduced awareness) that can potentially increase the risk of on-site accidents and injury to the individual and others working or living alongside them.

A survey by the Considerate Constructors Scheme (CCS) revealed that the majority of UK construction industry workers were concerned about how drugs and alcohol effect their workforces. 59% of those surveyed said they had concerns or issues related to drugs and alcohol in the workplace. Employee safety is already at high risk due to the nature of work within the construction industry. Statistically, a construction worker is six times more likely to be killed at work than employers in other industries. Adding drugs and/or alcohol to this mix can only lead to an increase in workplace accidents and potential fatalities.

It is easy to associate drug and alcohol misuse with individuals who are addicted to them. However, employers need to also take into account those who use drugs and alcohol infrequently. In addition, it is important to remember that there can be significant health and safety risks from individuals who have, for example, been drinking heavily the previous day or evening, or those who may have been taking either prescribed or over-the-counter medications.

 On average, 358,000 people are admitted to hospital every year where the main reason was attributable to alcohol. For further information, advice, guidance and support visit the Drinkaware website.

Successfully identifying, managing and supporting individuals with substance misuse problems is beneficial to them, your business and customers. For example, you would save on the cost of recruiting and training new employees to replace those who left work because of untreated misuse.

Raising awareness of managers, supervisors and operatives to ensure that effective identification, management and control measures are always put in place and monitored is important in helping to reduce the impact of drugs and alcohol on operatives and, where appropriate, occupants. There is a need to comply with legislation, including the Health and Safety at Work etc. Act, the Management of Health and Safety at Work Regulations, the Road Traffic Act and the Transport and Works Act, and a duty to provide safe systems of work and a safe working environment. In appropriate circumstances, employers may also be held liable for the acts of employees under the Misuse of Drugs Act.

 The CCS survey also revealed that 35% of workers have witnessed their colleagues working whilst under the influence of drugs or alcohol. This means that not only are these workers putting themselves at risk, but also everyone else working on their site. These numbers suggest that this issue is quite prominent in the construction industry.

4.2 Important points

● Managers and supervisors should be aware of the signs and symptoms of drug and alcohol misuse.

● People who misuse drugs and alcohol are likely to be still under the influence when they report for work, so are more likely to endanger themselves and others.

● Drinking coffee, taking a cold shower or eating junk food do not minimise the effects of alcohol. It is only time, and a rule of thumb is for every unit of alcohol consumed, it takes one hour for the body to remove it from the bloodstream.

● There is likely to be a negative impact on productivity, enhanced periods of sickness absence and lower morale generally.

● If people are under the influence of drugs or alcohol at work, decisive action needs to be taken to ensure it does not continue, and that the risk is mitigated.

- Companies should put into place and communicate an approach to managing employees who are unfit for work through drug and/or alcohol misuse.
  - This approach must be reflected in employee handbooks, induction processes and employment contracts. It must cover the right of search and testing (and the type of testing, e.g. for cause, post-incident, random, and the prescribed limits for alcohol and drugs), and identify the support in place to assist misusers only if they self disclose, as well as the approach to suspension or dismissal from work.
- Unless there is related misconduct, substance misuse should be seen as a treatable illness.
- Individuals who disclose that they have a problem linked to drugs, alcohol and or prescription medication should be offered support and rehabilitation in strict confidence – there are many agencies who can offer professional advice and help.
- Drug and alcohol workplace policies, supported by a testing programme, should ideally be compiled with the support of external occupational health providers. Any policy must be clearly communicated and understood by all employees, as well as any external stakeholders that would be party to the policy (e.g. sub-contractors or external consultants).
- Driving a motor vehicle on a public road whilst under the influence of drugs and or alcohol is a criminal offence.
- Driving on site under the influence of drugs and or alcohol is equally, if not more, dangerous than driving on a public road. Employers should consider how these risks are managed in their policies and procedures, and clearly outline the consequences if an employee operates vehicles and plant and is convicted of a drink or drug driving offence.
- Drug and alcohol misuse causes absenteeism, lack of awareness, loss of focus and lower productivity, as well as harm to the short and long-term health and wellbeing of individuals.

04

 Contrary to popular belief, the majority of people with a drinking or drug problem have a job.

 For the latest statistics on alcohol-related deaths, visit the Government website.

4.3　Legislative requirements

Under the **Health and Safety at Work etc. Act** (HSWA) all employers have a legal duty to protect employees' health, safety and welfare. Understanding the signs of drug and alcohol misuse or abuse will help in managing the ongoing health and safety risk in the workplace. Policies should be developed to tackle drug and alcohol-related problems, and offer appropriate support.

There is also a duty under the **Management of Health and Safety at Work Regulations** (MHSWR) to assess the risks to the health and safety of their employees.

If an employer knowingly allows an employee to work under the influence of alcohol or drugs in the workplace, and their behaviour places the employee or others at risk, the employer could be prosecuted. In accordance with HSWA, employees are required to take reasonable care of themselves and others who could be affected by their acts or omissions at work.

4.3.1　Transport and Works Act

- It is a criminal offence for workers to be unfit through drugs and/or alcohol while working on railways, tramways and other guided transport systems.
- The operators of the transport system would be guilty of an offence unless they had shown all due diligence in trying to prevent such an offence from being committed.

4.3.2　Road Traffic Act

- Any person who, when driving or attempting to drive a motor vehicle on a road or other public place, is unfit to drive, through alcohol or drugs, shall be guilty of an offence.
- An offence is also committed if a person unfit through alcohol or drugs is in charge of a motor vehicle on a road or other public place. A person shall be deemed not to have been in charge of a mechanically propelled vehicle if they prove that at that time the circumstances were such that there was no likelihood of their driving it, as long as they remained unfit to drive through alcohol or drugs.
- Courts, in determining whether there was such a likelihood of driving, may disregard any injury to individuals and any damage to the vehicle.
- A person shall be taken to be unfit to drive if their ability to drive properly is, for the time being, impaired.
  Note: this stipulation also applies to prescription or over-the-counter medicines, so you should always read the labelling and, if you're not sure, consult your pharmacist.

4.3.3　Misuse of Drugs Act

The Misuse of Drugs Act is the principal legislation in the UK for controlling the misuse of drugs. The Act makes the production, supply and possession of these controlled drugs unlawful, except when they have been prescribed by a doctor. The Act lists the drugs that are subject to control and classifies them in three categories, according to their relative harmfulness when misused.

Class A. Includes cocaine, crack, ecstasy (MDMA), heroin, LSD, magic mushrooms, methadone and methamphetamine (crystal meth).

Class B. Includes amphetamines, barbiturates, cannabis, codeine, ketamine, methylphenidate (Ritalin), synthetic cannabinoids and synthetic cathinones (such as mephedrone and methoxetamine).

Class C. Includes anabolic steroids, benzodiazepines (diazepam), gamma butyrolactone (GBL), gamma hydroxybutyrate (GHB) and piperazines (BZP).

The penalties for offences involving controlled drugs depend on the classification of the drug. Penalties for misuse of Class A drugs are more severe than those for Class B or Class C drugs.

It is possible that in certain circumstances charges may be brought against an employer or an employee under this Act, HSWA, or both. It would be up to the courts to decide on the circumstances of each case.

Not all drugs are illegal but that does not mean they are not harmful. Tobacco and alcohol are legal but they can still damage your health.

4.3.4   Psychoactive Substances Act

Psychoactive substances, previously referred to as 'legal highs' (though illegal), are designed to mimic similar effects to drugs such as cannabis, cocaine and ecstasy, whilst remaining chemically different enough not to be subject to control under the Misuse of Drugs Act.

Psychoactive substances are controlled by the Psychoactive Substances Act, which was introduced in 2016 and which established a blanket ban on the importation, production or supply of psychoactive substances not already covered by the law.

● There were 258 deaths registered from new psychoactive substances (NPS) in 2021. This is 88.3% higher than the previous year (137 deaths).

 A *psychoactive substance* is defined in law as anything which 'by stimulating or depressing the person's central nervous system affects the person's mental functioning or emotional state'.

The following points apply to the Psychoactive Substances Act.

● Makes it an offence to produce, supply, offer to supply, possess with intent to supply, possess on custodial premises, import or export psychoactive substances; that is, any substance intended for human consumption that is capable of producing a psychoactive effect. Offences are punishable by a fine or up to seven years' imprisonment.

● Includes provision for civil sanctions – prohibition notices, premises notices, prohibition orders and premises orders (breach of the two orders will be a criminal offence) – to enable the police and Local Authorities to adopt a graded response to the supply of psychoactive substances in appropriate cases.

● Provides powers to stop and search persons, vehicles and vessels, enter and search premises in accordance with a warrant, and to seize and destroy psychoactive substances.

● Exempts healthcare activities and approved scientific research from the offences under the Act, on the basis that persons engaged in such activities have a legitimate need to use psychoactive substances in their work.

● Legitimate substances (such as food, alcohol, tobacco, nicotine, caffeine and medical products) are exempt from the scope of the offence, as well as controlled drugs, which continue to be regulated by the Misuse of Drugs Act 1971.

4.4   Definitions

Alcohol. A colourless, volatile, flammable liquid that forms the intoxicating element in beer, spirits and wine.

Alcoholic. A person suffering from alcoholism.

Drug. A medicine or other substance that has a physiological effect when ingested or otherwise introduced into the body.

Drug misuse. The intermittent or continual use of drugs, which causes harm to the individual, their significant others or the wider community. Drug misuse can be detrimental to the employee's health, safety and work performance.

Substance abuse or misuse. The continued misuse of any mind-altering substance that severely affects a person's physical and mental health, social situation and responsibilities.

Company premises. All property owned, operated, leased by or otherwise under the control of the company, in whole or in part. This includes building and construction sites as well as company offices on or off site.

Under the influence. When there is a sufficient amount of the substance in a person's system to produce a positive result from a medical test or breathalyser and/or when the person shows behaviour likely to pose a risk to themselves or others or to interfere with their job performance. *(For further information refer to 4.7 Driving under the influence.)*

 A document detailing drug misuse and statistics can be found on the Office for National Statistics website.

For information on drug misuse at work refer to the Health and Safety Executive (HSE) Employers' guide.

4.5 Common drugs, effects and symptoms

There are many different types of drugs available, and these are continually changing. New substances are emerging and slang terms for drugs are constantly changing, meaning that it is difficult to keep up with terminology from around the whole of the UK.

It is important for site managers or supervisors to identify, manage and support individuals who misuse drugs. They should be aware of some of the common drugs, effects and symptoms.

 For up-to-date A to Z lists of drugs and currently-used slang terms, as well as free impartial information, advice and guidance on all of the different drugs available and their effects on people, visit the Talk to Frank website.

4.5.1 Class A drugs

4.5.1.1 Ecstasy

This is a Class A drug, meaning that it's illegal to have for yourself, give away or sell.

It produces a buzz and intense pleasure, but also causes dizziness, disorientation, breathlessness and sickness. It increases the pulse-rate and can leave you feeling flushed, restless, anxious and paranoid. Your jaw muscles tighten, pupils get bigger, energy increases and you may lose your appetite and desire to sleep. It enhances affection and energy but can make music and light seem more intense.

A penalty for its use or supply can range from a fine to life imprisonment. The drug is detectable in urine for two to four days.

- Some people are sensitive or allergic to ecstasy, which can cause illness or death.

- If you have a heart condition, you could have a seizure.

- It can cause heat stroke, especially if you're in a hot club and dancing a lot, which can cause death as your internal organs stop working.

- Drinking too much water can also be dangerous as fluid can build up on your brain leading to unconsciousness, coma and even death.

- If you have an existing condition (such as epilepsy), ecstasy could trigger it.

- You may develop long-term mental health problems and depression.

- You could do permanent damage to your internal organs (liver, kidneys, heart and brain).

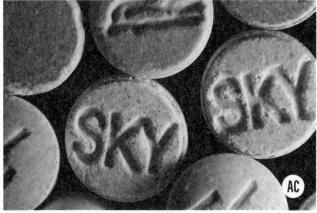
Ecstasy

4.5.1.2 Cocaine and crack

A Class A drug, it is a powerful stimulant that speeds up your central nervous system; your heart rate and blood pressure increase and your pupils get bigger. It makes you feel really powerful, as though you can do anything, and it gives you more energy and awareness.

The effects of crack are more intense than coke and you get a quicker hit, but the effects last for only a short time. A penalty for its use or supply can range from a fine to life imprisonment. The drug is detectable in urine from 12 hours to four days.

- You can easily get hooked – developing a real craving for it, but feeling rough when it wears off.

- It can cause death, mainly from heart failure or internal bleeding.

- Regular crack users will almost certainly suffer from breathing problems, because of damage to their lungs.

- If you snort cocaine regularly you can end up with a perforated septum (the wall between your nostrils).

- Even if you use cocaine only occasionally you could suffer from disrupted sleep patterns, appetite loss, fatigue, restlessness, anxiety and paranoia.

- It destroys some of the chemicals in your brain that control your mood, which can make you depressed and even suicidal.

- It increases adrenaline and this can cause restlessness, extreme paranoia and aggression.

- Mixing it with alcohol increases the risk of heart and liver damage.

Cocaine

4.5.1.3 Heroin

A Class A drug, heroin is an analgesic, which makes you feel relaxed and acts as a powerful painkiller.

It creates a sense of extreme pleasure and feeling good. Heavy use makes you sleepy, sedated and slurred. Many people are sick the first time they use it.

A penalty for its use or supply can range from a fine to life imprisonment. The drug is detectable in urine for one to two days.

- There is a high risk of death from overdose, especially if you've been drinking alcohol or taking other depressants (certain types of drugs, like tranquiliser pills prescribed by doctors).

- Regular use often means you stop looking after yourself and stop caring about the way you look.

- Injecting increases the risk of dangerous infections and abscesses.

- Your cough reflex can be reduced for long periods, so you're more likely to get chest infections.

- Regular users commonly suffer from constipation.

- You can become tolerant to heroin quickly, so you need more to get the same hit or to stop getting withdrawal symptoms.

- If you stop taking heroin for a while your tolerance drops, which means that if you start again and take your normal dose, there is a greater risk of overdosing.

- Heroin is physically addictive, and though withdrawal is not fatal it is extremely unpleasant.

Heroin

4.5.1.4 LSD

A Class A drug which takes between 30 and 60 minutes to take effect, and the effects can last from eight to 12 hours.

Trips are unpredictable and vary hugely from person to person. The drug works on the brain causing changes to thoughts, senses and perceptions. It can cause visual disturbance, hallucinations, anxiety, dizziness or disorientation.

A penalty for its use or supply can range from a fine to life imprisonment. The drug is detectable in urine for two to three days.

- The most common health risk is short or long-term psychological damage.

- It can trigger a range of mental problems and frequent long-term use can leave you feeling disorientated for quite a long time.

- Use of LSD can cause permanent eye damage.

- There is a risk that you could injure yourself when you've taken LSD, by doing something dangerous.

- You may experience flashbacks (reliving a few seconds or minutes of a trip) weeks, months or even years after taking it.

- It doesn't mix well with alcohol and cannabis, increasing the side effects (for example, sickness and anxiety).

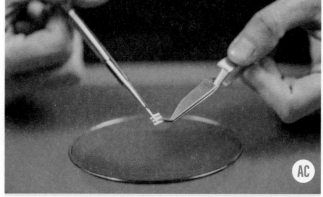
LSD

4.5.1.5 Methadone

A Class A drug which is only legal if it's prescribed. It has similar effects to heroin, though longer acting (24 hours) and less intense. Some users experience an intense allergy-like itchiness.

When prescribed for heroin users, it can stop withdrawal symptoms for 24 hours, to allow them to gain control of their lives.

A penalty for its use or supply can range from a fine to life imprisonment. The drug is detectable in urine for three to five days.

- Methadone is physically addictive and withdrawal can be longer and even more unpleasant than heroin.

- If you mix methadone with alcohol you are at more risk of passing out and, like heroin, your cough reflex is reduced, which means you could choke if you're sick.

- Overdose is common in users who are not used to the drug or have lost their tolerance.

- Injecting it or using undiluted 50 mg ampoules can lead to vein damage, and injecting crushed tablets carries serious risk of vein blocking and abscesses.

- Methadone is extremely poisonous to children.

4.5.2   Class B drugs

4.5.2.1   Amphetamines

These are Class B drugs, but are Class A if prepared for injection. They are stimulants, so they increase your heart rate and blood pressure and you feel more alert, talkative and have more energy. A penalty for its use or supply can range from a fine to seven years' imprisonment. The drug is detectable in urine for two to four days.

- Overuse can cause anxiety, panic attacks, irritability and aggressive behaviour, as well as weight loss and illness, because of eating poorly and generally not looking after yourself.

- Regular use can bring on a state of intense paranoia (feeling terrified of things around you).

- If you have a heart condition, there is a particular risk of death from heart problems.

- Depending on how you take it, an amphetamine can damage your nasal lining, gums or stomach. If you inject it, it can cause permanent damage to your body.

- It can also make your jaw feel tight, which can make you grind your teeth and chew constantly.

- Amphetamines can reduce sexual sensitivity and performance.

- The comedown can cause aches and pains, hunger, tiredness, depression and loss of self-esteem.

- If you snort drugs, the lining of your nose often breaks and bleeds, and you can easily get an infection.

- Injecting amphetamines is especially dangerous. It can badly damage your veins and there is the added risk of catching a blood-borne virus (for example, hepatitis B or C or HIV) if you share equipment.

Amphetamines

4.5.2.2   Cannabis

A Class B drug also known as marijuana, it is a stimulant, depressant and hallucinogen. It can make you relaxed, giggly, hungry, and appreciate sound and colour more. You may feel anxious and paranoid and the effects can be unpredictable. A penalty for its use or supply can range from a fine to 14 years' imprisonment. The drug is detectable in urine for two to three days.

- Smoking cannabis, especially with tobacco, can cause lung damage, with an increased risk of lung and throat cancers.

- Regular use can cause short-term memory loss and make you feel demotivated and listless.

- There is an increased risk of mental health problems (such as anxiety and paranoia), which can last into adult life.

- It interferes with learning, making it harder to study and work.

- Side effects (such as nausea, palpitations and anxiety) are sometimes made worse by alcohol.

- If you become dependent, you'll find stopping difficult due to symptoms like sleep disturbance, vivid dreaming, mood swings, irritability and possible aggression, headache and tiredness.

- Cannabis can stay in your body for up to 30 days and so can show up positive in drug tests for some time after your last use.

Cannabis

4.5.2.3   Mephedrone

A Class B drug, mephedrone is a stimulant (increasing alertness and energy) with similar effects to cocaine, amphetamines and ecstasy. The effects can come on in a head rush and be overpowering, which can make you feel sick (more likely if you've been drinking alcohol or smoking cannabis). The effects of a single dose can last for at least an hour, although some people report it going on for much longer. A penalty for its use or supply can range from a fine to life imprisonment. The drug is detectable in urine for up to four days.

- Taking it carries some serious risks so it should be treated with caution. These risks are greater if you use large doses, take it for extended periods of time or combine it with other drugs.

- The biggest risk is heart failure, so if you have an existing heart problem or high blood pressure you should especially avoid using it.

- Some prescribed medication can react badly with it.

- Drugs such as mephedrone and ecstasy can occasionally cause death because of a direct toxic effect on the body.

- Like other stimulants, it can cause jaw clenching and teeth grinding, which can damage your teeth.

- The comedown can make you feel exhausted, depressed, confused and disorientated, with a sore head. You won't be able to sleep properly after taking it.

4.5.2.4 Ketamine

A Class B drug which can make you feel disoriented, with a sense of numbness and a lack of co-ordination. Low doses can create a sense of extreme pleasure and mild hallucinations (K-holing – a feeling of travelling outside the body towards a tunnel of light). Effects shouldn't last for more than about three hours. A penalty for its use or supply can range from a fine to 14 years' imprisonment. The drug is detectable in urine for up to 14 days.

- Ketamine is an anaesthetic, which numbs pain, so you may injure yourself without realising it until the effects have worn off.

- There's a risk of mental health problems from the drug's disorientating experiences.

- It can cause sickness, headaches and diarrhoea, and may even paralyse you temporarily.

- If you drink alcohol or take other depressants (certain types of drugs, like tranquiliser pills prescribed by doctors) you increase the risk of heart failure, unconsciousness, vomiting and choking.

- Serious and permanent bladder problems can develop.

- If you inject ketamine there are the usual risks of dangerous infections through using needles.

4.5.3 Class C drugs

4.5.3.1 Benzodiazepine

A Class C drug (which is legal if you have a prescription for it) and also includes the following prescription medications: nitrazepam, mogadon, lorazepam, ativan, flurazepam, clonazepam, rohypnol, temazepam, librium, diazepam and valium. It relaxes you, reduces anxiety, your muscles feel less tense and it can also help you sleep. A penalty for its use or supply can range from a fine to 14 years' imprisonment. The drug is detectable in urine for one to two days.

- You may lose co-ordination, become forgetful and vague.

- You can become tolerant to the drug quickly, so after a few weeks the dose stops being effective.

- It can cause sleeplessness and anxiety if you take it for longer than a few weeks.

- It can cause vertigo, hypotension, loss of libido, urinary retention and blood disorders.

- If you are taking other depressants as well, there's a higher risk of overdose.

- If you crush and inject tablets, you're at risk of abscess-blocked veins as well as the usual risks of intravenous drug use.

4.5.3.2 Piperazines (BZP)

A Class C drug, piperazines (BZP) come in various forms and shapes. Pills can be red, blue, pink, white, off-white, purple, orange, tan and mottled orange-brown. BZP was originally evaluated as an antidepressant drug. Now it is found mainly as a substitute for MDMA (ecstasy). Stimulant effects are similar to MDMA, but dose for dose they are not as potent. Effects can last for six to eight hours and include feelings of euphoria, being alert, alive and full of energy, arousal, sleeplessness and loss of appetite. Physical health risks for users include the following.

- Users often suffer a hangover-like reaction that can last for up to 24 hours.

- Agitation, vomiting, stomach pain, fits, irregular heart rhythms, diarrhoea, allergic reactions and fever.

- As stimulant drugs, piperazines are particularly risky if taken by anyone suffering from high blood pressure or a heart condition. (Remember: the user may not know that they have a pre-existing heart condition.)

- Perfectly healthy young people can have a fit or heart attack after taking stimulant drugs.

- In rare cases, users may suffer from serotonin syndrome, which can cause high blood pressure and be fatal.

- The chemical composition of substances sold as piperazines is changing all the time, which is why you can never be sure of what you're getting and how it could affect you.

This is a Class C drug, which means it's illegal to possess for yourself, give away or sell. Penalties for possession can be up to two years in prison, an unlimited fine or both. Supplying someone else, even your friends, can carry a sentence of up to 14 years in prison, an unlimited fine or both.

4.5.4 Psychoactive substances

Psychoactive substances cannot be sold, purchased and advertised for human consumption.

It is likely that psychoactive substances may actually contain one or more substances that are illegal to possess.

 Employers should include psychoactive substances when writing and reviewing their substance misuse policies.

- Psychoactive substances can still cause harm and have similar health risks to other illegal drugs (for example, paranoia, coma, seizures and death).

- Risks are increased if used with alcohol or other drugs.

- There has been little research into the effects of short to long-term use of psychoactive substances.

- A large number of psychoactive substances can be known by:
  - a chemical name (for example, dimethocaine)
  - a slang name (for example, in some areas 'bubble' is a generic name for any synthetic white powder which has stimulant effects). It is not uncommon for the drug content of such white powders either to be unknown or to be incorrectly described. Therefore users don't know what they are really buying, how it will affect them, how strong it is or if it is legal.

4.5.4.1   Common psychoactive substances, effects and symptoms

Spice is a synthetic form of marijuana that contains artificial cannabinoids. Although it is not marijuana, it is mixed with unspecified compounds that vary with each batch. It is a blend of herbs and unknown substances: often, unnamed chemicals are sprayed onto the herbs to make the NPS mimic the appearance of marijuana.

Smoking, vaping, or consuming Spice produces mind-altering effects, and such effects can be much more potent and considerably more harmful than cannabis. If a person develops an addiction to this substance, it could give way to alarming physical and mental health consequences.

Spice and pre-rolled Spice cigarettes

Signs of spice addiction include the following.

- Feelings of euphoria.
- Physical and mental relaxation.
- Think about the drug all the time.
- See the drug as a necessity.

- Conceal the addiction to friends and family.
- Avoid social interactions.
- Only associate with others who use Spice.
- Neglect their physical appearance and personal hygiene.

People use psychoactive substances for many of the same reasons that they use illegal drugs, including:

- to experience the pleasurable short-term effects
- to cope with difficult life circumstances, such as stress, anxiety and depression
- to self-medicate for a mental health disorder.

4.5.5   Over-the-counter drugs

Over-the-counter drugs come in three different types.

Stimulants, such as cough and cold treatments and decongestants, especially non-drowsy (for example, Actifed Expectorant, Sinutab and Sudafed).

Depressants, such as cough and cold linctuses, painkiller analgesic capsules and diarrhoea preparations (for example, Nurofen Plus, Paracodol, Feminax and Syndol).

Sedatives, such as antihistamines, cough and cold treatments and some night-time sleep aids (for example, Piriton, Night Nurse, Benylin and Contac 400).

Stimulants can make you excited, alert, agitated and anxious, and increase your heart rate and blood pressure. Depressants can cause mild euphoria, relaxation, detachment, decreased heart rate and blood pressure, increased effects of alcohol and physical addiction. Sedatives can make you sleepy or drowsy, even at normal dosages, and increase the effects of alcohol.

- Misuse of these products often mimics the classic symptoms of a clinical drug addiction, with physical and psychological effects.

- Dependence doesn't always mean you're regularly taking large daily quantities of a drug. You can become dependent by having to take a daily amount, under the maximum recommended dosage, over many years.

- You can become unintentionally addicted to an over-the-counter drug. You may have simply bought it to treat a physical complaint, without being aware that it could be addictive.

4.5.5   E-cigarettes

E-cigarettes are a comparatively new and rapidly-evolving product. Many people are using e-cigarettes (also known as vapes) as an alternative to smoking tobacco.

They consist of a plastic electric cigarette with a heating element, and hold a cartridge containing liquid nicotine that, when heated, changes into a vapour. The nicotine and other ingredients are inhaled into the body.

Although e-cigarettes are almost certainly significantly less harmful than smoking tobacco, they aren't risk free. Most contain nicotine, which is highly addictive, as well as other ingredients such as propylene glycol, glycerine and flavourings. E-cigarettes have been regulated by the government since May 2016, and since April 2017 it is illegal to sell e-cigarettes to, or buy them for, under-18s.

04

If used as a complete replacement for smoking, they will almost certainly benefit the users health. The health benefit comes from stopping smoking, not using an e-cigarette. It will be some time until studies will show the long-term impact and any unforeseen risks of using e-cigarettes. They aren't the only option for smokers looking to stop. If someone is looking to quit, they could consider using proven methods of stopping smoking like nicotine replacement therapy (NRT) or prescribed medication to help to break their reliance on nicotine.

4.5.5.1   Illegal drugs and e-cigarettes

With around 2.6 million users across the UK, the popularity of e-cigarettes has increased substantially in recent years. A recent study by public health experts has revealed that an increasing amount of these users are modifying their devices to vape illegal substances like cannabis and heroin. Medical experts are now warning that this trend poses a serious public health risk.

Experts at King's College London surveyed 2,500 people, and 861 said that they currently or previously have used a vaping device, and 39% admitted to vaping illegal drugs. The most common illegal drug to be used in a vaping device is cannabis. The research team who conducted the investigation revealed that the main reason behind this trend was that users thought it was safer as well as being more discreet:

 Increasing availability, use and acceptance of vaping devices, especially amongst teens and young adults, may lead to greater use of recreational drugs by this route, thereby increasing overall drug exposure. The ability to vape deodorised drugs, especially cannabis, more discreetly with no smell – known as 'stealth vaping' – makes drug use harder to detect and therefore prevent.

A spokesperson for Young Addiction said health concerns around tobacco may also have contributed to this growing trend: "Young people don't want to use tobacco due to the health risks, but do want to use cannabis. As such, vaping is increasing in popularity."

4.6   Alcohol

Alcohol is a positive part of life for many people and most of the time drinking alcohol doesn't cause many problems. However, drinking too much at the wrong time can be harmful. The department of health recommends that alcohol intake is limited to 14 units per week (two units per day) for men and women, with at least one alcohol-free day a week. The usual advice that one glass of wine or one half-pint of beer is equal to one unit is misleading and can lead to misunderstanding and accidental over-consumption.

e.g. Formula for calculating alcohol units

The number of alcohol units is worked out by the formula:

Strength (ABV) x Volume (ml) ÷ 1,000 = units

where: ABV = percentage alcohol content of the drink.

If a person drinks one 200 ml glass of wine with 13% alcohol content:

13(%) x 200(ml) ÷ 1,000 = 2.6 units.

 Visit the Drinkaware website for an alcohol unit calculator.

Excessive and continued intake of alcohol can result in serious ill health, including scarring of the liver tissue, which then affects its function. Approximately 30% of people diagnosed with the condition of cirrhosis of the liver only survive five years after diagnosis. Furthermore, 3% of all cancer is directly caused by alcohol consumption.

 For an employers' guide to alcohol at work visit the HSE website.

4.7   Driving under the influence

4.7.1   Alcohol

Driving a motor vehicle on a public road whilst under the influence of alcohol is a criminal offence, with penalties that range from a fine, with or without disqualification, to a term of imprisonment. In line with the current UK (England, Wales and Northern Ireland) drink drive legal limits, it is an offence to drive with an alcohol concentration that exceeds the following legal limits:

- 35 micrograms per 100 millilitres of breath
- 8 milligrams per 100 millilitres of blood, or
- 107 milligrams per 100 millilitres of urine.

In Scotland, the legal limits are:

- 22 micrograms per 100 millilitres of breath
- 50 milligrams per 100 millilitres of blood, or
- 67 milligrams per 100 millilitres of urine.

There is no safe limit of alcohol that you can consume and then drive. Each person's body reacts differently to alcohol. There are a lot of factors that can affect how long alcohol remains in a person's system, but – on average – the liver can process one ounce of alcohol every hour, and it can be detected in the blood for several hours, while it can be detected in the urine for several days.

The speed at which alcohol is absorbed into your system (and how quickly your system gets rid of it) depends on a large number of factors, including your age, gender, ethnicity, body size, medications (such as anti-anxiety or anti-depressant tablets or antibiotics), the last time you ate and the last time you had an alcoholic drink.

It is impossible to know how long it will take to sober up after drinking. Drinking strong coffee, eating, sleeping and taking a cold shower **do not** sober you up any faster. Only **time** sobers you up.

Too many people are killed or seriously injured on our roads in drink-driving accidents. It is estimated that in Great Britain 1,490 people were killed or seriously injured due to drink driving in 2020 alone.

Alcohol affects sensory perception and reaction times – don't drink and drive

Penalties for driving whilst under the influence of alcohol			
Offence	Maximum penalty		Further restrictions
	Custodial sentence	Fine	
Being in charge of a vehicle while above the legal limit or unfit through drink.	Three months' imprisonment.	£2,500.	Possible driving ban.
Driving or attempting to drive while above the legal limit or unfit through drink.	Six months' imprisonment.	Unlimited.	Driving ban for at least one year (three years if convicted twice in 10 years).
Refusing to provide a specimen of breath, blood or urine for analysis.	Six months' imprisonment.	Unlimited.	Ban from driving for at least one year.
Causing death by careless driving when under the influence of drink or drugs (Section 3A of the Road Traffic Act 1988 (as amended by the Road Traffic Act 1991, Section 3)).	Life imprisonment.	Unlimited.	Ban from driving for at least two years and an extended driving test before your licence is returned.

 The maximum penalty is 14 years' imprisonment if the offence was committed before 28 June 2022. If the offence was committed on or after 28 June 2022, the maximum penalty is life imprisonment.

4.7.2   Drugs

It is an offence to drive whilst unfit through drugs. Many people think that if they drive under the influence of drugs a vehicle search and a potential charge of possession is all they have to be worried about, but the following should also be considered.

● Taking drugs will impair driving skills. Driving whilst under the influence of drugs is extremely dangerous and can affect driving in numerous ways.

● Drugged drivers can suffer from slower reaction times, erratic and aggressive behaviour, an inability to concentrate properly, nausea, hallucinations, panic attacks, paranoia, tremors (or 'the shakes'), dizziness and fatigue. In such a condition, it is a bad idea to be behind the wheel of a car, for the driver, their passengers and other road users.

● Whilst the effects of drugs are wearing off, the taker may feel fatigued, which will affect their concentration whilst driving.

Penalties for driving whilst under the influence of drugs			
Offence	Maximum penalty		Further restrictions
	Custodial sentence	Fine	
Being convicted of drug driving.	Six months' imprisonment.	Unlimited.	Driving ban for at least one year, with a drug-driving conviction on your licence for 11 years.
Causing death by careless driving when under the influence of drink or drugs (Section 3A of the Road Traffic Act 1988 (as amended by the Road Traffic Act 1991, Section 3)).	Life imprisonment.	Unlimited.	Ban from driving for at least two years and an extended driving test before your licence is returned.

 The maximum penalty is 14 years' imprisonment if the offence was committed before 28 June 2022. If the offence was committed on or after 28 June 2022, the maximum penalty is life imprisonment.

4.8   Managing work-related substance misuse

Workplace problems can be caused through drug and alcohol consumption both inside and outside of work, as the effects can be long-lasting. The following points should be taken into account when considering the scale of the drug or alcohol problem within a company.

- The risk of accidents due to impaired performance through drugs or alcohol.
- Inept and poor decision making.
- Lower standards of work.
- Low productivity caused by employees' inability to cope with workplace situations.
- Disruption and ill discipline by employees under the influence of substances.
- Time lost from the workplace due to absenteeism, lateness or habitual sick leave.
- Long-term health of the workforce.
- Stress factors on employees due to home circumstances.
- Financial stress on employees of feeding any habits or addiction.
- Impact on customers.
- Impact on company reputation.
- Security concerns.
- Potential compensation claims against the employer.
- Poor staff retention rates.

Successfully tackling alcohol and drug misuse can benefit your business and employees. For example, you would save costs on recruiting and training new employees. Offering support to employees who declare a drug-related problem will also help in the following ways.

- Reducing the risk of accidents.
- Creating a more productive environment and improving employee loyalty and morale.
- Enhancing company reputation as a responsible employer.
- Contributing to society's efforts to combat alcohol and drug misuse.

4.8.1   Identifying misuse

Alcohol, drug or solvent misuse by employees may come to light in a variety of ways. The following actions may indicate that a problem exists.

- Absenteeism without notice.
- Poor time-keeping.
- High accident levels and clumsiness.
- Confusion and disorientation.
- Poor performance and workmanship.
- Irritability, aggression and argumentativeness.
- Misconduct.
- Failure to remember, or failure to comply with, common instructions.
- A sudden need for increased supervision.
- Leaving site either without permission or at lunchtimes to visit licensed premises.
- Finding empty beer cans, bottles or drug-related paraphernalia.

Physical symptoms of substance misuse may include the following.

- Rapid loss of weight.
- Gaunt appearance.
- Tremors or sweating.
- Constant tiredness.
- Trackmarks, severe bruising or abscesses on arms.
- Over-dilated or very small pupils.
- Cravings (for example, ice cream, nicotine and sweet foodstuffs).

Behavioural symptoms may include the following.

- Degenerating personal appearance.
- Excessive care about personal appearance.
- Hyperactivity.
- Severe mood swings.
- Avoidance of authority or supervision.

- Deteriorating relations with other staff.
- Swings in morale.
- Minimum involvement with other staff.
- Obsessive or compulsive behaviour.

Communicating with and educating employees, supported by an effective workplace policy and community-based treatment, will improve the chances of the early detection of problems. Employees need to feel secure in asking for help and be made aware of the benefits this provides to all parties in supporting them. Supervisors and managers may require training and supporting information to enable them to identify problems and then manage and support individuals in line with company policy and legal requirements.

4.8.2   Addressing misuse

Known or suspected misuse should lead to consultation between the company, employees and representatives. To agree a way forward is essential if it is to be addressed adequately.

 Employer associations, solicitors and professional bodies (such as Alcohol Change UK, Phoenix Futures or DrugWise) can advise and help develop a workplace alcohol and drugs policy.

4.8.2.1   Developing and implementing workplace policies

A substance misuse policy that applies to all staff can be of benefit and may form part of a company's overall health and safety policy. The policy will need to take account of the particular needs of the company and the practical situations, including those brought about by working on building and construction sites. However, there are a number of minimum requirements (shown below) for such a policy.

- Contain a clear statement of the behaviour that is expected of employees.
- Apply equally to employees at all levels, including managers and supervisors, in the workplace.
- Result from full consultation with employees and, if appropriate, representatives (such as recognised trades unions) before it is adopted.
- Be made known to all employees.
- Be an integrated part of an overall health and safety policy.
- Include clear statements on the roles and responsibilities of all employees in relation to the policy (for example, site-based operatives, HR department, Occupational Health department, site managers).
- Address issues in the work environment that are likely to increase the use of alcohol or drugs.
- Encourage those with a problem to come forward under a promise of strict confidentiality and future support.
- To the greatest possible degree, be non-punitive.
- State the conduct likely to result in action being taken under the policy.
- Provide for appropriate treatment and rehabilitation for those with problems.
- Be evaluated after implementation and amended, if necessary, in line with the outcome of the evaluation.

The potential for the policy to interfere in an employee's private life must be lawful and proportionate. The policy is likely to be lawful and proportionate in the following situations.

- When it is instituted to protect and promote employee safety.
- If employees are aware of the policy.
- When the process of collecting, transporting and testing samples can be proven to be independent and beyond reproach.
- Where employees know what the employer will do with the test results.
- If the employer has no other reasonable alternative way of obtaining the same result.

 For a template on developing a substance misuse policy refer to Appendix A.

Implementing a substance misuse policy has four essential components.

1. The education and information of all levels of management, employees and their representatives.
2. The organisational support shown by the company.
3. The addressing of issues in the work environment.
4. The prevention and rehabilitation support offered by the company to its employees.

Information about a substance misuse policy, covering alcohol and drugs, must be provided to all employees, and be included as part of any induction training for new recruits. The policy must be supported by education about the harmful effects of alcohol and drugs, the rehabilitation services available and the means by which employers will help individuals to access these services.

It is important that management demonstrates its full support for the policy by ensuring observance by all staff, at whatever level, and endorsing changes to the working environment to facilitate the full and proper implementation of the policy.

The provision of treatment and/or referral services is an important component of implementing the policy. If problems are detected early, before serious physical and social effects occur, a brief intervention may be all that is needed.

Confidentiality for employees undergoing treatment and rehabilitation must be guaranteed. Equally, employees should not be disadvantaged in terms of promotion or seniority because they have sought or are accepting help. Treatment and rehabilitation should be covered by adequate leave entitlements.

However, as with all workplace health and safety matters, consultation with employees and the provision of education and information at an early stage, may prevent the onset of alcohol and drug problems at work.

4.8.2.2   Temporary and sub-contracted staff

The company substance misuse policy should address the employment of sub-contractors and other temporary staff. Sub-contractors are normally obliged to work within the main contractor's policies and this condition could form part of any contract.

4.8.2.3   Misuse outside of the workplace

Generally, an employee's conduct outside of the workplace is not within the employer's control. However, if drug or alcohol misuse during recreational times creates a risk to their health and safety or to that of others who may be affected by the employee's actions during working hours, consideration must be given to the situation and to what action should or can be taken.

A company's substance misuse policy may also need to consider situations where an employee's behaviour outside the workplace results in a conviction for a criminal offence, and the effect that this would have on the company's image and reputation.

 If a driver is convicted of a drink-driving or drug-driving offence and they drive for work, the employer will see the conviction when they produce their licence.

4.8.3   Disciplinary procedures

The majority of employers will have a disciplinary procedure in place. It may be appropriate to ensure the procedure covers the consumption of alcohol or drugs in the workplace. You may also wish for the policy to contain a provision that possession, dealing or trafficking in drugs will be reported to the police.

For a substance misuse policy to be effective, it is essential that it is consistent with disciplinary procedure.

Employees with a substance misuse problem or those suspected of misusing alcohol or drugs should have the same rights to confidentiality and support (or to any other company procedure, including those agreed with the recognised trades unions) as they would if they had any other medical condition, or if any other disciplinary matter were involved.

It can be difficult for employees to discuss or openly admit to having an alcohol or drug problem, because of the stigma or fear of reprisals, or the difficulty they have facing up to the issue.

It should also be considered that HSE inspectors may, in appropriate circumstances, issue improvement and prohibition notices and, if they were to find an employee under the influence of alcohol or drugs on site, they would have the option to take appropriate actions against the employer.

 For further information on improvement and prohibition notices refer to Chapter A02 The Health and Safety at Work etc. Act.

4.9   Drug or alcohol screening and testing

Introducing drug testing in the workplace is a difficult and potentially expensive initiative. It is essential to be completely clear on the reasons for doing so, or not. Testing is far from the whole answer and has inherent limitations.

Before any decision is taken by an employer to implement an alcohol or drug testing regime, care must be taken to ensure that a substance misuse policy is fully established, communicated to all employees and, where appropriate, accepted by their representatives.

It is legitimate for employers to take an interest in drug and alcohol use in their workforce. The independent inquiry into drug testing at work concludes that these circumstances are when:

- employees are engaging in illegal activity in the workplace
- employees are actually intoxicated during working hours
- drug or alcohol use is having an impact on work performance that goes beyond a threshold of acceptability
- the nature of the work is such that the public is entitled to expect a higher than average standard of behaviour from employees and/or there is a risk of corruption.

There remains an open question as to whether introducing testing for employees constitutes a solution to any of these circumstances. As yet, there is no clear evidence that this is so, but broadly speaking there are valid arguments for and against.

Supporters of drug testing claim the following.

- There are benefits for safety.
- The company is more efficient.
- There is a positive effect on the organisation's external reputation.
- It sends a strong message to employees that drug use is not acceptable.

Opponents of drug testing claim the following.

- Tests are unreliable for many reasons, chiefly that they do not necessarily prove impairment, dependence or current use.
- There is no clear evidence of any benefit in terms of deterring use, reducing accidents or improving efficiency.
- It is excessively invasive and a potential infringement of human rights.
- It is damaging to work relations and can hamper recruitment.
- It is costly, complicated and time-consuming.
- It is possible to cheat drug tests.

4.9.1 The legal position

The extent to which employers can require employees to undertake random drug or alcohol testing is limited, even where there is a right to test the employee in their contract of employment.

An unreasonable request to take a test will result in a breach of the implied duty of mutual trust and confidence. This could lead to an employee successfully claiming unfair constructive dismissal. Obtaining samples without consent could, in addition, constitute the criminal offences of assault or battery. In the absence of factors indicating that the employee is using, or is affected by, alcohol or drugs at work, the employer will have to ensure it can justify any testing it wishes to carry out.

There is no specific legislation relating to drug testing in the workplace. Consequently, there is a lack of clarity surrounding the legal issues. Case law is also relatively scarce. Important legal decisions hinge on an interpretation of a range of legal implications, the main ones are shown below.

- Health and safety at work.
- Data protection.

- Human rights.
- Disability discrimination.

It is clear, however, that no-one can be tested against their will. It is important to be aware that any attempt to test employees without their express individual consent would constitute a criminal offence.

4.9.2 Why test?

Drug testing might be introduced for a number of reasons. Other than where there is a clear clinical imperative (that is rehabilitation testing), the effectiveness of each approach has not been proven.

Recruitment screening usually refers to testing or assessing the health of potential employees during the recruitment process. Testing of this kind presents far fewer legal and logistical problems than introducing testing for existing employees.

Routine testing is done at specified times, and gives a clear message that it is not acceptable to be affected by alcohol or drugs when working. It might be used in situations where employees are in safety-critical posts (such as operating or driving construction plant on a public road, or operating machinery).

Random testing or unannounced testing is used as a deterrent to identify previously undetected drug or alcohol misusers. As with routine testing, any use in situations that are not safety critical may cause feelings of resentment amongst the workforce.

Reason or 'with cause' testing might be used if a manager has reason to believe that an employee or employees have been using drugs or drinking alcohol. This might be because of their behaviour or by physical signs (such as smelling alcohol or finding drug paraphernalia). It may also form part of a post-incident or accident investigation.

Post-incident testing can be used following an incident. Everyone involved in the work activity would be subject to testing as soon as possible. Post-incident testing can be used to determine whether drug or alcohol use was a contributing factor for accidents and injuries.

Rehabilitation testing may be used where an employee has agreed to treatment and the treatment provider is testing to ensure compliance with a prescription (for example, urine testing to ensure that an individual who has been prescribed methadone is not using heroin as well as the prescribed dose). Similarly, testing may be introduced as part of a return to work agreement between employee and employer.

4.9.3 Is testing necessary?

In the past drug and alcohol testing has been considered a controversial and complex issue that has scientific, ethical, legal, social, industrial and economic ramifications. However, many major contracts successfully implement such testing programmes.

It is reasonable to expect employees to be unimpaired by drugs or alcohol whilst at work.

In such a dangerous working environment with a high rate of accidents, it is vital that workers are of sound health and mind, and can conduct their activities to the best of their ability – which means there is no place for drugs and alcohol.

The mental health charity Mates in Mind estimates that around 350,000 construction workers experience health issues, which increase the risk of suicide. The construction industry has a responsibility to identify workers with a drug or alcohol problem, and ensure that company policies welcome full disclosure, so that support is given before the worst happens.

Whether testing is appropriate or necessary should be carefully considered, as the damage to employer-employee relations can potentially outweigh the benefits. However, it may also be a client requirement, which should be explained to the employee at induction.

Drug and alcohol testing in the construction and built environment sector is not currently governed by laws regarding drug and alcohol use, unlike other high-risk industries such as rail and aviation.

Whether you decide to introduce testing or not, it must be emphasised that it is not an end in itself. Drug and alcohol testing is no substitute for good management practice and should never be introduced without the following.

● Full co-operation from employees.

● A programme of education for managers and employees.

● Robust systems for referral to adequately-trained health professionals.

Before considering the introduction of a testing programme, employers should be able to fully answer the following questions

● Why do we want to test? (What do we hope to achieve by it?)

● What substances will we test for?

● Which employees will we test?

● How will we select them?

● When will we test them (for example, routinely, randomly, pre-employment)?

● How often will we test?

● How will we test (for example, by what method)?

● Who is best placed to conduct the test (for example, independent company/laboratory, Occupational Health department)?

● What will we do with a positive result?

● What training will be necessary and for whom?

● What will be the financial costs?

● What may be the other costs (for example, staff morale)?

● How will we involve the workforce and gain their consent?

● What will be our safeguards? (How do we ensure that test results are accurate and legally defensible?)

The conclusions that are drawn from these questions should guide you to a well thought out and rational decision.

4.9.4   Methods of testing

The variety of methods can be confusing for employers, and each testing company will advocate the advantages of their particular approach. It is vital that those wishing to introduce a testing programme are clear about the requirements of each, and consider logistical issues (refer to 4.9.3).

● Gaining employee consent.

● Clear explanations of the process to employees.

● Collection of samples.

● Second sampling.

● Legal defensibility (chain of custody).

● Employee confidentiality.

● Appropriate privacy.

● Clear testing protocols and prescribed testing limits.

There is a variety in both the methods used for employee testing and in the standards of service offered by drug-testing companies. As yet there is no universally accepted accreditation scheme or quality standard.

It should also be clearly understood that there is a significant difference between testing for alcohol and testing for other drugs.

Alcohol testing indicates whether an individual is under the influence **at that time**. Drug testing shows traces of drugs used in the past, but does not necessarily confirm impairment at the time of testing.

Alcohol use can be tested in two ways.

● Breath testing – a breathalyser measures the level of alcohol in the breath. This is convenient and inexpensive. Employees may be tested prior to commencing a shift, or immediately following an incident.

● Blood testing – this is the most accurate measure of alcohol in the body, although it is more invasive than a breath test. It is often inappropriate in a workplace setting because of a lack of staff suitably trained to take samples.

Drug use may involve the use of illegal drugs, or prescribed and over-the-counter medicines. These can be detected by gaining samples.

● Oral fluid – not as invasive as other methods but a relatively new technology so may be expensive or inaccurate.

● Hair – not accurate for recent use, but depending on hair length the sample may reflect the individual's drug use pattern over a course of months.

● Blood – invasive, but can be more accurate than sampling.

● Urine – potentially invasive, but a well-established science.

● Skin wipe – simple and quick to use. Drug metabolites (small molecules) are deposited on the skin by perspiration and remain when sweat evaporates.

04

Appendix A – Sample template for developing a substance misuse policy

Substance misuse policy

Introduction

<Company> recognises that alcohol and drug abuse related problems are an area of health and social concern. It also recognises that a member of staff with such problems needs help and support from their employer.

The Company also recognises that alcohol and drug abuse problems can have a detrimental effect on work performance and behaviour. The Company has a responsibility to its employees and customers to ensure that this risk is minimised.

Accordingly, Company policy involves two approaches.

1. Providing reasonable assistance to the member of staff with an alcohol or drug abuse problem, who is willing to co-operate in treatment for that problem.

2. Disciplinary rules, enforced through disciplinary procedures, where the use of alcohol or drugs (other than on prescription) affects performance or behaviour at work, and where either (1) an alcohol or drug dependency problem does not exist or (2) where treatment is not possible or has not succeeded.

The Company does not have the internal resources to provide or arrange treatment or other forms of specialist assistance. Such services are provided by GPs, hospitals and other agencies. Through this policy the Company will seek both to assist a member of staff in obtaining such specialist help, and to protect their employment.

Assistance for a member of staff

The Company will, where possible, provide the following assistance to a member of staff.

● Help the member of staff to recognise the nature of the problem, through referral to a qualified diagnostic or counselling service.

● Support them during a period of treatment. This may include a period of sick leave or approved other leave, continuation in post or transfer to other work, depending upon what is appropriate in terms of the staff member's condition and needs of the Company.

● The opportunity to remain or return to work following the completion of a course of treatment, as far as is practicable, in either the employee's own post or an alternative post.

The Company's assistance will depend upon the following conditions being met.

● The Occupational Health Service/company-approved doctor diagnoses an alcohol or drug dependency related problem.

● The member of staff recognises that they are suffering from an alcohol or drug abuse problem and is prepared to co-operate fully in referral and treatment from appropriate sources.

The Company and its employees must recognise the following limits, regarding what assistance the Company can provide.

● Where a member of staff fails to co-operate in referral or treatment arrangements, no special assistance will be given and any failure in work performance and behaviour will be dealt with through the disciplinary procedure.

● If the process of referral and treatment is completed but is not successful, and failure in work performance or behaviour occurs, these will be dealt with through the disciplinary procedure.

● A member of staff's continuation in their post or an alternative post during or after treatment will depend upon the needs of the Company at that time.

Disciplinary action

In line with the Company's disciplinary procedure, the following will be regarded as serious misconduct:

● attending work and/or carrying out duties under the influence of alcohol or drugs

● consumption of alcohol or drugs whilst on duty (other than where prescribed or approval has been given).

Breach of these rules will normally result in summary dismissal, and only in exceptional cases will either notice or the reduced disciplinary action of a final written warning be applied.

Where a breach of these rules occurs, but it is established that an alcohol or drug abuse related problem exists, and the member of staff is willing to co-operate in referral to an appropriate service and subsequent treatment, the Company will **suspend** application of the disciplinary procedure and provide assistance as described above.

Staff who do not comply with the treatment suggested or continue to abuse alcohol or drugs will be subject to the application of the disciplinary policy.

Substance misuse policy *continued*

Procedures

Nature of the procedures

The procedures define management responsibilities and provide guidelines on:

- where assistance to a member of staff should be provided and the nature of and limits to such assistance

- the application of the Company's disciplinary procedure.

Through the Occupational Health Service/company-approved doctor, the Company will provide advice and support to managers on:

- whether an alcohol or drug-related problem exists

- progress in treatment

- re-establishment or continuation at work of a member of staff or other appropriate arrangements

- assistance to members of staff with alcohol or drug abuse related problems.

This does not include directly providing treatment or specialist help, which is the responsibility of GPs, hospitals and other agencies working in the field. The Occupational Health Service/company-approved doctor, in close liaison with these persons and agencies, will assist staff referred in the following ways:

- through counselling, encouraging them to come to a better understanding of their problem and the benefits of seeking treatment or help

- providing advice and direction regarding obtaining treatment and specialist help

- assisting in continuing at or achieving a return to work.

Alcohol or drug abuse related problems can come to the notice of management through:

- failures in work performance or behaviour necessitating use of the disciplinary procedure. In such situations the procedure described above should be followed

- other means, whereby a member of staff seeks or agrees to accept assistance on a voluntary basis. In such situations, the procedures described above should be followed.

Situations where use of the disciplinary procedure is appropriate

Recognising the existence of a possible alcohol or drug abuse problem

Abuse of alcohol or drugs can affect performance and behaviour at work. This could be either through serious misconduct at work (where there is a direct and demonstrable breach of the disciplinary rules regarding alcohol or drug abuse at work), or where there is a falling off of standards of work performance or behaviour, and abuse of alcohol or drugs is a possible cause.

The immediate line manager will be responsible for responding to such situations, carrying out either counselling or disciplinary investigations and interviews, supported as appropriate by a more senior manager.

In such interviews the possible existence of an alcohol or drug abuse problem should be explored. The line manager is not required to diagnose the existence of an alcohol or drug abuse problem, merely to assess whether such abuse is a possible factor.

Any requirements of the disciplinary procedure regarding allowing the member of staff representation will be observed.

Diagnosing the existence of an alcohol or drug abuse problem

Should the interviews lead to the conclusion that an alcohol or drug abuse problem might exist and the member of staff accepts referral, the manager should refer the matter to the Occupational Health Service/company-approved doctor, who will be responsible for establishing whether or not a diagnosis of alcoholism or drug dependence can be made.

Disciplinary action should be suspended until diagnostic advice is obtained. Where appropriate, suspension arrangements in the disciplinary procedure should be followed.

If the interview fails to lead to the conclusion that an alcohol or drug abuse problem exists, or the member of staff rejects or fails to co-operate in referral, disciplinary action should be continued, where and as the situation justifies.

Confirming that an alcohol or drug abuse problem exists and arranging treatment

If a positive diagnosis of an alcohol or drug abuse problem is made, and the member of staff agrees to co-operate in treatment, treatment arrangements should commence.

Where necessary, the Occupational Health Service/company-approved doctor will advise the member of staff regarding treatment and will be responsible for monitoring progress and advising the manager concerned. This advice should be available at least monthly following commencement of treatment and thereafter as appropriate. (Disciplinary action should be discontinued unless the member of staff fails to co-operate with the treatment arranged.) Should a diagnosis of alcoholism or drug dependence not be confirmed, or should the member of staff refuse to co-operate in treatment, disciplinary action should be continued.

Substance misuse policy *continued*

The Occupational Health Service/company-approved doctor will advise on whether there is a lack of progress with treatment or lack of co-operation by the member of staff. Managers must then review the facts and consider whether or not there should be a return to the use of disciplinary procedures.

Where medical certificates are submitted, sick leave should be given. Should the employee continue to be fit for work during the period of treatment, they should be permitted to continue in their post (or alternative work), unless such an arrangement would have an adverse effect on Company services. In such circumstances, annual or unpaid leave should be approved or, exceptionally, suspension arranged.

If a member of staff has been off work during the period of treatment, before returning to duty, they will be seen by the Occupational Health Service/company-approved doctor who will advise management regarding capability for continuation in their own post and whether any special supervision or other arrangements are required.

Every effort should be made to comply with the advice provided by the Occupational Health Service/company-approved doctor. If it is not reasonably practicable to do so, and as a result the member of staff is not able to resume duty, employment may be terminated on the grounds of incapacity (ill health).

If a member of staff is again involved in disciplinary situations resulting from alcohol or drug abuse related problems, a second referral to the Occupational Health Service/company-approved doctor and suspension of the disciplinary procedure may be appropriate. If they advise positively on the possibilities of further treatment or help and the willingness of the member of staff to co-operate, the disciplinary procedure may be suspended again to permit treatment and help to be undertaken. This second referral will not apply if the further disciplinary problems involve serious misconduct. Third and subsequent referrals are not permissible.

Situations where a disciplinary situation does not exist

There may be situations where the possible existence of alcohol or drug abuse problems affecting a member of staff come to a manager's attention, although there is, or has been, no discernible effect on work performance or behaviour. This could arise if a member of staff confides in their manager about an alcohol or drug abuse problem, or a manager sees a need to approach a member of staff after observing possible indicators of an alcohol or drug abuse problem (such as an absence pattern or information provided by the member of staff's colleagues).

In such situations, the Company would wish staff to feel they could seek help from their employer (in complete confidence) without worry that their job security would be in jeopardy. Accordingly, if managers should be faced with a situation of this type they should:

● seek the advice of the Occupational Health Service/company-approved doctor regarding whether and how the matter could be dealt with

● counsel the member of staff and, if appropriate, arrange for the member of staff to be interviewed by the Occupational Health Service/company-approved doctor.

In the procedure described above, the Occupational Health Service/company-approved doctor serves as a facilitator; they will seek to establish whether a problem exists, and advise and direct the member of staff towards appropriate forms of treatment and help.

These steps cannot be taken without the co-operation of the member of staff. If the member of staff does not wish to co-operate, no further action should be taken.

Should a member of staff take up the opportunity of assistance on this voluntary basis there need be no further formal involvement of management in terms of action or the right to learn of progress with treatment. It may be, however, that the member of staff would wish, or agree to, further involvement of management as a means of assisting progress with treatment.

Use of the disciplinary procedures and/or the application of the approach described above would only be appropriate if, subsequently, the member of staff is involved in a breach of disciplinary rules.

Should the problems of the member of staff develop to an extent that their continuation in post or employment became impossible, it may be necessary to identify alternative work or arrange for termination, on the same basis as the Company operates for staff with problems of incapacity due to ill health.

04

Substance misuse policy *continued*

<OPTIONAL SECTION>

Drug and alcohol testing

<Company> will ensure that all its employees work within the laws of the land. The UK laws on use of drugs and alcohol are clear:

- it is a criminal offence for certain workers (such as drivers or operators of public transport systems) to be unfit for their work due to taking drugs or alcohol

- it is a criminal offence to be unfit to drive, attempt to drive or be in charge of a motor vehicle when under the influence of drugs or alcohol

- the possession, supply or production of controlled drugs is unlawful except for in special circumstances (such as when they have been prescribed by a doctor).

Employees are also legally required to take reasonable care of themselves and to behave in a way that does not pose risks to the health and safety of themselves or others in the workplace. This includes consideration of the effects that intoxication through taking alcohol or drugs may have.

In order to ensure compliance with the law, <Company> will undertake drug and alcohol testing for certain jobs within the Company. These will be carried out pre-employment, as part of a random testing scheme or as a result of an incident. These jobs are:

- <Insert jobs in Company that will be subject to testing – usually posts where safety is vital (such as driving or machine operating posts)>. The Company reserves the right to add to or amend this list as appropriate.

Individuals in these posts will be asked to agree to testing as part of their contract of employment.

To ensure the testing is legal and safe the following arrangements will apply.

- Testing will only be carried out as part of this policy, and only by trained staff who will carry out the test in a non-invasive way (usually by urine sample or exhalation).

- Samples to be collected under supervised conditions but respecting human dignity (two identical samples are taken, either on site or split in the test laboratory).

- Samples to be kept under chain of custody at all times.

- Screening test for alcohol or common drugs to be carried out on one sample with either positive or negative results.

- Any positive results from screening to be confirmed by approved scientific techniques.

- Results to be reviewed by an expert and reported back.

- Second sample to be kept for further analysis as part of any appeal by the employee.

- Confidentiality will be maintained at all times.

<Company> believes that effective workplace drug and alcohol policies are a better way of achieving results than drug and alcohol testing and that providing an environment where employees can discuss any drug and alcohol problems they have, with the prospect of gaining help and support, will be more effective than a testing regime. Therefore, the undertaking of drug and alcohol testing in the workplace will be minimal and used only where the Company has a reasonable belief that abuse is taking place.

04

04

First aid

05

Supporting
INFORMATION

GT700 Toolbox talks / supporting checklists and forms

Toolbox talks on some of these topics are available in the GT700 publication. Supporting checklists and forms covering some of these topics are available on our companion website.

FIRST AID

Overview

In the event of injury or sudden illness, failure to provide first aid could result in a casualty's death. The employer should ensure that an employee who is injured or taken ill at work receives immediate attention.

The Health and Safety (First Aid) Regulations require employers to provide adequate and appropriate equipment, facilities and personnel to ensure their employees receive immediate attention. The regulations apply to all workplaces, including those with fewer than five employees and the self-employed.

5.1   Introduction

First aid at work is covered by the **Health and Safety (First Aid) Regulations**, together with approved Health and Safety Executive (HSE) guidance that provides further information on such matters as first-aid equipment and training. The regulations provide a flexible framework within which employers can develop effective first-aid arrangements appropriate to their workplace and the size of their workforce.

Current HSE information says that as a minimum, a low-risk workplace such as a small office should have a first-aid box and a person appointed to take charge of first-aid arrangements, such as calling the emergency services if necessary. Employers must provide information about first-aid arrangements to their employees. Workplaces where there are more significant health and safety risks are more likely to need a trained first-aider. Completing a first aid needs assessment will help employers decide what first aid arrangements are appropriate for their workplace.

The following duties are placed on employers under the regulations.

- Provide adequate first-aid equipment and facilities appropriate to the type of work or operations undertaken.

- Appoint a sufficient number of suitable and trained people to render first aid to employees who are injured or become ill at work.

- Appoint a sufficient number of suitable people who, in the temporary absence of the first aider, will be capable of dealing with an injured or ill employee needing help from a medical practitioner or nurse, and who are able to take charge of first-aid equipment and facilities.

- Inform employees of the first-aid arrangements, including the location of first-aid equipment and personnel. This will require notices to be posted and signs displayed. Provision should be made for employees with language or reading difficulties.

Employers must provide first-aid equipment, facilities and training

The guidance sets out what employers and the self-employed need to do to address first-aid provision in the workplace. It provides guidance on the following points.

- Requirements and training for first aiders.

- Requirements for appointed persons.

- Managing the provision of first-aid (for example, first-aid kit, equipment and room).

- Making employees aware of first-aid arrangements.

- First aid and the self-employed.

- Cases where the Health and Safety (First Aid) Regulations do not apply.

> **!** **An employer shall inform their employees of the arrangements that have been made in connection with the provision of first aid, including the location of equipment, facilities and personnel.**

It is recommended that first-aid notices are displayed as an effective means of informing the workforce of the employer's arrangements for first aid. Signs should comply with the Health and Safety (Safety Signs and Signals) Regulations.

5.2   Important points

- Trained first-aid staff and first-aid equipment must be available on site.

- The level of provision of trained staff and first-aid equipment will depend upon the findings of a first-aid needs assessment.

- Everyone working on site should know where the first aiders and the first-aid kits can be found.

- All accidents causing injury must be recorded in an accident book.

- In an emergency, assess the situation but do not put yourself in danger.

- Don't move casualties who are obviously injured unless it is **absolutely** necessary to do so – summon the first aider and dial 999.

- Cover severe bleeding with a clean pad and apply direct pressure.

- First aiders have the potential to save lives.

 Adequate and appropriate

The definition of **adequate** and **appropriate** will depend on the circumstances in the workplace. This includes whether trained first aiders are needed, what should be included in a first-aid kit and if a first-aid room is required. Employers should carry out an assessment of first-aid needs to determine what to provide.

5.3 Definition of first aid

First aid is defined in the regulations as:

- in cases where a person will need help from a doctor or a nurse, treatment for the purpose of preserving life and minimising the consequences of injury or illness until such help is obtained

- treatment of minor injuries, which would otherwise receive no treatment or which do not need treatment by a doctor or nurse.

 It should be noted that the definition covers any illness at work and not just accidents. You must, therefore, plan for times when someone has a heart attack or collapses.

Emergency first aiders can give a restricted range of first-aid treatment to someone who is injured or becomes ill at work. Fully trained first aiders can do the above, plus apply first aid to a range of specific injuries and illnesses.

5.4 First-aid needs assessment

An employer should make an assessment of first-aid needs, appropriate to the hazards and risks of each workplace.

In assessing their needs employers should consider the nature of the work and workplace hazards and risks, as well as the work pattern and size of the organisation. Some of the factors that should be considered are listed below.

- The type of work or operations being carried out.

- Whether or not employees work alone or in scattered and isolated locations.

- Whether there are special or unusual hazards.

- Whether or not there is shift work (first-aid cover will be required at all times that work is being carried out).

- The maximum number of people likely to be on site at any one time.

- The remoteness of emergency medical services.

First-aid point

- Cover for first aiders' holidays and sickness absence (first-aid cover will be required at all times that work is being carried out).

- The presence of work-placement trainees.

- The organisation's history of accidents.

Unless arrangements have been made for the sharing of first-aid cover and facilities, all contractors on the site must make their own provisions for their own employees.

On sites where special or unusual hazards are present, a proportionately larger number of first aiders, having regard to the factors already mentioned, will be needed. Good practice should encourage all the contractor's site personnel to be trained in basic emergency first aid.

On major construction projects where there is a site nurse and/or a doctor on call, their advice in connection with first aid should be followed.

 A summary of considerations for assessing first-aid needs has been provided at Appendix B.

5.4.1 Mental health first aid

Following your employer's first-aid needs assessment, you might decide that it will be beneficial to train personnel so that they can identify and understand symptoms and are able to support someone who may be experiencing a mental health issue, known as a mental health first aider (MHFA).

Consider ways to manage mental ill health that are appropriate for your workplace and business, such as providing information or training for managers and employees, employing occupational health professionals, appointing MHFAs and implementing employee support programmes.

First-aid training courses covering mental health teach delegates how to recognise the warning signs of mental ill health and how to develop the skills and confidence to approach and support someone, while keeping themselves safe. An MHFA is someone who has undertaken training and attained a recognised qualification.

MHFAs have:

- an in-depth understanding of mental health and the factors that can affect wellbeing

- practical skills to spot the triggers and signs of mental health issues

- confidence to step in, reassure and support a person in distress

- enhanced interpersonal skills (such as non-judgemental listening)

- knowledge to help someone recover their health by guiding them to further support – whether that is self-help resources, assistance through their employer or the NHS, or a mix of these options.

5.4.1.1 Employer's support

An independent review was commissioned by the government and the mental health charity Mind to review the role employers can play to better support individuals with mental health conditions in the workplace.

The 'Thriving at Work' report sets out a framework of actions – called 'Core Standards' – that the reviewers recommend employers of all sizes can and should put in place. These standards have been designed to help employers improve the mental health in their workplace and enable individuals with mental health conditions to thrive.

The core standards are:

- Produce, implement and communicate a mental health at work plan that promotes good mental health of all employees and outlines the support available for those who may need it.

- Develop mental health awareness among employees by making information, tools and support accessible.

- Encourage open conversations about mental health and the support available when employees are struggling, during the recruitment process and at regular intervals throughout employment.

- Provide employees with good working conditions and ensure they have a healthy work life balance and opportunities for development.

- Promote effective people management to ensure all employees have a regular conversation about their health and well-being with their supervisor and support line managers and supervisors in effective management practices.

- Routinely monitor employee mental health and wellbeing by understanding available data, talking to employees, and understanding risk factors.

By taking action on work-related stress, employers will form part of a mental health at work plan, promote communications and open conversations, by raising awareness and reducing stigma.

 For further guidance and support, a free workbook called *Tackling work-related stress using the Management Standards approach* is available to download from the HSE website.

5.4.2 Emergency care services

The local emergency service should be informed about large sites and of any particularly hazardous operations being undertaken. It is helpful to supply a map locating the site and its entrances and, where appropriate, the first-aid room.

 Provide 'tear and go' printed map/directions to the nearest Accident and Emergency department, including phone number and sat-nav postcode.

5.4.3 Induction

Induction training for employees, contractors and visitors to the site should include actions to be taken in cases of injury or illness, details of the identity and location of qualified first-aid personnel and the location of first-aid kits.

5.4.4 Responsibility for visitors and other non-employees

The regulations require employers to make first-aid provision for their own employees. However, there is also a general duty upon employers in respect of their premises or work with regard to people who are not their employees, and first-aid arrangements should extend to cover visitors and other non-employees.

5.4.5 Shared facilities

Where employees of more than one employer are working together, arrangements may be made for one of the employers to take responsibility for providing first-aid cover. All employers should agree the arrangements and the employees should be kept informed. A written agreement between the employers is recommended.

In such circumstances, it is the responsibility of each employer to ensure that the agreed facilities are actually provided, and that all their employees are aware of these arrangements.

5.4.6   Self-employed persons

Self-employed persons must provide adequate first-aid provisions for themselves. However, if they are working from home and the risk is low, normal household first-aid requirements are sufficient.

Where the use of potentially dangerous tools and machinery present a hazard, an appropriate first-aid provision should be made. If a self-employed person is working under an employer or with another self-employed person, joint arrangements can be made.

5.4.7   Trained and suitable personnel

First aiders must have received training and hold a current first-aid certificate. They must remain competent and so they should undergo refresher training and re-examination as necessary. The employer must keep a written record of such training.

First aid at work certificates, which have been issued by, or in, another country, are not valid in mainland Britain.

5.4.8   First aiders

A first aider is someone who has undertaken training and attained a recognised qualification. They must hold a valid certificate in either:

- first aid at work (FAW)
- emergency first aid at work (EFAW).

At least one first aider should be provided where 25 people are employed. The needs assessment will help the employer decide how many first aiders are required, dependent on the size of undertaking, the hazards present and the number of people employed.

 The checklist in the HSE guidance *First aid at work* (L74) serves as a general guide on the number of first aiders and appointed persons required.

5.4.9   Appointed persons

An appointed person is someone who has been nominated by the employer to take charge of first-aid arrangements, including looking after equipment and facilities and calling the emergency services.

They will act in the absence of the trained first aider or in situations where it is deemed that a first aider is not required (such as in a small, non-hazardous working area) and where there is easy access to professional medical assistance (such as a hospital Accident and Emergency department).

Appointed persons do not need first-aid training. However, emergency first-aid training should be considered for all appointed persons.

Appointed persons must not be regarded as an alternative to qualified first aiders, but they can provide cover when the first aider is absent (excluding annual leave). They must not, however, be required to render first aid personally.

5.5   Equipment and facilities

Based upon the findings of a first-aid needs assessment, the employer must carry out the following.

- Provide and keep stocked suitable first-aid kits and other appropriate equipment (such as eyewash stations and burns kit), in places that can easily be accessed by all employees.
- Display notices giving the identity of first aiders and the location of first-aid equipment.

The needs assessment may indicate that additional equipment is required (such as foil blankets or disposable aprons). These may be stored in the first-aid kit, if there is room, or stored separately.

A suitable first-aid room(s) should be provided where the first-aid needs assessment identifies it as necessary. It is essential that all employees should have quick and easy access to the first-aid facilities on site.

Where employees are working in large numbers and in close proximity, facilities should be centralised in that area. With employees spread over a wider area, first aiders and equipment should be distributed accordingly. Sometimes, a combination of these arrangements may be appropriate.

All employees must be aware of the location of first-aid facilities and the arrangements for providing treatment. The location of first-aid facilities should be clearly marked with the appropriate symbol.

5.5.1   First-aid kits

Depending on the findings of the first-aid needs assessment more than one first-aid kit might be required. They should be strategically placed, easy to get to and clearly marked with a white cross on a green background in accordance with the **Health and Safety (Safety Signs and Signals) Regulations**.

The first-aid kit should hold first-aid equipment and nothing else, and should protect the contents from dust and damp. The recommended content of a first-aid kit is contained in the HSE publication *First aid at work.*

Medicines, pressure bandages and home remedies should **not** be kept in first-aid kits.

If workers require access to prescribed medication, it is recommended that they carry their own.

A first aider may assist the individual to take their own prescribed medication, but they **must not** administer it themselves.

It is essential that the contents of first-aid kits are replenished after use and checked frequently by the first aider or appointed person.

Some items are prone to deterioration after a certain period of time.

First-aid kit

 ## Medicine legislation restricts the administration of injectable medicines

Unless self-administered, injectable medicines may only be administered by or in accordance with the instructions of a doctor (for example, by a nurse).

Adrenaline is an exemption to this restriction. In an emergency, a layperson is permitted to administer adrenaline by injection for the purpose of saving a life. Using an EpiPen to treat anaphylactic shock falls into this category. Therefore, first aiders may administer an EpiPen if they are dealing with a life-threatening emergency, involving a casualty who has been prescribed and is in possession of an EpiPen, and where the first aider is trained to use it. *(Source: HSE)*

 The minimum recommended contents of first-aid kits are listed in Appendix A, which should be adjusted following an assessment of the first-aid needs of a specific site.

5.5.2 Automated external defibrillators

Sudden cardiac arrest (SCA) can affect anyone, at any time, and kills over 100,000 people each year in the UK. Although SCA is more common in people who are older or who have heart problems, many sufferers are fit and have no known risk factors or previous history. SCA occurs due to an electrical malfunction, which disrupts the heart's normal rhythm, but there is usually no warning that it is about to happen.

 Following an SCA the sufferer will lose consciousness instantly and, unless immediate cardiopulmonary resuscitation (CPR) and defibrillation is administered, it will cause death within minutes.

Evidence suggests that where automated external defibrillators (AEDs) have been used the outcomes are far more favourable for the individual suffering from a cardiac arrest or heart attack than if treatment is delayed until the emergency services arrive.

AEDs are becoming more prevalent within the wider community. For example, there are national strategies in place actively promoting their placement in schools and public places (such as railway stations). Many workplaces have voluntarily invested in this equipment. The Resuscitation Council UK guidance on AEDs is that this equipment is safe to use and can be readily used by untrained bystanders.

It is not compulsory for employers to purchase AEDs to comply with the Health and Safety (First Aid) Regulations and in-depth training in the use of AEDs is not currently part of either the emergency first aid at work or first aid at work courses. However, if your needs assessment identifies the need for an AED, or where an employer decides to provide a defibrillator in the workplace, then the HSE recommends that those who may need to use it should be fully trained in its use. Training can provide additional knowledge and skills and may promote greater confidence when using the defibrillator.

Automated external defibrillator (AED)

5.5.3 Travelling first-aid kits

Special or small travelling first-aid kits should be provided to the following employees (based on the assessment of their first-aid needs).

● Those who are working alone or in small groups in isolated locations (such as maintenance gangs).

● Those whose work involves travel in remote areas.

● Those who use potentially dangerous tools or machinery.

Organisations with employees who work in remote areas should consider issuing personal communication devices and also providing additional training.

5.5.4 Carrying equipment

Where first aiders are employed, stretchers or appropriate carrying equipment (such as a carrying chair or wheelchair) should be provided in an easy to access location, clearly identified by a sign. If a site covers a large area, or contains a number of distinct working areas, it will be necessary to provide such equipment at a number of suitable locations. However, it is recommended that, in most incidents, casualties are not moved before the emergency services arrive.

5.5.5 Water for eye irrigation

If mains tap water is not readily available for eye irrigation, at least one litre of sterile water or sterile normal saline (0.9% w/v), in sealed disposable containers, should be provided. If a site covers a large area, or contains a number of distinct working areas, it will be necessary to provide such equipment at a number of suitable locations.

5.5.6 First-aid rooms

A suitable first-aid room(s) should be provided where the first-aid needs assessment identifies it as necessary. The assessment will consider the number of people on the site, the type of work and whether a hospital or other emergency facilities are close to hand.

The first-aid room will normally be under the control of the first aider who should be nearby or on call, with access to the room when employees are at work. The name of this person should be displayed, together with the names and locations of all other first aiders and appointed persons. On some larger sites, the first-aid room will be staffed by a qualified nurse.

The room should be clearly identified, available at all times and used only for rendering first aid. It should be of sufficient size to contain a couch, with adequate space around it to allow people to work, and have an access door to allow the passage of a stretcher or other carrying equipment. Pillows and blankets should be provided and be frequently cleaned.

The room itself should be cleaned each working day, have smooth-topped, impermeable working surfaces and provision for privacy and refuse disposal. Heating, lighting and ventilation should be effective. In addition to the required first-aid materials, which should be stored in a suitable cabinet, the following could also be provided.

- A sink with running hot and cold water.
- Drinking water with disposable cups.
- Soap, nail brush and paper towels.
- A chair.

- A suitable container for disposal of clinical waste (yellow bags).
- A telephone, where possible, or other communication equipment (such as a siren or klaxon) to alert personnel on call.
- An accident recording book, for which the first aider or appointed person is responsible.

In first-aid rooms that are supervised by the site nurse, other items may be provided on their advice. If the first-aid room cannot be reserved exclusively for first aid, employers need to make sure that the first-aid facilities can be made available quickly, if necessary.

Consideration should be given as to whether:

- furnishings and equipment can be moved easily and quickly
- activities carried out in the room can be stopped immediately

- there is a storage room for first-aid equipment.

5.6 Training and qualifications

The employer is responsible for ensuring that those people who have been selected as fully qualified first aiders have undergone training and possess a recognised qualification.

In order to be able to demonstrate compliance with the regulations, employers must keep written records of all training that has been given to employees, along with results of that training. Additional training may be necessary to cope with any special hazards in a particular working environment.

The training of EFAW must meet the requirements of the Health and Safety (First Aid) Regulations. First aiders will hold a valid certificate of competence in either EFAW or FAW.

EFAW training enables a first aider to give emergency first aid to someone who becomes injured or ill while they are at work.

FAW includes EFAW and equips first aiders to apply first aid to a range of additional specific injuries and illnesses. Instruction in emergency first aid (such as cardiopulmonary resuscitation (CPR), control of bleeding and treatment of unconsciousness) is desirable for all staff.

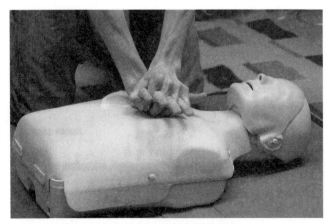

Performing chest compressions during first-aid CPR training

 For guidance on actions to take in an emergency refer to Appendix C.

5.6.1 Initial selection of first aiders

Whilst it is desirable to appoint staff who have already received first-aid training and utilise their skills, in many instances this may not be an option. On most new sites it is unlikely that a trained first aider will be available, and it will be necessary to arrange training for a suitable member of staff. In selecting people for this role, consideration should be given as to whether they:

- have a friendly, reassuring disposition

- are acceptable to male and female staff

- can cope with stressful and physically demanding emergency procedures

- are able to remain calm in an emergency

- are employed on a task that they can leave immediately in order to go to the scene of an emergency

- are capable of acquiring the knowledge and qualifications required

- understand the demands of the role.

5.6.2 Training organisations

Training organisations should use training material in accordance with the following.

- Current guidelines published by the Resuscitation Council (UK).

- The latest first-aid manual of Voluntary Aid Societies (St John Ambulance, British Red Cross and St Andrew's First Aid).

- Other published guidelines, which are in line with the points above, or are supported by a responsible body of medical opinion.

 The HSE provides guidance to assist employers in selecting a competent first-aid training provider.

5.6.3 Fully qualified first aiders

It may be necessary to provide specialised instruction in the use of protective equipment or rescue techniques, where these are important in the trainee's workplace or if special hazards exist. A FAW training course will involve at least 18 hours of training and will run over a minimum of three days. Where an alternative qualification is identified, in place of FAW or EFAW, the employer will need to seek assurance that the standard of training received, and the competence of the organisation that delivered the training, meet the criteria outlined in the guidance.

5.6.4 First aiders for special or unusual situations

First aiders should complete training in the subjects described for first aiders, and be given any specialised training related to the particular requirements of their workplace and its hazards. It is the duty of the employer to let the training organisation know if there are any particular hazards at their workplace, so that training can be tailored appropriately.

Some workers carry their own medication (such as inhalers for asthma) or EpiPens, which contain injectable adrenaline for the treatment of severe allergic (anaphylactic) reactions (for example, to peanuts). These medications are prescribed by a doctor. If an individual needs to take their own prescribed medication, the first aider's role is limited to helping them do so and contacting the emergency services as appropriate (adrenaline (EpiPens) is an exemption to this restriction).

Paramedic's response bag

5.6.5 Emergency first aiders

Emergency first aiders must undertake an EFAW course, which involves at least six hours of training and should be run over a minimum of one day. The certificate will be valid for three years. As with fully qualified first aiders, the HSE recommends that emergency first aiders undertake annual refresher training during any three year certification.

5.6.6 Appointed persons

To fulfil their role, appointed persons do not need first-aid training. They may benefit from an EFAW course (or suitable alternative).

5.6.7 Mental health first-aid training

Mental health first-aid (MHFA) training courses teach people to spot the symptoms of mental health issues, offer initial help and guide a person towards support. Mental health first-aid training does not teach people to be therapists but it does teach them to listen, reassure and respond, even in a crisis – and, potentially, to stop a crisis from happening.

There are a range of training options, including the following.

● Workplace MHFA two-day course – the qualification required to become a mental health first aider.

● Workplace MHFA one-day mental health awareness and skills course – the qualification required to become a MHFA champion.

● Workplace MHFA half-day course – an introductory four-hour session to raise awareness of mental health.

5.6.8 Expiry of certificates

All first-aid certificates, whether FAW or EFAW, are valid for three years.

Re-qualification training, with re-examination, will be required before re-certification. First aiders must undertake re-qualification training before their current certificate expires. FAW re-qualification courses are two days in duration.

EFAW re-qualification courses should be the same duration and content as the initial EFAW course. New certificates will be dated to continue from the expiry date of the previous one. Ideally, employers will take advantage of this period.

Where this is not possible or practical, if a certificate has expired, candidates will be required to complete the three-day FAW course.

It is up to the employer to decide what is the most appropriate training course to re-qualify an individual as a first aider.

 For further information on injury reporting, refer to the table in Section 1.3.2.

5.6.9 Annual refresher course

The HSE strongly recommends that first aiders undertake annual refresher training.

The suggested content of the annual refresher course includes administering first aid to a casualty who is unconscious, wounded and bleeding, or suffering from shock.

5.7 Accident records

First-aid treatment should be recorded. If the accident book does not allow enough detail to be gathered, an additional treatment book may be necessary.

Employers are required to keep accident records under the requirements of the **Social Security (Claims and Payments) Regulations**.

Records can be stored in any medium, including electronic, providing that printable copies are readily available if required.

Records must include the following details.

● Date, time and place of accident.

● Full name, address and job of injured or ill person.

● Details of injury/illness and what first aid was given.

● What happened to the person immediately afterwards (for example, went home, to hospital or back to work).

● Name and signature of the first aider or person dealing with the incident.

Details should be recorded by the injured person, but can be completed by any employee. However, some employers insist that records are completed by first aiders, which requires one to be available at all times. This is a company operating procedure, and not strictly necessary.

Completion of an accident record does not meet the employer's obligation to report specific accidents and dangerous occurrences to the HSE or Local Authority. This information can help identify accident trends and possible areas for improvement in the control of health and safety risks.

All records must comply with the **General Data Protection Regulation (GDPR)** to ensure the confidentiality of entries.

Accident Book BL510 enables each record to be detached and stored separately when complete, thus maintaining the confidentiality of the injured person's details.

All personal information must be kept in confidence, and in a secure location (such as a lockable cabinet).

 For further information on the Accident Book BL510 visit the HSE website.

Accident books designed and produced in-house may still be used, provided that:

● all details required by BL510 are recorded

● the requirements of GDPR are met

● information recorded electronically can be made readily available in hard copy.

5.8 Reporting of Injuries, Diseases and Dangerous Occurrences Regulations

People covered by the Reporting of Injuries, Diseases and Dangerous Occurrences Regulations (RIDDOR) include employees, the self-employed and non-workers who have been injured (such as members of the public).

 Trainees are not specifically mentioned within these regulations, but other regulations require that all trainees, including non-employed trainees, must be treated as employees for all health and safety purposes.

Employers, and others in control of premises, must report and keep the following records.

- Work-related accidents that cause death.
- Work-related accidents that cause specified (serious) injuries.
- Diagnosed cases of certain individual diseases.
- Certain dangerous occurrences.

RIDDOR apply to all work activities but not all incidents are reportable.

 For further details on RIDDOR refer to Chapter A13 Accident reporting and investigation and Chapter B01 Reporting of Injuries, Diseases and Dangerous Occurrences Regulations (RIDDOR).

Appendix A – Recommended contents of first-aid kits

There is no mandatory list of items that should be included in a first-aid kit, but the findings of the first-aid needs assessment will influence the contents. As a guide, for low hazard environments, a minimum stock is provided below.

Item	Quantity in first-aid kits	Quantity in travelling first-aid kits
First aid guidance card	1	1
Individually wrapped sterile adhesive dressings (assorted sizes)	20	6
Sterile eye pads, with attachment	2	Nil
Individually wrapped triangular bandages	2	2
Safety pins	6	2
Medium-sized, individually wrapped, sterile, unmedicated wound dressings (approximately 12 cm x 12 cm)	6	Nil
Large, sterile, individually wrapped, unmedicated wound dressings (approximately 18 cm x 18 cm)	2	1
Individually wrapped, moist cleaning wipes (pack of 10)	Nil	1
Disposable gloves (pair)	3	2

Where tap water is not readily available for eye irrigation, sterile water or sterile normal saline (0.9%) in sealed disposable containers should be provided.

 BS 8599-1 provides further information on the contents of workplace first-aid kits, but contents should reflect the outcome of the first-aid needs assessment.

Travelling first-aid kits

Small, travelling first-aid kits are designed for use where the workforce is dispersed widely (possibly with hazardous tools), for self-employed persons, and for employees working away from their employer's establishment.

 First-aid kits purchased from major chemists or suppliers can vary in size to cater for the number of people employed.

Appendix B – Considerations for assessing first-aid needs

First-aid provision

- How many employees are involved?
- How is the workforce distributed/grouped (is it widely dispersed)?
- Are remote locations involved? (How far are you from emergency services?)
- Are shifts worked?
- What is the nature of the work?
- Does it involve special operations?
- Have all significant hazards been identified (such as falls, electric shock and dangerous substances)?
- How many first aiders are needed (consider holiday and sickness cover)?

Training

- Which personnel require first-aid training?
- Does the training offered meet foreseeable needs?
- Is there a system to trigger a warning to management when a first aider is within three months of their certificate expiring?
- Are training records kept?
- Are individuals, who are working in isolated locations, trained to cope with emergencies?
- Where appointed persons are in charge, do they understand their duties?
- Does induction training cover first-aid arrangements?

Equipment

- Is first-aid equipment placed in locations where it is likely to be needed?
- Does it meet foreseeable needs and special hazards?
- Are travelling first-aid kits available when required?
- Is a first-aid room needed, or available, and suitably equipped?
- Are information signs provided?
- Are first-aid kits properly stocked and maintained?

General

- Has responsibility for first-aid provision and organisation been assigned to an individual?
- Are there established procedures for reviewing:
  - training and equipment needs
  - new work processes
  - special operations
  - changes in work patterns
  - site locations
  - size of labour force
  - arrangements with contractors?

Appendix C – What to do in an emergency

General first-aid guidance is given in the HSE publication *Basic advice on first aid at work*. The information in this leaflet, which is reproduced below, is not intended as a substitute for effective training.

Priorities

- Assess the situation – do not put yourself in danger.
- Make the area safe.
- Assess all casualties and attend first to any unconscious casualties.
- **Send for help – do not delay.**

Follow the advice given below.

Check for a response

If there is no response to gentle shaking of the shoulders and shouting, the casualty may be unconscious. Your priorities are to:

- shout for help
- open the airway
- check for normal breathing
- take appropriate action.

The priority is to check the **A**irway, **B**reathing and **C**irculation. This is the **ABC** of resuscitation.

A – Airway

To open the airway:

- place one hand on the casualty's forehead and gently tilt the head back
- lift their chin with two fingertips.

B – Breathing

Look along the chest, and listen and feel at the mouth for signs of normal breathing, for no more than 10 seconds.

If the casualty **is** breathing:

- place in the recovery position and ensure the airway remains open
- get help
- monitor that the casualty continues to breathe until help arrives.

If the casualty **is not** breathing:

- get help and call for an AED, if available
- get the help to dial 999 immediately
- start chest compressions (see CPR below).

C – CPR

To start chest compressions:

- lean over the casualty and, with your arms straight, press down (5-6 cm) on the centre of the breastbone, and then release
- repeat at a rate of about 100-120 times a minute (more than one compression per second!)
- after 30 compressions, open the airway again
- pinch the casualty's nose closed and allow the mouth to open
- take a normal breath and place your mouth around the casualty's mouth, making a good seal
- blow steadily into the mouth while watching for the chest rising
- remove your mouth from the casualty and watch for the chest falling
- give a second breath and then start 30 compressions again without delay
- continue with chest compressions and rescue breaths in a ratio of 30:2 until qualified help takes over or the casualty starts to breathe normally.

Bleeding

With all open wounds there is a risk of infection, so wash your hands and use gloves (if you have any) to help prevent any infection passing between you and the casualty. In the case of severe bleeding, your priority is to stop the bleeding.

- Protect yourself by wearing gloves.
- If the wound is covered by the casualty's clothing, remove or cut the clothes to uncover the wound.
- If there is an object in the wound it may be acting as a plug to reduce the bleeding. Do not pull it out but apply pressure either side of it with a pad (such as a clean cloth) or your fingers, until a sterile dressing is available.

To treat severe bleeding where there is no object in the wound, follow the steps below.

- Apply direct pressure.
- Call 999 or 112 for emergency help.
- Apply a dressing and secure with a bandage.
- Raise and support the injured limb (unless it is broken).
- Treat the casualty for shock (help them lie down and raise their legs, if appropriate).

Broken bones and spinal injuries

If a broken bone or spinal injury is suspected, **obtain expert help**. **Do not move casualties** unless they are in immediate life-threatening danger.

Burns

Burns can be serious so, if in doubt, **seek medical help**. Cool the part of the body affected with cold water until pain is relieved. Thorough cooling may take 10 minutes or more, but this must not delay taking the casualty to hospital.

Certain chemicals may seriously irritate or damage the skin. Avoid contaminating yourself with the chemical. Treat in the same way as for other burns but flood the affected area with water for 20 minutes. Continue treatment even on the way to hospital, if necessary. Remove any contaminated clothing that is not stuck to the skin.

Eye injuries

All eye injuries are potentially serious. If there is something in the eye, wash it out with clean water or sterile fluid from a sealed container to remove loose material. **Do not attempt to remove anything that is embedded in the eye.**

If chemicals are involved, flush the eye with water or sterile fluid for at least 10 minutes, whilst gently holding the eyelid open.

Ask the casualty to hold a pad over the injured eye. Seek medical help immediately.

Record keeping

It is good practice to use a book to record any incidents involving injury or illness that you have attended. Include the following information in your entry.

- The date, time and place of the incident.
- The name and job of the injured or ill person.
- Details of the injury or illness and any first aid given.
- What happened to the casualty immediately afterwards (for example, went back to work, went home or went to hospital).
- The name and signature of the person dealing with the incident.

This information can help identify accident trends and possible areas for improvement in the control of health and safety risks.

Appendix D – Suggested numbers of first-aid personnel required

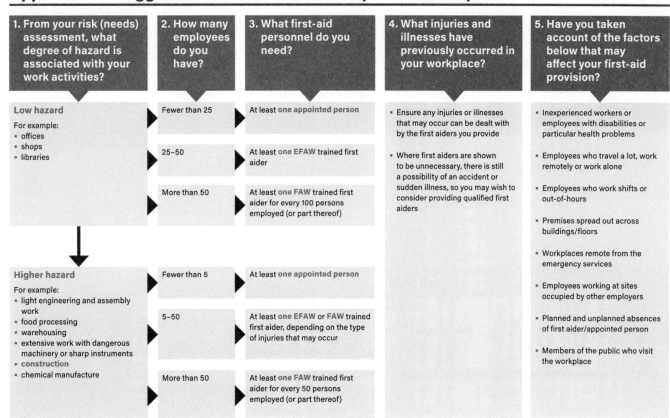

1. From your risk (needs) assessment, what degree of hazard is associated with your work activities?	2. How many employees do you have?	3. What first-aid personnel do you need?	4. What injuries and illnesses have previously occurred in your workplace?	5. Have you taken account of the factors below that may affect your first-aid provision?
Low hazard For example: • offices • shops • libraries	Fewer than 25	At least **one appointed person**	• Ensure any injuries or illnesses that may occur can be dealt with by the first aiders you provide • Where first aiders are shown to be unnecessary, there is still a possibility of an accident or sudden illness, so you may wish to consider providing qualified first aiders	• Inexperienced workers or employees with disabilities or particular health problems • Employees who travel a lot, work remotely or work alone • Employees who work shifts or out-of-hours • Premises spread out across buildings/floors • Workplaces remote from the emergency services • Employees working at sites occupied by other employers • Planned and unplanned absences of first aider/appointed person • Members of the public who visit the workplace
	25–50	At least **one EFAW** trained first aider		
	More than 50	At least **one FAW** trained first aider for every 100 persons employed (or part thereof)		
Higher hazard For example: • light engineering and assembly work • food processing • warehousing • extensive work with dangerous machinery or sharp instruments • **construction** • chemical manufacture	Fewer than 5	At least **one appointed person**		
	5–50	At least **one EFAW** or **FAW** trained first aider, depending on the type of injuries that may occur		
	More than 50	At least **one FAW** trained first aider for every 50 persons employed (or part thereof)		

Source: HSE First aid at work guidance on regulations Appendix 3 (L74)

05

05

Personal protective equipment

Supporting
INFORMATION

GT700 Toolbox talks / supporting checklists and forms

Toolbox talks on some of these topics are available in the GT700 publication. Supporting checklists and forms covering some of these topics are available on our companion website.

Overview

Construction workers may need to wear some items of personal protective equipment (PPE), such as safety helmets, high-visibility (hi-vis) vests, gloves, light eye protection and safety footwear, as indicated by the findings of the risk assessment.

PPE should always be considered as a last resort; over-reliance is sometimes placed on the need to wear PPE, as opposed to eliminating the risk at source.

6.1   Introduction

Personal protective equipment (PPE) is any item of equipment or clothing that is used or worn by a person to protect them from any identified risk to their health or safety. A sub-group of that, designed to protect the wearer against respiratory (breathing) hazards (such as the inhalation of dust and fumes), is known as respiratory protective equipment (RPE).

Within the construction industry PPE is commonly thought of as equipment that is used to protect the head, ears, eyes, respiratory (breathing) system, skin, hands and feet. However, it must be appreciated that PPE is also commonly used for the following reasons during construction:

- to prevent or arrest falls (for example, safety harnesses and lanyards)

- to enable a person in distress to be rescued from a confined space (for example, a rescue harness or escape RPE)

- to enable someone who has fallen into water to stay afloat and be rescued (for example, a lifejacket).

If it is found necessary for employees to wear PPE, its selection and use must comply with the Personal Protective Equipment at Work Regulations, to ensure that it will effectively protect the user against the hazard for which it has been selected.

All PPE should bear the CE mark to show conformity with European Standards. When employers are deciding how best to protect employees from a risk to their health and safety at work, the decision to issue PPE may only be made where it is found that the risk cannot be adequately controlled by other means that are equally or more effective. In effect, the issue and use of PPE is the last resort in terms of risk control.

PPE must be selected by a competent person who, if necessary in conjunction with the suppliers, can identify the most suitable PPE that will be effective against the hazards present in the workplace. An example of this is the selection of the correct type of respirator or filter to protect the user against the various types of airborne substances, either particles or gases.

It must be remembered that PPE is a last line of defence. Failure of an item of PPE, or the wrong type of PPE being used, could expose an employee to the possibility of occupational ill health, serious injury or death.

6.2   Important points

- The correct use of PPE is essential in many cases to protect the wearer from harm.

- On almost all construction sites there will be a risk of head injury. Therefore, safety helmets must be worn in areas where there is a risk of head injury.

- The use of PPE is the last resort; it only protects the wearer if it is:
  - the right PPE for the job
  - in good working order
  - being used properly.

- Employers have a legal duty to investigate the use of other protective measures before issuing PPE.

- Employees must look after the PPE that has been issued to them and inform their employer if it becomes defective, damaged or is lost.

- RPE is a sub-group of PPE.

- Managers and supervisors must set an example and wear PPE where required.

 Employers have a legal duty to supply the necessary PPE free of charge.

6.3   Personal Protective Equipment at Work (Amendment) Regulations 2022

The Personal Protective Equipment at Work Regulations cover the duties of employers and employees on the suitability, provision, maintenance, instruction and use of PPE. These regulations should not be confused with the European Union (EU) Personal Protective Equipment (Enforcement) Regulations, which came into force in the UK on 21 April 2018 and concern the supply and 'placing on the market' of PPE; they place duties on economic operators throughout the supply chain (the manufacturer, authorised representative, importer and distributor) to ensure compliance with the regulation. Other regulations cover the PPE that should be provided to protect the worker against hazards such as noise, vibration, asbestos, lead and other hazardous substances.

On 6 April 2022, the Personal Protective Equipment at Work (Amendment) Regulations extended employers' and employees' duties regarding PPE to limb (b) workers (dependent contractors), i.e. those who work under a contract of service, such as those carrying out irregular or casual work for more than one company.

If a risk assessment indicates that a limb (b) worker requires PPE to carry out their work activities, the employer must carry out a suitability PPE assessment and provide the PPE free of charge, as they do for their employees. The employer will be responsible for the training and instruction, maintenance, storage, and replacement of any PPE provided.

 The following regulations have alternative requirements

- The Ionising Radiations Regulations.
- The Control of Asbestos Regulations.
- The Control of Noise at Work Regulations.
- The Control of Lead at Work Regulations.
- The Control of Substances Hazardous to Health Regulations.

Where work is carried out under any of the above regulations, any PPE required must be provided to comply with the respective set of regulations. For example, hearing protection **must be** provided to meet the requirements of the Control of Noise at Work Regulations, not the Personal Protective Equipment at Work Regulations.

The Personal Protective Equipment at Work Regulations require that where a risk has been identified by a risk assessment and it cannot be adequately controlled by other means, which are equally or more effective, then the employer must provide **suitable** PPE and ensure that it is correctly used and cared for by employees.

Detailed requirements of any such risk assessment are specified in the regulations and require the problem to be thought through in a structured manner and the right equipment chosen for the right reasons. A vital factor is the competence of the person carrying out the assessments. If they do not get it right, the consequences for the health and safety of employees could be very serious.

In essence, PPE may only be used as a **last resort** after all other means of eliminating or controlling the risk have been considered.

In deciding which type to issue, the employer must take into account the hazard that the PPE is being used to protect against and ensure that the PPE will fit the wearer and allow them to work safely.

If more than one item of PPE is being used at any one time, the employer must make sure that individual items of PPE are **compatible** and do not adversely affect the performance of each other. This is of particular importance in the building and construction industry, since operatives often need to simultaneously wear a combination of PPE items (such as safety helmets, eye protection, ear protection or respiratory protection).

Employers are responsible for providing, replacing and paying for PPE for their employees. It is an offence to charge an employee for any item of PPE that the employer is required to provide under any legislation. The employer can charge a worker for PPE if they are genuinely self-employed. However, some employers come to an agreement with their employees whereby PPE (for example, safety boots) are purchased by the employee and then subsidised by the employer, or provided under other schemes or conditions.

Further complications can arise as to whether the employer is responsible for the safety of labour-only employees and some other categories of site-based staff. It is suggested that this is agreed at the start of the contract, and documented in the construction phase plan.

Whenever PPE is to be issued, the employer must ensure that employees have been given adequate and appropriate information, instruction and training to enable the employees to understand the risks being protected against, the purpose of the PPE and the manner in which it is to be used.

Whilst the employer must ensure that PPE is supplied and used, the employee has the following duties.

- Properly use the PPE provided, in accordance with the information, instruction and training that they have been given.
- Return PPE to its storage facility, where provided, after use.
- Know the procedures for reporting loss of any PPE or defects in it to their employer.

6.3.1 Supplying suitable PPE

PPE should only be used as a **last resort** and only when the risks to health and safety cannot be controlled adequately in other ways. It will only be deemed to be **suitable** in the following situations.

- If it is appropriate for the risks involved and the conditions of exposure.
- When it takes account of the ergonomic requirements and state of health of the user.
- When it can fit the wearer properly, if necessary after adjustment.
- As far as is practicable, when it effectively prevents or adequately controls exposure to risk without increasing the overall risk.
- When it complies with any relevant European Regulation or Directive.

Also supplying one-size-fits-all PPE (such as gloves) or one size of hi-vis vest (for example, XXL) may not offer everyone the same level of protection and could introduce other risks (such as entanglement or snagging). Provision of a range of sizes to fit the individual should be taken into account.

6.3.2   Assessing suitability

Employers must carry out assessments of the suitability of PPE regarding the nature of the risk, before selecting it. The assessment must consider the following points.

- The risks to health and safety that have not been controlled by other means.

- The nature of the risks to health and safety, against which the PPE is to protect the user.

- A comparison of the nature of the risks and the performance capabilities of the PPE.

- The compatibility of the PPE under consideration and any other PPE that will be worn at the same time.

6.3.3   Reviewing the assessment

Employers must ensure that the following points are adhered to.

- Review assessments if it is thought that they are no longer valid or if there has been a significant change in the matters to which it relates.

- Incorporate any changes that are indicated by the review.

6.3.4   Maintenance and storage

Employers must ensure that PPE provided to employees is maintained (which includes replacement or cleaning) in an efficient state, efficient working order and good repair. The same duty is on **self-employed** persons with regard to any PPE provided to them. Employers and self-employed persons must provide suitable storage facilities for PPE that has been issued, for when it is not in use.

6.3.5   Information, instruction and training

Employers who have provided employees with PPE must also provide **adequate and appropriate** information, instruction and training to enable employees to know the following.

- The risk(s) for which the PPE has been provided.

- The purpose for which, and the manner in which, the PPE is to be used.

- Any actions that they (the users) must take to keep the PPE in the correct condition.

- Any information that should be available to them.

To be adequate and appropriate, the information must be understandable by the people receiving it. Training can be theoretical and/or practical. Where appropriate the employer should, at appropriate intervals, arrange suitable demonstrations in the correct wearing of PPE.

6.3.6   Usage and defects

Legal duties are required of the following people.

- Employers, to take reasonable steps to ensure that the PPE provided to employees is used correctly.

- Employees, to use the PPE provided in accordance with any instruction and training provided.

- Self-employed people, to make full and proper use of PPE.

- Employees and the self-employed, to take reasonable steps to return PPE to any storage facilities provided.

- Employees, to report any defect in the PPE issued, or the loss of it, to the employer as soon as possible.

6.4   Using personal protective equipment

After carrying out a risk assessment, the employer or self-employed person must then implement measures to control the risks identified. This may involve the identification and issue of appropriate PPE. All other methods of controlling the risks arising from the work activity must have been considered and found not to be reasonably practicable before the decision is taken to use PPE as a means of reducing the risk.

Construction industry workers will need to wear or use PPE on many occasions. They will wear or use it for one of two reasons.

1. They have been told to (site rules).

2. It makes sense.

The more often that it is done for the second reason, the better. In circumstances when wearing or using PPE is necessary it must become second nature for those workers who are at risk. However, at present this is still often not the case. For example:

- cases of occupational asthma and dermatitis show that PPE that protects the skin and respiratory system are not being used where they should; the problem is not being taken seriously either by employers, supervisors or employees

- deaths have occurred through falls, either because a safety harness and lanyard were not being worn or because they were worn but the free end of the lanyard was not clipped onto a suitable anchorage point.

There is the temptation to ignore the need to wear PPE and the protection it gives because 'the job will only take a minute' ... but that 'minute' may be all the time that the job needs to kill or injure someone.

It must be remembered that, for PPE to be fully effective, the user must have received adequate training and instruction in its use and it must:

- have been designed to protect the user against the type of hazard that will be present
- be available at all times that it is needed
- be adjusted properly where necessary
- fit the wearer properly and be compatible with other PPE worn at the same time
- be worn/used during the period(s) of risk
- be treated with care and returned to its storage after use, where this is necessary
- be inspected and maintained as necessary
- be replaced if it becomes defective.

Failure of PPE, or using the incorrect type, could expose employees to the possibility of serious injury, ill health or even death. Employers are likely to be far more successful in persuading employees to wear PPE if they are involved in the selection process during purchase. PPE can be cumbersome and uncomfortable, and the cheapest may not be the most suitable. In such circumstances it likely will not be worn, at least not for long, leaving workers unprotected. It is much better to purchase PPE that fits comfortably and will be used willingly. Good quality PPE usually also lasts longer than cheaper PPE, the frequent replacement of which can be more expensive than just buying better quality PPE.

The PPE selected must offer the level of protection required for the hazard(s) identified. For example, whether the job involves the following.

- The use of substances that have the potential to create hazardous dust or fumes.
- The use of substances that could irritate or burn the skin.
- Creating airborne dust through cutting, grinding, and so on.
- Creating fumes from hot-work processes.
- Any process that could result in eye injuries.
- Working at height in circumstances where the wearing of a safety harness and lanyard is the only practical fall protection measure.

 As well as assessing PPE for the immediate task you must also assess the need for any additional PPE as a result of the surrounding site conditions or additional hazards (such as noise, dust, fumes, falling objects and so on).

Manufacturers and suppliers have a statutory duty to provide information regarding the performance characteristics of the PPE products that they manufacture or sell. If necessary, they should be consulted to ensure that PPE meets the standard requirements and only products that comply with the regulation are made available. For some basic PPE (such as a pair of general safety glasses) the exact fit may not be an issue. However, in selecting some PPE (such as in the examples below), achieving a satisfactory fit is essential.

- When a respirator is to be used, the effectiveness of the device is dependent upon the face fit of the individual, which in turn will require that the head-harness straps be adjusted to suit the wearer and their facial features.
- Adjusting the head-harness of a safety helmet to suit the wearer will ensure that it is comfortable and secure.
- Gloves should be a close fit to protect from chemical ingress, entanglement and to maximise dexterity (there are many different sizes available, and the correct size should be purchased to fit the individual).
- Adjusting the fit of a safety harness, which could at worst have to take the shock loading of an arrested fall, is essential if the harness is to be fully effective.

Where a satisfactory fit is not, or cannot, be achieved, the wearer is likely to suffer discomfort and is much more likely to stop using the PPE and also lose concentration. The employee's co-operation must be established in the selection of comfortable and acceptable PPE.

 Consider the potential wearers' physical needs. If they wear glasses and have to wear a mask, goggles or safety glasses, they may require a special type. If they have a beard and have to wear respiratory equipment, can they obtain an airtight seal? These are crucial considerations.

Supervisors must ensure that employees understand *why, what, who, how* and *when* there is a need for PPE.

Why is the PPE needed?

What will be the implications of not wearing it?

Who is going to provide the PPE along with all necessary information, instruction, training and supervision?

How is it fitted, worn or adjusted?

When must it be worn?

 Protection is available for the hazard that you are about to work with. Find it and use it.

6.4.1 Combinations of personal protective equipment

In many circumstances it will be necessary for operatives to simultaneously wear more than one item of PPE.

Whilst this is entirely acceptable, attention should be given to ensuring that the different types of PPE are compatible with each other, to avoid the possibility of a dangerous situation.

For example, hearing protectors that are fitted directly to a safety helmet will not be effective if the safety helmet is poorly fitted and, by moving around on the head, does not allow the hearing protectors to form an effective seal around the ears.

6.4.2 Counterfeit personal protective equipment

Wearing a combination of PPE

Ensure that any PPE you buy is UKCA marked (or CE marked in special circumstances). PPE should also have a Declaration of Conformity, and instructions on how to use the item. The marking signifies that the PPE satisfies certain basic safety requirements and, in some cases, will have been tested and certified by an independent body.

The British Safety Industry Federation (BSIF) is a trade body which, amongst other things, represents the interests of the manufacturers of PPE within the United Kingdom.

In recent years BSIF has become aware of the emergence of counterfeit PPE which, in many cases, looks identical to genuine PPE produced by reputable manufacturers. Much of the counterfeit PPE comes into the UK from abroad.

It is likely that the people within companies who are responsible for purchasing and issuing PPE will be unable to distinguish counterfeit and non-conforming items from the genuine article. Frequently these products are incorrectly (fraudulently) CE marked and do not perform to the required standard. The wearer or user of the PPE will almost certainly be unaware of any problems until it is too late.

It is recommended that PPE is only purchased from reputable suppliers and offers of unduly cheap PPE are resisted.

6.5 Head protection

Employers must provide suitable head protection (for example, industrial safety helmets (hard hats) or bump caps) to employees and ensure they are worn when there is a risk of head injury. Self-employed workers should also obtain and wear suitable head protection.

It is a requirement to wear suitable head protection on all building and construction sites, unless there is no risk of head injury, either from falling objects or by banging the head. Established good practice is to ensure that head protection is always worn by everyone on site, except when in designated safe areas (such as the site office or canteen).

There are many makes of safety helmet available that are constructed to British Standards, and it is the duty of the employer to provide safety helmets that are suitable for the job and the wearer. It is not a legal requirement that safety helmets are kite marked but it is recommended that helmets with kite marks are used. Safety helmets should also have a date of production. They should be replaced if they become damaged or show signs of wear and tear.

Employees, for their part, must follow their employers' instructions. They must wear their safety helmets at all times, when instructed to do so, and report any damage or loss to their employer.

Safety helmets are designed to offer a pre-determined level of impact resistance if they are correctly worn. Safety helmets may only be worn back to front if the helmet has been specifically designed with a reversible cradle, which allows it to be worn with a short peak or full peak at the front. Otherwise, this practice should not be tolerated.

The solvents in some paint, adhesives and indelible markers can reduce the strength of the plastic from which helmets are manufactured.

Provide safety helmets that fit properly and are suitable for the job

Employees must be discouraged from marking or decorating their safety helmets, other than applying official stickers (such as first aider) or confirmation of site induction.

Where the work involves leaning over exposed edges, or similar, chinstraps must be fitted and worn. Many safety helmets have in-built features that enable compatible ear defenders or a face shield to be securely attached.

06

A safety helmet that has fallen from height onto a hard surface may have suffered damage that will affect its strength even though no cracks are visible. In most circumstances, a replacement helmet should be obtained.

Bump caps could be used where the risk assessment has identified that the worker needs to be protected against low-level risks only. They protect the worker from bumping their head (for example, when walking into a fixed object). However, they do not offer adequate protection where there is a risk of falling objects, or moving or suspended loads.

Under Regulations 11 and 12 of the Employment Act, construction workers who are practising members of the **Sikh faith** are exempt from wearing a safety helmet whilst wearing a turban. No other workers are covered by this exemption. Sikhs who do not wear a turban are not exempt from the regulations and, therefore, are required to wear the same head protection as other operatives.

 For more detailed information on the requirements for head protection visit the Health and Safety Executive (HSE) website.

6.6 Foot protection

Accidents arising from the manual handling of items, materials and substances are common causes of injury to the feet, as well as to the hands.

Foot protection comes in many types and styles, such as safety trainers, safety shoes or boots, safety wellington boots and rigger boots. Properly manufactured and selected foot protection with steel toecaps and mid-soles can protect the feet against dropped objects and penetration of the sole of the foot by upward-pointing nails or glass. They can also be oil and slip resistant.

Safety trainers offer good grip on sloping or slippery surfaces and offer more comfort. They are more suitable to trades (such as floor layers) who repeatedly kneel and bend their feet.

Safety wellington boots are essential in preventing burns when operatives have to stand in wet concrete. The cement content, when mixed with water, becomes highly corrosive and will cause severe burns to body tissue. It quickly burns and kills nerve endings and can continue to burn deeply without the person feeling much immediate pain.

Safety boots, as commonly worn by construction workers, provide the required level of protection with steel toecaps and a steel plate moulded into the mid-sole, protecting the wearer against dropped objects and penetration through the sole by sharp objects.

Safety footwear

The ankle support provided by some styles of safety boot is important in the prevention of injuries resulting from walking on uneven surfaces and some industries insist on this type (for example, the rail industry).

Manufacturers offer advice on the most suitable footwear for specific types of hazard.

It is essential that protective footwear is worn when people are on site, both from an employer's point of view, in being able to provide a safe place and a safe method of working, and from an employee's position where safety footwear has a benefit in preventing injuries.

6.7 High-visibility clothing

High-visibility (hi-vis) clothing that protects the wearer against any risk to their health or safety is classified as PPE whereas clothing (such as uniforms), when the primary purpose is to promote a corporate image, is not.

There are wide ranges of hi-vis clothing and accessories (including vests, coats, fleeces, polo-shirts, trousers and overalls). Risk assessment or policy will determine the level of visibility required but all hi-vis clothing should comply with BS EN 20471.

There are three classes of hi-vis clothing.

Class 1 – low visibility.

Class 2 – medium visibility, required when working on or near A and B class roads or sites with vehicle or plant movements.

Class 3 – high visibility, required when working on or near dual carriageways, with a speed of 50 mph or above, or motorways.

Always wear appropriate hi-vis clothing

It can also be a requirement when working in high-risk areas (such as airports, highways maintenance and railways).

6.8   Weather-appropriate clothing

Clothing that is designed to protect the wearer against cold and/or wet weather (as in the examples below) is classified as PPE and must therefore be provided at no charge by the employer.

● Padded and/or waterproof jackets (either hi-vis or not), equipped with a hood that can accommodate a safety helmet where necessary.

● Padded and/or waterproof leggings.

● Suitable footwear.

● Thermally protective gloves and socks.

6.9   Hearing protection

Many types of building and construction activity and equipment generate excessive noise, which can cause permanent hearing damage in people exposed to it, unless appropriate control measures are put into place.

Excessive noise can also cause annoyance, fatigue, loss of concentration and disrupted communication, and may lead directly or indirectly to an increased risk of accidents. Whilst the law requires that the use of PPE as a control measure is only considered as the last resort, the practicalities of working in a construction site environment mean that hearing protection is often the only way of controlling personal exposure to noise.

Hearing protection helps block out hazardous noise. The amount of noise blocked out or reduced is known as attenuation. To achieve the stated attenuation levels it is vital that hearing protection is worn correctly.

All hearing protection must comply with the relevant British and European standards, and must therefore be CE or UKCA marked and be obtained from reputable suppliers to ensure that it meets these standards. As with all PPE for use at work, the selection should be undertaken by a competent person who can ensure that the equipment meets the following criteria.

● It provides an acceptable level of protection (this includes not over-protecting).

● It is compatible with other PPE.

● It does not create additional hazards.

Disposable earplug dispenser with catch plate to prevent wastage

6.9.1   Selection of hearing protection

Providing personal hearing protection should be one of the first considerations on discovering a risk to the health of your employees due to noise. It should not be used as an alternative to controlling noise by technical and organisational means, but for tackling the immediate risk while other control measures are being developed.

In the longer term, it should be used where there is a need to provide additional protection beyond what has been achieved through noise control. Where personal hearing protection is needed it is important that you select the right type of protection, and make sure that it is used and looked after.

The selection of hearing protection should initially consider two factors, namely the **type** and the **performance**. There are two basic types of hearing protection.

1.   Earplugs (either disposable or reusable).

2.   Ear defenders.

These types of hearing protection are available in many forms and are capable of providing a reduction in noise exposure. They will be provided with information to allow you to decide whether they provide adequate noise reduction for your work situation. Whichever type of protector is used, it will provide the best protection only if it is in good condition, is the correct size and is properly worn. It is important that hearing protection is selected by a competent person. Employers should seek specialist advice where necessary.

The following factors should be considered when selecting suitable hearing protection.

● Types of protector and suitability for the work being carried out.

● Noise reduction (attenuation) offered by the protector.

● Compatibility with other safety equipment.

● Pattern of the noise exposure.

● The need to communicate and hear warning sounds.

● Environmental factors (such as heat, humidity, dust and dirt).

● Cost of maintenance or replacement.

● Comfort and user preference.

● Medical disorders suffered by the wearer.

6.9.2 Earplugs

Earplugs take many forms (such as foam plugs, soft plastic valves and re-usable banded plugs). The following are considerations for earplugs.

- Foam earplugs need to be handled when fitted. Therefore, in environments where workers have dirty hands, these might not be suitable as dirt could be pushed into the ears, causing ear infections.

- Banded earplugs (or semi-aural plugs) can be fitted without touching, and so are better in dirty environments.

- Earplugs have a wide range of performance – generally in-ear earplugs have a higher performance than banded or semi-aural earplugs.

- Fitting is critical for in-ear earplugs. If not worn properly, their performance is drastically reduced. Workers should be trained to fit their earplugs correctly, and supervisors must also ensure that earplugs are being worn properly.

6.9.2.1 Disposable earplugs

These are made of fine mineral fibre, sometimes ready shaped. They must be inserted correctly and, if taken out, should not be reused. They should only be handled with clean hands. When it comes to protection from hazardous noise, earplugs are designed to be a safe distance from the sensitive eardrum, even when deeply inserted. Employees need to be instructed on how to insert disposable earplugs correctly. Disposable earplugs are frequently worn incorrectly, by users not inserting them deeply enough. A poorly-fitted foam earplug actually offers little or no protection from noise.

Foam in-ear earplugs worn incorrectly

Foam in-ear earplugs worn correctly

6.9.2.2 Reusable earplugs

These are made of rubber or plastic, and need regular and careful washing. They must be a good fit. A competent person should be responsible for instructing employees in their correct fitting and use. Different sizes may be required for each ear.

Reusable earplugs, like disposable ones, must be fitted with clean hands, as any contamination by dirt, grease or swarf may cause ear irritation or ear infections.

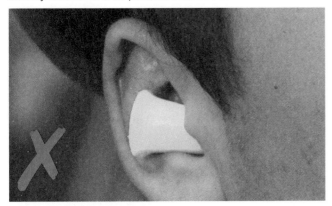

6.9.2.3 Moulded earplugs

These are individual moulded earplugs, which are moulded to the

Banded semi-aural earplugs with replacement buds

shape of the ear. Even though these are initially more expensive, they can offer a longer life span and potential cost savings. It is believed that moulded earplugs offer an improved level of hearing protection and comfort, compared to other earplugs and ear defenders.

6.9.3 Ear defenders

Ear defenders (sometimes referred to as earmuffs) cover the whole of the ear and make a seal against the head. They also come in a variety of forms, including overhead banded, helmet mounted, and those that contain radios and communication devices. Badly designed or badly produced ear defenders may give little or no protection against noise.

Ear defenders can be worn over safety glasses but the determining factor is the width of the eyeglass frame where it meets the earmuff cushion. Thin frames (thickness of 2 mm or less) cause very little obstruction to the seal, resulting in no measurable change in attenuation of the earmuff. Thicker frames (typically seen on safety glasses with adjustable sidebars) can reduce attenuation by 10 decibels.

The frames also need to be touching the head, as sidebars that sit away from the head will give poor performance. If workers must wear earmuffs over safety glasses, thin frames should be chosen for best attenuation. Alternatively, earmuffs can be fitted to certain types of safety helmets, and this might be a better solution for a worker who wears glasses.

 Wearing ear defenders over thick eyeglass frames or over long hair reduces attenuation.

Ear defenders are visible, so it is easy for supervisors to see if operatives are wearing them properly. Other considerations concerning ear defenders are listed below.

- They become sweaty, particularly in hot weather. If not regularly cleaned, they can become quite unhygienic. Users should be provided with cleaning kits, and the ear defenders should be replaced when they become excessively dirty.

- Although more substantial, ear defenders do not necessarily give a better performance than in-ear earplugs.

- The performance of ear defenders can be compromised by wearing them with glasses or over long hair.

- Ear defenders must be stored properly, to avoid them getting contaminated or damaged whilst not being worn.

- Sometimes workers wear earphones under their ear defenders, so that they can listen to music. This practice is dangerous, as it is distracting; the music may mask auditory warnings and reduce awareness of the environment.

Helmet-mounted ear defenders

6.9.4   Hearing protection performance

Any hearing protection equipment (whether earplugs or ear defenders) has a performance that varies across the frequency spectrum. Some provide better protection than others at high frequencies, whilst others provide more protection at mid or lower frequencies. It is important that hearing protection equipment is selected according to its performance, in relation to the noise that it is intended to protect against. This selection should be undertaken by someone who is competent to do so.

In the construction industry in particular it is important that hearing protection does not over-protect, since too much protection may prevent an individual from hearing warning sounds or from being aware of their environment. This may increase their risk, for example, from being struck by construction vehicles. Hearing protection that reduces the level at the ear to below 70 dB should be avoided. Below this level the wearer is likely to feel isolated and be unaware of their surroundings.

All hearing protection must be supplied with data regarding its performance, which should be used during the selection process. There are three types of data and methods of selection, each with varying degrees of complexity.

Single number rating (SNR). As the name suggests, this is a single number that represents the amount of noise reduction that could be expected when used against a broad-band (for example, not tonal) noise source.

High, medium, low (HML). This data broadly represents the level of noise reduction that could be expected at high, medium and low frequencies. It allows some selection in relation to the frequency content of the source noise. However, it requires some indication of the frequency spectrum of the source noise.

Octave band method. This applies noise attenuation data for each octave frequency band. It requires detailed information of the frequency spectrum of the source noise.

In construction, the SNR method is often used, as it simply requires the SNR figure for hearing protection to be subtracted from the measured broad-band noise level from the activity or equipment in question. However, care should be taken if applying this approach, as it may result in the wrong hearing protection being selected where the noise has a significant low frequency component.

6.10   Eye protection

- Many eye injuries occur to people at work each year because eye protection is not being worn.

- These accidents are easily preventable simply by wearing the correct type of eye protection.

- The loss of sight, even in one eye, will have a profound effect on the sufferer and is likely to affect future job prospects and earning power.

- Given the nature of most construction sites, in many cases protection of the eyes will be achieved by the issue and wearing of appropriate PPE.

- In common with other types of PPE, employers must:
    - identify the correct type of eye protection necessary
    - provide it at no charge to employees who need it
    - provide adequate information, instruction and training in use
    - make sure that it is worn.

- Users of eye protection must:
    - wear it when there is a risk of eye injury, as indicated by a risk assessment
    - look after it, particularly with regard to protecting the lenses or face shield
    - return it to any accommodation allocated to it when not in use
    - report to the employer any defect (such as scratched or crazed lenses) and obtain a replacement
    - report to the employer if it is lost and seek a replacement.

Wear eye protection

There are, on average, 1,000 injuries to people's eyes every working day. Some injuries are so severe that they cause partial or even total blindness. A person's eyes are vulnerable and an accident or injury can completely change that person's way of life. Analysis of eye injuries shows that damage is caused:

- 75% of the time by impact
- 10% by abrasion following ingress of dust or other foreign body
- 15% by burns or chemical contamination.

The majority of these injuries would have been prevented if the correct eye protection had been worn.

The Personal Protective Equipment at Work Regulations make provision for protection of employees' eyes at work, and also persons not employed, who may be at risk. Protection must conform to approved specifications, and includes goggles, visors, spectacles, face screens and fixed shields, either freestanding or attached to machinery or plant. Construction personnel involved in a wide range of work (for example, grinding, welding, cutting, hammering and handling chemicals) run the risk of eye injury. Some risks are listed below.

- Impact of solids.
- Ingress of liquid, dust or gas.
- Splashes of hot metal.
- Exposure to glare.

All types of eye protection must meet the following requirements.

- Comply with European Standard specifications.
- Suit the type of work or risk involved, including resistance to impact, heat, dust and chemical penetration.
- Suit the user to ensure minimum discomfort and ease of movement whilst working.
- Be marked to identify their type and suitability.
- Be kept clean and disinfected.

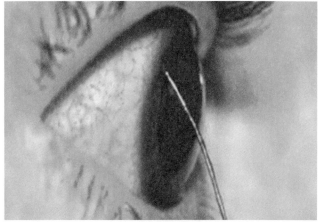

Eye injury sustained as a result of not wearing eye protection

6.10.1 Identifying the type of hazard

Only when the employer has carried out a risk assessment to determine the hazards can the correct type of eye protector be supplied.

Some of the types of hazard detailed require eye protectors to have sufficiently strong lenses or shield to withstand the impact of particles or fragments striking them. For example, some abrasive wheels (such as angle grinders and petrol disc cutters) can operate at speeds of up to 3,800 rpm (revolutions per minute), with a disc speed of up to 180 m per second – equivalent to the disc turning at over 400 mph. Any flying fragments or particles from the disc would travel at a similar speed. Suitable protection for this type of hazard would be impact-resistant goggles or a face shield to BS EN 166 B.1.B.3.4, suitable for high speed particles, medium energy impact.

The effectiveness of the seal made between the eye protectors and the operator's skin is important in affording protection against the type of hazard where irritant or corrosive materials are involved. The ability to withstand high temperatures or reduce strong light and glare is a main requirement for the other types of eye protector.

 For further information concerning specific requirements or combinations of different kinds of protection, manufacturers' literature should be consulted.

6.10.2 Types of eye protector

There are several types of eye protector, and it is important to select and issue the correct type to give the required protection.

 For eye protector types and their markings refer to Appendix A.

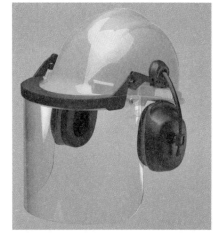

Safety glasses (low-impact eye protection)

Face shield

Eye protection safety checklist

- Have operations requiring eye protection been identified?
- Has the work activity been assessed to determine what, if any, hazards exist?
- Are appropriate types of eye protection available for the various work activities to be carried out?
- Does all eye protection comply with the relevant standard?
- Is the eye protection supplied on a personal basis to employees?
- Are there sufficient quantities of eye protectors available for occasional users?
- Is the use of eye protection satisfactorily monitored?
- Have employees been informed of work activities requiring eye protection?
- Have employees been trained in the correct use and maintenance of eye protection?
- Are employees aware of their responsibilities with regard to the care and reporting of loss or defective eye protectors?
- Are appropriate safety signs displayed?

All eye protectors and shields provided must comply with British and European Standard specifications and meet the following requirements.

- Be suitable for the type of work or risk involved.
- Be suitable for the user to give them minimum discomfort and ease of movement whilst working.
- Be marked to identify their type and suitability.
- Be maintained, kept clean and disinfected.

The following requirements are specific for **eye protectors**.

- Should be issued on a personal basis to the person at risk.
- Sufficient numbers should be maintained and readily available for persons occasionally employed.
- Sufficient numbers should be kept available so if any become lost, destroyed or defective they can be replaced.

The following requirements are specific for **fixed shields**.

- Must conform to the relevant European Standard specification.
- Must be cleaned regularly, disinfected and properly maintained.

Impact-resistant safety goggles

- Must be constructed and kept in position so that they protect the eyes.

6.10.3 Lasers

The Control of Artificial Optical Radiation at Work Regulations 2010 aim to protect workers from the risks to health from hazardous sources of artificial optical radiation. The artificial optical radiation includes light emitted from all artificial sources in all its forms (such as ultraviolet, infrared and laser beams) but excludes sunlight. This applies to a limited number of construction industry activities.

- Full training and information must be given to persons using lasers.
- There should be no unauthorised access to any laser equipment.
- All personnel must be aware of the hazards when working with lasers, the safe working procedures and accident reporting procedures.
- Any necessary eye protection equipment, hazard signs or barriers, for example, must be available and in use as necessary.
- Any eye protectors used in conjunction with lasers must be suited to the wavelength of the laser in use. General purpose safety glasses offer no protection whatsoever against lasers and should not be used.
- All hazard areas must be clearly defined with signs and barriers.
- The laser beam should only be directed at non-reflecting surfaces. Any adjacent reflective surfaces must be covered; otherwise the beam will diverge and could affect other areas and people not directly involved in the job.
- Extra care must be taken when working near reflective surfaces (for example, water, dust and spray) that cannot be marked or covered.
- Special precautions must be taken when working near roads, airfields and other public areas, where a stray beam could cause a hazard.
- When work requires the use of high-powered lasers, the work should, when possible, be undertaken when the site is vacated (such as evenings or weekends). If this is not possible, special precautions will be necessary to ensure that unauthorised persons do not enter the work area or any designated area.

Items of equipment producing light amplification by the stimulated emission of radiation, commonly known as lasers, are widely used on construction sites, mainly for alignment and levelling in civil engineering.

Most are of the helium or neon continuous wave type and emit visible light, but some lasers emit in the invisible infrared region of the electromagnetic spectrum, and these require extra caution.

The HSE says that it receives few reports of ill health or injury arising from the use of lasers. However, those that are reported arise from misuse of the equipment.

The optical radiation produced by a laser is absorbed by the first few centimetres of the body and so the skin and eyes are the tissues most at risk of damage.

Laser beam warning sign

All lasers should comply with BS EN 60825-1. This standard groups laser products into five classes (with some sub-classes), based on acceptable emission levels, and is intended to ensure that the manufacturer and user of laser products comply with current requirements.

It should be noted that if users modify instruments (for example, by adding lenses) they take on the responsibilities of a manufacturer for the class of laser.

The use of Class 1 and 2 products is preferred on construction sites because these represent the lowest risk of eye injury. However, even these lower power lasers can cause eye damage if they are misused (for example, staring directly into the beam or viewing the beam through any magnifying device).

Class 3R and 3B lasers, which may sometimes be in use, can involve hazards to both the user and other personnel. Those who maintain, operate and supervise the use of these products must be fully trained, competent and capable of implementing the necessary safety and hazard control procedures.

Where lower power lasers are used, the human blink reflex will offer some protection. However, this should not be relied upon and is unlikely to offer any protection from higher power lasers.

 For more information on lasers, view Chapter C05 Work equipment and handheld tools.

06

 For a table showing laser health risks visit the Government website.

 ## Laser eye injury

In the event of an eye injury, caused by a laser, ensure the following.

- No medication is applied to the eye.
- The eye involved should be covered with a clean, dry material.
- Immediate medical attention should be sought.

A thorough ophthalmic examination should be carried out within 24 hours, with a full biophysical investigation.

 ## Laser safety checklist

- Has a risk assessment been carried out?
- Are only suitably experienced and trained people allowed to operate laser equipment?
- Has the hazard area been defined and clearly marked?
- Has an exclusion zone been created if the more powerful classes of laser are being used?
- When work with lasers is taking place, are only authorised people allowed in the area?
- Is correct eye protection in use during all laser operations?
- Is there no danger to any other person(s) resulting from stray reflections or from any activity involving the use of lasers?
- Where necessary, is the source and direction of the laser beam clearly identified?
- Is the laser beam only directed at a non-reflecting surface?
- Are any other reflective surfaces covered?
- Does all laser equipment comply with BS EN 60825-1?
- Are beam attenuators and any other safety devices in use when using Class 3R and 3B products?

6.11   Hand and skin protection

Protective clothing and other PPE provides one of the most practical ways of limiting contact between the skin and other substances. To be effective, all protective clothing must be the right size, fit for the purpose, maintained in good condition, cleaned regularly and stored carefully when not in use.

Protective clothing may include gloves, overalls, eye protectors (such as goggles and face shields), aprons, boots and leggings, depending on the work being undertaken. Legislation requires the provision and wearing of protective clothing for specific processes and operations. The protective clothing provided must be suited to the requirements of the job.

Regular inspections must be made to ensure the protective clothing remains sound and adequate.

Hand protection must be suitable for the job

6.11.1   Gloves

British Standards cover many types of protective glove but care is needed in selecting the right type for a particular hazard. For example, a glove suitable for handling abrasive materials may offer no protection against chemicals, while the appropriate glove to protect the skin against contact with diesel oil may offer no protection against some solvents.

Manufacturers' charts and recommendations should be followed when selecting gloves to protect the wearer against specific hazards. A properly selected glove can be useful in the prevention of dermatitis, for example, if care is taken to avoid getting contaminants inside the gloves when putting them on and taking them off.

The modern materials from which gloves are now made enable them to be effective against hazardous substances whilst generally allowing the necessary amount of feel and dexterity where these factors are an issue.

All manufacturers and reputable PPE suppliers offer advice on the most suitable gloves for specific types of hazard, some of which are summarised in the following table.

Safety gloves must be worn

Industrial gloves – some types and uses	
Hazard	**Recommended type**
Acids, concrete, brickwork, stain removers, solvents and alkalis.	Neoprene, nitrile, PVC or rubber.
Esters, ethers, ketones (mastic, sealers), aldehydes and petroleum-based products.	Medium and heavyweight rubber, neoprene, nitrile or PVC.
High and low temperatures.	Nitrile, PVC or medium and heavyweight rubber.
Abrasion, unloading bricks and blocks and general materials handling.	Rubber, nitrile, PVC, neoprene or chrome-leather with reinforced palm.
Bitumen, hot work or similar.	Asbestos substitute or Nomex.

It should be noted that industrial safety gloves are rated from 1–4 for their resistance to abrasion, tear and puncture, and 1–5 for blade cut. People specifying and purchasing work gloves must ensure that the correct grade is obtained by speaking to the manufacturers or suppliers, if necessary.

🔍 For guidance on the selection of gloves refer to Appendix B.

6.11.2   Cuts and abrasions

Manually handling objects with rough surfaces and sharp corners can cause damage to the skin of the hands if appropriate gloves (such as rigger gloves) are not worn. Repetitive manual handling may even make the situation worse. Such damage breaks the surface of the skin making it more vulnerable to absorbing other substances that could potentially have severe health effects. Worn-out gloves must be thrown away and replacements obtained.

Where objects with sharp edges (such as sheet glass and sheet metal components) have to be manually handled, gloves with cut-proof material (such as Kevlar) woven into the fabric must be worn. Dependent on the findings of the risk assessment, long-sleeve Kevlar gloves or gauntlets, or close fitting Kevlar sleeves that extend up to the elbow, may be required to offer protection against cuts, slashes and abrasion to the forearms.

Ideally, work would be organised so that the manual handling of all such objects could be avoided. However, given the nature of construction, total avoidance is usually not possible. For example, a roof tiler may now use an inclined hoist to get the tiles up to roof level, but the hoist must still be loaded and the tiles distributed around the roof by hand.

6.11.3 Hot works

Work, such as welding and grinding, will require that the hands, forearms and face are protected against high temperatures and welding fumes or grinding sparks. To achieve this level of protection it may be necessary for those who carry out such work to wear specialist PPE made for the purpose (for example, welders should wear welding gauntlets that extend up to the elbow, a face shield and flame retardant overalls or apron).

6.11.4 Vibration

Some retro-fit products are available that are designed to protect operators from vibration. Only those approved by manufacturers should be used.

 Anti-vibration gloves

The wearing of anti-vibration gloves is not recommended as problems can include the following.

● Reduced flexibility at the hands resulting in higher grip and push forces and loss of precise tool control.

● The possibility of gloves amplifying the tool vibration in some cases (these cases are difficult to predict).

● They are only tested in one direction and vibration occurs in three directions.

● Field trials of gloves have shown that the vibration isolation materials are not always durable.

One benefit from work gloves is that they keep the hands warm and offer other protection.

If an employer intends to provide items of PPE as part of their strategy to reduce the risks from vibration in the workplace, it is important that the correct PPE is selected. As with all PPE for use at work, gloves or anti-vibration protection should be selected by a competent person who can ensure, in discussion with the supplier, that they carry the CE or UKCA mark and meet the appropriate standards. Most reputable manufacturers and suppliers will offer advice on the selection of different types of gloves and other PPE.

 For further information refer to Chapter B12 Vibration.

6.11.5 Hygiene

Personal cleanliness is an important factor in the prevention of skin diseases. The necessary washing facilities and an ample supply of clean warm water, soap and clean towels should be made available near to the workplace. Workers should be encouraged to use these facilities. Facilities for changing out of work-stained or contaminated clothing should be made available to workers. This will also help to promote personal cleanliness. All facilities should be kept clean and be inspected regularly.

6.11.6 Barrier substances

Where skin exposure is unavoidable, the use of barrier creams or other preparations may limit the degree of contact. These are applied before starting work, and removed by washing after. Re-application is necessary before resuming. Water-soluble barrier creams are unsuitable where wet work is involved, and some substances wear off. There are many types available, and it is essential that the right type is used for the work being done. Most barrier substances afford only limited protection, and should never be relied on as a sole means of protection.

6.11.7 Skin cleansers

Soap and water will help restore the skin to its natural state after the use of barrier creams. Skin cleansers may be required where soap and water are not adequate (such as insoluble barrier substances). With some skin cleansers (sanitisers), an additional moisturiser may be needed. Solvents (such as paraffin, turpentine, thinners and petrol) remove the natural oils from the skin, and with persistent use can lead to skin problems, so they must not be used for skin cleaning. Conditioning creams, designed to replace the natural oils of the skin, removed through frequent cleansing, should be used when necessary to help avoid future skin problems.

6.11.8 First aid

A healthy, intact skin is an effective barrier against some substances and infection, but the slightest cut or other injury may admit infection All abrasions to the skin, however minor, should be treated at once. However, be aware that some substances can penetrate unbroken skin, which can lead to a range of possible infections and other serious diseases. Employers must provide adequate first-aid equipment and facilities appropriate to the type of work or operations being undertaken.

6.11.9 Educating staff in risk prevention

Regular inspections of the workplace, work methods and precautionary procedures adopted will help ensure that the risk of dermatitis, or other skin complaints, is kept to a minimum. At-risk employees should be encouraged to carry out self-checks for the first signs of dermatitis or skin cancer and, ideally, supervisors should be trained to carry out skin checks and be able to identify signs or symptoms of dermatitis.

In appropriate circumstances, arrangements should be made for workers to have regular examinations by an occupational health professional to detect early signs of skin complaints. Active concern for employees' welfare will encourage their co-operation in early reporting of skin irritations. Workers are more likely to co-operate in preventative measures if they are informed of the different skin diseases and what can be done to prevent them from occurring.

 The HSE Skin at work webpages contain basic practical advice for employers and employees on the prevention of skin diseases. The webpages also contain in-depth technical advice for occupational health nurses and health and safety practitioners, plus other resources.

6.12   Protection from sun exposure

A sunny day usually makes most people feel good, but too much sunlight can cause life-long damage to the skin. It is not simply sudden exposure while on holiday that is harmful. Even a tan that has been built up gradually can be harmful to health. A tan is a sign that the skin has been potentially damaged.

Skin damage is caused by ultraviolet rays in sunlight. People whose jobs keep them outdoors for a long time (such as building, construction and civil engineering workers) may, if their skin is unprotected, get more sun on their skin than is healthy for them. They will then be at greater risk of developing skin cancer.

In the short-term, excess exposure of unprotected skin to the sun can cause blistering and peeling. Even mild reddening of the skin is a sign of skin damage.

In the long-term, too much sun will speed up ageing of the skin, making it leathery, mottled and wrinkled. However, the most serious issue is an increased chance of developing skin cancer.

There are two main types of skin cancer: **malignant melanoma**, which is less common but more serious, and **non-melanoma**, which is very common but not as serious.

Ultraviolet radiation from the sun is a major cause of skin cancer. Cases have doubled in the last 20 years. Around 800 construction workers are diagnosed with skin cancer every year as a result of sun exposure. Men most commonly develop skin cancer on their chest or back, whereas for women it is on their legs.

More than two adults (aged 15–34) are now diagnosed with skin cancer every day in the UK.

Some medicines, and contact with some chemicals used at work (such as bitumen products), can also make the skin more sensitive to sunlight (photosensitivity).

Site sunscreen dispenser with details of the day's UV level

 For images of malignant melanoma and non-melanoma visit the Cancer Research UK website.

6.12.1   Skin types

Some people are more at risk than others. People with white skin are most at risk. Workers with the following characteristics should take particular care.

● Fair or freckled skin that does not tan, or goes red or burns before it tans.

● Red or fair hair and light coloured eyes.

● A large number of moles.

The effect that strong sunlight can have on the different types of skin is explained below.

Type 1. White skin, never tans, always burns. Often person has red or fair hair, blue eyes, pale skin and freckles.

Type 2. White skin, burns easily, but may tan eventually. Person may have fair hair, blue eyes and freckles.

Workers with skin Types 1 or 2 must take extra care to avoid strong sunshine or cover up with tightly woven clothing and a hat.

Type 3. White skin tans easily and burns rarely. Person has dark hair and eyes and slightly darker skin.

Type 4. White skin, never burns, always tans. Person has dark hair, eyes and skin.

Workers with skin Types 3 or 4 should still take care in strong sunshine.

Type 5. Brown skin.

Type 6. Black skin.

Workers with skin Types 5 or 6 are still at risk from skin cancer. These skin types can still darken and even burn in stronger sunlight.

6.12.2 Protecting yourself

Even if their skin is not fair or freckled, workers should be particularly careful whilst working outside in summer in the three or four hours around midday when the sun is most intense. Workers should:

- protect themselves with the type of clothing outlined below

- try to avoid the mild reddening, which is a sign of skin damage, as well as being a sign of early burning

- try to work and take breaks in the shade if they can (this will reduce the danger of harming the skin)

- not be complacent (the skin's most vulnerable areas are the back of the neck and the head – where possible, keep these areas covered)

- try not to get a tan; it might look good but it indicates that the skin has already been damaged.

 A leaflet for workers about working in hot weather is available from the HSE.

Using **protective clothing** to cover up is the main way to avoid the dangers of developing skin cancer.

- Work clothing made from close-woven fabric, such as a long-sleeved shirt and jeans, will stop most of the UV rays.

- Wear a hat. A wide brimmed hat will shade the face and head. A safety helmet will afford protection and the addition of a hanging flap will protect the back of the neck.

- Keep a shirt or other top on.

Hats and other clothing are the best form of protection, but sunscreen and lotions can add useful protection for parts of the body that are not easy to shade from the sun. A sun protection factor (SPF) rating of 15 or more is recommended.

The first warning sign is often a small scabby spot that does not clear after a few weeks. Workers should be instructed to look for changed or newly formed moles or any skin discoloration. Workers should pay particular attention to any growths that appear on the face, especially around the eyes and nose, or on the backs of hands. If these signs are noticed, medical advice should be sought, either from the company's medical staff or a local general practitioner, drawing attention to any moles that grow, change or bleed.

Many of these symptoms may prove to be non-cancerous – but need to be checked to be absolutely sure. Even if a spot is cancerous, simple modern treatments can usually cure it. This type of cancer rarely spreads to other parts of the body. The smaller the spot, the easier to cure.

 Don't delay. If you think something might be wrong, get it checked out.

 Employers are strongly encouraged to develop a sun safety policy. For an example of a sun safety policy refer to Appendix C.

6.13 Fall protection

Items of equipment used by a person to avoid falling from height (as in the examples below) are classified as PPE.

- Safety harness.

- Fall-arrest or restraint lanyard.

- Inertia reel fall-arrest block.

All employer and employee duties that apply to other types of PPE also apply to this type of equipment. A major additional consideration regarding the use of this PPE is the prompt rescue of anyone who has fallen and is suspended in a safety harness. If a worker's fall has been arrested, any delay in rescuing them could result in suspension syncope or fainting. There are many kits available to rescue those suspended at height.

Worker using fall restraint to undertake maintenance work

 A site-specific rescue plan must be in place before any works from height are carried out using fall arrest equipment.

 For further information refer to Chapter D05 Fall arrest and suspension equipment.

6.14   Personal buoyancy equipment

Another category of PPE is that which enables the user to keep afloat should they fall into water or other liquids.

These are broadly divided into lifejackets and buoyancy aids.

 For further information refer to Chapter F05 Working over or near to water.

6.15   Respiratory protective equipment

6.15.1   Hazards

Dust is known to have a severe impact on workers' health, especially when inhaled for long periods.

While the health issues associated with asbestos are well recognised, the greater part of the dust problem in the industry currently relates to more common substances (for example, cement, plaster, wood, MDF, stone, silica, fillers and plastics).

High-speed sanding, grinding or cutting of most materials can produce sufficient dust to cause a health hazard.

Not all dusts are the same. Some dusts are more harmful than others. Excessive exposure to some types of dust has been linked to the development of particular health problems that can take may years to manifest, such as lung cancer or asthma. The development of occupational disease can mean some workers experience life-altering (and in some cases) premature life-ending illness.

Fumes from certain substances (such as solvents, paints and adhesives) can have serious health implications, especially in poorly-ventilated areas as well as using them in a confined space. This is a high risk issue, and can cause fatalities.

Such problems are unlikely to arise if occupational exposure limits and the Control of Substances Hazardous to Health (COSHH) Regulations are observed and safe systems of work maintained.

 For further information refer to Chapter B10 Dust and fumes (Respiratory hazards).

6.15.2   Selecting respiratory protective equipment

Under the Personal Protective Equipment at Work Regulations, the employer must carry out an assessment to determine **when** RPE is required and **what type** is appropriate for controlling exposure to the hazardous material.

Selecting RPE that is both suitable for the user and the job must be carried out by a competent person, because the choice will depend on a number of interacting factors.

● The nature of the hazards and materials.

● The measured dust concentrations.

● The period of exposure.

● If working outdoors, the prevailing weather conditions.

● Suitability for each user (field of vision, provision for communication and the need to move in cramped or difficult working places, such as confined spaces).

● Compatibility with any other items of PPE that may need to be worn at the same time.

Given the nature of some types of work, it is not always reasonably practicable to completely eliminate respiratory hazards.

In these circumstances, if no other control measure is reasonably practicable or, if after applying all other reasonably practicable measures, there is a residual risk from exposure, suitable RPE must be provided for each person exposed to the hazard.

Selecting the wrong type of RPE could have serious, even fatal, consequences. Selection must be carried out by a competent person and must be adequate in reducing exposure to an acceptable level, which must not exceed any applicable workplace exposure limit (WEL) and be as far below it as possible.

The equipment must also be suitable for the wearer, task and environment, to ensure the wearer can work freely and without additional risk caused by the RPE.

Manufacturers assign a protection factor to their RPE – the assigned protection factor (APF), which indicates the expected level of performance of the equipment. In simple terms, it predicts the ratio of the hazardous substance outside the RPE to the amount inside the RPE.

Protection factors

For example, for typical filtering half-mask respirators the following apply.

FFP1 or P1 is a low efficiency device offering a protection factor of 4.

FFP2 or P2 is a medium efficiency device offering a protection factor of 10.

FFP3 or P3 is a high efficiency device offering a protection factor of 20.

A protection factor of 10 means that in controlled conditions, for every 10 particles outside the mask, it is predicted that one particle would penetrate the filter material. A protection factor of 20 means for every 20 particles outside the mask, it is predicted that only one particle would penetrate the filter. Therefore, to properly select RPE it is necessary to know the following information.

- The concentration of the hazardous substance in the air to which the worker will be exposed.
- The WEL that applies to the substance.

For example, for a concentration of silica dust in air of 1 mg/m³, a P2 filter with an APF of 10 would be expected to reduce the concentration of the silica inside the mask to 0.1 mg/m³. The WEL for RCS is 0.1 mg/m³, so this would appear to be adequate protection. However, allowing for real world factors, it is good practice to go to the next level of protection up, to provide a margin of error. Therefore, a P3 mask would be selected, with an APF of 20, giving potential exposure of 0.05 mg/m³.

 It is recognised good practice to use RPE with an FFP3 or P3 rating to protect against dust (such as silica) that is created when mechanically cutting concrete, bricks, slabs and so on, even when wet cutting, which only removes around 60-75% of airborne particles.

There are various types of RPE approved for use. Details of types and typical uses should be obtained from the manufacturer. The main types are listed below.

- Disposable half-mask respirators.
- Reusable half-mask respirators.
- Powered respirators.

- Ventilated visors and ventilated helmet respirators.
- Air-fed breathing apparatus.
- Self-contained breathing apparatus.

 Respirators must not be used in oxygen-deficient atmospheres.

Breathing apparatus must be used where there is the possibility of reduced oxygen levels.

 Guidance and recommendations are provided in the HSE publication *Respiratory protective equipment at work: a practical guide* (HSG53).

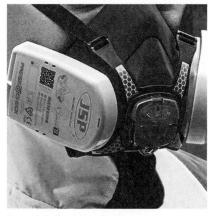
Reusable half-mask respirator

Ventilated visor and ventilated respirator

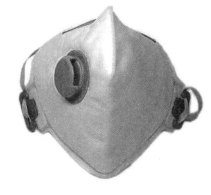
Disposable half-mask respirator

 Cheap nuisance dust masks (cup-shaped filters often held in place by a single strap) are not classed as PPE or RPE. They do not meet any current standards or legislative requirements and offer little or no protection to the wearer.

6.15.3 Face-fit testing

The performance of tight-fitting RPE facepieces depends on achieving a good contact between the wearer's skin and the face seal of the facepiece. People's faces vary significantly in shape and size so it is unlikely that one particular type or size of RPE facepiece will fit everyone. Inadequate fit will significantly reduce the protection provided to the wearer. Any reduction in protection can put the RPE wearer's life in danger or may lead to immediate or long-term ill health.

In line with the supporting Approved Codes of Practice (ACoP), face-fit testing for employees should be carried out. This test checks that the respirator matches the person's facial features and seals adequately to the wearer's face. It will also ensure that incorrectly fitting respirators are not selected for use. This test must be carried out by a competent person.

Research indicates that up to 50% of all RPE used does not offer the level of protection assumed. This is due to poor selection and fitting, rather than the product itself.

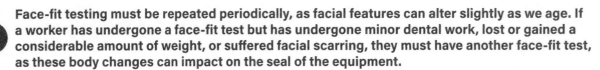

The presence of facial hair in the region of the face seal will significantly reduce the protection provided. A human hair is around 150 microns (150 μm) in diameter. Stubble or facial hair can lift the facepiece off the face, creating a gap of around 100 microns (100 μm), large enough for harmful dust to get past the seal.

Respirable dusts **are dusts with a particle size below 10 microns (10 μm), which have the ability to be deposited in the lungs. These tiny particles are too fine to be seen by the naked eye, but are the most harmful.**

Face-fit testing should be conducted by a competent person. Competence can be demonstrated through achieving accreditation under the Fit2Fit RPE fit test providers' accreditation scheme. This scheme has been developed by the British Safety Industry Federation (BSIF) together with industry stakeholders and is supported by the HSE. The scheme is not compulsory and employers are free to take other action to comply with the law. One way that employers can demonstrate good practice is by ensuring that the fit tester is appropriately accredited, for the type of service they offer, by the Fit2Fit scheme.

Face-fit testing must be repeated periodically, as facial features can alter slightly as we age. If a worker has undergone a face-fit test but has undergone minor dental work, lost or gained a considerable amount of weight, or suffered facial scarring, they must have another face-fit test, as these body changes can impact on the seal of the equipment.

For further information on the Fit2Fit scheme visit the website.

6.15.4 Training employees

Training employees in the correct use of RPE is essential before first use and should be repeated at suitable intervals. It is essential that training is carried out by a competent person and covers the following.

- Why the RPE is necessary.
- The hazards, the risks and the effects of exposure.
- What RPE is to be provided.
- How the RPE works.
- Why face-fit testing might be necessary.
- How to wear and check the RPE correctly.

- What maintenance is required and when.
- Where and how to clean the RPE and store it.
- How to report defects in the RPE or any other problem with it.
- Employer and employee responsibilities.
- Use and misuse of RPE.

The provision and use of RPE must only be considered when equally or more effective protective control measures cannot be used. The failure of RPE could have serious consequences. The importance of the correct type of RPE being provided and used cannot be overstated as it must be assumed that the user will be working in a hostile environment. However, there are several potential problems arising from the selection and/or use of RPE.

- The **failure** of an item of RPE where, for whatever reason (such as lack of routine maintenance), it fails to provide the necessary level of protection.
- The **misuse** of RPE (such as it being mistreated or not used in accordance with the manufacturer's instructions or the training given).
- It being the **wrong type** of RPE (for example, there would be no protection from a filtering respirator designed solely to capture airborne dust if being used where the workplace hazard is a toxic gas).
- The effectiveness of the **face fit**. Many types of RPE depend upon a good seal between the respirator and the skin of the user at all times, including where physical activity and exertion are required. Factors such as facial hair or the shape of the face can interfere with a good fit.

Where the wearing of RPE is inevitable, European Standard BS EN 529 recommends that employers and the self-employed define and document a policy covering selection, use and maintenance of RPE, which is communicated to, and understood by, all organisational levels.

6.15.5 Common failings

Research undertaken by the HSE targeted workplace RPE inspections. Their findings are shown below.

● A perception that using RPE was simple or obvious.

● Managers and supervisors had knowledge gaps on critical aspects of RPE.

● There was limited use of external information sources (for example, manufacturer's literature and websites).

● There was an assumption that workers know how to put on and use RPE.

● RPE misuse is common – but is generally blamed on workers.

● Limited input and involvement from management.

● Little information was provided to the worker.

● Poor standards of training, hazard awareness and RPE use.

● Little supervision and enforcement.

● Deficiencies in provisions for RPE storage and maintenance regimes.

● RPE pre-use checks were unlikely.

Additional failings include the following.

● Insufficient consideration given to the selection of RPE.

● Inadequate face-fit testing.

● Wearers having more than one day's stubble growth, which substantially reduces the RPE's face seal and reduces the protection factor.

● Mask straps not being adjusted or tightened, or straps in the wrong position on the head.

● Disposable RPE not being replaced as often as it should be.

Apart from correct selection, there are other important considerations in the use of RPE.

Replacement. Filters may become saturated and no longer provide sufficient protection, or give excessive breathing resistance. They must be replaced at appropriate intervals, depending on the level of use and level of contaminant in the air.

Hygiene. Masks can become unhygienic quickly. Provision must be made for non-disposable equipment to be cleaned by the user.

Face fit. Regular users of RPE must undergo face-fit testing as part of the selection process, to ensure that they are using the make of respirator that best fits their face shape. Many suppliers provide a face-fit service. Face-fit testing may need to be repeated (for example, after weight loss or dental work that has altered facial features, even minimally). Employers must keep records of face fits undertaken.

Facial hair. The manufacturer's specification for RPE is based on the user being clean shaven. Where the user has facial hair, the effectiveness will be reduced. Even light stubble can have an effect. This should be considered during selection and supervision. Types of RPE are available that can be worn with facial hair.

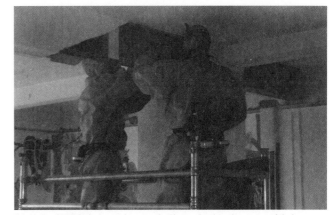

Storage. Where equipment will be used across shifts, it will need to be properly stored, not just left in a toolbox. Manufacturers often supply foil storage bags for reusable respirators, which should be used to ensure that the equipment is not contaminated when not in use.

Supervision. It is essential for the employer and principal contractor to ensure that the correct RPE is being properly worn for all of the time that it is needed. This requires effective supervision on site.

Example of RPE being worn incorrectly. The worker has the straps of their powered respirator over their overalls, meaning they would have to remove their mask in order to take off their overalls, exposing them to asbestos fibres

Training. Employers should not assume that workers know how to wear RPE properly. They need to be trained in how to do so. Workers should also be given information on the nature of risks from respiratory hazards for the site they are working on. This should be included in site induction as well as general training.

 For further information refer to Chapter B10 Dust and fumes (Respiratory hazards).

 The HSE has an easy-to-follow pocket card aimed at workers. It covers the key points about wearing a face mask to make sure it is effective. Download a copy from the HSE website.

6.15.6 Using and maintaining respiratory protective equipment

Both the employer and the employee have a duty to ensure that all RPE provided is used correctly and that it is stored correctly after use. Employers must also ensure that non-disposable RPE is thoroughly examined and tested at appropriate intervals.

The ACoP, which supports the Personal Protective Equipment at Work Regulations, specifies that such examinations and tests are carried out at least every month, and more frequently where conditions are particularly severe. Longer intervals may be more appropriate in the case of certain RPE (for example, half-mask respirators used infrequently for short spells against air contaminants of relatively low toxicity).

However, the longest interval between examinations and tests should not exceed three months. For disposable RPE, provided it is only used for one working shift and is then disposed of, the user should check it for defects and contamination before and during use.

Appendix A – Eye protection selection

The standards of eye protection

Hazard description	Standard	Symbol	
		Frames	Lenses
Optical class*			
Refractive power +/- 0.06	BS EN 166		1
Refractive power +/- 0.12	BS EN 166		2
Refractive power + 0.12	BS EN 166		3
Refractive power - 0.25	BS EN 166		3
Mechanical strength**			
Increased robustness (12 m/s).	BS EN 166	–	S
Low energy impact (45 m/s).	BS EN 166	-F	F
Medium energy impact (120 m/s).	BS EN 166	-B	B
High energy impact (190 m/s).	BS EN 166	-A	A
Field of use			
Droplets and splashes of liquid.	BS EN 166	3	–
Large dust particles.	BS EN 166	4	–
Gas and fine dust particles.	BS EN 166	5	–
Short-circuit electric arc.	BS EN 166	8	–
Molten metal and hot solids.	BS EN 166	9	9
Other			
Non-mist (resistance to fogging).	BS EN 166	–	N
Welding work equipment.	BS EN 175	–	–
Sun glare filters	BS EN 172	–	–
Infrared filters	BS EN 171	–	–
Ultraviolet filters	BS EN 170	–	–
Welding filters	BS EN 169 and 379	–	–

*   1, 2 or 3 indicates the optical quality of the ocular, with Class 1 being the best.
** S and F is for any type of eye protection
    B is for goggles and face shields only
    A is for face shields only

Notes

1. Eye protectors manufactured to the British and European Standard are subjected to a number of tests (including temperature, robustness and optical quality) before approval.

2. In the test of robustness, for example, general purpose goggles to EN 166.1.S must withstand the impact of a 6 mm steel ball travelling at 12 m/s (27 mph). Impact goggles to EN 166.1.F must withstand the impact at 45 m/s (100 mph) and for EN 166.1.B they must withstand an impact at 120 m/s (270 mph).

3. Safety goggles are marked with a combination of letters and numbers to indicate the standard of protection provided, for example:
   – BS EN 166.1.F is impact-resistant to a low energy projectile
   – BS EN 166.1.B.3.4 is impact-resistant to medium energy projectiles, droplets, splashes of liquid and large dust particles
   – BS EN 166.1.A.9 is impact-resistant to high energy projectiles, molten metal and hot solids.

 Safety glasses, commonly referred to as light eye protection, are either low or medium energy impact rated. They are not high energy rated and must never be used as a substitute for safety goggles during high-impact work (such as using grinders, petrol cut-off saws, cartridge guns, gas-powered nail guns and breaking out).

Selection

Eye protection must be selected in the light of the work activity to be undertaken and the assessed level of risk. A suitable and sufficient risk assessment will identify hazards and indicate the control measures required to minimise the likelihood and severity of potential risks.

 For further information on the selection of eye protection refer to the appropriate British Standard.

Appendix B – Glove selection guidance

Choosing the right glove for the right job

BS EN 420 – General requirements for gloves
■ Mark identifying the manufacturer.
■ Product identifying mark.
■ Size designation (normally in range **6** to **11**).
■ Date of obsolescence (if appropriate).
■ Dexterity performance in range **1** (lowest) to **5** (highest), if required.
■ Markings specific to individual risks, including pictograms where appropriate.

Mechanical hazard

Mechanical hazards are associated with the handling of rough or sharp objects that could abrade, cut or pierce the skin (such as glass, thin metal sheets and masonry blocks). A mechanical hazard is not associated with moving machinery; in fact it can be extremely dangerous to wear gloves that could catch in moving parts or serrated blades.

 Gloves should not be used when working with serrated blades – *use guards*.

4. 1. 4. 1.
BS EN 388

■ 4 = Abrasion. Performance index 0 to 4.
■ 1 = Blade cut. Performance index 0 to 5.
■ 4 = Tear. Performance index 0 to 4.
■ 1 = Puncture. Performance index 0 to 4.

Highest number equals greatest resistance.

Chemical hazard

Whether total immersion or merely splash is involved, any substance that would irritate, inflame or burn the skin is classed as a chemical hazard. In order that a more informed and relevant glove selection can be made, there is a list of 12 chemicals, identified by the letters A to L. Refer to the manufacturer for details of the specific chemicals.

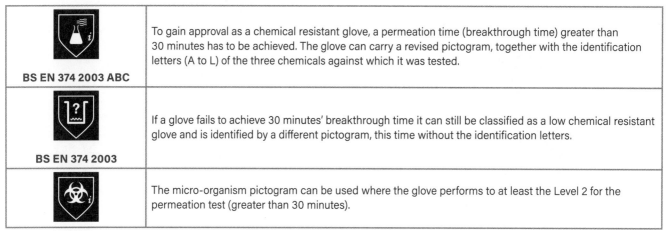

BS EN 374 2003 ABC	To gain approval as a chemical resistant glove, a permeation time (breakthrough time) greater than 30 minutes has to be achieved. The glove can carry a revised pictogram, together with the identification letters (A to L) of the three chemicals against which it was tested.
BS EN 374 2003	If a glove fails to achieve 30 minutes' breakthrough time it can still be classified as a low chemical resistant glove and is identified by a different pictogram, this time without the identification letters.
	The micro-organism pictogram can be used where the glove performs to at least the Level 2 for the permeation test (greater than 30 minutes).

Thermal hazards hot and cold

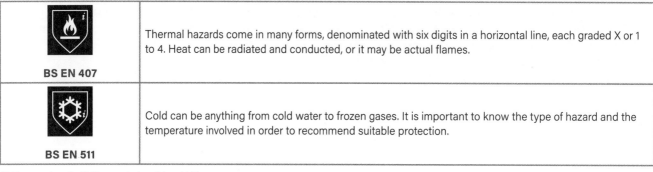

BS EN 407	Thermal hazards come in many forms, denominated with six digits in a horizontal line, each graded X or 1 to 4. Heat can be radiated and conducted, or it may be actual flames.
BS EN 511	Cold can be anything from cold water to frozen gases. It is important to know the type of hazard and the temperature involved in order to recommend suitable protection.

(Table reproduced with the permission of Arco Ltd.)

06

Appendix C – Sun safety policy example

1. This company is committed to protecting and educating its workers about the risks to health arising from excessive exposure to strong sunlight. The policy will be implemented as appropriate for all workers who are at risk.

2. Sun protection advice will be provided as part of routine health and safety training for all employees, including supervisors and managers. All new employees will be made aware of the sun safety policy.

3. Wherever possible, working hours and tasks will be scheduled to avoid the midday sunshine. Wherever possible, work that can be carried out indoors or in the shade will be scheduled during periods of strong sunshine.

4. All workers who are liable to be at risk will receive appropriate training on how to protect themselves from prolonged exposure to strong sunlight, regardless of their skin type or hair colour.

5. Workers who are at risk will be encouraged to wear full-length trousers and long-sleeved shirts throughout the year. They will be made aware that, ideally, clothing will be loose fitting and made from a close-weave fabric.

6. In most circumstances, the mandatory wearing of a safety helmet will provide the necessary protection for the head. In the rare circumstances where a safety helmet need not be worn, workers at risk will be advised to wear a suitable hat.

7. Workers at risk will be given information on the appropriate use of sunscreen and lotions, including advice on the minimum recommended level of protection.

8. Drinking water will be provided in the shade and all workers will be encouraged to drink plenty of water to avoid dehydration.

9. Rest areas in the shade will be provided and workers at risk will be encouraged to use them for their rest breaks.

10. All contractors working on the site will be made aware of the contents of the sun safety policy and will be required to adhere to its guidelines.

11. The effectiveness of this policy will be monitored and it will be reviewed and updated as necessary.

06

06

Control of substances hazardous to health

Supporting
INFORMATION

GT700 Toolbox talks / supporting checklists and forms

Toolbox talks on some of these topics are available in the GT700 publication. Supporting checklists and forms covering some of these topics are available on our companion website.

CONTROL OF SUBSTANCES HAZARDOUS TO HEALTH

Overview

The intention of the Control of Substances Hazardous to Health (COSHH) Regulations is to protect human health from harm through exposure to hazardous substances by either totally preventing exposure or, where that is not reasonably practicable, controlling the level of exposure to safe values, by appropriate means.

Substances covered by the COSHH Regulations can take on many forms, including chemicals, vapours, dusts, fumes, gases and biological agents.

Asbestos and lead hazards are commonly encountered during construction work, particularly during the refurbishment of older buildings, but they are not covered by the COSHH Regulations because they have their own regulations.

7.1   Introduction

The construction industry has worked hard over the years to improve its safety performance, and this is evidenced in the reduction in the number of fatal accidents.

Although the sector is becoming more aware of the exposure to occupational health hazards, there is still a lot of work to be done, as they remain a high-risk health issue to all construction workers.

Whereas the impact of accidents is immediately obvious (acute) and often dramatic, the onset of occupational health problems is often more subtle, slower to develop (chronic) and therefore easier to miss or ignore.

Failure to control exposure to COSHH substances can result in lung disease (such as asthma), silicosis, cancer and skin disease (such as dermatitis).

COSHH Regulations do not cover any flammable or explosive properties that the substances might possess (for example, solvent-based products may give off flammable vapours and clouds of dust from everyday materials, such as wood dust, which can explode if ignited).

These are covered by the Dangerous Substances and Explosive Atmospheres Regulations.

7.2   Important points

- Many of the substances **used or created** during work processes have the potential to cause harm to the health of anyone exposed to them.

- Many COSHH issues within construction relate to substances that are created through construction work processes and activities (such as dust or fumes), as opposed to chemicals that have been bought in.

- Hazardous substances that are already present on a site when it is first occupied can also pose a hazard to health.

- All purchased products that are hazardous to health must carry an appropriate warning symbol on the packaging. However, hazardous substances that are created by the work process (such as dust from cutting slabs) or those that are already present on site (such as contaminated ground) will carry no such health warning.

- Employers have legal duties to establish the health risks to their employees, and others who may come into contact with hazardous substances, by carrying out an appropriate assessment and putting in place adequate control measures.

- The assessment should take into account how the substance is used on site and should not merely be a copy of the supplier's information.

- Ideally, exposure to any hazardous substance would be rendered impossible by eliminating the use of that substance (for example, by changing the way that the job is carried out so that the substance is not necessary). Alternatively, risk can be reduced by:
  – the substitution of safer substances (for example, replacing solvent-based paint with water-based paint)
  – modifying the method of its use (for example, total enclosure of the process).

- If the prevention of exposure is not possible, the level of exposure must be controlled. This can be through a combination of engineering controls, safe systems of work and personal protective equipment (PPE).

- Using PPE to control exposure must only be considered as a **last resort**, after other methods have been explored and found not to be reasonably practicable.

- In some cases, employees exposed to hazardous substances must receive appropriate health surveillance.

7.3 COSHH Regulations

 The regulations can be downloaded from the Government legislation website.

The regulations place duties on both employers and the self-employed. These duties cover people actually working with substances and other people (such as the public or other contractors) who might be affected. The emphasis under the COSHH Regulations is to avoid exposure to hazardous substances unless it is not reasonably practicable to do so, in which case adequate control measures must be put in place to control exposure to a safe level.

If five or more people are employed, the significant findings of the COSHH assessment and the actions that will be taken to control exposures must be written down. The main requirements of the regulations are shown below.

- To assess the health risks to employees or other people, created by work that involves substances hazardous to health.

- To implement suitable control measures to effectively protect employees and others from exposure.

- To review the assessment if there have been any changes that may invalidate it, such as:

  – a change in the way the work is carried out, or

  – the results of monitoring indicating that existing control measures are not effective.

The regulations require the following thought process in relation to control.

- Can a less hazardous product or substance be used?

- If not, can the substance be changed (substituted)?

- Can the process be enclosed so the product will not escape?

- Can the emissions from the substance be extracted from the source?

If the answer to these questions is 'no' then the introduction of measures to control exposure will be necessary.

Engineering controls should be the first controls to be considered (such as pouring devices to stop splashes, the use of dust extraction, increasing ventilation and so on). PPE should not be considered as a control, until engineering control options have been exhausted, because of the following reasons.

- It can be expensive.

- It only protects the wearer and then only if being used and maintained correctly.

- It can be unpleasant to wear.

- It often requires considerable management effort to ensure that it is used correctly.

Removing the need to buy and use PPE makes good occupational health and business sense. The regulations apply to all industries and, while some fixed workplaces (such as factories and warehouses) may find it practical to introduce effective engineering controls, the nature of construction sites and work conditions mean that it will often be difficult to do anything other than use PPE. It is good practice to think of ways to reduce or minimise exposure to hazardous substances wherever possible. For example, purchasing prefabricated elements and systems that are manufactured off site, therefore removing the need for hazardous processes such as sawing and creating dust on-site.

It is, however, becoming easier to introduce engineering controls, as newer equipment is designed to overcome exposure problems (for example, powered hand tools can be fitted with dust extraction and collection attachments). Similarly, a number of hire companies stock air movers to enable improved ventilation. The requirements of the regulations are thorough, and one of those is to ensure that control measures that have been identified as suitable are properly used. To ensure that the control measures are effective, the regulations require the following.

- Extract ventilation systems must be thoroughly examined periodically.

- If using substances that are known to damage health, part of the assessment is likely to identify that health surveillance is necessary.

- Any health surveillance records must be kept for 40 years and made available to the people who have been exposed to the hazard.

- There is a duty to communicate the information and provide relevant training to people who may be exposed.

- Emergency arrangements with suitable first aid provision and equipment are available.

- Emergency arrangements are practiced.

- Make proper use of any control measures provided (including PPE).

- Return any control measure, where provided (mainly PPE), to its accommodation after use.

- Report any defects in the control measures to their employer.

- Attend health surveillance medicals where required (the employer must pay for the medical and it must be in paid work time).

07

7.4   Sources of harm

The regulations cover substances that can be either a natural or artificial substance, in solid or liquid form, or in the form of a gas or vapour. These substances are carcinogenic (cause cancer), mutagenic (cause mutation of the body) or reprotoxic (toxic for reproduction; for example, causing damage to the reproductive system and malformation of an embryo or foetus). These are known as CMR substances.

The purpose is to safeguard the health of people using or coming into contact with any substance that is harmful to health, apart from lead and asbestos (which are not covered by the COSHH Regulations because they have their own regulations).

 For more information, refer to Chapters B08 Lead and B09 Asbestos.

The regulations apply to those substances that are classified as being very toxic, toxic, harmful, corrosive or irritant. The symbols used on the containers of such substances are reproduced later in this chapter *(refer to 7.6.1)*.

In evaluating sources of harm, also consider the following points.

● Substances (products) bought in and used in the construction industry have the potential to harm the health of people using them.

● Many construction processes and activities can create potentially hazardous substances.

● There already may be harmful substances (including micro-organisms) on site before a project commences.

 Types of exposure

Hazardous substances can enter the body in four ways.

Inhalation (breathed) into the lungs, when the substance is in the form of a gas, vapour, fume, mist, aerosol or dust.

Absorption through the skin or eyes by contact with a substance that can penetrate unbroken skin, or is absorbed through unprotected cuts or grazes.

Injection by contact with contaminated sharp objects or high-pressure equipment (such as hydraulic systems or water jetting).

Ingestion (eating or drinking) by swallowing particles of a hazardous substance resulting from hand-to-mouth transfer.

7.4.1   Bought-in products

The first, and easiest, stage is to look at the substances that are bought in. This involves identifying what is used, what is hazardous to health and how much is used. Most construction processes are relatively simple as they rarely use a large number of substances or involve mixing of substances. Mechanical workshops (for example, where plant is serviced) tend to be more challenging simply because of the amount of chemicals present in the substances that they normally use.

Another consideration is the substances that will be brought onto site by other contractors, how those substances might affect other people or may react with other products on site. The contractor's COSHH assessments should reflect this information. Where and how the substances are stored needs to be considered: for example, cleaning materials required for welfare units and site offices must be stored appropriately and safely. Make a register of all hazardous substances being used and stored on site, and ensure that it is kept up to date.

 Identification of hazardous and non-hazardous substances

In the case of cleaning chemicals, washing-up liquid does not have any warning symbols on it and therefore, other than noting its presence, no further action is necessary. However, the information on a container of bleach should provide the basis for determining how it can be used safely. Of these two products, one requires no control measures to be identified but the second does.

7.4.2   Products created by the work process

The considerations become more complicated when potentially harmful substances (such as many forms of dust or fumes) are created by work processes. The situation is further complicated if the substance created has a workplace exposure limit (WEL) that must not be exceeded.

This may require that exposure levels are measured, unless exposure can be eliminated or controlled to a known safe level. Again, it will be necessary to also consider potentially harmful processes that will be carried out by other contractors.

Depending upon the complexity of the project, it may not be possible to complete this part of the exercise prior to the start of the project unless all work processes and substances that will be created are known.

In these circumstances, it will be a case of building up the COSHH information as the job progresses, but this must be achieved in such a way that no-one is exposed to a potentially harmful substance until the assessment of it has been carried out and appropriate controls are in place.

7.4.3 Products already present on site

A third category of potentially harmful substances includes those substances that may already be present on site.

Any number of hazardous substances might be present in the ground when former industrial (brownfield) sites are redeveloped.

- Land, heavily contaminated with fuels, oils and other hazardous liquids that have seeped into the ground over many years.

- Residues of hazardous substances left in pipework, underground tanks and drums.

- Substances, such as cyanides, paints, plastics, pesticides, synthetic fibres and polychlorinated biphenyls (PCBs), that were deliberately buried by the past users of the land.

There could also be the following sources of micro-organisms in contaminated land.

- Leptospirosis (Weil's disease) from the presence of infected rats or their carcasses.

- Infected syringes, needles and other items associated with drug taking (for example, where a derelict site is being refurbished).

- Tetanus from infected ground or other materials.

- A range of respiratory diseases arising from the disturbance of accumulated pigeon or bat droppings.

- Pipework and sumps containing sewage sludge residue.

7.5 Workplace exposure limits

Exposure to hazardous substances can have harmful effects on health. Some of these substances have a workplace exposure limit (WEL). This represents a concentration of the substance in the air that has been measured and averaged over a period of time, either long-term (eight hours) or short-term (15 minutes). The taking of these measurements (workplace monitoring) is a specialist activity that must be carried out by someone who is competent, has the necessary skills, knowledge, training and experience to do so and who possesses the appropriate equipment. If a substance has been assigned a WEL, it is subject to the requirements of the COSHH Regulations and exposure should be controlled. Control is only defined as adequate in the following circumstances.

- Where principles of good control practice are applied.

- When the WEL is not exceeded.

- If exposure to asthmagens, carcinogens and mutagens is reduced to as low as is reasonably practicable.

The following substances, all of which have a WEL, are commonly used in or produced by construction work.

- General dust.
- Hardwood dust.
- Softwood dust.
- Silica.
- White spirit.
- Pulverised fuel ash.
- Synthetic mineral fibre (rock wool/fibreglass).
- Asphalt.
- Welding/cutting fumes.

- Gypsum.
- Portland cement.
- Micro-organisms associated with:
  - blood products
  - Weil's disease
  - tetanus
  - sewage
  - certain black mould species
  - anthrax.

 This list is not exhaustive. Employers have a legal duty to establish that an in-use substance has a WEL, and to control exposure.

 A list of all WELs is published by the Health and Safety Executive (HSE) in Guidance Note EH40, available to download from its website.

 The absence of a substance from the list of WELs does not indicate that it is safe. For these substances, exposure should be controlled to a level that any person affected could be exposed to, day after day at work, without any adverse effects on their health.

Those who plan and carry out work that could result in exposure to hazardous substances may have difficulty in appreciating that there is a (real or potential) problem. This is particularly true when a hazardous substance is created by the work process.

 Hazardous substances created by the work process

A hardwood plank should not pose any serious health issues in the form that it is delivered to site. However, cutting or sanding it will produce dust that, unless controlled, has the potential to cause irritation of the nasal passages, sensitisation or, on rare occasions, nasal cancer.

Cutting, sawing, grinding or sanding any substance has the potential to liberate harmful dust. Furthermore, many types of hot works will create harmful fumes or gases that may be inhaled unless the process is closely controlled.

7.6 Identifying hazardous substances

7.6.1 Packaging or labels

The European regulation on classification, labelling and packaging of substances and mixtures (otherwise known as CLP) applies to all EU member states, including the UK. **Note**: *as with other EU exit legislation, the UK Government has taken the law as it is now, including all directives from the EU, and transposed it directly into new, post-Brexit UK law; it has made no changes to the legislation.*

The CLP Regulation adopts the United Nations' globally harmonised system (GHS) on classification and labelling of chemicals, shown in the table below. In time, under the GHS, the same classifications and labelling will be used worldwide.

Globally harmonised pictograms			
☠	Acute toxicity, very toxic or toxic. Can be fatal if swallowed or inhaled.	🌲	Hazardous to the environment and aquatic life.
🗲	Contains gases under pressure. May explode if heated and can cause burns.	🔥	Oxidising gases, liquids and solids. May cause or intensify fire.
!	Harmful skin, eye or respiratory irritation. May cause an allergic reaction, drowsiness or breathing difficulties.	☣	Serious health hazard/aspiration hazard. Damage to organs and may cause serious longer-term health hazards (such as carcinogenicity, respiratory sensitisation and reproductive toxicity).
🔥	Flammable gases, liquids, solids and aerosols. Heating may cause a fire.	🧪	Corrosive and can cause severe skin burns and eye damage.
💥	Explosive, self-reactive. Heating may cause an explosion.		

The following substances and physical agents can be potentially harmful to the skin.

- Pitch, tar and bitumen.
- Cement or lime.
- Brick, stone, tile and plaster dust.
- Paints, varnishes, lacquers and stains.
- Certain types of timber.
- Fibreglass.
- Certain epoxy resins.
- Acrylic and formaldehyde resins.
- Chromates (in primers and cement).
- Organic solvents.
- Petrol, diesel and paraffin oils.
- White spirit and thinners.
- Acids or alkalis.
- Ionising radiation.
- Solar radiation.
- Other materials (depending on individual reactions).

 Further information on labelling and packaging can be found on the HSE website.

7.6.2 Safety data sheets

Before a COSHH assessment is undertaken, it is important to collate information about the substance. Safety data sheets are available for substances that are dangerous for supply.

 Safety data sheets are not COSHH assessments. Employers should use the information they contain to undertake their own assessment of how the substance will be used on site.

Manufacturers and suppliers have a legal obligation to provide this information. Many have safety data sheets on their websites. Nevertheless, it should be possible to go into any builder's merchant, trade supplier or DIY store and obtain sufficient information about the products being purchased. The safety data sheet includes details of the hazards that the chemical presents, how it should be stored and handled, and emergency measures required in case of an accident. If the substance that is intended to be used is found to be a carcinogen or a mutagen (for example, capable of causing cancer or mutation of the body) every possible step should be taken to eliminate its use.

 It is considerably harder to find out information about substances created by the work process.

7.7   COSHH assessment

An assessment is the fundamental requirement of the COSHH Regulations, and it is in two parts.

Part 1. An employer must not carry out any work that is liable to expose employees to any substance hazardous to health, unless a suitable and sufficient assessment of the risks created by the work has been made.

Part 2. If the first part indicates that substances hazardous to health will be used or created, employers must identify the actions to be taken to comply with the remainder of the COSHH Regulations.

 Definitions

The meanings of the following words need to be clearly understood.

Substance means any natural or artificial substance, in solid, liquid, gaseous or vapour form, and includes micro-organisms.

Hazard is the potential for the substance to cause harm, illness or damage to health.

Risk is the likelihood that the hazardous potential of the substance will be realised.

7.7.1   Assessing the risk

Employers must carry out a risk assessment of health risks created by work involving substances hazardous to health. Each assessment must take account of the following.

- The hazardous properties of the substance.
- Information provided by the supplier on the potential harmful effects.
- The type, level and duration of exposure.
- The way in which the job will be carried out, including the amount of the substance used (or present in the case of substances created by a work process).
- Work (such as maintenance) where there is the potential for high levels of exposure.
- Any published WEL for the substance.
- The effects of any control measures that are, or will be, in place.
- The results of any health surveillance and/or exposure monitoring that has been undertaken.
- The risks where there is exposure to more than one hazardous substance at any one time.
- Other information that the employer may need or have in order to complete the assessment.

Any assessment must be reviewed regularly if there is reason to suspect that the assessment is no longer valid, or if there has been a significant change in the work to which the assessment relates, or exposure monitoring results indicate it is necessary.

 The HSE has developed a free internet tool (the COSHH e-tool) for identifying good control practice. It covers a wide range of processes and activities and also provides advice for products that have safety data sheets.

7.7.2   Who can carry out an assessment?

Employers have the duty to make an assessment, but they can arrange for anyone who is competent to do so to assist with the task, whether within the company or from outside. It is the responsibility of the employer to ensure that anyone who carries out any duties under the COSHH Regulations is competent to do so, has the necessary skills, knowledge and experience, and has received the necessary information, instruction and training, whether or not the assessor is an employee.

The majority of COSHH assessments for small building and construction work can be carried out without the need for the assistance of specialist outside consultants, provided the assessor is competent and meets the following requirements.

- Has access to the safety data sheets for the products concerned.
- Understands, in basic terms, what the COSHH Regulations require to be done.
- Is knowledgeable of the work process being assessed.
- Has the ability to systematically gather relevant information regarding exposures to hazardous substances and the subsequent risks to staff by:
  - observing working practices
  - obtaining information on substances used
  - asking questions in the workplace
  - making informed 'what if' judgements regarding possible divergences from standard working practices.

- Can specify the steps and control measures to be taken to comply with the COSHH Regulations.

- Can appreciate their own limitations; knowing when to call in specialists with certain skills (such as when there is a need to undertake air sampling).

- Has the ability to make valid conclusions, to make a report and communicate findings regarding risks and precautions to the employer and employees.

7.7.3   Carrying out a COSHH assessment

 The HSE, in collaboration with the TUC and CBI, has developed a COSHH essentials toolkit to help firms comply with the COSHH Regulations.

7.7.3.1   Know what products and substances you are using

- Compile a list of all the hazardous substances that are in use.

- Add to the list any hazardous substances that are created as a by-product of a work process.

7.7.3.2   Assess the health hazards they can cause

- From manufacturer's information and other relevant sources, determine the level of risk to health, the degree of exposure and what action is needed to eliminate or control exposure.

- Carry out a COSHH risk assessment to establish how the hazardous substances might cause harm.

- Record the findings of the risk assessment and the control measures to be taken.

- Review any assessment regularly or whenever the exposure monitoring results indicate that it is necessary.

7.7.3.3   Eliminate or minimise the risk of exposure

- Design a work process that prevents exposure to, or the creation of, hazardous substances (for example, use hydraulic croppers to cut brick pavers rather than disc cutting them, to reduce exposure to dust, or use hydraulic shears to cut steelwork rather than burning gear).

- Substitute or dilute the substance. Designers, managers and specifiers should look towards less hazardous options (for example, lead paint removal by a system that does not heat the paint sufficiently to liberate lead fumes).

- Use dust or fume extraction. This may be a standalone extractor unit or built-in to some hand tools.

- Use engineering controls (such as totally enclosing the process – often not feasible in the construction environment) or wet cutting.

- Issue suitable PPE, including respiratory protective equipment (RPE) and make sure it is worn (only after the use of all other risk control measures have been explored).

e.g. Eliminate or minimise the risk of exposure

- Alter the work method so the process that produces the exposure is no longer necessary (for example, use a demolition shear to cut structural steelwork rather than gas cutting and therefore avoid a process that may produce metal fumes and toxic gases).

- Change the work method to prevent the production of a hazardous waste product (for example, purchase panels of the correct size, rather than cutting oversize panels on site and producing dust). Given the pressure on reducing waste and manual handling, this is another example of where good health and safety is good business.

These examples of controlling the COSHH risk may indicate that some companies are already doing COSHH assessments without realising it.

Some control measures are very simple (for example, use a suitable vacuum cleaner to remove the dust on a floor slab instead of sweeping up with a brush). Other situations may require a little more thought and ingenuity. However, it is not always possible or reasonably practicable to introduce engineering controls and so the implementation of certain organisational controls may need to be used instead.

7.7.3.4   What to establish

- Who is exposed? Is it just the person using the substance or can it affect other people?

- What are they going to do with it? The decision to either spray or apply paint by brush may make a significant difference. Spray application will probably mean a much smaller droplet size, creating a more severe respiratory hazard. The assessment needs to be honest and objective. For example, paint removal gels state on the tin that they are only for brush application, although it is physically possible to spray them. However, the controls required to spray without potentially damaging the skin, eyes or lungs are completely different to those required for brush application.

- How often and how much of a substance is used, and for how long, are also important factors.

07

7.7.3.5   Personal protective equipment

Obtaining appropriate PPE for hazardous substances that can affect the skin might be as simple as identifying the correct type of gloves.

However, where there is a need for respiratory protection, selecting the correct type of RPE is critical. For example, a filtering face mask designed to filter out dust will be useless against gases, fumes or vapours.

The need for employees to work in masks or respirators is always the last resort. If RPE is necessary, it must meet the following requirements.

- Adequately control exposure to the hazardous substance(s) identified.

- Suit the wearer (comfort and fit).

- Be appropriate for the job and be used correctly.

Before selecting RPE, proper thought must also be given to the following.

- The physical condition of the employee (breathing through some types of RPE for extended periods can require effort) and whether facial hair or glasses would make the equipment ineffective.

- Providing face-fit testing and suitable training on the safe use and maintenance of the RPE.

7.7.3.6   Information, instruction and training

Information, instruction and training must be provided to employees who may be exposed to substances hazardous to health so that they are aware of the danger of exposure and the precautions that should be taken.

It is important that workers are not put at risk due to lack of information, instruction or training. Therefore, they should be knowledgeable of the health risks, the precautions they should take (including the control measures), and be able to use the supplied PPE efficiently. Managers and supervisors should ensure that all information is clearly explained and fully understood by workers.

Workers should also know what precautions to follow in the event of an emergency.

Information, instruction and training given must cover the following points.

- Details of the substances hazardous to health to which the employee is liable to be exposed, including:
  - the names of the substances and the risks that they present to health
  - any relevant occupational exposure standard, maximum exposure limit or similar occupational exposure limit
  - access to any relevant safety data sheet
  - other legislative provisions that concern the hazardous properties of those substances.

- Significant findings of the risk assessment.

- Appropriate precautions and actions to be taken by the employee in order to safeguard themselves and other employees at the workplace.

- Results of any monitoring of exposure and, in particular, in the case of a substance hazardous to health for which a maximum exposure limit has been approved, the employee or their representative shall be informed if the results of the monitoring show that the maximum exposure limit has been exceeded.

- Collective results of any health surveillance undertaken in a form calculated to prevent those results from being identified as relating to a particular person.

Before work starts, give information, instruction and training to employees relating to the following.

- The nature and degree of known risks.

- Access to any relevant safety data sheets.

- Safe storage of hazardous and volatile substances in appropriate containers.

- The control measures adopted and how they should be put into operation.

- Reasons for, and the correct use of, PPE.

- Any exposure monitoring arrangements that are in use.

- The purpose of, and arrangements for, any health surveillance, if appropriate.

 For an example of a COSHH assessment for the use of diesel refer to Appendix A.

7.7.4   Records

The COSHH assessment, training, briefings, monitoring arrangements and health surveillance must be recorded. Some records may need to be kept for 40 years.

In companies where there are union-appointed safety representatives, or representatives of employee safety, this information should be available to them.

7.7.5   Emergencies

Procedures to deal with accidents, incidents and emergencies involving hazardous substances must be provided. These procedures should include the following.

- First-aid provision.
- The use of safety drills and regular practising.
- Identification and details of all hazards.
- Specific hazards that are likely to occur during any accident, incident or emergency, together with warning and communication systems and emergency actions.

If significant or dangerous accidental releases or leakages of a hazardous substance are possible, despite the control measures that have been implemented, an emergency plan should be drawn up and instigated for achieving suitable control and for safeguarding the health of anyone who may be affected. This needs to be kept in context – spilling 500 ml of gloss paint is probably more of an environmental and quality issue than a serious occupational health hazard.

The emergency plan should include first-aid provisions and safety drills, including the testing of drills at regular intervals. Any particular hazards that are likely to occur as a result of the emergency must be specified. The emergency plan should be made available to all people potentially affected and be displayed on site. It should also be made available to the accident and emergency services.

Depending on the substance, a spillage may also be a pollution issue.

Emergency plans must be drawn up and consideration should be given to the following.

- Making appropriate first-aid provision.
- Developing and practising safety drills (for example, site evacuations) as appropriate.
- Identification and details of hazards.
- Making available details of specific hazards that are known to exist.
- Developing warning and communication systems.
- Displaying emergency plans and emergency procedures on how to deal with potential spills using a spill kit.
- Making relevant information available to the emergency services.

7.7.6   Summary

The assessment is a considered judgement that balances the hazardous properties of the substance, the method by which it will be handled and the environment in which it will be used.

The skill of the COSHH assessor is to:

- sift through the information contained on the safety data sheets and other sources (such as on the packaging or container)
- extract the useful information
- incorporate their knowledge of how, when and where the substance is used
- from the information available, produce a useful and useable COSHH assessment to guide those who will be doing the work.

e.g. **Insulating roof spaces with synthetic mineral fibre offers a number of challenges**

The material has a WEL for the concentration of fibres in air, and is irritating to the skin. The roof space is an unpleasant working environment as it can be extremely hot in summer and the level of natural ventilation may be low.

The obvious way to reduce exposure is to provide a Type 5 coverall and FFP3-rated RPE. However, whether this is sufficient must be considered under the requirements of the COSHH Regulations.

For a company that employs people full time to insulate lofts, the answer is probably not; they should be looking at the use of ventilation equipment to drive exposures, and possibly the temperature, down. However, a small contractor carrying out this type of work five or six times a year can be more selective about when to carry out the work, so it could be argued that, by carrying out the work during the cooler months, the lower level controls are sufficient.

The judgement is based on experience and backed up with paperwork to justify decisions.

  The HSE has compiled a set of example COSHH risk assessments for some industries, available on its website.

There is also excellent guidance on silica exposure on the HSE website.

7.8 Effects of contact with some materials on the skin

Skin contact with certain materials can cause a variety of reactions and some examples are given below. This list is not exhaustive.

Mineral oils, including fuel oils and mould oils, can lead to inflammatory skin conditions (such as dermatitis, oil acne or even skin cancer). These may be caused by constant contact with oil or oily clothes and rags (for example, when placed in overall pockets).

Chemicals, including strong alkalis, certain acids, chromates and formaldehyde, are substances that can penetrate the skin causing ulcers (for example, chrome ulceration) and dermatitis. Some chemicals can also cause skin cancer. The most significant chemicals for construction workers are polycyclic aromatic hydrocarbons (PAHs) from products containing coal tar or pitch. HSE research estimates that these caused over 450 cases of **non-melanoma skin cancer** in 2004. These risks are now significantly reduced as petroleum-based alternatives to coal tars are now used.

Cement and lime can cause chronic dermatitis. Wet cement and lime become more alkaline, corrosive and therefore potentially damaging to the skin.

Solvents and de-greasers, including paraffin, turpentine, petroleum products, thinners and similar solvents, affect the skin by dissolving the natural oils (de-fatting), which renders it more vulnerable to attack by other substances and bacteria.

Tar, pitch, bitumen products, including cresols, and phenols like mineral oil, cause inflammation, blisters and oil acne.

Radiation, light and heat radiation, including X-rays, beta and gamma radiation, extremes of radiation, temperature and humidity, make the skin more susceptible to dermatitis and other skin problems.

Epoxy resin hardeners, glass fibres, certain woods, fungicides and insecticides may irritate the skin and lead to dermatitis.

7.8.1 Industrial dermatitis

Industrial dermatitis is an inflammatory skin condition, which is neither infectious nor contagious. It is caused by certain irritants contained in many industrial materials. Although dermatitis itself is not an infection, it can lead to infection when the skin's natural barriers break down. It is a major cause of absenteeism, not only in the construction industry, but across the whole spectrum of industries, and it accounts for over half of all the working days lost through industrial sickness. It is essential that a risk assessment identifies the properties of the hazardous substance so that the correct type of gloves can be provided.

People may react differently to a substance, and some substances are known to have the effect of either an irritant or a sensitiser (such as turpentine). In the course of their work, many construction workers are likely to come into contact with one or more possible skin irritants, such as those shown below.

- Cement, lime and plaster.
- Certain types of wood, resins, fungicides and pesticides.
- Paint.
- Tar, pitch and bitumen.
- Solvents, thinners and degreasers.
- Mineral oils and grease.

There are two general types of dermatitis.

Contact (irritant) dermatitis is usually caused by the skin coming into contact with an irritant substance – usually a chemical, but it can be a mineral.

Repeated exposure to extreme heat or cold can lead to physical damage to the skin and make it more likely that irritant dermatitis will occur. Wet work, which involves the hands being wet for long periods (more than two hours a day) or repeatedly getting the hands wet, can also cause dermatitis. Anyone may be affected and the length of exposure, together with the strength of the irritant substance, will affect the seriousness of the complaint. Most cases of dermatitis are of this type.

Sensitising dermatitis, also known as allergic contact dermatitis, accounts for about 20% of all work-related dermatitis.

Some people develop a sudden allergic reaction following exposure to a specific substance. The reaction may be after weeks, months or even years of use or exposure to a substance without any ill effects.

However, once sensitising dermatitis has occurred, any future exposure to the substance will again produce an adverse reaction. The exposure may be to an everyday chemical or mineral, and may be as simple as exposure to nickel in jewellery or coins.

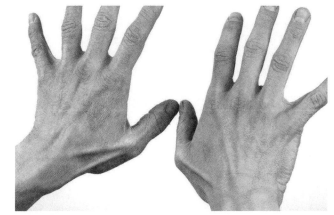

Contact (irritant) dermatitis

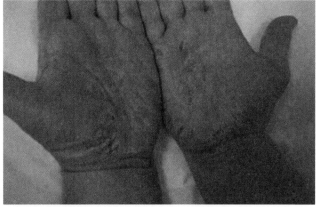

Sensitising dermatitis

07

The outer layer of skin forms a natural defence against irritants, providing it is undamaged by cuts and abrasions, or by solvents (such as hydrocarbons, benzene, tetrachloride, spirits and thinners) that remove the skin's natural protective oils. Reaction of the skin to an irritant varies from one individual to another. The reaction may be only a mild redness or it can develop into swelling, blisters and septic ulcers that are both unsightly and painful.

Personal hygiene is particularly important when working with materials that may be irritants, as resistance to an irritant varies with the type of skin. Pores, ducts and hair follicles in the skin may admit irritants to the sensitive inner skin layer and, therefore, washing thoroughly to remove dirt and grime with soap and water is an essential preventative measure. It is equally important that clothing is kept clean. Oil-stained overalls are a known cause of skin problems around the thighs.

The best course of action is to prevent skin contact with all potentially irritant substances, even if this is achieved by issuing suitable PPE. When total avoidance of skin contact cannot be guaranteed, it will be necessary in some cases to implement occupational health screening (depending on the hazardous properties of the substance). Initially this should involve establishing whether the persons involved in the job have had any previous adverse reaction to the substance(s) in use.

 A poster on skin checks for dermatitis is available to download for free from the HSE website.

Those people who are found to be allergic to one or more substance should be identified and not be allowed to handle or come into contact with them. Any part of the body that comes into contact with a skin irritant may be affected although it is usually the hands, wrists and forearms that are affected initially. Treatment for dermatitis should be sought as soon as possible because, if neglected, symptoms may spread to other parts of the body. Any treatment of dermatitis or its symptoms should be left to a doctor.

It should be noted that occupational dermatitis diagnosed by a doctor is notifiable to the HSE under the provisions of the Reporting of Injuries, Diseases and Dangerous Occurrences Regulations (RIDDOR).

 Refer to Appendix C for examples of timber materials known to produce dermatitis or other irritant effects.

For further information on RIDDOR refer to Chapter A13 Accident reporting and investigation.

 For further information on dermatitis visit the HSE website.

7.8.2 Skin burns

Many substances used in the construction industry have corrosive properties that can cause severe burns to the skin and kill nerve endings, resulting in long-term health impacts. These substances have either strong acid or alkali properties. Hot-work processes also have the potential to cause skin burns.

Wellington boots, for example, whether reinforced with protective toecaps, soles or not, are essential in preventing burns from wet cement or concrete.

The cement content, when mixed with water, becomes highly corrosive and will cause severe burns to body tissue. It quickly burns and kills nerve endings and can continue to burn deeply without the person feeling much immediate pain.

7.8.3 Acid and alkali burns

Some substances that are in common use in the construction industry have sufficiently strong acid or alkali properties that can

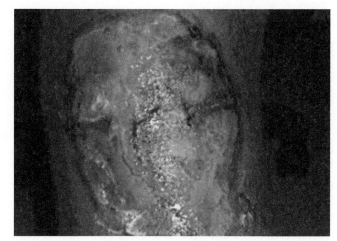

Irritant contact dermatitis 'pizza knee' from a cement burn

cause burns to the skin, such as hydraulic oils and fluids used plant, machinery and some types of tools and equipment. Plant mechanics can be at particular risk of exposure to this when carrying out maintenance or repairs. Gloves are available to protect the users of such substances from chemical burns.

7.9 Control measures

7.9.1 Hierarchy of control

The preferable method of prevention or control is to replace the substance or process with a non-hazardous or less hazardous substance or process. If this cannot be achieved, then controls shall be in the following order of priority:

● engineering controls

● organisational controls

● providing suitable PPE (as a last resort).

The control measures must:

- ensure the safe handling, storage, transportation and disposal of hazardous substances
- ensure maintenance procedures, which involve exposure to hazardous substances, are suitable
- reduce to a minimum the number of people exposed, the level and duration of exposure and the quantity of hazardous substances present in the workplace
- include control of the working environment, including the provision of adequate ventilation
- include adequate hygiene and washing facilities.

The COSHH Regulations contain further details of measures that must be taken to control exposure to carcinogens, mutagens and biological agents. With regard to this regulation, it is considered that control of exposure will be generally adequate if the following are met.

- Work is organised to minimise the release and spread of hazardous substances.
- Account is taken of the routes of exposure (inhalation, skin absorption, ingestion and injection).
- The control measures selected:
  - are proportionate to the degree of health risk
  - are effective in minimising the escape and spread of the substance
  - may, where necessary, include a combination of control measures, including PPE.
- The control measures selected are periodically reviewed for their effectiveness.
- Users of hazardous substances are informed of the hazards and risks and trained in the use of the control measures provided.
- The control measures do not increase the overall risks to health or safety from other sources.

Employers who provide any control measure are required to ensure that they are properly used or applied. All employees must ensure the following.

- They make proper use of any control measure (including PPE) provided.
- All steps are taken to return it to its place of storage after use.
- Any defects in the control measure are reported to their employer.

 The four routes of entry for a hazardous substance into the body are inhalation, absorption, ingestion and injection.

7.9.2   Use of control measures

Employers should have procedures in place to ensure that measures provided to control exposure to hazardous substances, including the provision of PPE, are properly used or applied. These procedures should include regular inspections of working practices and a system to ensure that, where remedial action is found to be necessary, it is promptly taken.

Employees' duties are shown below.

- Make full and proper use of any control measures and to properly wear any PPE provided for their use.
- Take all reasonable steps to return the PPE after use to the accommodation provided.
- Notify any defects at once to management.

These are all common sense measures. Working with hazardous substances also dictates that employees make every effort to practise a high standard of personal hygiene, for example, by adhering to the points below.

- Removing any protective clothing (this may be contaminated) and thoroughly washing hands and skin before eating and drinking.
- Consuming food and drink only in mess rooms or canteens.
- Making full use of showers and washing facilities.
- Using the storage facilities provided and keeping PPE clothing separate from ordinary clothing, to avoid possible contamination.
- Make sure that work clothing is washed regularly.
- Smoking only in designated areas and thoroughly washing hands before handling cigarettes or tobacco (including rolling cigarettes, or using vapes or e-cigarettes), otherwise contamination may spread from the hands to the mouth and be ingested into the stomach, which can lead, in some circumstances, to serious health problems.

7.9.3   Maintenance, examination and testing of control measures

Employers are required to ensure that all measures installed to prevent or control exposure to substances hazardous to health under the COSHH Regulations are maintained in efficient working order and in good repair.

Certain engineering controls require thorough examination and tests (as follows overleaf).

07

7.9.3.1 Local exhaust ventilation plant

Local exhaust ventilation plant should be examined and tested at least once every 14 months. This would be expected in, for example, a woodworking shop. Technically, using a vacuum cleaner as an extractor on a power tool is creating a local exhaust ventilation system. However, because this is not a fixed system, it is unlikely that this would be considered for formal testing, but it would need to work effectively and be subjected to pre-use checks and regular maintenance.

More frequent testing of local exhaust ventilation is required for those processes listed in Schedule 4 of the regulations, although none of those processes are directly related to construction. Any defects in local exhaust ventilation systems must be reported and promptly rectified.

7.9.3.2 Non-disposable respiratory protective equipment

Thorough examinations and tests of non-disposable RPE should be carried out, where appropriate, at suitable intervals.

The Approved Code of Practice (ACoP) that supports the COSHH Regulations (L5) specifies that such examinations and tests should be carried out at least every month, and more frequently where the conditions of use are particularly severe. Longer intervals may be more appropriate in the case of certain RPE (such as half mask respirators used infrequently for short spells against air contaminants of relatively low toxicity). However, the longest interval between examinations and tests should not exceed three months.

Face-fit testing by someone who is competent is required for most types of RPE. For full face respirators this needs to be quantitative testing using a computerised method.

 For further information on RPE refer to Chapter B06 Personal protective equipment.

7.9.3.3 Disposable respiratory protective equipment

No examinations or tests are required, provided that the disposable RPE is used for only one working day or shift and then disposed of.

Again, face-fit testing by a competent person is required. This can be qualitative testing using a bitter/sweet solution to check the effectiveness of the fit. (If the wearer can taste or smell the solution then the fit is not correct and the test is a fail.)

7.9.3.4 Records

All examinations, tests and repairs carried out on engineering controls and non-disposable RPE should be suitably recorded in any format provided they are easily retrievable. These records should be kept for at least five years.

 Detailed maintenance arrangements for engineering controls and non-disposable RPE are in the Approved Code of Practice (L5).

7.9.3.5 Review of assessments

An assessment should be reviewed regularly, and at once in case of the following.

- There is reason to believe that it is no longer valid (for example, new information on health risks has come to light).
- The work to which it relates has changed significantly (for example, new substances have been introduced, or the method of working is to change, such as the use of a spray gun to apply paint instead of a brush or roller).
- Environment and/or health monitoring results indicate it is necessary.

The definition of regularly will depend on a number of factors (such as the nature of the risk). However, the maximum period between reviews should not exceed five years. Each review should trigger an opportunity to consider whether exposure can now be prevented (for example, by substituting a less hazardous substance or by process changes). Similarly, control measures should be reappraised to see whether they are still adequate or if further improvements are necessary and possible.

7.9.4 Monitoring controls

Where control measures are provided in accordance with Regulation 7, adequate maintenance, examination and testing of control measures, including any PPE provided, must be undertaken to ensure they are in efficient working order and remain clean.

Where engineering controls are undertaken, the employer must ensure thorough examinations and testing are carried out on a regular basis.

Where indicated as necessary by the COSHH assessment, monitoring of the exposure to hazardous substances must be undertaken using suitable procedures, unless it can be demonstrated by another method of evaluation that exposure is adequately controlled.

It is important to monitor the effectiveness of any risk controls. Observation of the task and speaking to the people doing the job is one way to measure the effectiveness of controls. It may also require the regular testing of equipment (such as ventilation), which must be kept in efficient working order.

Organisational controls can be introduced. These are concerned with investigating whether the way in which the job is carried out can be changed so that individual exposure is reduced. For example, by carrying out a job out of normal working hours the number of persons exposed, who would otherwise have to wear PPE, will be significantly reduced.

Further examples include:

- job rotation so that no individual person is exposed to a substance above its WEL

- moving a work activity into the open air to prevent the accumulation of vapour or fumes.

In some circumstances, the application of control measures will continue after the actual work activity is completed. Some jobs (for example, working with heavily contaminated land) will require the operatives to go through a full decontamination procedure. Anyone who has been in the live working area may have to follow a strict procedure about where they take boots and overalls off, or even go through a shower, and it may involve wearing additional gloves to ensure that contaminants are kept off their skin when decontaminating.

Often, simply washing hands with hot soapy water will suffice. Good COSHH practice and the provision of good welfare facilities are closely linked. This may mean in some circumstances that eating and drinking are not allowed other than in designated clean zones.

In the past, the HSE has targeted a lack of adequate site welfare facilities in relation to occupational health issues. In order to serve a prohibition notice, the HSE has to consider whether or not there is imminent risk of harm to health and/or safety. Simply by looking at the substances present and their COSHH assessments may be enough.

It is easy to determine, for example, whether a lack of hot water and a hand cleanser has the potential to create a health problem. If there is a lack of such facilities, an HSE inspector may consider there to be an imminent risk to health and therefore justify the serving of a prohibition notice.

7.10   Monitoring exposure at the workplace

The Approved Code of Practice (L5) defines monitoring as the use of valid and suitable occupational hygiene techniques, by competent people, to measure the exposure of employees to substances hazardous to health.

There are certain situations, outlined below, in which the monitoring of exposure to a hazardous substance is required. Sometimes, however, it is so obvious that there is a problem that the money may be better spent on solving the problem rather than simply confirming what was already suspected.

Monitoring is required in the following circumstances.

- Where a serious health hazard could arise because of failure or deterioration of the control measures.

- Where it is necessary to ensure that a WEL or employer-imposed working standard is not exceeded. Significant exposure to silica dust may require monitoring.

- When it is necessary to carry out an additional check on the effectiveness of any control measure.

- Where work involves the use of any carcinogen or mutagen and any work with substances or processes listed in Schedule 4 of the COSHH Regulations (for example, work involving vinyl chloride monomer or chromium plating).

It is unlikely the competency for carrying out monitoring will be available in-house to many companies. A number of health and safety consultancies can carry out the work. If competent advisers are brought in, it is essential to establish that they have the necessary experience and resource to do it.

 The work would often be considered to be occupational hygiene so it is worthwhile contacting the British Occupational Hygiene Society.

In some situations, information about typical exposure values is available from trade bodies or HSE guidance. If the job being carried out is typical in all respects then, as a starting point, it would normally be acceptable to take these levels of exposure as being typical of the exposure levels actually experienced.

However, there are obvious dangers in relying heavily on typical exposure values, particularly if the way the job is being carried out starts to diverge from the norm. An example of monitoring would be the use of a personal sampler to monitor an airborne contaminant in the breathing zone of an employee.

7.10.1   Monitoring records

Monitoring records must be kept in a suitable format and be available either as individual records or as a suitable summary for five years. If they are representative of the personal exposures of identifiable employees, the records must be kept for at least 40 years.

7.11   Health surveillance

Regulation 11 requires that employees, who are or are liable to be exposed to substances hazardous to health, must be put under the appropriate health surveillance, provided by the employer.

The main purpose of health surveillance is to detect problems with the health of employees at the earliest possible stage. The purpose of control measures is to prevent damage to the health of employees; this is something that health surveillance cannot do. However, adverse health surveillance results may indicate that the existing control measures are not working properly.

In many cases, health surveillance must be carried out by an occupational health practitioner and recorded. Employees must have access to medical records that apply to them.

Health surveillance has to be undertaken when an employee is exposed to the following.

- A substance and process (as listed in Schedule 6 of the COSHH Regulations), although those listed are unlikely to apply to the construction industry. (The substances listed in Schedule 6 of the COSHH Regulations are used, for example, in the manufacture of nitro or amino derivatives of phenol and of benzene, and the making of explosives with the use of any of these substances.)

- A hazardous substance that is linked to an identifiable disease related to the exposure (for example, exposure is known to cause asthma) and there are valid techniques for detecting indications of the disease. For example, isocyanates used in two-pack paints are respiratory irritants and can result in sensitisation and asthma.

 The HSE has published online guidance, with guidelines on health surveillance needed where, even after all precautions are taken, there is still a risk that workers may be exposed to chemicals or other hazardous substances.

Where it is appropriate for protecting employees' health, health surveillance must be carried out and recorded.

Health surveillance is required to:

- protect the health of employees by early detection of adverse changes or disease

- collect data for detecting or evaluating health hazards

- evaluate the effectiveness of control measures.

 ## Providing health surveillance

Health surveillance must be provided in the following circumstances.

- If there is a disease associated with the substance (such as asthma, cancer or dermatitis).

- When it is possible to detect the disease or adverse change and reduce the risk of further harm.

- Where conditions of the workplace make it likely that the disease will appear.

Health surveillance can be visual checks, regular planned assessments, a test or a questionnaire. All results must be interpreted and the employer should take action to either eliminate the risk or control the exposure.

Where an employee requires health surveillance and it has been decided that the employee cannot continue in that work, the employer must take steps to ensure the employee adheres to the medical decision, unless it has been cancelled.

Working on contaminated land often requires some form of health surveillance. This may include lung function testing or direct analysis of blood, urine or hair samples. Normally this would occur before, during and after the work. It allows a personal baseline to be established and then simply acts as a check that the control measures are working.

Suitable health surveillance can range from surveillance under the supervision of an employment medical adviser, an appointed doctor or a registered medical practitioner, to enquiries about symptoms, or an examination by an occupational health nurse.

At the other end of the scale, health surveillance could simply involve a trained manager or supervisor inspecting an employee's hands and forearms, looking for the early signs of dermatitis.

Where the hazardous properties of a substance indicate, via the COSHH assessment, that health surveillance may be appropriate, advice on how to proceed can be sought from the Employment Medical Advisory Service (EMAS) of the HSE.

Health records must be kept for all employees under health surveillance. These records must be kept for at least 40 years from the date of the last entry, due to the often long period between the exposure and commencement of ill health.

The health record should include details of relevant health surveillance, including the date it was carried out, by whom, the outcome of any test, the decision made by the occupational health professional and any restrictions.

Health records are different to medical records and they should not contain confidential medical information.

Medical records are compiled by a doctor or nurse and may contain information obtained from an individual from their health surveillance. Medical records may include information relating to health issues that are not associated with work.

This information is confidential, and should not be disclosed without the individual's consent or by a court order. The doctor or nurse should only provide employers with information on their employee's fitness to work.

7.12   REACH Regulations

REACH concerns the **R**egistration, **E**valuation, **A**uthorisation and restriction of **Ch**emicals. The EU REACH Regulation was brought into UK law on 1 January 2021, and is known as UK REACH. The UK REACH and the EU Reach Regulations operate independently from each other. UK REACH regulates chemicals placed on the market in the UK.

REACH operates alongside COSHH and is designed so that better information on the hazards of chemicals and how to use them safely will be passed down the supply chain by chemical manufacturers and importers through improved safety data sheets.

REACH Regulations apply to substances manufactured or imported into the EU, in quantities of one tonne or more per year.

The regulations exclude the following.

- Radioactive substances.
- Substances under the customer's supervision.
- The transport of substances.
- Non-isolated intermediates.
- Waste.
- Some naturally occurring low-hazard substances.

Some substances are covered by more specific legislation and have tailored provisions.

 ## REACH aims

- To provide a high level of protection, for human health and the environment, from the use of chemicals.
- To make manufacturers and importers responsible for understanding and managing the risks associated with chemical use.
- To allow free movement of substances on the EU market.
- To enhance innovation in, and the competitiveness of, the EU chemical industry.
- To promote the use of alternative methods for the assessment of the hazardous properties of substances.

 To check your knowledge of your duties, as required by the COSHH Regulations, take the self-assessment quiz in Appendix B.

 ## Company director sentenced for sales of illegal chemicals

A Nuneaton company director has been sentenced to 10 months in prison for the online sale of products containing prohibited substances.

Warwick Crown Court heard that a complaint was raised that the company was selling a plant protection product containing sodium chlorate, a prohibited substance. An investigation by the HSE also found the company was selling paint stripper containing dichloromethane (DCM), which is restricted under REACH.

The company also failed to check at the point of sale that the paint stripper containing DCM was being sold either for use in industrial installations or, after October 2016, to appropriately certificated professionals, which is a condition of sale.

The HSE worked with online platforms to have the advertisements for these products taken down and served enforcement notices to prohibit further supply. However, the enforcement notices were ignored by the company.

The company director pleaded guilty to breaching Regulations 9 and 18 of the Plant Protection Products Regulations 2011 and Regulation 11(2) of the REACH Enforcement Regulations 2008, and was given a 10-month custodial sentence.

Speaking after the hearing, the HSE inspector said: 'Chemicals are carefully regulated to protect human health and the environment. Sodium chlorate is not approved for use in weed killers, as a safe level of use was not established for operators. Dichloromethane has been restricted in paint strippers due to concerns for human health during its use – it has caused fatalities when not used properly.

'Companies should be aware that HSE will take robust action against those who unnecessarily put the lives of workers and the public at risk, and against those who endanger the environment, through the inappropriate supply and use of chemicals.'

(Source: HSE.)

Appendix A – COSHH assessment example

Diesel fuel

Name of hazardous substance	Auto diesel.
Substance hazard classification	Flammable, harmful/irritant.
Trade name(s)	Any auto fuel production company.
Substance used for	Motive power for plant and other diesel powered vehicles.
Likely circumstances of exposure	Refuelling vehicles or filling other containers.

Potential hazards	Risk control measures	Emergency procedures
Inhalation can lead to nausea and headaches.	1. Avoid inhaling vapour or mist; dispense directly into tank using nozzle. 2. Refuel vehicles or otherwise decant in the open air.	Remove to fresh air. Seek medical attention if conditions are severe. Remove the casualty from exposure.
Skin contact can be irritating and have a defatting effect. Can cause contact or irritant dermatitis.	1. Avoid skin contact. Wear PVC gloves. Do not use as a cleaning agent. 2. Only refuel vehicles from a dispensing nozzle directly into fuel tanks. 3. Use funnel if dispensing into container.	Remove contaminated clothing. Wash skin thoroughly with soap and warm water.
Eye contact will cause irritation.	1. Wear eye protection if splashing can occur. 2. Ensure refuelling nozzle is fully inserted into fuel tank neck. 3. Dispense at a rate that avoids splashes.	Rinse immediately with water until irritation subsides. Seek medical advice.
Ingestion will irritate mouth, throat, and so on.	1. Do not eat, drink or smoke when handling. 2. Do not attempt to siphon using the mouth.	Do not induce vomiting. Wash mouth with water. Seek immediate medical attention.
Fire: flammable liquid. Products of combustion are toxic. Vapour/air mixture is explosive.	1. Do not smoke when handling. 2. Store bulk diesel away from heat, sources of ignition and flammable materials. 3. Do not allow to come into contact with hot engine parts during refuelling.	Clear the area. Do not inhale vapours or smoke. If trained, use foam or CO_2 extinguisher. Call emergency services to large fires.
Spillage: fumes/vapour likely to collect in low areas.	1. Do not allow to enter drains. Eliminate ignition sources. 2. Ensure good ventilation.	Contain with sand or granules. Remove into a container. Dispose of as hazardous waste. Call emergency services (FRS) to large spills.

Additional information. Environmentally damaging.

Are current controls adequate? Yes/No

Assessment date		Next review date	
Approved for use by			

Name		Position		Signature		Date	

Appendix B – Self-assessment quiz

Question	Emergency procedures
1. What is the main purpose of the COSHH Regulations?	The main purpose of the COSHH Regulations is to protect the health of employees working with substances hazardous to health.
2. When do you have to start complying with the regulations?	You must start now. The regulations are fully in force. Unless you act promptly, you could be breaking the law.
3. What is a substance hazardous to health?	(a) Substances listed as very toxic, toxic, harmful, corrosive or irritant. (b) Substances listed as having a workplace exposure limit (WEL). (c) Anything else that produces similar effects to any of the things mentioned above.
4. What is said about lead and asbestos?	They are not covered by the COSHH Regulations but, of course, you must comply with the Control of Lead at Work Regulations and the Control of Asbestos Regulations.
5. Are there any other exceptions to the regulations?	Yes, anything that is a hazard because it is radioactive, explosive or flammable is excepted, but only for those reasons. If the substances have other hazardous properties, like giving off a fume (solvents), these are covered by the regulations.
6. What must you make an assessment of?	The risk to employees of working with a substance hazardous to health and the actions needed to comply with the regulations. Substances may be hazardous solely at high or low temperatures or at high or low pressure.
7. If your assessment shows that an employee will be exposed to a substance hazardous to health, what should you do?	Prevent the exposure, if possible. If you cannot, you must adequately control it.
8. What is the main recommendation about control measures?	Control should be exercised without the use of PPE, if at all possible.
9. Whose responsibility is it to provide or use control measures?	The employer must provide them, and the employee must use them. The employer must also ensure use by properly supervising the workplace and employees.
10. When is monitoring of the workplace necessary?	When it is necessary to check on the effectiveness of control measures or to protect the health of workers.
11. When is health surveillance required?	Only where special circumstances require it (such as processes mentioned in the regulations or where certain diseases can be identified).
12. What can happen if you do not make the assessments?	The enforcing authority (the HSE or Local Authority) can issue an improvement or prohibition notice or even prosecute in the criminal court in certain circumstances.
13. If it is alleged that you have broken the regulations, what, if any, defence have you got?	You must prove that you took all reasonable precautions and exercised due diligence to avoid committing the offence.
14. Who has to make the actual assessments?	It is the responsibility of employers to ensure that assessments are done, although they can employ a competent person to carry out the assessment.
15. If a substance that can be inhaled does not have a control limit, what would be the adequate control standard?	Control would be considered adequate if the majority of the population could be regularly exposed to that substance at that level of exposure without any adverse effects on their health.
16. Where will you find a list of substances that have a workplace exposure limit?	In HSE Guidance Note EH40 Workplace Exposure Limits (regularly updated).
17. Which assessments have to be recorded?	All assessments must be recorded, unless they are very basic, simple and obvious.
18. Can you use other people's assessments?	Yes, provided that they exactly fit your circumstances, or can be modified or adapted to suit your needs.
19. When must you review an assessment?	When it is, or you suspect it may be, no longer valid because of changes in work methods, introduction of new types of control measures, or new information; or when monitoring shows that controls may not be working and, of course, when new substances are introduced.
20. Define the terms **hazard** and **risk**.	A **hazard** is the potential of a substance to cause harm. A **risk** is the likelihood of that harm occurring in the circumstances that exist.

07

Question	Emergency procedures
21. To whom do you have a duty under the COSHH Regulations?	To employees and anyone else who may be affected, such as contractors and people working or passing nearby.
22. What is the first step in the assessment process?	List all of the products and substances that you use, and determine which are substances hazardous to health.
23. Who has the right to ask to see your assessments?	Enforcing authority inspectors (either the Health and Safety Executive inspector or Local Authority environmental health officer). If you have safety representatives, they may also have a right to see your assessments. Principal contractors or your customers could also be included here, although they may not have a legal right.
24. What is the best recommended control measure?	Elimination of the substance altogether or substituting a non-hazardous substance.
25. When can the use of PPE or RPE be considered?	Only as a last resort, after every other type of control has been considered and PPE or RPE is found to be the only reasonably practicable method of achieving control.
26. What is the general rule about the maintenance and inspection of control measures?	Anything provided as a control measure, except single-use RPE, must be properly maintained, regularly inspected and records kept. The regulations give details of inspections and records.
27. What information, instruction and training do you have to give your employees?	Information, instruction and training on the risks to health of the substances that they work with, the precautions they must take and any controls they must use.
28. What is monitoring?	The use of a valid occupational hygiene technique to properly assess the exposure of employees to substances hazardous to health.
29. When is monitoring necessary?	When it is necessary to ensure the adequacy of the control methods in use or it is otherwise needed to protect the health of employees.

How did you do?

Check which questions you could not answer, or got wrong. List the points covered then take a second look at the sections of this chapter that deal with them. Try the test again later.

07

Appendix C – Some timbers known to produce dermatitis and other irritant effects

Commercial name	Harmful effects	Severity	Frequency of exposure
Afrormosia	Dermatitis and asthma.	Can be severe.	Quite frequent.
African mahogany	Dermatitis.	Severe.	Infrequent.
Boxwood	Dermatitis, rhinitis and asthma.	Mild.	Frequent.
Chestnut	Dermatitis, conjunctivitis and asthma.	Usually mild.	Infrequent.
Dahoma	Irritation of the chest and dermatitis.	Severe.	Frequent.
East African camphor wood	Asthma and dermatitis.	Fairly severe.	Infrequent.
Ebony	Irritation of nose and throat, and dermatitis.	Fairly severe.	Frequent.
Guarea (also West African cedar)	Nasal irritation, severe vomiting, chest irritation, blisters and dermatitis.	Effects vary from mild to severe depending on sensitivity.	Quite frequent.
Iroko	Skin and eye irritation, asthma and symptoms of the common cold.	Usually mild, occasionally serious.	Very infrequent.
Machaerium	Dermatitis.	Severe.	Infrequent.
Mansonia	Irritation of mucous membrane, nasal haemorrhage, sore eyes, dizziness and dermatitis.	Severity varies with individuals.	Frequent.
Satinwood	Dermatitis, headache and coughing.	Quite severe.	Infrequent.
Teak	Dermatitis and eye inflammation.	Can be severe.	Frequent.
Western red cedar	Asthma, bronchial trouble, dermatitis and septic wounds from splinters.	Severe.	Fairly frequent.
Yew	Bronchial asthma and dermatitis.	Quite severe.	Infrequent.

07

07

Lead

08

Supporting
INFORMATION

GT700 Toolbox talks / supporting checklists and forms

Toolbox talks on some of these topics are available in the GT700 publication. Supporting checklists and forms covering some of these topics are available on our companion website.

Overview

Old, lead-based paint and dust are still likely to affect the majority of UK buildings, although lead paint was completely removed from retail sale by 1992. If there is a possibility that workers will be exposed to lead then the employer should assess the risk to their health and decide what precautions are needed.

Exposure to lead, lead dust and fumes constitutes a major and widely underestimated hazard to the health of those whose work involves lead, lead products and lead-containing materials (LCMs), such as lead-based paint, or leaded exhaust particle contamination in lofts and roof voids, known as ceiling dust.

Lead paint and consequent dust exposure risks are greatest within pre-1970 buildings and structures, especially during repair, maintenance, refurbishment and demolition, if proper precautions are not followed.

The build-up of lead dust contamination in lofts, and roof, ceiling and floor voids continued until the general sale of leaded petrol became illegal in 2000.

This chapter sets out to explain the risks and controls that are required.

8.1   Introduction

Exposure to lead dust, fumes and vapour constitutes a major hazard to the health of industrial workers, including those in the construction industry, who work with lead, lead products and lead-containing materials (LCMs) (such as old lead-painted surfaces).

Construction workers most at risk are described below.

- Those carrying out blast-removal and burning of old lead paint.

- Those stripping old lead paint from doors, windows, and so on.

- Those carrying out surface preparation of previously lead-painted surfaces. Even stripped surfaces can contain significant lead residues.

- Those stripping old wallpaper and disturbing underlying lead-based paint.

- Demolition operatives involved in hot-cutting in demolition and dismantling operations.

- Plumbers working on lead-flashing, upstands and gutters.

- Operatives handling old, architectural lead work.

- Anyone involved in structural renovation or refurbishment, including conservation or heritage projects.

Exposure risks from lead paint, dust and fumes are most likely to occur in pre-1970 buildings but can be present in any building, especially during repair, maintenance, refurbishment and demolition, if proper precautions are not followed.

It should be noted that, wherever paintwork or coatings are likely to be damaged or disturbed, the Health and Safety Executive (HSE) advises that, **when preparing paintwork, an assessment for the workers' potential exposure to lead should be completed, regardless of the age of the building or the extent of the works.**

 Information on working safely with lead can be found on the HSE website.

The **Construction (Design and Management) Regulations** (CDM) impose a duty on clients to identify and collect information about hazardous materials likely to affect a project as part of pre-construction information. Lead-containing paint is one such material. If the client has information regarding this in their possession, they must pass the information onto other duty holders (for example, the designer and contractors).

The **Control of Lead at Work Regulations** (CLAW) and its associated Approved Code of Practice, together with guidance notes and information from the Lead Paint Safety Association (LiPSA) and the Painting and Decorating Association (PDA), enable employers to interpret the legal duties placed upon them by the regulations and to take the appropriate actions to protect the health and safety of their employees, who have to work with lead, and other people who may be affected by the way the work is carried out.

Clients have a duty to identify lead hazards before a project commences. One way to do this is an incremental three-stage approach, involving preliminary indicative DIY testing with a simple chemical test, followed by limited professional paint-on-base-material analysis and/or a full lead survey. This provides a cost-effective approach to meeting this widely unknown requirement.

Employers have a legal duty to protect their employees (and any building occupants). For employees where exposure to lead is *significant* this includes monitoring their blood-lead levels, so that those individuals whose work involves *significant* exposure to lead at work (as defined by CLAW can be taken off such work if the legal threshold for blood-lead levels is exceeded.

Lead contaminated waste must be disposed of in accordance with the Hazardous Waste Regulations.

8.2   Important points

● Lead and LCMs (such as lead-containing paint) are hazardous. They can become a *significant* exposure risk if lead dust, fumes or vapour are not prevented or adequately controlled. Any work involving lead must be in accordance with CLAW.

● Unless adequate precautions are taken, children and pregnant women are particularly at risk when decorators, for example, are disturbing old lead-containing paint in homes or schools.

● Lead is a cumulative poison that is absorbed into the bloodstream. Over time it will also collect in the kidneys and soft tissues, before accumulating in the bones.

● Lead is likely to get into the body through the:
  – **inhalation** of fumes or dust
  – **ingestion** of lead particles through hand to mouth contact (especially for smokers).
  Note: lead is not absorbed through the skin, except in the form of lead alkyls (an additive to petrol) and lead naphthenate. Any lead absorbed at work will circulate in the blood. The body gets rid of a small amount of lead each time you go to the toilet, but some will stay in your body, stored mainly in your bones. It can stay there for many years without making you ill.

● Workers' families may indirectly be exposed to lead as a result of the lead remaining on the workers' clothes when they arrive home.

● All work with lead or LCMs must be subject to a risk assessment, which includes consideration of the amount of lead involved.

● General builders, carpenters and decorators who remove or disturb old lead-containing paint, particularly if involved in window replacement, repairs and general refurbishment or demolition, may be exposed to *significant* quantities of lead without realising it. Scaffolders are also a *significant* exposure risk group.

● Where the risk assessment indicates that employees' exposure to lead is likely to be *significant*, certain monitoring actions must be taken with regard to the employees affected and the workplace itself. These include sampling to determine blood-lead levels, air-monitoring for airborne lead-dust levels and surface dust contamination checks.
  Note: although there are no legal threshold levels relating to surface dust contamination this is something that HSE inspectors are required to consider during CLAW inspections, as set out in Operational Circular 298/15.

● *Significant* exposure is defined in the regulations as: **where there is liable to be a substantial ingestion risk**.
  Note: it is the ingestion risk that needs to be substantial, not the amount of lead.

● *Significant* exposure risk also exists where airborne lead-dust levels are greater than or equal to 50% of the occupational exposure limit (OEL) for airborne lead.

● During health surveillance, employees' exposure to lead is most commonly measured by the concentration of lead in their blood.

● Above a certain level of exposure, employers have a legal duty to temporarily suspend the affected worker(s) from further work with lead and lead-containing materials.

 An extract from an observational study undertaken on lead exposure on scaffolders during refurbishment construction activity is available online.

In the context of this chapter, the main consideration is identifying where and how much lead could be present. This allows appropriate actions to be taken to protect the health of workers exposed to lead risk and, if necessary, other people who may be affected by the work (such as occupant families at home or children at school, or workers' families).

Although it is possible for lead exposure risks to be contained and controlled in occupied buildings, it is worth noting the advice from the Department for Levelling Up, Housing and Communities with respect to stripping and preparing lead-based paint in older homes. It is contained within its lead worked example risk assessment under the *Housing health and safety rating system* (HHSRS).

 The occupants should be temporarily rehoused during the stripping and re-painting.

This guidance is consistent with advice in paint manufacturers' material safety data sheets (MSDS).

 ...exclusion of other personnel and especially children from the building during actual work and the subsequent clean-up operations.

8.3   Control of Lead at Work Regulations

The regulations aim to give greater health protection to people at work, whether directly or indirectly exposed, by reducing their exposure to lead and thus the concentrations of lead in their blood. Where concentrations are too high, employers are required to remove employees from work with lead. This is known as the **suspension level**. If employers cannot transfer employees to other work not involving exposure to lead, they must pay them suspension pay under the Employment Rights Act.

Concentration levels of lead in blood, which are below the suspension level and known as **action levels**, have been set. If these lower levels are breached, employers have a duty to investigate and remedy the cause. Employers are also required to take steps to reduce the concentrations of lead in air to a level not exceeding the occupational exposure limits stated in the regulations.

08

Women of child-bearing age and young people are particularly at risk of lead poisoning, and therefore have lower blood-lead action and suspension levels than other workers.

 Lead exposure risks are not covered by the Control of Substances Hazardous to Health (COSHH) Regulations. Only CLAW should be applied to lead hazards and their exposure risk assessment.

It should be noted that CLAW place a number of legal duties on employers, as well as limited legal duties on employees.

8.3.1   Duties under the regulations

The main requirements of CLAW are shown below.

- An employer who is working with lead, or with a substance or material containing lead, has to protect from exposure anyone who may be affected by the work as well as their own employees. This includes:
  - the workers of other employers, including those not involved in work with lead (such as maintenance staff and cleaners)
  - visitors to the work site
  - the families of those who are exposed to lead at work who may become affected by lead carried home unintentionally on the clothing and footwear of the employee
  - the occupiers of premises, including private dwellings, irrespective of whether the occupiers are present whilst the work is carried out or they reoccupy the premises later.

- Every employer is required to make a suitable and sufficient assessment of the risk to the health and safety of employees while at work. This includes other people who are not employees but who may be exposed as a result of the way the employer carries out the work concerned.

  The assessment must be reviewed as often as is necessary and in other certain specified circumstances, and a record made of any significant findings if more than five people are employed. Such an assessment is to allow the employer to make a decision whether the work concerned is likely to result in an employee being *significantly* exposed to lead, and to identify the measures needed to prevent or adequately control exposure.

8.3.1.1   Control of exposure

- Every employer must ensure that the exposure of employees to lead is either prevented or, where this is not reasonably practicable, adequately controlled, by means of appropriate control measures.

- As the preferred control measure, the employer must consider the use of alternative materials or processes as a means of eliminating or reducing the risks to the health of employees.

- Where it is not reasonably practicable to prevent exposure to lead, the employer must introduce protective measures that are appropriate to the work activity and consistent with the findings of the risk assessment. In order of priority, these must be:
  - the design and use of the work process, systems and engineering controls
  - control of exposure at source, including ventilation systems and wet methods
  - where adequate control cannot be achieved by other means, the provision and use of suitable respiratory protective equipment (RPE) and personal protective equipment (PPE).

 Painters and decorators should be aware that most paint manufacturers' material safety data sheets (MSDS) advise the use of wet sanding for surface preparation regardless of whether the surface contains lead or not. Wet sanding prevents airborne dust generation and provides a superior finish.

- The control measure(s) must include:
  - the safe handling, storage and transportation of lead and waste that contains lead
  - suitable maintenance procedures
  - reducing, to the minimum required for the task in hand, the number of employees exposed, the level and duration of exposure and the quantity of lead present in the workplace
  - control of the working environment, including where appropriate, extract ventilation and appropriate daily clean-up using a combination of vacuuming and wet mopping
  - appropriate hygiene measures, including washing and showering facilities. Decontamination units (DCUs) are an increasingly common choice.

  Irrespective of these control measures, where the exposure to lead is, or is likely to be, *significant* the employer must provide suitable and sufficient protective clothing.

- Where the inhalation of lead fumes is possible, the control measures will only be regarded as adequate if the occupational exposure limit is not exceeded, or the employer identifies the reason and takes immediate steps to rectify the situation.

  Inhaling lead fumes from the uncontrolled use of heat guns or torches is the most likely cause of acute lead exposure and hospitalisation. Up to 90% of the lead content of any lead fumes can be absorbed through the lungs and passed directly into the bloodstream.

- Employers must take reasonable steps to ensure that any control measure provided is properly used or applied.

- Employees must make full and proper use of any control measure provided, and:
  - take all reasonable steps, where appropriate, to return anything provided as a control measure to its accommodation (storage) after use
  - report any defect in any control measure provided to the employer.

- Adequate control of exposure to lead covers all routes of possible exposure (such as inhalation, ingestion and absorption through the skin).

- When eating, drinking and smoking, adequate steps must be taken to control the ingestion of lead. An employer must ensure that, as far as is reasonably practicable, employees do not eat, drink or smoke in any place which is, or is liable to become, contaminated by lead. In practical terms, employees must be warned against doing so. Furthermore, under this regulation employees have a legal duty not to eat, drink or smoke in any place that they have reason to believe is contaminated by lead. All control measures provided, including RPE and PPE, must be well maintained, kept in a good state of repair and cleaned as necessary. Any defect in the equipment, or failure to use and apply it properly, which could result in a loss of efficiency or effectiveness, thus reducing the level of protection, should be identified and rectified as soon as possible.

  Colorimetric (colour change) testing of dust contamination can be used to ensure welfare areas are sufficiently lead-free.

8.3.1.2   Air monitoring

Where employees are liable to receive *significant* exposure to lead, employers must establish a programme of personal air monitoring, including keeping records of the findings of such monitoring.

8.3.1.3   Medical surveillance

Where exposure to lead is *significant*, as defined in Regulation 2, the employer must ensure the following.

- Employees are under medical surveillance by either a medical inspector (employment medical adviser) or a relevant doctor.
- Suitable facilities for health surveillance to be carried out are provided, where the procedures are to be carried out at the employer's premises.
- Health surveillance records are maintained and then retained for 40 years.
- Employees are allowed reasonable access to their personal health records.
- Copies of personal health records are provided to the HSE upon request.
- All records are made available to the HSE if ceasing to trade.
- Steps are taken to determine the reasons why any employee's blood sample exceeds the appropriate action level and appropriate remedial action is taken, where required.
- The necessary actions, including reviewing the risk assessment, are taken where an employee's blood or urine sample reaches the suspension level.

 If an employee's test shows concentration levels have been reached, they should have the test repeated urgently. Employers should ensure that every effort is made to obtain the result of the repeat test within 10 working days of the initial result becoming available.

Employees for whom health surveillance has been arranged must, when required by the employer (and at the cost of the employer), make themselves available for the necessary health surveillance procedures and supply the relevant doctor with such health-related information as the doctor may require.

An initial assessment, including blood-lead levels, should always be carried out on new employees who are employed in an activity liable to expose them to lead, and who are likely to have been exposed to lead at work in a previous job, within the last three months, *irrespective* of whether their exposure to lead in their new employment is likely to be *significant*.

The variety and variability of any lead exposure levels in previous employment in refurbishment and related activities are such that it would be safest, at the very least, to check the blood-lead levels of all new employees. If this is not done, then every new project involving activities liable to expose employees to lead should be seen as an opportunity to rectify this oversight and establish a person's base line or reference levels for comparison in case of future problems.

8.3.1.4 Information, instruction and training

Employers who undertake work liable to expose employees to lead shall provide such information, instruction and training as is suitable and sufficient to know the risks to health and the precautions which should be taken (*refer to 8.5 Training*).

 What employers must provide

In addition to this, the Code of Practice requires that an employer should issue a copy of the HSE's free leaflet entitled *Lead and you* to all employees at the start of their first employment on work with lead, and make copies available for issue at the request of any employees or their representatives.

It is thought that this requirement is often not followed with regard to painters and decorators because the information is not sufficiently trade-specific. The Painting and Decorating Association's (PDA) *Health and safety manual* provides a useful source of more relevant information.

Employers must additionally provide employees with written records of concentrations of lead in air to which they have been exposed, the results of the measurements of lead in their blood or urine, and an explanation of the significance of these results.

Note: *in construction, blood lead is the most common measure of exposure to inorganic lead (as found in compounds used in old lead paint), with action and suspension levels being expressed in micrograms of lead per decilitre of blood. Urine sampling tends to be used for assessing exposure to organic lead (such as the fumes from tetraethyl lead).*

8.3.1.5 Arrangements for accidents, incidents and emergencies

The employer, in attempting to protect the health of employees (and others) from an accident, incident or emergency, must ensure that procedures, including the provision of first-aid facilities and safety drills, have been prepared and can be put into effect should such an occasion arise. The employer must also ensure that information on such emergency arrangements has been notified to accident and emergency services and that all such information is displayed within the workplace and for occupants in the same premises.

Colorimetric qualitative lead paint and dust-test kits can be kept on site to allow an immediate assessment of likely lead exposure risks when these emerge. Follow-on quantitative analysis should then be used to quantify the severity and extent of the problem.

8.3.1.6 Exemptions

A certificate of exemption may be granted by the HSE. For further information refer to the regulations and seek competent advice.

8.4 Approved Code of Practice

CLAW should be read in conjunction with the supporting Approved Code of Practice (ACoP) and guidance, which interprets the regulations and sets out standards relating to controlling any type of work activity liable to expose employees and any other persons to lead. The regulations achieve this by means of risk assessments, control measures, air monitoring, the setting of an occupational exposure limit (OEL), medical surveillance and the setting of an action level and suspension level for lead in the blood.

8.5 Training

Training and supervision are an ongoing process involving the education of workers about the hazards and risks of working with lead, how to use controls, what to do if something goes wrong and checking periodically that workers are following instructions. With regard to CLAW (as amended), there is a specific requirement to ensure that the information, instruction and training provided for persons working with lead includes the following.

● The type of lead being worked, the potential health hazards and symptoms.

● The relevant occupational exposure limit, action level and suspension level (as explained later – *refer to 8.8 Controlling exposure to lead*).

● Any other sources of information (such as a lead survey and/or a lead register).

● Any other legislative provisions relevant to working with lead.

● The significant findings of the risk assessment (such as the amount of lead involved).

● The control measures that are in place and that must be used to enable work to be carried out safely.

● The results of any personal air monitoring or surface dust contamination checks.

● The results of previous health surveillance, in such a way that the confidentiality of individual cases are not breached.

8.6 The effect of lead on health

Lead is a cumulative poison that will find its way into the bloodstream, collect in tissue and be stored in bones. Lead poisoning may occur through exposure to lead in its pure form or exposure to products containing lead. Lead affects the body's ability to produce haemoglobin, which is the protein in blood that carries oxygen to the tissues. Lead exposure can initially go unnoticed because there may be no obvious physical symptoms of an underlying problem.

Blood-lead levels are the best measure of current exposure. If the level of lead in the body gets too high, it can cause headaches, tiredness, irritability, constipation, nausea, stomach pains and loss of weight. Continued uncontrolled exposure could cause far more serious symptoms (such as kidney, nerve and brain damage).

The regulations are specifically intended to protect women of child-bearing age and young persons. A developing unborn child is at particular risk from exposure to lead, particularly in the early weeks before a pregnancy becomes known. Thus, women of child-bearing age who may be exposed to lead should take special care to follow good work practices and observe a high standard of personal hygiene.

The employer has a duty to assess the nature and extent of the exposure to lead and, on the basis of this assessment, to determine the measures necessary to control exposure and comply with the regulations.

Action should be taken to reduce the amount of lead breathed in by operatives to below the lead-in-air standard. Air monitoring should be used to ensure the controls are adequate. Good welfare facilities should also be provided.

Although inhalation has always been considered to be the major source of lead exposure, current thinking recognises the much greater contribution of hand-to-mouth contact and the *significant* exposure risk that can arise from ingestion.

Many sections of the regulations relate to the prevention of the inhalation or ingestion of lead dust, fumes and vapour. **The basic need is to prevent the liberation of lead dust, fumes or vapour into the workplace.**

8.7   Testing for the presence of lead

There are a number of ways to test for the presence of lead, shown below.

- A variety of destructive tests for paint sampling, although these can result in damage to painted surfaces in order for samples to be taken.

- Disposable test kits: instant, on-site lead/no lead result with 95% accuracy. (These are an indicator only, **not** a laboratory-standard test and are unsuitable and insufficient for risk assessment purposes.)

- Paint-sampling kits, which are ready to use (for non-lab professionals) for submission of samples for chemical analysis. (A laboratory-standard test.)

- Dust-wipe sampling kits, which are ready to use (for non-lab professionals) for submission of samples for chemical analysis. (A laboratory-standard test.)

- Professional sampling for accredited or non-accredited laboratory analysis.

- Hand-portable devices that use XRF-i (x-ray fluorescence isotope) technology to obtain laboratory standard readings instantly, on site.

 When taking physical samples for off-site analysis, it is almost impossible to ensure 100% recovery of all of the lead from a given substrate, whether timber, metal, plaster or any other materials – occupationally *significant* quantities of lead residue tend to be left behind. For this reason laboratory analysis of samples removed from site can significantly understate the severity of the actual on-site hazard.

Paint-on-base-material analysis, instead of the customary use of paint flakes or scrapings, provides the best starting point for determining the full extent of potential lead exposure risks, as found on site.

8.8   Controlling exposure to lead

8.8.1   Risk assessments

Employers must not carry out any work that may expose employees to lead unless a suitable and sufficient risk assessment has been carried out. Given the CLAW requirement to **'consider the amount (of lead) involved'**, a suitable and sufficient risk assessment cannot be based on the assumption that lead-based paint is present.

The purpose of the risk assessment is to enable the employer to assess whether the exposure of employees to lead is likely to be *significant* and to identify the measures necessary to prevent or control exposure.

8.8.2   Control measures

Control measures involve substituting lead with less hazardous substances or, if this is not possible, using engineering and organisational methods, similar to those outlined for COSHH, to control exposure.

The control of exposure to lead (by inhalation) will only be regarded as adequate in the following circumstances.

- If the concentration of lead in the air is kept below the OEL *(see below)*.

- If, where the OEL is exceeded, the employer identifies the reasons and takes immediate steps to remedy the situation.

Where old, lead-based paint is concerned, removal is not necessarily the best option. Leaving it in situ is often safer, especially if it can be encapsulated with a proprietary coating or rigid covering. Encasement behind plasterboard is also an alternative.

8.8.3   Air monitoring

Where a risk assessment indicates that employees may be liable to *significant* exposure to lead, the employer must arrange for preliminary personal air monitoring to be carried out to establish the levels of lead in the air at the place of work.

Air monitoring will involve using specialist equipment, fitted to the employee being monitored, to take an air sample from the employee's breathing zone over a set period of time. Using static air-monitoring equipment to take air samples is not acceptable for preliminary monitoring as the results will not be representative of any employee's personal exposure.

Generally, depending upon the circumstances, monitoring must be carried out for each individual process likely to generate different levels of exposure. The work environment, choice of equipment and the amount of lead in the material being worked on, can all contribute to significant variations. Air monitoring will determine whether the OEL has been breached.

The employer has a duty to retain records of air monitoring results for a period of five years.

Given the temporary nature of construction sites, and the even shorter periods when employees might actually be exposed to lead, this requirement is considered to be largely academic for the construction industry. With tradespeople (such as plumbers and painters) being potentially exposed to lead many times but over relatively short periods, it will be for the employer to decide how frequently air monitoring should be carried out to confirm whether or not existing control measures are adequate.

8.8.4   Occupational exposure limit

The standard for inorganic lead in the air is **0.15 mg** (milligrams) or **150 µg** (micrograms) of **lead per cubic metre** of air determined on an eight-hour time-weighted concentration.

 Significant

Significant in relation to exposure to airborne lead dust means exposure where any employee is, or is liable to be, exposed to a concentration of lead in the atmosphere exceeding half the occupational exposure limit for lead.

From the above it can be seen that the *significant* level would be **0.075 mg** (milligrams) or **75 µg** (micrograms).

 Units are shown here in micrograms because blood-lead levels are reported in micrograms per decilitre (µg/dL), helping to explain the use and relevance of these numbers and making it easy to relate them to each other.

This quantifies the standard to be met by the control measures for airborne lead under the regulations.

 Even if the *significant* exposure risk threshold for airborne lead dust is not exceeded, a *significant* lead exposure risk can still exist because of a substantial ingestion risk.

8.8.5   Medical surveillance

Medical surveillance to detect exposure to lead involves measuring the concentration of lead in the blood or urine and therefore necessitates the involvement of suitable, trained medical staff.

 Blood-lead levels

A saliva check or screening test is now available to determine blood-lead levels from the laboratory analysis of saliva samples. This is not a legal requirement but it is an accurate, non-invasive and easy-to-take sample. And, because it is a painless, non-medical procedure, it should encourage compliance. A high blood-lead level from a saliva test should be followed up by a (second) blood sample, which is a legal requirement.

Where a risk assessment indicates that employees' exposure to lead is likely to be *significant*, the employer has a duty to arrange medical surveillance for the affected employees.

 There is an important difference between everyday use of the word *significant* and its definition/ application under CLAW. The amount of lead in an exposure situation can be low or high, but the substantial risk of ingestion can be *significant* in both cases.

If biological monitoring detects blood-lead concentrations at or above those outlined below, this will trigger continued medical surveillance.

● Women of reproductive capability: **20 micrograms** of lead, or greater, per decilitre of blood.

● All other employees: **35 micrograms** of lead, or greater, per decilitre of blood.

(For further information refer to 8.3.1.3 Medical surveillance.)

8.8.6 Action levels

The action levels for lead are shown below.

- Women of reproductive capability: **25 micrograms** of lead per decilitre of blood.

- Young persons (aged 16–17): **40 micrograms** of lead per decilitre of blood.

- Any other employee: **50 micrograms** of lead per decilitre of blood.

If medical surveillance detects blood-lead concentrations at or above these action levels, the employer must carry out the following.

- Recognise that the employee's blood-lead level is near the suspension level.

- Investigate the effectiveness of existing control measures and take the necessary actions to reduce employees' blood-lead levels below the action level.

- Prevent the blood-lead level of affected employees from reaching the suspension level.

8.8.7 Suspension levels

If medical surveillance reveals that an employee's blood-lead level has reached or exceeded the levels outlined below, a doctor must decide whether to temporarily suspend them from work that exposes them to lead.

- Women of reproductive capability: **30 micrograms** of lead per decilitre of blood.

- Young persons (aged 16–17): **50 micrograms** of lead per decilitre of blood.

- Any other employee: **60 micrograms** of lead per decilitre of blood.

In such circumstances, the employer must carry out the following.

- Ensure that a doctor makes an entry in the health record of affected employee(s) as to whether, in the doctor's professional opinion, they should be suspended from further work liable to expose them to lead.

- Review the relevant risk assessment.

- Review the actions taken to prevent exposure to lead.

- Provide for a review of the health of any other employees who may have been similarly exposed.

If the doctor thinks that there is no need to suspend the affected employee(s) from work, the doctor must note in their health records the reasons for that decision and any conditions under which working with lead may continue.

Doctors practising in this specialist medical field are familiar with the regulations, and if there are some exceptions to the rule, such doctors will be able to explain them. An employer must act on the doctor's decision and an employee will not be able to work with lead again, or be exposed to it, until the doctor considers it safe to do so.

 Level of concern

The so-called 'level of concern' for the general population is 10 micrograms of lead per decilitre of blood. In some countries a lower threshold of 5 micrograms has been set for children under six years old. Contractors employing operatives with proper training, supervision and equipment should be able to maintain blood-lead levels below 2 micrograms of lead per decilitre of blood. For grit-blasting operations, keeping blood-lead levels below 15 micrograms is practicable and achievable.

 Annexes 1–5 and Appendix 6 of the ACoP record details of an employee under medical surveillance because of exposure to lead.

8.8.8 Understanding lead levels

Tiny amounts of lead can have a significant effect on a person's health, hence why lead exposure must be carefully assessed and controlled.

1 microgram (µg) = one grain of sugar ÷ 1,000
One grain of sugar = 1,000 micrograms (µg)

1 deciliter (dL) = 100 ml
or 1/10th litre (about half a glass of wine)

For employees the action level is **50 micrograms (µg)** of lead per **decilitre (dL)** of blood. This is the equivalent of dissolving 1/20th of a grain of sugar into half a glass of wine. Case studies have demonstrated that **36,100 micrograms (µg)** can be found in just **1 cm²** of old lead paint. The same exposure risk situation arises after paint stripping – even if all of the visible paint has been removed.

8.8.9 Significant levels

Significant exposure to lead can occur in the following circumstances.

● Where any employee is, or is liable to be, exposed to a concentration of lead in the atmosphere exceeding half the occupational exposure limit for lead.

● If there is a substantial risk of any employee ingesting lead.

● If there is a risk of contact between the skin and lead alkyls or other substances containing lead that can be absorbed through the skin.

Employers must provide employees with protective clothing, monitor lead-in-air concentrations and place the employees concerned under medical surveillance, including biological monitoring of blood-lead levels.

 The more stringent suspension levels and the action levels introduced by the regulations are intended to tighten controls on exposure to lead and reduce the risk to workers' health. In order to see further improvements in the control of employees' exposure to lead, the HSE has made known its intention to review the suspension levels with a view to reducing the limits further.

In such cases, all the regulations will apply; blood-lead levels must be monitored and air monitoring must be carried out regularly to confirm the effectiveness of control measures. The results must be recorded. PPE will be required where control measures are not practicable.

8.9 Activities liable to result in significant exposure

Some types of work with lead, carried out as part of construction or decorating (such as in the examples listed below), have the potential to result in *significant* exposure to lead unless the employer provides adequate controls and ensures that they are used.

● Burning off old paint.

● Dry-sanding old paint.

● High temperature lead-work (such as lead-smelting, burning and welding).

● Working with metallic lead and alloys containing lead (for example, soldering).

● Disc abrasion of lead surfaces and cutting lead with abrasive wheels.

● Spray painting with lead-based paints.

● Grit-blasting operations.

● Work inside tanks that have contained petrol.

● Manufacture of leaded glass.

● Hot-cutting, demolition and dismantling operations.

● Removing or disturbing old lead sheet, thereby raising contaminated dust.

● Recovering lead from scrap and waste.

● Perforating top floor ceilings or ceilings below roof voids holding quantities of settled leaded exhaust particles, known as ceiling dust.

● Disturbance and/or removal of loft insulation where leaded exhaust particles have settled.

● Disturbance of floor voids containing accumulated lead particles.

● Welding galvanised metal and flame cutting steelwork that has been painted with lead-based paint.

 The molten metal in a galvanising bath for hot-dipping steelwork typically used to contain 1% lead (approximately) to assist with run-off after the component had been dipped. In the industry it is well known that older galvanised coatings, once dried, typically had a 0.5% lead content. Although this lead content has been reduced over time, it has not yet been completely eliminated. So it is not simply leaded paint that can create or contribute to a person's overall lead exposure risk in this example.

Those operations that do not usually produce *significant* levels of airborne dust or fumes include low temperature work, ordinary plumbing, soldering, handling clean sheets or pipes of lead and rough painting. In some cases, however, even these can present a substantial ingestion risk, and consequent *significant* exposure risk, if not managed properly. Examples of types of work producing exposures above and below *significant* levels are given in the ACoP. Frequently, however, these are not sharply divided. For example, if the character of the lead is changed by the work itself, **work with materials containing LESS than 1% lead can be liable to result in significant exposure.**

8.10 Working with lead-containing paints

The residues of lead-containing paints are a health hazard. Operatives carrying out work involving the disturbance, preparation or removal of old lead-containing paint, and anyone else who might be adversely affected, must be adequately protected when applying or removing it. Similarly, the occupiers of premises (including the residents of private housing) must be protected by not being allowed to return to their premises (or contaminated parts of those premises) until they have been thoroughly and effectively cleaned.

The findings of a risk assessment carried out by a competent person, with specialist lead knowledge and before any surface finish is disturbed, will indicate the most appropriate method of removal and the safety precautions that must be taken.

8.10.1 Sanding or flatting

Wet sanding, wet scraping and wet abrasion, regardless of whether or not a coated substrate contains lead, are considered good practice methods for minimising airborne dust and paint chips during surface preparation. Wet residues should be cleaned up before they dry out and become chalky, with the potential to become airborne dust.

Lead-containing paintwork should never be dry-sanded by hand as this activity will liberate lead-rich dust into the air. Mechanical or power sanding should only be used if the sander is fitted with a H or M class dust extraction or collection unit.

 Not all methods of stripping paint remove the residual lead from the grain of the wood. As a result, the subsequent dry sanding of apparently clean wood can liberate a *significant* amount of lead-containing dust into the air. Whichever of these methods is chosen toxic dust-rated RPE (minimum FFP3 or P3) should also be worn.

8.10.2 Burning

Blowlamps or gas torches must not be used to burn off old lead paint as these will heat the paint sufficiently to liberate toxic lead fumes into the air. The use of heat guns, unless carefully supervised for low-heat use, is likely to generate toxic fumes.

8.10.3 Solvents

Lead paint may be removed by using a solvent or water-rinsable paint remover. If a solvent is used, the work area must be well-ventilated and no smoking or naked flames allowed. Suitable RPE and other appropriate PPE should be used.

8.10.4 Hot-air gun

These must not be confused with blowlamps and gas torches. Used on a low-heat setting **only** (for example, below 360ºC) a hot-air gun will not raise the temperature of the paint sufficiently to allow lead fumes to be released. When using a hot-air gun, the old paint must be scraped off as soon as it is sufficiently soft and before it re-hardens. Care must be taken to ensure that the paint does not burn as this indicates that it is reaching too high a temperature where fumes may be given off. The use of RPE to protect against lead-containing dust will be necessary. Care should also be taken to prevent lead dust and paint from being blown everywhere, especially into people's homes or schools during external redecoration works.

Some hot-air gun manufacturers warn against using their products on lead paint surfaces, others advise low-heat working. Hot-air guns should be avoided on commercial projects because of the near impossibility of supervising their correct use. Unless a device has a pre-set operating temperature that cannot be overridden, allowing hot-air gun use on site is prone to problems.

8.10.5 Infrared heating

A product is available that safely lifts the old paint from the base material by heating it to a safe temperature using an infrared heater. Whilst warm, the paint can be safely scraped off. This method is particularly suitable where large, flat surfaces have to be stripped.

The main benefits of using this method, which acts by heating the resins in the wood and breaking the bond between the wood and the first layer of paint, are shown below.

- All layers of paint are removed in a single action.
- As a static heat method, the spread of air-blown lead contamination is avoided.
- Virtually all residual lead is removed from within the grain of the wood.
- Large flat surface areas can be safely stripped more quickly than by using other methods.

8.10.6 Spraying

Spraying methods should not normally be employed for applying lead-based paints.

8.10.7 Cleaning up the work area

All exposed surfaces in areas where lead paint stripping or removal has taken place should be washed down thoroughly, either with a proprietary lead-specific detergent or with a solution of dishwasher detergent in hot water, and then wiped down again with clean water.

08

In areas that will be reoccupied by children, all washed down and rinsed areas should be towel dried to remove or prevent the formation of chalky residues. Any residual dust and other debris should be removed using a vacuum cleaner fitted with a H or M class extraction unit. Appropriate RPE (FFP3) should be worn whilst doing this.

 Normal vacuum cleaners (domestic or industrial) should not be used as their filters are not sufficiently fine to retain the lead-containing dust. H or M class extraction units should be used.

 For further information refer to Chapter B10 Dust and fumes (Respiratory hazards).

8.11 Personal protective equipment

In the context of this chapter, the regulations require that where a risk of exposure to lead has been identified by a risk assessment and it cannot be adequately controlled by other means, which are equally or more effective, the employer must provide PPE and they must ensure it is properly used by employees. Users of PPE must be trained in its use and care as appropriate. In essence, PPE may only be used as a **last resort** after all other means of eliminating or controlling the risk have been considered and are not reasonably practicable.

8.11.1 Respiratory protective equipment

Where control measures do not reduce the lead in air levels to below the control limits, RPE of a type suited to the hazard or process involved must be provided and all employees must be properly trained to use it. All such equipment should be serviced, cleaned, maintained and stored correctly, as is appropriate. Depending upon whether the hazard is lead dust or fumes, adequate protection will be given by the use of compressed air-line breathing apparatus, self-contained breathing apparatus, or a full face positive pressure-powered respirator fitted with a P3 filter. Wearers of RPE must be face-fit tested.

 Half-face respirators fitted with P3 filters or their disposable equivalent (FFP3) are suitable for toxic dusts (such as lead), subject to an assessment of the suitability of their assigned protection factor.

Because lead is both an ingestion and an inhalation risk, airborne lead levels below the OEL (and even below the *significant* exposure level) can nevertheless present a substantial ingestion risk. By providing a physical barrier around the nose and mouth, suitable RPE specified to protect against lead dust can also help to minimise ingestion from hand-to-mouth contact. Sole reliance on RPE is insufficient to avoid *significant* exposure.

8.11.2 Protective clothing

Wherever exposure is substantial, protective clothing must be provided. It must be suited to the hazard or process involved, should resist the permeation of lead dust, and not collect or harbour dust (for example, overalls with no pockets on the outside). Laundry facilities should be available so that contaminated clothing is not taken home for laundering. Employees must be instructed to report any damaged or defective ventilation plant or protective equipment, without delay, to their supervisor or safety representative. All contaminated clothing and footwear should remain on site to prevent the potential of workers' families being exposed to lead – a known problem.

 For further information refer to Chapter B06 Personal protective equipment.

8.12 Welfare arrangements

CLAW requires the provision of adequate welfare facilities, particularly in respect of personal hygiene. Contractors must provide or make the following items available.

- Suitable and sufficient washing facilities, including showers if necessary, due to the nature of the work (decontamination units (DCUs) are becoming more commonplace for this).

- Hot (or warm) and cold running water, soap or other cleanser and roller towels or other effective means of drying.

- Suitable and sufficient changing rooms.

- Lockers or other facilities in which to secure work clothing that is not taken home and personal clothing that is not worn at work.

- Suitable rest facilities where meals may be prepared and eaten.

Regular checks (such as dust wipe sampling) should be made to ensure welfare facilities are sufficiently free of lead contamination.

 In accordance with HSE *Operational circular* OC 298/15 for inspections under CLAW, inspectors may seek from employers evidence of surface contamination levels.

8.12.1 Changing and washing facilities

This includes accommodation for clothing where necessary.

To avoid any risk to health or damage to the clothing concerned, the employer must also provide separate accommodation for an employee's own clothing and any protective clothing the employee may have to wear at work.

This requirement will normally apply for protective clothing worn for work with lead.

Adequate and suitable washing facilities are required where operatives are exposed to lead. The ACoP requires that, where employees are exposed to lead, washing and changing facilities provided should allow them to meet a high standard of personal hygiene so as to minimise the risk of them ingesting or otherwise absorbing lead.

The design of the washing facilities should be related to the nature and degree of exposure to lead as indicated by the assessment. Where employees are *significantly* exposed to lead, and if washbasins alone would not be adequate, the washing facilities should include showers or baths.

An example would be where work is carried out in dusty conditions that could result in the whole body being contaminated by lead. The provision of showers or baths would then be essential.

Washing facilities should provide the following, as a minimum.

- Basins should be of sufficient size to permit arms to be immersed up to the elbow.
- A constant supply of hot (or warm) and cold water (running water where reasonably practicable).
- Soap or other cleaning materials.
- Nail brushes.
- Warm air dryers or roller towels; communal towels should not be used.

For certain types of work (such as lead paint removal work), carried out at premises or sites where such work is not regularly done (for example, certain tank cleaning, lead burning and grit-blasting operations), mobile caravan-type washing/showering DCU facilities of suitable design should be provided.

8.12.2 Eating, drinking and smoking

The regulations specifically require employers to reduce the risk of ingestion of lead by ensuring that employees do not eat, drink or smoke in places that are contaminated, or likely to be contaminated, by lead arising from work. The legal ban on smoking in enclosed places of work may, in many cases, render this legal requirement irrelevant.

Therefore, employers should reduce the risk of employees ingesting lead by ensuring that they are given adequate information on the specific areas that might be contaminated by lead and in which they should not eat (including chewing gum or tobacco), drink or smoke.

The information should be reinforced by displaying a prominent notice to identify those areas in which employees may, or may not, eat, drink or smoke.

The following points should be noted.

- Clean areas, canteens or mess rooms should be isolated from lead-contaminated work areas and checked regularly for levels of surface lead-dust contamination.
- Protective clothing should be removed before entering these areas.
- Washing should take place before eating meals or drinking.
- The employer must advise employees where they may not eat, drink, smoke or use e-cigarettes.
- A legal duty is placed on employees not to eat, drink or smoke in any place where there is risk of contamination by lead.

Even with a total ban on smoking in enclosed workplaces, those who work with lead but smoke elsewhere (such as at home) must be aware of the need to remove all traces of lead from their hands and clothes at some time between carrying out the two activities.

 Smokers are likely to ingest between 200–400% more lead than non-smokers.

8.12.3 Personal hygiene

Anyone who works with lead, lead-containing materials and old lead paint, should take simple personal hygiene measures to prevent the inhalation or ingestion of lead during and after work.

Interestingly, the ACoP that supports CLAW indicates that nail-biting and roll-your-own cigarettes are often implicated in high levels of lead absorption.

08

8.13   Provision and use of work equipment

The Provision and Use of Work Equipment Regulations (PUWER) require that an employer only supplies work equipment that is correct and suitable for the job for which the equipment is going to be used.

The regulations also require that users of work equipment are trained in its use, as appropriate.

8.14   Reporting of diseases

The Reporting of Injuries, Diseases and Dangerous Occurrences Regulations (RIDDOR) require the responsible person to report to the enforcing authority (normally the HSE) any case of lead poisoning suffered by any person at work that results from exposure to lead whilst at work.

Lead poisoning, when diagnosed by a medical practitioner, is a reportable occupational disease under RIDDOR and must be reported in accordance with requirements of the regulations.

The regulations contain strict provisions as to medical surveillance and require that employers ensure that basic details of all those who need to be under medical surveillance are recorded.

There are additional forms specified by the regulations in respect of the following.

● The initial medical assessment, which also contains the past occupational medical and clinical details of the employee, including a smoking history.

● A surveillance record for persons exposed to lead.

● A notification to an employer of biological test results and a record of medical surveillance.

● A certification of unfitness or fitness to return to work.

● An annual return of persons under medical surveillance, to be completed by employers.

 For further information on RIDDOR refer to Chapter A13 Accident reporting and investigation.

8.15   Supporting information

8.15.1   Lead Paint Safety Association UK

The Lead Paint Safety Association UK is a not-for-profit organisation. It is at the forefront of efforts to promote awareness and good practice in lead paint safety and compliance. Its overall objective is to prevent, and ultimately eliminate, unnecessary childhood and occupational lead poisoning.

8.15.2 Painting and Decorating Association

The Painting and Decorating Association (PDA) represents thousands of painters and decorators across the UK and is the largest trade and employers' association for contractors. The PDA offers health and safety advice to all its members.

 For further information visit the PDA website.

Asbestos

GT700 Toolbox talks / supporting checklists and forms

Toolbox talks on some of these topics are available in the GT700 publication. Supporting checklists and forms covering some of these topics are available on our companion website.

ASBESTOS

Overview

Asbestos is a hazard to health when airborne fibres are breathed in. Asbestos fibres are biopersistent (the human lung is not able to expel or break down asbestos fibres). The greater the number of fibres inhaled, and the longer the period over which they are breathed in, the greater the risk of incurable asbestos-related diseases developing. These include cancers in the lungs and chest lining.

9.1   Introduction

An understanding of this chapter alone will not be deemed sufficient for any person to be considered as a competent person under the Control of Asbestos Regulations (CAR). The purpose of this chapter is to give users information on the subject of asbestos.

- What to look for.
- The dangers to health that can occur due to exposure.
- The requirements of the current regulations.
- The duty to manage asbestos.

 Around 5,000 people die each year as a result of past asbestos exposure.

Asbestos removal work will normally be considered to be construction work as defined in the Construction (Design and Management) Regulations 2015 (CDM). Asbestos removal work must always be undertaken in accordance with all relevant legislation, regardless of the size and complexity of the asbestos removal task.

The Health and Safety Executive (HSE) has previously expressed a number of concerns regarding aspects of health and safety, often related to working with asbestos, but which can be overlooked (such as working at height, the risk of fire, working in confined spaces, the use of machinery, burning, cutting and lifting). It is important not to view asbestos as a hazard in isolation. All associated hazards must be effectively managed, with due consideration given as to how the use of respiratory protection may exacerbate some of these risks. For example, a respirator used for confined space work may not be suitable for working with asbestos.

Not surprisingly, the emphasis of the regulations is on exposure risk management, not only for those who may be working directly with asbestos but also for those who undertake work in premises where asbestos might be present. Work with the most high-risk (dangerous) products must be carried out by a licensed contractor and appropriately trained operatives. Work with less hazardous products can, in most cases, still be carried out by people who are trained and competent and who are maintaining records of these non-licensed works.

The key to safe working is a risk assessment, which must be carried out by someone who is competent in terms of the following.

- Assessing the likelihood and extent of exposure to asbestos.
- Implementing the requirements of the legislation and supporting guidance.
- Understanding the controls needed.

All work with asbestos must comply with CAR. The classification of work and risk are determined by a material's friability. Those **materials capable of releasing high levels of fibre will generally require a licensed contractor**.

Generally, work with undamaged asbestos-cement products, older textured coatings (such as Artex) and some other **materials where the asbestos fibres are tightly bound into a base material is non-licensed**, but in some circumstances may require *notification*.

Some work with asbestos-cement products (for example, clearing up fire damaged debris where the cement has been badly damaged and the asbestos fibres are no longer well bound into the base material matrix) is likely to need the services of a licensed contractor.

Damaged asbestos lagging

 Asbestos is a risk to health when airborne fibres are breathed in. The greater the number of fibres, the earlier the age of first exposure and the longer the period over which they are breathed in, the greater the risk of incurable asbestos-related diseases developing. These include cancers in the lungs and chest lining. Smokers exposed to asbestos have a greatly increased risk of lung cancer.

It is essential that everyone working in construction-related sectors is fully aware and educated about the risks. The HSE is conscious that there is a new generation of workers that are much less aware of the risks, and do not see the dangers or that the risks are current and relevant to the work that they do.

Due to the long time it takes for symptoms to appear following exposure, there is a perception among younger workers that asbestos only impacts older generations who were working around it before it was banned. To improve awareness, the HSE launched a new campaign, **Asbestos & You**, in March 2023, the objective of which was to reduce exposure to asbestos among tradespeople, and thus decrease the number of those afflicted by or dying from asbestos-related disease.

The campaign's focus was to remind individuals that asbestos is still present, and target behaviours and awareness across numerous trades (with more of a focus on domestic properties). It highlighted that we are living with asbestos and must be aware of the dangers.

To reduce future work-related ill health, it is paramount that everyone working in construction, whatever their age, takes the risk from asbestos seriously, knows how to recognise the dangers, and takes the right actions to protect themselves and others from exposure.

 To find out more about the Asbestos & You campaign, visit the campaign's website.

9.1.1 Asbestos-related diseases

Exposure to asbestos can cause asbestos-related lung cancer, asbestosis, mesothelioma and pleural thickening.

Asbestos-related lung cancer is similar to lung cancer caused by smoking but it is caused by exposure to asbestos fibres.

Asbestosis is scarring of the lungs that occurs after heavy exposure to asbestos. It can cause progressive shortness of breath as your lungs cannot hold as much air as they used to. There is no cure for asbestosis. The lung damage it causes cannot be reversed. In its advanced stages, the disease may cause cardiac failure.

Mesothelioma is a cancer of the thin, protective membrane (pleura) surrounding the lungs, heart and abdominal cavity, which is only caused by exposure to asbestos. It can take up to 50 years after exposure before symptoms develop, and the condition is often diagnosed at an advanced stage. Mesothelioma is fatal in all cases, with death often occurring within months of diagnosis. Only around 5% to 10% of people diagnosed with mesothelioma will survive for five years or more.

Pleural thickening can occur after heavy exposure to asbestos. The lining of the lung thickens and swells, meaning that your lungs cannot expand as far, causing discomfort in the chest and shortness of breath.

The use of asbestos materials in construction products was common from the mid-1940s, reaching its peak in the mid-1970s. However, asbestos that is in a good condition, which is not damaged and is not likely to be worked on or disturbed, does not pose any immediate problem and may not need to be removed. The HSE advises that it is usually better to leave it in place, and then to manage its presence on an ongoing basis. However, on construction projects the HSE states: *'in the case of demolition or major refurbishment, the plan of work must specify that all asbestos is removed before any other major work begins, where this is reasonably practicable and does not cause a greater risk to the employees than if the asbestos had been left in place'.*

In the past, asbestos was widely used in the manufacture of building materials and products. Current legislation now prohibits the use of asbestos for all of these purposes. As a result, there should be no asbestos issues with any new-build premises or refurbishment after 1999, where the full removal of asbestos has been undertaken. It is important to note that asbestos has not been banned worldwide and from time to time may be found in imported products. Appropriate due diligence should be applied to imported plant and machinery arriving from areas around the world where asbestos is not a banned material.

Although asbestos building materials and products have been largely replaced by safer alternatives, there remains the issue of the ongoing and long-term management of existing asbestos where its removal is not practicable. Consequently, the regulations place a duty to manage asbestos on the owners or occupiers of non-domestic premises.

 There are many resources available on the HSE website, including video support, which can indicate the likely locations where you may find asbestos.

9.2 Important points

- CAR applies to employers, as well as those who manage premises or who remove asbestos.

- The regulations are designed to protect everyone who might be at risk from asbestos exposure, not just those tasked with the removal of asbestos-containing material (ACM).

- ACM is hazardous when airborne and dangerous when fibres are inhaled.

- Asbestos was widely used in the UK until it was banned in late 1999; disturbance of the fabric of any building built before this time has the potential to expose asbestos.

- As part of the requirements of the duty to manage, all non-domestic premises should have an asbestos management plan in place. This document should be available to anyone who might work within or will undertake any maintenance of the building.

- The requirements for the control of asbestos removal are cascading, and relate to the friability of the material. The most friable materials require higher levels of control and competency than the least friable materials.

09

ASBESTOS

- Anyone who may encounter asbestos as part of their daily work operations (this includes most people within the construction and maintenance sector) should have asbestos awareness training, which must be repeated at least annually. It is currently estimated that 20 people from the construction sector die each week as a result of past asbestos exposure.

- All work with asbestos must comply with CAR. The requirements for licensed work remain the same: in the majority of cases, work with asbestos needs to be done by a licensed contractor. This work includes most asbestos removal, all work with sprayed asbestos coatings and asbestos lagging and most work with asbestos insulation and asbestos insulating board (AIB). Other types of asbestos may require the use of a licence subject to an assessment of risk and potential fibre release.

- If you are carrying out non-licensed asbestos work, this still requires effective controls.

- Some non-licensed work needs to be notified to the relevant enforcing authority. This is referred to as notifiable non-licensed work (NNLW).

- Written records should be kept of non-licensed work, which has to be notified (such as copy of the notification with a list of workers on the job), plus the level of likely exposure of those workers to asbestos. This does not require air monitoring on every job, if an estimate of degree of exposure can be made based on experience of similar past tasks or published guidance.

- Before any work that has the potential to expose anyone to asbestos is carried out, a survey must be carried out and a written risk assessment made.

- The priority for any employer is to prevent exposure to, and the spread of, asbestos. This is not only important during asbestos removal operations, where effective containment is required, but it should also be considered during maintenance and refurbishment work.

- A written, site-specific plan (or register) of work must be kept on site and followed.

- Anyone who does any work with asbestos must be specifically trained to do it, and this training must be repeated at least annually.

- Contractors producing hazardous asbestos waste must check that the site receiving your asbestos waste is authorised to receive asbestos. They should have an environmental permit.

- Be aware of other hazards that may arise from working with or managing asbestos (such as working at height, in a confined space or where the presence of live services must be managed) and how the use of respiratory protective equipment (RPE) can change these risks by, for example, restricting all round visibility.

- The HSE, or the appropriate authority, must be notified of the following.
  - All work involving the disturbance of asbestos. This applies to licensed asbestos work and notifiable non-licensed asbestos work. Only non-licensed work does not require notification to the HSE.
  - Separately, if the project is notifiable under CDM.

- CAR require anyone who issues a site-clearance certificate to be accredited to ISO 17025 by an appropriate accreditation body as competent to carry out such work. In the UK the sole source of this accreditation is through the United Kingdom Accreditation Service (UKAS).

- CAR require all those who may be exposed to asbestos to have had appropriate asbestos awareness training. The HSE has identified specific groups deemed at risk, which includes all construction personnel.

 The HSE has developed Managing my asbestos, a material and priority scoring tool, to use online at the HSE website and aimed at helping to protect you and your workers from asbestos exposure.

 HSE research suggests that annual mesothelioma deaths are expected to reduce in the UK over the period between 2020 and 2030.

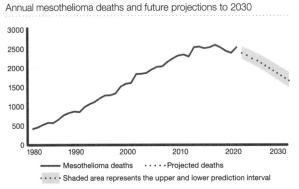

Annual mesothelioma deaths and future projections to 2030

— Mesothelioma deaths · · · · Projected deaths
Shaded area represents the upper and lower prediction interval

Credit: Health and safety at work - Summary statistics for Great Britain 2022, HSE

 For further information on research into the dangers of asbestos visit the HSE website.

09

9.3   Control of Asbestos Regulations

CAR define the following terms.

Licensed work. All high-risk work, other than very minor work, with the following products.

- Asbestos insulation.

- Coating (excluding textured coatings and paint).

- Asbestos insulation board.

- Work on any material that exceeds the control limit of 0.1 fibres per cm^3 over four hours, or the short-term exposure limit of 0.6 fibres per cm^3 over ten minutes.

Notifiable non-licensed work. Work that will normally fall into this category may involve minor work involving the repair of asbestos insulation, minor work with AIB that meets the short duration criteria, maintenance of and removal of damaged asbestos cement and removal work of decorative coatings that contain ACM.

For work not to require a licensed contractor, an assessment by a competent person must conclude that the planned exposure is sporadic and low intensity, and will not exceed the control limit.

The work itself must meet the following requirements.

- Be short, non-continuous maintenance; or removal of materials where the asbestos fibres are firmly linked to the base material matrix.

- Encapsulate or seal the materials that are in good condition.

- Be subjected to air monitoring, gathering samples or other analytical work.

Work with the following materials will be notifiable and non-licensed providing the risk assessment accurately confirms that the exposure over a four-hour period will not exceed the control limit of 0.1 fibres/cm^3, and the maximum exposure will be below a peak of 0.6 fibres/cm^3 averaged over ten minutes. It is worth noting that 0.1 fibres cm^3 equates to 100,000 fibres per m^3.

- Asbestos cement.

- Textured decorative coatings containing asbestos.

- Paints that contain asbestos.

- Items of bitumen, plastic, resin or rubber, which do contain asbestos, but the asbestos was not used for its thermal or insulation properties (such as damp-proof course, roofing felt, vinyl floor tiles and toilet seats).

- Gaskets, packers and washers.

- Items (such as asbestos rope) **where the material is not being used for insulation** (for example, asbestos rope used as a gasket/packer in the joint between two sections of an asbestos-cement drainpipe). (It should be noted that asbestos rope wrapped around a pipe, to keep the heat in or stop it from freezing, is acting as insulation.)

 Written records should be kept of notifiable non-licensed work.

Non-licensed work. Work that will normally fall into this category is shown below.

- Short, non-continuous work with asbestos insulating board (attaching cables, cleaning light fittings and lifting ceiling tiles for inspection).

- Short, non-continuous maintenance and removal work with asbestos cement that is in good condition.

- Short, non-continuous work with decorative coatings (drilling and fixing screws).

It includes minor work on the repair or removal of asbestos-containing items, where the asbestos is well bonded and the removal of these items will not result in the degradation of the materials. Some examples are shown below *(for further information refer to 9.10.5 Non-licensed work).*

- Work with asbestos-cement sheets, where the material is in a good condition and can be removed intact.

- Work on textured decorative coatings, applied to plasterboard, where the material can be removed while attached to the plasterboard.

- Thermoplastic floor tiles.

Sporadic and low intensity. The concentration of air cannot exceed, or be liable to exceed, 0.6 fibres/cm^3 in air measured over a ten-minute period by a UKAS laboratory.

Control limit. Average exposure measured by a UKAS laboratory for a four-hour period, which is currently set at 0.1 fibres/cm^3 for all types of asbestos fibre. This should not take into account any RPE worn.

Risk assessment. An assessment of the risk of anyone being harmed through exposure to asbestos, as carried out by someone with both the theoretical and practical experience of the intended work with ACMs. This degree of specialism necessary to carry out such a risk assessment may be beyond the competence of many people who would otherwise be considered to be a source of competent health and safety advice under the Management of Health and Safety at Work Regulations.

9.3.1   Prohibitions

Part 3 of the regulations prohibit the importation, supply, use and reuse of all types of asbestos, as articles or substances for use at work, and also prohibit the supply of products containing them. Further restrictions prevent their use for the manufacture and repair of any product. Any existing products that contain asbestos should be properly disposed of.

If, for example during a refurbishment, asbestos-cement sheeting is removed from the roof of a building, it cannot be sold or given away. It must be disposed of properly.

It is important to note that the requirements of the REACH Regulations may apply in circumstances where items of plant and machinery, which have an asbestos content, are being sold or moved.

9.4   Types of asbestos

Asbestos is a naturally occurring fibrous silicate mineral material, which does not burn, is resistant to most acids and alkalis, does not dissolve in water or evaporate, and is mechanically strong.

The fire protection, insulating properties and its resistance to chemical and biological degradation were the main reasons for its use over the years in the building trade. The vast quantities that were available meant it was also an economical building resource for many countries around the world.

CAR apply to all asbestos types, but the three predominately used in the UK construction industry are shown below.

1.   Chrysotile (white).

2.   Amosite/grunerite (brown).

3.   Crocidolite (blue).

Although the colours are often quoted to differentiate between the types of asbestos when in its natural form, the actual colour of a material suspected of containing asbestos is not an accurate indication as to whether or not it contains asbestos, or what type of asbestos is in the material; or, if it is, of what type.

Only laboratory testing can definitively prove that a material is asbestos and confirm what type.

Asbestos mining

🚫 **It is impossible to rely on colour or appearance to identify different types of asbestos. This can only be ascertained by laboratory analysis.**

Asbestos fire blanket

Asbestos (AIB) panels at high level

Damaged, spray-applied asbestos acoustic ceiling material

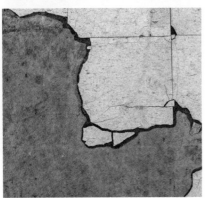

Asbestos floor tiles

Asbestos soffit

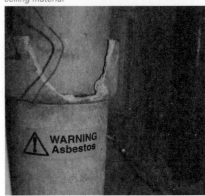

Damaged asbestos flue

Changes in colour may occur due to the following.

- It ageing or simply becoming dirty.
- The effects of heat.
- Surface coatings or dyes being applied.
- Encapsulation.
- Oil or chemical splashes.

It is important to ensure that a full depth sample is taken whenever materials are suspected of containing asbestos. In the case of lagging of boilers and pipework this can be particularly difficult, as differing layers may have different contents. Repairs and modifications can mean that boilers or pipework may be lagged by a mixture of different types of asbestos, and it was widely used as fire protection in building materials, for thermal insulation and also as a sprayed coating to steel structural members. All of these uses now present significant management issues associated with the maintenance of the asbestos over the remaining life span of the building, or the removal of the asbestos during renovation, refurbishment or demolition. Safe working in situations where asbestos might be exposed or damaged demands stringent control, and compliance with recommended precautionary measures and methods of work. These are detailed in the Approved Code of Practice (ACoP) *Work with materials containing asbestos* and CAR.

 The HSE publication *Asbestos: the licensed contractors' guide* (HSG247) provides specific guidance for high-risk (licensed) asbestos work.

9.5 Locating asbestos

This is often a job for an asbestos surveyor, and it can be difficult, as the appearance may be changed by surface coatings, heat or ageing. It may also be encapsulated by, or be concealed beneath, other materials, particularly if removal was carried out to a poor standard in the past. However, original plans or specifications may help to confirm its presence. It is important to note that it might have been introduced to properties through historic maintenance and refurbishment, and it will not always be possible or practicable to locate all asbestos within a building. If it was constructed or refurbished prior to the year 2000, there is a strong probability that it may contain asbestos. The asbestos industry estimates that over 3,500 products have been produced with asbestos content, many of which have been used for a variety of reasons within construction. Its high tensile strength made it ideal for incorporation into fabrics and yarns. This quality also made it a perfect binding material with cement and other matrices.

9.5.1 Products that asbestos can be found in

The following items are an example of the types of products that asbestos can be found in.

9.5.1.1 Insulation and sprayed coatings using moulded or pre-formed lagging

- Boilers, plant and pipework.
- Fire protection to steel work.
- Thermal and acoustic insulation of buildings, including loose packing.

9.5.1.2 Insulation board

- Fire protection to doors.
- Claddings on walls and ceilings.
- Partitioning.
- Ceiling tiles.
- Fire breaks in ceiling voids.
- Electrical equipment and service risers.
- General building board.

9.5.1.3 Asbestos cement

- Corrugated roof sheets.
- Flat sheets for cladding and partitions.
- Roof and rainwater drainage goods.
- Underground pipes.
- Bath panels.
- Artificial roof slates.
- Flue pipe.
- General building board.

9.5.1.4 Other materials

- Vinyl or thermoplastic floor tiles.
- Insulation of electrical equipment.
- Some textured coatings.
- Bakelite sanitary ware, and other products.
- Bitumen.

Asbestos-based friction materials were widely used in brake and clutch linings in vehicles and plant, including lift equipment, together with gaskets and packing in engines and heating or ventilation systems. Substitute materials have been developed in most cases.

 For further information on places and materials that can contain asbestos refer to Appendix C.

09

9.6   Duty to manage

This is perhaps the most important part of CAR for the long-term protection of the health of employees and others. It states that any person who owns, occupies, manages or has responsibility for part or all of non-domestic premises that may contain asbestos has a legal duty to manage the risk from asbestos or ACMs within those premises, or co-operate with whoever has the duty to manage the risk.

It should be noted that domestic housing that is owned and/or managed by Local Authorities, housing associations, or similar is deemed to be non-domestic property and therefore the duty to manage under the regulations will not apply to the owner or manager. However, the common parts of blocks they control are deemed to be within scope of the requirements of Regulation 4 of CAR 2012.

 It should also be noted that although Regulation 4 of CAR does not apply wherever maintenance or refurbishment work is planned in any property, including domestic dwellings, Regulation 5 places an obligation on the employer to identify asbestos before work starts, regardless of whether the requirements of Regulation 4 apply.

 The HSE has revised the ACoP *L143 Managing and working with asbestos*. This contains updated information about the requirements to manage asbestos under Regulation 4 of CAR 2012.

The requirements of the duty to manage can be a shared responsibility depending upon contractual requirements. In the construction industry when taking possession of a site you are likely to be taking on an element of duty holder responsibilities. Responsibility may also change during the contract, as work progresses. A contractor in charge of a site during development is likely to be the duty holder.

 The HSE publication *Managing asbestos in buildings – A brief guide* provides simple precautions to be undertaken, explains the duty to manage in general terms, and is available as a free download.

If you have any maintenance and/or repair responsibilities for non-domestic premises, either through a contract or a temporary agreement, or because you own or occupy the premises, then you have a duty to manage. It is important to note that the responsibility can be shared, and several people could have duty holder responsibilities at any time. Your duty will require you to manage the risk from asbestos by the following.

Asbestos insulating board (AIB)

Asbestos panels

1. Find out if there is any asbestos or suspected ACMs in the premises, how much of it there is, where it is and what condition it is in.

   Note: if work will be carried out that will disturb the fabric of pre-2000 premises, an appropriate asbestos survey must be carried out by a competent person, as outlined in the HSE publication Asbestos: the survey guide *(HSG264). There are now two types of survey:*

   – management survey   *– refurbishment or demolition survey.*

   (These are treated as two different survey types by many surveying organisations. Refer to Appendix A for further details of commissioning a competent asbestos surveyor to carry out a suitable survey.)

   Prior to any refurbishment or demolition work, it is a client's duty to ensure an invasive refurbishment or demolition asbestos survey is undertaken in accordance with HSG264. It is important to ensure that this survey has considered the work planned and is reviewed should the work change, to ensure it provides an appropriate record of asbestos materials.

2. Always presume that it is asbestos or an ACM unless you know or you have strong evidence proving otherwise.

   Note: it is better to overprotect than to expose employees and others to asbestos.

3. Make, and keep up-to-date, a record (an asbestos register) of the location and condition of all the asbestos, ACMs or presumed ACMs in your premises.

   Note: a plan of the premises showing where the materials are will always be extremely useful, and will be essential in larger premises. Such a plan would form an integral part of the ongoing management of the asbestos or ACM. Where applicable, details of asbestos should also be added to the health and safety file.

4. Assess the risk that the materials pose to employees and others.

   *Note: a risk assessment should be undertaken by a competent person who has sufficient knowledge of the subject. If the materials are in good condition, not liable to be damaged, and will not be disturbed or worked on, then the risk is probably low. If the materials are flaky, crumbling or in a place where they can be damaged by, for example, forklift trucks, then the risk is high. Given the known ill health caused by asbestos, a high risk of damage calls for urgent action. When assessing this risk the surveyor may need additional information about how the space containing the ACM will be used. This is known as the **priority assessment**. Completion of this is the responsibility of the duty holder.*

5. Prevent any work on the premises that may disturb asbestos or ACMs until control measures to manage the risk have been put in place.

   Note: this could be work by your employees or any contractors or sub-contractors brought in for carpentry, flooring, partitioning, ceiling fixing, plumbing, electrical, data or telecoms cabling, or other work.

6. Prepare a plan that sets out in detail how you are going to manage the risk from the material.

   Note: if material is not going to be removed by a licensed asbestos removal contractor, consider how you are going to manage the long-term presence of the asbestos. If it is in good condition and not liable to be damaged, then routine inspection and monitoring may be enough if records are kept.

   A sealing coat may be needed, or other protective work necessary, to lower and to further control the risk.

7. Take all of the steps needed to put your plan into action.

   Note: make it happen. What is the organisation, what are the arrangements for the implementation of the plan and who has the responsibility?

8. Review and monitor your plan and the arrangements that you made to put it in place.

   Note: a regular review of the action plan will ensure that it is working, that the control measures are still effective and that inspection, monitoring and recording are in fact taking place.

   It may be the case that procedures, notices and policies that have been in place for a length of time tend to be overlooked. A fresh approach may therefore be needed.

9. Provide information on the location and condition of the material to anyone who is liable to work on it or to disturb it.

   Note: part of this information involves the use of the signs that will have been placed to identify the location of asbestos or ACM.

   In a large workplace or premises, this will also mean keeping a detailed plan of the building or register that describes every individual room or workplace and the asbestos or ACM that is in there. This will inform staff, visiting contractors, maintenance workers and visiting specialists (such as IT data installers) of the areas and features of the building that they must not disturb.

   Wherever possible, it should be ensured that actions are traceable and contractors should sign to confirm they have inspected the register or management plan before starting work.

   Asbestos will pose a significant risk to health if it is in a condition that allows easy release of fibres that can then be inhaled.

10. Ensure that anyone who has information on the whereabouts of asbestos in your premises makes this available to you as a duty holder.

    Note: those who are not duty holders but who control access to the premises (for example, contractors who remove panelling and find what could be asbestos or ACM) have a duty to tell you what they have found. However, you may need to remind them about this duty before they start work.

    Regarding the control of premises, the duty may be with the landlord or management agency. The regulations also impose duties on employers for the protection of employees who may be exposed to asbestos at work, and other persons affected or who may be at risk of being affected by such work. Similar duties are placed on self-employed persons.

11. Provide information to the emergency services.

    Note: in practice this is more important where buildings have large amounts of asbestos products in them. The presence of, for example, one or two rainwater goods products is unlikely to be a major issue.

12. If you are a contractor working on someone else's premises where asbestos is likely to be present, you must be given access to the asbestos register, which must outline the location and condition of known asbestos within the building. You should check that this information is appropriate for your use (for example, it covers all of your work areas) and for your work. If your work involves alterations to the fabric of the building a management survey is unlikely to be suitable.

 If you are not given access to the asbestos register, you should not start any work that will disturb the fabric of the building.

 For a checklist on managing asbestos visit the HSE website.

 Failure to provide asbestos information – Example 1

A building contractor failed to plan, manage and properly monitor the construction work at a school.

He was fined £50,000 and ordered to pay £26,217 after admitting a breach of Section 3(1) of the Health and Safety at Work etc. Act 1974.

After the hearing, the HSE inspector said: 'This was a serious failing on the part of the company.

'Having correctly commissioned an asbestos survey, it looks as though no-one at the company bothered to read it. Or, if they did, they disregarded its contents and failed to act to protect site workers from exposure to what is the single greatest cause of work-related deaths in the construction industry.

'As a result, several people, including the young apprentice, were unnecessarily exposed to the risk of inhaling asbestos fibres. One can only wish and hope that there are no serious consequences for these workers in the future.

'It is vital that companies are fully aware of not just the duty to get an asbestos survey done, but then to act on its findings. There is considerable guidance freely available from the HSE to assist duty holders to deal with asbestos materials properly.'

(Source: HSE)

09

Failure to provide asbestos information – Example 2

A court heard how an employing company failed to ensure that information about the location and condition of asbestos materials was provided to those liable to disturb it. The contractor had conducted the work without carrying out the necessary assessment to determine whether asbestos was present, and had failed to take any measures to prevent the spread of asbestos fibres. The personal involvement of both directors meant that they had also been prosecuted as individuals.

The work carried out by the contractor meant that asbestos debris was scattered over the working area, which exposed workers there, and on neighbouring sites, to a potential health risk. The employing company had to have the site environmentally cleaned.

The contractor was fined a total of £12,000 and ordered to pay £3,804.20 in costs after pleading guilty to breaching Regulations 5(a) and 16 of CAR. The employing company was fined £10,000 with £2,243.40 costs after pleading guilty to breaching Regulation 4 of the same legislation. A director was fined £1,000 and ordered to pay £204.80 in costs after pleading guilty to breaching Regulation 5(a) of the same legislation. A second director was fined £650 (with no order for costs) after pleading guilty to breaching Regulation 16 of the same legislation.

Speaking after the case the HSE inspector said: 'Asbestos is the single greatest cause of work-related deaths in the UK and there is a lot of industry in the area that still uses or occupies premises that have old chemical processing plant dating back to the 60s. Almost all of it was lagged with asbestos in those days. Site operators and contractors working at these sites should always assume that old pipework is lagged with asbestos, unless there is reliable evidence that says otherwise. Those involved in the construction and refurbishment industry also have a clear duty to ensure that work is managed so as to prevent the spread of asbestos.

'This incident occurred because the employing company's asbestos management systems did not include anything relating to informing others of the presence of asbestos on the site. The contractor failed to carry out an asbestos assessment before starting work and did not take any measures to prevent the spread of asbestos fibres. This put the directors themselves, their own employees and others working nearby at risk of exposure to asbestos fibres and the court agreed that both companies were equally culpable for the offences.' *(Source: HSE)*

9.7 Representative sampling

If representative samples are needed for laboratory analysis, they must be taken in a prescribed manner to retain their integrity and the safety of anyone who may handle them. It is a legal requirement that any laboratory carrying out analysis has the necessary facilities, expertise and quality control procedures. Laboratories that meet these standards are accredited under ISO 17025 by the United Kingdom Accreditation Scheme (UKAS).

To confirm or identify the type of asbestos or ACM on the premises, a series of bulk samples may have to be taken for laboratory analysis by a UKAS-accredited laboratory. Methods employed in taking samples of asbestos will vary according to its type and location. HSE guidance on taking samples should be followed.

Anyone removing samples for analysis must be competent to do so and use appropriate protective clothing and respiratory equipment, particularly if the work involves cutting, boring, drilling or otherwise creating airborne dust or fibres.

 Guidance covering licensed asbestos removal, sampling, analysis and clearance procedures is available from the HSE.

9.8 Asbestos surveys

Two types of survey are defined within the HSE publication HSG264.

1. **Management survey.**

2. **Refurbishment or demolition survey.**

To understand the difference between a management and a refurbishment or demolition survey, the simplest explanation is to consider a studwork wall that forms a firebreak. It was originally clad in asbestos insulation board, which was later covered over with plasterboard. In a management survey, the surveyor would correctly identify the outer surface as being plasterboard. However, as there would be no invasive testing, the asbestos would remain undiscovered. An invasive refurbishment or demolition survey would break through the plasterboard and discover the inner asbestos cladding.

Just because the surveyor did not find any asbestos does not mean that no asbestos is present. In all cases it is important to remember that surveying is as much an art as a science. Within some types of building asbestos will only be found by dismantling the building in a controlled manner.

There are also some ACMs that would only be found by luck rather than judgement (for example, asbestos-cement shuttering in a concrete slab, or asbestos insulation board used as packers inside a studwork wall). It is important to be wary of unidentified building products and for everyone to have sufficient asbestos awareness training. Management should be in a position to stop work if necessary and question the presence of any 'funny looking plasterboard' found.

A growing number of UKAS-accredited organisations are treating refurbishment or demolition surveys as two different surveys. A refurbishment survey can and will often be limited in its nature to, for example, a single room or an area where work may be being carried out (for example, the installation of a door opening). Demolition surveys are more encompassing and will require greater surveyor competence. The skillset required for the simple refurbishment survey in a house will be different to the skillset required to conduct a demolition survey of an office complex. This differentiation in the survey types is present to help clients understand the differences in the complexity of the works.

It is important to consider the type of building, especially system build properties, where information about concealed ACMs can be found on similar types of property. In such an instance, it could be reasonable to assume that ACMs will be in similar locations to that of a surveyed property. It is also important to note that other trades might be required when undertaking these surveys (such as lift engineers, electricians and specialist access contractors). These elements should be considered in any survey plan and cost proposal.

The HSE strongly recommends the use of UKAS-accredited organisations to carry out asbestos surveys. It is the employer's responsibility to ensure surveying organisations are competent. This can be achieved by the use of UKAS-accredited organisations. If the employer chooses a non-accredited organisation they should keep records of the checks undertaken to assess competence.

 Refer to Appendix A for further details on asbestos surveys.

9.9   Working with asbestos

The following is a brief overview of the main requirements of the regulations, as they are likely to affect the readers of this chapter, as opposed to the detail of the much more stringent requirements that affect asbestos-removal contractors and others whose business involves working with asbestos.

 The HSE website provides comprehensive and understandable guidance on the types of work methods to be used.

An employer or self-employed person who is required to carry out any work in a building or structure must ensure the following.

- Have appropriate awareness training, as detailed in CAR Regulation 10.

- Make a suitable and sufficient assessment as to whether asbestos is, or is liable to be, present in the premises where work is being carried out. Under CDM, the client has a duty regardless of the size of the project to provide information to the contractor on the known hazards associated with the structure (such as the presence of asbestos).

- Note that:
  - this information should normally be in the form of refurbishment or demolition surveys, as defined in HSG264 for most invasive construction work
  - any existing information on the presence of asbestos, supplied by the client based on a management survey, must be closely scrutinised to ensure that the construction work will not disturb more of the structure than the surveyor checked (do not regard a management survey as appropriate for any construction work; a management survey is for occupation and day-to-day operational needs, not construction needs). Asbestos surveys typically focus on buildings so it is important that other areas (such as external ducts) are considered within any survey.

- Identify that the material does not contain asbestos or assume it contains brown or blue asbestos if not known (fail-safe system).

- A competent person carries out an assessment to decide the likely exposure for the proposed work methods and if the work will, therefore, be licensable or non-licensed.

- Prepare a suitable written plan of work.

- Provide adequate information, instruction and training for employees and others.

- Training is repeated on an annual basis for any work with asbestos.

- When working with asbestos, prevent or reduce asbestos exposure to the lowest level reasonably practicable by means other than the use of RPE (for example, use an asbestos H class vacuum cleaner (BS 8520-3:2009) or other fibre suppression techniques (BS 8520-1:2009)).

- When working with asbestos, the proper use of RPE and that face-fit testing is carried out (minimum FFP3 or P3 filter).

- When working with asbestos, maintain respiratory equipment in a clean and efficient state, good order and repair. Regularly examine and test exhaust ventilation equipment (BS 8520-2:2009).

- Provide adequate and suitable protective clothing (minimum Type 5/6 overall) and ensure that it is cleaned or disposed of appropriately.

- Prevent the spread of asbestos from the workplace.

- Premises and plant involved in work with asbestos are kept clean.

- Monitor the air where employees are exposed to asbestos and keep suitable records for a specific period.

09

ASBESTOS

- Provide medical surveillance of staff, where necessary, and retain records for a period of 40 years.
- Air monitoring is only carried out by an accredited laboratory.
- Provide washing and changing facilities that are adequate and suitable for employees exposed to asbestos and provide storage for protective clothing and personal clothing (not worn during working hours).
- Regulate raw asbestos, asbestos waste storage and disposal, ensuring adequate packaging, sealing and marking in accordance with the regulations.

(For further information refer to 9.14 Asbestos waste.)

Simon's Story:
Living with an asbestos related disease

 View the video *Simon's Story: Living with an asbestos related disease* on CITB's YouTube page.

Working with an expired asbestos licence

An asbestos removal contractor was fined £15,000 and ordered to pay £4,000 in costs after admitting breaching Regulation 8(1) of CAR. After the hearing the HSE inspector said: 'The contractor obviously decided to ignore the fact that its asbestos licence had expired and also that the application to renew had been refused. Instead it carried on regardless and went ahead with work at the premises, removing a ceiling that contained asbestos insulation board. When the contractor's licence expired, the firm should have ceased to carry out any work with asbestos-containing materials that is required by licence. The company were fully aware of what types of activities are covered and knew perfectly well that it was illegal to undertake the work they did'. *(Source: HSE)*

Property developer guilty of exposing employees to asbestos

A property developer pleaded guilty to a total of 12 breaches, including exposing employees to asbestos. He was sentenced to eight months in prison, suspended for two years, for the breach of the prohibition notice. He was also fined £55,000 and ordered to pay a further £45,000 in costs. The court was told that the defendant disregarded the presence of asbestos insulation board at the site of a former school. He knew the potentially dangerous material formed part of the pre-fabricated buildings on the site, but ignored advice on its safe removal.

The HSE visited the school, which was being converted into a retirement complex, during a construction safety initiative. An inspector identified the type of building known to contain asbestos, and gave the defendant advice on what he needed to do to comply with the relevant legislation surrounding its removal.

Eight days later, the HSE received a complaint from a member of the public advising that the asbestos was not being removed properly. The contractor was told to have surveys carried out and to arrange for the licensed removal of the material. However, when inspectors later re-visited the site they found building rubble containing asbestos that had not been properly disposed of. A prohibition notice was immediately served to stop all work with, or liable to disturb, the material asbestos and a direction to 'Leave undisturbed' was imposed on the piles of contaminated rubble.

HSE inspectors made a third unannounced visit later that year and found workers in breach of the prohibition notice. They found two workers putting asbestos insulation board into a lockable skip and dry sweeping the dust, which resulted in large clouds of contaminated dust billowing across the site. Work was again stopped until arrangements were made for safe and proper removal of the asbestos materials.

The court heard that although employees had been wearing disposable overalls and face masks, no other controls were in place, so not enough was done to protect them from the risk of exposure. Dust would have contaminated their clothes and there was no water on site to enable decontamination. The asbestos-containing material should have been dampened down and double-bagged in special bags, before being removed by a licensed contractor. High efficiency vacuum cleaners should then have been used to remove smaller pieces of asbestos and dust, rather than a broom.

Speaking after the hearing, the HSE inspector said: 'The defendant showed a wilful disregard for the health and safety of his employees and others. Our investigation uncovered a catalogue of serious errors, safety failings and a general ignorance of the laws around the safe and correct removal of asbestos. This was an appalling case of failing to properly plan, manage and resource this project, which led to workers being exposed to risks to their health from asbestos. Workers who have been exposed to asbestos could have posed a health risk to others in the long-term, even their families and loved ones, by taking home their contaminated clothing. Asbestos is the single greatest cause of work-related deaths in the UK. Building owners and contractors have a duty to ensure they protect their workers from risk of exposure. The defendant failed in that duty by choosing to ignore the dangers of this hidden killer'. *(Source: HSE)*

For a summary of ways to prevent exposure to asbestos, which can be given as a toolbox talk, refer to Appendix B.

9.9.1 Medical surveillance

Asbestos removal contractors must ensure that their employees, who are liable to be exposed to asbestos above the control limit, are under regular medical surveillance by an HSE-appointed doctor; the local HSE office can supply the names of the appointed doctors who are able to carry out this specialist health surveillance.

Medical examinations should be provided before work with asbestos starts and at prescribed periods thereafter, currently every two years.

Health records containing information on medical examinations have to be maintained and kept for 40 years after the date of the last entry.

9.9.2 Washing and changing facilities

Asbestos removal contractors must provide adequate and suitable washing and changing facilities for their employees.

Where protective clothing and respiratory equipment are in use, storage must be provided for contaminated items. Separate storage must be provided for personal clothing not worn during working hours.

The hygiene facilities (decontamination unit) are usually mobile units with three compartments: a dirty room, a shower room (with one or more showers) and a clean room.

They should always be accompanied with the appropriate test certificates (electric, gas, dioctyl phthalate, and so on) and have a clean air-test certificate from the previous job (unless it's a new unit).

9.10 Licensed and non-licensed work

All work with asbestos must comply with CAR. Some materials are licensed because they present a high risk and require the use of licensed contractors. Other work is deemed lower risk and therefore lower levels of control and requirement apply.

CAR has a hierarchical approach to asbestos controls and, based upon this approach, identifies three categories of asbestos removal work.

1. **Licensed asbestos work.** Applies to the highest risk materials.

2. **Notifiable non-licensed asbestos work (NNLW).**

3. **Non-licensed asbestos work.** Applies to the lowest risk materials.

 For guidance visit the HSE website for advice on work with asbestos.

9.10.1 Licensed work

The regulations prohibit the removal or work on all types of sprayed asbestos, asbestos insulation, asbestos coating and asbestos insulation board, unless it is carried out by a company holding a licence granted by the HSE.

● An exception is made in the case of repair or maintenance work of short duration.

● An assessment made by a competent person will determine whether work should be licensed.

● Work with most other forms of ACM will not generally require a licensed contractor.

● A licence is not required for undertaking sample collection, analysis or air monitoring.

The decision on whether work is licensed or not licensed is the responsibility of the contractor undertaking the work (not the client). In some instances a licensed asbestos removal contractor may choose to notify work in order to avoid any ambiguity in the notification requirements, or where certainty cannot be guaranteed on the duration of the work.

9.10.2 Licences

There are three types of asbestos licence.

1. **Full removal licence** normally held by a licensed contractor.

2. **Supervisory licence** required where a third party actively supervises the work. A client, principal or main contractor does not need one. This type of licence is gradually being phased out as unnecessary. This is not to be confused with laboratories or consultants undertaking monitoring of contractor performance, who do not need a licence for these activities.

3. **Ancillary licence** needed to carry out work associated with the main asbestos removal work, typically by scaffold companies who erect scaffolds to form enclosures for licensed asbestos removal work. A separate notification must be sent to the HSE by the company carrying out the ancillary work.

   Companies that service and maintain asbestos removal equipment may also require this type of licence, particularly where there is a high probability of disturbing high-risk asbestos materials.

 All licences for work with asbestos insulation, AIB or asbestos coatings are granted by the licensing unit of the HSE.

ASBESTOS

A new asbestos licence will last one year and, upon renewal, it may, depending on performance, be renewed for a period of three years. However, this is not guaranteed and the HSE can grant licences of any duration, up to three years. The HSE can revoke the licence completely, shorten the term of the licence or impose extra conditions on the licence. It is good practice to look at the licence held by a licensed contractor and question the period of its validity, along with any conditions.

Licensing conditions are not obvious on a licence so you may need to ask the contractor to clarify the conditions that are applicable. Many conditions are standard but some contractors can have special conditions applied to the licence that may restrict the type of work they can undertake.

9.10.3   Notification of work with asbestos

Licensed asbestos removal contractors are required to notify the HSE or Local Authority (whichever is the enforcing authority) of all proposed licensed work at least 14 days in advance, using the ASB5 form. Where a scaffold is to be built, that will be used to give access to a workplace where asbestos will be removed or will provide a working platform, then the scaffold contractor may need to be an ancillary licensed contractor.

 Notification is not an approval of the work by the HSE.

The HSE uses notifications, along with contractor information, to undertake focused site visits based on contractor performance and risk.

In an emergency, it is sometimes possible to obtain a dispensation (waiver) from the 14-day period of notification. This should be discussed with the proposed licensed contractor. However, these dispensations are only available for emergencies and should not be applied for as a result of bad planning.

All questions on the removal of asbestos should be referred either to the HSE or a competent person.

 Details of where to find competent advice can be found in Appendix A.

The unlicensed removal of asbestos, as well as being an offence under the regulations and potentially subject to a prison sentence, may also expose employees and others to high levels of airborne asbestos fibres and the subsequent risk of later ill health.

9.10.4   Notifiable non-licensed work

Work that will normally fall into this category may involve minor work on low-risk materials that are already in a poor condition (for example, a textured coating ceiling affected by fire or flood), or those where the materials are likely to deteriorate during work (such as falling fragile asbestos-cement sheeting).

Other examples include involving the repair of asbestos insulation, minor work with AIB that meets the short duration criteria, maintenance of and removal of damaged asbestos-cement and removal work of decorative coatings that contain ACM.

A contractor who does not hold an asbestos licence may normally carry out work with certain low-risk asbestos products in situations where the planned exposure is sporadic and low intensity, and will not exceed the control limits (0.1 fibres/cm^3 in four hours or 0.6 fibres/cm^3 in ten minutes).

Any measurements required to check the exposure limit must be carried out by a UKAS-accredited laboratory and should not take into account the effect of any RPE used.

Since April 2015, if a job is notifiable non-licensed work (NNLW) it must be done by persons who have had a medical examination in line with the requirements in the law.

 Notification of this type of work will be necessary. Once you have confirmed the work is NNLW, you need to notify it to the relevant enforcing authority. Do this using the online notification form.

The online notification form is the only method of notification. You cannot notify by phone or post.

Notice should be given before the work starts – there is no minimum notice period. You do not need to wait for permission from the enforcing authority – the database will provide a PDF copy of your notification. A licensed asbestos contractor carrying out NNLW work will still need to notify.

 Any other work with ACMs is subject to the requirements of CAR and may require an asbestos licence.

9.10.5   Non-licensed work

Work that will normally fall into this category is work that is not licensed or is not NNLW. Some materials can be both NNLW and non-licensed. For example, where a textured decorative finish has been applied to a concrete surface the work will be NNLW, as to remove the material requires its deterioration, whereas the same material applied to a plasterboard finish will be non-licensed as it can be removed intact with the plasterboard.

09

The key distinction is whether the material is already in a less than good condition and whether, during the removal work, the material is likely to suffer further deterioration or degradation.

 Where employers are considering undertaking small works themselves, they should read the relevant HSE publications and ensure they have appropriate insurance cover in place.

There is an absolute requirement for anyone who undertakes any work with asbestos to have received practical training within the preceding 12 months for the tasks they will be performing, and more frequently if the method or equipment used changes.

The following products are likely to fall into non-licensed work.

- Short, non-continuous work with asbestos insulating board (attaching cables, cleaning light fittings and lifting ceiling tiles for inspection).
- Short, non-continuous maintenance and removal work with asbestos cement that is in good condition.
- Short, non-continuous work with decorative coatings (drilling and fixing screws).

The work itself must meet one of the four following conditions.

1. A short, non-continuous maintenance task, with only non-friable materials (materials that will only release a small number of fibres during work).

2. A removal task where ACMs are in a reasonable condition and will remain in a firmly contained matrix (for example, the asbestos will remain coated, covered or contained in a material such as cement, paint or plastic).

3. A task where the ACMs are in a good condition and are being encapsulated or sealed to ensure they are not easily damaged in the future.

4. An air monitoring or control task to gather samples for analytical work.

Asbestos insulation board

 For advice and examples of non-licensed work on asbestos visit the HSE website.

Non-licensed work does not require the following.

- Notification to the relevant enforcing authority.
- A licensed contractor to carry it out.
- Asbestos medicals or health records for the workers doing it.
- Specific emergency procedures.
- The area around the work to be identified as an asbestos area.

 The HSE publication *Asbestos: The licensed contractors' guide* (HSG247) provides comprehensive practical guidance on how a licensed asbestos removal contractor should work.

09

9.11   Assessment prior to the removal of asbestos

In the planning phase, and before carrying out any work involving asbestos or ACMs, including minor repairs, the employer must make an assessment to determine the following.

- Type of work and its possible duration.
- Type and quantity of asbestos involved (using analysis results if available) and if more than one type of asbestos is present.
- Likely nature and degree of exposure to the asbestos.
- Steps that need to be taken to prevent or reduce such exposure to asbestos (the control measures).
- Procedures for the removal of any waste from the site.
- Procedures in place for dealing with any emergencies.
- Reasons for the choice of the proposed work method.

Some of the information should come from the asbestos management plan for the building. This may be augmented, if necessary, with additional survey work. Under CDM, the client has a duty to provide information on the presence of asbestos. These requirements will be the responsibility of the contractor when working upon domestic premises. However, in the case of the Local Authority or housing associations, some of this information may already be available.

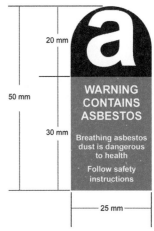

Asbestos warning label

The assessment should be prepared in writing, including where it is for maintenance, repair or small-scale work involving:

● the handling of existing pre-formed and package bonded asbestos materials in situ

● small-scale repair or maintenance work not involving the cutting or breaking of asbestos or ACMs.

A competent person with adequate knowledge of the job should carry out the assessment. Where work is of a repetitive nature, covering various locations within a building or site, then a single assessment may be sufficient.

When planning any asbestos removal it is important to consider what might be present behind the ACM. For example, if removing plasterboard that has been covered with an asbestos-containing textured finish, what would happen if asbestos lagged pipes were present in the ceiling void?

The assessment should also consider what additional risks could be present (for example, electrical risks if working on ceiling tiles).

Large quantities of asbestos board were previously used within premises to form fire compartments. Where clients are planning the removal of these materials, consideration should be given to the potential impact that this could have upon the building and its fire protection.

9.11.1 Designated areas

Where licensed asbestos contractors are working, designated areas may be created (such as one or more asbestos area and respirator zone).

In most situations, the asbestos area and respirator zone will be the same. However, in certain circumstances, there may only be an asbestos area, where the control limits are not exceeded (for example, a transit route/waste route for asbestos). It is advisable to exclude non-essential persons from this asbestos area. Where this is not possible, appropriate monitoring should be undertaken.

9.11.2 Asbestos areas

Where a licensed asbestos removal contractor is undertaking the removal of asbestos, in order to ensure that people other than those involved in asbestos work are not exposed to asbestos by entering asbestos areas, such areas should be designated and clearly identified, using notices that meet the requirements of the Health and Safety (Safety Signs and Signals) Regulations.

9.11.3 Respirator zones

Areas where the removal contractors are working, and where control limits for exposure to airborne fibres are liable to be exceeded, will be designated as respirator zones to ensure that only removal contractors wearing RPE are allowed to enter.

 Workers exposed to asbestos during refurbishment work

A cladding installation business owner was fined after he exposed workers to a potentially fatal risk from airborne asbestos fibres at a house.

The employer instructed an employee and a casual labourer to remove and replace soffit boards during refurbishment work at a property. The Magistrates' Court, however, heard that the employer had not carried out a suitable survey in advance to determine whether asbestos was present and did not hold a licence to undertake work with the dangerous material.

A neighbour informed the employer that the soffits were made of asbestos insulating board, but he allowed work to carry on. A complaint was made to the HSE and an inspector visited the site and immediately halted further work.

The HSE investigation found the employer was aware from some of his previous jobs that soffit boards may contain asbestos but had not taken this into account when assessing this job. He had also failed to provide information and training to workers who could be exposed to asbestos fibres. The employer was fined £7,015 and ordered to pay £3,200 in costs after pleading guilty to four breaches of CAR.

After the hearing an HSE inspector said: '[The employer], as a person running a cladding installation business, should have been in no doubt about the dangers posed by asbestos and of the regulations governing work with this material. Despite this, he progressed this work without testing the material to be removed for the presence of asbestos. This resulted in those working there being exposed to risk of inhaling airborne asbestos fibres without taking any suitable precautions.

'This incident was entirely preventable and highlights the importance of having a robust asbestos management system in place. Duty holders should identify the type, location and condition of all asbestos-containing materials, and establish appropriate precautions, before starting removal operations.

'This is all the more important for this type of higher risk notifiable work, which should only have been performed by a licensed contractor.' *(Source: HSE)*

9.12 Air monitoring

The HSE strongly recommends that the client of the licensed contractor, rather than the licensed contractor, appoints the UKAS analysts who will carry out any **air monitoring**. It is felt that this is likely to give a greater degree of independence.

The HSE is currently undertaking a research project into these types of contractual relationships and the impact they have upon quality. Evidence suggests that the quality of final work is improved where the analyst has been employed by the client, and this is increased further where the analyst acts in a management or supervisory capacity for the client.

The analyst is one of the few people, apart from the contractor, with the necessary skills and equipment to enable them to enter a live asbestos enclosure, if required.

There are various types of monitoring that can be performed. The analysts carrying out the air monitoring must either hold the Royal Society for Public Health (RSPH) Certificate for Asbestos Analysts (Air) or the British Occupational Hygiene Society P403 and P404 certificates.

Background monitoring is usually carried out before any asbestos removal work starts to enable the fibre concentration to be measured and any possible problems identified.

Static monitoring can be carried out during work with asbestos. Typically, this will be outside the asbestos enclosure to demonstrate that there are no leaks (leak monitoring), or it may be performed on the site boundary during work with asbestos cement to show that there is no off-site fibre emission.

Personal monitoring may be carried out for two reasons.

1. Specifically to demonstrate that the RPE being used is effective.

2. To measure the fibre levels that whoever is carrying out the work with asbestos is being exposed to.

It would be important to discuss what type of personal monitoring is required with the UKAS analyst, as the monitoring strategy would be different.

Any employer or self-employed person must monitor the exposure during work with asbestos unless they know that the exposure will not exceed the control limit, or they have access to other ways of showing what the level of exposure is. This may be done by referring to previous monitoring.

Air monitoring, to reduce the risks from the spread of asbestos, is required for the following reasons.

- Measure the background concentration of asbestos fibres in the work area during work.
- Check that control measures are effective.
- Measure background fibre levels outside the enclosure, particularly when the enclosure is in occupied premises.
- Check for fibre leaks around the perimeter of the enclosure and at the air lock and bag lock positions.
- Conduct testing at the discharge location of the air extraction equipment, where it is sited internally.
- Measure the background fibre levels inside the enclosure when the asbestos work is complete, to ensure that it has been thoroughly cleaned and decontaminated before dismantling.
- Carry out measurements for reassurance (for example, after accidental release of asbestos fibres).

For non-licensed and notifiable non-licensed work asbestos monitoring can be used to confirm that effective controls are in place. Examples of appropriate monitoring would include perimeter monitoring during asbestos-cement sheeting removal or monitoring within dwellings that are to be occupied immediately after floor tile removal.

This data can be used to reassure occupiers or those in the immediate vicinity of the work.

Where licensed asbestos work is being undertaken, consideration should be given to the need for monitoring to determine the effectiveness of controls. Prior to the commencement of any work, the asbestos enclosure should be subject to a smoke test to ensure the adequacy of the containment measures.

Where possible, this should be witnessed by a third party (such as the analyst), who will undertake subsequent monitoring of the work.

Where work is going to result in the removal of friable asbestos or is in areas where building occupants or other trades may be present, consideration should be given to leak monitoring outside of the enclosure.

This monitoring is designed to identify when asbestos fibres are escaping from enclosures as a result of containment failures, or failures in decontamination procedures.

Monitoring should also be undertaken within the asbestos work area to ensure that controls on fibre release are effective and in accordance with the contractor's plan of the work.

09

9.13   Certificate of reoccupation

A certificate of reoccupation is testing undertaken following the encapsulation and removal of ACMs within an enclosure. This is a four-stage process and is sometimes referred to as a *four stage*.

The importance of ensuring that a previously contaminated area is totally clear of asbestos before reoccupation cannot be stressed too strongly. The wellbeing of everyone who will occupy the premises is dependent upon it.

The Control of Asbestos Regulations require that anyone who certifies premises as being safe to reoccupy following licensed asbestos work must be accredited by an appropriate body as competent to carry out such work.

Organisations accredited under UKAS to ISO/IEC 17025 will have appropriate quality management schemes in place.

Clearance monitoring is carried out as part of the four-stage clearance.

1. Verification of work through document review.

2. Visual inspection of the enclosure, waste and transit routes (to ensure no visible asbestos remains).

3. Disturbed air tests in the enclosure to ensure the levels are <0.01 fibres/cm^3.

4. Subject to satisfactory previous stages, a post enclosure removal inspection.

These stages involve the analyst following a set procedure of looking at the site set-up and the cleanliness of the asbestos enclosure and asbestos decontamination unit.

Having completed a detailed visual inspection (which is likely to include a search on hands and knees), the analyst carries out an air monitoring clearance test.

This will include vigorously brushing the floor, and surfaces around each air monitoring pump, to disturb any trapped asbestos. The analyst then allows the removal contractor to take down the enclosure before a final visual check of the area is undertaken. **A certificate of reoccupation is then issued.**

Finally, prior to the decontamination/hygiene unit leaving site, it is inspected and air tested to ensure the asbestos levels are less than 0.01 fibres/cm^3, followed by a UKAS analyst leaving an air test certificate in the clean end of the unit.

It is important to review these documents and add any additional information to the management plan. It is also important to note areas where asbestos has not been removed, for whatever reason (for example, where insulation material has to be left in situ where pipes pass through walls).

The HSE is currently undertaking a project within the asbestos industry, looking at the quality of work and links to contractual relationships. Evidence has indicated that, where appointed directly by the client, the quality of the work is completed to a higher standard.

 The HSE strongly recommends that the organisation undertaking this monitoring is appointed independently of the asbestos removal contractor.

9.14   Asbestos waste

There are slight differences in the respective legislation for England and Wales, Northern Ireland and Scotland. Contractors who work in any of these areas must comply with the relevant national legislation. In essence, there is a duty of care put on everyone in the waste disposal chain.

Clients, whether they are at work or domestic, have a responsibility to ensure that the waste is disposed of correctly. You can be prosecuted if waste is fly-tipped.

Where asbestos has been removed as part of a project, a prudent contractor would ensure that proof of disposal formed part of the information that was given to the client.

In England, where a site waste management plan or demolition audit is utilised, it should include details of the disposal of the asbestos waste and the waste carrier.

The principal contractor should ensure that disposal records are passed to the principal designer to ensure that this information is placed in the health and safety file to confirm that the asbestos has been transported and disposed of legally.

 For further information on asbestos waste refer to Chapter E10 Waste and material management.

9.15 Training

The regulations have a framework of training requirements, based upon risk of exposure. The training needs to be appropriate for the work and the roles undertaken by individuals. There are three types of asbestos training.

1. Awareness training.

2. Training for work with asbestos that does not require a licence from the HSE. It includes practical training based on the tasks to be performed.

3. Training for asbestos work that does require a licence from the HSE. It includes practical training based on the tasks to be performed.

9.15.1 Awareness training

This training is for persons who are liable to disturb asbestos while carrying out their normal everyday work, or those who may influence how work is carried out. This could include, for example, general maintenance staff, electricians, plumbers, gas fitters, painters and decorators, joiners, plasterers, demolition workers, construction workers, roofers, heating and ventilation engineers, telecommunications engineers, fire and burglar alarm installers, computer installers, architects, building surveyors and other such professionals. However, this list is not exhaustive, and there are other occupations that are liable to disturb asbestos in addition to those listed.

Training should, in the first instance, be delivered in a classroom environment. It should then be supplemented with e-learning or toolbox talks, and updated as regulations and requirements change. It may also be prudent, on sites where asbestos is present and construction work is planned, to have site-specific asbestos awareness training incorporated into site induction processes.

9.15.2 Asbestos work that does not require a licence (non-licensed asbestos work)

This training is for workers who plan to carry out any work with asbestos that does not require a licence and who may knowingly disturb lower risk ACMs. It should be provided in addition to asbestos awareness training and should be job specific. Typically, workers who may need this training include those listed under asbestos awareness training, and who carry out tasks on site such as the following.

- Drilling holes in asbestos materials (including for sampling and analysis purposes).

- Laying cables in areas containing undamaged asbestos materials.

- Removing asbestos-containing floor tiles.

- Cleaning or repairing asbestos-cement sheet roofing or cladding.

Topics covered by this type of training are shown below.

- How to make suitable and sufficient assessments about the risk of exposure to asbestos.

- Safe working practices and control measures, including an explanation on the correct use of control measures, protective equipment and work methods.

- Selection and appropriate use of protective equipment.

- Waste handling procedures.

- Emergency procedures.

- Relevant legal requirements.

This training should incorporate elements of both classroom-based training and practical training for the tasks that will be performed. Any training programme for employees undertaking this work will also need to consider refresher training.

9.15.3 Asbestos work that does require a licence (licensed asbestos work)

Most work with higher risk ACMs must be carried out by licensed contractors. Only suitably trained workers, using appropriate RPE and who are under suitable medical surveillance, can undertake licensed asbestos work. This type of training is therefore required for operatives, supervisors and managers working for a licensed contractor, but note that the training requirements for operatives and supervisors are different. This training should incorporate elements of both classroom-based training and practical training for the tasks that will be performed. Any training programme for employees undertaking this work will also need to consider refresher training.

9.15.4 Refresher awareness

Refresher awareness should not be a repeat of the initial training. It should be given at least once a year and be appropriate to the workers' familiarity with the work. It should be tailored to the work each worker is doing, and be based on training needs analysis (TNA) that will help to decide what is needed. It could be a structured update training session or a short toolbox talk refreshing experienced workers on the main principles and expectations. The training should be tailored and reviewed if, for example, work methods change, the type of equipment used to control exposure changes or the type of work being carried out changes significantly.

09

9.16   Insurance

It is imperative to ensure that anyone who proposes to carry out work with asbestos is insured to do so. In addition to employers' liability insurance, asbestos contractors also usually have public liability insurance for carrying out asbestos work.

Employers' liability insurance provides insurance cover in the event of an injury or death caused to an employee. As such it does not exclude risks but insurers will refuse cover if they discover asbestos work is being carried out that has not been declared on proposal forms.

Public liability insurance is in place to protect members of the public from the acts and omissions of contractors. Unless working with asbestos is specified, this cover will be specifically excluded for almost all construction related public liability insurance policies. It is important to check that this is in place for any contractor who is employed.

If people are insured to work with asbestos it normally states this openly on the insurance documents.

If in doubt you should check with the broker or underwriter of the insurance policy to confirm the mandatory employers' liability insurance covers them for work with asbestos, noting any specific exclusions (for example, non-licensed work only).

There have been instances of roofing contractors working with asbestos cement who created contamination of occupied premises and were not insured for the clean up costs.

When employing contractors to undertake asbestos survey and testing work they must be competent and hold employers' liability and public liability insurances. They must also hold appropriate levels of professional indemnity insurance, which protects clients where the standard of service is below the acceptable threshold.

9.17   Compensation cases

Compensation cases for asbestos-related health consequences continue to increase and considerable publicity has been given to those claimants who would not traditionally be viewed as being exposed to asbestos. Recent cases have been brought by school teachers, former pupils and employees of high-street retailers, who have never been involved in construction.

 Landmark legal victory for the family of a woman who died after low-level exposure at secondary school

The Supreme Court has upheld a £240,000 compensation claim, by a 49-year-old woman, in the first case of a former pupil successfully suing a Local Authority for negligent exposure to the risk of deadly asbestos dust while she was a school pupil in the 1970s. The woman joined the newly built comprehensive school in Knowsley, Merseyside in 1972 at the age of 11 and left in 1979. She was diagnosed as suffering from mesothelioma in March 2007.

As a pupil, she was exposed to asbestos on several occasions. Asbestos insulation ceiling tiles had been taken down and stacked in a busy corridor while electricians worked on cables in the ceiling void, and bullies took children's satchels and blazers and hid them above the ceiling tiles. There had also been vandalism in the girls' toilets, where asbestos ceiling tiles were stacked.

The woman died from malignant mesothelioma in October 2009, just hours after the Court of Appeal ruled she was entitled to compensation. The claim was subject to a number of appeals by the Local Authority. Mercifully, said her family, she did not know of Knowsley Metropolitan Borough Council's intention to appeal.

Lord Justice Sedley said at the Court of Appeal: 'It has to be remembered that where asbestos is involved, a risk of exposure is a risk of harm.'

One of the country's leading mesothelioma consultants gave evidence that: 'Mesothelioma can occur after low-level exposure and there is no known threshold dose below which there is no risk'. *Significant* is defined in accordance with the definition adopted in relation to mesothelioma causation by the Industrial Injuries Advisory Council in their 1996 report (Cm 3467): a level above that commonly found in the air in buildings and the general outdoor environment. It would be appropriate for the court to conclude that each such exposure materially increased the risk that she would develop mesothelioma.' *(Source: HSE)*

 Employee paid undisclosed sum by Marks & Spencer

An employee, who worked for Marks & Spencer between 1978 and 1987, claimed she was exposed to asbestos at the store. At the age of 53, she developed mesothelioma as a result of this exposure. In 2011, Marks & Spencer was fined £1 million as a result of failings during asbestos work.

The HSE stated: 'The court heard that the client, Marks & Spencer plc, did not allocate sufficient time and space for the removal of asbestos-containing materials at the store. The contractors had to work overnight in enclosures on the shop floor, with the aim of completing small areas of asbestos removal before the shop opened to the public each day. The HSE alleged that Marks & Spencer plc failed to ensure that work at the store complied with the appropriate minimum standards set out in legislation and Approved Codes of Practice. The company had produced its own guidance on how asbestos should be removed inside its stores, and the court heard that this guidance was followed by contractors inappropriately during major refurbishment.' *(Source: HSE)*

9.18　Supporting information

The trade associations listed below can provide information on their members (who can demonstrate having met certain standards of performance) and general advice on work with asbestos.

Asbestos Control and Abatement Division (ACAD).

Asbestos Removal Contractors Association (ARCA).

Asbestos Testing and Consulting (ATAC).

 The British Occupational Hygiene Society (BOHS) and the Royal Society for Public Health (RSPH) offer a range of competency training courses for those undertaking asbestos assessments and asbestos monitoring.

The United Kingdom Asbestos Training Association (UKATA) and the Independent Asbestos Training Providers (IATP) are organisations offering membership to other organisations who offer asbestos training to people undertaking asbestos removal activities.

 ## Taking risks with asbestos

Over 5,000 people per annum die as a result of asbestos exposure. It is estimated that over 75% of these deaths have a construction-industry link.

HSE Research Report RR558 outlines the reasons why people still take chances when working with asbestos even though they know the risks. The report highlights the fact that many people deny the importance or relevance of the risk because they think:

- as most asbestos has been removed, there isn't enough around to worry about

- exposure only occurs in extreme cases (such as when handling asbestos lagging)

- some levels of asbestos are actually safe

- new materials (such as MDF) pose a greater risk

- more visible risks (such as working at height) are more important

- contact with asbestos is a lottery – there is always some present.

There are also economic factors and pressure from employers (creating a fuss versus keeping your job) and the lack of safety culture (a failure of the employer to promote safe working practices). However, the Working Well Together (WWT) initiative, in conjunction with commercial organisations and local safety groups, run Safety and Health Awareness Days (SHADs) around the country for SMEs. These raise awareness of asbestos and other hazards encountered when undertaking maintenance work.

 Information on the risks from asbestos can be found on the HSE website.

09

Appendix A – Asbestos surveys in accordance with HSG264

Survey planning

Good planning is essential to ensure the effectiveness of any survey. The level of planning required will largely depend upon the complexity of the structure to be surveyed and the extent of the survey.

As part of the planning process, the client should be clear as to why the survey is needed and what they want to get out of the survey report. Adequate planning, particularly with regard to establishing the areas where the surveyor would need access (to carry out the survey) and overcoming potential access problems, and agreeing the amount of intrusive inspection to be carried out could significantly reduce the number of caveats in the survey report.

It is important that due consideration is given as to why the survey is needed. A management survey, for example, will be sufficient for the occupier's needs to manage asbestos. However, it is unlikely that the same survey will be sufficient for a contractor refurbishing a floor within the building. Therefore, an appropriate refurbishment survey should be conducted, which should be designed around the project's requirements. A demolition survey will focus on the project requirement to demolish the property.

Prior to the survey

1. What the surveyor will need from the client.

- The details of the structure or part of it to be surveyed.
- The structure's use, work processes, known hazards and any priority areas.
- Plans and prior survey reports on design, structure and construction.
- Safety and security information (such as fire alarm testing).
- Access arrangements and any permit systems in operation.
- Contact details of relevant staff for operational or health and safety issues.
- The opportunity to carry out a walk-through inspection of the structure in the interests of familiarisation to enable potential problem areas to be identified.

2. What the client should expect from the surveyor.

- Details of qualifications and experience.
- The significant findings of their risk assessment.
- References from previous work.
- Details of professional indemnity insurance.
- Costs.
- Proposed scope of work.
- Plan of work.
- Timetable of work.
- Details of any caveats (for example, restrictions or limitations in the survey).

After the survey has been completed, the surveyor must supply the client with a comprehensive survey report that includes details of any areas not accessed or surveyed.

Competence of surveyors

The duty holder who commissions the asbestos survey must be satisfied that the prospective surveyor, whether an organisation or an individual, is technically competent to carry out the range of work required and will allocate adequate resources to it.

In line with the principles of CDM, it is essential that searching questions are put to each prospective surveyor to ensure their technical competence will be translated into a satisfactory survey that fully meets the duty holder's requirements. The client can satisfy themselves that these requirements have been met by appointing a UKAS-accredited asbestos surveying organisation.

 For further information on asbestos surveys, refer to the HSE publication *Asbestos: The survey guide* (HSG264).

Alternatively they can check by making reasonable enquires via a two-stage process.

Stage 1. Assess the company's or individual's survey expertise, along with their knowledge of health and safety.

Stage 2. Assess the company's or individual's experience and track record to establish if they are capable of doing the work and that they recognise their limitations.

As a minimum this should entail the following.

- Seeking evidence of their training and experience in such work.
- Confirming that they are qualified and experienced in carrying out the type of work to be done.
- Checking that they are going to carry out the survey in accordance with the HSE guidance contained in *Asbestos: the survey guide* (HSG264).
- Ensuring that at least two surveyors will carry out the survey and that in doing so **they will** be working together.
- Seeking evidence that they have suitable liability insurance.
- Details of quality assurance and audit arrangements.

If choosing to follow this path it is important that evidence of these investigations is retained, in the event that a decision may need to be justified at a later date.

Personal competence

Individuals may be able to demonstrate sufficient competency through a combination of qualifications and experience.

As a minimum, an individual should hold a British Occupational Hygiene Society (BOHS) P402 certificate, or a RSPH asbestos survey qualification, plus a minimum of six months' full-time, relevant, field-based experience, working under the supervision of an experienced and suitably qualified surveyor. Currently, no third-party quality assurance schemes are in operation to validate individual competence.

Corporate competence

Organisations can demonstrate their technical competence to carry out asbestos surveys through accreditation to ISO/IEC 17020, which is the quality standard against which the performance of inspection bodies (such as asbestos surveying companies and analytical laboratories) can be independently assessed. The standard is awarded by UKAS.

Survey risk assessment

Before a survey begins, the risks to the surveyor, sampling staff and others, including the building occupants, must be assessed. The risk assessment would normally be conducted by the asbestos surveyor and should cover asbestos risks and non-asbestos risks. Depending upon the type of survey to be carried out and the nature of the premises, the non-asbestos risks could include the following.

- Working at height.
- Working in confined spaces.
- Noise, vibration and machinery hazards.
- Lone working.
- Electrical and chemical hazards.

The above list is not exhaustive.

Types of survey

Since the introduction of HSG264 there have been two categories of asbestos survey.

Management survey. The purpose of this type of survey is to locate, so far as is reasonably practicable, the presence and extent of any suspected ACMs, which could be damaged or disturbed by daily work (such as normal occupancy and building maintenance). Management surveys will often involve minor intrusive work and some disturbance, and can involve sampling of materials and/or presumptions that asbestos is present.

Management surveys have replaced the older surveys commonly referred to as Type 1 or Type 2 surveys. These surveys may still be appropriate but they often excluded areas where routine maintenance is required (such as false ceiling voids), so it is therefore important to ensure that any report caveats do not exclude these areas. When using or relying on a report it is important to ensure it is robust and up-to-date. This will include ensuring any recommended actions have been completed and that the client has undertaken the necessary re-inspections.

Refurbishment or demolition survey. As its name suggests, this type of survey must be carried out before any refurbishment or demolition is commenced. (It replaces what used to be called the Type 3 survey.) However, this type of survey might also be necessary for other work (such as engineering construction projects).

The survey will locate and describe, as far as is reasonably practicable, all ACMs in the area to be refurbished or the whole structure if it is to be demolished. This type of survey is fully intrusive and involves destructive inspection, as may be necessary, to gain access to all areas, including those that are difficult to reach.

It is important that both the surveyor and client understand the scope of the survey, as the degree of investigation within a survey may differ from a refurbishment project to a demolition project. Refurbishment surveys may be very specific in the areas in which they apply (for example, a survey focused on the installation of a new door opening). It is therefore important that the remit of the survey is clearly understood, especially if the survey is being provided by a third party. This, in part, explains why some organisations treat refurbishment or demolition surveys as two types of survey.

Construction work is rarely fixed so the survey should be reviewed following any revisions to the scope of work.

09

Additional consideration should be applied to demolition sites where work may involve ground work. In these instances it is important to ensure the survey has considered the presence of underground services away from buildings (for example, central boiler systems with buried services).

It is also important to consider whether additional investigation work should be undertaken behind identified ACMs. Typically, the asbestos survey will stop when a suspected ACM is identified, but this may not represent the true extent of the work. For example, an asbestos survey might identify an asbestos insulation board ceiling, at which point the survey would cease. However, it is possible that additional ACMs may be present in the ceiling void, which could delay the work, or the materials could mean a significant change to the contractor's notifications (such as the discovery of pipe insulation), which would warrant a re-notification of the work and a delay of at least 14 days.

Within the life cycle of a building the expectation should be that the building will have at least one management survey, numerous refurbishment surveys and, finally, a demolition survey.

Caveats

Anyone applying the results of a survey should initially check if the surveyor has written any caveats on the survey. In the past it was common for surveyors to exclude access to areas that are over 3 m above ground level, as it is not possible for a single surveyor to safely use a ladder higher than this because they cannot foot it. Hence, in such circumstances there should always be a minimum of two surveyors. There may be other areas that have not been accessed.

Caveats are restrictions put on the scope of the survey, or the investigative methods to be used. Caveats can be imposed by either party.

- They can be imposed by the building owner to reduce the intrusive damage that would otherwise occur to the building as a part of the survey process or on a listed building.

- Conversely, the asbestos surveyor may find it necessary to include caveats in the survey report to cover areas of the building where asbestos could be present but, for whatever reason, access could not be achieved (this may apply to live plant or, in the case of refurbishment surveys, areas that are permanently occupied).

Hence, caveats can seriously reduce the usefulness and value of a survey and should only be imposed when absolutely necessary and where they can be fully justified.

Asbestos surveyors are taught to identify the spaces where asbestos is likely to be found and to survey accordingly. The meaning of spaces can be anything from a boiler room to a roof void, an office, an underground duct, a cavity between the two leafs of a wall or anywhere else that asbestos or an ACM might have been used. By preventing access to an area or restricting the investigative method necessary, the client could seriously reduce the usefulness of the survey report.

A 'no access' comment on an asbestos report could be simply for any of the following reasons.

- The door of a room was locked and the surveyor could not gain entry.

- The space was an underground duct and lifting equipment was required to lift the covers.

- A suspended floor had no access other than by destroying the floor.

- The electrical system was live during the survey.

Effective planning should help to overcome such obstacles.

Survey report

The outcome of the survey should be a survey report that fulfils the requirements of the client.

A comprehensive report will include a plan of the building with the areas where ACMs have been identified clearly marked on the plan. Similarly, areas where access could not be gained, but where asbestos could be present, should also be marked on the plan.

HSE guidance recommends that the information is also presented in a tabulated format, room by room, for ease of interpretation. This table could then be incorporated into the asbestos register for the building.

The survey report must identify the following.

- Locations where ACMs have been found.

- The extent of the ACM in each location.

- What type of ACM it is.

- The level of confidence that it is an ACM (for example, identified through analysis, strongly presumed or presumed).

- The asbestos type within the ACM.

For management surveys (and refurbishment or demolition surveys where work will not start for some time), the following information should also be provided.

● How easy to access the ACMs are.

● The extent of damage or deterioration.

● If it has received any surface treatment.

● An indication of the priority for dealing with each ACM identified.

● How each ACM should be dealt with.

Some asbestos surveys will be prepared with both a material assessment and a priority assessment. The priority assessment is the responsibility of the duty holder, as it forms part of the management plan and, where provided, this information should be carefully reviewed.

The client must ensure that the asbestos report fulfils the requirements for which it was commissioned. This will entail checking that the report meets the following conditions.

● Complies with the tender requirements.

● Contains no unagreed caveats or disclaimers.

● Confirms the survey was of the type required.

● Covers all the rooms and areas required.

● Contains clear and accurate diagrams and plans.

● Confirms that an adequate number of samples were taken.

● Indicates that sample numbers reflect variations in the same ACM (for example, where two types of suspended ceiling tile have been used in the same room).

● Does not contain any other obvious omissions, discrepancies or inconsistencies.

09

Appendix B – Preventing exposure to asbestos

Manager

- Avoid disturbing ACMs, if possible.
- If you are not a licensed contractor, make sure you know what work can be carried out on ACMs.
- Ensure that anyone going to work on asbestos material has received adequate training.
- Use the HSE's *Asbestos essentials* to ensure the job is carried out properly.
- Prepare a plan of work, explaining what the job involves, the work procedures and what controls to use.
- Ensure that those doing the work understand the plan of work.
- Provide the right protective clothing and equipment, including properly fitted respirators and overalls.
- Make sure the work area is inspected visually at the end of the job and there is no debris or dust.
- Make arrangements for the safe disposal of any asbestos waste.
- Consult with others who may be affected by the work.

Worker

- Make sure you have been properly trained for work with asbestos and understand what is required of you in the plan of work.
- Use the HSE's guidance to help you carry out the job properly and ensure that exposure to asbestos is kept as low as possible.
- If you have any concerns, stop work and talk to your supervisor.
- Don't eat, smoke or drink in the work area.
- Use any equipment provided, including that for personal protection; ensure it is clean and in good working order.
- Make sure the work area is clean at the end of the job. Don't sweep up dust and debris – use a Type H vacuum cleaner and wet rags.
- Ensure asbestos waste is disposed of safely.

Links to HSE guidance

 A range of HSE *Asbestos essentials* task sheets can be found on the HSE website.

Planning – prioritising decisions and managing risk

- Identify where there might be ACMs.
- Consider eliminating the need to work with asbestos. Can you avoid disturbing asbestos by doing the job some other way?
- Does the work need to be done by a licensed contractor?
- Where it is not possible to eliminate the risk, develop a plan of work that highlights the risks and identifies the controls that must be used. Communicate this so that it is understood by all involved.
- Workers must be provided with the appropriate RPE and any other protective equipment identified in the plan of work. This must be properly fitted, clean and in full working order.
- Ensure all workers are trained in non-licensed asbestos work and follow the appropriate task guidance sheets.
- Use an asbestos waste container and dispose of asbestos waste safely.

09

Appendix C – Places and materials that can contain asbestos

Building fabric

- Corrugated roofing, tiles, slates, soffits, gutters, downpipes, walls and panels.
- Insulation under the roof, on beams and stanchions.
- Boards and panels, and any insulation between these.
- Insulation around pipes, on a heater, boiler, calorifier, in storage heaters.
- Decorative coatings on walls or ceilings.
- Insulation around windows.
- Water cisterns.
- Flues, waste water pipes.
- Plastic floor tiles.

Also check **outbuildings**.

Equipment

- Oven, brakes, soundproofing, ironing surfaces and insulating mats.
- Fire blankets, fire insulation in or on doors and insulating gloves.

Note down the **condition** and **amount** of materials that might contain asbestos.

Where you can't get access (for example, roof void, undercroft or wall cavities) presume that these contain asbestos.

Materials that do not contain asbestos

The following materials **do not** contain asbestos, but they **may conceal** asbestos:

- stone
- brick or breeze-block and mortar
- concrete
- metal

- glass
- wood
- most furnishings and fabrics (but see 'Equipment' above).

 Steel frames that were clad in asbestos for fire protection may have underlying lead paint coatings and thus a lead paint survey will also be required.

 The HSE website contains further guidance on asbestos

The guidance covers the following areas.

- Identifying asbestos risk.
- Licensed work with asbestos.
- Other work with asbestos.

- Waste.
- Instruction and training.

09

09

Dust and fumes (Respiratory hazards)

Supporting
INFORMATION

GT700 Toolbox talks / supporting checklists and forms

Toolbox talks on some of these topics are available in the GT700 publication. Supporting checklists and forms covering some of these topics are available on our companion website.

DUST AND FUMES (RESPIRATORY HAZARDS)

Overview

Each year, thousands of construction workers contract respiratory diseases from breathing in dust, vapours, gases or fumes. The amount breathed in each day can seem small or insignificant, but respiratory hazards often have a cumulative effect. In some cases, the effects of exposure may be immediate, but generally it can take years before the symptoms of ill health become apparent. Because of this, these respiratory hazards are often not given sufficient attention or are overlooked altogether.

Respiratory diseases can result in occupational cancers. It is estimated that past exposure from construction activities causes over 5,000 occupational cancers and approximately 3,700 deaths annually.

In this chapter, the nature of respiratory hazards is explained, along with what must be done to minimise exposure and protect the workforce.

10.1   Introduction

Respiratory hazards are substances that threaten human health by inhalation. They can affect the lungs and respiratory system, and they may have systemic effects on other parts of the body.

These hazardous substances are normally inhaled in the form of dusts, vapours, gases or fumes.

The exposure to respiratory hazards can result in debilitating or fatal chronic respiratory illnesses. These illnesses normally take many years to become apparent and include cancer, silicosis, asthma and chronic obstructive pulmonary disease (COPD).

Asbestos fibres, silica and lead dust are particularly hazardous if inhaled. Such diseases are often totally disabling, causing those affected to be unable to work.

In addition to chronic illness, respiratory hazards may cause acute illness (such as from exposure to carbon monoxide or welding fumes). Such exposures can cause illness or even death after short exposures, and the effects may appear rapidly.

Some substances may have both chronic and acute effects, depending on the dose received.

Managing and controlling long-term exposure to respiratory hazards is a challenge facing the industry. Many workers are exposed daily, but may only work for short periods of time on various sites and frequently change employers.

As a result it is difficult to establish their cumulative exposure over time.

Work-related ill health may have devastating consequences for individuals and their families, but it is often both misunderstood and underestimated.

- There are approximately 12,000 deaths each year as a result of occupational respiratory diseases. About two-thirds of these are due to asbestos-related diseases or COPD. These are long latency diseases (they take a long time to develop following exposure to the agent that caused them). Therefore, current deaths reflect the effects of past working conditions.

- There are an estimated 10,000 new cases of breathing or lung problems caused or made worse by work each year.

- Health and Safety Executive (HSE) statistics show that each year around 7,000 people in the UK develop occupational asthma.

- Every year, approximately 600 construction workers die from silica-related lung diseases (caused by dust from cutting blocks, kerbs and other items). Silica is the biggest risk to construction workers' health after asbestos.

- When asked about exposures contributing to their illness or condition, almost 20% of workers reporting with work-related respiratory problems identified dusts from stone, cement, bricks or concrete.

Raising the awareness of managers, supervisors and workers, to ensure effective control measures are always put in place and followed, is fundamental in helping reduce these numbers.

The Construction Dust Partnership has been formed to raise awareness within the construction industry about lung diseases related to hazardous workplace dust.

It is also in place to promote good practice to prevent these diseases, particularly for those undertaking high-risk tasks. It offers advice for both employers and workers.

 For further details on the Construction Dust Partnership visit the CITB website.

 At any one time, far more people are off work through occupational ill health than through work-related accidents.

10.2   Important points

● The presence of respiratory hazards should be prevented or eliminated where reasonably practicable, by:

– substituting and using a less harmful substance or material

– using a different process (such as a block splitter instead of mechanical cutting)

– manufacturing or cutting materials off site.

● Where the prevention of respiratory hazards is not possible, the extent of exposure must be controlled to a level that is safe. Respiratory protective equipment (RPE) should only be used to control residual risk after other controls have been applied to either reduce or eliminate exposure.

● The risk from respiratory hazards depends upon the nature of the substance, as well as the concentration (amount) in the air, and the period over which someone is exposed. It is essential that workers and managers understand the nature of the risks from the substances they are using.

 Some respiratory hazards may be harmful even at low concentrations or from short-term exposure. Risk assessments must identify all respiratory hazards, and may require the measures selected to control them. A method statement may also be used to describe a step by step procedure for the use of these control measures.

 For further information on lead and asbestos refer to Chapters B08 and B09.

10.3   Types of respiratory hazard

Respiratory hazards refer to substances that may be inhaled which will cause acute or chronic ill health. The substances may be present in the workplace in a range of forms. The hazard is dependent not only on the nature of the substance but also on its form, since this dictates its ability to enter the body and reach the sites where damage may be caused. The principal forms of respiratory hazard that may be encountered on site are described below.

10.3.1   Dust

Dust is produced when solid materials are broken down into finer particles. The size of the dust particles has a major influence on the degree of risk posed by the dust. Dust can either be respirable or inhalable.

Respirable dusts are most harmful. These are dusts of particle size below 10 microns (10 μm), which have the ability to be deposited in the lungs. Larger particles are generally deposited in the respiratory tract, and are generally referred to as **inhalable dust**. Current evidence suggests that the most harmful particles are those below 2.5 microns (2.5 μm). Some particles below this size have the ability to cross the alveolar wall and enter the bloodstream, enabling hazardous substances to have effects beyond the lungs.

The most harmful dusts are not visible. Dusts that are too fine to be seen by the naked eye are the cause of many serious health problems. Where a dust exists in sufficient quantities, it may be considered hazardous even if dust is formed from a non-hazardous substance.

 One micron (1 μm) = 1,000th of 1 mm. A human hair is around 150 microns (150 μm) in diameter.

The inhalation of dust can cause a range of conditions, from nuisance effects (such as coughing and sneezing) to chronic diseases *(refer to 10.4 Chronic respiratory diseases)*.

10.3.1.1   Construction dust

This is a general term used to describe different dusts that you may find on a construction site. Construction dust is not just a nuisance, it can seriously damage your health and cause life changing lung diseases. There are three main types of construction dust:

● **Silica dust** – created when working on silica-containing materials like concrete, mortar and sandstone (also known as respirable crystalline silica or RCS)

● **Wood dust** – created when working on softwood, hardwood and wood-based products like MDF and plywood

● **Other 'general' dust** – created when working on other materials containing very little or no silica. The most common include gypsum (e.g. in plasterboard), limestone and marble.

10.3.2   Mists and aerosols

Tiny liquid droplets are formed by the atomisation of the liquid (for example, when spraying or using an aerosol). Mists and aerosols may be hazardous because of the nature of the liquids from which they are formed. In addition, mists and aerosols may carry bacteria and enable them to be deposited in the body at a location where they can cause harm, infection and disease, such as is the case with legionella bacteria.

10

10.3.2.1 Legionella

This is the collective name given to the pneumonia-like illness caused by the legionella bacteria. This includes the most serious Legionnaires' disease, as well as the similar but less serious conditions of Pontiac fever and Lochgoilhead fever. Legionnaires' disease is a potentially fatal form of pneumonia, and everyone is susceptible to infection. However, some people are at higher risk, including:

- people over 45 years of age
- smokers and heavy drinkers

- people suffering from chronic respiratory or kidney disease
- anyone with an impaired immune system.

The bacterium *Legionella pneumophila* and related bacteria are common in natural water sources such as rivers, lakes and reservoirs, but usually in low numbers. Since legionella bacteria are widespread in the environment, they may also contaminate and grow in purpose-built water systems, such as cooling towers, evaporative condensers, hot and cold water systems and whirlpool spas.

There are also a number of other systems that may pose a risk to exposure to legionella, for example humidifiers, air washers, emergency showers, and indoor ornamental fountains. Many of these are systems that construction workers can come across in relinquishment or demolition works.

10.3.2.2 Legionella risks in the workplace

Any water system that has the right environmental conditions could potentially be a source for legionella bacteria growth. There is a reasonably foreseeable legionella risk in your water system if:

- water is stored or re-circulated as part of your system

- the water temperature in all or some part of the system is between 20 and 45°C

- there are sources of nutrients such as rust, sludge, scale and organic matters

- the conditions are likely to encourage bacteria to multiply

- it is possible for water droplets to be produced and, if so, they can be dispersed over a wide area (for example showers and aerosols from cooling towers

- it is likely that any of your employees, residents, visitors and so on are more susceptible to infection due to age, illness or a weakened immune system, and whether they could be exposed to any contaminated water droplets.

10.3.2.3 Employers' duties

An employer or person in control of a premises (site welfare) needs to take suitable precautions to prevent or control the risk of exposure to legionella. The employer must carry out a risk assessment to establish any potential risks and implement measures to either eliminate or control those risks. The person must be competent with the necessary skills to carry out the assessment.

 For more information and guidance on Legionnaires' disease, visit the HSE website.

10.3.3 Vapours

These are the gaseous state of substances that are liquids or solids at room temperature. They usually form when substances evaporate. One example is the vapour from a tin of glue or solvent that has been left open. Some substances form vapours at room temperature, whilst others need to be heated before they will give off vapours. Liquids which give off vapours at room or low temperatures are described as being highly volatile (such as petrol and organic solvents). Solvent vapours can often be toxic by inhalation, causing dizziness, unconsciousness and death. They may also have chronic effects (such as causing liver damage or sensitisation). Harmful vapours are particularly hazardous in enclosed spaces, where the vapours can quickly build up to dangerous concentrations.

 For further information refer to Chapter D08 Confined spaces.

10.3.4 Fumes

The definition of a fume may be confusing as it is often misused and applied to any mixture of gases and particles.

 A *fume* is actually defined as 'solid particles generated by chemical reactions or condensed from the gaseous state, usually after volatilisation from melted substances' (HSE – EH40/2005).

In terms of occupational health, fumes arising from the heating of metal (for example, when welding and gas cutting) are particularly hazardous, because as the fumes cool they form microscopic particles of the metal, which may be inhaled. For example, a common form of respiratory illness, known as metal fume fever, which has flu-like symptoms, is caused by the inhalation of welding fumes. There is scientific evidence that exposure to all welding fumes, including mild steel welding fumes, can cause lung cancer. There is also limited evidence linked to kidney cancer. When welding is taking place, the temperature of the metal at the weld is sufficiently high for the elements in the metal to become gaseous. However, 2–3 mm away from the weld, the gases have cooled down sufficiently for the fumes to solidify out as small particles. Usually, metal fumes are actually a solid particle by the time they are inhaled.

Other sources of hazardous fumes are the use of equipment and plant powered by internal combustion engines. This is particularly hazardous when the engine is operated in an enclosed space, allowing concentrations of harmful constituents to reach dangerous levels. Such fumes may contain carbon monoxide, soot and unburnt hydrocarbons. These constituents may be acutely fatal as well as having long-term consequences (such as lung cancer).

The physical properties of fumes can be confusing, particularly when identifying suitable RPE. Consequently, when purchasing RPE to protect against fumes, knowledge of the nature of the fume is necessary to ensure that the correct equipment is selected.

10.3.5 Gases

Gases are generally substances that are in gaseous form at room temperature and normally mix with the air that we breathe (for example carbon dioxide, carbon monoxide and hydrogen sulphide). As well as having toxic qualities, gases may also be flammable or explosive. Inert gases can also be dangerous in sufficient levels in confined spaces, where they dilute the concentration of oxygen in the air to dangerously low levels.

10.4   Chronic respiratory diseases

With an accident on site, the injury or other effects are usually immediate and obvious. However, the effects of exposure to most work-related ill health hazards are not immediate or not even felt.

As workers are repeatedly exposed to small doses of dust and fumes, these start to damage their body. Workers may go home from work feeling more or less the same each day and are none the wiser.

It can take many weeks, months or even years before symptoms of exposure become a problem to them and irreversible damage may well have occurred.

Chronic respiratory disease (such as those listed below) can often result in employees being unable to work as hard or as efficiently as before, and sometimes they may never work again.

Silica dust can cause irreversible lung damage

- Chronic obstructive pulmonary disease.
- Silicosis.
- Asbestosis.
- Respiratory cancers.
- Pleural thickening.
- Occupational asthma.

10.4.1   Chronic obstructive pulmonary disease

Chronic obstructive pulmonary disease (COPD) is the name for a collection of lung diseases, including chronic bronchitis, emphysema and chronic obstructive airways disease. People with COPD have difficulties breathing, primarily due to the narrowing of their airways. This is called airflow obstruction. The following are typical symptoms of COPD.

- Increasing breathlessness when active.
- A persistent cough with phlegm.
- Frequent chest infections.

It is caused by the inhalation of substances that irritate the lungs and airways causing inflammation. Over many years, the inflammation leads to permanent changes in the lung. The walls of the airways thicken and more mucus is produced. Damage to the delicate walls of the air sacs in the lungs causes emphysema and the lungs lose their normal elasticity. The smaller airways also become scarred and narrowed. These changes cause the symptoms of breathlessness, coughing and phlegm, associated with COPD.

Smoking is the main cause of COPD, but there are many occupational causes, such as exposure to silica dust, isocyanates (which are found in many construction products), cadmium dust and grain dust.

10.4.2   Silicosis

Silica dust exposure is the biggest risk to construction workers after asbestos exposure. Respirable crystalline silica (RCS) is found in stone, rock, sand and clay, and so is contained in many construction products (such as concrete blocks, bricks and ceramics).

Common day-to-day work produces RCS, and many workers are exposed to it both knowingly and unknowingly by breathing in silica particles. Some of this dust is fine enough to get deep into your lungs in the form of RCS, and the harmful silica particles are too small to see with the naked eye or under normal lighting.

silica dust

The amounts needed to cause serious damage are not large. The most you should be inhaling during a day after using the right controls is shown next to the penny.

Prolonged exposure to RCS can cause lung cancer and other serious respiratory diseases. The HSE estimates that RCS has been responsible for the death of over 500 construction workers every year, and in addition to the risks from lung cancer, silica is also linked to other serious lung diseases. Exposure to RCS at low levels over a long period can cause silicosis, which causes fibrosis (hardening or scarring) of the lung tissue, with a consequent loss of lung function.

10

Sufferers are likely to have severe shortness of breath and may find it difficult or impossible to walk even short distances or upstairs. The effect continues to develop after exposure has stopped and it is irreversible. Sufferers usually become house- or bed-bound and often die prematurely due to heart failure. Higher levels of exposure may cause **accelerated silicosis**, which can be present as little as four years after exposure, but normally occurs between five and 15 years after exposure.

Acute silicosis is a rare complication of short-term exposure to large amounts of silica, and may lead to significant health consequences. This can develop within months of exposure. Silica may also be linked to lung cancer. Precautions taken to control the risk of fibrosis will serve to control the risk of lung cancer. Workers with silicosis are at an increased risk of tuberculosis, kidney disease and arthritis. Exposure to RCS may also cause COPD.

 For further information on silica dust, exposure levels and good practice, refer to 10.11 Silica.

 Visit the HSE website to view a video case study of a former stoneworker suffering with silicosis.

10.4.3 Asbestosis

This is a chronic lung disease, characterised by scarring of the lung tissue. It is caused by long-term asbestos exposure. It is only caused by exposure to long, thin asbestos fibres. Extended exposure can lead to an accumulation of fibres in the lung tissues, which can then create scarring (fibrosis). Over time the lung tissue thickens, causing pain and restricting breathing. Individuals may not be diagnosed until years after the exposure occurred.

Asbestosis is not a form of lung cancer or mesothelioma, so people can live with the disease. However, the condition is incurable and will get worse over time; therefore treatment is required.

10.4.4 Respiratory cancers

Respiratory cancers include lung cancer, which may be caused by a range of exposures (such as asbestos, silica, diesel engine exhaust emissions and mineral oils) and mesothelioma.

Mesothelioma is a form of cancer only caused by exposure to asbestos. It affects the thin, protective membrane surrounding the lungs, heart and abdominal cavity. When microscopic fibres are breathed in or swallowed the human body is sometimes unable to release them. These fibres can then become trapped and cause inflammation, scarring and damage.

The disease can lay dormant for years. It can take from 20 to 50 years after exposure before signs and symptoms develop. Mesothelioma is fatal in all cases, with death often occurring within months of diagnosis.

10.4.5 Pleural thickening

This is also known as diffuse pleural thickening. It causes chest pain and a decline in breathing, and is one of the most commonly diagnosed symptoms of asbestos exposure, although it may have other non-occupational causes (such as infection).

Pleural thickening is a lung disease caused by inhaling asbestos fibres. These fibres become embedded in the pleura (the thin membrane that covers the lungs), which then triggers scarring. The scarring thickens the pleura and, as the scar tissue grows, it can encase the lung and close off the space between the lungs and the pleura. Pleural thickening caused by asbestos is not the same as asbestosis; in these conditions, the pleura is damaged by asbestos but the lungs themselves are unharmed.

10.4.6 Occupational asthma

Occupational asthma is caused by exposure to respiratory sensitisers at work, which are inhaled into the lungs over a period of time. It can be a serious condition, leading to severe chronic asthma, if there is a prolonged exposure to respiratory sensitisers. A worker with asthma may suffer an asthma attack when exposed to a range of irritants (such as smoke, dust and cold air). Note that the attacks are not only brought on by the agent that caused the development of the condition. Respiratory sensitisers can be chemicals, such as isocyanates (from spraying), wood dusts, colophony (from soldering) or some glues.

10.5   Workplace exposure limits

Employers must protect workers from exposure to hazardous substances, including dust, fumes, chemicals, vapours, mists, nanotechnology, gases, biological agents and germs that cause disease.

Where substances have been classified as carcinogens, mutagens or asthmagens, to comply with the Control of Substances Hazardous to Health Regulations 2002 (COSHH), exposure must be controlled to as low as reasonably practicable (ALARP).

The harmful effects of respiratory hazards are dependent upon the amount inhaled and the period of inhalation. The combination of the concentration in the air inhaled and the period of exposure is referred to as the dose. In occupational health, the dose is normally expressed as a time weighted average (TWA) over a nominal eight-hour working day or, where the substance may have acute effects following a short-term exposure limit (STEL), a 15-minute TWA.

 The HSE has published a revised edition of EH40/2005 Workplace exposure limits that contains the list of workplace exposure limits for use with COSHH (as amended).

Workplace exposure limits (WELs) are British occupation exposure limits, and are set in order to help protect the health of workers. WELs are concentrations of hazardous substances in the air, averaged over a specified period of time referred to as a time-weighted average (TWA). Two time periods are generally used:

● long-term (eight hours); and

● short-term (15 minutes).

Because dust is a mix of small particles, all dusts have been assigned a concentration in air above which they are considered hazardous. It is important to remember that this applies to all dusts, irrespective of their constituents. The hazardous constituents of dusts may have their own WELs, in which case the lowest of the levels will apply.

Also significant to the construction industry is the WEL for RCS of 0.1 mg/m^3. *(For further information refer to 10.11 Silica.)*

 Any dust in sufficient quantity is classified as a substance hazardous to health.

10.6   Managing the risk

COSHH require that employers shall not expose any employees to any hazardous substance, unless a suitable and sufficient assessment of the risks has been carried out and adequate controls are applied. Under the regulations, an employer has not exerted adequate control unless they have applied the principles (listed below) of good control practice.

● Design and operate processes and activities to minimise emission, release and spread of substances hazardous to health.

● Take into account all relevant routes of exposure (inhalation, skin absorption and ingestion) when developing control measures.

● Control exposure by measures that are proportionate to the health risk.

● Choose the most effective and reliable control options, which minimise the escape and spread of substances hazardous to health.

● Where adequate control of exposure cannot be achieved by other means, provide, in combination with other control measures, suitable personal protective equipment (PPE).

● Check and review regularly all elements of control measures for their continuing effectiveness.

● Inform and train all employees on the hazards and risks from the substances with which they work and the use of control measures developed to minimise the risks.

● Ensure that the introduction of control measures does not increase the overall risk to health and safety.

Therefore, employers are required to assess the health risks to their employees arising out of exposure to respiratory hazards and, if reasonably practicable, put control measures in place to eliminate the work processes and the use of substances that cause exposure. If this is not reasonably practicable, employers must ensure the following.

● Exposure is controlled to an acceptable level.

● Employees are informed of the hazards involved and the control measures in place.

● The effects of any exposure are mitigated by providing health surveillance where necessary.

Under the Construction (Design and Management) Regulations 2015 (CDM), designers are required, when preparing or modifying designs, to eliminate, reduce or control foreseeable risks that may arise during construction, maintenance and the use of a building once it is built, as outlined in the examples below.

 Specifying construction materials that are cut to size at the point of manufacture, eliminating the need for cutting, planing and sanding on site. Designing paving that does not require complex cutting, or cutting for drainage channels, to reduce the need for cutting on site.

Principal contractors must ensure that the methods to be applied are specified in the construction phase plan, and that there is sufficient monitoring and supervision on site to ensure that the control measures are applied.

 For further information refer to the Construction News supplement *Taking control of dust*, which can be accessed on their website.

 The Healthy Lung Partnership (HLP) was set up to co-ordinate activities to reduce work-related lung disease. Members include HSE, other Government departments, trade associations, trade unions and professionals across the UK. The partnership shares, promotes and encourages good control practice in the workplace to prevent and reduce exposure to hazardous substances that damage the lungs.

 More information on the HLP can be found on the HSE website.

10.7 Respiratory protective equipment

Given the nature of some work, it is not always reasonably practicable to completely eliminate respiratory hazards. In these circumstances, if no other control measure is reasonably practicable, or if, after applying all other reasonably practicable measures there is a residual risk from exposure, suitable RPE must be provided for each person exposed to the hazard.

For further information on RPE and its selection refer to Chapter B06 Personal protective equipment.

10.8 Monitoring

Monitoring is sometimes necessary to establish or confirm the level of respiratory hazards in the air. However, in construction, levels of exposure are often known from past experience, and are not always necessary to monitor in every case, provided that a valid assessment can be made from other data sources.

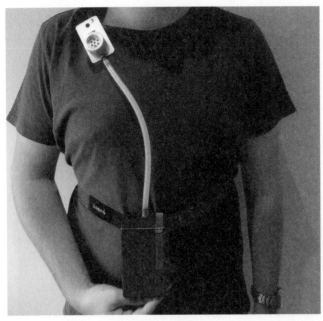
Gravimetric dust sampling using pump and filter

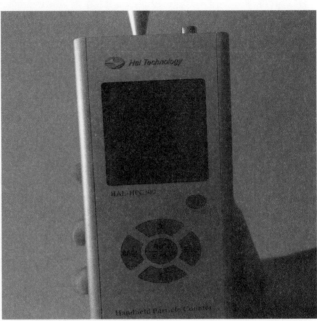
Hand-held direct reading particle analyser

Dusts are generally measured gravimetrically, which involves collecting a sample of dust from a known volume of air and determining its weight. Sampling is usually carried out by using metered pumps with fibreglass filters worn by workers on site. The dust collected is weighed in relation to the amount of air sampled to determine the concentration of dust in the worker's breathing zone. For comparison against WELs, levels should always be determined from personal monitoring, rather than static or area monitoring. Static monitoring may be useful to show variations in dust levels over time, or to monitor boundary dust levels for nuisance prevention purposes.

Direct reading dust sampling monitors are also available, which are useful for undertaking widespread site surveys. Many have particle size capability, which is useful for establishing risks from respirable particles. For hazardous dust (such as silica), samples may need laboratory analysis (for example, by X-ray diffraction) to determine the proportion of the dust that is silica. This allows proper selection of RPE. However, an approach often taken is to assume that 100% of the dust is silica, and select RPE accordingly – this builds in a good safety factor.

Other respiratory hazards may be monitored by a wide range of methods, such as organic vapour passive monitoring badges for solvents. It is important that the method to be used is chosen accurately and undertaken properly in order to obtain meaningful results. Competent advice should be sought from an occupational hygienist.

10.9 Training and supervision

Employers must provide employees with adequate information, instruction, training and supervision to be able to carry out any work task safely and without risks to their health. Induction training must be provided to any person new to a particular site, even if they have previously worked on similar sites. Employees should receive full instruction before starting work. This includes the following.

- Health risks associated with the respiratory hazards present on the site and preventative measures in operation, as identified by the risk assessment.

- The correct method of use of PPE, and in particular RPE, including its maintenance, cleaning, storage and replacement.

Good practice: using the correct PPE and dust extraction

● Their duties in respect of the correct use of equipment and of safe systems of work in operation.

● Procedures for reporting defective or inadequate equipment.

Managers and supervisors involved in the selection, management and supervision of RPE should receive training to enable them to do so. All contractors and the principal contractor must have adequate arrangements for monitoring the application of the control measures, and in particular the correct use of RPE used to control respiratory hazards.

10.10 Other ways to control respiratory hazards

10.10.1 Choice of work methods

The primary focus should be on reducing the risk at the design stage.

● Paving can be planned so that the smallest number of cuts is needed.

● Different sized materials can be chosen so that cutting is minimised.

● Routes for services can be designed in.

Where a risk remains, this can be reduced by working another way.

● Cables can be protected and covered with plaster or board instead of chasing.

● Brackets and cable trays can be directly fixed instead of using drill holes.

● A block splitter can be used instead of a cut-off saw.

10.10.2 Water suppression

Water can be used with some tasks to effectively dampen down the dust. Most modern cut-off saws can be attached to a water supply. The water can come directly from the mains or a portable source (such as a hand-pressurised freestanding container). Other devices (such as masonry saw benches) can be selected that come with an in-built water reservoir. Water suppression is not suitable for controlling all dust risks. It cannot be used with most electric tools, on wood or where the waste slurry would create a problem (such as in an inhabited building). Supervisors and workers should receive training on the correct use of equipment, safe systems of work in operation and procedures for reporting defective or inadequate equipment.

10.10.3 Local exhaust ventilation and on-tool extraction

Extraction is an effective alternative to water suppression. This sucks the dust away as it is being created and stores it until emptied. An extraction vacuum can also be used for general cleaning instead of dry sweeping.

Correctly working on-tool extraction is made up of a number of different parts. A specially-designed hood is needed to collect the dust at the point it is being created. This should be shaped and designed around the cutting or contact point. The hood is attached to an industrial vacuum extraction unit via a hose. If using local exhaust ventilation (LEV) this needs a statutory thorough examination and test, by a competent person, at least once every 14 months to ensure it is working as expected.

The extraction unit is like an industrial vacuum cleaner. It is a portable unit and also an important part of the LEV system. The extraction unit removes dust from the captor hood, filters it and then stores it for safe disposal. Extraction units can often be used with different makes and models of tools. It is important to choose parts that are compatible and work together, and selecting the correct extraction unit is vital to achieving this, otherwise the dust may be poorly controlled.

10.10.3.1 On-tool extraction units

The specification of the unit must be suitable for the tool and the task. The most suitable extraction units are fitted with high efficiency particle arrest (HEPA) filters. There are three main classes of dust extraction: L class, M class and H class.

An H (high) or M (medium) class unit should be used for construction, as these classes of unit provide effective and reliable extraction capability and should be fitted with low-flow indicators.

The units are marked with a special label, which will indicate their suitable uses and what they are not suitable for. Don't just use a HEPA filter in a general commercial vacuum. *Note: an L (low) class unit is only suitable for lower-toxicity dust (such as gypsum in plasterboard).*

Check that the unit creates and maintains enough air suction to cope with the amount of dust the work will create (manufacturers or suppliers can advise). It needs to remove the dust as fast as it is created.

Circular saw with M (medium) class extraction unit

Consider how often the unit will need emptying and check the waste capacity is correct for the work. Use the correct disposable waste bags. Seal and place them in the appropriate waste container. Do not empty these bags to recycle them.

10.10.3.2 Supervision and training

The equipment needs to be operated correctly and be properly maintained. Supervisors and workers need to be provided with the right training before using on-tool extraction. This includes information on the following.

- Selecting the right on-tool system.
- Pre-use checks and maintenance.
- How to use the system correctly.
- Common faults, how to spot them and the action to take.

- What to do if there is a problem.
- Other controls that may be needed (e.g. RPE) and how to use them.

10.10.3.3 Regular checks and maintenance

Pre-use checks should be undertaken before first use to ensure that the system works properly first time, every time. Formal maintenance checks should be carried out at least once a week, but you may have to do this more frequently if there is a high risk of the equipment being damaged. Checks should concentrate on the following.

- Damage to parts of the system (such as the hood or ducting). Repair or replace straight away.
- Maintaining the extraction unit's flow of air. Follow the manufacturer's instructions. Check that the airflow indicator and any built-in cleaning mechanism work properly.
- Replacing filters, when needed.
- Replacing worn cutting discs and similar items.

Equipment needs proper servicing and testing to make sure that it remains effective over a long period. A **thorough examination and test** is a detailed and systematic examination that ensures the equipment can continue to perform as intended by its design. A person with the right knowledge, capabilities and experience should carry out a thorough examination and test at least every 14 months, but more frequent testing may be required if regular wear and tear could limit the effectiveness of the system more quickly.

10.11   Silica

Silica occurs as a natural component of many materials used in construction work. Crystalline silica is present in substantial quantities in sand, sandstone and granite, and often forms a significant proportion of clay, shale and slate. Products such as concrete and mortar also contain crystalline silica.

The health hazards of silica come from breathing in the dust. Work that can expose workers or members of the public to the dust includes working with stone, grit blasting, scabbling, cutting or drilling (such as kerbs and paving slabs) and demolition. The use of power tools leads to high exposures if exhaust systems or wet cutting processes are not used and maintained. For some work, exposure will depend upon how confined the working space is, and the presence or absence of ventilation. For example, tunnelling through dry, silica-bearing rock will always lead to high exposures for workers at or near the cutting face, unless precautions are taken.

 Principal contractor fined after workers exposed to silica dust

A construction and carpentry building contractor has been fined after failing to plan, manage and monitor work under its control, leading to gross exposure of workers to RCS.

Westminster Magistrates' Court heard that the company was undertaking a project that included the refurbishment of a building at Netherall Gardens, London. A proactive site inspection by the HSE found workers in a basement had been dry cutting approximately 250 bricks to shape them for use in bay windows.

An investigation by the HSE found that failures in health and safety management had led to numerous issues on site. Workers were not informed of the dangers of inhaling the dust, they were not made aware of the correct controls and the work was not supervised by a competent person. The company pleaded guilty to breaching Regulation 13(1) of the Construction (Design and Management) Regulations 2015. They were fined £40,000 and ordered to pay costs of £2,313.10.

Speaking after the hearing, the HSE inspector said: 'Over 500 construction workers are believed to die from exposure to silica dust every year. It is the biggest risk to construction workers after asbestos. This number can be reduced by those in control of the work through adequate planning, managing and monitoring of the work on site. This company has been repeatedly warned by HSE about the dangers of silica, and has today been held to account for failing to take adequate action to protect the health and safety of its workers.' *(Source: HSE.)*

 For further information on silica dust, including the HSE guidance *The control and exposure to silica dust* (NDG463) and the Construction Information Sheet No 54 *Dust control on cut-off saws used for stone or concrete cutting*, visit the HSE website.

10.11.1 Health surveillance for silicosis

Health surveillance must be considered when there is a reasonable likelihood that an employee could contract silicosis or other diseases through exposure to respirable silica dust. However, if there is only a low exposure risk then health surveillance, involving x-rays and a survey, could be unnecessary. A health professional would be able to advise on the type of surveillance techniques that would be required. This may involve chest x-rays, lung function tests and symptom questionnaires. The type and frequency of interventions would depend on the nature of the exposure. However, it is recommended that pre-employment or baseline surveillance is undertaken for potentially exposed workers.

 For further information refer to the HSE guidance *Health surveillance for those exposed to respirable crystalline silica* (G404).

10.11.2 Good practice methods – Silica

Drilling masonry	Control measures
	■ Determine if material can be pre-drilled.
	■ Ensure drill bits are sharp.
	■ Avoid drilling, especially horizontal at chest or eye level, or above head.
	■ Where possible use dust collection systems that use a vacuum (not clip-on dust bags).
	■ Avoid sweeping; instead, vacuum up drill dust, otherwise the dust will disperse around the area and continue to be a hazard.
	■ Use RPE (P3 or FFP3-rated).

Cutting slabs, kerbs or concrete	Control measures
	■ Purchase pre-sized material if possible.
	■ Use a block splitter rather than a rotary cutter.
	■ Use a cut-off saw with a constant water feed.
	■ Use RPE (P3 or FFP3-rated).
	Note: *water feed on its own will only remove approximately 75% of the airborne particles. RPE still needs to be worn.*

Chasing walls	Control measures
	■ Use a proprietary system that incorporates a dust extraction system.
	■ Regularly empty the vacuum collector and clean or replace filters.
	■ Use additional dust extraction where tool extraction is not sufficient.
	■ Use RPE (P3 or FFP3-rated).

Sweeping up – General	Control measures
	■ Vacuum the area rather than sweeping, where possible.
	■ Dampen down the area before sweeping.
	■ Dispose of dust in sealed bags.
	■ Provide a vacuum to clean down equipment and clothing.
	■ Use RPE (P3 or FFP3-rated).

10

 For further information refer to the HSE information sheet *Construction dust* (CIS36).

10.12   Wood dust

Wood dust can cause serious health problems. It can cause occupational asthma, which carpenters and joiners are four times more likely to get compared with other UK workers.

COSHH require that employers protect their workers from the risks of exposure to wood dusts.

Airborne or settled wood dust contains the fine particles that are most likely to damage the respiratory system and lungs.

Softwood dusts can cause asthma, and hardwood dusts can cause cancer, particularly of the nose.

Both hardwood and softwood dusts have a WEL which must not be exceeded. This is a combination of the concentration of the air inhaled and the period of exposure is referred to as a dose.

Drilling, cutting and sanding wood can create harmful dust

- The WEL for hardwood dust is 3mg/m3 (based on an eight-hour time-weighted average).

- The WEL for softwood dust is 5mg/m3 (based on an eight-hour time-weighted average).

- For mixtures of hardwood and softwood dusts, the WEL for hardwood dust of 3mg/m3 applies to all wood dusts present in that mixture.

Warning on deadly wood dust cancer

A carpenter who was given a false negative cancer result at an Eastbourne hospital died of an occupational tumour, an inquest has heard. The carpenter died at his home on Christmas Day 2009 from cancer of the nose.

At an inquest at Eastbourne Magistrates Court into the death of the 67-year-old, the coroner was told the deceased had been transferred to the hospital by his doctor after complaining of sinus problems.

After various examinations and tests, samples from the tumour were sent for analysis. The tests came back as benign, but two-and-a-half months later the carpenter was diagnosed with cancer.

The coroner recorded a verdict of industrial disease.

10.12.1 Control measures

Educate workers about the risks from wood dust and ensure that control measures are installed and maintained. Workers should know how to use extraction systems properly.

Fitting air flow indicators will help, as these will show them if it is working correctly, for example if dampers are open or shut, and also if maintenance is required.

Keep the extraction system properly maintained and working correctly (it is a legal requirement to have it examined by a competent person at least every 14 months). Follow the extraction manufacturer's guidance for maintenance requirements.

Never sweep up or use compressed air lines, as this will disturb the dust and allow it to become inhaled. Always clean up using a suitable industrial vacuum cleaner that at least meets the Class M classification.

Additional protection may be needed and suitable RPE (face mask) should be worn as well as using the extraction. More details and video guidance on how to fit effective extraction with regard to the control of wood dust can be seen on the HSE website.

 The HSE has produced an information sheet, *Wood dust, controlling the risk* (WIS23), to help LEV users. It provides practical guidance on the health and safety risks from wood dust, and how to control them. This revision contains new information on the use of airflow indicators and dust lamps, as well as advice on how to improve dust control on circular saws.

10.12.2 Health surveillance for wood dust

Businesses should seek advice from an occupational health professional (doctor or nurse) who has the relevant skills, competence and experience for health risks in woodworking. Your health surveillance programme should cover all of your workers who might breathe in wood dust.

You should assess workers' respiratory health ideally before exposure, but if not, then as soon as possible after exposure starts (for example, within six weeks) to provide a baseline. You must have ongoing assessments at appropriate frequencies, usually annually, although more frequent assessments are appropriate for new workers. Your occupational health professional can advise you on how frequently you should do this.

10

Health surveillance should involve an appropriate questionnaire and the performance of spirometry. Occupational health professionals should interpret the heath surveillance results for both individuals and groups of similarly-exposed workers, taking into account any previously available results.

This allows you to identify any need to revise your risk assessment, review exposure controls, and where necessary move workers to alternative roles.

 Visit the HSE website for further information and guidance on health surveillance for those exposed to wood dust.

10.13   Carbon monoxide

Carbon monoxide is a respiratory hazard that is of particular importance to the construction industry. Carbon monoxide is a toxic gas formed by incomplete combustion and is colourless, odourless and tasteless.

Managing and controlling exposure to carbon monoxide is a vital challenge facing the industry as it can impact, sometimes lethally, both operatives working on site and also any occupants of properties where work is being undertaken.

Every year, 200 people are taken to hospital with suspected carbon monoxide poisoning, with around 40 subsequent deaths.

Carbon monoxide is an issue in the construction industry in the following situations.

● For site security workers and office staff where portable liquefied petroleum gas (LPG) heaters or LPG cookers are being used and there is inadequate ventilation.

● Where combustion engine powered equipment, including generators, is used in enclosed or confined spaces, exposing the operative and others to exhaust emissions containing carbon monoxide.

● Where refurbishment or other work is undertaken on existing buildings containing gas systems. Interference with gas equipment or flues can lead to construction workers or end users being exposed to carbon monoxide.

10.13.1 Symptoms of carbon monoxide intoxication

When carbon monoxide is inhaled, it crosses the alveolar walls in the lungs and enters the bloodstream. Here, it combines with the haemoglobin in the red blood cells to form carboxyhaemoglobin.

Normally, the haemoglobin in the red blood cells binds with oxygen to transport it throughout the body. However, molecules that have bound to carbon monoxide are not available to transport oxygen. Hence carbon monoxide is a chemical asphyxiant, and its effects are largely caused by oxygen deprivation in the body tissues.

Carbon monoxide intoxication is often mistaken for other illnesses (such as viral infection or chronic fatigue syndrome). Symptoms will increase with the concentration, so that low levels of intoxication may just cause headaches and tiredness.

These symptoms will normally disappear when the person leaves the environment where the carbon monoxide is present.

Higher concentrations can cause the following symptoms.

● Pains in the chest or stomach.

● Erratic behaviour and decreased mental performance.

● Visual problems.

● Nausea.

● Breathlessness.

● Collapse and loss of consciousness.

Typically, the concentration of gas will build up in a poorly ventilated space, and so a victim will progress through some or all of the symptoms if they continue to be exposed. This can eventually lead to death.

Generally, if a victim is removed from the exposure before death, a full recovery can be expected. There is some evidence, however, that long-term sub-acute exposures, such as may occur with a faulty boiler, may have chronic effects on mental functioning.

First aid for people intoxicated by carbon monoxide is immediate removal to fresh air and then, if necessary, treatment with 100% oxygen by the emergency services.

10.13.2 Exposure of site workers in site security and staff facilities

LPG cookers and heaters (and similar appliances using other forms of fuel, such as diesel) produce carbon monoxide gas, which can build up to dangerous levels if there is not adequate ventilation. Flammable gas may also escape from leaking cylinders.

Site workers and night security staff have died from carbon monoxide poisoning on construction projects where such gas-fired appliances have been used in site welfare or rest facilities.

10

Security guard dies from carbon monoxide poisoning

A construction company and a security company manager have been fined after a security guard died from carbon monoxide poisoning while at a work.

The Central Criminal Court heard how the deceased had been working as a security guard. The semi-derelict building was due to be turned into a self-storage facility. The construction company was managing the refurbishment and had employed a security company to provide 24-hour security to the site. That company engaged a self-employed security guard.

A petrol-powered electricity generator had been provided by the construction company to power a portable heater and lights, as there was no electricity supply to the building.

The security company manager attended the site at about 13:45. He had not heard from the security guard, who was on the night-patrol shift and had been due to call in at 06:00. The security guard was found lying on a second-storey office floor, with the generator in another room off the same corridor. An ambulance was called and the security guard was declared dead at the scene. The post-mortem revealed he had died of carbon monoxide poisoning.

The HSE investigation showed that the construction company failed to take reasonable measures to ensure, so far as was reasonably practicable, that the generator provided for their use was safe and without risks to the health of the security guards. The manager of the security company failed to take effective steps to ensure that the petrol generator, provided for the use of the security guards, was not operated within the building and he did not carry out or implement the findings of a risk assessment for the provision of a 24-hour security presence. He had also not provided the security guard with appropriate information, instruction and supervision in respect of the use of the generator.

The construction company pleaded guilty to breaching Section 4(2) of the Health and Safety at Work etc. Act 1974. The company was fined £60,000 and ordered to pay costs of £24,515.

The manager of the security company pleaded guilty to breaching Section 3(2) of the Health and Safety at Work etc. Act 1974. He was fined £30,000 and ordered to pay costs of £15,000.

Using properly maintained electrical equipment instead of LPG cookers and heaters can eliminate the risks associated with using LPG. If LPG is used, the risks can be reduced in the following ways.

- Using and storing the cylinders in safe, well-ventilated places, outside of the accommodation (including overnight) or in purpose-built ventilated storage areas.

- Ensuring that appliances have been properly installed, checked and maintained by a competent person.

- Providing adequate combustion ventilation with fixed grilles at high and low level. Adequacy to be checked by a competent person.

- Regularly checking that the ventilation provided is not blocked (for example, by newspaper or rags in cold weather to stop draughts).

- Ensuring that users of the room are aware of the need to maintain ventilation, not to obstruct any existing flues or chimneys, and also know what the early signs of carbon monoxide intoxication are.

- Checking that cylinders are properly turned off when not in use.

- Using wall or ceiling mounted CO detectors.

Typical LPG-powered heater

10.13.3 Use of combustion engine powered equipment

Exhaust emissions from any internal combustion engine contain carbon monoxide. Catalytic converters reduce the amount of carbon monoxide. However, these are not normally fitted to the majority of internal combustion engines used in the construction industry.

In addition to carbon monoxide, exhaust emissions contain many toxic and carcinogenic substances such as soot (diesel engines), polyaromatic hydrocarbons and oxides of nitrogen and sulphur. Long-term exposure to diesel fumes in particular is associated with chronic illness (such as lung cancer).

In construction, the principal risk from using combustion engine powered equipment arises where they are used in enclosed spaces. The use of such equipment in an enclosed space may cause that space to be considered as a confined space under the Confined Spaces Regulations, since the hazards produced by the use of the equipment may well create one or more of the specified risks.

For further information refer to Chapter D08 Confined spaces.

The use of any combustion engine powered equipment in construction must be preceded by a risk assessment, which considers the environment in which the equipment is to be used.

 Where possible, electrical powered equipment or alternative methods of work not involving combustion engine powered equipment should be used if there are issues with adequate ventilation.

 Workers refurbishing a large industrial warehouse became ill and were taken to hospital suffering from the effects of carbon monoxide. They were using diesel-power floats and even though the doors were left open, there was insufficient ventilation.

Where combustion engine powered equipment is used in locations where ventilation and the free movement of air may be restricted, carbon monoxide monitoring should be employed to ensure that levels of carbon monoxide to which workers are exposed are safe. This could include both area monitoring and personal monitors in high-risk situations.

Carbon monoxide analyser

Inadequate ventilation may occur in rooms, but also in the following places.

- Basements.
- Deep excavations.
- Chambers.
- Pits.
- Sewers.
- Tanks.

It is a myth that carbon monoxide is heavier than air and will therefore accumulate at low level. In fact it is slightly lighter than air, and will mix quite evenly with the ambient air. Since exhaust emissions are hot, they will be quite buoyant, which might actually cause the carbon monoxide to rise.

 The risk assessment and method statement for any diesel plant must address the potential hazard of build-up of exhaust emissions. Extraction fans can be hired and carbon monoxide levels can be monitored by a suitable gas monitor.

10.13.4 Refurbishment work on existing buildings

Members of the public have died from carbon monoxide poisoning after refurbishment work (such as roof work) has disrupted gas flues or ventilation systems in their property, causing carbon monoxide to build up. The impact of refurbishment work on existing gas-fired systems must be identified during the planning stage and managed throughout the project.

Prior to the commencement of work. During the planning stage, a competent Gas Safe engineer should undertake an assessment to determine whether there is any likelihood that refurbishment work will affect gas-fired systems.

During the work. Gas systems should be isolated where possible, and the work planned so that the gas system is unaffected. Any work to the gas installation must be undertaken by a competent Gas Safe engineer.

On completion. The gas installation must be re-inspected by a competent Gas Safe engineer prior to re-commissioning if there has been any work that has interfered with the gas installation, including changes to the ventilation regime.

 ## Loft conversion work causes risk of carbon monoxide poisoning

Two partners in a home improvement company have been fined after building work at a house exposed a woman and her foster children to the risk of carbon monoxide poisoning. The company was contracted to carry out loft conversion work at a property. As part of the improvement work, the company had to replace a flue from the gas fire. However, this was then left in an immediately dangerous condition, with potentially lethal fumes escaping into the loft space.

The householder had concerns about the quality of the work carried out by the company, and found that there were faults with the plumbing system. The Gas Safe register sent an officer to investigate. They found that the flue from the gas fire had been removed just below the level of the loft, allowing poisonous carbon monoxide gas into the loft space. This was classified as immediately dangerous.

The HSE's investigation identified that the company did not obtain advice from a Gas Safe registered engineer before the chimney and flue were removed. The gas fire was still connected and used during the winter, resulting in potentially deadly carbon monoxide gas building up within the loft space.

The householder said: 'My son started complaining of headaches and feeling sick and I put it down to him playing computer games, not carbon monoxide. When the Gas Safe register inspector found that the flue had been removed, I realised just how lucky we were.'

The company partners each pleaded guilty to a breach of the Gas Safety (Installation and Use) Regulations and were fined £1,500.

An HSE inspector said: 'The partners failed in their duty to ensure the gas fire was made safe before they removed the chimney and flue. The shoddy and careless work by the contractors could have cost a family with young children their lives. Anyone carrying out work on or near a flue should get advice from a Gas Safe registered engineer, before starting work, to ensure it is made safe. It is never acceptable to assume that a gas appliance will not be used after a flue has been removed.' *(Source: HSE)*

10

10.14   Gas Safe register

All gas work carried out in domestic properties and workplaces (such as shops, restaurants, schools and hospitals) must be undertaken by a Gas Safe-registered engineer.

Gas work includes installing, repairing or servicing a gas boiler and installing or repairing a gas fire, gas cooker or hob. In other workplaces, gas work must be undertaken by a competent person. It is the employer's responsibility to check that they are competent.

If the engineer is on the Gas Safe register, with the qualifications to do the work required, then they will be a competent person.

The Gas Safe register is the only gas engineer registration scheme approved by the HSE under the Gas Safety (Installation and Use) Regulations.

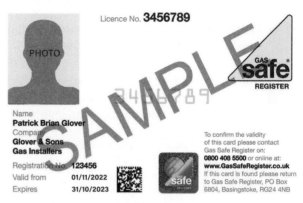

Example of a Gas Safe register identity card

For further information and details on how to find or check a Gas Safe engineer, visit the Gas Safe website.

Gas engineers will often have a range of qualifications that allow them to carry out specific types of gas work. Every gas engineer carries a Gas Safe register ID card with their own unique licence number. This shows the type of gas work they are qualified to do. Before any gas work is carried out, ensure that the engineer is competent by checking their card or looking on the Gas Safe website.

Noise

11

Supporting
INFORMATION

GT700 Toolbox talks / supporting checklists and forms

Toolbox talks on some of these topics are available in the GT700 publication. Supporting checklists and forms covering some of these topics are available on our companion website.

Overview

Construction work can create levels of noise that have the potential to cause permanent damage to the hearing of those affected.

In addition to the long-term health implications, noise can also affect safety on site by interfering with spoken communications and auditory warnings to the point where the risk of accidents is increased.

Noise from construction activities is also a common reason for complaints from neighbours, both residential and commercial, and control of environmental noise can often be an important factor on construction sites.

Noise is a physical health risk and the construction industry has one of the highest rates of ill health caused by exposure to noise.

11.1   Introduction

Noise from construction activities can come from a wide range of common equipment and activities (for example, demolition, excavation, piling, compressors and concrete mixers). Operations (such as hammering, disc cutting, the use of breakers and the use of cartridge-operated fixing tools) are sources of noise that pose a particularly high risk of hearing damage because the source is close to the operative.

Exposure to high levels of noise can cause permanent damage to hearing, in the form of hearing loss and tinnitus. Hearing damage is irreversible, and is often compounded by the natural loss of hearing that occurs with age. It causes a great deal of distress to sufferers, often leading to social isolation and depression.

Environmental impacts from noise are common and are generally related to the nature of the noise generated, as well as its intensity. Intermittent noise can be more disruptive than a continuous noise, and high-pitched sounds are generally more disturbing than low frequency ones. The time of day when the noise occurs is also an important factor in whether it causes a nuisance.

11.2   Important points

- Noise exposure, from work activities and from outside work (such as listening to loud music), contributes to noise-induced hearing loss.

- Early signs of hearing damage (such as tinnitus and the inability to follow conversations where there is background noise) should not be ignored.

- Employers must assess the risk of hearing damage to their employees, and formulate an action plan if the assessment indicates a problem.

- In addition to hearing loss, excessive noise can have other health and safety implications, such as not being able to hear auditory warnings.

- Construction noise is a common source of nuisance to the public and generates many complaints.

- Planning to reduce noise on site can prevent delays caused by nuisance complaints from the public.

- Employers are required to seek noise engineering and organisational control measures before resorting to the use of hearing protection.

- The labour force survey (LFS) estimates that around 20,000 individuals every year consider that their hearing is damaged or made worse through work.

 Many workers do not get enough protection from their hearing protection because they wear it incorrectly.

11.3   Control of Noise at Work Regulations

The Control of Noise at Work Regulations 2005 impose duties on employers and employees to reduce exposure to noise. The aim of these regulations is to ensure that workers' hearing is protected from excessive noise at their place of work, as this could cause them to lose their hearing and or to suffer from tinnitus (permanent ringing in the ears).

 For further details on the regulations and guidance visit the HSE website.

11.3.1   Requirements of the regulations

The requirements of the regulations (summarised on the following pages) are triggered at the two action levels: exposure action values and exposure limit values.

11.3.1.1 Assess the risks

● Identify noise hazards.

● Estimate the likely exposure to noise of workers.

● Identify measures required to eliminate or reduce risks, control exposures, and protect employees.

● Make a record of what measures are to be taken in the form of an action plan. In construction, this action plan would generally be part of the construction phase plan, produced by the contractor or principal contractor under the Construction (Design and Management) Regulations 2015 (CDM).

11.3.1.2 Protect employees

● Eliminate or reduce risks using technical or organisational noise control measures, with the degree of cost and effort depending on the size of the risk.

● Make sure the legal limits on noise exposure are not exceeded.

● Protect employees with hearing protection, making its use mandatory in high-risk cases (however, ensure that the use of hearing protection is only considered after other measures have been taken into account).

● Manage the use of hearing protection, with signed zones where practicable, instruction and supervision.

11.3.1.3 Worker information and training

● Consult workers on noise issues, and allow their participation.

● Give employees information, instruction and training about the risks from noise, control measures, hearing protection and safe working practices.

11.3.1.4 Health surveillance

● Provide health surveillance (including hearing checks) for those at risk.

● Use the results of the health surveillance to review controls and further protect individuals.

11.3.1.5 Maintain and use the equipment

● Maintain any noise control equipment and hearing protection.

● Ensure that anything supplied in the interests of safety is fully and properly used.

11.3.2 Noise assessment

It is the employers' duty, where employees are likely to be exposed at or above the lower exposure action value *(refer to 11.3.3)*, to make a suitable and sufficient assessment of the risk from that noise to the health and safety of those employees. The risk assessment must identify the measures that need to be taken to effectively manage the noise. The assessment must consider, among other factors, the level, type and duration of exposure. A record of the assessment must be maintained and the assessment reviewed when circumstances (such as equipment or work methods) change. Noise assessments are to be undertaken by someone who is competent to do so.

Calibrated noise level meter

In construction, it is common to base exposure assessments on experience of common activities, rather than undertaking measurements on each site. In any case, it must be ensured that the exposure estimates are representative, so that an effective control regime can be implemented. Where the noise emission levels of items of equipment or activities are known, the HSE noise level calculator can be used to work out daily or weekly exposure levels, for comparison against the exposure limit and action values.

The competent person carrying out the assessment may also use a calibrated sound level meter or noise meter to measure sound levels for specific activities, to help calculate exposure levels. There are also noise meter apps available to download to mobile devices, which can be used by site managers to help gauge noise exposure levels and whether any further action needs to be taken.

 Noise meter apps may be used for approximate measurements only. With many different apps available from various sources, it is difficult to verify calibration or accuracy. They are not calibrated in the same way as noise meters, so readings should not be relied upon for the purposes of calculating exposure in a noise assessment.

 For further information refer to the noise exposure calculators and ready-reckoners on the HSE website.

11.3.3   Exposure limits and action values

The Control of Noise at Work Regulations establish exposure limit values and action values.

Lower exposure action values (LEAVs).

● Daily or weekly personal noise exposure of 80 dB(A).

● Peak sound pressure of 135 dB(C).

Upper exposure action values (UEAVs).

● Daily or weekly personal noise exposure of 85 dB(A).

● Peak sound pressure of 137 dB(C).

Exposure limit values (ELVs).

● Daily or weekly personal noise exposure of 87 dB(A).

● Peak sound pressure of 140 dB(C).

The ELVs are to take into account any hearing protection worn by the employee.

11.3.4   Rules of thumb

The various action values quoted in this chapter will be meaningless to anyone who does not have a way of accurately calculating the noise levels on site, taking into account the time factor. There are, however, two rules of thumb that should give a rough indication of noise levels.

One-metre rule. If two people standing one metre apart (about an arm's length), who are not wearing hearing protection, have to raise their voices to hear each other, the noise level is around or above 90 dB. Hearing protection must be worn to reduce the noise at the ear to below the ELV, or the noise must be reduced to the ELV by other means. Employers must identify why ELV has been breached and modify organisational and technical measures.

Two-metre rule. If two people standing two metres apart (double arm's length) have to raise their voices to hear each other, the noise level is around 85 dB and hearing protection must be worn.

There is also a third rule that, if there is any doubt, everyone affected should be wearing hearing protection in the interests of their health.

11.3.5   Elimination or control of exposure to noise in the workplace

There is a requirement on the employer to either eliminate the risk to their employees from noise exposure or, where this is not reasonably practicable, to reduce the risk to as low a level as is reasonably practicable. In particular, if an employee is likely to be exposed at or above a UEAV, the employer must reduce the exposure as far as is reasonably practicable by means other than the use of personal hearing protection. The actions to be taken by the employer, other than the issue of hearing protection, must include the following considerations.

● The use of other working methods that reduce exposure to noise.

● Choice of appropriate work equipment emitting the least possible noise.

● Design and layout of workplaces, work stations and rest facilities.

● Suitable and sufficient information and training for employees, such that work equipment may be used correctly and procedures followed properly, in order to minimise their exposure to noise.

● Reduction of noise by technical means, such as the use of silencers, low-noise bearings, enclosures, and so on.

● Appropriate maintenance programmes for work equipment and systems.

● Limitation on the duration and intensity of exposure to noise.

● Appropriate work schedules with adequate rest periods.

If an employer is unable to adequately reduce the exposure of their employees below an UEAV by the means specified above, then suitable hearing protection must be provided to any employee exposed at the UEAV or above. The area where employees are likely to be exposed at or above the UEAV must be designated a hearing-protection zone. Such zones must be demarcated and identified by means of signs specified for the purpose of indicating that ear protection must be worn.

On construction sites, due to the mobile nature of the work, it is not usually practical to demarcate hearing-protection zones within the site. Generally the whole site is designated as a zone, and the wearing of hearing protection is enforced for particular activities.

 It should be noted that blanket use of hearing protection may be hazardous, as it prevents workers from perceiving other hazards (such as site traffic). The construction phase plan should clearly indicate how this will be managed on the site.

If an ELV is exceeded, the employer must reduce the exposure below the ELV as soon as possible, identify the reason for the ELV being exceeded and modify the organisational and technical measures to ensure that the ELV is not exceeded again. Where the assessment determines that an employee is likely to be exposed at or above the LEAV, but below the UEAV, the employer shall, upon request, make hearing protectors available to any worker who is exposed.

 Whilst not a requirement of the regulations, it is advisable to designate areas where exposures are typically between the LEAV and the UEAV as advisory hearing-protection zones and erect suitable signs.

In some cases, due to the levels of noise and the location of the site, the whole site may be designated as an advisory hearing-protection zone, and this can be indicated on the site signage.

11.3.6 Health surveillance

The regulations include a requirement for employers to provide health surveillance for employees at risk from noise at work. Health surveillance is a programme of systematic health checks to identify early signs of hearing loss and prevent its progression.

It is also useful for monitoring the effectiveness of controls. Health surveillance for those at risk should include hearing checks, also known as audiometry.

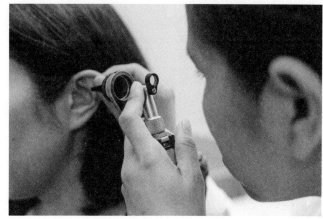

The guidance accompanying the regulations recommends that those exposed at or above the UEAV should receive regular health surveillance, whilst those exposed at or above the LEAV should receive health surveillance if they have a particular sensitivity, family history of hearing problems, existing hearing damage or previous work history at high noise levels.

Hearing checks should be undertaken for at-risk workers

Where the health surveillance shows that there is identifiable hearing loss, the employer must ensure that the employee is examined by a doctor or specialist. The employer must maintain records of all health surveillance, and make those records available to the enforcing authorities and the employees themselves, as necessary.

 For further information on health surveillance refer to Chapter B01 Management of health.

11.3.7 Information, instruction and training

Any employee exposed to noise at or above the LEAV must be provided with sufficient information, instruction and training. This should include the following.

- A description of the nature of risks from exposure to excessive noise.

- The organisational and technical measures taken by the organisation in order to reduce the risk from noise.

- A description of the exposure action value and exposure limit value contained in the regulations.

- Significant findings of the noise assessment, including any measurements taken, with an explanation of the findings.

- Arrangements for the provision, storage and maintenance of hearing protection, along with a description of the various types of equipment available.

- How to use and maintain the various types of hearing protection.

- How to detect and report signs of hearing damage and the reasons why.

- Entitlement to health surveillance and a description of what is involved.

- Safe working practices to minimise exposure to noise.

- Collective results of any health surveillance, in a form that does not identify any particular person.

11.4 Nature of construction noise

By its nature, construction involves activities that can generate high levels of noise.

This noise is often intermittent, meaning it is prone to stop and start, and making it more likely to cause a nuisance.

It is often tonal in nature, with dominant tones (such as screeching, whining or beeping) that also make it more likely to cause a nuisance.

However, it is the high intensity of many sources that create its potential to cause hearing damage.

The figures displayed in the table to the right are some typical noise levels of construction equipment measured at 1 m from the source.

Construction equipment	Noise level
Hammer drill	102 dB(A)
Concrete mixer	104 db(A)
Hand-held breaker	105 db(A)
Circular bench saw	107 db(A)
Sheet piling rig	>120 db(A)

 It is not just the user of a noisy tool who is at risk of hearing damage – those working nearby are also at risk and must be protected.

11.5   Effects of noise

11.5.1   Hearing loss

The most common effect of excessive noise at work is noise-induced hearing loss. The occurrence and the amount of hearing loss are related to the noise dose. Therefore, high noise levels may cause hearing loss within a short period and, in extreme cases, instantaneously (for example, when caused by explosions).

Lower levels of noise will have a cumulative effect over a period of years. Therefore, hearing loss is often slow and secretly harmful, coming on without being noticed, until significant damage has been caused.

It is a common misconception that hearing loss simply reduces the volume of sound perceived by the sufferer. In fact, hearing loss generally varies at different frequencies, so that some sounds are more difficult to discern than others. Noise-induced hearing loss typically affects the frequencies around 4 KHz, creating a characteristic 4 K dip on an audiogram *(refer to the chart to the right)*.

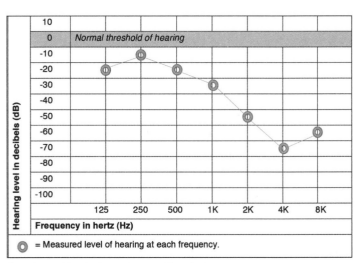

Noise-induced hearing loss audiogram (illustrative)

This causes 't', 'd' and 's' sounds to become indistinguishable, making speech difficult to understand. If the person continues to be exposed to high levels of noise, the dip becomes deeper and the hearing loss more severe with time. Most people naturally lose their ability to hear high frequencies as they get older, and this natural loss will be superimposed on the noise-induced hearing loss, making the situation even worse.

Often associated with noise-induced hearing loss is a condition called tinnitus. This causes the sufferer to experience ringing, whistling, buzzing or other noises in one or both ears. Often sufferers can tolerate it during the day, when there are many background noises to mask the tinnitus, but at night, in the absence of background noise, the tinnitus can cause sleep interference and often distress. Many sufferers use background noise generators at night, or attempt to sleep with the radio on to mask the noise.

The HSE website contains an audio file that demonstrates the effects of noise-induced hearing loss

11.5.2   Nuisance noise

Noise from construction activities can affect those around the workplace, other than construction workers, by causing nuisance. Whilst not directly damaging to health, nuisance noise can cause unacceptable disruption to other people and, if prolonged, may cause some distress. Nuisance noise may affect people in residential areas, as well as people at work (such as those in nearby offices). Most complaints relating to construction noise come from residential areas.

The Local Authority has powers to deal with noise nuisance, including construction noise, under the **Environmental Protection Act 1990**, and may issue abatement notices to prevent noise nuisance. The Local Authority also has powers under the **Control of Pollution Act 1974** specifically in relation to construction noise. A notice served under Section 60 of the Act enables the Local Authority to stipulate requirements as to the way in which the works are to be carried out. In particular, the notice may specify the following.

- Plant or machinery that is, or is not, to be used.
- Hours during which the works may be carried out.

- Level of noise that may be emitted.

Prior to the start of construction work, a contractor may apply for **prior consent** for noise generating activities during the construction project. If the Local Authority grants consent to the activities and hours of operation, the contractor may use this as a defence if any subsequent noise nuisance complaints are received. This noise planning process may prevent problems during the construction phase, and avoid delays caused by Local Authority abatement action.

11.6   Managing noise levels during construction

A hierarchical approach should be adopted to both occupational and environmental noise control from construction activities. For noise, the following hierarchy should be applied.

11.6.1   Control at the source

This is the best option. Some of the available techniques are described on the next page.

11.6.1.1 Buy quiet

By specifying low-noise equipment, noise can be effectively reduced at source. Manufacturers are required to provide noise emission data for all of their equipment. Whilst this data is not good enough for noise exposure assessments (because it is laboratory data and not real world measurements) it can be used to compare different makes and models of equipment. Inherently quiet equipment is also a good approach to reduce the risk from nuisance complaints – effectively silenced generators can reduce much of the constant noise that often originates from construction sites.

The HSE has launched an initiative called *Buy quiet*. It aims to help manufacturers, importers, suppliers and users of work equipment to work together to reduce the risk of noise-induced hearing loss in the workplace.

 For further information on the *Buy quiet* initiative visit the HSE website.

11.6.1.2 Selection of work method

Where possible use work methods that are inherently quieter, or where the noise source is further away from the operative. Some examples are shown below.

- Use a rotary diamond cutter to cut large holes in brickwork, rather than chain drilling with a tungsten drill bit which requires hammer action. Although more expensive to buy, it is faster and gives a cleaner hole. It is also much quieter and produces less vibration.

- Use an excavator-mounted pecker breaker rather than a hand-held breaker. Although pecker breakers are noisy, and may not be suitable where nuisance is a potential problem, the noise is generated at a much greater distance from the operator and so noise exposure is less. They are also quicker and therefore exposure is shorter. In addition, hand-arm vibration issues are avoided.

- Specify prefabricated components (such as factory-cut paving slabs) to avoid the need for on-site cutting (which also avoids hand-arm vibration and silica dust issues).

- Use equipment that is powerful enough for the job. Underpowered equipment operating at or near its limit will be noisier and take longer, increasing noise exposure.

11.6.1.3 Maintain equipment

Tools and equipment should be serviced and maintained in accordance with the manufacturer's instructions and maintenance schedules. This will help to prevent high noise levels, ensure efficient operation and reduce wear. Maintenance may include the following.

- Keep cutting tools sharp.

- Correctly dress abrasive wheels.

- Replace worn parts.

- Check and replace worn vibration dampers, bearings and gears.

- Sharpen chainsaw teeth and keep correct chain tension.

- Keep tools and equipment well lubricated.

- Tune and adjust engines.

11.6.2 Control in the sound path

Control in the sound path is the next best option. Some of the available techniques are described below.

11.6.2.1 Siting or location

Position equipment so that it is as far away from the receivers as possible. This is particularly effective for the control of environmental noise. Sound levels generally reduce rapidly with distance, depending on the nature of the environment.

Effective siting includes the following.

- Siting the source of noise as far from the sensitive environmental receiver as possible.

- Orientating the plant to direct the noise away from the work area or sensitive environmental receiver.

- Placing site buildings, stores, and so on, between noise sources and the sensitive environmental receivers. This is particularly effective if the buildings block the sight of the noise source, since people generally perceive a greater nuisance if they can see the noise source.

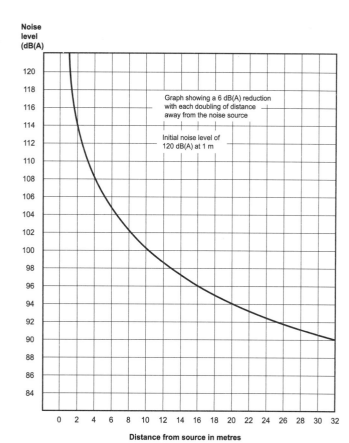

How sound levels might typically reduce with distance

11.6.2.2 Use of barriers or enclosures

A barrier placed correctly between a noise source and the receiver can reduce received noise levels significantly. Of course, this is not always practicable (such as for operatives using hand-held tools). However, in some situations (such as those listed below) this is an effective technique.

● Siting spoil between noisy areas and sensitive receivers to create a noise bund.

● Using continuously boarded site hoarding that will act as a noise barrier, provided it is properly constructed with no gaps or openings.

● Housing plant (such as generators) in soundproof enclosures.

In general, for maximum effect, a sound barrier should be placed as close to the source or receiver as possible.

11.6.2.3 Reducing the number of people

Temporary noise barrier utilising acoustic curtains

By the use of effective training and supervision, operatives should be encouraged not to stand near hazardous noise sources. It is common to see construction workers standing close to a colleague who is using a road breaker or other piece of high-noise equipment, and whilst the worker using the equipment is wearing hearing protection, those around are not.

11.6.3 Control at the receiver

This is the last and least preferred option. This largely refers to the use of hearing protection to control the exposure of workers.

In construction, it is often necessary to use hearing protection as part of the noise control strategy, as sufficient control may not be achieved using the control at source and control in the sound path methods. This requires careful management in order to be successful.

The management of hearing protection must include the following.

● Careful selection of hearing protection equipment.

● Training of employees on the use of the equipment.

● Supervision to ensure the equipment is used properly.

11.7   Personal hearing protection

It is not always possible to eliminate all noise hazards. Where a noise risk remains, suitable hearing protection must be provided to each worker who is exposed to the hazard.

 For further information on hearing protection refer to Chapter B06 Personal protective equipment.

Appendix A - Definitions

Acoustics is the branch of physics that deals with sound and noise. This is a complex field, and some understanding of the basic definitions is necessary to understand the concepts and the Control of Noise at Work Regulations 2005 requirements.

Sound is the sensation caused by rapid pressure variations in the ear. The variations are converted to nerve signals and sent to the brain, which interprets them into what we hear.

Noise is often described as unwanted sound. The perception of what is noise will vary from person to person.

Decibel (dB) is the measurement unit for sound, and is a logarithmic unit, which means a small increase in decibels still indicates a large increase of sound energy reaching the ear.

Frequency is the rate of variation of the pressure waves in air. Humans can perceive from around 20 Hz to 20,000 Hz (20 KHz), although this range is affected by age and hearing damage.

Sound intensity is a function of the sound pressure, and hearing damage is related to the intensity and duration of sound. A doubling of sound intensity equates to a 3 dB increase.

Loudness is the perception of sound level. Loudness is not directly related to sound intensity. A doubling of perceived loudness is around 10 dB, although this is ten times the sound intensity.

Weighting is the adjustment made to measured sound levels for various reasons. The most commonly used weighting is the 'A' weighting, which mimics the human response to sound, making the measurements more meaningful. It is used for the main noise criteria referred to in the Control of Noise at Work Regulations. The 'C' weighting is also widely used, and is effectively a linear measurement used for peak sound measurements from impulsive noises (such as cartridge tools and hammer tools). These are expressed as dB(A) and dB(C) respectively.

Daily dose ($L_{EP,d}$) is the equivalent continuous noise level over an eight hour period. This measure allows noise exposures of different intensities and durations to be directly compared, and is the basis of the criteria levels in the Control of Noise at Work Regulations.

Lower exposure action value (LEAV) is the lower threshold for employers to take action under the Control of Noise at Work Regulations *(refer to 11.3.3 and Appendix B)*, and is represented by a daily personal noise exposure ($L_{EP,d}$) of 80 dB(A) or a peak sound pressure of 135 dB(C).

Upper exposure action value (UEAV) is the higher threshold for employers to take action under the Control of Noise at Work Regulations *(refer to 11.3.3 and Appendix B)*, and is represented by a daily personal noise exposure ($L_{EP,d}$) of 85 dB(A) or a peak sound pressure of 137 dB(C).

Exposure limit value (ELV) is the level of personal exposure that must not be exceeded under the Control of Noise at Work Regulations *(refer to 11.3.3 and Appendix B)*, taking into account the effect of any hearing protection worn. It is represented by a daily personal noise exposure ($L_{EP,d}$) of 87 dB(A) or a peak sound pressure of 140 dB(C).

Appendix B – Summary of the requirements of the Control of Noise at Work Regulations

An employer may decide to implement a number of measures at lower noise exposure levels (for example, health surveillance for employees with existing hearing damage or previous work history at high noise levels).

Employers' duties	Where exposure is below the lower exposure action value of 80 dB(A)	Where exposure levels are likely to be at or above the		
		lower exposure action value of 80 dB(A) or peak sound pressure of 135 dB(C)	upper exposure action value of 85 dB(A) or peak sound pressure of 137 dB(C)	exposure limit value of 87 dB(A) or peak sound pressure of 140 dB(C)
Assessment of noise exposure				
■ Risk assessment to be carried out and reviewed as necessary.		✔	✔	✔
■ Record of significant findings and control measures put in place.		✔	✔	✔
■ Risk assessment to include extra considerations in higher risk situations.			✔	✔
General duty to reduce risk				
■ Risk of hearing damage to be eliminated or reduced to the lowest level reasonably practicable.		✔	✔	✔
■ Implement organisational and technical control measures, excluding issue of personal hearing protection.			✔	✔
■ Reduce exposure below exposure limit value (ELV); if ELV breached, identify why and modify organisational and technical measures.				✔
■ Ensure noise exposure in rest facilities is kept to an acceptable level.		✔	✔	✔
■ Adapt control measures as necessary to take account of employee(s) who may be particularly at risk from exposure to noise.		✔	✔	✔
■ Consult with employees or their representatives on protective measures taken.		✔	✔	✔
Provision of hearing protection Ensure that personal hearing protectors are: ■ provided to employees who ask for them		✔		
■ provided to all those exposed			✔	✔
■ used by all those exposed.			✔	✔
Create hearing-protection zones, designated by appropriate signs and: ■ restrict access if justified by the level of risk			✔	✔
■ ensure as far as is reasonably practicable that all who go into a marked hearing-protection zone use hearing protection.			✔	✔
Maintenance and use of equipment Ensure so far as is reasonably practicable that: ■ all equipment provided under the regulations, except personal hearing protectors, are fully and properly used			✔	✔
■ all equipment is maintained in an efficient state and good working order.	✔	✔	✔	✔

11

Employers' duties	Where exposure is below the lower exposure action value of 80 dB(A)	Where exposure levels are likely to be at or above the		
		lower exposure action value of 80 dB(A) or peak sound pressure of 135 dB(C)	upper exposure action value of 85 dB(A) or peak sound pressure of 137 dB(C)	exposure limit value of 87 dB(A) or peak sound pressure of 140 dB(C)
Information instruction and training Provide adequate information, instruction and training and update it as necessary, on:				
▪ the nature of the risks to hearing from noise		✔	✔	✔
▪ the organisational and technical measures taken		✔	✔	✔
▪ the action and limit values		✔	✔	✔
▪ the significant findings of the risk assessment		✔	✔	✔
▪ how to obtain a personal hearing protector		✔	✔	✔
▪ how to detect and report signs of hearing damage		✔	✔	✔
▪ the entitlement to health surveillance		✔	✔	✔
▪ the results of any **collective** health surveillance.		✔	✔	✔
Provide information, instruction and training for anyone who has responsibilities for ensuring the employer's legal duties are carried out.		✔	✔	✔
Health surveillance Provide as appropriate if the risk assessment indicates there to be a risk to employees' health resulting from noise at work.		✔	✔	✔
Keep and maintain records of health surveillance and enable employees access to their own health surveillance records and allow the HSE to access records as necessary.		✔	✔	✔
Where employees are found to have hearing damage: ▪ ensure the employee is informed by a suitably qualified person		✔	✔	✔
▪ review the risk assessment and control measures		✔	✔	✔
▪ consider assigning the employee to alternative (non-noisy) work		✔	✔	✔
▪ continue with health surveillance.		✔	✔	✔
Employees' duties				
Use of equipment Employees must: ▪ make full and proper use of personal hearing protectors			✔	✔
▪ use any other control measures provided by the employer		✔	✔	✔
▪ report any defects discovered in the protective measures to the employer.	✔	✔	✔	✔
Health surveillance Attend health surveillance procedures as required by the employer in working hours and at the employer's expense.		✔	✔	✔

11

Appendix C – Exposure levels

The effect on maximum working times due to exposure without protection

Average noise level dB(A)	Maximum exposure in one working day if 80 dB(A) ($L_{EP,d}$)* is not exceeded
80	8 hours
83	4 hours
86	2 hours
89	1 hour
92	30 minutes
95	15 minutes
98	7.5 minutes
101	3.75 minutes

* See page 184, Daily dose, for how this formula should be presented.

Increase of protection gained in relation to time if ear protectors are worn

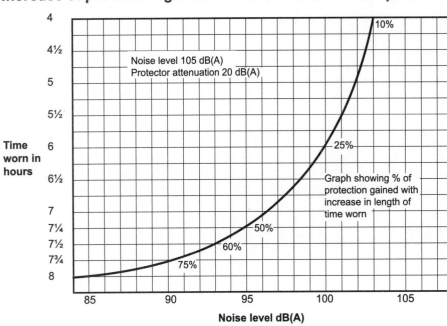

Vibration

12

Supporting **INFORMATION**

GT700 Toolbox talks / supporting checklists and forms

Toolbox talks on some of these topics are available in the GT700 publication. Supporting checklists and forms covering some of these topics are available on our companion website.

Overview

Exposure to vibration can have serious health effects. Vibration from hand-held tools can cause hand-arm vibration syndrome (HAVS), which affects many workers in the construction industry. Whole-body vibration (WBV) is also a health risk in the construction industry and may affect operators of construction vehicles, often resulting in back injury.

Employers have a duty to assess and control the vibration to which their workers are exposed. The careful selection of work methods (including selecting low-vibration tools) and limiting exposure times are important aspects in the control of exposure to vibration in the construction industry.

Vibration is a physical health risk and the construction industry has one of the highest rates of ill health caused by vibration.

12.1   Introduction

The injuries and ill health effects that can be caused by excessive exposure to hand-arm or whole-body vibration are often debilitating and painful, and can have a chronic effect on the sufferer's quality of life. Both are serious issues in the construction industry, but hand-arm vibration is by far the most significant, leading to many cases of disablement each year. Sufferers may have damage to nerves, tendons, blood vessels, bones and ligaments, which cause chronic pain and can lead to difficulties performing everyday tasks.

In addition to the pain and suffering caused to individuals, employers have to deal with the effects of long-term absence of people affected, and the civil claims and criminal law sanctions that often arise in organisations where vibration risks are not properly managed.

12.2   Important points

- The HSE estimates that over two million workers are at risk from vibration at work in the UK.

- Failure to control vibration risks can result in disabling, painful, chronic health conditions among workers.

- Employers have a duty to undertake an adequate risk assessment from vibration risks. This must be undertaken by someone competent to do so.

- The Control of Vibration at Work Regulations set action criteria and limit values. However, employers are required to keep vibration exposures as low as is reasonably practicable, irrespective of these criteria and limit values.

- Changing work methods, limiting exposure times and using low-vibration tools are among the most common control methods.

- Employees exposed to vibration risks must receive adequate training so they are aware of the risks and what to do to control them.

- Regular health surveillance of workers exposed to vibration risks is an essential method of ensuring that symptoms are prevented from occurring or from getting worse.

12.3   Control of Vibration at Work Regulations

The Control of Vibration at Work Regulations 2005 implement the requirements of the European Directive regarding the exposure of employees to vibration. They impose duties on employers to protect employees (and others) who may be exposed to the risk of ill health because of vibration at work. The regulations are, in places, very technical, particularly in relation to the measurement of vibration. The services of a qualified occupational health professional may be needed where the measurement of vibration is necessary. The regulations place legal duties on employers and employees with regard to the control and management of employees' exposure to vibration.

12.3.1   Employers' duties

If employees are likely to be exposed to risks from vibration in the course of their work the employer must ensure the following.

- An assessment of the risks to the health and safety of the employees exposed to vibration is carried out. The risk assessment must identify the measures that need to be taken to meet the requirements of these regulations.

- As part of the risk assessment, the daily exposure of individual employees to vibration is determined.

- Assess whether any employee is likely to be exposed to vibration at or above the action values and limit values in the regulations.

- Where exposure is likely to be at or above the exposure action value (EAV), reduce exposure to vibration to as low a level as is reasonably practicable, by implementing organisational and technical measures that are appropriate to the work activity being carried out.

- Employees are not exposed to vibration above the exposure limit value (ELV) or, if they are, immediately carry out the following.
  - Reduce exposure to below the ELV.
  - Identify the reasons for the ELV being exceeded.
  - Take appropriate actions to prevent it occurring again.

- Actions taken to comply with the above requirements are based upon the principles of prevention set out in the Management of Health and Safety at Work Regulations and include consideration of the following.
  - Alternative work methods that eliminate or reduce exposure to vibration.
  - Alternative work equipment or an appropriate ergonomic design which, taking account of the task, produces the least vibration.
  - Provision of effective maintenance programmes for equipment that can create vibration.
  - Provision of information and training for at-risk employees.
  - Limiting the duration and intensity of exposure to vibration.
  - Adjusting work schedules and ensuring adequate rest periods.
- Employees likely to be exposed over the EAV, or who have other risk factors (such as HAVS), receive regular health surveillance.
- Significant findings of the risk assessment are documented, along with the measures taken to control risk and provide information, instruction and training.

 The HSE has produced a range of free resources, information and guidance on hand-arm vibration at work, including the publication *Hand-arm vibration at work: A brief guide* (INDG175), to help both employers and employees understand what is required to comply with the Control of Vibration at Work Regulations 2005.

12.3.2 Health surveillance

Health surveillance should be provided for the following vibration-exposed employees.

- Those who are likely to be regularly exposed above the EAV.
- Those who are likely to be exposed occasionally above the exposure action value and where the risk assessment identifies that the frequency and severity of exposure may pose a risk to health.
- Those who have a diagnosis of HAVS (even when exposed below the exposure action value).

Where health surveillance indicates that a worker is being adversely affected by vibration, the employer must ensure the following.

- The risk assessment is reviewed.
- Existing control measures are reviewed, taking into account any advice given by a doctor, occupational health professional or enforcing authority.
- Consideration is given to reassigning the employee to other work where there is no risk from further exposure.
- The health of any other employee who has been similarly exposed is reviewed, including the provision of a medical examination where recommended by a doctor, occupational health professional or the enforcing authority.

The HSE recommends a five-stage system of health surveillance for HAV.

Stage 1	An initial questionnaire to be answered when employees first move into any job that involves exposure to vibration.
Stage 2	A short questionnaire answered annually by employees exposed to vibration.
Stage 3	A formal HAVS health assessment carried out by a qualified person (for example, an occupational health nurse).
Stage 4	A formal diagnosis made by a doctor who is qualified in occupational health, and who will assess fitness for work.
Stage 5	(Optional) If considered necessary, the doctor refers the employee for certain tests for HAVS to assist the doctor in making the judgements required in Stage 4.

Employers who consider that their employees are at potential risk from HAVS should appoint a person to manage the health surveillance programme and be actively involved in the initial stages.

Requirements of that person are listed below.

- Does not need to be medically qualified.
- Should not attempt diagnosis or be judgemental as to the cause of HAVS with regard to individual cases.
- Should be trained by an occupational health professional.
- Must be able to describe the symptoms of HAVS.
- Should have experience of the working environment.
- Must be able to gain the trust and co-operation of employees, and understand the importance of confidentiality.

 The HSE recommends that employees known to be at risk of HAVS, but who report no symptoms for three consecutive years on their annual questionnaire (Stage 2), should be referred to an occupational health specialist for an independent view of symptoms that may have been overlooked.

 For WBV, detailed health surveillance is not possible, as there are many non-vibration causes of back pain. Therefore, the HSE recommends health monitoring, which is a structured system for self-reporting symptoms.

12

12.3.3 Training and information

Where the risk assessment shows a risk to the health of employees who are (or are liable to be) exposed to vibration at or above the EAV, the employer must provide the employees and their representatives with suitable and sufficient information, instruction and training, including the following.

● The organisational and technical measures taken to eliminate or control exposure to vibration.

● The EAV and the ELV.

● The significant findings of the risk assessment, including details of any measurements taken, with an explanation of the findings.

● Why and how to detect and report signs of injury resulting from exposure to vibration.

● The employees' entitlement to health surveillance.

● How to work safely to minimise exposure to vibration.

● The collective results of any health surveillance carried out. These must be anonymous so as not to reveal the personal health record of any individual.

The information, instruction and training provided (as above) must be updated by the employer to take account of any significant changes in the type of work carried out or methods of working.

12.3.4 Vibration risk assessment

The vibration risk assessment is intended to identify those workers who are at risk from workplace vibration, and attempt to quantify the degree of exposure. There are many potential sources of error for such an assessment, particularly with regard to the measurement of vibration emission from equipment. Therefore it is essential that employers obtain suitable competent advice and assistance to help with any assessment. The assessment requires two fundamental sets of reliable data.

1. **Vibration emission** from the equipment currently in use. For the assessment of hand-arm vibration risks, this would be any hand-held equipment that produces vibration. This data may be obtained in one, or a combination, of the following ways.

   – Direct measurement of the equipment currently in use, preferably whilst being used by the operatives who normally use it, on the materials and using the attachments normally used.

   – From a database of measurements from comparable equipment doing comparable tasks – the reliability of such data is lower, and therefore a larger margin of error should be accommodated. This may be an internal company database or an external commercial database.

2. **Usage data** for the workers using each piece of equipment. Vibration exposure is dose-based, being a combination of the level of emission and the time for which it is actually used. The daily usage time for a piece of equipment is known as *trigger time*, being the time that the equipment is actuated (in use).

 Manufacturers produce vibration emission data for their equipment. This is not 'real world' data and should only be used for comparing equipment as part of a selection process. It should NOT be used for the assessment of individual risk.

Some issues with data collection are shown below.

● Accurate measurement of vibration emission is dependent upon a good measurement technique being employed. Even with good technique it is estimated that the error could still be as much as +/- 20%.

● Vibration emission can vary due to a number of factors, such as:

   – operative technique   – the state of maintenance of the equipment

   – the speed the equipment is operated at   – the choice of tool, bit, disk or fitting.

● Operatives asked to self-report usage times tend to overestimate trigger times.

● In the construction industry in particular, usage times are highly variable, and within a day an operative may use a number of pieces of equipment for varying periods, depending on the needs of the work in progress.

Vibration risk assessors should plan the assessment so as to minimise these factors as far as possible. For example, trigger time can be determined more accurately by the use of a tool timer, which records the trigger time for a piece of equipment.

Vibration risk assessments must be suitable and sufficient, to enable appropriate controls to be planned, and must also be recorded. They must be repeated when it is suspected that they are no longer valid.

Given the issues with data reliability, it is reasonable to include a margin for error in any conclusions, and take a worst-case approach to the interpretation of data.

12.3.5 Quantification of vibration exposure

Vibration is measured as acceleration of the vibrating surface. It is measured in metres per second squared and therefore has a unit of ms^{-2} or m/s^2. Vibration exposure direction is also important and is measured in defined directions. Hand-arm vibration and whole-body vibration are measured in three axes (x, y and z) and combined to give an overall level.

Measurements are frequency-weighted by the instrumentation to represent the human response to vibration. In order to assess the risk to individuals, the dose is required, which is expressed as a time-weighted average over an eight hour working day. This is expressed as **ms^{-2} A(8) or m/s^2 A(8)**.

The **exposure action values (EAVs)** are:

- hand-arm vibration　　　2.5 ms^{-2} A(8)

- whole-body vibration　　　0.5 ms^{-2} A(8).

Individual exposure at or above this level requires that employers implement a range of managerial and technical measures to control exposure to as low a level as is reasonably practicable.

The **exposure limit values (ELVs)** are:

- hand-arm vibration　　　5.0 ms^{-2} A(8)

- whole-body vibration　　　1.15 ms^{-2} A(8).

Vibration exposure of individuals must not exceed the ELV. If exposure of individuals exceeds the ELV, action must be taken to identify the reason and ensure that it does not happen again.

12.3.6　Employees' duties

Under the regulations, employees have a legal duty to make themselves available for health surveillance checks (during working hours) as required by the employer.

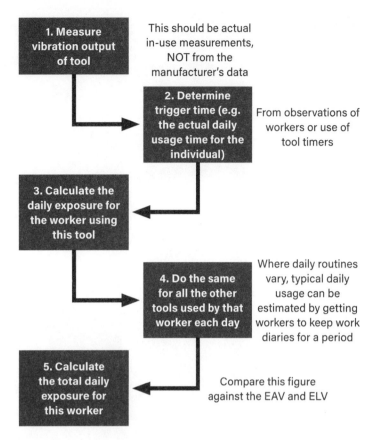

Vibration assessment for powered tools

 Compensation and civil claims

Many cases reach the civil courts in which employees pursue claims for compensation after having reportedly developed ill health or physical conditions through the use of plant and equipment that generated vibration.

Complying with the Control of Vibration at Work Regulations, following the guidance on the regulations and implementing an occupational health programme that monitors and manages employees' exposure to vibration will help to reduce the number of employees suffering from symptoms, hence reducing the number of such cases.

Evidence that the regulations are being complied with will also be evidence that the employer has been reasonable, and can be used as a defence in civil claims. Employers need to keep records of their management programmes and monitoring (such as health surveillance).

12.4　Hand-arm vibration

The most common form of vibration affecting those who work in construction is hand-arm vibration, which has the potential to damage the circulation, nerves, joints and bones in the hands and arms.

12.4.1　Sources of hand-arm vibration

Below are some tools and plant used in the construction industry that could cause exposure to risks from hand-arm vibration.

- Road and concrete breaking drills.
- Sanders and similar reciprocating tools.
- Concrete pokers.
- Cut-off saws or disc cutters.
- Plate vibrators or wacker plates.
- Power hammers and chisels hammers.
- Demolition picks.

- Percussive (hammer) drills.
- Compressor guns.
- Chainsaws.
- Pneumatic drills.
- Needle guns or scabblers.
- Angle grinders.
- Woodworking machinery.

This is irrespective of the tool's power source.

Other equipment that may occasionally be used and is a source of vibration includes plaster or paint mixers (whisks), impact wrenches, rotavators, lawnmowers and brushcutters.

12

Examples of tools that could cause hand-arm vibration if control measures are not implemented

The factors below can influence the magnitude of the vibrational acceleration reaching the hand and the effect of the vibration.

● Frequency at which the tool vibrates.

● Exposure pattern (length and frequency of work and subsequent rest periods).

● Sharpness and suitability of the cutting tool or blade to cut the material being worked on.

● Grip, push and other forces used to guide and apply the vibrating tools. The tighter the grip, the more vibration energy is transferred to the hands. (Vibration may increase as a tool becomes blunt and the user pushes harder.)

● Other factors that potentially affect blood circulation (such as workplace temperature, whether the person smokes and individual susceptibility).

● Hardness of the material being worked.

● Posture of the tool user, because tense muscles are more susceptible to hand-arm vibration (for example, using vibrating tools at arm's length increases the effect).

12.4.2 Effects of hand-arm vibration

Hand-arm vibration can cause a range of symptoms collectively known as **hand-arm vibration syndrome (HAVS)**, as well as specific conditions, such as carpal tunnel syndrome (CTS). The effects of HAVS can broadly be subdivided into the following areas.

● Vascular – affecting the blood vessels.

● Neurological – affecting nerves and sensory nerve endings.

● Musculoskeletal – affecting muscles, soft tissues (tendons, ligaments, cartilage, and so on) and bone.

12.4.2.1 Vascular HAVS symptoms

The principal vascular symptom of excessive exposure to hand-transmitted vibration is finger blanching.

It should be noted that, although vibration causes the condition, the symptoms are precipitated by cold, not vibration. Hence, someone suffering from this condition may be fine whilst carrying out work with a vibrating tool, but when they get cold hands, they will suffer the characteristic blanching, with painful red throbbing on re-warming. After many years' exposure, permanent discolouration of the fingers may occur.

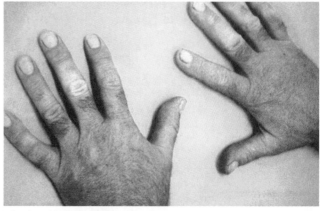

Vibration white finger (VWF)

This collection of symptoms is known as vibration white finger (VWF), or secondary Raynaud's disease (primary Raynaud's disease is where the symptoms are caused by existing factors within the body).

12.4.2.2 Neurological HAVS symptoms

Damage to nerve tissue in the hand caused by vibration may lead to the following types of symptom.

- Tingling.
- Numbness.
- Loss of sensation.
- Loss of manual dexterity.
- Painful throbbing.

12.4.2.3 Musculoskeletal HAVS symptoms

Muscles, bones and soft tissues may be affected by exposure to vibration in the following ways.

- Muscle fatigue and loss of grip strength.
- Disorders of the bones (such as cysts and vacuoles).
- Joint disorders of the upper arm (such as tennis elbow and rotator cuff degeneration).

In addition, CTS is a common result of excessive exposure to hand-transmitted vibration. The carpal tunnel is a small tunnel that runs from the bottom of the wrist to the lower palm. Symptoms arise due to entrapment or compression of the median nerve in the palm. CTS caused by hand-held vibrating tools is reportable under the Reporting of Injuries, Diseases and Dangerous Occurrences Regulations (RIDDOR).

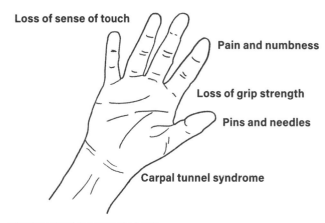

Loss of sense of touch

Pain and numbness

Loss of grip strength

Pins and needles

Carpal tunnel syndrome

Vibration-related damage to the hands

These symptoms, as well as being painful or uncomfortable, can cause a loss of amenity, affecting work and home life. Inability to do fine work (for example, assembling small components) or everyday tasks (such as fastening buttons) is typical. Vibration damage is very much dose-related. The greater the exposure to vibration, the more likely there is to be damage. At high levels of exposure, early signs of damage can appear after months rather than years.

12.5 Whole-body vibration

Whole-body vibration (WBV), as its name suggests, is vibration or jolting of the whole body through the surface that is supporting the body (such as a machine seat or floor).

WBV, which often results from driving or operating some types of construction plant or vehicle, has the potential to cause back injury or make an existing back condition more painful.

Back pain can be caused by many work and non-work activities. It can lead to time off work, loss of productivity and compensation claims. Mobile machine operators and drivers (especially those who work off-road) are at increased risk from back pain.

Listed below are some tools and plant used in the construction industry that could cause exposure to risks from WBV.

- Rough-terrain forklift trucks and telehandlers.
- Vibratory rollers.
- Mobile crushers.
- Dumper trucks and other forms of earth-moving machinery.

Equipment that can cause exposure to whole-body vibration

Among those most likely to experience high vibration exposures are regular operators and drivers of off-road machinery listed below.

- Construction, mining and quarrying machines and vehicles, particularly earthmoving machines (such as motor scrapers, bulldozers and construction site dumpers).

- Tractors and other agricultural and forestry machinery, particularly when used in transportation, tedding (turning hay), primary cultivation and mowing.

WBV can be controlled in different ways, such improved technology in mobile plant (like improved suspension and air-cushioned drivers' seats), operator training, smooth operation of machines and job rotation, and using devices to measure the amount of vibration.

12.6 Managing and controlling vibration

Once the vibration risk assessment has established that there are at-risk employees, the employer must design and implement a control programme to reduce the exposure to a level as low as is reasonably practicable, and in any case below the ELV.

12.6.1 Principal vibration control methods

The most effective means of controlling vibration exposure is by **changing the process**. Avoiding the use of hand-held equipment will effectively eliminate the incidence of hand-arm vibration.

Using a machine-mounted breaker instead of a hand-held version will eliminate the risks associated with hand-arm vibration

If there is no option to change the process in this way, the next option should be to **ensure equipment generates the lowest possible amount of vibration**. This may be achieved in the following ways.

- Adopting a *buy/hire smooth* policy, whereby the manufacturers' or hirers' published vibration emission data is used comparatively to select low vibration equipment (**note:** *that the manufacturer's data is not to be used for assessing individual exposure levels as part of a risk assessment*). Keep in mind that some tools might emit less vibration than others but be relatively inefficient, resulting in increased exposure times and higher grip and push forces, therefore resulting in an overall higher exposure.

- Maintaining equipment so that it continues to operate at the lowest possible vibration levels. This includes ensuring bearings, bushings and vibration-resilient components are regularly serviced and replaced if necessary.

- Using the correct bit, disk or attachment for the work, and keeping them sharpened, or replacing items such as sanding disks when worn. Using blunt or worn out bits, disks and attachments causes workers to exert more force on the tool, which increases the transmission of vibration to the hand.

- Operating the equipment at a speed that gives the lowest vibration. Often by increasing the rotational speed, the vibration emission can be minimised. The best speed can be determined by experimentation and accurate measurement.

Correctly installed and smooth running machines will, in time, vibrate as the machinery parts become worn. The following list indicates the parts of machinery and vehicles that contribute to vibration.

- Worn bearings.
- Dirty fan blades (unbalanced fans).
- Worn mountings or worn anti-vibration pads.
- Misaligned shafts.
- Unbalanced rotating parts.
- Loose bolts.

- Damaged gear teeth.
- Blunt cutting tools and blades.
- Worn suspension components.
- Incorrect tyre pressures.
- Damaged or incorrectly adjusted seats.
- Damaged tyres or tracks.

If the above methods do not adequately reduce the vibration exposure of individuals, then **limitation on individual daily use** can be used as a managerial control of vibration exposure. This approach is commonly used in construction, using the hourly vibration exposure point method, as described on the following page.

- During the initial risk assessment, the hourly vibration exposure point is calculated for each piece of equipment.

- During use, the operative keeps a running total of the points accumulated during the day by multiplying the cumulative trigger time by the hourly vibration exposure point for the tool.

- If using multiple tools, the method is used for each tool, and the points added together.
  - 100 per day = EAV 2.5 ms^{-2} A(8) for hand-arm vibration.
  - 400 per day = ELV 5.0 ms^{-2} A(8) for hand-arm vibration.

- When an agreed number of points is reached (which must be below the ELV, allowing a suitable margin for error and uncertainty), the operative reports to their supervisor and is allocated work that does not involve use of vibrating hand tools.

- Exposure records should be kept as useful data, which can be used as part of the vibration management program.

- Tool timers are available that attach to the tool and measure the trigger time directly. By entering the vibration emission level for the tool, the tool timer will give an audible and visual alert when the trigger point level is reached. This will then alert the user that they need to take a break from the tool.

Tool timer on a hammer drill

Some devices work as a pairing system, with a small unit fitted to the tool and paired with a watch-type device worn by the user. Others may just be worn by the individual. When used correctly, these devices can provide accurate records of exposure for the individual worker.

e.g. Vibration exposure point

If two tools, with one hour exposure points of 20 and 80, are in use for two and two-and-a-half hours respectively, then it is simple to calculate the combined exposure using the one hour points system. The score for each tool is (2 x 20) = 40 and (2.5 x 80) = 200, so the combined exposure gives a total score of (40 + 200) = 240 points. Therefore, the operator's daily exposure is 240, which is above the EAV of 100 but below the ELV of 400. At this level, the employer should stop the operative from being exposed to vibration.

The measured tool vibration in m/s^2 relates to the points per hour, as shown in the table below.

Tool vibration (m/s^2)	3	4	5	6	7	10	12	15
Points per hour (approximate)	20	30	50	70	100	200	300	450

 Visit the HSE website for a calculator to assist in calculating exposures for hand-arm vibration.

12.6.2 Other vibration control methods

 HSE information on practical ways to avoid or reduce use of vibrating equipment (HSG170) can be found on its website.

In addition to the principal vibration control methods **described earlier**, the following should also be implemented.

- Ensure workers have regular short breaks, particularly if experiencing acute symptoms (e.g. pins and needles in the hands and fingers).

- Maintain blood circulation in the fingers, which makes a significant contribution towards preventing damage from hand-arm vibration. The following measures can help to achieve this.
  - Wearing gloves to keep the hands warm.
    Note: *the use of so-called anti-vibration gloves is* **NOT** *recommended. In most cases they have little or no effect on vibration transmitted to the hand, and in some cases can make matters worse.*
  - Using proprietary heating pads for the hands.
  - Using tools with heated handles.
  - Avoiding tools that have pneumatic exhausts that discharge towards the hands.
  - Encouraging operatives to warm up before starting work, and helping them to stay warm.
  - Providing warm, weatherproof clothing in cold, wet areas, and ensuring it is worn.
  - Massaging and exercising fingers during work breaks.

- Ensure that workers are aware of the course of action they should take if they are experiencing early symptoms of over exposure to hand-arm vibration, such as reporting to an appointed manager, supervisor or occupational health service.

- Training and information provided to all workers, supervisors and managers *(for more information refer to 12.3.3 Training and information).*

- Ensure all workers exposed at or above the EAV, or otherwise at risk from vibration at work, are subject to a program of health surveillance *(for further information refer to 12.3.2 Health surveillance).*

12

Appendix A - Some typical vibration levels for common tools

Tool type	Lowest	Typical	Highest
Road breakers	5 m/s^2	12 m/s^2	20 m/s^2
Demolition hammers	8 m/s^2	15 m/s^2	25 m/s^2
Hammer drills/combi hammers	6 m/s^2	9 m/s^2	25 m/s^2
Needle scalers	5 m/s^2	–	18 m/s^2
Scabblers (hammer type)	–	–	40 m/s^2
Angle grinders	4 m/s^2	–	8 m/s^2
Clay spades/jigger picks	–	16 m/s^2	–
Chipping hammers (metal)	–	18 m/s^2	–
Stone-working hammers	10 m/s^2	–	30 m/s^2
Chainsaws	–	6 m/s^2	–
Brushcutters	2 m/s^2	4 m/s^2	–
Sanders (random orbital)	–	7–10 m/s^2	–

Note: the table above provides an indication only. Vibration magnitudes associated with tools, equipment and machines may change (up in some cases, down in others) and you should, as far as possible, try to obtain up-to-date information for the specific item or tool intended for use.

Manual handling

13

Supporting **INFORMATION**

GT700 Toolbox talks / supporting checklists and forms

Toolbox talks on some of these topics are available in the GT700 publication. Supporting checklists and forms covering some of these topics are available on our companion website.

Overview

All construction and building work involves lifting, handling, pushing and pulling activities. When assessing the risk of injury to workers, the first consideration should always be whether the load needs to be handled, thus eliminating any risk. Where handling cannot be avoided, mechanical lifting aids or an automated process should be considered and utilised wherever possible.

Manual handling injuries can result in upper and lower limb disorders and/or repetitive strain injury. These conditions are known as musculoskeletal disorders (MSDs). MSD is the term used to describe damage, injury or disorder to the muscles and soft tissues, causing pain and discomfort of the back, shoulders, neck, lower arms and hands. The pain can be caused by overuse of the affected muscles and tissues, and it is often made worse by work.

The risk of injury can be greatly reduced by involving the workforce and taking into account the nature of the task, the load and the working environment when implementing the required control measures.

13.1   Introduction

Over a third of all reported work-related accidents each year result from poor manual handling techniques. Many cause absence from work and, in the worst cases, permanent disability and physical impairment. Therefore, there are good social and health reasons why MSDs should be reduced and, if possible, prevented.

Where it has been identified that there is a risk of MSD to the employee, the Management of Health and Safety at Work Regulations and the Manual Handling Operations Regulations require that a risk assessment is carried out. In addition to assessing and controlling the risks, giving employees the appropriate training in the correct manual handling techniques and the use of mechanical lifting aids is highly cost effective.

Adequate supervision is necessary to ensure that employees then use the proper equipment and techniques and do not take shortcuts. This will reduce accidents, the amount of time lost on site, and the disruption to work that is caused when something goes wrong.

The part of the body most vulnerable to injury if bad manual handling techniques are used is the back, particularly the lower back. Once it has been damaged, it is usually weakened for the rest of a person's life. Poor posture, obesity, poor physical fitness and exposure to whole-body vibration can also result in back pain. All the other major joints and muscle groups can also be easily damaged if the correct manual handling techniques are not used.

The consequences of an injury due to bad manual handling or MSD injury can be a long-term absence or incapacity, or permanent inability to work. The cost to the employer is reduced productivity and having to find others to carry out the work.

 ***Manual handling* includes lifting, lowering (putting down), carrying, pushing, pulling or moving a load by hand or bodily force.**

13.2   Important points

- Poorly thought out or badly performed manual handling is the cause of many injuries to construction workers.

- Factors that determine whether it is safe for an individual to manually handle a load include the **task**, **individual**, **load** and **environment** (**TILE**).

- Employers must:
  - avoid, so far as reasonably practicable, their employees having to carry out manual handling likely to result in an injury
  - where that is not reasonably practicable, assess the risks to the employee
  - put in place control measures to prevent such an injury occurring.

- Employees must:
  - make full and proper use of the employer's safe system of work
  - use (lifting) equipment and machinery in accordance with instruction and training given
  - report to the employer any situation where it is considered the system of working is not safe.

- Where manual handling cannot be avoided mechanical lifting aids should be used where possible.

13.3   Manual Handling Operations Regulations

Regulation 4(1) sets out a hierarchy of measures to reduce the risks of manual handling. These are shown below.

- Avoiding hazardous manual handling operations, as far as is reasonably practicable.

- Assessing any hazardous manual handling operations that cannot be avoided.

- Where a risk is identified, which cannot be avoided, reducing the risk of injury, so far as is reasonably practicable (for example, by implementing risk reduction control measures).

The regulations do not have an approved code of practice (ACoP) due to the diversity of subject areas covered. However, the regulations are supported by guidance that should be followed.

The **Management of Health and Safety at Work Regulations** require that a general risk assessment is undertaken. If this risk assessment identifies there is a possibility of injury from manual handling, then a specific manual handling assessment should be carried out.

In addition, employers must provide the following.

- Safe systems and places of work.

- The safety of their employees and, where possible, the absence of risks in the handling, storage and transport of all types of articles and substances.

- The information, instruction, training and supervision necessary to ensure the health and safety of their employees.

13.3.1   Employers' duties

Each employer shall, so far as is reasonably practicable, avoid the need for employees to undertake any manual handling operations at work, that involve a risk of their being injured; or where this is not reasonably practicable, each employer shall:

- make a suitable and sufficient assessment of all such manual handling operations to be undertaken by their employees, having regard to those points contained in a manual handling checklist.

- take appropriate steps to implement control measures, thereby reducing the risk of injury to those employees undertaking any manual handling operations, to the lowest level which is reasonably practicable

- take appropriate steps to provide any of those employees who are undertaking any manual handling operations with general indications and, where it is reasonably practicable to do so, precise information on the:
  - weight of each load
  - heaviest side of the load whose centre of gravity is not positioned centrally.

Any assessment that an employer has made must be reviewed where there is reason to suspect that it is no longer valid, or there has been a significant change to the manual handling operations to which that assessment relates.

Where changes to an assessment are required, as a result of any review, an employer shall make the changes.

For the purposes of this regulation, when determining whether manual handling operations at work involve a risk of injury, and to determine the appropriate steps needed to reduce that risk, particular care shall be taken to check the following.

- The physical suitability of the employee to carry out the operation.

- The clothing, footwear and other personal effects worn by the employee.

- The employee's knowledge and training.

- The results of any relevant risk assessment carried out under the Management of Health and Safety at Work Regulations.

- Whether the employee is within a group of employees identified by that assessment as being especially at risk.

- The results of any health surveillance provided under the Management of Health and Safety at Work Regulations.

13.3.2   Employees' duties

The following duties are required of each employee, while they are at work.

- Make full and proper use of any system of work provided by the employer in connection with manual handling.

- Use any machinery or equipment provided by the employer in accordance with any training or instruction received.

- Inform the employer, or anyone else responsible for safety, of any dangerous work practice or shortcomings in the employer's arrangements for safety.

13.4   Common injuries

Injuries resulting from unsafe or incorrect manual handling can affect the following parts of the body.

- Whole body.
- Back.
- Shoulders.

- Arms.
- Hands.
- Feet and toes.

Back injuries are the most common, but hernias, ruptures, sprains and strains are all conditions that can result from poor manual handling techniques. Gloves, safety footwear, safety helmets and overalls all play an important part in reducing the type and severity of accidents arising from manual handling.

There are conflicting views on the benefits of wearing a back-support belt. Some authoritative bodies believe that wearing one may render some people more likely to suffer an injury. There is no evidence to support the theory that they reduce manual handling injury rates. There may be some negligible benefit derived from the fact that wearing a back support will keep the lower-back muscles warm. People tend to start wearing back-support belts at work only after they have already suffered some discomfort, pain or back injury. Wearing a back-support belt may not aid recovery if manual handling activities continue, and may increase the likelihood of suffering further, more serious injury or damage to the back.

The cost of physical injury can be high for the employer through lost production and raised costs, and legal liabilities leading to possible prosecution. For the employee, the physical injury may cause pain and even permanent disability, leading to lost wages. Anyone who believes that they have suffered a manual handling injury, particularly a back injury, should be encouraged to seek prompt medical advice.

13.4.1   Musculoskeletal disorders (MSDs)

MSDs cover any injury, damage or disorder of the joints or other tissues in the upper limbs or the back, neck and shoulders; less often they affect the lower limbs. Health problems range from discomfort and minor aches and pains to more serious medical conditions.

13.4.2   Strains, sprains, torn ligaments, disc trouble and hernias

Strains and sprains to muscles and joints, torn ligaments and tendons, disc trouble and hernias are often caused by sudden and awkward movements (for example, twisting or jerking while lifting or handling heavy loads). They are also caused by persons attempting to lift loads beyond their physical capabilities. The muscles of the abdominal wall are particularly vulnerable, and excessive strain may lead to ruptures.

13.4.3   Cuts and abrasions

Personal protective equipment (PPE) and clothing (such as leather gloves to protect the hands) should be worn as necessary to help protect against cuts and abrasions from rough surfaces, sharp or jagged edges, splinters, projections, and so on.

Radiated pain from a spinal injury

13.4.4   Back injuries

Back injuries are most frequently sustained while lifting and handling manually. They may be the cumulative effect of repeated minor injuries, or the result of an abrupt strain. Stoop lifting should be avoided; it greatly increases the likelihood of sustaining back injuries. Laboratory tests show that the stresses imposed on a rounded back during stoop lifting is six times that experienced if the trunk is kept straight while bending at the knees.

13.4.5   Crushing of limbs

Limbs can be crushed by falling loads, or fingers, hands or feet can become trapped by loads. Correct positioning of hands and feet in relation to the movement of the load is essential. Timber wedges or other blocks should be used when beginning to raise or lower heavy loads. The likelihood of injury can be reduced through knowledge of correct lifting techniques and by not attempting to lift excessively heavy loads without assistance.

 Manual handling and lifting injuries are often for life.

13.4.6 Upper limb disorders

Upper limb disorders (ULDs) affect the arms (from fingers to shoulders) and the neck. They affect the muscles, tendons and ligaments. ULDs are often called repetitive strain injuries (RSIs), cumulative trauma disorder or occupational overuse syndrome.

13.4.6.1 Repetitive strain injury (RSI)

RSI is usually an upper limb disorder caused by carrying out the same task (for example, typing, twisting or bending) over and over again. It can be more damaging where a load is involved in the task. The Chartered Society of Physiotherapy (CSP) has indicated that there has been a sharp rise in the number of cases of RSI in the workforce in general. Those in construction most likely to experience RSI are plumbers, carpenters, painters and plant operators. Methods by which workers can limit the potential for RSI are shown below.

- Avoiding long periods of repetitive tasks (job rotation).
- Alternating use of hands (picking up left then right-handed).
- Taking more short breaks rather than one long break.
- Wearing looser clothing to increase ease of movement.
- Keeping warm (cold muscles don't expand properly).
- Not overstretching (moving closer to the task).
- Reporting pain or other symptoms immediately – RSI is easier to treat in the early stages.

Employers can make a big difference to the health of their workers (which will have business benefits) by taking the following actions.

- Assessing each job for the potential for RSI.
- Encouraging early reporting.
- Allowing workers to organise their work and take breaks as necessary.

13.4.6.2 Carpal tunnel syndrome

Carpal tunnel syndrome (CTS) is a relatively common condition that causes pain, numbness and a burning or tingling sensation in the hands and fingers. The carpal tunnel is a small tunnel that runs from the bottom of the wrist to the lower palm.

Several tendons that help the fingers to move pass through the carpal tunnel, as does the median nerve, which controls hand sensation and movement. When the median nerve becomes compressed, this can disrupt nerve signals, affecting sense of touch and hand movements. It can become compressed if the tendons that run through the carpal tunnel are swollen and inflamed.

Activities that may lead to CTS include vibration from hand-held tools, using a computer keyboard, craftwork (making decorative items by hand) and work that involves manual labour.

13.4.7 Lower limb disorders

Lower limb disorders (LLDs) affect knees, hips and legs, and usually occur due to overuse. Workers may experience lower limb pain, aching and numbness, without a specific disease being identified.

Carpal tunnel syndrome

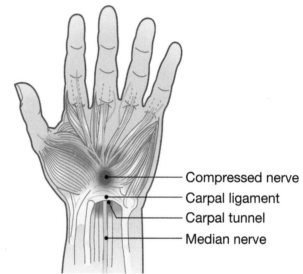

The inner workings of the hand and how they cause CTS

13.4.7.1 Osteoarthritis

Osteoarthritis is the most common joint disease worldwide, affecting an estimated 10% of men and 18% of women over 60 years of age. It is a degenerative condition that occurs when the cartilage coating the joints within the body (for example, the knees, hips or spine) becomes damaged or worn away. There is a significantly increased risk of knee osteoarthritis among individuals whose occupations involve hard, repetitive and physically demanding use of their knee joints. Building trades and construction workers have approximately three times the risk of developing knee osteoarthritis compared to those in more sedentary types of work.

Debilitating symptoms include knee pain, knee swelling, stiffness and reduced mobility, all of which can become a significant cause of disability requiring knee joint replacement surgery. Adequate, fit-for-purpose knee protection should be worn where necessary in order to protect knees in three key areas: penetration resistance, force distribution and shock absorption. Hip involvement, which refers to the level of pain and limited range of motion which evidences hip arthritis, is more common in those doing heavy work, prolonged lifting and standing.

The overall impact of osteoarthritis varies depending on the joint(s) involved. The severity of symptoms can vary greatly from person to person, with symptoms including swelling, tenderness, and grating or cracking sounds when moving the affected joint. Complications may include chronic pain, joint deformity, functional impairment and disability affecting grip and pinch strength (and causing difficulty with activities such as opening jars, turning keys or door handles, fastening buttons and writing), and difficulty walking, climbing stairs, dressing and driving.

13.4.7.2 Knee bursitis

Knee bursitis (also known as coal miners' knee, carpet layers' knee or housemaids' knee) is caused by repetitive kneeling or activities that strain the knee. Workers who develop bursitis generally report tenderness, swelling and a reduction in knee movement due to pain and tightening of the skin over the kneecap. Beat knee or hyperkeratosis is the thickening of the skin over the knee due to pressure. It is an acute and extreme form of bursitis, and is common among those regularly involved in straining activities (such as kneeling and squatting).

13.4.7.3 Meniscal lesions or tear damage

If the knee is bent or twisted whilst lifting or carrying a load, the force may cause meniscal lesions or damage to occur. Overuse trauma (for example, repetitive squatting or kneeling) can also cause meniscus injury or damage.

This damage can often result in the injured knee being more susceptible to degenerative changes typical of osteoarthritis.

13.4.7.4   Stress fracture or stress reaction injuries

Stress fracture and reaction injuries are the result of repeated micro injuries to the bone. They usually affect people who regularly march or stamp their feet. Construction workers could suffer from this injury if they have had previous military service or run long distances.

13.4.7.5   Varicose veins

Varicose veins are any dilated subcutaneous veins in the leg. Workers may complain of heaviness and pain, a sensation of swelling, night-time calf cramps and restless legs. These symptoms can increase during the day, especially after prolonged periods of standing.

13.5   Manual handling assessment

An ergonomic approach to the problems of manual handling and lifting can help to overcome many of the problems. Ergonomics have been described as *fitting the job to the person, rather than fitting the person to the job*. This requires attention to the following.

Task. What has to be achieved and by when?

Individual. Male or female, large or small frame, age, stature and state of health or previous injuries?

Load. Is it too heavy to lift and, if so, can it be broken down into smaller loads? Can two people lift it?

Environment. Consider hazards en-route (such as uneven floor surfaces, slopes, steps and narrow passages).

 Task, individual, load and environment can be remembered using the acronym TILE.

Where the assessment indicates potential risks to the health of employees from the manual handling of loads, the employer must develop a safe system of work that avoids the risks. The employer must consider the following.

- Task.
    - Can manual handling be avoided completely?
    - Can the distance a load has to be moved be reduced by better on-site planning?
    - Can lifting aids be used?
    - Does the load have to be raised to, or lowered from, above head height?
    - Does the task involve repetitive lifting?
    - Is it possible to avoid lifting from the floor?
    - Can it be carried close to the body?

- Individual.
    - Do they need manual handling training?
    - Do they need additional PPE?
    - Is there any known reason why they might not be suitable for the job (existing injuries or conditions)?

- Load.
    - Can it be broken down into smaller loads?
    - Is the weight known and, if not, can it be found out?
    - Are there adequate handholds?
    - Does it have sharp edges?
    - Can lifting accessories be built or cast in, or fixed into position?

Safe working using a mechanical aid

    - Is it evenly balanced (centre of gravity)?
    - Can the centre of gravity move (fluid loads)?
    - Are there any manufacturers' recommendations or constraints for methods of lifting?
    - Should it be carried by two (or more) people?

- Environment.
    - Is the floor surface sufficiently level?
    - Are there any obstructions, space constraints or trip hazards that should be removed?
    - Is the level of lighting adequate?
    - Is the workplace temperature satisfactory?
    - Is the surface slippery? (Consider varying weather, such as rain, frost, ice and dew in the mornings.)

Employees must co-operate in the following way.

- By using the appropriate equipment supplied in accordance with their training and instructions.
- By following the systems of work laid down by their employer.

13.5.1 Online assistance

The Health and Safety Executive (HSE) has developed online tools to assist employers carrying out manual handling assessments.

- **Manual handling assessment chart (MAC) tool.**
- **Variable manual handling assessment chart (V-MAC) tool.**
- **Assessment of repetitive tasks (ART) tool.**
- **Risk assessment of pulling and pushing (RAPP) tool.**

The **MAC** tool helps users identify **high-risk manual handling** by helping them to understand, interpret and categorise the level of risk of the various known risk factors associated with manual handling. The tool incorporates a numerical and colour coded scoring system to enable priorities to be identified.

The **V-MAC** is a tool for assessing manual handling operations where **load weights vary**. It gives a better indication of risks associated with the weight of the load, the distribution of the weight and the number of times it is handled. It should be used in conjunction with the MAC tool.

The **ART** tool, which uses a numerical score and a traffic light system, assists employers in assessing the risks of MSDs arising out of **repetitive, upper limb tasks**.

The **RAPP** tool helps employers to analyse the risks of pushing and pulling a load. Around 10% of RIDDOR related manual handling accidents involve **pushing and pulling**.

13.6 Lifting and handling

The weight an individual can lift safely will vary according to personal physique, age, condition of health and practice, and the techniques employed. Lifting capacity declines with age and an older person may not be capable of lifting the same load as a younger person; this, however, can be offset to some extent by employing a better technique.

The general rule is that the load should not be lifted if it causes any feeling of strain. Assistance should be available if required, and employees must not be required to lift loads beyond their capability. Youthful exuberance and bravado often tempt younger employees to try to lift loads that are too heavy. While they may succeed in the short-term, long-term damage may be done to the ligaments, muscles and back.

If single person handling is required of building blocks, and cannot be avoided after all other precautions (such as mechanical handling) have been considered, then smaller, lighter blocks should be specified. With blocks or other materials weighing less than 20 kg, manual handling risks are still significant and suitable precautions should be taken to minimise these risks as much as possible.

 For a brief guide on manual handling at work visit the HSE website.

13.6.1 Avoiding manual handling

Reducing the risk of injury can be helped by using the following types of mechanical aids. Some of the solutions listed below will require a degree of training and expertise; some will require an appropriate operator's competence card or licence.

- Genie lifts.
- Kerb lifters.
- Sack trolleys.
- Pallet trucks.
- Skids.
- Telehandlers.

- Correct delivery locations.
- Built-in lifting attachments.
- Wheelbarrows.
- Stillages.
- Conveyor belts.
- Suction pads.

- Temporary handles/grips.
- Material hoists.
- Excavators/dumpers.

 Bricklaying – stacking bricks and mortar on a platform at waist height allows more of the work to be done between waist and shoulder height, thus avoiding stooping.

13.6.2 Preparing to lift

Before lifting and handling any load, the following points should be established.

- What has to be moved?
- Does it really have to be moved?
- What does it weigh?

- Can it be broken down into smaller loads?
- Can the process that requires it to be moved be changed?
- Where is the load's centre of gravity?

13

- Can it be safely handled by one person?
- Will assistance be required?
- Can the move be carried out more safely with mechanical assistance?
- How far does it have to be moved and from where to where?
- Is the route clear of obstructions?
- Can it be put down safely?

Suitable protective clothing should be worn. This may include gloves, safety footwear, safety helmets, and special overalls if hot or corrosive substances are to be carried. Ensure that the lifting and lowering areas are clear of tripping hazards, and likewise check the route over which the load is to be carried.

Kerb lifter and layer used to reduce manual handling

13.6.3   The load

Large, heavy loads should, if possible, be broken down into smaller, lighter and more manageable sizes. It is obviously easier to lift 10 kg five times than to try to lift 50 kg once. Where the load has to be moved by a woman, the weight should be reduced by approximately 30%.

As a rough guide, the HSE has produced lifting and lowering guidelines for the weights that an individual should lift (shown in the diagram on the right).

Each box in the diagram contains a guideline weight for lifting and lowering in that zone. As you can see, the guideline weights are reduced if handling is done with arms extended, or at high or low levels, as that is where injuries are most likely to happen. The size and shape of a load may be as significant as its weight in determining whether assistance is required.

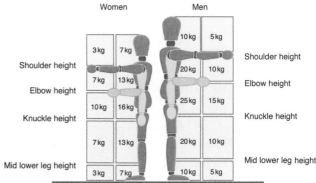

Lifting and lowering guidelines for men and women

Large awkward loads that require the arms to be extended in front of the body place more strain on the back and abdomen than compact objects carried close to the body. The absence of natural or designed handling points can also make it difficult to raise and carry objects without strain so barrows or other lifting and handling aids may be required to move the load. Not all loads need to be carried, of course. It may be easier to roll or push them, depending on the contents. Even so, assistance might still be required to avoid the risk of injury.

13.6.4   Manual handling techniques

13.6.4.1   Plan the task

- What has to be moved?
- Where to; where from; how far; is the route suitable, safe and clear of obstructions?
- Is it safe for one person to do it alone?
- Will help be required? If so, how much and for what purpose?

13.6.4.2   Use your body wisely

- Let the leg and thigh muscles do the work. They are larger, better developed muscles and cope better than the smaller, lesser developed back muscles.
- Try to keep your spine straight (not necessarily vertical, but straight) and the muscles relaxed. However, slight bending of the back, knees and hips is permitted if necessary to maintain the natural curve of the spine, and is certainly preferable to fully flexing the back (stooping) or fully flexing the hips and knees (deep squatting).
- Once you have started to lift (taken the full weight) don't flex your back any further, which can happen if you begin to straighten before you have raised the load.
- Avoid twisting the back or leaning sideways, especially whilst the back is bent.
- Use the movement and inertia of your own body weight as you start to lift. Do not snatch the load.

13.6.4.3   Bend your knees

Feet slightly apart; one foot slightly forward; balance; keep the back straight. Avoid tight clothing that prevents you from bending your knees.

13.6.4.4   Get a good grip

Use your hands – not fingers. Tilt the load slightly to get a secure grip as close to the body as possible. Keep your elbows tucked in.

13.6.4.5 Lift with your legs

Do not jerk or snatch. Let the thigh muscles do the bulk of the work. Lift in stages, if necessary, from the ground onto a low platform.

13.6.4.6 Putting the load down – plan ahead

- To floor level: it will probably be a reversal of the lifting process. Attention must be given to the positioning of the feet and back.

- To a higher level: depending upon the height of the surface to which the load is to be positioned, it may be less of a stress on the body to lower the load and assistance may be required.

- If loads are to be manually handled, heavier loads should be stored at waist height.

 There is a case study on the HSE website for reducing plasterboard manual handling, which could be delivered as a toolbox talk.

13.6.4.7 Team lifting

If the load is large, heavy or awkward, get assistance, preferably from someone of about the same size and build as yourself to help maintain the balance of the load during lifting. Always plan the lift with your helper and agree who will give directions as to when and how you will lift. Good levels of clear communication are vital if you are planning, or are involved in, team lifting.

13.6.5 Simple mechanical aids

Steel pipes and round timbers make effective rollers or mechanical aids, and should be used when necessary, but great care must be taken to ensure the following.

- The movement of the load is co-ordinated with the positioning of the rollers.

- The hands of the person who positions the rollers are kept well out of the way of the moving load.

The use of a wheelbarrow or sack trolley will make the manual handling of suitable loads that much easier. Using lifting straps or hand-held suction devices will assist in moving some sheet materials. The use of simple mechanical aids lowers the level of risk, can prevent accidents and avoids unnecessary fatigue and strain, which can also improve efficiency on site.

Whenever practical, mechanical handling and lifting should replace manual handling techniques.

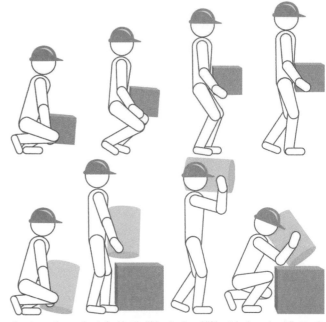

Good practice methods for kinetic lifting (top) and lifting/placing a load (bottom)

A team lift to move an awkward load (top); hoist for roof materials (bottom)

e.g. Handling building blocks

- Specify/order blocks that weigh less than 20 kg.

- Store blocks where they will not get wet (which will increase their weight).

- Arrange work so that lifting over shoulder height is not carried out.

- Deliver blocks as close to the point of laying as possible.

13.6.6 Scaffolds

Manual handling is linked to the erection, alteration and dismantling of scaffolds, so those who work from scaffolds will be involved in manual handling, and employers must assess the risks. This is usually undertaken as part of the general risk assessment and method statement/scaffold plan. Specific techniques and skills are required for scaffolding, and are comprehensively covered by the CISRS training courses. Labourers, trainee scaffolders and scaffolders not trained through a CISRS scheme should receive specific manual handling training.

13

Appendix A – Examples of how risks from frequent and heavy lifting can be avoided or reduced

	Storing, warehousing/order picking	Moving sheet materials	Packing and unpacking pallets, stillages and containers	Bales, reels, barrel, drum, keg handling	Bag, sack, box etc handling
Powered trucks and trolleys, vehicles etc	Battery-operated truck	Lift truck	Pallet converter	Drum/reel rotator	Lift truck
Non-powered trucks, trolleys and aids	Shelf trolley	Pallet truck	Pallet tilter	Keg truck	Truck with hydraulic lift
Tracks, conveyors, slides/chutes/roller balls	Conveyor with turntable	Gravity rollers	Roller track	In-line weighing	Ball table and rollers
Adjustable height devices, rotary and tilt tables	Adjustable height turntable	Sheet/trolley table	Auto-leveller	Reel trolley	Rotary table
Mechanical hoists and vacuum lifting devices	Conveyor and vacuum hoist	Vacuum hoist	Tub hoist	Reel lifting head	Vacuum hoist
Other	Gravity feed racking	Lifting hook	Bin tilter	Battery-powered tug	TV trolley with suction cups

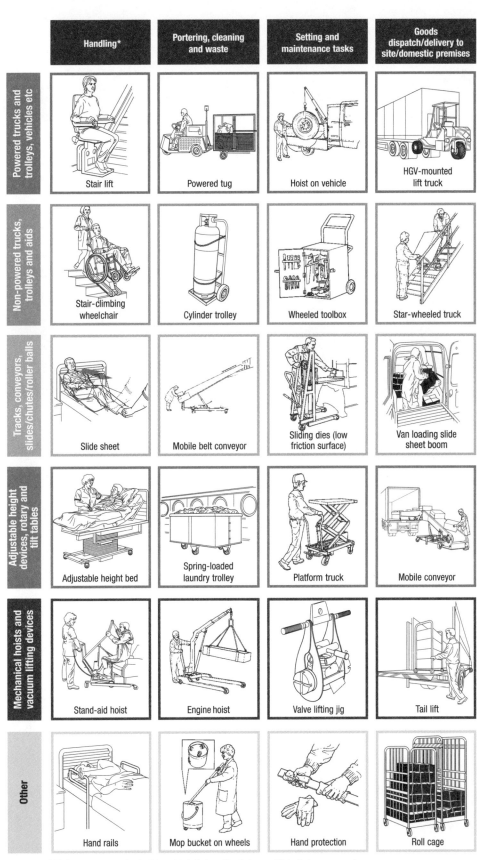

	Handling*	Portering, cleaning and waste	Setting and maintenance tasks	Goods dispatch/delivery to site/domestic premises
Powered trucks and trolleys, vehicles etc	Stair lift	Powered tug	Hoist on vehicle	HGV-mounted lift truck
Non-powered trucks, trolleys and aids	Stair-climbing wheelchair	Cylinder trolley	Wheeled toolbox	Star-wheeled truck
Tracks, conveyors, slides/chutes/roller balls	Slide sheet	Mobile belt conveyor	Sliding dies (low friction surface)	Van loading slide sheet boom
Adjustable height devices, rotary and tilt tables	Adjustable height bed	Spring-loaded laundry trolley	Platform truck	Mobile conveyor
Mechanical hoists and vacuum lifting devices	Stand-aid hoist	Engine hoist	Valve lifting jig	Tail lift
Other	Hand rails	Mop bucket on wheels	Hand protection	Roll cage

* Take care to select aids which take clients' condition into account

 For further information visit the HSE website.

13

Index

INDEX

INDEX

CONTENTS

C

General safety

CONTENTS

Site organisation

GT700 Toolbox talks / supporting checklists and forms

Toolbox talks on some of these topics are available in the GT700 publication. Supporting checklists and forms covering some of these topics are available on our companion website.

Overview

In this chapter we provide practical guidance on factors to be considered when preparing to set up a construction site. Details on the other sections of GE700 that will support this work, including information for security, logistics, safety, signs, access and egress, and the environment are also referenced.

Generally, much of construction work is transient and therefore the hazards on site can change from day to day. Many accidents occur on site as a result of poor design and planning during the pre-construction phase.

1.1   Introduction

This chapter aims to give employers and managers general practical guidance on site set-up, organisation and layout, how a site should be run and its impact on site workers, people living nearby and visitors. The chapter also introduces some of the topics found in other sections of GE700. Its content should be read alongside, not instead of, those sections.

 The construction phase plan must record health and safety arrangements for the construction phase, site rules and measures to control particular risks (such as work near high-voltage cables, risk of drowning and working below ground, for example, working in excavations).

 When planning site set-up and logistics, use site drawings to outline (or use scale cut-outs to lay out) site accommodation, plant and vehicle turning circles, material storage, buildings and temporary works (such as scaffold) and excavation working space. Also, when planning the safe management of deliveries to and from the site, consider the proximity of the site to nearby housing, schools, hospitals or shopping centres. Remember to take into account the finished building or structure when decommissioning the site.

 It may be helpful to use a sheet of clear Perspex over a site plan that outlines items such as site accommodation, fencing and temporary roads. Work (such as excavations, crane positions and material storage) can then be colour coded and plotted daily, making it easier to identify and plan for potential logistical and safety issues.

The **Construction (Design and Management) Regulations 2015** (CDM) place specific duties on commercial clients, the contractor or the principal contractor to ensure that authorised personnel have access to appropriate information to keep them safe on site. In addition, these duty holders have a duty to ensure that unauthorised persons do not gain access to site. Unauthorised persons will not be familiar with site rules and site hazards, so access to site could expose them to hazards that they may not be aware of.

 For further information on what to do when setting up and managing a site refer to the CDM industry guidance documents for contractors and principal contractors.

In accordance with the **Occupiers' Liability Act**, trespassers and non-employees have a right to be protected from risk if entering a site. A higher standard of care must be given by site management where children are concerned, for both authorised and unauthorised access.

1.2   Important points

The term *site organisation* generally includes the following areas.

- Management of the site.
- Preparation and communication of information.
- Pre-job briefing.
- Competence.
- Site discipline.
- Welfare requirements.
- Site security.
- Safe storage of materials.
- Safety signage.
- Utilities.
- Communication with neighbours.

1.3 Considerations when setting up a construction site

1.3.1 Existing site features

● Consider previous uses of the site, including contaminated ground, underground tanks or unexploded ordnance that may need to be cleared. Also consider any previous storage of dangerous goods or hazardous substances in buildings, cellars or tanks, which might require substantial decontamination, resulting in controlled site transport movements and additional time and cost.

● Check if any existing health and safety files or historic records are available detailing any hazardous previous use of existing buildings or structures on site.

● Check that an asbestos survey has been carried out to identify areas that need protection or isolation.

● Consider whether demolition is required as part of the project.

● Confirm if any underground services need to be isolated or if barriers and goalposts are required to avoid contact with live overhead power lines. Consider the impact on existing, or planned, access routes on site.

● Are there any protected wildlife or plants?

● Check if any invasive species (such as Japanese knotweed) are present.

● Are there watercourses (underground or surface) that need to be protected from contamination?

● Are there archaeological features that need protection?

● Check neighbouring activities to identify sensitive receptors and plan to avoid nuisance.

 For further information refer to Chapter D07 Underground and overhead services and Chapter B09 Asbestos.

1.3.2 Site security

A principal contractor – or, where there is only one contractor, the contractor – must take the necessary steps to prevent access to the site by unauthorised persons or trespassers.

In accordance with the Occupiers' Liability Act, trespassers and non-employees have a right not to be put at risk if they enter a construction site.

The contractor must not start work until the following steps have been taken, either by themselves (on a one-contractor project) or by the principal contractor (on a project involving more than one contractor).

● Secure the boundary immediately on possession, preferably with lockable gates and suitable hoarding to prevent unauthorised access or fly-tipping.

● The perimeter of a construction site must be identified by suitable signs, so it can be recognised, and it should be fenced off or secured where practicable.

● Consider installing CCTV. Even on small sites this can prevent or deter unauthorised entry and can support other HSE monitoring.

● Any hoarding or barriers provided to maintain site security and control unrestricted access must be checked regularly to ensure that they remain safe throughout the duration of the construction project.

● If the whole site cannot be secured then ensure areas with potentially hazardous operations are appropriately secured.

A facial recognition system for controlling access to a site

● Make specific security arrangements for particular areas (such as hazardous substances or plant and equipment storage).

● On larger sites, access for site personnel may be controlled by a biometric system, which can provide a solution for ensuring site security. Biometric verification is any means by which a person can be uniquely identified, evaluating one or more distinguishing biological traits, such as fingerprint, retinal scan, or facial recognition.

● Make provision for card reading facilities to identify individuals and confirm competency (often the CSCS card reader).

In planning for site security, remember that children often think that construction sites are exciting places to play. It is therefore important that access to the site is controlled during and after normal working hours.

Any evidence of trespass must be reported to site management immediately and appropriate action should be taken.

Seven year old boy trapped and suffocated on construction site

A civil engineering firm was fined £600,000 for safety breaches after a seven-year-old child became trapped and suffocated on a construction site.

The boy went missing from home and was found the next morning by workers at the construction site in South Yorkshire.

An investigation by the Health and Safety Executive (HSE) found that he had become trapped in a drainage pipe, which had been fixed into the ground in preparation for the installation of fencing posts. Tragically, he had suffocated before being found the next morning when work restarted on site.

Howard Civil Engineering Ltd pleaded guilty to breaching regulation 13(4)(b) of the Construction (Design and Management) Regulations 2015 and to breaching Section 3 (1) of the Health & Safety at Work etc. Act 1974. The company was fined £600K and ordered to pay £42,952.88 in costs at Sheffield Crown Court today.

The construction site was a new-build housing development next to an existing housing estate and adjacent to busy pedestrian footpaths and roads. The HSE found that there was insufficient fencing in place to prevent unauthorised persons from accessing the construction site due to a combination of poor planning, management and monitoring of the site and its perimeter.

Speaking after the hearing, the HSE inspector said: "The child should never have been able to be on that site. He should have been kept out. The construction industry should be aware of the dangers of construction sites to members of the public and any other unauthorised persons.

"The dangers to children gaining access to construction sites and treating them like a playground is an ongoing problem which must be addressed at all types of sites no matter what their complexity or size.

"The industry must do all it can to ensure children can't access construction sites and be exposed to the inherent risks they present to prevent further tragedies like this from occurring."

(Source: HSE.)

1.3.3 Temporary site structures

A competent person must ensure the following.

- They must carry out a foundation assessment and check whether the area for site cabins or other temporary structures is suitable.

- Assess temporary site roads for their capability to withstand loads during construction works, especially if they cross existing services.

- Undertake checks of the ground-bearing capacity of any hard standing for the positioning of lifting equipment.

- Ensure that material storage areas are planned carefully, with an awareness of shallow services that could be damaged.

- Design the site hoardings and gates to withstand local wind loadings, particularly to ensure swing gates are managed during high wind conditions. The Temporary Works forum can provide additional information about other conditions for site hoardings.

- If a 110-volt distribution system is required, check if a live 230/400 volt system is available to power it. Check who will design and install it, and who will test it and ensure that it meets ECA/NICEIC standards.

 For further information refer to Chapter C04 Temporary works.

1.3.4 Pedestrian and traffic routes

- Ensure safe vehicle operations and safe management of deliveries are considered at the design stage of a project, by specifying suitable profiles and removing hazardous gradients and embankments.

- Traffic and pedestrian management should be planned and then covered during the site induction. A plan of the construction site and traffic management plan could also be provided at the entrance for visitors and delivery drivers.

- Minimise risk to pedestrians by providing separate routes and entrances for vehicles and pedestrians. Use physical segregation where possible.

- Ensure the safety of the public on a partially-completed housing development site, by having phased occupation of dwellings: so that site traffic can be excluded from occupied areas, and public vehicle and pedestrian routes can be segregated from site vehicle and site worker routes.

- Ensure site entrances and exits minimise traffic hazards on public roads.

- Any traffic route must not be so uneven, potholed, sloped or slippery that any person using it is exposed to a risk to their safety.

- Provide a car park for privately owned vehicles, preferably accessed directly from a public road, with vehicle entry to the construction area prevented, if practicable.

- Parking areas should be clearly signposted, firm, level or with an acceptable gradient, well lit and not slippery.

- Ensure that site offices and other facilities are connected to the parking areas or pedestrian entrance, avoiding the need for visitors to cross site to gain access.

- Ensure safe, designated pedestrian routes, separate from vehicle routes where possible, are available to all work locations and are maintained as work progresses.

- Ensure pedestrian routes are wide enough to accommodate the number of people likely to use them at peak times.

- Provide pedestrians with a clear view of traffic movements at crossing points.

- Make use of a turning area if space is tight and try to avoid the need for reversing on site – one way systems are ideal.

- Set standards for driver competence and vehicle safety.

- Ensure availability of competent vehicle marshallers if reversing is required, entry onto a site is awkward, or pedestrians cannot be completely segregated.

- Roads should be wide enough for the vehicles using them.

- Sharp and blind bends should be avoided. Additional control measures (such as mirrors, stop signs or signals) could be used to help drivers and pedestrians see what is around the corner.

- Consider the possible requirement for a wheel wash and/or a road sweeper to keep site and public roads clear of mud and other debris, avoiding the creation of hazardous driving conditions or nuisance.

- Reduce the likelihood of pedestrian injury in areas of ongoing work with suitable temporary control measures.

The safe separation of construction plant and pedestrians avoids accidents

Access from car park directly to site offices

Pedestrians have a clear view of traffic movements at crossing points

WISA block impalement protection in use on steel reinforcing bars

1.3.5   External and internal site access routes and housekeeping

- Access routes should be on an even surface, signposted and have adequate lighting.

- If a route becomes muddy or slippery it should be treated with hardcore or a similar material.

- If internal access routes are icy, they should be treated with grit or given a temporary covering to make them safe to walk on.

- Careful consideration should be given to location and routing of temporary electrical supplies to minimise trip hazards and protect electrical supply cables from damage.

- Maintain high standards of housekeeping to keep all access routes clear, reduce tripping and fire hazards and project a positive company image.

- All obstructions should be kept out of access routes. This can be achieved by providing designated areas for deliveries and waste.

Good housekeeping – cables routed along ceiling and over doors to minimise slips and trips

1.3.6   Site lighting

The Provision and Use of Work Equipment Regulations (PUWER) require that:

 Every employer shall ensure that suitable and sufficient lighting is provided at any workplace.

The Construction (Design and Management) Regulations 2015 (CDM) require that adequate lighting is provided at every place of (construction) work and approach to the workplace, and that secondary (back-up) lighting is provided where failure of the primary lighting would result in risks to health or safety.

These two legislative provisions place a duty on employers to ensure that well-planned and adequate lighting be installed on site where necessary for safe working and access. To obtain such lighting conditions, you should consider the following.

- Installing suitable lighting to provide the required level of illumination for the nature of the work being carried out.

- Mounting the lights at a suitable height above the work level to give the required spread of light.

- Positioning lights to avoid glare, dazzle and reflection.

- Changing the position of lights as work proceeds.

- Screening or shielding lights from reflective surfaces, on traffic routes, neighbouring properties and so on.

- Routing of lighting cables to avoid trip hazards or damage to the cable.

- Installing back-up lighting if failure of the primary sources would result in risks to health and safety.

 Certain forms of lighting can constitute a heat source and, therefore, a fire hazard. They also retain heat for a period after being switched off. Avoid locating lights in close proximity to combustible materials very employer shall ensure that suitable and sufficient lighting is provided at any workplace. Halogen floodlights get particularly hot, and have been the cause of several fires.

1.3.7   Material unloading and loading

The loading and unloading of vehicles has been the cause of a number of fatalities. Drivers and operatives unloading cargoes have been hit and crushed by objects falling from the vehicles because of the following circumstances.

- Cargo moving during transit and not being securely held.

- Failure of wagon straps, resulting in the release of loads suddenly and without warning.

- Changes in load distributions leading to uncontrolled collapse of the loads.

In addition, access and falls from height from the flat bed of a wagon need to be controlled.

The following measures should be considered.

- Loading stations with fixed platforms.

- Vehicle based systems (such as handrails).

- Soft-landing systems placed around the wagon.

- Inertia harnesses.

- No-slip surfaces.

- Keeping the area clear of debris and rubbish.

- Unloading checks to confirm the integrity of the retaining mechanisms.

- Checks to confirm the locations of lifting points.

- Checks to confirm the load's centre of gravity.

Reduce the risk of accidents involving mobile plant and vehicles by designing groundworks and landscaping that reduce the need to import fill or take spoil off site.

Materials that are unloaded or tipped from plant should be deposited in designated locations where they will not cause an obstruction, environmental issues or a hazard.

A vehicle marshaller should assist the driver during any manoeuvring or tipping operation to ensure that it is safe to tip and that there are no other hazards to be encountered during the operation.

Consideration should also be given to additional precautions that may be required (for example, increased signage, entry and exit signs into and out of delivery areas, restricted pedestrian movement, proximity sensors and/or convex mirrors).

Ensure that any plant being used is in good condition, is appropriate for the task and is operated by competent, certified employees.

Operatives working with plant or vehicles, or on sites where there are regular vehicle movements, should be provided with the appropriate personal protective equipment (PPE), which should include high-visibility clothing.

1.3.8 Materials storage and lay-down areas

- Develop a materials delivery schedule and ensure that it is communicated to all relevant personnel.

- Ensure all contractors and suppliers are aware of any delivery issues or restrictions specific to the site or surrounding area (such as schools, low bridges or one-way systems).

- Make provision for designated and safe storage areas to protect materials and ensure site and access roads are kept clear of obstructions.

- Make provision for safe and secure storage of any hazardous, flammable and polluting substances (such as bottled gases, oils and fuels).

- Make sure pallets of materials are stored in stable stacks with a safe limit designated for each different material.

- Consider what access is needed to reach these materials and what lifting equipment may be required (such as telehandlers, forklift trucks, mobile or tower cranes).

- Consider ways of moving materials on site without using vehicles.

- Try to place heavy items that need to be moved by hand near to where they are required, to minimise manual handling and avoid double handling.

Marking access routes and providing designated storage areas helps keep walkways tidy and free from obstruction

Designated plant accessory storage area

Supervisor convicted of manslaughter after a member of the public is crushed and killed

A 43-year-old woman was walking along a public pavement past a central London construction site when three large, unglazed window frames, weighing 655 kgs, fell and killed her. The window frames had been delivered the previous day and had been left on the public pavement overnight, leaning against the building. No efforts had been made to secure them to prevent them from falling and nor had any barrier been placed around them to protect members of the public using this busy thoroughfare.

The construction site was under the control of Westgreen Construction Limited (Westgreen), which was the principal contractor on a project to refurbish the ground floor and basement of the building to create a gallery space on behalf of the client. This included installing new ground floor windows and doors.

By the time of the accident, the construction phase of the project was well under way but it was running behind schedule. As the principal contractor, Westgreen was responsible for planning, managing and monitoring the construction phase of the project to ensure, so far as was reasonably practicable, that it was carried out without endangering those working on the project or members of the public. On at least one occasion in the days before the accident, a plywood hoarding had fallen from one of the apertures on the building, almost hitting a member of the public.

After identifying a catalogue of failures which led to the accident, the following convictions were secured.

- A construction supervisor was convicted of manslaughter (12 months' imprisonment) and breaching Section 7 of the Health and Safety at Work etc. Act 1974 (nine months' imprisonment). The supervisor was employed by IS Europe Limited, which was contracted by Drawn Metal Limited, to install the window frames.

- The site manager, working for the principal contractor Westgreen, was sentenced to six months' imprisonment, suspended for two years. Westgreen contracted Drawn Metal Limited to manufacture, deliver and install the window frames.

Failures

- Poor assessment of contractor competence.
- Non-compliance with an established construction phase plan and safe systems of work.
- No lifting plans in place for the operation.
- No procedures for checking risk assessments or method statements.
- Failure in the identification of hazards and mitigation of risk.
- Unsuitable, insufficient and out-of-date risk assessments and method statements.
- Contravention of existing risk assessments and method statements.
- Inadequate levels of communication and co-operation.
- Failure to postpone or refuse the delivery of the frames.
- Inappropriate storage of materials.
- No segregation between members of the public and construction activities.
- No segregation between members of the public and stored construction materials.
- Unsuitable storage and security of materials on site.
- Failure in monitoring the activities of sub-contractors working on site.

Following the verdict, the deceased woman's parents said: '[Our daughter] was a bright, lovely, professional woman living her life to the full and making plans for the future. Her future was taken from her when she was crushed to death by half-tonne window frames which took two seconds to fall on her. The frames had been left standing, almost vertically, at the side of a public pavement, unsecured to anything, unattended and with no safety barriers around them. If construction companies and the people who work for them are not held to account for such high levels of negligence and incompetence, then none of us is safe walking the streets next to construction sites.'

(Source: Homicide and Serious Crime Command, Metropolitan Police)

 Materials must be stacked and secured appropriately to avoid them falling and injuring someone.

 For further information visit the HSE website for *A guide to workplace transport safety* (HSG136).

 For further information refer to:
- **Chapter C06 Mobile work equipment**
- **Chapter C07 Lifting operations**
- **Chapter C08 Lifting equipment.**

1.3.9   Utility services

Give early consideration to the following points.

● The provision of a 230 or 400 volt three-phase (mains) supply when there may be heavy electrical loads (for example, a tower crane).

● The supply of clean water, which must be suitable for drinking, and may require installation and commissioning by the local water company.

● The drainage of surface and foul water. The Local Authority needs to be aware of any new connections and discharge of waste effluents into foul sewers. Discharge consents are required if water pumped from excavations or site run-off are discharged into rivers or other watercourses.

● The provision of telephone and/or broadband connections.

● The provision of gas or oil as required for heating.

● The size of the site and emergency requirements to determine what communication links are needed.

● The provision of an appropriately sized generator (if required) and supply of fuel.

● The incorporation of renewable energy and rainwater harvesting systems.

 For further information refer to Section E: *Environment*.

1.3.10   Work at height

● A comprehensive risk assessment will determine the most appropriate type of equipment required.

● Consider methods of fall prevention on or around vehicles for the unloading of site resources (such as accommodation units and site fencing).

● Temporary site accommodation, welfare units and containers can be pre-slung or slung using a method that attaches to the bottom of the unit's legs rather than having to access the roof to attach slings to the top of it.

Various working at height activities

● If scaffolding is being used, it must be erected, altered or dismantled by, or under the direct supervision of, a competent person and be inspected periodically by a competent person.

● If mobile elevating work platforms (MEWPs) are used they must be suitable and operated by competent persons. Ground conditions need to be checked and proximity hazards (such as overhead cables, rivers and basements) must also be identified and controlled.

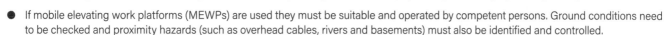 **For more information refer to Chapters C07 Lifting operations and D01 Work at Height Regulations.**

1.3.11   Excavations

● Sufficient working space for spoil heaps, earthwork support, laydown areas, pipes, and plant and machinery must be considered when planning the work.

● Suitable equipment (such as guardrails) will be required to form effective, physical barriers around excavations to prevent falls of persons, machinery or vehicles.

● Provide suitably anchored stop blocks or similar devices to prevent vehicles, especially tipping dumpers, from falling into excavations.

● If sides of an excavation cannot be battered, then they must be supported to prevent collapse of soil, rock or materials. A system of support must be designed by a competent person.

● Ensure safe means of access and egress for persons who need to enter the excavation; this should be by a secured ladder, or using adjustable lightweight staircase or towers.

● Never use underground service lines as a stepping point to get into and out of an excavation.

Physical barrier around an excavation

● Arrangements must be in place for statutory inspections of all excavations.

● Provide equipment to facilitate cy evacuation of injured personnel.

● Give consideration to groundwater removal from excavations.

 For further information refer to Chapter D06 Excavations.

1.3.12 Site office

- If the site office has more than one level, particularly where non-construction staff are employed, then temporary planning permission may be required. Also check for any planning restrictions in the contract documents at this stage.

- When temporary accommodation is required, consider its environmental performance and select on the basis of high insulation, double glazing, door closers and PIR (passive infrared sensor) lighting.

- Administrative staff and others, who may not have personal protective equipment (PPE), should be provided with safe access to the site office without having to pass through operational areas. If this cannot be achieved at all times then they must be issued with appropriate PPE.

- Site offices should offer comfortable accommodation for all types of weather and ranges of temperature.

- Provide a suitable and safe form of heating.

- Provide a suitable and safe electrical supply and telecommunications.

- Compile registers for portable appliance testing, fire alarms and other emergency planning.

- Ensure the site visitors' log is available at the entrance to the site, is completed by all visitors on arrival and departure and is monitored.

1.3.13 Welfare facilities

- It is a legal requirement to provide clean and hygienic areas, where workers can securely store personal items and dry clothing, get changed, make a hot drink, heat and eat meals and take shelter in bad weather.

- Suitable provision must be made for toilets, washing (if necessary, shower) facilities, changing rooms and rest facilities. Where there are both women and men on site, separate conveniences must be provided, with doors capable of being secured from the inside.

- It may be necessary to provide alternative temporary arrangements until the welfare facilities, power or water connections are made. A variety of standalone, self-contained units are available to suit site-specific needs.

- Additional welfare facilities may be needed for peak workforce levels and provision should be made for their delivery and installation.

Facility for heating food and with access to running hot water

Separate male and female site toilets

 For further information refer to Chapter B02 Welfare facilities.

1.3.14 First aid

- The appropriate number of appointed persons, emergency first aiders or qualified first aiders will be needed, depending on the number of people on site and the findings of the first-aid needs assessment.

  As a guide:

  - **fewer than five** – at least one appointed person (person responsible for the first-aid kit and calling the emergency services)
  - **five to 50** – at least one person trained in emergency first aid at work (EFAW) or first aid at work (FAW), depending on the type of injuries that may occur
  - **more than 50** – at least one person trained in FAW for every 50 people employed (or part of 50. For example, if there are 51 people on site, two persons trained in FAW will be required).

- The following information must be displayed and communicated, and should be covered as a topic during site induction.

  - The details of people who are first aiders, and the means of identifying them.
  - The location of first-aid kits, and the means of summoning first aid and medical assistance.

- Make sure the first-aid equipment has been ordered.

- Make sure appropriate signs are in place to identify first-aid locations and to direct personnel to them.

- Make sure you have the contact numbers and directions for emergency services, local hospitals and doctors.

 For further information refer to Chapter B05 First aid.

1.3.15   Fire safety

- Gather all relevant pre-construction information, including any existing general fire precautions (GFPs), building layout and the presence of flammable or combustible materials

- Contact the emergency services to inform them of your location, the means of access and any planned specialist activities.

- Work with the emergency services to agree site layout and identify areas and routes to be kept clear for emergency vehicle access.

- Complete a fire risk assessment and develop this into a fire safety plan for the site.

- Think about the level of risk from work activities and flammable substances that may be stored and used during the project.

- Provide a sufficient number of fire extinguishers, suitable for the types of fire that might occur, and place them in highly visible fire points in appropriate places, including offices and welfare accommodation.

- Train a suitable number of staff in the use of fire extinguishers.

- Keep fire exits and emergency escape routes clear of obstructions. Make sure they are easily visible and have adequate, illuminated signage.

Emergency routes should be clearly marked and indicate the direction to the nearest place of safety

- Ensure routes to the emergency assembly point are clearly indicated. The assembly point will be in a safe area, ideally outside of the confines of the construction site.

- Maintain any third-party fire arrangements (for example, working in shared or occupied premises). Close liaison is vital.

Be aware that the points above need to be reviewed regularly, given the changing nature of construction sites.

 For further information refer to Chapter C02 Fire prevention and control.

1.3.16   Emergency plans

- From the start of any project, plans must be put in place for the safe evacuation of the site.

- On complex or refurbishment projects, it is good practice to liaise with local fire authorities to identify fire-fighting strategies for the plan, together with the locations of fire-fighting cores, dry risers and lifts or hoists to be used or not used.

- Emergency escape routes must be identified and labelled with appropriate signs and communicated to everyone on site.

- A suitable assembly point should be identified. This should accommodate the maximum number of people on site at any time, be a safe distance from potential hazards and not be an obstruction or hazard to the emergency services.

- Display information about actions to be taken in an emergency, including what the alarm sounds like, days and times when it will be tested and where the assembly point(s) are.

- For larger sites, the emergency plan may be part of the construction phase plan. Fire wardens may need to be appointed for specific areas of the site. Emergency plans should be covered as part of any site induction programme.

- Identify the responsible person, who will carry out a head count of people, to account for the people registered as being on site (this may be more than one person on large sites).

- Ensure that Environment Agency contact details are available and that suitable equipment is provided for use in the event of an environmental emergency (such as spill kits for use with a fuel spillage).

- It is important that workers are trained in the use of spill kits, rescue lines or other emergency equipment provided.

1.3.17 Contact with emergency services

● Ensure the local emergency services are informed about the site's location, particularly if it is difficult to find.

● Provide details on the means of access and any specialist activities being undertaken.

● If you are running a large site, you should nominate an emergency controller to liaise with the emergency services and oversee site emergency actions and any communications with the press or neighbours.

 Display a road map in the site office, showing the quickest route to the nearest hospital and police station. This information should also be included in the site induction.

Valuable time can be wasted if the emergency services (police, fire or ambulance) are not aware of your location

1.3.18 Personal protective equipment

● Employees (including agency workers if they are legally regarded as employees) must be supplied with appropriate PPE free of charge. The site management team should ensure that workers understand how, where and when to use it, what to do if it is lost or damaged and how to care for and maintain it.

● A stock of relevant PPE will need to be available on site, to cover specific tasks undertaken by employees, to replace damaged PPE and to issue to site visitors.

● For specialist work you may need to seek advice when selecting respiratory protective equipment (RPE), eye protection, hearing protection, gloves and some other forms of PPE.

● There should always be adequate means to clean, maintain and store PPE.

 For further information refer to Chapter B06 Personal protective equipment.

1.4 Safety signs

All safety signs are colour coded, as required by the Health and Safety (Signs and Signals) Regulations.

There are five types of sign, shown below.

● Prohibition.

● Warning.

● Mandatory.

● Emergency escape and first aid.

● Fire-fighting.

1.4.1 Prohibition signs

Prohibition signs are round, with a black pictogram on a white background, with red edging and a diagonal red line. They prohibit behaviour likely to increase or cause danger by informing people of things they **must not do.**

No smoking

No naked flames

No access for pedestrians

Do not extinguish with water

Not drinkable

No mobile phones

No access for industrial vehicles

Do not touch

1.4.2 Warning signs

Warning signs are triangular, with a black pictogram on a yellow background, and black edging. They warn people of a hazard or danger.

Combustible or flammable material

Explosive material

Toxic material

Corrosive material

Radioactive material

Overhead load

Industrial vehicles operating

High voltage

General sign (where necessary, accompanied by another sign)

1.4.3 Mandatory signs

These are round, with a white pictogram on a blue background. They prescribe specific behaviours by informing people what they **must do.**

Protective eyewear must be worn

Safety helmet must be worn

Hearing protection must be worn

Respiratory equipment must be worn

Safety boots/shoes must be worn

Safety gloves must be worn

Safety overalls must be worn

Protective face shield must be worn

Safety harness must be worn

Pedestrians must use this route

General sign (where necessary, accompanied by another sign)

1.4.4 Emergency escape and first-aid signs

These signs are rectangular or square, with a white pictogram on a green background. They give information on emergency exits, assembly points and first-aid facilities.

1.4.4.1 Emergency escape route and assembly point signs

1.4.4.2 First-aid signs

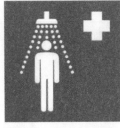

First aid   *Stretcher*   *Emergency shower*   *Emergency eyewash*   *First aid emergency telephone*

1.4.5 Fire-fighting signs

These signs are rectangular or square, with a white pictogram on a red background. They indicate the location of fire-fighting and safety equipment.

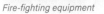

Fire hose reel   *Fire ladder*   *Fire-fighting equipment*   *Fire emergency telephone*

Fire extinguisher   *Fire alarm call point*

1.4.6 Signs and notices

The Health and Safety (Safety Signs and Signals) Regulations require employers to provide safety signs where other methods, properly considered, cannot deal satisfactorily with certain risks and the use of a sign will further reduce that risk. Employers should ensure that their employees are aware of, and understand the meaning of, safety signs and signals, providing training where necessary.

- Signs should be displayed at the site entrance(s) to inform all persons entering the site about the health and safety requirements for the site. These should include, for example, minimum standards of PPE and state that all visitors must report to the site office.

- Other signs to be displayed include a selection of mandatory, warning, prohibition, emergency escape and first-aid signs.

- Ensure there is adequate fire signage (such as signs showing escape routes, fire assembly points and where the fire alarm call points (alarms and extinguishers) are located).

- Signs will also be required to identify the presence of liquefied petroleum gas (LPG), fuels and other flammable substances.

- Some signs may be used together with other types of communication, for example:
  - illuminated signs and acoustic signals
  - illuminated signs and verbal communication
  - hand signals and verbal communication.

- Traffic management signs will also be required and should meet the requirements of the latest (road) Traffic Signs Regulations and General Directions, as appropriate to the specific site. These may also include directional signage to site and instructions for deliveries.

Signs for workers to use, to highlight hazards as working environments change

 Signs should not be used as the only means to convey important information. They should be used to reinforce the information you have already covered in a site induction.

1.5 Environmental considerations

Construction work can have a severe impact on the environment. Therefore, measures must be taken to prevent or reduce the potential for harm or nuisance.

The risks should be recorded in the environmental impact assessment (EIA) and the construction environmental management plan (CEMP). Review the CEMP, as follows.

- Identify and protect watercourses and drainage systems.

- Ensure you have licences for discharges of water or effluents and arrange for settlement tanks, if appropriate.

- Identify, enhance and protect habitats and areas occupied by protected species of animals, insects and plants.

- Identify and protect areas of archaeological and historic importance.

- Create an action plan detailing measures to be taken in the event of a spillage to prevent ground or watercourse contamination. Include emergency contact details for the relevant Environment Agency.

- Identify how you propose to reduce noise and dust levels, as far as reasonably practicable. You may need to consider restricting some construction processes to certain times of the day.

- Ensure correct handling, storage and disposal of hazardous and non-hazardous waste.

- Avoid nuisance to neighbouring properties by locating noisy activities away from boundaries. Ban the use of radios, do not leave engines running when not in use and avoid inconsiderate parking on public highways.

- Clearly identify and explain environmental issues in inductions and briefings.

- Consider methods of communicating with the local community to keep them informed about site activities that may have an impact on them.

- Demonstrate a caring attitude towards local residents with regard to site lighting and CCTV use during the hours of darkness.

- Consider electing an environmental champion for the site.

 For further information refer to Section E: *Environment*.

1.6 Waste storage and disposal

If you are involved in managing waste, you have a legal duty of care.

The duty of care applies to everyone involved in handling the waste, from the person who produces it to the person who finally recovers or disposes of it.

Waste that is created on a site must be disposed of appropriately by licensed contractors. Hazardous waste will need to be stored in appropriate containers and removed by contractors with the appropriate hazardous waste licence (special waste in Scotland), with the transfer recorded using appropriate waste consignment notes.

A plan to reduce and manage waste should be developed before the project commences. Relevant content should also be communicated to suppliers, contractors and those carrying out the work.

The following will need to be considered.

- Will the project be carrying out any waste treatment activities requiring permits or exemptions?

- Can any treated waste be reused on site or transported for use on a registered cluster site (a site that utilises surplus materials)?

- Is the waste suitable for transporting (hazardous or non-hazardous) and does it require special handling by competent persons?

- All waste must be transported by a registered waste carrier and be supported by a waste transfer note or, in the case of hazardous waste, a consignment note (special waste in Scotland) to an authorised facility.

- The provision of an adequate number of suitable, clearly marked skips or secure space to allow waste (for example, plasterboard, metal, timber and electrical waste) to be segregated prior to removal. This can help improve recycling and reuse, and reduce the amount of waste going to landfill.

For further information refer to Chapter E10 Waste and material management.

A waste chute and tipping skip provide a safe and easy method of collecting and removing waste from under a scaffold (ideally, the chute and skip would be shrouded to reduce dust generation and escape).

1.7 Human factors

1.7.1 Skills, knowledge, training and experience

- To work safely, everyone on site needs to be competent or be closely supervised by someone who is.

- Anyone responsible for recruiting must ensure that the people they employ have, or are registered with an official process of obtaining, the necessary skills, knowledge, training and experience to gain competence in the job or task in hand (often demonstrated by ownership of an appropriate competency card).

- You will need to confirm and check the competence of contractors and persons coming onto site (such as those persons installing welfare facilities, erecting, altering or dismantling scaffolds, operating site plant, digging excavations and installing the supports or installing traffic management systems).

1.7.2 Consultation

- Employers must consult and engage with employees or their representatives in good time on issues that may affect their health, safety and welfare.

- Employees must be encouraged and be able to raise health, safety and welfare issues with their employer, directly or through their representatives.

- Where a trade union is recognised, ongoing issues requiring consultation should be facilitated through union appointed health and safety representatives. In non-unionised workplaces, consultation should be either directly with workers or through their elected representatives.

- As part of the site set-up, consideration must be given as to how effective employer/employee consultation will be achieved.

1.7.3 Co-operation

- CDM require all duty holders involved in a construction project to co-operate with each other in the interests of health and safety.

- How to achieve this co-operation is best decided at an early stage and, where possible, before the site is set up.

Regardless of your job and employer, on a construction site you have a legal and a moral responsibility to ensure you work safely and don't endanger yourself or others by your actions or omissions. You must communicate, co-operate and co-ordinate your actions with site management and other interested parties.

CONTENTS

Fire prevention and control

GT700 Toolbox talks / supporting checklists and forms

Toolbox talks on some of these topics are available in the GT700 publication. Supporting checklists and forms covering some of these topics are available on our companion website.

Supporting INFORMATION

Overview

Every year fires occur during construction, demolition, refurbishment and maintenance contracts. Fires are often small and are not reported to the client or enforcing authorities. Larger construction site fires or explosions tend to make the headlines and are reported.

Fires not only put workers' lives at risk but can also result in damage commercially and to reputation, and they invariably lead to lengthy delays in completion time. This chapter covers the requirements of duty holders to properly plan, manage and co-ordinate fire safety. It also gives advice on how fire risks can be identified and the control measures that should be implemented.

2.1   Introduction

Fire precautions should be implemented from the outset through design, procurement and completion of all construction projects. The risk of fire is an ever-present threat during all phases. As the work progresses, the nature of the fire risk is likely to change as different work starts and is completed. Therefore, not only must the risk of fire be managed continuously, but the management process must allow for the changing nature of the risk. Proper planning and adoption of safe working practices can prevent the majority of fires. Planning includes addressing fire risks at the design stage, and ensuring that the principal contractor, or contractor (if only one), enforces safe working practices. The client, principal designer and principal contractor must be satisfied that the risk of fire is, and will be, proactively managed.

 It is essential that everyone on site knows what to do if the fire alarm sounds, whether it is for real, a practice drill or a false alarm.

 The Fire Protection Association's *Fire prevention on construction sites* (Joint Code of Practice) is the code that applies to activities carried out before and during the procurement, construction and design process – not the completed structure – and should be read in conjunction with all current legislation and HS(G)168: *Fire safety in construction*.

If compliance with this code forms part of the insurance contract, non-compliance could possibly result in insurance ceasing to be available or being withdrawn, resulting in a possible breach of a construction contract that requires the provision of such insurance.

2.2   Important points

- Fire safety must be an integral part of a construction project, from planning and monitoring through to completion.

- Legislation requires a suitable and sufficient fire risk assessment to be carried out by a responsible person, or someone appointed to do so with sufficient experience and qualifications.

- The correct fire safety materials and resources should be budgeted for and procured.

- Everyone involved in the construction project should know who the responsible person is. (They may change during the project.)

- Fire risk assessments should comply with the Regulatory Reform (Fire Safety) Order 2005.

- Fire risk assessments must address fire prevention and protection measures. They must be reviewed periodically due to the changing nature of the construction activities and introduction of new hazards, processes and personnel.

- Fire safety procedures should be developed and adhered to. These should be communicated to everyone on site so they know what action to take in the event of an emergency.

- A hot-work permit scheme should be implemented to control the way hot-work activities are managed and controlled.

- Plan where flammable materials (such as timber, gases, adhesives and flammable liquids) will be stored.

- Additional fire precautions may be required where on-site accommodation is provided.

 Fire safety can be a complex issue on large, fast-moving sites with significant numbers of people to evacuate. Where the expertise is not present on site or within the company, it is advisable to seek the advice of a fire safety specialist.

 In this chapter, in most cases, where the word *construction* appears the point being made will also be applicable to demolition. However, for simplicity's sake, only the word *construction* will be used.

2.3   Nature of fire

2.3.1   How a fire can start

Three factors need to be present to enable a fire to start.

Fuel or combustible material. These can be liquids, solids, gases or any materials that will burn and support the combustion, given sufficient amounts of heat and air or oxygen.

Heat or ignition source. Every fuel has an ignition temperature. All solids and liquids give off vapour when heated, and it is this vapour that ignites.

Air (or other supporter of combustion, such as oxygen) which is always there to sustain fire, providing that the other two factors are present.

Once a fire has started, combustion will continue as long as these three factors are present. If any one of these factors is removed, the fire will be extinguished. This can be achieved by:

● removing the fuel, leaving nothing to burn

● removing the heat by applying water to cool the burning material

● reducing or excluding the air by smothering the burning material. Foam, dry powder, CO_2 and fire blankets are all smothering agents.

The fire triangle

2.3.2   How fire can spread

Fire can spread in four ways.

1. Conduction.

2. Convection.

3. Radiation.

4. Direct burning.

Conduction is where heat is transmitted from one place to another along or through solid material (such as along a metal pipe or through a door or wall). The conduction of heat therefore has the potential to start a fire in a location that is remote from the original source of heat.

Convection occurs where superheated gases or heat arising from a fire ignite other combustible material or when particles of burning material in the circulating air are deposited in another place, causing another fire.

Radiation is the transfer of heat from the fire, through the air, to other flammable materials nearby, causing the temperature of those materials to be raised to their ignition point and then burn.

Direct burning is a combination of conduction, convection and radiation and is where the fire spreads and reaches other combustible materials and ignites them, adding further fuel to the fire.

2.4   Classes of fire

Fires can be placed into one of the following categories.

Class A. Carbonaceous material (such as paper, cloth, wood and rubber) often referred to as solid fuel fires.

Class B. Flammable liquids or liquefiable solids (such as oil, fat, paint and fuel). These can be subdivided into:

   B1. Fires involving liquids that are soluble in water (such as methanol). They can be extinguished by CO_2, dry powder and water spray

   B2. Fires involving liquids that are not soluble in water (such as petrol and oil). They can be extinguished by foam, CO_2 and dry powder.

Class C. Flammable gases or liquefied gases (such as propane, butane, hydrogen or acetylene).

Class D. Combustible metals (such as magnesium, sodium and phosphorus). They can be extinguished by specialist dry powder.

Class F. High temperature cooking oils or fats (such as those used in deep fat fryers in large catering establishments or restaurants).

Electrical fires (fires involving electrical apparatus or equipment) are not a specific fire class, as electricity is a source of ignition rather than a fuel.

However, they are still important to mention because they have their own special fire safety requirement.

 For further information on classes of fire refer to Appendix A.

2.5 Legislative requirements

The main legal requirements that cover fire prevention and control on construction sites are the **Regulatory Reform (Fire Safety) Order (England and Wales),** the **Fire Safety (Scotland) Regulations,** the **Fire Safety Regulations (Northern Ireland)** and the **Construction (Design and Management) Regulations 2015** (CDM).

 For further guidance refer to the HSE's *Fire safety in construction* (HSG168).

2.5.1 Regulatory Reform (Fire Safety) Order and Fire Safety Regulations

There are three main pieces of fire legislation in the UK that apply to all workplaces and premises.

- Regulatory Reform (Fire Safety) Order (England and Wales).
- Fire Safety (Scotland) Regulations.
- Fire Safety Regulations (Northern Ireland).

These apply to both the actual construction site and site offices, as well as to the head offices of a company that could be separate from the actual site address. The legislation covers fire prevention, detection, fire-fighting and emergency lighting routes during construction. The legislation requires that the project should have in place a valid **fire risk assessment**. The fire risk assessment should be reviewed periodically to take into account any changes in the construction activities and processes.

The legislation places duties on the **responsible person**: the employer or person who has control of any part of the premises. During the construction phase, the principal contractor or contractor will often be identified as the responsible person, and they must appoint a **competent person** who is sufficiently skilled and knowledgeable to help them fulfil the required duties. This person must be clearly identifiable during all stages of the construction project.

If the project involves refurbishment of occupied premises, the client may also have control or partial control. Therefore, both parties will need to agree and be sure of their responsibilities. The responsible person must make sure that the fire risk assessment is in place and remains up-to-date.

2.5.2 Construction (Design and Management) Regulations

The CDM Regulations (part 4) cover the following requirements on construction sites.

- The prevention of risk from fire, flooding or asphyxiation.
- Emergency procedures.
- Emergency escape routes and exits.
- Fire detection and fire-fighting.

There is a requirement under CDM for all duty holders to co-operate and co-ordinate their activities at all phases of the project.

Clients must make sure that arrangements are in place to manage health and safety from the start to completion of the project. This includes ensuring that a construction phase plan (including the **fire safety and evacuation plan**) is in place before work starts. During the construction phase the **principal contractor** or **contractor** (if only one) must make sure that the construction phase plan, along with the fire risk assessment and fire safety and evacuation plan, remain up-to-date.

The responsible person should be named in the fire safety and evacuation plan. This person may change throughout the construction phase. The named person must be aware of their responsibilities and any management actions or duties they are required to perform/ **Principal designers** and **designers** need to identify and ensure that all potential fire hazards have either been eliminated or reduced so far as is reasonably practicable. They should consider the use of non-combustible and non-flammable materials to reduce the fire load.

If specifying a timber-frame design they must give consideration to the surrounding environment to assess the potential risk of fire spreading to neighbouring properties. They should also look to avoid processes that require hot works on site, therefore reducing the risk and amount of controls and management associated with hot-work permits. Additionally, they should work closely with site managers to ensure that compartmentation of the structure happens as early as possible, smoke dispersal arrangements and escape stairs are in place and to allow for the early installation and use of fire alarm and fire-fighting systems to protect against the rapid spread of fire during the construction phase.

 Compartmentation

Compartmentation should be given priority by designers and contractors when considering fire precautions during construction. Effective compartmentation will stop fire spreading rapidly from one part of a building to another. A building can be sub-divided by means of fire-resisting walls, floors and ceilings. Holes and openings must be protected by using fire-resisting materials.

Whilst this publication looks at the issues about fire risk during construction, it is worth noting that the final *Independent Review of Building Regulations and Fire Safety* places greater responsibility on duty holders for maintaining the 'golden thread' of information about the building structure and materials, detailing the maintenance, testing and inspection routine as well as how fire risk assessments have been undertaken and actions implemented. A comprehensive Fire and Emergency File and digital record will be transferred from the client to the dutyholder, giving them the golden thread of information needed to manage the building safely, and evidence to inform the safety case. This must be updated by the dutyholder so that it remains accurate throughout the lifecycle of the building.

 For detailed information on the *Independent Review of Building Regulations and Fire Safety* visit the website.

2.5.3 The Building Safety Act

The Building Safety Act 2022 became law in England. It is designed to improve the safety of buildings and minimum standards in response to the Grenfell Tower fire in 2017. This Act makes changes which mean owners will manage their buildings better, and the home-building industry has the clear, proportionate framework it needs to deliver more, and better, high-quality homes.Many of the detailed provisions in the Act will be implemented over the coming years through a programme of secondary legislation.

 For further guidance refer to the Building Safety Act 2022.

2.6　Liaison with the fire and rescue service

During the design phase the principal designer or designer should contact the fire and rescue service (FRS) and discuss access requirements and arrangements.

At the construction phase the principal contractor or contractor should make contact with the FRS and provide an initial site plan. This plan should be updated and made available on site.

The site layout plan should include the following.

- The fire and rescue access point(s).
- Emergency escape routes and stairs.
- Fire-fighting shafts or cores, lifts and hoist facilities.
- Location of fire call points and other fire-fighting equipment.
- Location of hazardous material (such as flammable and highly flammable material storage areas).

- Location of the assembly points.
- Floor loading limitations.
- Sprinkler installations.
- Positions of hydrants and any wet or dry risers.
- Details of any temporary buildings.

 Specialist fire-fighting access equipment will be required where construction work will take place above 18 m. This must be brought to the attention of the FRS.

2.7　Responsible person

As mentioned earlier (refer to 2.5.1) a nominated responsible person is required under legislation. Often during construction this role will fall to the principal contractor, where appointed, or the contractor.

 The Regulatory Reform (Fire Safety) Order – Responsible person

- This will be the employer, in relation to a workplace, if the workplace is to any extent under their control.
- In relation to any premises not falling within the bullet above:
  - the person who has control of the premises (as occupier or otherwise) in connection with the operating by them of a trade, business or other undertaking (for profit or not), or
  - the owner, where the person in control of the premises does not have control in connection with the operating by that person of a trade, business or other undertaking.

 Refer to the Fire Safety Act 2021, which amends the Regulatory Reform (Fire Safety) Order 2005.

The responsible person must be competent and must ensure the following:

- Carry out a suitable and sufficient fire risk assessment of the site, record the findings in full, and ensure that the assessment is reviewed and remains relevant.
- Tell workers about the findings of the risk assessment.
- Take general fire precautions to ensure, so far as is reasonably practicable, the safety of employees and relevant persons. These can be persons who are lawfully on the construction site or in the immediate vicinity of the site.
- Put in place and maintain fire safety arrangements. These arrangements must be appropriate to the size of the construction site and the nature of the activities. These arrangements should include safe storage and transport of flammable materials, maintenance of fire safety equipment, hot-work permits, monitoring and inspection arrangements.
- Plan for an emergency. This detail can be written into the fire safety and evacuation plan and should include adequate emergency escape routes and exits, fire-fighting and fire detection arrangements and liaison with the emergency services.
- Provide workers with fire safety information, instruction and training. This can include displaying fire evacuation procedures, information on the arrangements to take in the event of discovering a fire, fire evacuation drill practices and fire extinguisher training.

- Co-operate and co-ordinate where two or more responsible persons have duties at the same premises.
- That they do not appoint a person to assist them in making or reviewing a fire risk assessment unless that person is competent.
- Record the identity of any person appointed to assist them.
- Record the fire safety arrangements.
- Take reasonable steps to ascertain whether there are any other responsible persons who share or have duties in respect of the premises.
- Record the other responsible person's:
  - name and address in the United Kingdom at which they, or someone acting on their behalf, will accept notices and other documents
  - area of responsibility, i.e. the part of the premises for which they consider themselves to be responsible.
- If someone takes over as the responsible person, the previous one must hand over any relevant fire safety information to maintain records.

A fire safety co-ordinator and fire warden(s) can be appointed to help the responsible person to perform their role.

 The responsible person could invite their local fire and rescue service to attend site and carry out a site inspection and familiarisation tour.

2.7.1 Fire safety co-ordinators and fire wardens

On larger or higher-fire-risk sites, the responsible person can appoint others to assist with the management of fire safety on site, and provide an increased level of management oversight in relation to fire safety. These can be either fire safety co-ordinators or fire wardens (and deputies). The appointment of deputies would be regarded as good practice on a complex site. The number of wardens will depend on the layout, site complexities and number of workers on site (a fire warden may also be known as a fire marshal).

On site, fire wardens or the fire safety co-ordinator (if appointed) would have the following responsibilities.

- Assist in implementing the fire safety and evacuation plan.
- Conduct weekly inspections of escape routes, fire-fighting equipment, access for emergency services and testing of alarms at detection devices on site.
- Keep records of all checks, inspections, tests and fire drills.
- Ensure that the hot-work permit systems are being followed and managed correctly.
- Liaise with security guards (where appointed) and fire and rescue services.
- Assist in fire evacuations.
- Ensure that offices and other accommodation are completely evacuated in the event of the fire alarm sounding (including practice drills) and conduct a roll call at the assembly point.

On large sites it is good practice for each sub-contractor to appoint a fire warden to account for their company's staff in the event of an evacuation. The location and number of staff can be identified by the use of an in/out board, signing in/out book or swipe card system that can be taken to, or accessed at, the assembly point and used for the roll call. Arrangements must be made for visitors to be logged into and out of offices so that, in the case of an emergency, they can be located quickly and escorted to a safe place.

Fire wardens and fire safety co-ordinators should be given sufficient time to perform their fire safety duties. They should receive training, specific to the role, which should be refreshed on a regular basis.

2.8 Fire risk assessment

There is a legal requirement for the responsible person to ensure that a site-specific fire risk assessment is carried out. They can either do this themselves or nominate a competent person to do it on their behalf. The responsible person on site will normally be the principal contractor or contractor. Fire specific legislation and CDM apply here, to ensure that risks are identified and managed. The risk assessment should identify the activities carried out on site and the likelihood that a fire could start and harm people in and around site. If an enforcing authority (such as the HSE or the fire and rescue service) visit site, they will expect to see a copy of the risk assessment.

 If you do not properly assess the risks, there is no way that you can adequately control them.

The principles of carrying out a fire risk assessment are broadly the same as for any other risk assessment.

There are five steps to carrying out a fire risk assessment.
1. **Identify the hazards.** Consider how a fire could start and what could burn, and the types of construction material used and stored on site, as well as the location of the build and how close it is to other buildings. This process should start at the design stage.
2. **Identify the people at risk.** Consider employees, contractors, visitors, immediate neighbours and people who may not be on site. Extra arrangements may be required for people with disabilities.
3. **Evaluate the risks and plan** how to remove or reduce them and how to protect people from any risks that remain (residual risk).
4. **Record, plan, inform, instruct and train.** Keep a record of the risks and actions taken, develop a fire safety and evacuation plan and ensure that people understand what they need to do in the event of a fire.
5. **Review** the fire risk assessment regularly to ensure it remains valid and takes account of any changes on site.

On smaller projects the initial assessment might be valid all the way through to completion.

On larger or complex projects, where there are a greater number of people to evacuate or there are long travel distances to a place of safety, someone with a detailed knowledge of fire risk management (such as a consultant) may be required.

In this scenario, it is likely that conditions around site will change as the project progresses meaning that periodic reviews and updates of the assessment will be required.

Irrespective of the size or complexity of the project, anyone carrying out a fire risk assessment must be competent to accurately identify the hazards, assess the risks and put effective control measures in place.

 For further information on the process of fire risk assessment refer to Appendix B.

 A guide to choosing a competent fire risk assessor **has been published by the Fire Risk Assessment Competency Council. For this and further documents to help you ensure you are competent to undertake risk assessments, visit the Fire Industry Association and Institution of Fire Engineers websites.**

2.9   Fire safety and evacuation plan

The fire safety and evacuation plan should be based on the findings of the fire risk assessment.

Like the fire risk assessment, the plan should be reviewed periodically so that it remains up-to-date and reflects the changing nature and hazards of the site.

A **fire safety co-ordinator** could be appointed to take responsibility for the fire safety and evacuation plan and its implementation.

The person who completes the fire safety and evacuation plan could be a member of the existing site management team or, where particular expertise is required, from a consultancy or specialist fire safety organisation.

The following are examples of sites where external expertise might be required.

● Those large in area, with a high number of people to evacuate via multiple escape routes.

● Where the structure being built or refurbished has several floors with limited access between them.

● Sites and structures with long or complex escape routes, with changes in direction and levels.

As a minimum the plan should include details of the following.

● The organisation and named individuals who have responsibility for fire safety.

● Arrangements for recording fire safety training given to site workers.

● Details of general site fire precautions, for example:

  – fire detection and alarm systems

  – temporary emergency lighting

  – fire extinguishers and fire points

  – fire escape arrangements and communications

  – procedures for calling the fire and rescue service.

● Fire service access facilities and co-ordination, including the provision of operational rising mains.

● Fire drills and training.

● Hot-work permit procedures, where hot works cannot be avoided.

● Site accommodation, including location, fire protection, construction and maintenance.

● Location and control of smoking arrangements.

● Security measures to minimise the risk of arson on site.

● Material storage arrangements and waste control regime, particularly where flammable and highly flammable materials will be stored on site.

● Maintenance of temporary electrical installations.

● Any coverings that will be used (for example, monoflex sheeting), as well as a record of checks made to ensure that they are fire retardant.

● Arrangements for plant and vehicles, in particular storage and refuelling arrangements.

● Measures to prevent the spread of fire on site and to any adjoining properties.

2.10 Common sources of fire risk

2.10.1 Hot work

Failure to adequately control hot work has been the cause of many construction site fires, many of them on refurbishment and maintenance jobs due to cutting, burning and welding operations and intense heat from halogen lights.

The Fire Protection Association (FPA) introduced a hot work passport scheme to enhance the level of competence of those involved in work with the potential to produce ignition sources. The passport is valid for five years and is suitable for employees involved in carrying out hot works or with responsibility for supervising or managing hot works.

 Hot work

An activity or process that generates flame, heat or spark and introduces a foreseeable risk of fire or explosion through a source of ignition created by tools or equipment, such as the examples shown below.

- Intentional source of ignition arising from working methods with or without the use of a naked flame (for example, welding, flame-cutting, soldering, blazing, heat-stripping of paint and heat-sealing of roof membrane).

- Unintentional generation of heat or sparks, by the use of power or hand tools (for example, grinding and the use of disc cutters).

A hot-work permit system must be introduced to make sure that such work can be carried out in a safe and controlled environment.

It is essential that anyone involved in hot works is:

- aware of the fire risk in the particular location where work is to be carried out

- aware of how heat might be transmitted to other areas

- trained and competent to use the equipment that will produce the source of heat

- trained and competent to select and use portable fire extinguishers.

Precautions must be taken where heat from a work process could be transmitted to other combustible materials (for example, where hot works are carried out on steelwork or pipes adjacent to, or passing through, flammable materials, such as studwork walls or timber floors). Where this kind of operation is anticipated, it is essential that all combustible materials, including liquids, are protected before any work is allowed to start. Special care should be taken when cutting or welding is carried out above flammable materials. Precautions must be taken to prevent sparks or hot fragments of metal from dropping onto and igniting the flammable material below (such as removing it or covering it with fire-resisting material).

Hot work should cease at least **one hour**, or **two hours** on high-risk sites (such as large, timber-frame projects), before the site closes, with the area actively monitored for signs of fire until the site is vacated.

Checks must include an inspection of cavities, around eaves, behind studding and into other voids where smouldering material would otherwise go undetected.

The introduction of a permit system should be considered for all hot work, except where the risk of fire is considered to be low. Hot-work permits are formal management documents that should only be issued by someone with official authority to do so.

Hot-work permits should normally include the following.

- The location where the work will be carried out.

- A description of the hot work to be carried out.

- The proposed start time and duration of the work activity.

- The time at which the permit expires (the work must be completed or cease at that time).

Other precautions to be taken, which should be reflected in the hot-work permit, include instructions for:

- clearing all combustible material from the surrounding area

- checking for combustible material in adjacent hidden locations

- having at least two suitable and serviceable fire extinguishers at the place of the work

- maintaining a careful watch for the early signs of fire during the work

- protecting combustible material that cannot be cleared (for example, by the use of non-combustible matting)

- on completion of the hot works, carrying out checks and monitoring the area until the site closes.

Even where a formal hot-work permit system is not in operation, because of a perceived low risk of fire, basic fire safety precautions (such as having a serviceable fire extinguisher to hand) are still required.

The following precautions must be observed when using **bitumen boilers**.

- The distance between the boiler and LPG cylinder must be at least 3 m, unless a suitable protective shield is fitted.
- Do not place boilers inside a building or in an enclosed space.
- Stand the boiler in a tray, with a capacity greater than the boiler, to capture any spills or leaks.
- Additional LPG bottles must be stored at least 6 m away from the boiler.
- The boiler must never be left unattended, moved or towed whilst the burner is alight.
- For extra safety only use boilers that are thermostatically controlled.
- If possible avoid taking boilers onto roofs; if this cannot be avoided, place the boiler on a non-combustible, insulating base.
- Appropriate fire-fighting equipment must be located nearby.

 Never use water to fight a bitumen fire.

 For detailed information refer to the HSE document *Health and safety in roof work* (HSG33).

2.10.2 Flammable liquids and gases

 You must be careful when LPG is being used on your site; the person doing the job must be competent and you must ensure that they are.

LPG should be stored in purpose-designed, fireproof compounds or cages that prevent the accumulation of vapour in the event of a leak. Compounds should have a level base of compacted earth, concrete or paving slabs and be surrounded by a secure chainlink fence at least 1.8 m high.

There should be sufficient shelter to prevent cylinders from being exposed to extremes of weather. Signs must be clearly displayed indicating the presence of LPG, and prohibiting smoking and the use of any naked flame in the area of the store.

Precautions for the use of LPG include the following points.

- Minimise the amount of LPG on site at any one time.
- Turn off cylinder valves before connecting or disconnecting any equipment.
- Check cylinders and all associated equipment before use; do not use if there are signs of damage or leaks.
- Small, easily portable LPG cylinders and canisters should ideally be removed from site after work.
- Use leak-finding fluid or soapy water to try to detect the exact location of leaks; the smell should provide the initial indication.
- Store LPG cylinders:
    - with their valves uppermost, apart from cylinders used to provide fuel for LPG-powered plant, which are used and stored on their side
    - away from oxygen cylinders, highly flammable liquids, oxidisers, toxic or corrosive gases or substances
    - away from untrapped drains and cellars
    - a distance of at least 3 m from other substances, although they may be kept in the same compound.
- **Never** store LPG cylinders below ground in cellars or basements.

 LPG cylinders must never be stored in unventilated metal boxes or site accommodation.

Ignition of released LPG, where the concentration exceeds 2%, can result in fire or, if confined, an explosion. If a leak does not ignite immediately, and the LPG and air mixture drifts from the point of release, it will gradually become more diluted. However, if the concentration still exceeds 2%, ignition could cause a flash or cloud-fire back to the point of release.

A leak of LPG may be noticed either by the smell or the noise of the gas escaping. Leaks must not be traced with a lighted match or naked flame as this would almost certainly cause an explosion. Only soapy water or a proprietary leak-finding fluid should be used. If it is suspected that LPG has leaked inside a building, no attempt should be made to touch any electrical apparatus.

 Never turn on light switches or any other electrical equipment if a leak of LPG is suspected.

Open all doors and windows, if it is safe to do so, and leave immediately. Do not re-enter the building until advice has been sought and you are told it is safe. Where LPG is used for fixed heaters, cookers and lighting within welfare facilities, the cylinders and regulators must be kept outside and the gas supplied using rigid copper piping.

FIRE PREVENTION AND CONTROL

The use of flexible hosing is permitted only between the cylinders and changeover valves or manifolds, and for the final connection to appliances, but this must be kept as short as possible. There should be ventilation grills at low and high level to maintain ventilation.

Check that these have not been blocked or covered to prevent cold drafts and install carbon monoxide alarms.

All pipework should be easily accessible for inspection, but protected against accidental damage. Any work on LPG pipework or other parts of a fixed installation, including testing, must only be carried out by appropriately trained (Gas Safe registered) persons.

Inspections of all appliances must be carried out before use. If soot forms or smells occur, place the appliance in quarantine. Find out the reason for the problem and have it corrected.

Before using LPG equipment in an enclosed space a risk assessment must be carried out. It is essential to ensure that there is adequate ventilation, which may have to be forced. This is necessary to ensure full combustion and also to make certain that the products of combustion, other fumes and excess oxygen from any cutting apparatus are removed. Enhanced fire safety precautions and the use of atmospheric monitoring should be considered.

Wherever practicable, cylinders used with operations in confined spaces should be located in a safe area, preferably in the open air. The supply pressure should be reduced to the lowest practicable level on leaving the source of supply.

When working below ground, the number of cylinders must be kept to a minimum. All cylinders and hoses should be removed as soon as work has finished or if it is interrupted for a substantial period (for example, overnight).

LPG cylinders must not be taken into confined spaces, as defined in the Confined Spaces Regulations, unless exceptional safety precautions are taken.

Highly flammable and explosive substances (such as adhesives, solvents and paint) should be stored as follows.

● Where site conditions allow, in an external, secure, purpose-built compound.

● Where external storage is not practical, in a suitable secure, internal, fireproof storeroom with fire detection and suppression systems installed.

● In a metal, lockable cabinet or bin, for immediate or imminent use at the place of work.

Where it is necessary to store bulk quantities of highly flammable substances, the requirements of the storage area are shown below.

● Located outdoors in a position away from watercourses and drains and protected against vandalism or impact from vehicles or plant.

● Be stored within an impervious bund with a capacity greater than 110% of the total potential stored contents. For multi-tank storage the capacity must be 110% of the largest tank or 25% of the total combined tank capacity, whichever is greater.

● Protected against direct sunlight.

● At least 2 m away from nearby buildings or boundaries, except where the boundary of the store forms part of a solid wall; cans or drums may be stacked up against that wall up to 1 m from the top.

● Fitted with appropriate signage to indicate the content (such as 'highly flammable' or 'flashpoint below 32°C').

● Fitted with an 'EX' sign when an assessment under the Dangerous Substances and Explosive Atmospheres Regulations (DSEAR) indicates that an explosive atmosphere could be present in the event of a leak.

Image showing bad practice. Designated refuelling and cutting points should be used or, better still, another type of powered equipment when working in timber-frame or enclosed buildings

● Fitted with 'No smoking' or 'No naked flames' signs.

● Kept locked when access is not required.

● Equipped with intrinsically safe electrical circuits and fittings where electrical supplies are necessary.

● Equipped with dry powder or foam fire extinguishers.

● Equipped with a quantity of absorbent material, to soak up any spilt liquids, and a suitable container for the collection and safe disposal of the contaminated absorbent.

● If necessary, equipped with racking made from a non-ferrous metal or other non-combustible material.

EX icon hazard sign indicating an explosive atmosphere

❗ The secure storage of dangerous materials in a proper compound or cabinet is as equally important as using them in a safe manner.

If for any reason it is not practical to store highly flammable or other dangerous substances outside (for example, if the footprint of the structure under construction completely fills the land available), conditions for outdoor storage above apply, and the DSEAR assessment must consider whether the risks of storage indoors are acceptable. If the DSEAR assessment concludes that it is not safe, off-site storage and transportation must be arranged.

In deciding whether or not the risks associated with indoor storage are acceptable, it is likely that expert advice will be required to determine the suitability of the proposed storage area with regard to its fire and explosion resistance.

It is recommended that the maximum quantities that may be stored in cabinets and bins are no more than 50 litres for highly flammable liquids (and flammable liquids with a flashpoint below the maximum ambient temperature of the workroom/working area) and no more than 250 litres for other flammable liquids with a higher flashpoint of up to 55°C.

Under no circumstances should storage areas be located underground as this would prevent the dispersal of leaks from gases and vapours that are heavier than air.

All signs must conform to the Health and Safety (Safety Signs and Signals) Regulations.

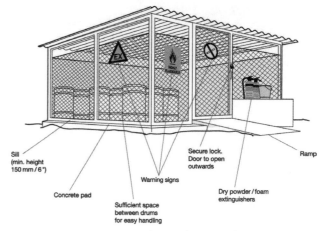

A secure dangerous substances storage area

 When storing highly flammable materials at the workplace, ready for use, only store one day's supply or less.

On many sites there will be a need to store bulk quantities of vehicle fuels, particularly diesel oil, usually in a bowser or drum. If storage drums are used, the same conditions apply as for the storage of other highly flammable and explosive substances.

 Carelessly dispensing fuel into vehicles or plant when the engine is still hot has been the cause of many serious fires and injuries.

Where fuel oil is to be dispensed into containers or vehicles, the outlet must be fitted with a valve or nozzle, which closes automatically when not in use and cannot be fixed in the open position unless an automatic cut-off nozzle is used on the end of the hose.

The hose and nozzle should be housed in an enclosed, secure cabinet with a drip tray when not in use, or have a lockable valve where the feed leaves the tank. Hoses should be kept locked or kept within the bund when not in use.

Any permanent valve or tap that opens directly from the tank must:

● be located within the secondary containment system (bund wall)

● discharge vertically downwards

● be locked off when not in use.

Finally, no vent must discharge outside of the bund in the event of an overfill.

Generally, petrol is only used in relatively small quantities for generators and some hand tools (such as chainsaws) but, however small the quantity, it must be stored safely.

Petrol will usually be stored in 20 litre metal jerry cans or five-litre, purpose-made plastic containers. The jerry cans or containers must be kept closed, except when the content is being decanted.

The positioning of fire extinguisher points, and the types of extinguisher, must be based in part upon where flammable construction materials will be stored and used.

Storage areas for flammable substances and gas bottles should be located away from emergency escape routes and assembly points.

 For more detailed information on flammable liquids refer to the following HSE guidance.

● *Safe use and handling of flammable liquids* **(HSG140).**

● *Storage of flammable liquids in tanks* **(HSG176).**

2.10.3 Material storage

Many materials (such as timber) and substances used in the construction process will readily catch fire if exposed to a source of ignition.

Where practical, all combustible materials should be stored outside – not within a building. Ideally, all materials will be stored in a locked compound or storage container, with adequate separation between different types of product. Where internal storage is inevitable, the storage area must:

● be constructed and arranged so that the spread of fire would be limited

● be separated from the rest of the structure by a partition that provides a **minimum of 30 minutes' fire resistance** and doors must be fire resistant and self-closing

● be located away from evacuation routes so that it does not pose a threat to people trying to evacuate the site.

2.10.4 Storage of waste

Most construction sites generate large quantities of waste that present a potential fire risk. Good housekeeping should be maintained and waste should be cleared from site on a regular basis. Poor housekeeping will increase the fire loading and has the potential to block access to fire alarms, fire-fighting equipment and escape routes, putting people at risk.

Examples of poor planning and housekeeping that increase fire risk are shown below.

- Work being carried out in designated escape routes (for example, tower scaffolds erected on staircases).

- Flammable liquids and gases not being returned to their designated storage areas after use.

- Access routes for the emergency services being blocked, preventing access to all parts of the site.

A build up of combustible material causing a fire risk

Skips and other waste disposal containers should be placed **a minimum of 3 m away** from the structure under construction or the means of escape from it. If this cannot be done, the following actions should be taken.

- Encourage the regular clearing and segregation of waste.

- Prevent build up of a significant fire load.

- Make sure skips are easily accessible to vehicles that are facilitating removal or replacement of the skips.

- Place skips away from canopies and overhanging eaves.

- Place skips against a fire-resisting wall, which is high enough to prevent fire from reaching other flammable parts of the structure.

- Ensure that personnel working on site use only a chute made of non-combustible materials.

- Restrict the amount of flammable material placed within waste disposal containers.

The following points should also be considered.

- Site rules should state that contractors must keep their areas clear of waste at intervals appropriate to the nature and volume of the waste created, but at least daily.

- Skips should be emptied or replaced before the contents represent a fire risk.

Flammable waste materials should not be allowed to accumulate but instead be cleared away promptly to hazardous waste skips located outside the structure; the more waste material there is within the structure, the greater the fire loading.

2.10.5 Electrical installations

Electrical installations should be professionally designed, installed, inspected and maintained, in accordance with the **Electricity at Work Regulations**. This will ensure that the installation has the required capacity to cope with the intended loads and will remain in a safe condition. A regime of regular inspection and maintenance of the system will be required, with any necessary alterations being designed and installed by competent persons.

 Unauthorised alterations must not be made to the distribution system.

Halogen light fittings can get hot and cause materials near them to ignite. Historically, they have been a common source of ignition for site fires and it is good practice to only use them where other forms of task lighting are not suitable and the fire risk assessment shows that it is safe to do so (some sites have banned the use of halogen lights). The failure of electrical hand tools and mains-powered office equipment has also been the cause of fires. The regular testing of portable electrical appliances and hand tools (PAT – portable appliance testing) will confirm whether the internal insulation is breaking down or there are other defects rendering the equipment a potential fire hazard.

PAT testing helps an employer maintain regular maintenance checks on portable electrical appliances and equipment, and evaluate the regularity of those tests according to the risk. Portable electrical equipment should be switched off and disconnected from the supply when not in use for extended periods. This extends to equipment that might be left on overnight (such as computers or photocopiers).

Possible causes of electrical fires are shown below.

- Overheating of poorly maintained or damaged equipment and hand tools.

- Overloading of electrical circuits.

- Overloading of electrical sockets in site accommodation.

- Accumulation of combustible rubbish alongside cables (frequently in ceiling voids) or distribution boards.

- Bypassing of circuit safety devices, rendering them inoperative.

- Fitting of the incorrect rating of fuse, circuit breaker or residual current device (RCD).

- Unauthorised modification of the site electrical distribution system.

- Failure to carry out the periodic testing and maintenance of electrical circuits and safety devices.

- Sparking within electrical equipment or tools igniting explosive airborne particles (dust) or fumes.

- Accidental damage to equipment and conductors that have not been adequately protected.

 For further information refer to the following HSE publications.

- *Maintaining portable electrical equipment* **(HSG107).**

- *Maintaining portable electric equipment in low-risk environments* **(INDG236).**

2.10.6 Bonfires

Environmental factors, risk of uncontrolled fire and/or Local Authority restrictions make the controlled burning of rubbish on site an unacceptable practice. The potential for the reuse or recycling of waste materials should always be considered with alternative arrangements made for the proper disposal of rubbish and waste.

2.10.7 Plant and equipment operations

Most engine-driven plant and equipment will generate heat during use. Excessive heat can be generated if the plant or equipment is poorly maintained or if it is being used beyond its design capacity. Furthermore, plant represents a fire hazard when it is being refuelled or stored away, under cover, whilst still hot. The lead-acid batteries used in plant and other vehicles give off an explosive gas when the batteries are being recharged, if the batteries are of a type where the filler caps have to be removed or loosened. The same will apply to any type of electrical equipment (for example, temporary traffic light units, which incorporate this type of battery).

2.10.8 Protection of finished surfaces

Once a building is nearing completion, it is common practice to use temporary coverings to protect finished surfaces and installed equipment during the remaining fitting-out phase. These coverings often take the form of plastic sheeting, fibreboard or similar materials, some of which may be flammable. They can consequently assist in spreading fire. Ideally, purpose-made, fire-retardant materials should be used.

 All temporary flexible covering materials used for the protection of internal surfaces or fittings incorporated into the building or structure should be compliant to *Fire requirements for protective covering materials* (LPS 1207 (internal) and LPS 1215 (external)).

If non-fire-retardant materials are used, the protective covering should be fitted as late as possible in the project and the fire-protection measures must be suitable to cover the enhanced risk.

2.10.9 Scaffolding sheeting

If scaffolding is to be sheeted and used as a means of escape, the sheeting must be made to a flame-retardant standard (LPS 1215). Consideration should be given to ventilation (to clear smoke) and access for the emergency services.

2.10.10 Arson

Arson has been the suspected cause of many construction fires. It should be identified on the risk assessment as a potential hazard, and the control measures should be written down and included in the site fire safety and evacuation plan. Flammable materials should not be stored where they can be seen and set alight from outside the site boundary. Therefore, hoarding and fencing around the site perimeter, and securing access points, can help prevent arson or the temptation of arson. Security measures (such as 24-hour security, CCTV cameras and intruder alarms) can help to secure the site from arson risks. If security guards are to be used, part of their patrol can include fire checks during the day, night, holidays and weekends.

Some other ways to prevent arson are listed below.

- Only allow authorised people on site.

- Employ site security to prevent unauthorised access to the site out of normal working site hours.

- If necessary, remove flammable liquids, LPG and other gases and combustibles whilst the site is closed.

- If the completed project includes security fencing, this should be brought forwards and used during the construction phase.

- Provide security lighting.

- Log any suspected incidents so that preventative action can be taken.

 If employing security personnel the duties they undertake must be covered by a risk assessment.

2.11 Higher-risk projects

Projects that will require extra precautions could be timber-frame structures, multistorey buildings or high rise construction sites, or those where significant risks have been identified during the risk assessment. Some of these are explained in more detail below.

2.11.1 Timber-frame structures

Large, timber-frame buildings under construction without the appropriate protection measures and controls in place pose a significant risk to construction workers, fire-fighters, adjacent buildings and members of the public.

Timber-frame structures are at their most vulnerable when they are being erected and before any cladding or protective skins are installed. Each structure should be compartmentalised and clad at the earliest practical opportunity. Designers should give consideration to the use of materials that have been given a fire protective or retardant treatment.

Compartmentalising the structure at the earliest opportunity prevents the rapid spread of fire and supports safe travel distances for anyone who has to evacuate the structure in an emergency.

! High-risk timber-frame buildings require additional fire-prevention measures.

Consideration must be given to using fire-resistant boarding to temporarily fire-stop ducts and shafts until the permanent fire-engineered solution is installed. Temporary or permanent fire-resisting doors, panels and fire stopping should be installed as early in the construction programme as is practical.

Temporary accommodation units, site cabins and offices should be situated at least 20 m away from the timber-frame structure to act as a fire break if a potential fire did break out.

Where there are multiple, timber-frame structures on a site, the fire risk assessment must consider how a fire in one of them could be prevented or slowed from spreading to the others or to adjacent premises. To this end, temporary non-combustible cladding could be used to cover exposed timber and other combustible construction materials prior to the final cladding being installed.

High-risk timber-frame buildings require additional fire-prevention measures

The Structural Timber Association has published several guides (freely downloadable from its website) related to fire safety in timber-frame construction, as part of its safe site strategy.

- *Fire risk induction pack for site workers.*
- *Design guide to separating distances during construction.*
- *Risk assessment checklist.*
- *Guidance notes on wireless fire alarms.*
- *16 steps to fire safety.*

2.11.2 Multistorey buildings

It is advisable that the fire and rescue service are informed that any construction work or renovations are taking place. The Building Regulations, for example, require additional measures on buildings above 18 m (or seven storeys or more). The important factor, in relation to construction site fire safety, is that the risks associated with the build can be adequately controlled, and that the GFPs needed in the event of a fire are sufficient to ensure that every person on site can return to the ground and to a place of safety.

More-complex and very high-rise projects are beyond the scope of this guidance. You may need additional help with these from a competent specialist with the necessary skills, knowledge and experience of both fire safety and construction of high-rise buildings.

This type of structure, during construction or refurbishment, can pose particular problems with regard to the management of fire risk. Incomplete or absent fire-engineered solutions can result in the rapid spread of fire, leaving workers on the upper floors particularly at risk. Furthermore, it is possible that in some circumstances it will not be practical to supply sufficient water for fire-fighting purposes to the higher levels. In these circumstances a specific risk assessment must be undertaken to establish how the safety of those working on the upper levels can be assured in the event of a fire.

Designers have a major impact on fire safety, not only in their selection of materials and methods of work, but also in ensuring the following.

- Temporary, fire-resistant compartmentalisation or other fire-engineering solutions are incorporated until permanent fire stopping is in place.

- With new-build or refurbished premises, a working fire alarm system is extended as each level of the building is completed so that it can be heard in all parts of the building at all stages of construction.

- The fire alarm system is electrically operated (hard-wired or wireless) with break-glass call points and sounders at each level.

- The rising water main(s) is installed and commissioned at an early stage before interior work starts.
- If some floors are already occupied, the risk assessment and fire safety and evacuation plans allow for:
  - the integration of the fire alarm systems for both the construction areas and the occupied floors
  - any restrictions that prevent construction workers accessing the occupied part of the building, particularly escape routes
  - the possibility that construction workers may not be allowed access to occupied parts of the building.
- Access to all staircases, or other protected routes, is maintained at all times, as far as possible.
- One staircase is designated as a fire-fighting staircase for the sole use of the fire and rescue service during an emergency.
- Fire doors with self-closers are fitted to protect the escape stairways and provide adequate fire stopping.

2.12 Fire detection and emergency planning

As detailed in Regulation 32 of CDM *'suitable and sufficient fire-fighting equipment and fire detection and alarm systems must be provided and located at suitable places'*. This requirement includes examination, testing, maintenance and signage. Additionally it stipulates that *'each person at work on a construction site must, so far as is reasonably practicable, be instructed in the correct use of fire-fighting equipment that may be necessary for the person to use'*.

The responsible person must consider the following aspects, *2.12.1 to 2.12.6* below, at all stages of the project and review and revise as necessary. Changes identified should be reflected in the fire risk assessment and fire safety and evacuation plan and communicated to those who are at risk.

 The emergency plan must be reviewed and updated on a regular basis as the structure develops and site conditions change.

2.12.1 Fire alarm systems

In the event of a fire it is essential that the alarm is raised as quickly as possible so that everyone on site can evacuate and reach a place of safety. As the site changes, the fire alarm system may need to be modified so that coverage across site is maintained.

- Alarms must be sufficient in number and located so that everyone on site is aware that the alarm has sounded.

- Manually operated sounders (such as hand bells, whistles and klaxons) will only be practicable for use on sites where they can be heard above any site noise and they must be readily available.

- Temporary hard-wired systems operated from call points are best when the site is large and covers multiple floors.

- If using a wireless fire alarm system, consideration must be given to ensure that the signal remains constant and uninterrupted. The Fire Protection Association's Joint Code of Practice states components of an automatic fire detection and alarm system should be marked as complying with BS EN 54.

- Flashing lights or vibrating pagers could be used if it has been identified that the alarms cannot be heard or where there is continuous loud noise.

Sites must have an effective fire alarm system

The operation and effectiveness of the fire alarm system should be routinely checked and serviced. Records of these checks should be maintained. If the project is a high-risk site or includes temporary accommodation units then automatic fire detection systems should be linked to the sounders. Domestic-type smoke alarms are not considered suitable on sites. However, they may be suitable on low-risk sites or in a small, temporary site office.

2.12.2 Fire detection systems

During the early stages of new build projects it is inevitable that the only way of detecting fire is visually; someone will see a fire and raise the alarm. However, on larger and high-risk sites and as the areas become enclosed, with increasing amounts of flammable materials present, the benefits of an automatic fire detection system become obvious.

Where a permanent automatic fire detection system is planned, phased activation of the system should be programmed in to follow the progress of the construction as early as possible.

During refurbishment work, if an automatic fire detection system already exists it should remain live throughout the work, where it is practicable to do so.

2.12.3 Fire action notices

Fire action notices should be displayed in prominent locations across site and should include the following.

- Actions to take in the event of a fire.
- Instructions for calling the fire and rescue service.
- The location of the nearest fire assembly point.

Certain people on site may have additional duties in the event of a fire. For example, security guards may be responsible for providing unobstructed access for emergency vehicles, and supervisors may be responsible for undertaking a head count of their workers to ensure everyone is accounted for at the assembly point.

Principal contractors or contractors must ensure they have briefed everyone on site about the site emergency procedures. This is normally covered during the induction. However, they may need to provide additional briefings (such as a toolbox talk) as escape routes change.

2.12.4 Fire drills

Emergency procedures should be tested by carrying out regular fire drills, at least once every six months. Details of these tests should be recorded (for example, in a designated fire log book).

Details of the test could include a note on how long it took everyone to evacuate and any findings (for example, if workers reported they couldn't hear the alarm or if fire escape routes were blocked or unavailable) so that corrective action can be taken.

Fire drills will also identify if there are any bottlenecks, so alternative routes can be identified before a real emergency occurs. No-notice fire drills provide the most useful information on the effectiveness of the evacuation procedure. However, it is recognised that these may not always be practicable.

2.12.5 Means of escape

Escape routes must be located so all parts of the site have access to a place of safety, in the open air and at ground level. There should be at least two means of escape from the structure at all times, including from the basement and from roof level. Travel distances must be appropriate for the level of fire hazard.

Where dead ends exist they should be closely monitored and travel distances must be kept to a minimum in these situations. Any openings along a dead end route must be able to restrain a fire for half an hour.

Maximum travel distances from the fire to the safe area			
	Low level of fire hazard	**Medium level of fire hazard**	**High level of fire hazard**
Enclosed structure			
Alternative	60 m	45 m	25 m
Dead end	18 m	18 m	12 m
Semi-open structure			
Alternative	200 m	100 m	60 m
Dead end	25 m	18 m	12 m

The following points add clarity and detail to the table above and show factors to be considered when planning and selecting escape routes.

- Dead end travel distances are measured as a person walks.
- Alternative escape routes should be in the opposite direction.
- Semi-open structure: structures where there are substantial openings that would allow smoke and heat from a fire to disperse.
- Low hazard areas: very few flammable materials and the risk of fire occurring is low.
- Medium (normal) hazard areas: include materials that may be flammable. Any fires in this type of area will initially be localised.
- High hazard areas: locations where flammable materials are present in significant quantities. If a fire occurs in this area it will spread rapidly.

During the construction phase escape routes are likely to change and therefore they must be reviewed and alternative routes identified and communicated to everyone on site. Escape routes should be identified at design stage and permanent routes, including fire escape stairs, should be installed as soon as possible.

Escape routes must be:

- adequate for the number of workers on site at any one point of the project
- always available in the event of a fire
- kept free from obstructions and checked that they are unobstructed, at least weekly

- altered as necessary as the project advances

- equipped with adequate signage and lighting (old signage must be removed as the escape routes change)

- provided with a second protected escape stairwell for buildings over four storeys high (if not reasonably practicable, due to cost or disruption, an external staircase can be provided instead).

Where an external escape route is constructed against an existing wall, the wall should not have holes or gaps and should provide half an hour of fire resistance for 9 m below the stairway and 1.8 m either side and above (these distances should be measured from the stair treads).

If any opening (such as a window) that is not fire resisting is present, this can be protected with plasterboard, steel sheets or reinforced cement panels.

Doors onto an escape route or the final exit should open outwards (revolving and sliding doors may jam). Doors leading to the escape routes must be self-closing and have half an hour of fire resistance. If doors are required to be locked when the site is unoccupied, due to security reasons, then they must be unlocked as soon as the site is opened.

Preferably all locks should be escape locks that comply with relevant British safety standards, therefore removing the need for a key lock.

 Fire doors must comply with BS 476 and their installation must comply with BS 8214.

2.12.6   Emergency lighting and signs

Emergency lighting is required to ensure that escape routes can be seen. In the event of failure of the primary lighting, emergency lighting needs to come on immediately. Batteries or an emergency generator can be used to power the emergency lighting.

Emergency signs should comply with the Health and Safety (Safety Signs and Signals) Regulations. In low light areas or where lighting cannot be guaranteed photo luminescent escape signs should be provided.

2.13   Fire-fighting equipment

Portable fire extinguishers, hose reels, hydrants and fire blankets are all types of fire-fighting equipment.

2.13.1   Portable fire extinguishers

Fire extinguishers do not prevent fires. However, they can be used by trained employees in an attempt to aid escape and minimise loss and damage after a fire has started. It goes without saying that preventing the fire in the first place is a far better option.

Where there is a realistic possibility that staff will have to use fire extinguishers (for example, if they are involved in hot works), they should be trained in their use. CDM (Regulation 32) require that each person at work on a construction site, so far as is reasonably practicable, must be instructed in the correct use of fire-fighting equipment, which may be necessary for the person to use.

In line with the risks identified in a fire risk assessment, adequate numbers of suitable types of portable fire extinguisher must be provided and kept available throughout the premises.

Extinguishers must be located in clearly visible locations near exits on each floor. They should be fixed to the wall with their carrying handles approximately 1 m above the floor level. Where this is not possible, they should be fixed in position (for example, using base plates or stands) at floor level.

In the open, extinguishers should be situated in red painted boxes, which are either sitting on the floor or raised 500 mm above ground level, with a 'Fire point' sign at a height readily seen above any obstructions. Care must be taken during winter months to ensure that extinguisher contents do not freeze.

To protect electrical distribution panels and items of electrical equipment, appropriate extinguishers (usually carbon dioxide, or CO_2) must be provided near but not dangerously close to the equipment concerned.

For large or costly items of equipment (such as computer suites) consider installing automatic fire detection and extinguishing systems.

 All mechanically propelled site plant should carry an appropriate fire extinguisher.

2.13.1.1   Colour coding of fire extinguishers

It is essential that staff who may be called upon to use a fire extinguisher have been trained in their use and have a clear understanding of the colour coding system.

All fire extinguishers are painted red with a contrasting colour somewhere on the casing (such as a contrasting panel or handle), which indicates what extinguishing agent the extinguisher contains.

Colour coding enables a trained person to rapidly identify the type of extinguisher needed in an emergency.

The coloured panels must cover a minimum 5% of the surface area.

Extinguishing medium	**Water:** for wood, paper, textile and solid material fires	**Foam:** for flammable liquid fires, such as petrol, diesel, and paint	**Powder:** for liquid and electrical fires **Specialist dry powders:** for metal fires	**Carbon dioxide (CO_2):** for flammable liquid and electrical fires	**Wet chemical:** for wood, paper, textile, cooking oil and solid material fires
Colour of panel	Red	Cream	Blue	Black	Yellow
Where not to use	**Do not** use on flammable gas and liquids, fires involving electrical equipment or metal fires	**Do not** use on fires involving electrical equipment or metal fires	**Do not** use on metal fires **unless** M28 or L2 text is printed on the extinguisher, which means it is suitable for metal fires	**Do not** use on metal, wood, paper or textile fires	**Do not** use on flammable liquid, gas or electrical fires

 Dry powder extinguishers may be provided in addition to or substituted for water, foam or CO_2 extinguishers. Extinguishers used to control Class B fires will not work on Class F fires because of the high temperature generated.

A few extinguishers may still be in use that complied with a much earlier standard of colour coding. This standard required that the whole body of each extinguisher was painted in the same contrasting colours that are now used in the later standard. In addition, a small number of extinguishers are bright silver or self-coloured metal with a designated panel stating the medium they contain. The colour coding of the panel should be the same as that listed above.

 For further information on the selection and use of fire extinguishers refer to *Fire safety in construction* (HSG168).

2.13.1.2   Inspection and maintenance

Fire extinguishers must be tested by a competent person annually, and there should be an appropriate management system to ensure that they are regularly checked and properly maintained along with other firefighting equipment. These examinations and tests should be in accordance with a recognised procedure, such as that in BS 5306–3:2017 and BS 5306–1:2006. The work should be carried out by a competent person who has received appropriate training. Record the date and results of the examinations, preferably on a service sticker attached to the individual piece of equipment, so that the particular extinguisher or hose reel checked is identifiable.

 No extinguisher should be more than 20 years old, have any damage or be unusable in any other way. In that situation, it needs to be replaced or serviced immediately. Clearly, if it has been discharged it will need to be replaced straight away.

Inspection and maintenance

Fire-fighting equipment must be maintained and regularly inspected. Monthly checks should be carried out to ensure that:

● extinguishers are in place and are suitable for the type of work in the adjacent area

● extinguishers are fully charged and in a good condition, with no visible signs of rust or damage

● all hydrants are clear from obstructions and are clearly marked.

Hose reels and extinguishers must be serviced annually.

 Fire extinguishers need to be checked more often if they are in locations where they are likely to be tampered with.

2.13.1.3   Hazardous vapours from fire extinguishers

The discharge of a CO_2 extinguisher in any small, enclosed or confined space will reduce the percentage of oxygen in the air. The dust cloud from a dry powder extinguisher may, in a confined space, produce local and temporary breathing difficulties and poor visibility. Once an extinguisher has been discharged in such circumstances, the user should leave the area immediately. When it is safe to do so, the area should be thoroughly ventilated before allowing anyone to re-enter. If there is a need to re-enter before the air has cleared, suitable breathing apparatus must be worn.

2.13.1.4 Staff training in the selection and use of fire extinguishers

There is a legal requirement for employers to ensure that all employees are familiar with fire procedures, and that an appropriate number of employees are trained in the use of fire-fighting equipment.

Training in the selection and use of portable extinguishers is essential if they are to be used effectively in fighting small fires. It is also important that the right type of extinguisher is used on certain types of fire.

Attention should be given to the physical strength of persons who may have to use extinguishers. Some extinguishers weigh 20 kg.

During staff training on the use of extinguishers, the following points need to be emphasised.

● Think of evacuation first.

● Only use an extinguisher if it is safe for you to do so.

● Do not let the fire come between you and your escape route. You may become trapped if the fire develops.

● If the extinguisher does not appear to be working or is ineffective on the fire, get out immediately.

● If the fire starts to increase or gets out of control, get out immediately.

During induction training or ongoing staff training, the following points should be made to all staff.

● Do not use a fire extinguisher unless you have been trained to do so.

● Do not misuse fire extinguishers.

● Do not move fire extinguishers from their allocated positions (for example, do not use fire extinguishers as door stops).

● Immediately report any fire extinguishers that appear to have been used, misused or damaged.

2.13.2 Hose reels

Hose reels can be used instead of water-based extinguishers. They are more likely to be found in a live state on projects where premises are being refurbished. One hose reel is recommended for each 800 m² of floor area. In making this assessment, care must be taken to ensure that the hose reaches all of the area to be covered.

On new build projects, or where the water supply to existing hose reels has been drained, it is good practice to make the supply live in progressive stages as the fire loading of the structure increases.

Training employees in the correct use of hose reels is essential if fire-fighting is to be effective. Staff need to be fully aware of how the hose reels work, and what type of fire they would be effective on, before they use them in an emergency.

2.13.3 Water supplies

Water supplies for fire-fighting must be available as early as possible. Water can be drawn from the normal mains and hydrants, or from swimming pools and rivers.

As part of the design specification, rising and temporary mains must be provided as the building increases in height, with temporary caps being used, as required, to seal the riser.

Water supplies for fire-fighting must be tested as the work progresses.

Water supplies for high rise buildings must be agreed with the fire and rescue services before work commences. The on-site water flow should be tested and recorded before work commences and all valves should subsequently be tested every three months.

 Fire hydrants must be clearly marked to support identification and be kept clear of obstruction at all times.

2.13.4 Fire blankets

Fire blankets are usually sufficient to deal with small, contained fires involving tea-making facilities, frying pans and so on, and are usually found next to cooking facilities. To fight a small fire using a fire blanket you actually have to approach the fire, so it is important that prior training takes place.

Before attempting to extinguish such fires, the electricity or gas supply must be turned off.

The following points describe how to use a fire blanket.

● The blanket must be pulled from its container with the corners wrapped around the hands of the person using it, making sure that their hands and forearms are completely covered. The blanket must be held at chest level and gently placed over the burning container to exclude the air from the fire.

● The blanket must not be thrown because it may miss the burning container or cause it to spill, spreading the fire.

● The blanket must be left in place until the container has cooled down. It is essential that no-one lifts a corner to check if the fire is out as this may let in enough air to reignite the fire. The container must not be moved before it is cold.

2.14 Temporary accommodation units

In the drive to get the project built, it is easy to overlook the potential fire risks of the site accommodation.

Temporary accommodation units (TAUs) include site offices, canteens, rest rooms, drying rooms and toilets. They are often of timber construction, with fire-resisting surface materials. From site to site they will range from a single site cabin, combining the functions of office and canteen, to a range of single-storey, interlinked units, or they may form a multi-floor administrative complex.

The Confederation of Fire Protection Associations in Europe provides guidance on the fire protection of temporary buildings on construction sites, covering fire risks, fire protection requirements for escape and protection against the spread of fire.

For further information on the recommended frequencies for the inspection and testing of most electrical installations in temporary buildings refer to the Institution of Engineering and Technology.

For further guidance refer to the HSE's *Fire safety in construction* (HSG168).

2.14.1 Location of temporary accommodation units

A fire risk assessment is required for any TAU. The risk assessment will determine the correct location, siting and use of a TAU. They should ideally be located in the open air and separated from the building under construction and storage compounds by a fire break of at least 6 m (20 m on timber-frame and other high-risk sites). If such separation is not possible, the TAU should be designed to meet the following criteria.

● Walls, roof, windows and doors to achieve 30 minutes' fire resistance to BS 476.

● Fire doors must be fitted with self closures.

● Doors and windows should be shut when the area is unoccupied.

● If temporary buildings are to be stacked vertically, the floor or roof assembly and the supporting members must be protected to achieve a minimum of 30 minutes' fire resistance.

For TAUs that are located inside the building under construction, their fire resistance needs more careful consideration and they must include a fitted fire detection system. Under no circumstances should they be located in timber-frame structures. TAUs should be designed and constructed of materials that would not contribute significantly to the growth of a fire or increase levels of smoke or corrosive fumes. Where TAUs do not sit flush on the ground, measures must be taken to prevent the accumulation of rubbish in the space beneath the floor, a gap which will also enhance under floor ventilation.

For an example of a completed fire risk assessment for temporary accommodation units refer to Appendix C.

2.14.2 Sleeping accommodation

Sleeping accommodation could include facilities provided on site or a separate caravan or mobile home site provided solely for the use of the construction project. This accommodation needs a specific fire risk assessment, and sites should aim to provide a fire break at least 10 m wide. If caravans are to be used, they must be spaced in accordance with the Local Authority's requirements, and the necessary fire alarm and fire-fighting equipment must be provided. There should be no interconnecting route between sleeping accommodation and site.

2.14.3 Fire alarm systems

The fire alarm system for TAUs will inevitably vary between sites. For a single or double site cabin set-up, a verbal shout of 'fire' would be acceptable providing it can be heard throughout the TAU in normal circumstances. Where a fire could remain undetected for a period of time, smoke alarms should be installed.

The more TAUs there are, the more sophisticated the alarm system should be. For small TAU complexes, a hand-operated fire bell might be sufficient, providing it is audible throughout the complex. For larger complexes and areas where cooking is carried out, an electrical break-glass system with multiple call points and sounders may be required. Automatic fire detection should be fitted in canteens and drying rooms.

For TAUs that are within the building under construction, the TAU fire alarm should be integrated with the main building's fire alarm system. Fire alarm systems should be tested weekly to confirm that they are audible throughout the complex. For multiple points, the testing of these points should be rotated. Consideration must be given to fitting automatic fire detection systems and intruder alarms to temporary buildings where flammable substances are stored.

Automatic fire detection must be installed where flammable liquids and gases are stored and in temporary accommodation used for either cooking or for drying clothes.

2.14.4 Means of escape

The site fire safety and evacuation plan should detail the emergency evacuation procedures. In the event of a fire, the first priority is to get everyone out of the TAUs and account for them. How difficult this will be depends upon the size of the TAU complex, how many people are involved and whether they have full mobility. Visitors must also be accounted for.

Toxic smoke is the main cause of fatalities from fires, which makes it a greater hazard in enclosed spaces. Prompt evacuation is paramount. Suitable means of escape from a TAU depends on the travel distance (which determines the position and number of exits and stairs) and the occupancy level (which determines the width of escape routes, including doorways and doors).

For single and double cabin set-up, the means of escape will generally be obvious and special considerations will not be necessary. Ideally, in all TAU complexes there will be escape routes in at least two different directions from all points within the complex.

Where there is only one escape route:

● it must be adequately protected from fire so that it will always be available, if needed

● any high-risk equipment or materials must not be located adjacent to it.

Where the TAU assembly consists of more than three temporary buildings stacked vertically or more than four linked horizontally then specialist advice should be sought from the HSE. Wherever practical, doors should be hung so that they open in the direction of the escape. Employers (or the responsible person) must have regard for the requirements of the Disability Discrimination Act when considering means of escape.

Fire escapes can be blocked unintentionally

 For information on fire safety routes and distances refer to the FPA Joint Code of Practice *Fire prevention on construction sites*.

2.14.5 Fire-fighting equipment

All TAUs should be equipped with fire-fighting equipment. A hand-held fire extinguisher should be provided as a minimum. The appropriate type of extinguisher will depend upon the class or classes of fire that could occur *(refer to 2.13.1 for information on different types of fire extinguisher)*. A fire blanket will be required in any TAU where cooking oils are heated (such as kitchens and canteens) *(refer to 2.13.4)*.

2.14.6 Other considerations

Emergency lighting should be installed in TAUs if they are to be used outside of normal daylight hours and there is no illumination from other lighting (such as street lighting). Lighting provided should be self-contained or from a separate power source and last for a minimum of one hour.

Heaters in drying rooms and in office spaces must be fixed (preferably at floor level), fitted with security guards and maintained. Heating appliances cover a range of equipment (from wall mounted, electric cabin heaters, to large, forced air LPG heaters). Carelessly drying clothes on heaters can cause fires, so coat stands and drying lockers should be provided at a safe distance from the heaters to prevent the risk of fire. Care must be taken to see that combustible materials are not allowed to build up around such heaters.

 For information on carbon monoxide poisoning refer to Chapter B10 Dust and fumes (Respiratory hazards).

Any room where a gas fire is used must be fitted with a permanently open vent or louvre at high and low level to provide sufficient ventilation to enable the fire appliance to operate properly, without producing excess CO_2 (a window that could be closed in cold weather, for example, is not acceptable).

Gas fires, including associated pipework, connections and valves, must be regularly serviced by **Gas Safe registered engineers**. Spare cylinders must not be stored in site cabins or anywhere else where they may be subjected to being heated. All heaters and stoves, including cookers, must be turned off at the end of the working day, with the supply valve on the cylinder closed.

Cooking appliances must be properly installed and have adequate ventilation. To reduce fire risk, provide microwaves instead of electrical or gas cookers. High and low ventilation will also be required, and for heaters and cookers must be permanent and adequate, divided equally between vents at high and low level (for example, a two-burner cooker in a site hut needs approximately 150 mm x 150 mm ventilation. A 3 kW convector heater needs approximately 225 mm x 225 mm ventilation).

TAUs should contain the minimum amount of **furniture and fittings** and, where possible, these should be treated with flame retardants.

Cooking appliances should only be installed and maintained by a competent engineer

Appendix A - Classes of fire

Fires can be placed into one of the following categories.

Class A. Carbonaceous material (such as paper, cloth, wood and rubber) often referred to as solid fuel fires.

Class B. Flammable liquids or liquefiable solids (such as oil, fat, paint and fuel). These can be subdivided into:

> **B1.** Fires involving liquids that are soluble in water (such as methanol). They can be extinguished by CO_2, dry powder and water spray

> **B2.** Fires involving liquids that are not soluble in water (such as petrol and oil). They can be extinguished using foam, CO_2 and dry powder.

Class C. Flammable gases or liquefied gases (such as propane, butane, hydrogen or acetylene).

Class D. Combustible metals (such as magnesium, sodium and phosphorus).

Class F. High temperature cooking oils or fats (such as those used in deep fat fryers in large catering establishments or restaurants).

Electrical fires (fires involving electrical apparatus or equipment) are not a specific fire class, as electricity is a source of ignition, rather than a fuel. However, they are still important to mention because they have their own special fire safety requirements.

Class A. Carbonaceous material

On the majority of building or construction sites, the following carbonaceous items are freely available sources of fuel.

- Cardboard, paper and cloth.
- Wood.
- Dirty rags, oily rags and clothes.
- Packaging materials.

If a fire occurs involving carbonaceous material, a hose reel or a water extinguisher should be used. The jet of water should be aimed at the base of the fire first, and then moved progressively over the whole of the burning area. Always remove the material from the source of heat if possible, but without endangering the person involved or starting a fire in another location.

Class B. Flammable liquids or liquefiable solids

Includes any fire involving flammable liquids (some examples are shown below).

- Petrol or diesel.
- Oil.
- Paraffin.
- Paint.
- Resin and adhesive.

This type of fire should be dealt with using foam, CO_2 or dry powder extinguishers, depending on whether the fire is contained or flowing.

If the fire is contained, use a foam extinguisher with the jet of foam directed at the back of the container. This allows a blanket of foam to build up and spread across the surface of the burning liquid. If the fire is flowing, a dry powder extinguisher should be directed at the front edge of the fire, in an attempt to separate the flames from the fuel. This will smother the fire, remove oxygen and extinguish it.

The aim of using extinguishers in such a way is for the fire to be covered with a blanket of either foam or dry powder. This will cut off the supply of air, and thus the oxygen, to the fire. Once the blanket has been laid, do not disturb it until the liquid has cooled. Any reintroduction of air may cause the fire to re-ignite.

 Never use a water extinguisher or a hose reel on a fire involving any flammable liquid. The water will react violently with the burning liquid and cause an explosion.

Class C. Flammable and liquefied gases

Extreme caution is necessary when dealing with fires involving liquefied gases as there will always be the danger of an explosion.

LPG expands to a ratio of 274:1 so a leak of just one litre of liquid would produce a cloud of gas, if diluted in air to the right concentration, large enough to fill a room 3 m x 2 m x 2 m. This would cause an explosive atmosphere.

If a fire occurs in which a compressed gas cylinder is directly involved the following actions should be taken.

- Call the FRS and tell them the location of the cylinders and type of gas involved.
- Attempt to turn the gas off at the cylinder, if it is safe to do so.
- Attempt to turn off any gas appliances, if it is safe to do so.
- Activate the emergency evacuation procedure and clear the site.

Do not try to fight a fire in which a compressed gas cylinder is directly involved; leave it to the FRS as an overheated cylinder can explode.

If a fire involves other combustible materials (for example, timber that might cause the fire to spread to the location of the cylinders) a decision based upon personal safety will have to be taken on whether to attempt to fight the fire to prevent an escalation of the situation.

Class C fires are best dealt with by the use of dry powder extinguishers.

Class D. Combustible metals

Fires of this type involve magnesium, sodium, phosphorus and similar metals, and should only be dealt with by trained firefighters.

 Never apply water to any burning metal fire or a fire involving powdered metal. It would cause an immediate explosive reaction.

Specially-formulated powders are available for use in controlling fire in metals but, as a last resort, if no proprietary powder is available dry sand or earth may be applied to smother the burning area. The proprietary powder should be carefully placed and not thrown onto the burning metal. Throwing the powder will cause the burning material to spread. Be sure either to wear darkened safety glasses or to look away from the extreme brightness whilst attempting to cover the fire. Failure to take these precautions could damage your eyes.

Class F. Cooking oils

Class F fires are fires involving cooking oils or fats. These differ from conventional liquid fires due to the high temperatures involved, with auto ignition temperatures in excess of 340°C. They are difficult to extinguish using conventional extinguishers with a Class B capability, where other flammable liquids (for example, petrol) have a low flash point and so auto ignition temperatures make them easier to extinguish.

Extinguishers designed for cooking oil fires typically include wet chemical, dry chemical, or foam with special additives. These react with the burning oil to create a thick, soapy, heat-resistant crust on top of the cooking oil, preventing flammable vapours from reacting with oxygen. This reaction is called saponification. The alkalinity of the extinguishing material quickly reacts with burning oil to create the soap layer.

Due to the high heat, using an incorrect extinguisher on these fires can be extremely dangerous. Some reasons for this are given below.

- A water jet extinguisher directed at the surface of burning cooking oil will create an explosion. The water is quickly converted into steam, resulting in the possible expulsion of burning oil, which could spread the fire and harm the person using the extinguisher.

- Conventional foam extinguishers can put out flames, but heat quickly destroys the foam blanket, exposing the oil and allowing re-ignition.

- CO_2 and powder extinguishers are effective, but without sealing the oil's surface from oxygen it will rapidly re-ignite.

- Conventional powder, foam or CO_2 extinguishers are normally too powerful and direct, easily splashing the oil and spreading the fire.

Other types of fire

Electrical fires

Electrical equipment fires can be dealt with using CO_2 or dry powder. In staff training, the following simple safety rules should be emphasised.

- Do not use water on any fire involving electrical equipment. You may be electrocuted.

- Switch off the electricity supply, if possible, before fighting the fire. It is then just an ordinary fire.

- Do not approach closer than 1 m to any fire where the electrical supply has not been switched off.

- CO_2 is the best extinguishing medium if the concentration of gas can be confined (for example, within an electrical distribution cupboard).

- Direct the discharge from the extinguisher to one edge of the fire and, with a sweeping movement, pass to the far edge until extinguished.

Electrical equipment used on building and construction sites sometimes incorporates devices to protect against overheating and fire. Most electrical equipment fires are due to misuse or neglect, where appliances have not been properly maintained or are being used for a purpose, or in a manner, for which they were not designed. A fuse larger than the appliance rating will negate the purpose of the fuse and render the appliance potentially unsafe. All staff should be properly trained so that they do not misuse equipment, and to ensure that damaged or defective equipment is reported, taken out of use and professionally repaired.

Flammable adhesives and flammable liquid stores

For such fires, use dry powder or foam. Extreme care must be taken if the adhesive is petroleum or spirit-based, due to explosive vapours.

Cooking ranges

For range fires, use foam, dry powder, CO_2 or a fire blanket. Never move burning pans, as contents may splash and cause serious burns.

Petrol and diesel in stores

For fires involving petrol or diesel in stores use foam or dry powder.

Petrol or diesel-powered plant

For fires involving petrol or diesel-powered plant use foam or dry powder.

Hot work with cutting or welding equipment and bitumen boilers

For fires of this type use foam, dry powder or CO_2. Turn off the heater. The correct types of fire extinguisher must be provided and kept close at hand, with a careful watch being maintained for fire breaking out whilst work is in progress.

Appendix B – Stages of a fire risk assessment

Stage 1. Identify the fire hazards

Anything that burns is fuel for a fire; in general, fires start in one of three ways.

1. Accidentally (for example, failure of a hot work inspection to discover smouldering materials).

2. By act or omission (such as in the example above, if the inspection was simply not carried out).

3. Deliberate arson attack on the structure or, for example, a waste skip.

Therefore, the assessor should consider how a fire could start and what could burn.

Some considerations, relating to the risks, are shown below.

- The use of any equipment that incorporates a naked flame, hot air stream or hot surface.

- Making sure that electrical equipment is not misused (for example, by overloading circuits).

- Grinding and cutting wheel operations (for example, angle grinders or petrol cut-off saws).

- Checking electrical equipment for faults (such as damaged cables or sockets).

- Carrying out periodic testing and inspection of electrical circuits and equipment, including safety devices.

- Discarded smoking materials in areas where smoking is allowed.

- The use of non-fire retardant temporary protection and coverings.

- Build up of combustible waste, materials and packaging.

- Refuelling in non-designated safe areas.

- Asphalt and bitumen boilers.

- The use of heating and cooking appliances.

- The use of radiant heaters.

Potential fire risk due to a build up of materials and packaging near to a radiant heater

For a new-build timber-frame project, it is important to consider these additional areas when compiling the risk assessment.

- The location of the build.

- The proximity to other buildings already in situ.

- Can the materials being used and stored on site be reduced or substituted for less combustible materials?

Stage 2. Identify the people at risk

Everyone is at risk if there is a fire. Therefore, the assessor should consider the following.

- Decide who are the individuals and/or groups of people likely to be at risk if a fire breaks out and if anyone could be at a greater risk (for example, shift workers, visitors who are unfamiliar with the site, and so on).

- Consider whether anyone is at an enhanced level of risk because of their work activity, or because of a disability (such as a lack of mobility or reduced hearing). The Equality Act requires employers not to discriminate against any person because of their disability and to make reasonable adjustments to match the needs of disabled personnel. A personal emergency evacuation plan (PEEP) may be required in these circumstances.

- Consider the impact that a fire would have on neighbouring properties and all forms of traffic passing the site. For example, the FRS will impose a 200 m cordon and evacuation zone around any fire in which gas cylinders are involved. Such a fire can involve evacuating many people and closing major traffic routes, including railway lines.

Stage 3. Evaluate, remove, reduce and protect from the risk

Having determined the hazards and who is likely to be harmed, the responsible person must take the necessary actions to remove or reduce the risks to an acceptable level.

This is a two-stage process that involves considering the following questions.

1. What are the risks of the fire starting?

2. What are the risks to people on the site and nearby?

There are potentially many practical measures that can be taken to reduce the risk of a fire occurring (listed on the following page).

- Ensuring that electrical office equipment, electrical appliances and portable hand tools are PAT tested at appropriate intervals to identify any defects.

- The effective quarantine of defective electrical equipment awaiting repair (or disposal if not repairable).

- Routinely testing electrical distribution systems.

- Storing and locating flammable and highly flammable liquids in appropriately constructed and secure stores that prevent the escape of spillages or impact by traffic or plant.

- Storing gas cylinders in secure stores that allow any leakage to disperse, with the separation of some gases as is necessary.

- Prohibiting the refuelling of petrol or diesel-powered equipment and plant whilst it is still hot.

- The regular inspection and maintenance as necessary of any system that carries a flammable gas or liquid (such as the supply pipework to oxy-fuel sets, cabin heaters, the canteen cooker or a standby generator).

- Not allowing oxy-fuel sets to be used unless flashback arrestors are fitted to the pipework.

- Preventing arson by putting in place effective security measures, both within and outside of site operating hours.

- The introduction and effective implementation of a hot-works permit system for high-risk activities.

- Ceasing hot work at least one hour (two hours for higher risk sites, such as large, timber-frame projects) before site closure, and regularly monitoring the work area and surrounding structure in the intervening time.

- Maintaining a strict smoking policy; if smoking is permitted in certain areas of the site, provide safe means of disposing of used smoking materials.

Similarly, there are many practical measures that can be taken to reduce the risk to people if a fire should occur.

- Making fire safety and evacuation procedures part of site induction, so site staff know what to do if there is a fire, who will call the emergency services, what escape routes should be used, and so on.

- Understanding how fires spread and what actions to take in the event of a fire.

- Maintaining a strict regime of clearing up waste materials and putting them in skips.

- Ensuring that any flammable liquid waste is stored safely and disposed of at the first opportunity.

Stage 4. Record the findings, prepare an emergency plan and provide training

Record

Where there are five or more employees, the significant findings of the risk assessment, including details of any actions taken to reduce the fire risk, must be recorded in a manner that can be easily retrieved should it be necessary to do so.

Even when there are fewer than five employees, it is good practice to record the **significant** findings of the fire risk assessment. The risk assessment will also assist in developing the emergency plan and will show more clearly where there are weaknesses in fire risk management.

If called upon by the enforcing authority to provide evidence of sound fire risk management practices, a written risk assessment is far preferable to a verbal briefing.

The word **significant** allows the risk assessor to ignore trivial risks of fire. The dividing line between trivial and significant is subjective but it is advisable to err on the side of caution. The risk assessment must be suitable and sufficient for the area it is covering.

Points that require recording include the following.

- Significant fire hazards identified.

- How the hazards will be eliminated.

- Preventative measures that will be taken to reduce the risk of fire from those hazards that cannot be eliminated.

- People who are at risk.

- Actions that have been taken to reduce the spread of fire and smoke if a fire should occur.

- Details of the general fire precautions (such as the maintenance of escape routes, and the location and maintenance of fire-fighting equipment), plus any fire extinguisher training given.

- Details of any instructions given to individuals regarding the actions to take to prevent fires and to escape from the site safely if a fire does occur.

- Details of people with particular fire safety responsibilities (such as the responsible person, fire safety co-ordinator and fire warden).

 Record other fire-related issues, including the delivery of appropriate toolbox talks and other fire-related briefings. These records could be useful at a later date.

Prepare emergency plan

The findings of the fire risk assessment will help prepare a plan of how the fire can be prevented and how the site staff will be kept safe in the event of a fire. If the site adjoins occupied premises (for example, a hospital or existing business) your plan may need to be co-ordinated with their emergency plan.

Train

All site staff need to know what action to take in the event of a fire and if necessary understand any specific roles they may be required to carry out.

Correct training should be given, as required, and should include the following.

● The significant findings of the fire risk assessment.

● The measures that have been put in place to reduce the risk.

● What people should do in the event of a fire, including temporary staff.

● The identity of people with responsibilities for fire safety (such as fire wardens).

● Any special arrangements that are necessary to protect people on site from serious or imminent danger from fire.

It will also be necessary to provide training on the selection and use of portable fire extinguishers to an appropriate number of staff.

Stage 5. Review and update the fire risk assessment regularly

Due to the ever-changing nature of construction sites, the review of the fire risk assessment is important. A review provides the opportunity to critically examine the effectiveness of the fire risk assessment with regard to site conditions at that time and to update it as necessary. If significant changes in risks are identified or changes are made to the plan, site staff and those in adjoining premises must be informed, as required.

Workers should know what to do in the event of a fire

For example, consider the changes that might be necessary as a result of the following.

● Last week's escape route becoming a dead-end today.

● The increasing complexity of escape routes as large structures are built.

● A significant increase in people on site since the last review.

● The start of a hot-work system.

● The start of a new activity that necessitates the storage of flammable substances (such as LPG and other gases) in bulk.

● The need to extend the fire detection system.

● A poorly carried out practice evacuation.

● The occurrence of a fire-related near miss.

Many local FRS will provide guidance on carrying out fire risk assessments.

Appendix C – Example of a fire risk assessment for temporary accommodation units

Record of significant findings			
Risk assessment for		**Assessment undertaken**	
Single-storey site accommodation comprising five interlinked cabins Site address: *Premier Place, Carrow Road, Anytown*		Date:	*4th January 2023*
		Completed by:	*Chris Hughton (Site manager)*
		Signature:	*C Hughton*
Part of temporary accommodation units (TAUs) covered, if not whole area as identified above: *N/A*		This area is used for: *General office work* *Meeting room and inductions* *Canteen* *Toilets, changing and drying room*	

Step 1. Identify the fire hazards		
Sources of ignition	**Sources of fuel**	**Sources of oxygen**
Electrical appliances and office equipment *Electrical heater units* *Cleaning chemicals if mixed*	*Rubbish bins* *Office furniture and equipment* *Project paperwork and drawings*	*None above ambient level*

Step 2. Identify the people at risk
Office-based and visiting site staff, workers in canteen and toilets and other visitors *It is NOT considered likely that the work carried out within the office accommodation could pose any risk of harm to anyone outside the site boundary (12 m away)*

Step 3. Evaluate, remove, reduce and protect from risk	
(3.1) Evaluate the risk of the fire occurring	*Meeting room sometimes used for storing used packaging material prior to disposal* *Desks too close to electric heaters in project office* *Chairs or clothes too close to electrical heaters in canteen*
(3.2) Evaluate the risk to people from a fire starting in the premises	*A fire in the meeting room could be undetected for some time* *A fire in the canteen on ground floor could prevent access to the rear emergency exit* *Otherwise, emergency evacuation not considered to be problematic*
(3.3) Remove and reduce the hazards that may cause a fire	*Improved housekeeping required to prevent accumulation of flammable waste materials* *Furniture to be re-arranged – requires relocation of telephone connection point* *Drying room has enclosed oil-filled covered heaters with hooks for drying clothes – emphasise during induction* *Fit cages around electrical fires in canteen*
(3.4) Remove and reduce the risks to people from a fire	*When the defects noted above have been rectified, the existing fire precautions will be considered to be adequate* *It is noted that the fire extinguishers are due inspection in early April 2023*

Assessment review		
Review due before *2nd August 2023*	**Completed by**	**Signature**

Review outcome (where substantial changes have occurred a new record sheet should be used)

Fire action plan
Will this risk assessment result in a fire action plan being drawn up? YES / NO Delete as applicable

CONTENTS

Electrical safety

GT700 Toolbox talks / supporting checklists and forms

Toolbox talks on some of these topics are available in the GT700 publication. Supporting checklists and forms covering some of these topics are available on our companion website.

ELECTRICAL SAFETY

Overview

This chapter highlights the dangers associated with working on or near to live electrical circuits, and the good working practices that must be adopted to ensure that such work can be carried out safely.

Each year, accidents involving electricity cause deaths, injuries and burns on construction sites. Furthermore, over the years electricity has been a contributory factor to the starting of several fires on construction sites.

3.1   Introduction

Electricity can be regarded as a hidden killer. Unlike many other hazards, it cannot be seen, smelt or heard; it may not become obvious that a cable is live until someone touches it. There may be occasional circumstances where the hum from a transformer or the noise from a motor running indicates that at least some circuits are live, but relying upon this as a risk control measure is certainly not a safe method of working.

A risk of electrocution on site could be created from any of the following.

● Contact or arcing with live parts of the electrical distribution system in any structure being renovated or worked upon, and in associated site accommodation.

● Contact or arcing with overhead power lines.

● Contact or arcing with underground cables.

● The use of defective electrical equipment, including hand tools.

The presence of live electrical cables may not be obvious. Whilst it might be expected that cables run vertically from sockets and switches, this is often not the case and cables may have been run horizontally (and in worst case scenarios, diagonally). These unexpected cable runs, as well as cables that have been run inside partition walls or other hidden voids, need to be given due consideration to avoid accidental damage that can result in serious injury or death.

The temporary electrical distribution systems found on site often operate in a harsh environment and must be treated with care and respect.

The Health and Safety Executive (HSE) regards refurbishment work in buildings as presenting the highest risk. Many of the accidents resulting from such work arise out of the following.

● Confusion and lack of communication as to what circuits have been made dead.

● Hitting cables buried underground, hidden by wall coverings, in voids, and so on.

● Untrained workers knowingly working on live equipment.

Electric shock may not be the only consequence of contact with live electrical circuits; a fault within a circuit or equipment can result in heating or sparking, with the potential to cause a fire or explosion, as well as disrupt services to adjacent properties.

 An electrical safety poster should be prominently displayed in several locations, if necessary. It should show basic first-aid procedures for treating someone who has received an electric shock.

There should be somebody on site who is trained in first aid.

3.2   Important points

● No-one other than a qualified electrician should install, maintain or alter the electrical distribution system and the installation must comply with the Electricity at Work Regulations.

● Electrical safety **must** be covered during site induction and refresher training, where it must be emphasised that unauthorised alteration to, or extension of, the site electrical distribution system is strictly prohibited.

● Ideally, apart from mains-powered (230/240 volt) equipment in site offices, all other electrically powered equipment (such as electrical hand tools) should be battery-powered or run off a 110 volt supply.

● The power supply for 230/240 volt equipment must be fed through a safety device in addition to a fuse or circuit breaker (for example, a residual current device (RCD)). Fuses only protect equipment; they do not 'blow' quickly enough to prevent an electric shock to the user of the equipment.

● The reason behind any safety device tripping, apart from deliberate testing, must be investigated, if necessary by bringing in a qualified electrician; attempts to reset a tripped safety device must not be made until further investigation has been carried out.

● Work on or near to live, exposed cables or equipment poses an obvious danger. Competence is required and such work must only be carried out under a formal **permit to work**.

● Electrical circuits must be tested periodically by a competent person.

- Safety devices (such as RCDs) must be tested frequently by the user in accordance with established guidance.

- Hand-held electrical tools used in construction environments should be subject to a combined inspection and test before first use, and every three months thereafter.

- Electrical equipment must comply with the Electrical Equipment (Safety) Regulations and have the UKCA marking. If imported from the EU, the product must also show the UKCA mark alongside the CE mark.

- A permit to work system must be introduced and enforced for higher risk work (for example, where a danger from exposed live electrical wires or equipment exists).

 For further information on the dangers associated with electricity refer to Chapter D07 Underground and overhead services.

3.3   Legislative requirements

The regulations are concerned with the safety of electrical installations and equipment and apply to all situations involving electricity, at any place of work. They place legal obligations on duty holders, who may be either an employer or an employee. The details, in the main, are technical and not of general interest to site management staff, providing they have employed competent contractors to carry out electrical work. However, there are some fundamental requirements within the regulations (shown below) which require close observation.

- Working on or near to live electrical parts can only be carried out where:
    – it is unreasonable in all circumstances for the live electrical equipment to be made dead; and
    – it is reasonable in all circumstances for the worker to be at work on or near to the live electrical equipment; and
    – suitable precautions (including, where necessary, the provision of suitable protective equipment) are taken to prevent injury.

- Electrical wiring and equipment, which may be exposed to hostile environments or mechanical damage, should be constructed or protected and/or positioned to avoid danger. Consideration should be given to armoured cabling and conduits.

- All electrical wiring that could result in personal danger must be insulated, otherwise protected or positioned out of harm's way.

- A suitable means must be provided for:
    – cutting off the supply to any item of electrical equipment
    – enabling the supply to be securely isolated
    – identifying all electrical circuits.

! **Everyone who potentially will come into contact with live electrical wiring or equipment must be fully trained and competent in how to protect themselves and others.**

3.3.1   Management of Health and Safety at Work Regulations

These regulations require that employers carry out a suitable and sufficient risk assessment of the work they do and put in place measures to control the risks arising from the work. In the context of this chapter, this will mean that procedures and practices are put in place to eliminate or reduce the risk of anyone being harmed as a result of coming into contact with electricity.

 For more information refer to Chapter A05 Risk assessments, method statements and permits to work.

3.3.2   Electricity at Work Regulations

The requirements of these regulations cover fixed and temporary electrical distribution systems rather than electrical hand tools and equipment. The supply system that feeds mains power onto the site and distributes it to site offices, canteens and so on, must be installed, inspected and maintained in accordance with these regulations.

3.3.3   Provision and Use of Work Equipment Regulations (PUWER)

Electrical equipment and hand tools are classified as *work equipment* as defined under PUWER. As such, employers have a duty to ensure that electrical hand tools and equipment:

- are suitable for their intended purpose
- are well maintained and inspected as necessary
- are fitted with suitable controls

- are fitted with guards as necessary
- can be effectively isolated from the supply
- carry appropriate markings and warning notices.

Furthermore, employers have a duty to ensure that users of work equipment receive adequate training and health and safety information, including written instructions, where appropriate, on the use of the equipment.

 For further information on PUWER refer to Chapter C05 Work equipment and hand-held tools.

3.4 Site electrical supply

The supply of electricity on construction sites will ideally be provided from the public supply by the local electricity company. It is generally accepted that temporary supplies installed in line with the *Requirements for electrical installations* (BS 7671) will meet the requirements of the Electricity at Work Regulations.

Consideration should also be given to opportunities to use renewable energy sources, where practical.

3.4.1 Public supply

A public supply of electricity being provided depends on the following.

- Written application being made to the local electricity company, as soon as possible during the planning stage.
- Name, address and telephone number of the contractor, or principal contractor where appointed, and client, giving the full site address and a location plan.
- Details of the maximum demand load (in kilowatts) that is likely to be required during construction.
- Details of the maximum final demand load (in kilowatts) that will be required when the project is complete and operational.
- Dates when the supply is needed.
- Discussion with electricity company staff to determine the necessary precautions to avoid damage or hazards from any existing overhead or underground cables.
- Establishment of supply points (where incoming cables will terminate), switch gear, metering equipment and requirements for earthing.

3.4.2 Generators

Where a public supply cannot be installed, generators powered by petrol or diesel engines may be used as the main supply. Where a public supply is installed, generators can be used as a back-up supply in emergencies or where the public supply fails. Attention should be given to the siting of generators in order to minimise nuisance caused by noise and fumes. Other environmental issues to mitigate against are fuel spillage and leaks from generators causing water or ground pollution. Consideration should be given to the use of drip trays and bunds.

Site generators range from relatively small portable machines used to power one or two electrical tools to large, permanently sited standby generators capable of powering an extensive distribution system should the public system fail. In the event of unexpected failure, it is normal for standby generating systems to auto-start to avoid any risk associated with a sudden loss of power.

It should be noted that some of the smaller machines have dual outputs (230/240 volt and 110 volt). Therefore, separate arrangements for a 110 volt supply are not necessary. Generally, the output of larger generators is a 400 volt, three-phase supply, aligning with the public supply arrangements.

3.4.3 Calculating power requirements

The calculation for power requirements should be left to an experienced person or to the electricity supply company.

To enable the total site requirements to be established, an electrical demand table, which itemises all anticipated electrical loads, must be compiled. It is likely that a member of the site management team will become involved to advise on the electrical loads that will be in use.

The person compiling the demand table will apply a diversity factor that acknowledges that not all electrical equipment will be in use at the same time.

3.5 Site distribution systems

On new-build projects, the term *site distribution system* refers to a temporary and flexible electrical system that distributes electrical power around the site for construction purposes. However, with regard to refurbishment work or similar, the distribution may comprise a combination of the fixed electrical system within the building (providing it is safe to leave it live) and elements of a temporary distribution system to enable hand tools, task lighting, and so on to be used.

3.5.1 Safe voltages

 Mains voltage (230/240 volts) can be a killer. Battery-powered or 110 volt equipment should always be used, wherever possible.

Generally, the site distribution system comprises of a combination of mains (230/240 volts or 400 volts) and low voltage (110 volt) circuits. To ensure that the appropriate supplies are available where they are required, and that there is no overloading of any part of the system, it must be designed and installed by competent persons.

Whilst it is likely that the main incoming supply will be at 230/240 volts or 400 volts, by using a transformer, the voltage will be reduced to a maximum of 110 volts for hand tools, task lighting and so on.

In some high-risk situations, transformers are available to provide extra low voltages of 25 or 50 volts.

The way in which 110 volt systems are earthed means that the maximum voltage shock that anyone can receive is around 55 volts, which is regarded as relatively safe for healthy adults. However, this voltage can still induce current flow, which can block the electrical signals between the brain and the muscles. This can stop the heart from beating properly, prevent the person from breathing and cause muscle spasms. Factors that will affect this are the voltage, the parts of the body involved, how damp the person is and the length of time that current is flowing.

3.5.2   Distribution equipment

Electrical distribution equipment must be obtained from a reputable supplier or hire company, to ensure that it has been manufactured to a recognised standard and tested. This is particularly important where electrical distribution equipment is to be sited outdoors, where the ingress of water and dust could be a problem.

There are many types of distribution equipment available, all of which are suited to different situations and environments.

Supply incoming units (SIU) generally have a rating of up to 300 amps per phase. These units include main switch gear and metering equipment.

Mains distribution unit (MDU) for the control and distribution of electricity on site, either 400 volts three-phase, or 230/240 volts single-phase AC.

Supply incoming distribution unit (SIDU) may be used in some installations. This is a single piece of equipment that combines the supply and distribution system, which comes as one piece of kit.

Transformer units (TU) are either single-phase (reducing 230/240 volts to 110 volts) or three-phase (reducing 400 volts to 110 volts). Such transformer units can be used for portable tools and plant, and general lighting.

Outlet units (OU) 110 volt socket outlet units rated at 16 or 32 amps. Such outlet units can be used for portable tools, floodlighting and extension outlets. They are not usually protected by circuit-breakers.

Extension outlet units (EOU) equipped with one or more 110 volt socket outlet, rated at 16 amps. Such units can be used for portable tools, local lighting and hand lamps. They are not usually protected by circuit-breakers.

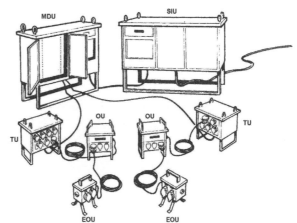

Example of a site electrical distribution system and different types of distribution equipment

In most cases at least part of each piece of distribution equipment will be **colour coded** to indicate its output voltage. Furthermore, the arrangement and number of pins within the electrical connectors are different for each voltage, which prevents, for example, a 110 volt power tool being plugged into a 230/240-volt supply unit.

The colour coding for distribution equipment is shown below.

	Violet	25 volts
	White	50 volts
	Yellow	110–130 volts

	Blue	220–240 volts
	Red	380–400 volts
	Black	500–650 volts

 Case study example

On these projects, the site team planned ahead and installed temporary supplies and general lighting to the soffit of main access routes. The lights in the foreground were fixed drops, each with two 110 volt sockets for equipment, which could be moved into rooms as and when required.

3.5.3 Residual current devices

All attempts should be made to use battery-powered or 110 volt tools where possible. However, it is inevitable that some 230/240 volt equipment will be in use, even if only in the site office. In such circumstances, the 230/240 volt supply must be supplied through a residual current device (RCD). Under fault conditions, RCDs detect an imbalance in the circuit current and disconnect the supply before the person at risk can receive a potentially fatal electric shock. There are two types of RCD.

1. Those that are fitted as part of an electrical distribution system and are most often found within the supply panel for a site office (this type of RCD can only be installed by a competent electrician). The user should check these daily at the start of every shift, with a more formal inspection every week, and a combined inspection and test before the first use and then every three months.

2. Plug-in RCDs (commonly known as power-breakers) that are plugged into a mains supply socket and have an in-built socket into which an individual mains-powered electrical tool or other appliance is plugged. Plug-in RCDs must undergo a combined inspection and test before the first use and then every month. The user should then check them daily at the start of every shift, with a more formal visual inspection every week.

Both types of RCD have a test button that simulates a fault and operates the device.

The following points should be noted

- *Maintaining portable electrical equipment* (HSG107) suggests that portable residual current devices (RCDs) used on construction sites should have a combined inspection and test before first use.

- RCDs do not reduce current flow or the voltage, only the time that the current flows (about 30 milliseconds), and thereby the severity of the shock.

- RCDs are delicate devices and should be treated with care. Advice on suitable RCDs for construction sites should be sought from manufacturers or suppliers.

- The use of an RCD does not give a 100% guarantee of safety.

- The RCD does not have a fail-safe feature and will not give an indication if it is faulty.

3.5.4 Site accommodation

The incoming electrical supply to site accommodation must be properly designed, installed and commissioned by competent electrical contractors. Site offices and welfare facilities are the only locations where electrical equipment that runs off a 230/240 volt supply should be in use. The electrical supply panel for such facilities must incorporate an RCD in each circuit. The correct operation of each RCD must be confirmed daily by operating the test button, which should trip the device and switch off the circuit running through it.

All portable electrical equipment should be electrical safety tested (portable appliance testing – PAT) at appropriate intervals as decided by a competent person. This includes:

- common types of office equipment (such as scanners and photocopiers)

- kitchen-type equipment (such as kettles, microwave ovens, and so on)

- small items (such as chargers for site radios and battery-powered tools).

 For further information refer to the HSE publication *Maintaining portable electrical equipment* (HSG107).

3.6 Safe working practices with electricity

A number of people are killed and injured each year through accidents where electricity was a contributory factor. These accidents occur equally to electricians as to other site operatives. Most fatal accidents involve contact with overhead power lines or unidentified live circuits. Some examples of why these accidents occur are shown below.

- The risks of doing the job had not been adequately assessed.

- Shortcuts in working practices were being taken.

- Pre-work investigation had failed to identify live electrical circuits (particularly in renovation projects).

- Circuits that had been made dead were re-energised by someone who did not realise that the system was being worked on by others.

 For further information on working close to overhead cables refer to Chapter D07 Underground and overhead services.

 For further details refer to the HSE publications *Electrical safety and you: a brief guide* (INDG231) and *Electricity at work: safe working practices* (HSG85).

3.6.1   Assessing the risks

Working near to live electrical circuits and equipment can only be carried out safely once the significant risks of injury or death have been identified and effective control measures put in place to eliminate the risks or reduce them to an acceptable level. The people doing the work and anyone else who might be adversely affected by it must be informed of the significant risks arising out of the work and the part they must play in ensuring the work can be carried out safely.

Most electrical accidents occur because people are working on or near to equipment that is thought to be dead but which is live, or people are working on equipment known to be live but those carrying out the work do not have adequate training, competency or the correct equipment or adequate resources including, where necessary, accompaniment, to prevent injury.

The person carrying out the risk assessment, and reviewing and updating it at a later stage, must be sufficiently competent to identify the significant risks and to devise effective control measures. The risk assessment must also be reviewed on a regular basis.

3.6.1.1   Accompaniment for authorised live working

It is the senior duty holder's responsibility to determine whether someone carrying out work should be accompanied. This should be based on considerations of how injury is to be prevented. If an accompanying person can substantially contribute towards safe working practice, then they should be present. They should be trained to recognise danger and, if necessary, to render assistance in the event of an emergency.

Below are some examples where a person carrying out electrical work must be accompanied.

- Electrical work involving manipulation of live, uninsulated power conductors at 230 volts or above, using insulated tools.

- Other work on or near to bare live conductors where someone working on their own would not be capable of undertaking the work safely without assistance in, for example, keeping other people away from the work area.

3.6.1.2   Protective equipment

Protective equipment suitable for the work activity should only be used as a last resort (for example, when all other ways to eliminate or reduce risks have been considered). Examples of equipment that can protect someone from the effects of electricity are listed below.

- Suitable clothing, including insulating helmets, goggles and gloves.

- Insulating materials used as fixed or temporary screening to prevent:

  – electric shock   – short circuit between live conductors and earth.

  – short circuit between live conductors

- Insulating mats and stands to prevent electric shock current via the feet.

- Insulated tools.

- Insulated test probes.

There must be procedures for the periodic inspection, maintenance, examination, testing and/or replacement of this protective equipment.

3.6.2   Managing the risk during refurbishment work

Refurbishment projects pose particular risks if the whole electrical system to the building is not made dead. A number of electrocutions have involved workers who were not electricians but who were carrying out other works (such as plumbers and joiners). The likelihood of these incidents could have been reduced or eliminated by the following.

Understanding the system. Those responsible for planning and managing refurbishment work must understand the electrical system of the building in which the work takes place and liaise with the building occupier. This will enable building work to be planned and managed so that the integrity of the electrical system is not compromised and the workforce remains safe.

System isolation. Relevant parts of the electrical system should be isolated if the refurbishment work (such as joinery or plumbing) is liable to disturb or damage the existing electrical system and expose people to electrical danger.

Portable electrical equipment. Tools, plugs and cables designed for DIY and domestic use are not suitable for site conditions. You should use efficient, robust tools that are battery powered or operate from a 110 volt supply system, earthed so that the maximum voltage does not exceed 55 volts. Regularly inspect power tools and take them out of service if they are damaged. Tools should be serviced by qualified electricians. Do not carry out makeshift repairs.

Protected lighting systems. These protect cabling and bulbs against breakage. If a bulb breaks, the exposed filament may present a hazard. Have a system for checking bulbs regularly to maintain electrical safety and to keep the site well lit.

3.6.3   Effective isolation of circuits

3.6.3.1   Making sure the power is off

If a worker is working next to electrical circuits and is not competent or authorised to check and confirm that the power is off, they must ask a competent person to do it for them, and watch them doing it. If they have any doubts about the method used, they should report the matter to their supervisor immediately.

ELECTRICAL SAFETY

When checking that the power is off the competent person should be **sure** of the following.

● The isolation device being used is suitable for the purpose.

● The isolator being used to turn off the power is working correctly and reliably.

● The switch being isolated is the only way that the circuit can be fed with electrical power.

● The switch being used is **locked** in the off position and cannot be turned on again until the task is complete.

● The equipment and methods being used to check for voltage are in working order and are reliable.

● Isolation has been successful by confirming the circuit is no longer live, using an approved test unit.

Some electrical systems and equipment must be earthed before it is safe to work near them.

Check whether this is necessary, and, if it is, ensure that this is done properly.

 Use the lock out, tag out, try out (LOTOTO) procedure.

 For further information refer to the Electrical Safety Council guide *Guidance on the management of electrical safety and safe isolation procedures for low voltage installations* (Best practice guide 2).

3.6.3.2 Making sure the power stays off (secure isolation)

If the electrical power has been turned off to allow work to be carried out on an electrical circuit safely, it is essential that the power stays off until the work is finished.

The person doing the work must make sure that **they** are in control and **stay** in control throughout the job. A good way is for that person to have the only key to the switch or to a locked room or cabinet containing the switch.

Removing a fuse may seem to be a safe way of isolating a circuit but someone else could insert another one. Displaying notices is not acceptable, as people often ignore them or do not notice them.

If the person doing the job has any concerns that the electricity may be turned on again without them agreeing, they must be given the authority to stop work without delay and without having to check with a supervisor first.

Electrical systems should be locked out and tagged during any works

 ## Contractor sustains electric shock after failure to isolate power supply

A self-employed contractor sustained 415-volt electric shock injuries from the bare electrical wires supplying an overhead travelling crane while working from a 'cherry picker' installing computer cabling.

The defendant company failed to follow their procedures for safe isolation of the power supply to the crane.

Action

The company was prosecuted under the Health and Safety At Work etc. Act 1974 (Section 3, Sub Section 1) and The Management of Health and Safety at Work Regulations 1992 (No 4, paragraph 1) due to the high risk of serious or fatal injuries from the energised electrical wires. This resulted in a £15,000 fine.

Comment

The company should have undertaken a risk assessment of the cabling activity that should have identified the hazard from the electrical wires. It should have taken action to warn the contractor of the presence of electrical wires near where the work was being carried out.

The company should have taken steps to only allow work when the electrical power had been turned off and to ensure that power remained off for the duration of the work.

(Source: HSE.)

3.6.4 Permit to work

Permit to work systems are essential to ensure safe working where live electrical supplies, cables and equipment are present, particularly in installation, maintenance or construction work.

The Electricity at Work Regulations require employers to implement safe systems of work in circumstances where a person could be exposed to live conductors or equipment. A permit to work must be a part of that safe system.

In the case of construction sites, permits to work are more commonly used whilst the site electrical distribution system is itself being worked on, or connections made to it, thereby potentially exposing live parts. Tight control of the permit system is essential if it is to be effective. The person issuing this permit must be competent, and have the appropriate technical knowledge and experience. This is often the electrical contractor's site manager, who must be appointed to raise, issue and co-ordinate permits.

People making the work area and circuit to be worked on safe and the person directly in charge of the work must be involved in completing parts of the permit and signing accordingly. Some companies use permits printed on carbonised paper, which provide identical second or even third copies, where the company's record-keeping system demands them. Most permits contain provisions for the physical locking off circuits, and the retention or display of keys and permits.

Before work starts, the authorised person should ensure that the permit to work will cover the making safe of the part of the system to be worked on, from all possible sources of supply. If the work is handed over from one competent person to another, the permit is to be endorsed by the authorised person and transferred to the second operative. One copy of the permit must be retained for the duration of the work by the person to whom it is issued. Before apparatus is made live again, the permit must be returned for cancellation. Then it must be countersigned by both the holder and the authorised person.

03

The authorised person should keep a record in the job file of the issued permits and their cancellation.

 Under no circumstances should anyone work on, maintain, repair or otherwise adjust high-voltage equipment, except in accordance with the instructions and terms of a formal permit to work.

3.6.5 Locating hidden electrical wiring

The presence of electrical wires may not be obvious at the location where work is to be carried out but, as many people have found out that does not mean they are not there. Even if some wiring is visible, there may be further wiring buried within or hidden by the fabric of the building. Electrical wiring may sometimes look like pipes, and may be a range of colours. The person in charge of the job must complete the following before anyone is allowed to start drilling or cutting into surfaces.

- If feasible, remove the risk by turning off the electricity to the building or area of work.

- Look for the presence of electrical wires and any other hazards (such as asbestos). Remember to look on both sides of walls.

- Inspect plans of the electrical installation, and use these as a guide to finding electrical wiring.

- Use a suitable cable detector if competent, or get a competent person to do it. Remember that some cable detectors will not find a wire carrying a small, or no, current – consult the user guide.

- Identify nearby electrical equipment or installations and try to establish from which direction the wiring runs to them (this will not always be in a horizontal or vertical path).

- Identify and provide equipment that will minimise the risks during the work (for example, cable detectors and insulated tools).

- Ensure that suitable personal protective equipment (PPE) is identified and used.

- Make it clear to the person doing the job that they must **stop work** and check with their supervisor if they have any doubts as to the safety of what they are about to do.

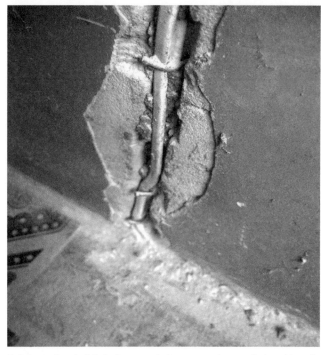

Before a surface is disturbed, a competent person must ensure that a cable and pipeline survey and search are undertaken

 An arc flash is an explosive release of energy caused by an electrical short circuit. The temperatures inside an arc flash incident can reach 19,000°C.

3.6.6 Dealing with electric shock

- Could you, or your workers, help someone who has had an electric shock?

- Do you know that what you do could make the difference between life and death?

- Have you and your employees been trained how to apply resuscitation correctly?

- If you were the casualty, is there anybody who could treat you?

- Do you have the 'Danger of electric shock' notices available?

- Can these notices or posters be seen by everyone? Are they well positioned?

- Are they read and, more importantly, understood?

3.6.6.1 Electric shock action

If the casualty is in contact with what could be a live electrical supply, switch off the power if possible and shout for help. Never assume the power has been turned off.

If the power cannot be switched off, you must respond in the following way.

- Do not touch the casualty with bare hands.

- If practical and safe to do so, move the casualty away from the electrical source, or the source away from the casualty, with a broom or something else wooden – never use an object which could conduct electricity (such as a metal pole).

- Seek prompt help from a first aider, calling the emergency services immediately to get qualified medical assistance if required.

 Electricity can kill. The correct information, instruction, training and supervision help to keep workers and others from coming into contact with unsafe electricity. Never put yourself in danger.

3.6.7 Monitoring contractors

In addition to electrical contractors, many other trades (examples of which are shown below) will have an electrical element to their work.

- Heating and ventilation engineers.

- Lift and escalator engineers.

- Plumbers.

- Fire detection and control engineers.

- Security and CCTV engineers.

- Crane installers.

The work of such contractors and others installing electrical circuits, or simply connecting to electrical equipment installed by others, must be carefully monitored to ensure that they do not jeopardise electrical safety or leave an installation in a dangerous condition.

The **person in charge** of the site, or the appointed responsible person, must complete the following.

- Inspect the risk assessments of these contractors to establish if their work could possibly adversely affect the safety of others working nearby, or those who might otherwise be affected by their work.

- Inspect any written scheme of work (method statement) to establish if any element will conflict with other works.

- Periodically liaise with the contractors to establish if the risk assessment should be reviewed and updated.

- Co-ordinate work, as necessary, to make sure that no-one is put at risk unnecessarily.

- Ensure that higher risk work is carried out in accordance with a permit to work system.

- If there have been any changes on site impacting the original electrical permit-to-work, a new permit must be issued covering the changes. Modifications to the original permit are not permitted.

- Monitor the work of the contractors on a periodic basis to make sure that it is carried out in accordance with the method statement and any permits.

- Make sure that the equipment used by the contractors is suitable for the job in hand, particularly in higher risk situations (such as working in cramped conditions where there is a lot of earthed metalwork or in a damp or wet environment, for example inside a tank).

- Make sure that the contractors implement a strict locking-off procedure where there is potential for them or others to come into contact with live equipment due to circuits being made live again whilst work is still being carried out.

- Where necessary ensure that appropriate signage is displayed to warn others of the dangers, but also appreciate that signage in itself is not an adequate safety measure for isolating a circuit.

- Ensure that contractors do not allow any combustible waste materials to accumulate in areas where it could become the fuel in the event of fire.

Particular care is needed in respect of any alterations and extensions to existing installations (for example, in renovation work), particularly in the identification of circuits where some circuits could remain live for at least part of the work.

With regard to **electrical contractors** working on site, as far as is practical, the site management team must assure themselves of the following.

● The contractor has compiled an accurate assessment of the risks to their employees and other people who may be affected by the work.

● The people at risk are aware and know what to do to protect themselves.

● An objective decision has been taken over whether the job can be carried out with the circuit(s) live or dead.

● The work will be properly planned, which includes the contractor informing site management of the circuit(s) to be worked on, and the implications for others (for example, if they have to disable a fire detection system).

● The job will be adequately supervised, with permanent accompaniment where necessary.

● The contractors will implement a permit to work system, where justified by the risks. The person issuing this permit must be competent, and have the appropriate technical knowledge and experience.

● A written safe system of working (incorporating the method statement) will be produced, communicated to those doing the job, and followed.

● The contractor will provide briefings to their employees and to others, as necessary.

● The contractor has employed only competent employees.

● The contractor will provide the correct tools and test equipment.

● The contractor's employees will be provided with suitable and sufficient PPE.

Where it is necessary to work on **live equipment**, it will be necessary for the person doing the work to be accompanied by another person. It is essential that this accompanying person:

● can recognise the signs of danger

● is able to administer first aid for electric shock

● can otherwise give assistance in the event of an emergency

● knows how to switch off the supply

● can assist in restricting access to the area.

 High-risk work should always be carried out in accordance with a permit to work system.

 As an indicator of competence the National Inspection Council for Electrical Installation Contracting (NICEIC) provides assessment and certification services for contractors working across the building services sector.

ELECTRICAL SAFETY

03

CONTENTS

Temporary works

04

Supporting
INFORMATION

GT700 Toolbox talks / supporting checklists and forms

Toolbox talks on some of these topics are available in the GT700 publication. Supporting checklists and forms covering some of these topics are available on our companion website.

TEMPORARY WORKS

04

4.1　Introduction

An important element of all construction projects relates to those items used to assist in the construction, but which do not usually form part of the final (permanent) works.

Temporary works are described in BS 5975:2019, clause 5.1.1.1 as:

 providing an "engineered solution" that is used to support or protect either an existing structure or the permanent works during construction, or to support an item of plant or equipment.

Temporary works are wide ranging, but some examples are shown below.

● Site hoardings and signboards.

● Temporary access roadways and working platforms for plant.

● Temporary earthworks.

● Reinforcement.

● Excavations and excavation supports.

● Propping systems for removal of load bearing walls and façade retention.

● Scaffolding and other proprietary systems used for access or support.

Two other terms related to temporary works are given below.

Falsework, which is the temporary support given to structures until they are able to sustain their own loads.

Formwork, which is the temporary form/mould (usually steel or timber) used to contain concrete until it has attained sufficient strength to withstand its own weight.

Although, on completion, it is the permanent works that receive attention, without temporary works being properly thought out, planned and managed, the project will not be successful. Effective, safe and perhaps imaginatively designed temporary works solutions can bring significant benefits and improve projects in terms of safety, certainty, productivity, efficiency, quality, completion times and cost.

On the other hand, poorly planned, designed, managed, supervised or constructed temporary works leave projects open to risks such as injuries or fatalities, the failure or collapse of both temporary and permanent works, damage to adjacent premises, and the consequent delays, increased costs and possible criminal charges.

4.2　Important points

Temporary works are important for several reasons.

● They can form a significant part of the overall cost of the project.

● They are often safety-critical (for example, if they fail, there is a high probability that people will be injured or killed).

● Often they have important characteristics that do not apply to permanent works *(refer to 4.3)*.

● They have the potential to cause delay and additional cost if not planned in adequate detail.

As for all aspects of construction projects it is important that, at all stages:

- all parties have adequate competence, resource and information to fulfil their role
- it is clear who is responsible for what
- all parties on site are aware of where their responsibilities start and finish.

This is particularly critical at interfaces, between temporary works and permanent works, between different elements of temporary works or where there are abnormal loads in the permanent works during construction.

e.g. Tower crane

Consider the following situation.

The permanent works foundation is to be used as a base for a tower crane. Some modifications of this foundation are required to accommodate the tower crane fixings.

Element	Designation	Comment
Foundation	Permanent works	Used as temporary works to found tower crane (with permanent works designer approval).
Foundation adaptation	Temporary works	Included to facilitate fixings; will become permanent works if it is not removed on completion (with permanent works designer approval).
Fixings into base	Temporary works	Co-ordinated with foundation layout and reinforcement details. Requires design check and co-ordination with permanent works designer.
Tower crane	Plant	Removed on completion.

The elements described above will involve several parties: permanent works designer, temporary works designer, contractor (foundation), supplier (fixings) and supplier (crane).

Unless the design and construction interfaces between these organisations and activities are adequately managed, and considered in advance of the work, delay or failure could result.

04

4.3 Characteristics of temporary works

Temporary works often have characteristics that are not present in permanent works or which present themselves differently.

You can view these in the table below.

Construction accuracy	Although some temporary works have specified/recommended accuracy (specifically in respect of how upright they should be), some do not. Experience shows that, generally, accuracy is less likely to be achieved with temporary works than with permanent works. However, accuracy can be important in order to achieve the assumed strength and robustness.
Misalignment of components	Assemblies made up of small components (such as proprietary falsework towers) may incorporate misalignments between sections.
Reuse	Unlike the permanent works, temporary works components are reused and hence the risk of damage, fatigue cracking or distortion should be recognised and managed.
Changes	Unauthorised changes (for example, in the layout or by the removal of components that obstruct trades) can seriously compromise the safety of temporary works (such as scaffolds).
Abuse	Temporary works can be prone to abuse in the form of overloading, impact and poor quality control (such as welding), unless adequately managed.
Utilisation	As temporary works are designed for a specific task, they are usually loaded to their full design load. Permanent works are rarely loaded to this extent.

Site management procedures should recognise these characteristics to ensure that none occur to an extent that would be detrimental to the effective use or safety of the temporary works being used.

4.4 Responsibilities

Responsibilities for temporary works arise in two ways: via statutory law and through contract.

4.4.1 Statute

Statutory requirements are legally binding and they override any contractual stipulations. There is no differentiation between temporary works and permanent works under the law: all hazardous work must be managed safely.

The main requirements, which stem from the Construction (Design and Management) Regulations 2015 (CDM), are set out, in summary, in the following table.

Communication, co-operation and co-ordination	All parties must communicate, co-operate and co-ordinate to ensure that temporary works are safe, and will not endanger or cause unnecessary ill effects upon the health of those involved.
This requirement is common sense. It will not only help to avoid accidents and ill health but also is an essential ingredient for a successful project. Contract requirements need to set out how this can be achieved (such as site meetings and information flow mechanisms). **Risk thrives at interfaces.**	
Competency	It is obligatory on all parties to be satisfied that they have the training, knowledge, skills, resources and adequate supervision to carry out the tasks assigned to them, and for the client to be equally satisfied.
The employment of a sub-contractor or designer who is not capable of safe or efficient working, or lacks experience, will sooner or later create a liability. It is important to have control over any further sub-contracting by sub-contractors themselves.	
Timing and resources	All parties must be afforded sufficient time to plan, mobilise and execute the works. They should also be provided with adequate resources. This includes those involved in the design or execution of temporary works. Hence, good project planning is essential.
To facilitate early and effective planning, designers and those who will execute the work must be provided with pre-construction phase information to establish interdependencies, constraints, sequencing and resource requirements.	
Pre-construction information	Under CDM, the principal contractor or contractor (if only one) should have received pre-construction information from the client, the principal designer or the design team; some of this may be relevant to temporary works design or execution. If so, it is important that it is passed to those sub-contractors or designers who are involved. Ensuring the timely distribution of all necessary information is one of the duties of the principal designer. This duty is also imposed on the principal contractor.
One of the recurrent complaints from sub-contractors is that they do not receive such information.	
Construction phase plan	This is the document that records the health and safety rules and management arrangements relating to the construction phase of a project and includes any temporary works.
Those elements of the plan that impact or may be relevant to others must be passed to them by the principal contractor or contractor.	
Inspections	Some temporary works (such as scaffolding and falsework, cofferdams and excavations) are required to have statutory inspections before use and at regular intervals (often before each shift or weekly) after alteration or after any significant adverse event (for example, inspecting a scaffold after high winds).
All such inspections must be carried out by competent persons and a record of the inspections must be retained.	

Other regulations will also apply, such as the Provision and Use of Work Equipment Regulations (PUWER), the Lifting Operations and Lifting Equipment Regulations (LOLER) and the Work at Height Regulations.

All of these have inspection requirements.

4.4.2 Contract

Although on multi-contractor sites the principal contractor will have the overall responsibility for temporary works, it is important that all sub-contractors are clear as to what obligations are passed on to others and how sub-contractors are to interact with other sub-contractors and the principal contractor.

Contracts should require the use of good practice approaches (such as British Standards, industry guides, and so on).

(For good practice on avoiding ambiguity and disputes, and to ensure high standards are attained, refer to 4.6.1)

The site manager will play an important role by ensuring this interaction occurs in a timely manner, that decisions are recorded and that designers (of permanent or temporary works) are consulted when appropriate.

Although most of this action will be undertaken by the temporary works co-ordinator (TWC) it is important that the site manager maintains an overview and that the interface between site manager and TWC is set out in the company procedures and detailed in the construction phase plan.

4.5   Hazards arising from temporary works

Temporary works produce similar hazards to those within permanent works. Generic hazards for safety and health are shown below.

- Safety.
    - Structural adequacy and integrity.
    - Work at height.

- Health.
    - Manual handling.

    - Falling objects.
    - Operational management.

    - Operational management.

Other hazards will apply on specific projects.

e.g. Operational management failure (safety)

A façade scaffold collapsed in Milton Keynes, causing the death of a worker and injuring several others, because of poor operational site management.

Specifically:

- failure to inspect the scaffold on a regular basis

- insufficient ties

- unauthorised changes

- overloading.

Each of these issues may have been considered small in itself but cumulatively, and over time, they caused a tragic failure.

Poor management of temporary works resulting in a scaffolding collapse

4.6   Good practice

Good practice, drawn up by industry itself, will not only help in the management of temporary works and site safety but also in creating a productive site. Good practice may be divided into **management** and **technical**.

4.6.1   Management

The accepted core document is BS 5975: *Code of Practice for temporary works procedures and the permissible stress design of falsework.* This should be embedded in all contracts to avoid any dispute or uncertainty as to the expected procedures. Main items are shown below.

Designated individual	There should be one person in each organisation who establishes and implements procedures (temporary works design and construction), including appointing competent TWCs. Site managers should be familiar with procedures.
Temporary works co-ordinators (TWC)	Whilst it is not a legal requirement, it is seen as good practice (as outlined in BS 5975), that on each contract the principal contractor or the contractor (on single contractor sites) should appoint one of its own personnel as TWC (known as the principal contractor's TWC (PC's TWC)). It is important that the duties are in writing, accepted, and made known. The TWC is responsible for ensuring that all aspects of the organisation's procedures relating to the management and co-ordination of temporary works are implemented on site.
	However, if another sub-contractor has control of a specific part of the site and manages their own temporary works, they appoint their own TWC. A schedule of TWC duties is provided in BS 5975. It is preferable that the TWC is not responsible for day-to-day progress of temporary works on site. Where unavoidable, the TWC should ensure that decisions relating to temporary works are safety-based and not influenced by commercial concerns.
Temporary works supervisors (TWS)	On larger or more-complex projects, it may be more desirable to appoint one or more TWS to assist the TWC. It is important that the appointment and duties are in writing, accepted, and made known.
Temporary works register	All sites should have a register of the temporary works. It should include a list of all identified temporary works that will be required throughout the project, giving: ■ a brief description ■ which parties are designing and executing the work ■ significant dates (for example, date design completed and date design checked). The first entry is likely to be site hoarding.
Permits to load/ unload	No load-bearing temporary works should be loaded or unloaded without the authorisation of the TWC (in the form of a permit to load or a permit to dismantle).
Information flow	The code stresses the importance of good information flow and co-ordination. Specifically, designers should always have a written brief.

TEMPORARY WORKS

There are occasions when choosing a solution with greater initial cost may have overall benefits that outweigh the expense. Some examples are shown below.

- Use of prefabricated staircase assemblies to gain vertical access, instead of ladders. Staircases allow quick access and exit in emergencies, multiple usage and are safer for the carrying of tools.

- Use of proprietary barrier systems allows quick installation.

- Formwork with integrated working platforms allows instant, safe and effective access.

4.6.2   Technical

BS 5975 also contains rules for design. Falsework should be designed to these rules or to the European Standards (for example, BS EN 12812) by competent persons with experience in falsework design. Detailed advice is outside the scope of this chapter.

All temporary works should be constructed from drawings and sketches authorised for use by the TWC. Some important watch-points, not requiring explicit technical expertise, are shown below.

- Adequate foundations to falsework (if it doesn't look right, it probably isn't).

- Lateral bracing of adjustable steel props at forkhead level (although some systems and arrangements do not need bracing, it is better to check if none are present).

- All scaffolding requires a formal engineered design, unless it is a basic scaffold, as defined in TG20.

- General standard of construction (such as vertical alignment).

- Adequate protection to those working in excavations.

4.7   Use of equipment and materials

Temporary works often utilise materials and equipment that have been used previously. These should:

- come from a reputable source

- have the previous use authenticated, when relevant

- come with guidance if its safe use is dependent upon the manner in which it is used

- be inspected (usually prior to, and during, delivery) for condition, cracks and distortion, depending upon the component.

The contractor ordering temporary works equipment should have procedures in place to ensure these points are recognised and actioned.

It is particularly important, when using proprietary equipment, to be satisfied that all the components are compatible and are the genuine article.

4.8   What can go wrong?

Most temporary works, following statutory requirements and good practice, are executed without any problem. Nonetheless, there are numerous examples of failure where significant cost, delay and human suffering have resulted. The most common factor of failing is lack of management. This is shown in the table below.

Aspect	Example
General	Insufficient oversight and understanding of the interdependencies between permanent and temporary work packages and the lack of clarity of the responsibilities between sub-contractors. Failure to appoint a TWC or to provide adequate technical back-up.
Change control	Inadequate processes to avoid unauthorised changes (such as removal of scaffold members to allow access for another trade).
Loading	Stacking of materials on working platforms that are only designed for access or light loads.
Time	Insufficient time allowed for the supply chain contractors to undertake their task. This often happens at sub-sub-contract level.
Information	Poor appreciation by the instructing party of the information required by designers and others to deliver a compliant (and safe) output.
Lateral support	Insufficient ties into adjacent structures to provide the necessary lateral support.
Sheeting	Adding sheeting to scaffolds and other above-ground structures (for protection or advertising), which have not been designed to accommodate the additional loading.

 Remember, risk thrives at interfaces.

4.9 Briefing and receiving data

4.9.1 Briefing

It is important that those being employed as temporary works contractors or designers are fully briefed (i.e. provided with relevant information, such as design briefs, surveys and investigations). Notwithstanding the requirements of CDM, BS 5975 sets out requirements, as does BS EN 12812 but only for design Class B2. It is important to check that these clauses are sufficient for the particular needs and to appreciate that they do not always apply.

 Advice should be sought where the temporary works are beyond the experience of site management.

4.9.2 Receiving data

Equally important is that those employed to design or construct temporary works provide information on any limitations or requirements relating to their work that might impact on others. Examples of the important data required are shown below.

- Pour rate assumed (for vertical formwork).
- Whether the structure may be sheeted.
- Size of tie bolts assumed.

- (Batter) slope inclination for excavations.
- Lateral stability assumptions (such as vertical assemblies relying on the permanent works).

04

4.10 Generic checklist

It is not possible to produce specific checklists, as temporary works come in a wide range of forms and all are influenced by site-specific situations. However, the following provide an overall reminder.

? Is the proposal safety-critical (for example, if it failed could anyone be hurt or have their health adversely affected)?

- If 'Yes', all organisations (and individuals) have statutory responsibilities. Clear procedures are essential.
- If 'No', a problem can nonetheless still cause delay or direct financial loss. Hence, it is a sensible contractual precaution to follow the same guideline principles.

? Is there a TWC appointed, acting in accordance with BS 5975?

- If 'Yes', ensure the interface between the TWC and site management is clear and operational. If you are the TWC, ensure you know your obligations and whether you may need to seek assistance.
  - If you are also responsible for site management ensure you are able to exercise the TWC duties independently from other management pressures.
- If 'No', you should refer the matter to the designated individual. The designated individual is the person within the organisation with specific, allocated responsibilities for the setting and implementation of temporary works procedures.

 Some small sites can produce substantial risk (such as refurbishment work involving structural alterations, basement construction and deep excavation work).

4.11 Temporary Works forum

The Temporary Works forum (TWf) aims to encourage open discussion of any matter related to temporary works. The group is open to any organisation within the industry and sharing this intent.

The TWf's primary objectives are listed below.

- Give authoritative guidance and, when required, professional leadership to the industry.
- Consider aspects of permanent works and interfaces between permanent works and temporary works as relevant.
- Consider both current practice and future development.
- Be aware of trends and innovations in design, construction and use.

 For further information visit the Temporary Works forum website.

4.12   Supporting information

- *Code of Practice for temporary works procedures and the permissible stress design of falsework* (BS 5975:2019)

- *Good practice guidance for tube and fitting scaffolding* (NASC TG20.21).

- *Temporary works – Principles of design and construction* (Thomas Telford, 2019).

- Checklist for erecting and dismantling falsework (The Concrete Society, 2014 (CS123)).

- Checklist for assembly, use and striking of formwork (The Concrete Society, 2014 (CS144)).

- Retention of masonry facades, *Best practice site handbook* (CIRIA, 2003 (C589)).

- *Ground conditions for construction plant* (a good practice guide, Strategic Forum Plant Safety Group, 2014).

- *Management of shoring in excavations*, Part 1, Management process (CPA, 2016 (STIG 13/01)).

- *Management of shoring in excavations*, Part 2, Hazard identification and risk assessment (CPA, 2016 (STIG 1501)).

- Safety in shoring, *The proprietary shoring and piling equipment manual* (CPA, 2006).

- *Temporary works – frequently asked questions*, HSE website.

 For further information on the *Preventing catastrophic events in construction* report visit the HSE website.

CONTENTS

Work equipment and hand-held tools

05

Supporting INFORMATION

GT700 Toolbox talks / supporting checklists and forms

Toolbox talks on some of these topics are available in the GT700 publication. Supporting checklists and forms covering some of these topics are available on our companion website.

WORK EQUIPMENT AND HAND-HELD TOOLS

Overview

There are a significant number of fatalities involving work equipment every year. The majority could have been avoided by effective planning and control of equipment use, adequate checking, inspection and maintenance, and thorough training, assessment and briefing of personnel.

This chapter gives an overview of the legal requirements for work equipment and hand-held tools and the steps required to ensure that these obligations are met, so that work equipment can be used safely and efficiently.

5.1 Introduction

All tools and plant used on construction sites are defined as work equipment by the Provision and Use of Work Equipment Regulations (PUWER), and have the potential to cause harm. Reducing the risk of harm caused by work equipment requires the following steps.

● Assessment of the hazards and risks involved in using work equipment.

● Implementation of measures to eliminate or reduce those risks.

● Ensuring that operators of work equipment are trained, competent and medically fit.

● Ensuring that work equipment is properly maintained and inspected regularly.

 For detailed information refer to Chapter C06 Mobile work equipment: 6.7 Training and competence of personnel, and 6.8 Maintenance, checks and inspections.

 Problems with work equipment operations often occur because of poor communication when planning the work and briefing personnel.

5.2 Important points

● The term *work equipment* is wide ranging and refers to any item of equipment, machinery or tools being used to carry out work.

● The word *used* means any activity involving the work equipment, including starting, stopping, repairing, modifying, maintaining, servicing or cleaning.

● Examples of work equipment are an excavator, a crane, a hammer, an angle grinder and portable fixing tools.

● All items of work equipment must comply with certain legal requirements.
  – The effort necessary to comply with the requirements will depend upon the complexity of the equipment and its potential to cause harm (for example, a trowel will not require the same level of inspection as a passenger goods hoist).

● The law also requires anyone who uses an item of work equipment to be trained, authorised and competent to do so.
  – The effort and time needed to achieve the required level of competence will depend upon the complexity of the equipment and its potential to cause harm.

● Work equipment must be maintained and inspected as necessary to ensure that it can continue to be used safely.

● Certain types of work equipment must also be subjected to thorough examination, which is generally much more detailed than a routine inspection and can involve dismantling and testing parts of the equipment.

5.3 Legislative requirements

The following is a brief summary of the legislative requirements for plant and work equipment operations.

5.3.1 Provision and Use of Work Equipment Regulations

Under PUWER, *work equipment* means any machinery, appliance, apparatus, tool or installation for use at work (whether exclusively or not). This includes equipment that employees provide for their own use at work. The regulations are concerned with suitability for purpose of work equipment, safeguarding of dangerous parts of machinery, provision of appropriate controls, training of operators and maintenance of all work equipment. PUWER place duties on any person who has control to any extent of any of the following.

● Work equipment.

● A person at work who uses, supervises or manages the use of work equipment.

● The way in which work equipment is used at work (including maintenance).

PUWER apply to employers in respect of work equipment provided for, or used by, their employees, self-employed persons and other persons (such as visitors).

5.3.2 Pressure Systems Safety Regulations

The Pressure Systems Safety Regulations deal with the specific risk arising from both fixed and portable pressure systems. The regulations set out requirements for the following.

- Design and construction.
- Provision of information and marking.
- Installation.

- Use.
- Maintenance, modification and repair.
- Examination.

 Safe operating limits should be clearly marked on equipment such as mobile compressors and shot blasting equipment.

5.3.3 Work at Height Regulations

The Work at Height Regulations impose health and safety requirements for equipment that facilitates work at height. Some of these requirements are shown below.

- Steps to be taken to avoid risk from work at height.
- Hierarchy of control for the selection of control measures.
- Organisation and planning, including rescue from height.

- Competence and supervision.
- Selection of work equipment.
- Inspection and testing of work equipment.

 Work at height

The regulations define *work at height* as:

- work in any place where, if there were no precautions in place, a person could fall a distance liable to cause personal injury, including at or below ground level
- obtaining access to or egress from such a place while at work, except by a staircase in a permanent workplace, where, if measures required by these regulations were not taken, a person could fall a distance liable to cause personal injury.

5.3.4 Construction (Design and Management) Regulations

The Construction (Design and Management) Regulations (CDM) place duties on duty holders, including clients, designers and contractors, for the planning, management and monitoring of health, safety and welfare in construction projects and of the co-ordination of the performance of these duties by duty holders. These include a duty on every person working under the control of another to report anything that they think is likely to endanger health or safety. Certain individual regulations have implications for the way in which plant and work equipment operations are carried out.

- There must be safe places of work, including getting to and from the place of work.
- Traffic routes must be suitable for the vehicles that will have to pass over them (for example, dumpers must be used and moved in a way that does not put pedestrians at risk).
- There must be suitable and sufficient lighting for every place of work and traffic route.

5.3.5 Control of Vibration at Work Regulations

These regulations require employers to assess the vibration risk to their employees and eliminate or reduce exposure. Some other employer requirements are listed below.

- Provide information and training to their employees.
- Keep records of risk assessments and control measures.

- Regularly review and update risk assessments.
- Provide suitable health surveillance and keep records.

5.3.6 Control of Noise at Work Regulations

The Control of Noise at Work Regulations require employers to complete the following.

- Assess the risks to their employees from noise at work.
- Take action to reduce the noise exposure that produces those risks.
- Provide their employees with hearing protection if the noise cannot be reduced adequately by using other methods.

- Make sure the legal limits on noise exposure are not exceeded.
- Provide their employees with information, instruction and training.
- Carry out health surveillance where there is a risk to health.

5.3.7 Supply of Machinery (Safety) Regulations

The Supply of Machinery (Safety) Regulations are the UK's implementation of European Union Directive 2006/42/EC, the Machinery Directive, which requires that all machinery (including lifting accessories) supplied into the European Union, meets the essential health and safety requirements detailed in Schedule 2 of the regulations. Each machine must be accompanied at the time of supply by an EC declaration of conformity, declaring that the machinery fulfils all the relevant provisions of the regulations.

 Plant must be CE marked and meet the essential health and safety requirements of the Supply of Machinery (Safety) Regulations. Consequently, most items of lifting equipment are designed to a harmonised European Standard (such as EN 474-5 for excavators, EN 1459 for telehandlers and EN 12001 for concrete pumps).

5.3.8 British, European and ISO standards

Standards do not generally have the force of law. The application of a standard is almost always voluntary, but compliance with a standard is sometimes quoted in legislation as offering a route to discharging legal obligations. A good example of this is the references to the BS 7121 series in the guidance to the Lifting Operations and Lifting Equipment Regulations (LOLER).

British Standards are generally restricted to Codes of Practice (CoPs) for safe use of equipment (such as BS 7121-1:2016 *Safe use of cranes*), whilst European (EN) Standards cover requirements for basic principles (Type A), common product requirements (Type B) and specific product requirements (Type C) (such as EN 474-6 *Earth-moving machinery. Safety – Requirements for dumpers*).

International Standards (ISO) cover both the safe use and specification of lifting equipment. They do not have any legal status but are often taken as good practice and are cited as normative references in some EN product standards.

 For more detailed information on legislation refer to Section A: *Legal and management*.

5.4 General work equipment

The building, construction and civil engineering industry uses a vast range of plant and equipment, all of which has to comply with PUWER. It is all referred to as work equipment and includes the following.

- Hand tools (such as hammers and screwdrivers).

- Powered tools, including petrol driven, electric and pneumatic (such as hand drills and circular saws).

- Lifting equipment and accessories (covered under PUWER as well as having requirements under LOLER).

- Testing and laboratory equipment (such as cube crushers).

- Complex structures and machines made up of other components and equipment (such as scaffolds).

- Remote controlled work equipment and, increasingly, unmanned aerial vehicles (UAVs), often referred to as *drones*.

- Static plant (such as concrete mixers and pumps).

 For further information refer to the HSE publication *Safe use of work equipment* (L22).

5.4.1 Suitability for purpose

All equipment that is used to carry out a work activity must be suitable for that work.

Improvisation is dangerous and can lead to serious accidents (for example, using a hand-held circular saw instead of a router to cut grooves or rebates in timber, or using a dumper to transport persons, creates a dangerous situation).

All work equipment must be regularly maintained to be kept in effective working order and in good repair. It must also be subjected to regular inspection and thorough examination, predetermined by the manufacturers (or scheduled sooner if operated in aggressive environments)

5.4.2 Conformity with UK health, safety and environmental protection requirements

Employers should ensure that any work equipment that is in use or acquired, either new or second-hand, has a CE or UK Conformity Assessment (UKCA) mark. This indicates that it complies with the relevant requirements and has been manufactured to appropriate standards.

The United Kingdom officially left the European Union on 31st December 2020. Before this, products marked with the CE mark were identified as meeting the regulatory standards required, and if they are still in good working order will continue to comply.

UKCA and CE markings

Any equipment purchased from 1st January 2021 within the UK must show the UKCA marking. If imported from the EU, the product must also show the UKCA mark alongside the CE mark.

5.4.3 'Grey' imports

Machines originally supplied from outside the EU frequently do not comply with the requirements of the Machinery Directive and are not CE marked for goods sold in the European Economic Area. If such machines are brought into the EU they cannot be used until they have been modified to meet health, safety and environmental protection requirements. This is a time-consuming and costly process that often negates the benefit of purchasing second-hand machines from outside of the EU.

5.4.4 Mobile plant

This includes excavators, dumpers, forklifts, telehandlers, rollers, mobile elevating work platforms (MEWPs) and mobile cranes. Mobile plant may either be controlled by the operator riding on the machine or they may be pedestrian controlled. Increasingly, some mobile plant is available as specialist, remote controlled equipment.

 For further information on mobile plant and remote controlled equipment refer to Chapter C06 Mobile work equipment.

5.4.5 Static plant

This includes items such as construction hoists *(refer to Chapter C08 Lifting equipment)*, compressors and pumps *(refer to 5.8 and 5.9)*, batching plants, concrete mixers, and rebar benders and cutters.

5.4.6 Lifting equipment

Both mobile and static plant may be designed as lifting equipment. This includes mobile cranes, tower cranes, MEWPs, hoists, telehandlers and excavators used for lifting.

 For further information refer to Chapter C07 Lifting operations and Chapter C08 Lifting equipment.

5.4.7 Manually operated hand-held power tools and work equipment

Selection of the correct equipment for the task is vitally important. Choosing modern equipment that reduces the risk of injury or ill health is fundamental to creating and improving safe working environments.

The environment in which the equipment is used also has a bearing on the safety of the operative. In certain circumstances it may be safe to use hand tools in a confined space, but to use powered equivalents that create dust and fumes could have fatal results.

Hand-held power tools, whether powered electrically, by internal combustion engine, hydraulically, by cartridge or by compressed air, are covered by the definition.

As the use of these types of tool has increased, so has the potential for serious injury. Old type, hand-operated smoothing planes could cause serious cuts if incorrectly used, but those injuries bear no comparison with the injuries that could occur when incorrectly using their modern electrically powered equivalent.

Cutting chases in a wall using an older type cutting disc produces unacceptable amounts of dust. Modern equipment that is fitted with a dust suppression mechanism is safer and much healthier.

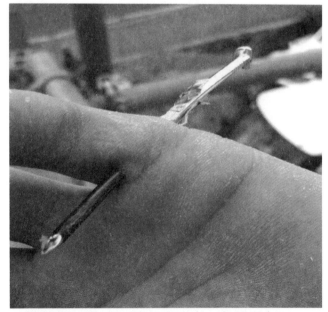
A lack of training and/or supervision, concentration and poor practice can result in serious injury

Also included within this category is the type of equipment that requires human effort in its operation (such as jacks, bar-bending machines, pipe-threaders and other machines where the principles of leverage or torque are utilised).

Many jobs (such as nailing slate battens on a roof), which traditionally would have been completed by using a hammer, are now carried out using nail guns powered by gas canisters.

Equipment of this type is open to abuse, which can result in horrific consequences. It is possible to propel a nail in free flight from a nail gun, giving it the lethal potential of a firearm *(for further information refer to 5.6 Cartridge and gas-operated fixing tools)*.

05

5.4.8 Hand tools

The general requirements of PUWER apply as much to hand tools as they do to more complex items of work equipment. Unfortunately, this is often not appreciated by those managing hand tools, who tend to only deal with problems when they occur, rather than eliminating hazards in the first place.

Two common hazards are listed below.

1. Cold chisels with burred-over mushroom heads can result in a serious eye injury that may result in the loss of an eye if a burr shatters and breaks off during use.

2. A hammer head becoming detached from its shaft can cause a serious injury to the user or a person nearby.

In both examples, the potential to cause harm can be substantially reduced if a system of regular checks, inspection and maintenance, as required by the regulations, is instigated and followed.

5.4.9　Non-mechanical access equipment

5.4.9.1　Scaffolds

If incorrectly erected or misused, scaffolds can be the cause of accidents. Therefore, they must meet the following requirements.

● Be suitably designed.

● Use suitable components that have been inspected prior to use.

● Be inspected every seven days, after alteration, and after any unexpected occurrence (such as impact damage or high winds), the results of the inspection recorded, and proactive maintenance regimes put into place.

● Not be interfered with or altered by unauthorised persons.

Many accidents have occurred due to the installation of scaffold with damaged equipment (such as split boards and bent tubes).

 For further information on access scaffolding refer to Chapter D04 Scaffolding.

5.4.9.2　Ladders and other wooden access equipment

HSE guidance is that ladders and stepladders should be used only as a place of work when the nature of the work meets the following criteria.

● It is of short duration (up to a maximum of 30 minutes).

● It is of a light (up to 10 kg) nature, requiring no heavy lifting, carrying or a destabilising pressure applied by the user or equipment in carrying out the work (i.e. minimal manual handling).

● It allows one hand to be available at all times for holding on to the ladder or stepladder.

● It requires nothing to be carried that would cause instability of the ladder, stepladder or user.

Additionally, when stepladders are used as a place of work they should be positioned so that the user faces the work as the stepladder is climbed. A stepladder must not be positioned so that the user is side-on to the work, where the nature of the work would apply a sideways pressure and cause the stepladder to become unstable.

 For further information on the selection and use of ladders and stepladders refer to Chapter D03 Common access equipment.

 For further guidance refer to the HSE leaflet *Safe use of ladders and stepladders* (INDG455) and the Ladder Association website.

The following are example of **types of ladder** that are available.

Standing ladders are a single stage ladder up to 6 m in length.

Pole ladders are a variant of standing ladders, but with the stiles having been made from a long, wooden pole cut centrally to give even strength and flexibility. Lengths can vary up to a maximum of 10 m.

The practice of shortening a pole ladder to fit a particular situation should be discouraged. Care must be taken to ensure that the fabric of the ladder remains stable if a tie wire is removed.

Extension ladders consist of two or three sections coupled together and extended by sliding over or inside each other. Longer multi-stage ladders are extended by means of a rope and pulley. The maximum reach of a single run ladder is 9 m. At this height and above, resting points must be provided.

Stepladders are of various types, have flat rectangular treads and are usually free standing.

Platform stepladders have a built-in working platform, and newer models can have wheels for ease of movement, handrails and restraint chains. Due to the provision of a platform, these are usually a better option for work that is regularly carried out at the same height.

Roof ladders are ladders with a hook on the top end for securing over the ridge of a roof.

Aluminium and steel ladders are available in various types. Their main advantage is that they are light and weather resistant. They can be prone to slipping at the base if the rubber feet are not properly maintained.

Telescopic ladders are a variation of leaning ladders, but they do not all work the same way. They should always be used, stored and transported with care and kept clean, and is always important you read and follow the user instructions provided by the manufacturer.

 Portable ladders, steps, trestles and lightweight staging are covered by BS 1129:1990, BS 2037:1994 and BS EN 131.

 The Ladder Association, a not-for-profit body dedicated to promoting safe ladder use, has produced a safety guide for users of telescopic ladders – an increasingly popular piece of equipment for working at height – following recent reports of unsafe products in the UK. Visit the Ladder Association website to download a free copy of the guidance.

In November 2017, the British Standards and regulations for ladders and steps changed. BS 2037 Class 1 Industrial and Class 3 Domestic standards were withdrawn to create two European-wide categories: **EN 131 Trade and Industrial** – heavy duty and industrial use (for professional users) and **EN 131 Domestic** (for non-professional users; not suitable for construction sites).

The new standards will ensure products are built with additional safety standards, such as wider bases and stabilisers on ladders over 3 m in height.

05

5.5   Abrasive wheels

Abrasive wheel machines are potentially dangerous if not used correctly by competent persons. Most accidents result from selecting the wrong type of wheel or from over-speeding. It is essential that:

- the right abrasive wheel for the job is chosen
- the wheel is correctly mounted by a competent person on a compatible machine
- it is run at the correct speed and guards are fitted
- high-impact eye protection is used.

In most circumstances abrasive wheels rotate at high speeds and contact with the revolving wheel can cause serious injury.

When using a grinding or cutting wheel, a stream of hot, abrasive particles is thrown off, which can cause injury, particularly to the eyes. Finally, there is always a risk of the wheel disintegrating or bursting as it revolves.

Fragments of the wheel can be projected a great distance, at great speed and in all directions.

5.5.1   Types of abrasive wheel

An abrasive wheel is generally defined as a power-driven wheel, cylinder, disc or point having abrasive particles. It may consist entirely of abrasive particles, or be of metal, wood, cloth, felt, rubber or paper, with a surface covered with abrasive material.

It may also be formed as a ring or segments of abrasive materials. These types of abrasive wheel are used for shaping material via grinding operations. Other types of abrasive wheel are those used for cutting rather than grinding operations. These are circular metal blades, usually with diamond impregnated tips, used for cutting through concrete, steel, and so on.

5.5.2   Choosing the correct wheel

The majority of accidents involving abrasive wheels are the result of using the wrong type of wheel for the job in hand. Had the manufacturer's recommendations been complied with then these accidents would have been avoided.

Abrasive wheels should comply with the requirements of BS EN 12413 and BS ISO 525.

Many types and grades of abrasive wheel are available, and the correct selection is important. As a general rule, soft grade wheels are most suitable for use on hard materials and hard grade wheels are for use on soft materials. Coarse grains are for the rapid removal of material and fine grains are for polishing.

The use of an unsuitable wheel may result in the wheel face becoming loaded as the pores are clogged by the material being removed. If the wheel is too hard or too fine it may become glazed or polished.

The consequence, in both cases, may be that the operative will press too hard, in an attempt to get the work done, and cause the wheel to break. It is important that only reinforced, resin-bonded abrasive wheels should be used with portable grinding machines.

Abrasive wheels should be marked to conform to Annex A of BS EN 12413.

 For further guidance refer to the HSE publication *Safety in the use of abrasive wheels* (HSG17).

5.5.3   Maximum permissible speed

The maximum permissible speed in revolutions per minute (rpm) and metres per second (m/s) specified by manufacturers should be marked on every abrasive wheel larger than 80 mm in diameter, or on the blotter or identification label that is sometimes attached to it. Since it is not practicable to mark smaller wheels, the maximum permissible speed in rpm of wheels 80 mm in diameter or less should be stated in a notice posted in a position where it can easily be read. For speeds of 50 m/s and above, colour coded stripes will appear on the wheel.

Metres per second	Colour	
50 m/s		Blue
60 m/s		Yellow
80 m/s		Red
100 m/s		Green
125 m/s		Yellow/blue

5.5.4   Restrictions of use

Annex A of BS EN 12413 and BS ISO 525 specify how wheels should be marked to indicate specific restrictions for use.

- RE1: Not permitted for hand-held and manually guided grinding.
- RE2: Not permitted for hand-held cutting-off machines.
- RE3: Not suitable for wet grinding.
- RE4: Only permitted for totally enclosed working areas.
- RE6: Not permitted for face grinding.

5.5.5   Shelf life

All organic bonded wheels for hand-held applications will have a use-by date, which is generally three years from the date of manufacture. The organic bond will break down over a period of time, increasing the likelihood of wheel burst during normal use.

5.5.6   Traceable number

A code number should be marked on the wheel to indicate the source and manufacturing details of the wheel.

5.5.7   Wheels bursting

The two main causes of abrasive wheels bursting are over-speeding and the incorrect mounting of the wheel.

5.5.7.1   Over-speeding

Abrasive wheels must not be run in excess of the maximum permissible speed recommended by the manufacturer. This should be clearly marked in rpm on all wheels over 80 mm (approximately three inches) in diameter.

For smaller wheels, a notice stating the maximum speed permissible should be displayed on or adjacent to where the machine is being operated. Any type of record may be kept, from computer database to a written record. The only restrictions are that a hard copy of the information must be available on request.

Speed of spindle. Every power-driven machine for use with abrasive wheels should have a notice fixed to it, specifying the maximum and minimum spindle speeds. Machines that are not marked with their spindle speed must **not** be used.

Sometimes these markings are very small. If this is the case, consideration should be given to painting or engraving the spindle speed clearly on the machine. Always keep the markings clean and in good condition so that they are easy to read.

Maximum spindle speeds must never be exceeded. Governors, or other devices to control or limit speed, must be properly maintained and in good working order.

The maximum spindle speed on equipment should be checked on a regular basis. This is particularly important on engine driven machines where the speed can change over a period of time as a result of component wear.

Peripheral speeds. Care must be taken to operate the wheel at the optimum speed that is recommended by the manufacturer.

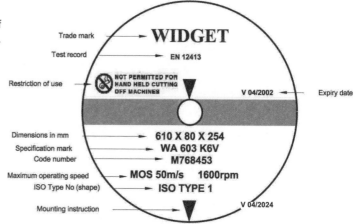

Abrasive wheel marking

Spindle speeds can be checked by using a stroboscopic light meter

As an abrasive wheel wears down, its peripheral speed (at the edge of the wheel) is reduced and this, in turn, reduces its efficiency. A wheel operated at too low a speed will not cut properly and there will be a tendency to press the wheel hard against the work piece. This may damage the wheel and cause it to burst.

5.5.7.2 Mounting of wheels

In order to be able to demonstrate compliance with legislation, abrasive wheels should only be mounted by a trained, competent and authorised person appointed to this duty by their employer.

 Never attempt to mount a wheel onto a machine unless you are authorised, trained and competent to do so.

5.5.8 Training

Training for the mounting of abrasive wheels must **only** be given by a competent person, which often involves attending an external course. It must cover the grades, types and marking of wheels, the use, hazards, speeds, storage, handling, inspection, testing, dressing, adjustments and the functions of associated components (such as flanges, blotters, bushes and locking nuts).

 Details of suitable training courses and training providers can be found on the British Abrasives Federation website.

5.5.9 Maintenance

In addition to checks immediately before and after each use, every machine should be regularly serviced by a competent person in accordance with manufacturer instructions. A maintenance record should be kept. It is good practice to record the type and serial number of all abrasive wheel machines, together with the date each machine is due for service. When servicing has been carried out, ensure that details of any completed work are entered, together with the date that the next service is due. All records should be kept up-to-date.

5.5.10 Diamond blades

A diamond blade is a circular steel disc with a diamond bearing edge. The edge of the blade may be smooth or textured, with a continuous rim, or a segmented rim with smaller, individual sections. The blade core is a precision-made steel disc and may have a continuous or slotted rim. The slots (also called gullets) provide faster cooling by allowing water or air to flow between the segments. The slots also allow the blade to flex under cutting pressure.

As with bonded abrasive wheels, people working with diamond blades must be properly trained and competent. Most of the safe procedures and precautions for using bonded abrasive wheels on hand-held machines apply to diamond blades. Additional advice and information can be obtained from suppliers and manufacturers. Diamond blades are **directional** and must be mounted so that they rotate in the direction marked on the blade. Different wheels are designed to cut different materials, a requirement that must be strictly adhered to.

 Diamond blades can significantly deteriorate and become unsafe if they are used to cut the wrong type of material.

Use the correct equipment for the task

A worker used a concrete blade to cut a series of post holes through an asphalt surface to receive concrete fence posts. As a result, the blade failed and several 50 mm long segment blade tips broke off at high speed, two of which embedded deep within his knee cap. He suffered high blood loss, was airlifted to hospital and the tips were removed during reconstructive surgery. He was off work for over six months and never fully recovered. Providing an additional asphalt blade would have avoided the accident.

Diamond blades can be used on hand-held machines at peripheral speeds of up to 100 m/s, provided that the machine is designed for this speed and the marked maximum permissible operating speed of the blade is not exceeded. Under no circumstances must the blade be allowed to overheat.

Periodically, it may be necessary to redress (sharpen) the blade by making cuts in a special dressing block or abrasive block. These wheels can last a comparatively long time. Before use and with the power disconnected, make a special point of checking the condition of the spindle bearings, as these can deteriorate considerably during the lifetime of a diamond cutting wheel. Pre-use checks for wheel defects should be carried out before each use.

 Reputable manufacturers will provide inspection guides for their blades.

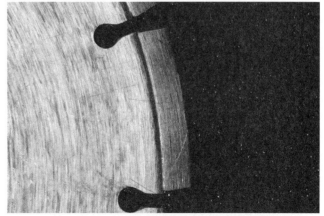

Diamond blades need to be inspected on a regular basis for defects

5.5.11 In-use considerations

5.5.11.1 Guards (fixed and hand-held machines)

● The guard should be designed, and be sufficiently robust, to contain any fragments in the event of the wheel bursting.

● The guard must be securely attached to the body of the machine, properly adjusted and maintained.

● The guard or shield supplied by the manufacturer must be adjusted to permit exposure of the minimum amount of wheel or disc to enable the job to be carried out. It must not be left off or altered in any way.

5.5.11.2 Defects

Employees are required to report any defects in work equipment, including abrasive wheels, guards or tool rests, to their employer.

5.5.11.3 Tool rests

Rests should be secured and adjusted so that they are as close as practicable to the wheel and no more than 3 mm away. If the gap between the wheel and the rest is too great, the work piece may become trapped and an accident may result.

 Continue to display cautionary notices concerning the dangers of abrasive wheels, wherever abrasive wheels are used or changed. This also serves as a useful reminder to employees of the training they have received.

5.5.12 Health considerations

5.5.12.1 Respiratory protection

Depending upon what material is being cut, it is possible that the user of an abrasive wheel may be vulnerable to inhaling hazardous dust. With fixed machinery (such as bench grinders or fixed concrete saws), it may be possible to reduce airborne dust to a safer level by installing a fixed local exhaust ventilation system.

The following would be more applicable to portable machines.

● Purchasing abrasive wheel machines that incorporate a facility for wet cutting.

● The attachment of a standalone dust extraction/collection unit (on-tool extraction).

A petrol-driven disc cutter with the facility for wet cutting

It is not always reasonably practicable to completely eliminate respiratory hazards. If, after applying all other measures, there is a residual likelihood of exposure, suitable respiratory protective equipment (RPE) should be provided to each person exposed. Therefore, the operator in both examples listed above would need to be issued with appropriate RPE and also be face-fit tested.

 For further information refer to Chapter B06 Personal protective equipment.

5.5.12.2 Vibration

The very nature of grinding or cutting work using abrasive wheels is likely to subject the operator to a degree of hand-arm vibration. In extreme cases, this can lead to permanent and disabling injuries.

Employers must assess the risk and exposure levels to employees who carry out such work, and put preventative and protective measures in place to ensure that employee health is not adversely affected.

 For further information on control of vibration refer to Chapter B12 Vibration.

5.5.12.3 Noise

Grinding and cutting operations using abrasive wheel machines will inevitably result in an increased level of noise, both from the machine itself (for example, a petrol-driven disc cutter) and from contact between the cutting disc or grinding wheel and the material being worked upon. In many cases, the level of noise generated will exceed the upper exposure action value, meaning that, unless other control measures can be put in place, personal hearing protection must be made available and worn. Depending upon the level of noise and the proximity of other people, it may be necessary for them also to wear hearing protection.

 For further information on control of noise refer to Chapter B11 Noise.

5.5.13 Safety considerations

During cutting or grinding processes, a stream of dust or abrasive particles and hot sparks is thrown off. These particles could be travelling at speeds in excess of 170 mph and can cause serious injury to the eyes.

Because there is an obvious risk of eye injuries when an abrasive wheel is being used, **high-impact resistant** eye protection should be provided in accordance with the Personal Protective Equipment Regulations (goggles, a face shield or visor, to BS EN 166).

 For further information on eye protection refer to Chapter B06 Personal protective equipment.

- The machine must have an efficient starting and stopping device that is easy to access and operate.

- The floor area of the workplace must be kept in good condition, free of loose material and trip hazards, and should not be slippery.

- Abrasive wheels should be properly stored, flat and preferably in their boxes, and in accordance with the manufacturer's guidance. Care must be taken to ensure that any manuals are retained so that the manufacture's guidance and instructions can be read. Labels on the discs themselves should be kept clean and undamaged so that the information can be easily read.

 For detailed information on abrasive wheels refer to the HSE publication _Safety in the use of abrasive wheels_ (HSG17).

5.6 Cartridge and gas-operated fixing tools

Portable fixing tools use the power of an explosive charge or a gas propellant (from cartridges or a gas canister) to drive a fixing device into position in a base material. They are particularly useful if there are a large number of repetitive fixings to be made, where a portable fixing tool reduces the time and labour expended in this area. However, the resemblance of the tools to the shape and action of a gun can lead to their misuse, especially by young and inexperienced workers.

They can be extremely dangerous if used incorrectly. Operatives must be trained, competent and authorised and be of a sufficiently mature and responsible disposition.

Poor technique, or the use of incorrect equipment, will result in poor or defective fixing. The tool, type of cartridge or fuel cell, type of fixing and the base material must all be compatible.

In most cases, items of additional personal protective equipment (PPE) (such as hearing, respiratory and eye protection) will have to be worn. At the end of the job all unused cartridges must be accounted for.

 It should always be remembered that portable fixing tools are potentially lethal if they are used recklessly or incompetently.

5.6.1 Cartridge-operated tools

A cartridge-operated tool works by using a firing cap or cartridge to provide propellant to drive a fixing home. These tools must not be used in areas where a flammable atmosphere or risk of dust explosion may exist. Listed below are the primary factors that will ensure the proper and safe use of cartridge-operated tools.

- Adequate information, instruction, training and supervision.

- Competent and responsible users, who are over 18 years old and are not colour blind (cartridges are colour coded for different levels of power, _see 5.6.1.4_).

- The compatibility of the base material, the type of fixing and the cartridge strength.

- Restricting access to the work area during fixing activities.

- The provision and use of appropriate PPE.

- Carrying out work in accordance with _Code of Practice for safe use of powder actuated fixing systems_ (BS 4078-1).

- Using cartridge-operated tools that comply with _Specification for tools_ (BS 4078-2).

 High-powered cartridge-operated tools can operate at the same velocity as a small firearm.

5.6.1.1 Types of tool

There are two main types of cartridge-operated tool.

Indirect-acting, where the driving force is transmitted to the fixing by means of the expanding explosive gas acting on a piston. These tend to be low power.

Direct-acting, where the explosive force of the cartridge acts directly on the fixing, driving it along the barrel into the background material. These tend to be high power.

5.6.1.2 Power level of tools

Cartridge tools are generally classed as high power and low power.

Low power is defined as giving the pin a kinetic energy not greater than 3.5 m/kg/f and a velocity not greater than 98.5 m per sec.

High power applies to any values greater than those above. Using high-power tools can result in dangerous through-shoots. This is where the fixing is fired right through the background material.

Most of the commonly available tools are low power and indirect acting. These are by far the safest. There are high-power tools for special applications, and some old, high-power (direct-acting) tools are still in use.

Hammer-activated tools are nearly always low power.

Some modern tools have provision for varying the power level (within the low-power range) by means of an adjustment that changes the size of the gas expansion chamber. There are also interchangeable pistons for different fixings or depths of penetration. Tools incorporating these features require a smaller range of cartridges.

5.6.1.3 Safety devices

All tools should incorporate a contact pressure safety device, which prevents them being fired unless the muzzle is pressed hard against the workface. They should always incorporate a drop-firing safety device that prevents the tool from firing when it is dropped onto a hard surface.

In addition, some tools are also equipped with an unintentional firing safety device. This prevents the tool from firing if the trigger is pulled before the tool is pressed against the work surface.

It should **only** be possible to fire the tool when it is correctly pressed against the material being fixed.

5.6.1.4 Cartridges

Any premises or any place where the cartridges for a cartridge tool are stored should be secure, dry and cool, and may need to be licensed. Checks should be made with the local police station or Local Authority as to whether this is necessary and, if so, where such a licence can be obtained.

Cartridges are designed for specific brands or types of tool and are not interchangeable, even if they are of a similar type or appearance. They are available in different strengths. It is preferable to start with a lower strength cartridge for a test fixing and then change to a more powerful cartridge if the depth of penetration is not sufficient.

BS 4078 requires the strength of the cartridges to be marked on the packaging and each cartridge to be colour coded to indicate its strength. The colour codes set out in BS 4078 are shown on the right.

Cartridge strength	Colour	
Extra low (XL)		Brown
Low (L)		Green
Low/medium (LM)		Yellow
Medium (M)		Blue
Medium/high (MH)		Red
High (H)		White
Extra high (XH)		Black

 For further information refer to *Cartridge operated hand-held tools. Safety requirements. Fixing and hard marking tools* (BS EN 15895).

It should be noted that the code is not universally followed, and that colour coding alone must never be relied on as an indicator of the cartridge strength. Cartridges should be retained in the packaging (which identifies their strength) and not carried loose.

Both cartridges and fixing nails are now available on plastic strips.

 ## ❗ Controls for dispensed and unused cartridges

Proper controls must be put in place to account for all dispensed and unused cartridges.

Fully dispensed cartridges in single or strip form are not classed as hazardous waste, and can be disposed of in accordance with normal rules of non-hazardous waste.

Unused or unserviceable cartridges that cannot be fired are hazardous, and in **no circumstances** should be exposed to fire or heat, or be subject to mechanical impact.

For the purpose of waste classification, unused cartridges often have a hazardous European waste code entry of *16 04 01* Waste ammunition*, but this should be checked in each case from the safety data provided by the supplier of the cartridge.

The supplier should be contacted to discuss suitable arrangements for the return/disposal of any unused or unserviceable cartridges.

Cartridges should be returned to their original packaging so that they can be properly identified.

5.6.1.5 Suitability of base materials

Attempting to fix into unsuitable materials with cartridge tools is dangerous. Before firing the first fixing, a simple test should be made by driving a fixing of the intended type into the base material with a hammer. The result will show whether the material is suitable. No attempt should be made to fix into unsuitable materials. The table below provides general guidance.

Material	Result	Conclusion
Plaster, plywood and lightweight blocks	Sinks in easily	Too soft (not suitable)
Marble, some rock, hardened steel and weld metal	Fixing blunted	Too hard (not suitable)
Glass, glazed tiles, slates and some cast-iron	Material cracks or shatters	Too brittle (not suitable)
Sound wood, concrete and mild steel	Clear impression of fastener point	Suitable

5.6.1.6 Hazards in use

Hazards from the use of cartridge tools generally arise from one or more of the following three factors.

1. Lack of competence, knowledge or training.

2. Misuse, whether deliberate or due to ignorance of proper use.

3. Poor maintenance, rendering the equipment defective or unsafe.

Two conditions that specifically need to be guarded against are **through-penetration**, where the fixing goes through the material emerging in free flight on the other side, and **ricochet**, where the fixing and debris is deflected after firing, possibly towards the operator.

5.6.1.7 Causes of through-penetration

- Cartridge too powerful for the material being fixed to.

- Fixing into voids in the structure.

- The background material being fixed into is too thin.

- Changes in type or consistency of the material penetrated.

- Not establishing the density of the material being fixed into.

To avoid these hazards:

- check the suitability of the material for cartridge-fired fixing

- if necessary, make a trial fixing using a low-powered cartridge

- check and guard the area behind the material or structure into which the fixing is being fired, to prevent access of unauthorised persons

- use an indirect (lower powered) acting tool.

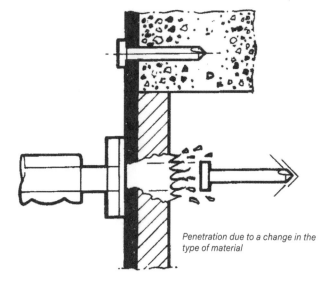

Penetration due to a change in the type of material

5.6.1.8 Causes of ricochet

- Firing into the hole of a previously attempted fixing.

- Attempting to fix into excessively hard materials (such as hardened steel or welded areas).

- Cartridge tools not held square onto the work surface, causing the pin to strike at an angle and then be deflected.

- Attempting to fix too near to an edge.

- Hitting a reinforcing rod or dense aggregate hidden just under the surface.

To avoid ricochets:

- fixings should be at the recommended distance (or greater) from failed attempts

- do not fix into unfamiliar background materials without first safely checking their suitability for cartridge fixing

- tools should be at right angles to the work surface. The whole rim of the splinter guard should be firmly placed against the workface so as to stabilise the tool and not leave gaps.

Ricochet due to firing too near to edge

The risk of ricochet is reduced by the use of low-powered, indirect acting tools. If high-powered tools are used, there is a risk that the fixing can be deflected and come back towards the operator.

5.6.1.9 General precautions

Recoil of a cartridge tool can lead to loss of balance, which is made worse if working from an unstable workplace. In this instance, only low-power tools should be used. Operators not familiar with cartridge tools, should test the tool for recoil before use. In all circumstances, an adequate and safe footing is a necessity. Makeshift platforms should not be used.

In the event of a **misfire**, the cartridge tool should be kept pressed in position against the workface for at least **30 seconds**, to allow for any delayed detonation. Following this time period, the cartridge must then be removed strictly in accordance with the manufacturer's instructions. Cartridges that have misfired should be stored in a metal box and returned to the supplier.

 Misfired cartridges should not be removed from the tool by levering under the rim. Some types are rim detonated and could be fired by this action. Only the proper extraction tool, as supplied by the manufacturer, should be used.

Loading of tools should be carried out immediately prior to use. Once the tool is loaded, it must never be pointed towards other people or at any part of the operator's body. Unused cartridges must be removed from the tool as soon as possible.

Storage and issue of tools. Only responsible and competent persons should supervise and check the acquisition, issue, use, return and maintenance of cartridge-operated tools.

Cartridge-operated tools and cartridges should be stored in a place that is secure, dry and cool. The issue of such tools and cartridges should be strictly controlled, and licensed if necessary. The following points should be clearly noted and understood.

- Cartridge tools should only be stored in an unloaded state.
- Different strengths of cartridge should be clearly identified and kept separate.
- The use of different makes of equipment on one site should be limited as far as possible.
- The manufacturer's instructions on the safe use of the cartridge tool should always be made available.

Personal protective equipment, complying with the relevant British Standards, should be used by operatives using cartridge-operated and gas-operated tools.

- High-impact resistant eye protection to the applicable BS EN 166 impact rating must be provided and worn at all times when handling and operating cartridge-operated tools, their cartridges or gas-operated tools.
- Noise levels will vary with the make of tool but all tools create a high intensity, short duration noise, so suitable hearing protection should be worn.
- Safety helmets to BS EN 397 should be worn while cartridge tools are in use.

The safety of other people in the vicinity of where cartridge-operated or gas-operated tools are being used, is a factor which should have been covered in the risk assessment, must be considered and all necessary precautions taken.

 For further information refer to Chapter B06 Personal protective equipment.

5.6.1.10 Safe battery charging

Good practice when charging the Lithium-Ion batteries of hand-held tools and equipment, in order to reduce the risk of potential fire risk, would be to:

- Never charge batteries near flammable materials or objects.
- Never charge batteries in places where high temperatures or exposure to direct sunlight may be expected.
- Never cover the batteries when charging.
- Ensure that overheat protection is installed at the charging socket.
- Never overcharge or leave to charge over night on a trickle charge; use time-out protection.

5.6.2 Gas-powered tools

Lighter duty gas-powered tools can be used for the fixing of timber and other low density materials. These fixing tools are generally lighter in weight and use a battery and fuel cell, either propane or other gas, to act as a propellant rather than a cartridge. The fuel cell, typically a small aerosol canister, is mounted within the tool. The safety issues that need to be considered when using a gas-powered tool are shown below.

- Operators must be trained. Usually this can be provided by the supplier of the equipment. Operators must also be in possession of, and be familiar with, the relevant equipment instructions.
- When firing, the operator must be in a stable position and holding the tool at right angles to the work.
- Firing must not take place when others are behind the work. As with cartridge tools, through-penetration can occur.
- If a malfunction occurs the tool can usually be fired again (unlike when using a cartridge tool). However, the manufacturer's instruction manual should be consulted.

- The tool and the fuel cells must not be exposed to extremes of heat or used within a flammable atmosphere.

- Harmful fumes are expelled during use and therefore the tool should be used in a well-ventilated area.

- Because of the mode of operation and speed of use, the tool can become hot. Reference should be made to warnings of hot areas on the tool.

- Fuel cells must not be damaged, pierced, punctured, burnt or opened, even after use.

- Fuel cells should be disposed of in accordance with local regulations for aerosol products.

5.7 Woodworking machinery

- Woodworking machines are classified as work equipment and must therefore comply with certain legal requirements.

- Many items of woodworking equipment, with their partially exposed blades or cutters, have the potential to cause serious personal injury if they are not properly used and maintained.

- Operators of woodworking machinery must be trained on each type of machine that they are required to operate and be judged as competent by their employer.

- Hand-held, bench-mounted and free-standing woodworking machines of all types present particular hazards to the operator and, in some cases, other people.

- The use of woodworking machines has the potential to cause occupational health problems if appropriate preventative measures are not taken to address the risk from dust, vibration and noise.

Several hundred accidents on different types of woodworking machinery are reported annually to HSE.

Of these, approximately 40% occur on circular saws and 25% on planing machines.

Woodworking machine cutters can inflict serious injuries and it is essential that the regulations for guarding them are strictly observed.

Neglect or ignorance of the regulations governing the use of such machinery creates the conditions in which accidents occur.

5.7.1 Types of machine

The following non-exhaustive list gives examples of different types of woodworking machine.

- Circular saws.
- Sanding machines.
- Bandsaws.
- Routing machines.
- Planing/thicknessing machines.
- Chainsaws.
- Mortising machines.
- Tenoning machines.
- Vertical spindle moulding machines, including high-speed routing machines.
- Multi-cutter moulding machines having two or more cutter spindles.
- Trenching machines.
- Boring machines.
- Automatic and semi-automatic lathes.

5.7.2 Health and safety risks

Some examples of occupational health problems caused by using woodworking machines are listed below.

- **Noise-induced hearing loss, caused by exposure to noisy environments.**
- **Hand-arm vibration syndrome (HAVS), caused by vibration of equipment.**
- **Chronic respiratory diseases, caused by the inhalation of fine dust particles.**
- **Eye injury.**
- **Dermatitis, caused by contact with fine wood dust.**

5.7.2.1 Noise-induced hearing loss

Woodworking machines can be particularly noisy when in use and the noise generated will be a significant hazard to health unless adequately controlled. Ideally, the level of noise will be controlled by means other than issuing PPE (for example, using screening or anti-vibration mountings).

 For further information on control of noise refer to Chapter B11 Noise.

5.7.2.2 Hand-arm vibration syndrome

In the context of using woodworking machines, the predominant problem is considered to be hand-arm vibration. The necessary training and on-going health surveillance should be implemented to prevent occurrence.

5.7.2.3 Respiratory problems

Woodworking machines inevitably produce dust that may affect the operator and persons in the vicinity. Dust should be treated and assessed in accordance with the Control of Substances Hazardous to Health (COSHH) Regulations. It should be controlled by effective extraction, collection systems or using dampening techniques in addition to wearing **face-fitted** RPE. Fumes can also be generated from adhesives and substances used for the treatment or finishes of the wood.

 For further information on control of dust refer to Chapter B10 Dust and fumes (Respiratory hazards).

5.7.2.4 Eye injury

Depending on the machine being used and the nature of the work being carried out, it may be necessary for machine operators (and anyone assisting them) to wear eye protection (such as goggles) or a full face shield of a suitable impact-resistant grade.

5.7.2.5 Dermatitis

It may be necessary to provide operatives with suitable gloves and protective creams to protect against skin damage whilst handling woods, particularly unplaned timber. Furthermore, the skin of a small number of persons can be adversely affected by the natural oils that occur in some woods, notably cedar.

 For further information refer to Chapter B06 Personal protective equipment.

5.7.3 Controls

Every machine must be fitted with start and stop controls that can be quickly and easily accessed by the operator.

5.7.4 Braking

An essential safety feature of most woodworking machinery is the provision of an automatic brake. This is to ensure that, if there is a risk of an employee coming into contact with the cutters during the rundown period, the machine stops within a period defined by CEN European standards.

5.7.5 Guarding cutters

Cutters include saw blades, chain cutters, knives, boring tools, detachable cutters and solid cutters. These must be guarded to the greatest practicable extent, having regard to the work being done. Guards must be of substantial construction, properly secured and adjusted, and constantly in position while cutters are in motion.

Adjustments **must not** be made to any guard whilst the cutters are in motion, unless safe means (that is mechanical adjusters) are provided for those adjustments to be made. Every dangerous part of any woodworking machine must be securely fenced, or be in such a position or of such construction that it is as safe to every person on the site as it would be if it were fenced.

5.7.6 Portable, electrically powered saws

Portable, electrically powered saws must always be disconnected from the electrical supply before any adjustments, repairs, cleaning or maintenance is carried out.

Whenever possible, to reduce the risk from electric shock, all portable, electric tools should be battery-powered or 110 volts and, if 110 volt supply, be earthed or double insulated. The mains input to a 110 volt transformer should be protected by a residual current device (RCD), commonly known as a power breaker.

Portable, electrically powered saws must never be carried by their power cable and, when operating, the power cable must always be kept clear of the saw blade. The power plug must be inspected each time, prior to use, for damage and security of the cable. All electrically powered saws should be inspected regularly by a competent electrician.

Care should be taken to ensure that the spring loaded, lower blade guard returns to cover the blade after every cut. This guard, also known as the swivel guard, is designed to uncover the saw teeth when material is being cut, and then automatically cover the saw teeth when the saw is withdrawn. This guard must **never** be wired in the open position.

5.7.7 Chainsaws

Due to their high potential to cause serious injury, the use of chainsaws on building and construction sites is not generally recommended. While they are not illegal, site rules may prohibit their use. Where chainsaws are used on site, they must only be used by operatives who are fully competent, have received specific and nationally approved training, and who are authorised to carry out the intended operation.

A specific risk assessment should be carried out and a written method statement produced for the operation, including the need for full PPE, safe working at heights and, if necessary, a workplace located safely away from other workers.

 For specific guidance on the use of chainsaws refer to the HSE leaflet *Chainsaws at work* (INDG317).

5.7.8 Other woodworking equipment

 For guidance on the safe use of other specific types of woodworking equipment refer to the HSE woodworking information sheets, which can all be downloaded, without charge, from its website.

05

5.8 Compressors

Air compressors are used in construction as a power source for a range of tools and equipment. They can be either diesel or electric powered, trailer mounted or static, and range in output from 60 to 900 cubic feet per minute of free air delivered, with working pressures of between seven and 12 bar (100 to 170 psi).

5.8.1 Selection

When selecting a compressor for a particular application the following points should be taken into account.

- How many tools are going to be run from the compressor?
- What is the total airflow required?
- What is the working pressure required?
- Does the compressor need to be trailer mounted for ease of movement?

- Where will the compressor be located?
- Are diesel fumes an issue?
- Are there any noise limitations?
- How long will the compressor be required?

5.8.2 Compressed air safety

A compressed air system presents a range of hazards.

- Unintended release of pressure from the air receiver, piping or a loose hose-tool connection.
- Hoses that become disconnected from a tool, whipping in an uncontrolled fashion.
- Noise from compressed air leaks and pneumatic machinery.
- Hand-arm vibration from pneumatic tools (this is also a hazard with electric tools).
- Hot discharge pipes.
- Moving parts of compressor.
- Trip hazard from trailing air hoses.

Some ways to reduce the risks associated with the use of compressors and air tools are shown below.

- Train users in safe working practices, and supervise activities.
- Select low vibration tools from reputable suppliers.
- Ensure guards protecting the belt and pulley drive are in place.
- Provide adequate ventilation.
- Fit a safety valve, pressure gauge and drain valve to air receivers.

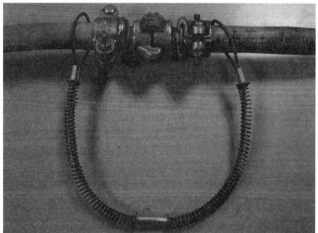

Whip checks should be used on every hose joint to prevent break away

- Fit whip checks across all hose connection points.
- Consider replacing quick disconnect hose connections with safer two-stage disconnect components.
- Maintain a written scheme of examination, as required by the Pressure Systems Safety Regulations.
- Wear the correct PPE (the last resort).

When compressed air is misused, it can cause serious injury or even death

A boilermaker was making repairs on a boiler. Upon emerging from the firebox, he disconnected the air hose from a riveting gun and began to blow dust from his clothes. There was one spot on his jacket sleeve that was so embedded in the fabric that the air did not readily remove it. In order to direct more air into the spot, he placed his index finger over the end of the air hose to partially close the opening. Air entered his finger through a small puncture wound, causing swelling and pain. Foreign material, apparently made up of dust and soot from the air, and oil from the compressor, was later removed from the wound. Even with proper medical treatment, gangrene set in and the finger had to be amputated.

As shown by this accident, using compressed air to blow dust or dirt off clothing or the body is a dangerous practice. A strong blast of air can dislodge an eye from its socket, or rupture lungs, intestines or an eardrum. Air forced into the bloodstream can even cause death.

 For further guidance on the use, maintenance and examination of compressors and compressed air systems refer to the HSE publications *Safety of pressure systems – Approved Code of Practice* (L122) and *Compressed air safety* (HSG39).

5.9 Pumps

Pumps are used in the construction industry for a number of tasks (such as dewatering excavations, pumping bentonite for diaphragm walls, pumping concrete and pumping sludge or sewage). Pumps can be diesel, petrol, electric or air powered and range in capacity from around 2 m³/hr to 1,200 m³/hr. They may be trailer or skid mounted and are available in silenced versions and as submersible units.

5.9.1 Selection

When selecting a pump for a particular application the following points should be taken into account.

- What type of fluid is being pumped?
- What is the flow required?
- What are the suction and delivery heads required?
- Does the pump need to be trailer mounted for ease of movement?

- Where will the pump be located?
- Are diesel or petrol exhaust fumes an issue?
- Are there any noise limitations?
- How long will the pump be required?

Providing the pump supplier with this information will assist in getting the correct pump for the application.

 For detailed guidance on the safe use of concrete pumps refer to the Construction Plant-hire Association *Code of Practice for the safe use of concrete pumps* (BCPG0401).

5.10 Lasers

If used correctly, lasers should not pose a health or safety hazard. The operating movement of a rotating laser means that, in practice, it is difficult to look directly at the beam for more than an instant. Static lasers (such as pipe lasers) pose more of a risk. Exclusion zones and warning signs must be in place if high-powered lasers are being used.

Laser equipment is commonly used in the construction industry. It is important to know the different classifications, the dangers and their safe use. The British Standard BS EN 60825-1:2014, *Safety of laser products Part 1: Equipment classification and requirements*, classifies laser products according to the laser beam hazard.

Rotating laser level. Photo reproduced by kind permission of Hilti

The standard sets out eight classes of laser products, consisting of the following:

- Class 1
- Class 1C
- Class 1M
- Class 2

- Class 2M
- Class 3R
- Class 3B
- Class 4

The classification scheme for lasers indicates the potential risk of adverse health effects; the higher the class number, the greater the radiation hazard posed by the laser.

05

Government guidance states that any Class 1 laser product is regarded as 'safe', for example barcode scanners, laser printers and laser levels. When working with laser equipment, it is important to follow the following points.

- Read operating instructions for the equipment before use.
- Set up laser equipment above or below normal eye level.
- Never point the laser at other persons.
- Keep lasers out of reach of children.
- Never look into a laser beam.

'Hazardous' lasers, which cover all Class 3B and 4 lasers, present a 'reasonably foreseeable' risk of harming the eyes and skin of workers, and are where control measures are needed. These are specified as 'hazardous' because of the potential to cause eye damage including blindness, burns to the skin, and their ability to cause a fire. Workers using this class of equipment and above must be trained and competent.

 For detailed guidance on the safe use of laser equipment, refer to the HSE *Guidance to Employers on the Control of Artificial Optical Radiation at Work Regulations* (2010) and examples of 'safe' and 'hazardous' lasers based on definitions in the British Standard BS EN 60825-1:2014.

5.11   Unmanned aerial vehicles (drones)

Small unmanned aerial vehicles (UAVs) are becoming more widely available for construction activity.

More popularly known as *drones*, they can carry out surveys at height and in inaccessible areas. Perhaps most importantly, they can remove the need for people to enter dangerous environments for inspections and surveys.

It must be acknowledged that if drones are not used responsibly they can create dangers for operatives and members of the public. Because of recent incidents, the use of drones is subject to specific safety regulations relating to the way they are operated. These rules are underpinned by UK law.

The regulations are contained within the Air Navigation Order 2016 (ANO 2016) and there are some specific additional steps that must be taken if a drone is being flown for commercial operations.

A drone in flight

In summary, ANO 2016 requires that anyone carrying out commercial drone flights must have permission from the Civil Aviation Authority (CAA) and abide by the regulations in relation to the size of aircraft being flown, areas of flight, due care and attention for aeroplane flight paths and for the safety of the general public.

5.11.1   Possible risks associated with drones

Failure of propulsion and/or control could cause the drone to hit people, property or the ground with the potential to cause serious injury or death (for example, a drone incident might cause a fire or a road traffic collision). Improper use of drones poses a threat to, and may breach, the privacy of people and property both on and adjacent to construction sites. This is of greater concern where sites are located in built-up areas that include houses, roads, schools and highways.

Appropriate airspace separation between unmanned and manned aircraft is essential. Regulations govern where, when and how drones may be operated. This includes the height at which drones may be flown, as well as permitted proximities to airfields. Professional and competent drone operators will be well informed as to how to carry out and complete their work safely and in compliance with all current regulations.

 Reportable occurrences

Be aware that certain types of incidents and accidents involving a drone may be reportable to the CAA and/or the Air Accidents Investigation Branch (commonly referred to as the AAIB). Your drone operator should know when and to whom such reporting is required. Mandatory reporting is the responsibility of the drone operator.

5.11.2   Reducing the risks associated with the use of drones

The following steps can be taken to reduce the risks posed by operating drones on construction sites.

Undertake basic drone training. Prepare staff who may be responsible for overseeing drone operations on site with a simple and broad appreciation of drone operations and their implications in the construction environment.

Choose a qualified and competent operator. Choose a drone operator (pilot) who is appropriately qualified and competent. Ask to see the operator's qualification and confirm their level of experience of carrying out similar tasks in similar environments.

Check permissions. All commercial drone operators are required by law to be holders of a permission issued by the CAA. Ask to see the operator's permission, check that it is in date and that the operator's planned activities are within the scope of the permission.

Task feasibility. Ensure that the operator is satisfied that the intended task is feasible for a drone to complete safely, effectively and in compliance with current regulations, and within the operator's permission.

Aircraft suitability and serviceability. Ask the operator to confirm that the drone is suitable for the task, has been regularly inspected and maintained and will function safely in the prevailing site conditions.

Suitable and sufficient resources. Check that the operator has allocated a competent pilot and identified sufficient support resources to complete the aerial data collection safely and effectively.

It is common for a drone operator to be accompanied by support personnel who will help monitor and manage the drone in flight, operate the payload (for example, a camera), and provide assistance on the ground (for example, managing pedestrian and vehicular traffic).

 All personnel should be trained and properly briefed by the drone operator before being assigned any duties.

Pre-flight planning. Before allowing any drone flights on site, ensure that your operator has undertaken and completed preflight planning and an on-site survey. Such planning should include a detailed risk assessment and the proposed method for carrying out the aerial work.

 All operational procedures should be detailed within the drone operator's operations manual, sight of which is recommended, prior to allowing any flights to be conducted.

Site induction. See that the operator and supporting personnel receive a full site induction before being allowed to carry out any work. Make sure that the operator is made aware of all site hazards which could pose a risk to the health, safety and welfare of personnel and/or which could compromise flight safety. Consider overhead hazards (for example, cranes, overhead power lines, tall structures and tree canopies).

Minimise flight time. Undertake detailed planning with the drone operator to minimise flight time and support the safe completion of the task.

 Reduced flight time generally equals reduced flight risk.

Establish a safe operating zone for the operator and support personnel, liaising on safe on-site locations for the following.

● An area for the operator to store and prepare equipment.

● A primary take off and landing zone.

● A secondary take off and landing zone (in case the primary location becomes unavailable).

● An appropriate place for the pilot and other personnel to stand, allowing safe and effective work whilst avoiding conflict with other site activities.

A safe, clearly marked take-off and landing zone

 Avoid unnecessary communication with the pilot during flights. This will allow them to focus on safe operation, minimising flight safety risks.

5.11.2.1 Minimise risk to those on the ground

Flying directly over people on the ground should be avoided. If flying above people cannot be avoided, it is essential that appropriate safety measures are put in place or that the persons affected are placed under the control of the person in charge of the drone.

 Risk mitigation measures to reduce the likelihood of causing harm include choosing a time when there are fewer people in the operating location (for example, during lunch or break periods, or at the start or end of the day).

5.11.3 On-site communications and emergency procedures

Discuss, agree and establish robust communication between the drone operator and the site management team. These must be appropriate to the site environment, the task and the operating conditions and risks. Discuss with the drone operator what emergency procedures are in place, in the event of an incident or accident involving the drone. Make sure that you are satisfied that these are appropriate, and that everyone understands what they need to do if there is an emergency.

5.11.4 Pilot considerations

Pilot health. Check that the pilot is satisfied that they are in a fit state of health to be able to operate the drone safely.

Avoid coercion or pressure on the pilot. The drone pilot must be satisfied that any proposed flight can be safely made. The pilot must not be pressurised or coerced to contravene safe operating protocols or to operate an aircraft when they do not consider it safe to do so.

 For further information about drones and UAVs visit the Civil Aviation Authority website and the Air Accidents Investigation Branch website.

Mobile work equipment

06

Supporting
INFORMATION

GT700 Toolbox talks / supporting checklists and forms

Toolbox talks on some of these topics are available in the GT700 publication. Supporting checklists and forms covering some of these topics are available on our companion website.

MOBILE WORK EQUIPMENT

Overview

A significant number of fatalities occur every year as a result of people being struck by moving vehicles. Many of these fatalities are caused by mobile plant. The majority could have been avoided by effective planning and control of mobile work equipment, adequate checking, inspection and maintenance of the plant, and thorough training, assessment and briefing of personnel.

This chapter gives an overview of the legal requirements for mobile work equipment and the steps required to ensure that these obligations are met so that mobile work equipment can be used safely and efficiently.

6.1   Introduction

The use and movement of mobile work equipment, whether over site roads or within specific areas, involves different and continually changing hazards. These have the potential to cause harm, such as persons being struck or run over, or thrown from or crushed by moving plant or equipment.

 Problems with mobile work equipment often occur because of poor communications when planning the work and briefing operators.

6.2   Important points

- Many accidents occur with mobile work equipment because operations were not properly planned in advance.

- Mobile work equipment should only be operated by trained, competent and authorised persons who have been properly briefed on the task to be carried out.

- The rated capacity or safe working load (SWL) of any item of mobile plant must never be exceeded.

- Mobile work equipment designed for specific operations must only be used for those operations. The design limitations and permitted modes of operation specified by the manufacturer must be complied with.

- All mobile work equipment must be subjected to a schedule of maintenance, inspections and thorough examination.

- Attention must also be paid to site features, such as overhead cables, excavations, unstable ground conditions and traffic and pedestrian routes.

- Mobile work equipment, first supplied after 1 January 1995, must be CE marked and meet the essential health and safety requirements of the Supply of Machinery (Safety) Regulations. Any equipment purchased from 1st January 2021 within the UK must show the UKCA marking. If imported from the EU, the product must also show the UKCA mark alongside the CE mark. Consequently, most items of lifting equipment are designed to a designated standard (such as BS EN 474-5:2022 for excavators, BS EN 1459 for telehandlers and BS EN 280-1:2022 for mobile elevating work platforms (MEWPs)).

6.3   Legislative requirements

 For a brief summary of the legislative requirements for mobile work equipment refer to Chapter C05 Work equipment and hand-held tools.

For more detailed information on legislation refer to Section A: *Legal and management*.

6.4   Types of mobile plant

By definition, mobile plant is plant that moves around a construction site, generally under its own power, and is driven or controlled by an operator. Mobile plant is subdivided into the four areas listed below.

6.4.1   Ride-on plant

Ride-on plant is where the operator sits/stands on the machine or in a cab (examples being rollers, excavators, loading shovels, rough terrain cranes, crawler cranes, self-propelled MEWPs, telehandlers, road planers, asphalt spreaders and dumpers).

Plant that is not designed to carry passengers should be provided with a notice clearly stating 'No passengers'.

People can only be carried if the vehicle has been designed for such a purpose.

Passengers and drivers must not be carried unless proper seating, correctly fitted to the main structure of the vehicle, is provided.

Where passengers are permitted to be carried, additional restraining devices must be provided for each person.

Where on-board work has to be carried out, seating should be provided, if possible, with work platforms fitted with suitable barriers or guard-rails to stop operatives falling from the equipment whilst it is in motion.

6.4.2 Pedestrian-controlled plant

This type of equipment relies heavily on the experience and competence of the operative for its safe operation. Small pedestrian-operated rollers, vibrating plate compactors and surface grinders are among the types of equipment within this category.

Common accidents involving pedestrian-operated equipment occur when operators are crushed between the machine and adjacent obstructions. This is one reason why the regulations require efficient emergency stop controls to be fitted.

This micro-surfacing machine is designed to carry more than one person

It is also essential that operators are provided with, and wear, strong protective footwear to prevent their feet from being injured.

6.4.3 Remote-controlled plant

The use of remote-controlled equipment is undertaken by specialists and is increasingly common on construction sites. It removes the operator from areas of danger as the equipment can be manoeuvred into hazardous or aggressive environments (such as enclosed spaces or unstable structures). The operator can then position themselves away from the dangers of falling material, dust, noise, fumes, vibration and moving parts of the machine. The equipment takes all of the risk and the operator is protected against hearing damage, deafness, hand-arm vibration syndrome (HAVS), whole-body vibration (WBV) and crushing from falling structures.

Common activities using remote-controlled equipment include demolition, core drilling, floor sawing and excavations in hazardous locations (for example, where there is a risk of rock fall).

6.4.4 Lifting equipment

 For further information on the lifting aspects of mobile plant that is also lifting equipment (such as mobile cranes, lorry loaders, MEWPs, telehandlers and excavators used for lifting) refer to Chapter C07 Lifting operations and Chapter C08 Lifting equipment.

6.5 Planning and use of mobile work equipment

The **Management of Health and Safety at Work Regulations** require that all tasks carried out at work are subject to a risk assessment to identify hazards and assess the risks associated with the task.

Planning a safe site should begin before the construction phase. In accordance with the **Construction (Design and Management) Regulations 2015** (CDM) there are specific duties placed on all of those involved within the construction process, including clients, principal designers, designers, principal contractors and contractors. The planning process for the use of mobile plant is similar to that for most other tasks, and consists of the following steps.

Step 1	Identifying the task to be undertaken.
Step 2	Identifying the hazards associated with the task.
Step 3	Carrying out a risk assessment.
Step 4	Identifying and implementing control measures.
Step 5	Developing the method to be used.
Step 6	Recording the planning in a method statement (including any contingency plans for rescue).
Step 7	Communicating the plan to all persons involved.
Step 8	Reviewing the plan before the task starts, periodically and incorporating any changing circumstances.

6.5.1 Practical measures for safe workplaces

The following practical measures should be considered to ensure that mobile work equipment can be used safely on site.

● Pedestrian routes should be established on site to facilitate safe pedestrian movement and access to work areas.

● Pedestrian routes should be segregated from mobile plant and vehicles, either by a safe distance or by physical barriers.

● Traffic routes should be planned in order to minimise disruption to neighbours, protect the public, avoid congestion and risk of collision. These routes should be kept free of obstructions and properly maintained, with access points restricted and clearly marked.

- Appropriate speed limits should be introduced.

- Set up vehicle-only areas, especially where space is limited or traffic is heavy.

- One-way traffic systems should be implemented, where possible.

- Parking places should be designated for delivery vehicles and other vehicles left temporarily on site.

- The operating area should be clear, as far as possible, on all sides.

- Operators must be informed of the location of any overhead power lines, sensitive areas, underground cables, sewers, ducts or services before operations commence.

- Excavations should be fenced or otherwise guarded.

- Ground conditions should be stable and sufficiently level for the operations being carried out and the equipment being used.

- Where equipment fitted with outriggers or stabilisers is used, the load-bearing capacity of the ground should be assessed so that the imposed loads do not exceed this capacity. An additional safety factor should also be applied.

- Where site vehicles are employed in tipping material into excavations, baulks of timber or other effective blocks (stop blocks) should be provided to prevent the vehicle over-running the edge.

- Excavations may require extra support or shoring to prevent the weight of adjacent vehicles causing a collapse (surcharging).

 For detailed guidance on the measures to be taken in planning for the use of mobile work equipment refer to the Health and Safety Executive (HSE) guidance *The safe use of vehicles on construction sites* (HSG144) and *Protecting the public: your next move* (HSG151).

6.5.2   Selection of mobile work equipment

In selecting the work equipment, every employer must take account of the working conditions and the risks to the health and safety of persons who are working in the vicinity of where the mobile equipment is to be used.

The design of some vehicles presents hazards, such as restricted visibility, lack of driver protection, exposure to noise and vibration and the risk of overturning.

6.5.2.1   Choosing the right equipment for the job

This is an essential part of effective management for mobile work equipment. The equipment selected needs to be capable of performing its designated tasks safely. Some important factors to consider are given below.

- Stability under all foreseeable operating conditions (for example, ground and weather conditions).

- Safe access to and from the cab and other working locations on the vehicle.

- Effective braking systems.

- Adequate visibility for the driver all around the vehicle, especially when reversing.

- Headlights, a horn, windscreen wipers and warning devices (such as reversing alarms).

- Physical guards to protect dangerous parts (such as power take-off shafts, chain drives, trapping points and exposed exhaust pipes).

- Protection for the driver from work hazards (such as working at height and falling from the vehicle, falling objects and the effects of the vehicle overturning).

- Protection for the driver from the weather, noise, vibration, fumes and dust.

Manufacturer's specifications need to be considered when selecting vehicles for construction and civil engineering work. In particular, load and stability limits need to be taken into account for vehicles intended to be used on uneven and sloping ground. Some vehicles, especially those involved in lifting operations (such as some lift trucks and telescopic handlers), require flat, compacted surfaces to operate safely.

6.5.2.2   Concrete pumps

All concrete pumping pours should be planned to ensure that they are completed safely and that all foreseeable risks have been taken into account. Planning should be carried out by personnel who have the appropriate expertise. In cases of repetitive concrete pours, this planning may only be necessary in the first instance, with periodic reviews to ensure that no factors have changed.

 For detailed guidance on the safe use of concrete pumps refer to the Construction Plant-hire Association's *Code of Practice for the safe use of concrete pumps*.

 Visit the Concrete Structures Group website for more information and guidance on the dangers of concrete pumping and pours, checks and inspections of pipelines, clearing of blockages, and the cleaning out process.

6.5.3 Braking systems

Effective braking systems are essential for the safe use of vehicles. In accordance with the Road Traffic Act parking brakes should be fitted on trailers over 0.75 tonnes maximum gross capacity. Where parking brakes are not fitted, trailer wheels need to be chained or locked to prevent movement when the trailer is parked. Wheel chocks should be used to prevent unintended vehicle and trailer movements. Trailers with maximum gross weights between 0.75 tonnes and 3.5 tonnes should have at least an overrun brake (such as an inertia brake), whereas trailers over 3.5 tonnes should be fitted with braking systems linked to the towing unit.

6.5.4 Roll-over protective structures

Where there is the risk of mobile work equipment rolling over, it should be fitted with roll-over protective structures (ROPS), such as reinforced cabs or a roll-cage, thereby minimising the risk of a person being crushed. The structure should give adequate clearance for operatives to escape if the equipment does completely overturn.

Where there is a risk of an operator being thrown then crushed by equipment rolling over, a suitable restraining system (such as a seat belt) should be fitted **and worn by the operator**. New mobile plant is fitted with green flashing lights on the outside of the cab that indicate that the seat belt is being worn.

This requirement may also apply to equipment fitted with a fully enclosed cab if there is a risk of a person who is thrown from their seat being injured by coming into contact with the internal cab structure.

Restraining systems must be fixed to a designated anchorage point on the main structure of the equipment.

In areas of limited access, ROPS may be removed only if a suitable and sufficient risk assessment has been carried out and there is no risk of overturning. The ROPS structure should be refitted when the machine is put back to work in areas where space is not restricted. An assessment should be made of the likelihood and potential consequences of a vehicle roll-over or overturn on site, and the nature of the mobile work equipment and any attachments or accessories fitted to it.

ROPS and FOPS cab

 Wearing seat belts

Telehandler cabs are provided with seat belts to restrain the operator and reduce the risk of serious injury in the event of the machine overturning. A survey of telehandler accidents in the UK carried out by the Health and Safety Executive (HSE) shows that in seven years there were at least 72 lateral overturns of telehandlers. In three cases, the operator was killed by being ejected from the cab and crushed; in a further two cases, the operator was ejected from the cab and received serious crushing injuries. Had these operators been wearing their seat belts, their deaths or injuries would probably have been avoided.

6.5.5 Falling object protective structures

Where there is the risk to persons operating mobile work equipment of being struck by falling material, falling object protective structures (FOPS) or a manufacturer's strengthened cab must be fitted to stop any falling material striking the operator.

6.5.6 Prevention of unauthorised start-up

Unauthorised persons must be prevented from starting up self-propelled mobile work equipment wherever it is parked. Additionally, it must be possible to isolate the drive mechanism. This can be achieved by simple measures (such as the removal of ignition keys or starting handles), the use of more sophisticated systems (such as keypad or smart card isolators), or remotely controlled systems and effective vehicle immobilisation systems and key custody procedures.

 Some old designs of site dumpers allowed the vehicle to be knocked easily into gear as the driver dismounted.

6.5.7 Lighting and warnings

When self-propelled mobile work equipment is used in the dark or in reduced visibility, lights must be fitted and used to enable the work area to be adequately illuminated. In addition, amber flashing beacons that give warning of the presence of the vehicle should be fitted and used. The site traffic management plan may dictate that construction vehicles are fitted with audible reversing warning devices or CCTV.

6.5.8   All-round visibility

Accidents involving mobile work equipment and pedestrians frequently involve poor visibility where the plant operator has not seen the pedestrian. Current standards aim to ensure that the operator of the plant or vehicle has all-round vision from the operating position.

Therefore, plant needs to be assessed to ensure that the existing levels of visibility meet the requirements of the Provision and Use of Work Equipment Regulations (PUWER), published guidance and your own safe system of work.

All-round visibility

❗ It is generally accepted that the operator should be able to see, at all times, an object positioned 1 m above ground level and 1 m away from the plant through 360° visibility.

All-round visibility can usually be achieved by the use of aids, such as additional mirrors, convex mirrors or CCTV.

Where this is not possible, consideration should be given to providing a competent, qualified vehicle marshaller working exclusively with the plant operator and implementing exclusion zones to prevent unauthorised access into any danger zones. *(For further information on plant safe zones refer to 6.6.)*

6.5.9   Forward-tipping dumpers

Amongst mobile work equipment, forward-tipping site dumpers are worthy of special note because they are involved in a disproportionately high number of accidents.

This applies to both rigid-frame and articulated dumpers.

In recognition of the high number of accidents, and to improve the welfare and working conditions of operators, dumpers are now available with protective cabs and enhanced safety features.

Forward-tipping dumper - bad practice: travelling with a raised skip

✋ Over 60% of dumper-related deaths involve the driver when the vehicle overturns. Most other deaths occur when pedestrians are struck by the dumper whilst it is in operation.

The common causes of these accidents are shown below.

● Overturning on slopes, rough ground and at the edges of excavations.

● Travelling with a high-lift skip in the raised position.

● The operator failing to observe pedestrians, who are then run over by the front wheels.

● The operator being thrown from the vehicle whilst travelling over rough or sloping ground.

● Operator error due to lack of experience and training, including accidental operation of the controls.

Efforts to reduce dumper accidents should focus on the following.

● Selecting the correct machine for the job.

● Effective site management and control of how dumpers are operated generally.

● Ensuring that machines are routinely inspected, serviced and withdrawn from use if unsafe.

● Ensuring that site roads and operating areas are suitable, maintained and safe for the use of dumpers.

● Ensuring that only trained, competent and authorised operators are allowed to operate dumpers.

🌐 For detailed guidance on the safe use of forward-tipping dump trucks refer to the HSE publication *Construction site transport safety: safe use of site dumpers* (CIS52) and the Construction Plant-hire Association's *Staying safe when operating forward tipping dumpers*.

The HSE has produced an ACoP on *Rider-operated lift trucks* (L117), which outlines the main legal requirements of use.

6.5.10 Quick hitches

The quick hitches fitted to excavators and other earthmoving equipment make a valuable contribution to the construction process by enabling buckets and other attachments to be attached and detached rapidly.

Unfortunately there have been a significant number of accidents involving the use of quick hitches, which have included fatalities.

When using quick hitches, the important safety precautions (listed below) should be observed. These precautions are applicable to all types of quick hitch – manual, semi-automatic and all fully automatic types, including those that lock onto both pins.

All types of quick hitches can be safely used by competent people within a safe system of work. This will involve planning, training, instruction, communication, supervision and maintenance.

 Site management should familiarise themselves with the different types of quick hitches, and any related company policy, to assess and monitor what contractors should be doing to manage the risk.

- Keep other workers away from the machine's working range. Never work under the bucket or attachment and ensure that the operator isolates the controls if there are other workers in the machine's working range. Ensure that your site supervisors or vehicle marshallers enforce this rule.

- Make sure that your operators are aware of their personal and legal responsibility to use all quick hitches safely. Serious misuse of quick hitches should always be treated as gross misconduct, which could lead to dismissal or individual prosecution.

- Prohibit practices (such as pick and place) that involve moving attachments without properly engaging the locking devices.

- Check that all operators confirm that the quick hitch is in place every time they change an attachment. It is essential that this is done by close inspection at the quick hitch, which will normally entail the operator getting down from the cab. It is good practice to make this a requirement for all quick hitches.

- Check that site supervisors understand that the operator has to fully confirm that the quick hitch is in place and allow operators time to do this.

- Check that site supervisors monitor that operators are confirming proper engagement, by spot checks. (Avoid conflict by ensuring that all operators understand and buy into the reasons why the supervisor has to carry out spot checks.)

- Check that machines are in good order, and all quick hitches are included in the maintenance plan and subject to proper maintenance.

- Check that operators and maintenance personnel have specific manufacturer instructions for the combination of machine, quick hitch and attachment.

- Confirm that operators are competent to use the specific quick hitch in accordance with the manufacturer's instructions and the safe system of work.

Keep other workers away whilst changing buckets or attachments

e.g. Using quick hitches with other attachments

Contractors may want to use quick hitches with attachments other than a bucket in normal configuration.

However, if a specific application (such as the fitting of vibratory hammers or reversing of buckets) is not explicitly referenced by the manufacturer, the user should assume that it is not allowed, and should not use the quick hitch for this attachment or application.

Quick hitches should be used only with attachments and in applications as specified by the manufacturer.

 It is essential that operators get out of the cab to physically ensure that all quick hitches are securely locked before starting work with a newly fitted attachment.

 For detailed guidance on quick hitches refer to the Strategic Forum for Construction's *Safe use of quick hitches on excavators* (Best practice guide).

6.6 Plant safe zones

The following diagrams are for guidance purposes, and show the safe zones applicable to a range of plant machinery likely to be used on site.

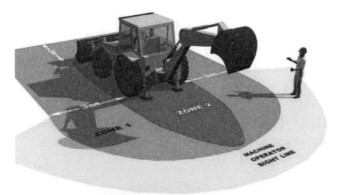

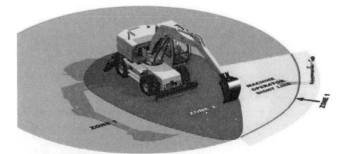

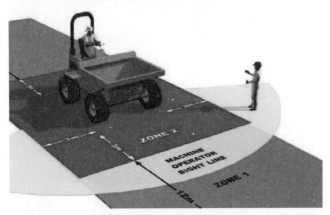

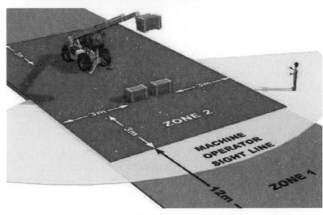

(Reproduced from The Delivery Hub health, safety and environment – Raising the bar 1 – Plant and equipment *from the Highways Agency, under licence of the Controller of Her Majesty's Stationery Office.)*

❗ Always signal the operator and receive a positive response before entering Zone 1.

Keep out of Zone 2 at all times.

6.7 Training and competence of personnel

It is essential that all involved in planning, supervising and carrying out mobile plant operations are adequately trained and competent. There are a number of nationally-recognised card schemes that provide evidence of training. The Construction Plant Competence Scheme (CPCS) also provides proof of competence, evidenced by endorsement with the CSCS logo on their card. It is, however, each employer's responsibility to ensure that employees and those working under their control are competent to undertake the tasks they have been allocated.

It is also important that mobile plant operators hold appropriate qualifications and endorsement for each different plant category they operate. Before allowing employees to operate plant, check that they are trained and that their industry card is endorsed with the right category (for example, 360 excavator, dumper, or telehandler). In addition, operators must be familiar with the specific machine they are operating.

Mobile work equipment comes in many shapes and sizes, with significant differences in control layouts and operating characteristics. It is therefore essential that operators are given **adequate familiarisation** before use. This is generally carried out by an experienced person employed by the equipment owner. Training should include control layouts for particular machine models, starting and stopping (including emergency stops), operating characteristics, emergency procedures (such as for spills, fire and overturn), and inspection and maintenance checks. Records should be maintained for all familiarisation training, clearly indicating makes and models covered.

www Details of the Construction Plant Competence Scheme (CPCS) can be found online.

Worker's head struck with an excavator bucket

A construction worker has been prosecuted after he struck another worker on the head with the bucket of an excavator. He was prosecuted after an investigation found he had been using a mobile phone whilst operating the excavator on a building site, and had not noticed his colleague.

The construction worker was working alongside a colleague who was driving a site dumper truck. The operation involved excavating and dumping material into the truck for transport to another location at the site. The court heard that the driver of the dumper truck had returned to the excavation site to await the next load of material. The construction worker had been using his mobile phone and, not realising his colleague had returned, rotated the upper body of the excavator, causing the metal bucket to strike the driver on the side of his head.

The driver sustained multiple fractures to his jaw, as well as a punctured and collapsed lung. He was hospitalised for ten days and did not return to work until 14 months later, with further surgery still required on his jaw. The construction worker was ordered to pay compensation of £2,500 to the injured worker, and costs of £1,554 after pleading guilty to a single breach of the Health and Safety at Work etc. Act 1974.

Speaking after the hearing, the HSE inspector said: 'Construction site vehicles are extremely powerful and, if the operator becomes distracted, can be highly dangerous. Road users are rightly banned from using mobile phones when driving cars. It's clearly important that those in control of machinery – weighing up to 40 tonnes in some cases – need to be equally attentive and concentrate solely on the job at hand. This incident could easily have been avoided if the operator had followed site rules and not become complacent about his responsibilities when operating his vehicle.' *(Source: HSE.)*

 For detailed guidance on plant operator competence refer to the Strategic Forum for Construction Plant Safety Group's *Competence to operate construction plant* (Good practice guide).

6.7.1   Medical fitness

People who operate mobile equipment have the potential to injure both themselves and others in the workplace and the surrounding area. Ensuring that operators are medically fit to operate is primarily an issue for employers, who have a duty to ensure that any employee is physically and mentally capable of undertaking the tasks they are required to carry out. Others in the construction sector (such as principal and sub-contractors) will also have an interest in ensuring operators have an appropriate level of fitness.

 For detailed guidance on medical fitness refer to the Strategic Forum for Construction Plant Safety Group's *Medical fitness to operate construction plant* (Good practice guide).

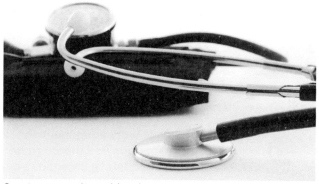
Operators may need to participate in an assessment to ascertain medical fitness

6.7.2   Supervision

An essential part of the safe use of mobile work equipment is supervision of the operator. The supervisor is required to re-brief the operator and others on the task and ensure they are put to work safely.

- Reinforce the main elements of the safe system of work, including:
  - strict adherence to exclusion zones
  - the correct safe methods when fitting/removing attachments (such as the use of quick hitches)
  - consulting the operator and others regarding any issues/comments they have in adhering to or the effectiveness of the safe system of work and, where appropriate, instigate changes.
- Check that the operator has undertaken the relevant daily checks.
- Check the required maintenance has been undertaken.
- Ensure the inspection/maintenance log/check sheet has been completed and signed. The supervisor's signature on the check list/log may be used as verification that they have carried out the check.

As part of the supervisor's ongoing duties, they must, throughout the day, monitor that the safe system of work is being adhered to. This should include maintenance of exclusion zones, checking that no-one is working below attachments at any time, and ensuring quick hitches are being used according to the manufacturer's recommendations, including correct use of any safety pins or locking devices. They should regularly check that the manufacturer's manual for operating the machine is in the cab, that any relevant instructional decals (durable stickers) are displayed in the cab and/or on the machine, and that the next service or inspection date has not expired. The daily checklist for the machine will provide evidence of some of these points.

6.8   Maintenance, checks and inspections

Maintenance, checks and inspections of mobile work equipment are essential if they are not to deteriorate, break down and ultimately fail.

All maintenance should be carried out by a competent person who is familiar with the equipment and has the knowledge and experience to identify and repair existing or potential faults.

The maintenance should be in accordance with the manufacturer's instructions and be carried out, as a minimum, at the recommended intervals.

All mobile work equipment should have a pre-use check carried out daily or at the start of each shift and any defects reported to a supervisor. This is normally undertaken by the operator who should be trained to carry out the checks.

In addition to pre-use checks, inspections should be carried out at appropriate intervals, either as part of the maintenance process or at more frequent intervals.

The frequency of inspections will depend on the working environment and assessment of the risk of failure of the equipment, and should be guided by the manufacturer's instructions.

A mobile lighting tower may not have a designated operator but should still be subject to pre-use checks

The results of all checks and inspections should be recorded and there should be a system in place to ensure that all reported defects are rectified and recorded.

Keep the following points in mind when planning for checks, maintenance and inspections.

- The equipment's potential to cause serious harm (powered machinery, such as a circular saw, will require more regular attention than a hammer).

- Type, class and complexity of equipment (some equipment requires weekly maintenance, others less frequent maintenance).

- Equipment in regular use will probably require more frequent maintenance than equipment used infrequently.

- Likely deterioration of work equipment when not in use.

- The environment in which the equipment is used (for example, an excavator used in a civil engineering project, such as sea defence work during the winter, will have the potential to deteriorate faster than an identical machine used in a less hostile environment).

 Each item of mobile work equipment should have a history file containing all records of maintenance, inspection and thorough examination, so that maintenance trends can be established and adequate maintenance demonstrated in the event of an accident.

 For guidance on construction plant handover and inspection reports refer to Appendix A.

Appendix A – Construction plant handover and inspection report guidance

These guidance notes are provided to assist the persons appointed by the site manager to complete reports.

Mobile plant is defined as mechanical or electrical plant that is self-propelled. The types of plant typically covered by the mobile plant handover report are as follows.

- All types of excavator.
- All forward or rearward tipping dumpers/trucks.
- All types of cranes.
- All types of compacting rollers.
- Rough terrain forklift trucks.
- Tractors and their trailer units.

In the case of plant provided by a plant hirer, then, at the site manager's discretion, a competent person appointed by the plant hirer may conduct the inspection and complete the report.

In the case of plant owned or hired by a contractor, then a competent person employed by the contractor may conduct the inspection and complete the report.

All completed mobile plant handover reports should be retained for inspection on site.

The report is produced in a checklist format for ease of use and is intended to provide a means by which the condition of all plant delivered to site can be checked by the appointed person. All questions should record an answer, with a suitable comment or action included when necessary.

The appointed person is also required to confirm the validity of relevant statutory documentation (such as test certificates, thorough examination and inspection reports).

An aide memoire is provided below to assist the appointed person on statutory requirements that apply to certain items of plant.

Plant	Thorough examination	Comments	Documentation
All types of cranes used for lifting people and mobile elevating work platforms (MEWPs).	Current six-monthly thorough examination report.	■ Fitted with suitable devices to prevent persons being crushed, trapped, struck or falling when riding or working from carrier. ■ Provision of suitable devices to prevent risk of a carrier failing. ■ Safe means of escape for persons trapped in a carrier.	Evidence of daily or weekly inspection and six-monthly thorough examination, including certification of the rated capacity (SWL).
Excavators used as cranes without any restriction and a fixed or variable rated capacity (SWL) greater than one tonne.	Current 12-monthly thorough examination report.	■ Fitted with controlled lowering devices (check valves). ■ Provided with a properly fitted hook or lifting shackle marked with the rated capacity (SWL). ■ Supplied with a register for the weekly inspections of the excavator and, where fitted, rated capacity indicator. ■ Have the rated capacity (SWL) clearly marked on the machine or displayed in the cab.	Evidence of daily or weekly inspection and 12-monthly thorough examination, including certification of the rated capacity (SWL).
All types of cranes and excavators used as cranes without restrictions and a fixed rated capacity (SWL) of one tonne or less.	Current 12-monthly thorough examination report.	■ Provided with properly fitted hook or lifting shackle marked with the rated capacity (SWL). ■ Supplied with a register for weekly inspections of the machine and, where fitted, a rated capacity indicator. ■ Have the rated capacity (SWL) clearly marked on the machine or displayed in the cab.	Evidence of daily or weekly inspection and 12-monthly thorough examination, including certification of the rated capacity (SWL).

 Following completion of the report at receipt of the plant on site, formal inspection/examination must be repeated at least at the intervals specified by legislation or policy.

06

Lifting operations

GT700 Toolbox talks / supporting checklists and forms

Toolbox talks on some of these topics are available in the GT700 publication. Supporting checklists and forms covering some of these topics are available on our companion website.

Supporting
INFORMATION

LIFTING OPERATIONS

Overview

There are a number of fatalities and a significant number of specified injuries in the construction industry each year as a result of poorly-planned lifting operations. In addition, many more incidents lead to property, material and equipment damage, resulting in costly delays.

The majority of these could have been avoided by effective planning and control of the lifting operations, thorough examination of lifting equipment and thorough training, assessment and briefing of personnel.

This chapter gives an overview of the legal requirements for lifting operations and the steps required to ensure that these obligations are met so that lifting operations can be carried out safely and efficiently.

7.1 Introduction

Experience has shown that lifting operations can be a hazardous activity if not properly planned and carried out.

Safe lifting operations will depend upon the following.

● Thorough pre-planning of each lifting operation.

● The availability of suitable lifting equipment, which is properly maintained.

● The provision of adequate information, instruction, training and supervision for everyone involved.

● Compliance with safe systems of work, as detailed in risk assessments and method statements (lifting plan).

Although regulations require that safe systems of work are developed, accidents occurring during lifting operations indicate that all too often these are not in place or are not complied with.

Lifting operations have the potential to cause death and serious injury to site workers and members of the public off site. In addition to the terrible cost in human suffering, accidents have a financial cost.

There is a strong business case for improving safety performance in this area.

 Problems with lifting operations often occur because of poor communication during planning and when lifting.

 The requirements for installing, operating, checking, maintaining, inspecting and thoroughly examining specific types of lifting equipment and lifting accessories are covered in Chapter C08 Lifting equipment.

7.2 Important points

● Many accidents occur during lifting operations that were not properly planned in advance.

● All site features (such as overhead cables, unstable ground conditions and adjacent properties) must be identified and adequately controlled as part of the planning process.

● All lifting operations must be carried out by, and under the control of, trained and competent persons who have been properly briefed on the lifting plan.

● Effective communication during any lifting operation is vital to ensure the safety of those involved and to protect people in the vicinity. This also applies to the planning phase.

● Specific requirements apply to the lifting of people.

● A contract lift will transfer the majority of the legal responsibility for carrying out the lifting operation in a safe manner to the contract lift company. (Companies without the specialist knowledge to plan lifts safely should always procure contract lifts.)

 The collapse, overturning or failure of any load-bearing part of a hoist, crane or other lifting equipment is a reportable dangerous occurrence, even if nobody is injured.

 For further information refer to Chapter A13 Accident reporting and investigation.

7.3 Legislative requirements

A brief summary of the main legislative requirements for lifting operations is listed below.

7.3.1 Provision and Use of Work Equipment Regulations (PUWER)

PUWER are concerned with such matters as the selection of suitable work equipment, safeguarding of dangerous parts of machinery, provision of appropriate controls, training of operators, and the inspection and maintenance of work equipment, including lifting equipment and accessories.

 For further guidance on PUWER refer to the HSE's ACoP and guidance *Safe use of work equipment* (L22).

7.3.2 Lifting Operations and Lifting Equipment Regulations (LOLER)

LOLER deal with the specific risks arising from the use of lifting equipment (including lifting accessories). They build upon PUWER in many areas and apply to all lifting operations, equipment and accessories. LOLER requirements are shown below.

- All lifting operations are planned, supervised and carried out safely.
- Pre-use checks and inspections at appropriate intervals are carried out on lifting equipment.
- Specific requirements are applied to the lifting of people.
- Lifting equipment must be thoroughly examined by a competent person (equipment examination) on specified occasions and at specified intervals.

 For further guidance on LOLER refer to the HSE's ACoP and guidance *Safe use of lifting equipment* (L113).

 For a list of definitions refer to Appendix A.

7.4 Planning of lifting operations

The siting, setting up and use of equipment for lifting operations requires careful planning to ensure the safety of all involved and others who could be affected. One person with sufficient training, practical and theoretical knowledge and experience should be appointed to be responsible for planning and supervising the tasks, known as the *competent person* in LOLER or the *appointed person* in the *Code of Practice for the safe use of cranes* (BS 7121). For the purposes of clarity in this chapter, *competent person* and *appointed person* are referred to as the *competent person (lift planner)*. Where reference is made to a competent person in relation to equipment examination, they will be referred to as *competent person (equipment examination)*. The competent person (lift planner) must ensure that the planning for each task includes the following.

- Identifying the task to be undertaken.
- Surveying the site.
- Identifying the hazards associated with the task.
- Categorising the lift (1, 2 or 3, dependent on complexity).
- Carrying out a risk assessment.
- Identifying the need for over-sailing licences for neighbouring properties (see 8.5.1.1 for more detail).
- Identifying control measures.
- Developing the method to be used.
- Selecting lifting equipment and lifting accessories.
- Recording the lifting plan with a method statement (including any contingency work for rescue).
- Communicating the plan to all persons involved.
- Reviewing the plan immediately before the task starts and responding to any changing circumstances.

Lifting operations, no matter how large or small, must be properly planned

The planning of lifting operations includes the consideration of 'temporary works', such as working platforms, outrigger pads, lifting beams and load spreaders (see Chapter C04 Temporary works). This necessitates liaison between the appointed person (competent person/lift planner) and the TWC(s).

07

LIFTING OPERATIONS

7.4.1   Identifying the task to be undertaken

As the first stage in the planning process, the task to be undertaken should be clearly identified, together with the location and sequence.

Certain lifting operations require particular care and attention. Further advice can be found in BS 7121 Part 1. The competent person (lift planner) should be familiar with these and plan the lift accordingly.

7.4.2   Surveying the site

The planning of a lift may involve a site survey, carried out by the competent person (lift planner) or their representative. This involves visiting the location where the lift is to be carried out so that both the task and any hazards involved can be identified. For simple lifts the remainder of the planning process may be completed at the same time, whilst for more complex jobs the person carrying out the survey may need to complete the process off site. The survey should include the assessment and confirmation of ground conditions (ground bearing capacity).

A further site survey may be required immediately before the lifting operation is to be started to ensure no changes have been made to the environment.

7.4.3   Identifying the hazards associated with the task

The hazards associated with the task should be identified. These might be associated with the location where the work is to be carried out, the nature of the lifting equipment, the load to be lifted or the people associated with the task or located in the vicinity.

7.4.4   Categorising the lift

To enable lifts to be planned, supervised and carried out effectively, three categories of lift are detailed below. The category into which a particular lift will fall depends on the assessment of the hazards associated with both the environment in which the lift is to be carried out and with the load.

As shown in the table, increases in environmental and/or load complexity (the *complexity index*) will lead to the lift being allocated a higher category. Having identified the hazards associated with a particular lift, a hierarchy of control measures should be applied to eliminate or control those hazards.

Relationship between complexity index and lift category

7.4.4.1   Basic lift

For a basic lift, the duties of the competent person (lift planner) should include the following.

● Establishing the complexity of the lifting operation, including load and environmental complexity.

 – Load complexity will include characteristics such as weight, centre of gravity and presence of suitable lifting points. This can be established by an authentic and reliable source of information, measuring and weighing the load, or calculation.

   Note: where the weight of the load cannot be accurately established, the notional weight must be multiplied by an appropriate factor (typically 1.5) to allow for possible inaccuracies.

 – Consideration of environmental hazards at the location of the operation will include the access and egress required for the lifting equipment, the location of overhead power lines or existing structures and the suitability of the ground to take the loads imposed by the lifting equipment during preparation for the lift and during the lift itself.

● Selecting the lifting equipment, based on the load characteristics (including weight of the load and any lifting points and accessories), the maximum height of lift and the maximum radius required. The rated capacity (safe working load (SWL)) of the lifting equipment should be specified by the manufacturer/installer in the user information supplied with the lifting equipment. **In cases where the lifting equipment has been derated at the time of thorough examination, the rated capacity (SWL) stated on the current report of thorough examination, issued by the competent person (equipment examination), should be used.** Manufacturer's sales leaflets and model classifications marked on the machine should not be relied on for the rated capacity (SWL) of specific lifting equipment.

● Ensuring that the lifting equipment is not operated in wind speeds in excess of those given in the instruction manual for the lifting equipment. The wind area of the load should also be taken into account to ensure that movement in the wind does not present a hazard.

● Ensuring that the lifting equipment has been thoroughly examined within the previous 12 months (or six months for equipment used for the lifting of persons). It is essential that the report of thorough examination, which confirms that the equipment is safe to use, is available. After installation or assembly ensure the equipment is inspected and checked before first use to confirm it has been installed correctly.

 Note: the report of thorough examination for the lifting equipment should be carried with the machine.

● Selecting appropriate lifting accessories, including their method of attachment to the load, configuration and any protection used to prevent damage.

- Ensuring that lifting accessories have been thoroughly examined, within the previous six months, inspected and checked before use. It is essential that the report of thorough examination is available to confirm that the lifting accessories are safe to use.

- Ensuring that a system for reporting and rectifying defects is in place.

- Designating a suitable person to check the lifting accessories and any lifting points that are provided on the load to ensure they are free from any obvious defect before attaching the load to the lifting equipment.

- Ensuring that the outcomes of the planning process are recorded in a risk assessment and method statement, which should be signed by the competent person (lift planner).
  Note: in many instances, a basic lift may be covered by a generic risk assessment and a generic method statement, provided that no additional hazards are identified on site.

- Selecting and defining the roles of the members of the lifting team. In many instances it may be possible to combine some of the roles of members of the lifting team.

- Briefing all persons involved in the lifting operation to ensure that the safe system of work described in the method statement is understood. All persons involved in the lifting operation should be instructed to seek advice from the competent person (lift planner) if any change is required to the lifting operation, or if any doubts about safety arise. If one or more handlines/taglines are required to give more control of the load, the competent person (lift planner) should designate persons to handle the lines.

- Where numerous repeat loads are to be lifted over a long period of time regular checking must be in place to confirm that no environmental changes have occurred requiring changes in the safe system of work.

- Ensuring that there is a lift (crane) supervisor designated to direct personnel and that the operation is carried out in accordance with the method statement.

The competent person (lift planner) and lift (crane) supervisor should be aware of the limits of their knowledge and experience concerning lifting operations and, when conditions exceed these limits, further advice should be sought.

7.4.4.2   Intermediate lift

For an intermediate lift, the duties of the competent person (lift planner) should include the following, in addition to the duties listed above.

- Identifying all significant hazards in the operating area, including any areas required for access or setting up of the lifting equipment.
  Note: this may involve the competent person (lift planner) visiting site if there are any concerns about the detail and quality of the information with which the competent person (lift planner) has been provided.

- Ensuring that a site/task-specific risk assessment and method statement, detailing control measures for the identified risks, is prepared.

- Liaising with any other person or authority, as required, to overcome any hazard, by including any necessary corrective action or special measures in the safe system of work.

- Determining any requirement for extra personnel in addition to the lifting equipment operator (such as a slinger, signaller or dedicated lift (crane) supervisor).

- Considering the effect of the lifting operation on surrounding property or persons, including the general public, and arranging for appropriate action to minimise any adverse effects, giving appropriate notice to all persons concerned.

7.4.4.3   Complex lift

For a complex lift the duties of the competent person (lift planner) should include the following, in addition to the duties listed for basic and intermediate lifts.

- Identifying all exceptional hazards in the operating area, including any areas required for access or setting up of the lifting equipment. This will require the competent person (lift planner) to visit the location of the planned lifting operation as part of the planning process.

- Ensuring that the method statement includes the exact sequence of operations when lifting the load.

- Preparing a sufficiently detailed and dimensioned drawing of the site, lifting equipment and the load, identifying the load path, pick up and set down areas, together with the position of any exceptional hazards in the area (for example railway lines). The information provided should be sufficient to enable the operator to position the lifting equipment accurately.

It is good practice for the competent person (lift planner) to be present on the site during a complex lift.

 Complexity of a lift

The case study in Appendix B illustrates the way in which both the complexity of the load being lifted and the environment in which the lift is taking place affect the overall complexity of the lift. The case study takes a typical construction lifting operation: the lifting of a generator and fuel tank.

Three different situations are evaluated, with examples of the hazards encountered and the control measures required to eliminate or reduce those hazards to an acceptable level.

It should be noted that this is an example, and does not identify all the hazards that may be present in a given circumstance.

LIFTING OPERATIONS

7.4.5 Carrying out a risk assessment

Having identified the hazards associated with the task, a risk assessment should be carried out to identify who might be harmed, the chance of them being harmed and the consequences of any harm.

This assessment should be recorded.

7.4.6 Identifying control measures

Once the risk assessment has highlighted the risks involved in the task, the procedures and measures required to control them should be identified and implemented.

7.4.7 Developing the method to be used

Having identified the hazards, evaluated the risks and worked out the control measures required to carry out the task safely, these components should be developed into a coherent plan. Any contingency measures and rescue procedures should be included in the plan.

7.4.8 Selecting lifting equipment and lifting accessories

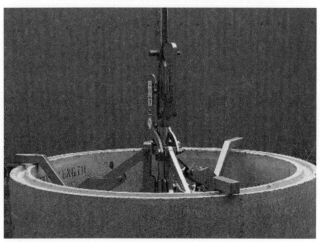

A proprietary inspection chamber lifting attachment

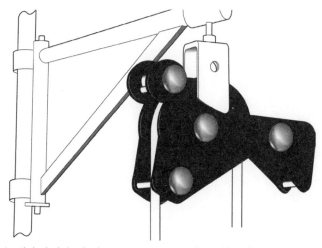

Inertia braked gin wheels are now common practice and far safer than traditional gin wheels

LOLER require that lifting equipment and lifting accessories are of adequate strength and stability for the load being lifted.

Consider the following when selecting lifting equipment and lifting accessories for a particular task.

- Weight, dimensions and characteristics of the loader (lifting equipment) and the loads to be lifted.
- Operation, speed, radius and height of lift and areas of movement.
- Number, frequency and types of lifting operation.
- Space available for lifting equipment access, deployment (including the space required for correct deployment of stabilisers), operation and storage for accessories and times of inactivity.
- Control position that will be most suitable for the lifting operation (the control position should be selected to ensure that the operator has an adequate view of the load path and is adequately protected from crushing hazards).
- Need for motion-limiting devices (such as slewing arc or height limiters).
- Effect of the operating environment on the lifting equipment.

7.4.9 Recording the method in a lift plan

Once the method has been developed, it should then be recorded in a lift plan. The length and detail of this document depends on the complexity of the task to be undertaken, and on the risks involved.

A simple, low-risk job (such as a routine delivery and unloading of bulk materials or blocks to site) might only require the use of a brief, generic plan, whilst a more complex and high-risk job (such as delivering, unloading, assembling and lifting into position a loading platform on a construction site) would require a more detailed job specific plan.

The method statement covering all planned lifting on a site is often referred to as the lift plan.

Telehandlers should have, and follow, a lift plan

07

The lift plan should include a lifting schedule, listing each type of item to be lifted, together with the following information.

- Item description.
- Weight.
- Dimensions.

- Lifting points and method of attachment.
- Type of lifting accessories to be used and configuration.
- Pick up and landing locations referenced to the site plan.

7.4.10 Communicating the plan to all persons involved

One of the most important aspects of successful planning is to ensure that the contents of the plan are communicated effectively to and between all parties involved, taking account of language differences. Arrangements should be made to ensure that copies of any method statements are given to the appropriate people and that others involved or affected by the operation are fully briefed. Similarly, any changes to the plan should be communicated to all parties.

7.4.11 Reviewing the plan before the job starts

Immediately before a job starts, the risk assessment and method statement (lift plan) should be reviewed to check if any aspects of the operation or working environment have changed and assess the effect that these changes could have on the safety of the people involved. Where changes are identified, the competent person (lift planner) should amend the lift plan and sign any significant changes with their initials. If any modifications to the plan are required these should be communicated to all those involved.

For further guidance on planning of lifting and installation refer to:

- *Code of Practice for safe use of cranes – Part 1 General and Part 3 Mobile cranes* (BS 7121)
- HSE leaflet *Risk assessment. A brief guide to controlling risks in the workplace* (INDG163)
- CIRIA publication *Crane stability on site* (C703).

7.4.12 Hired cranes

In construction, mobile cranes are generally hired by the user on site from the crane owner. The two ways of doing this are by hiring a crane (hired crane) or employing a contractor to carry out the lifting operation (contract lift). The difference between the two options is summarised below.

7.4.12.1 Hired crane (hired and managed)

With a hired lift you are hiring the crane and crane operator. You will be provided with a lift supervisor, slinger or an appointed person. The employing organisation should ensure the following.

- Carry out all work in accordance with BS 7121.
- Supply the competent person (lift planner).
- Plan the lift and operate a safe system of work.

- Confirm that the crane hired is of a suitable type and capacity.
- Check the credentials of the crane company and certification supplied.

The crane owner has a duty to provide a crane that is properly maintained, tested and certified, and a competent operator.

7.4.12.2 Contract lift (fully contracted)

With a contract lift you will not only be hiring the crane and operators, you will also be hiring the services of the crane company to organise and carry out the whole lift operation. The employing organisation should specify the following.

- That all work is to be undertaken in accordance with BS 7121.
- The ground bearing capacity.
- The dimensions and weight of the load to be lifted.

- That the lifting contractor is to supply the competent person (lift planner).
- What other information and/or services will be provided to the lifting contractor by the employing organisation.

The lifting contractor is responsible for the following.

- Supplying the competent person (lift planner).
- Planning the lift and operating a safe system of work.

- Organising and controlling the lifting operation.

If an individual or organisation does not have expertise in lifting operations they should not hire cranes but should opt for a contract lift.

Before entering into a contract, the employing organisation should satisfy itself that the contractor has the necessary competence to carry out the work.

For further detailed guidance on crane hire and contract lifts refer to the Construction Plant-hire Association's *Crane hire and contract lifting* (Best practice guide).

7.5 Siting of lifting equipment

For further detailed guidance on the siting of lifting equipment refer to:

- *Code of Practice for safe use of cranes – Parts 1, 3, 4 and 5 (BS 7121)*

- *Code of Practice for the safe use of construction hoists (BS 7212)*

 - *Code of Practice for the installation, maintenance, thorough examination and safe use of mast climbing work platforms (MCWPs) (BS 7981)*

- *Code of Practice for the safe use of MEWPs (BS 8460)*

- CIRIA publication *Crane stability on site* (C703)

- Strategic Forum Plant Safety Group publication *Ground conditions for construction plant* (2014).

The area where lifting equipment is to be sited must be carefully assessed, before the equipment is brought to site and put into service, to ensure it is suitable. During this assessment the following points should be considered.

7.5.1 Clearances

The area chosen must be of a sufficient size to enable the lifting equipment to be manoeuvred into position, assembled, set up or installed, operated and stowed (fixed closed position), with sufficient clearances between the lifting equipment and surrounding structures, as detailed in the manufacturer's operation and instruction manual.

This is to ensure that crush zones are not created, and that damage does not occur to either the lifting equipment or the surrounding structures.

A gap into which persons may enter, which may be reduced by a slewing motion, should be at least 500 mm, but preferably never less than 600 mm (see diagram opposite).

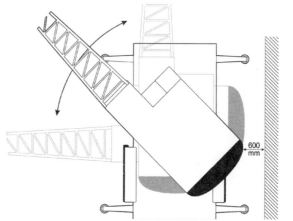

Recommended clearance of 600 mm between moving parts and other structures

7.5.2 Ground conditions

 Insufficient consideration and assessment of ground conditions has been found to be a major cause of accidents with lifting equipment.

The stability of most mobile lifting equipment relies on the ground structure or surface on which it stands being able to withstand the loads and pressure imposed by the machine. Most lifting equipment manufacturers supply information on the loads imposed by the machine in the various operating and set-up configurations of the equipment.

These generally consist of the following.

- Dimensions of stabiliser support plate (pad).

- Ground-level pressure on stabiliser support plate.

- Maximum vertical load per stabiliser (or wheel for free-on-wheels machines).

 An assessment of the ability of the ground or surface to accept these loads should be made by a competent (appointed) person (lift planner).

This assessment may indicate that the proposed surface has insufficient bearing capacity to accept the loads imposed by the lifting equipment, in which case additional measures will need to be taken before the equipment can be set up. These may include using timber sleepers, proprietary mats or, in extreme cases, concrete pads to spread the applied load to an acceptable bearing pressure.

Where timber is to be used, it is important that the timber sections employed are of sufficient dimensions and strength to transmit the applied loads to the ground and that the timbers are pinned together to form a grillage (timber frame creating a foundation for the lifting equipment). The use of individual loose timbers has been found to be a major cause of accidents.

It is essential that any stabilisers are deployed in the manner specified by the lifting equipment manufacturer. When siting equipment, consideration should be given to the length of time that it will be erected in one position and the likely deterioration of supporting ground or foundation over time (such as timber rotting, undermining by water or frost, drying out and collapse of any adjacent excavations).

The hazards that need to be considered when assessing the ground or surface include the following.

- Underground services.

- Paved areas.

- Uncompacted fill.

- Open excavations.

- High water table.
- Basements.
- Cellars.

- Proximity to canals and rivers.
- Changes to site conditions during construction.
- Slope and camber of ground.

Details of any foundation or load spreading arrangements should be recorded in the method statement by the competent person (lift planner).

 For further guidance on assessment of ground conditions and lifting equipment foundations refer to the CIRIA publications *Crane stability on site* (C703) and *Tower crane foundation and tie design* (C761) (CIRIA, 2018).

7.5.3 Overhead hazards

When siting lifting equipment care must be taken to ensure that the extending structure will not make contact with, or approach, overhead hazards (such as power lines, communications cables or overhead structures). Pre-planning of safe working procedures is important. The first step in avoiding danger is to find out whether there are any overhead power lines within or immediately adjoining the work area, or across any route or plane the crane may take.

If there are any overhead power lines over or near to the work area, the site boundaries, or over access roads to the work area, consult with the owners of the lines so that the proposed safe system of work can be discussed. Allow sufficient time for the line to be diverted or made dead, or for other precautions to be taken.

 If any such lines are found it should be assumed that they are live until this has been proved otherwise by their owners.

 For further information on working close to overhead power lines refer to Chapter D07 Underground and overhead services.

7.5.4 Proximity to railways and airports

If lifting equipment is to be sited adjacent to a railway or in the vicinity of an airfield or airport, the competent person (lift planner) should contact the railway or airport operator, as they may well impose restrictions on the height, lifting capacity and use of the lifting equipment.

The competent person (lift planner) should consult the aerodrome/airfield manager for permission to work if lifting equipment is to be used within 6 km of the aerodrome/airfield and its height exceeds 10 m over that of the surrounding structures or trees. When the project is near to a railway the competent person (lift planner) must contact Network Rail in all circumstances where the tower crane and its load can collapse within 4 m of a railway asset or property boundary.

 The Air Navigation Order makes it an offence to act recklessly or negligently in a manner likely to endanger aircraft.

Further guidance on the use of lifting equipment in the vicinity of airfields or railways is given in the following publications:

- ***Operating tower cranes in the vicinity of aerodromes, notification and en-route obstacle lighting* (TIN039). Construction Plant-hire Association**
- ***Guidance to crane users on the crane notification process and obstacle lighting and marking.* Civil Aviation Authority**
- ***Requirements for tower cranes alongside railways controlled by Network Rail.* Construction Plant-hire Association**

7.5.5 Access to and egress from the site

It is important when siting lifting equipment to ensure that there is adequate access to the set-up position for both the machine and any supporting transport. It is equally important to ensure that adequate egress will be available when the lifting equipment is removed from site.

 A self-erecting tower crane

A self-erecting tower crane was being used for lifting on a refurbishment project in a town centre. The crane stood in a courtyard for the duration of the project and the only way into the courtyard was through a single archway, which was just high enough to allow the folded self-erecting tower crane to pass below.

During construction a beam was inserted at the top of the arch to support a wall being constructed above. When it was time to remove the crane from site it was found that the headroom had been reduced to such an extent that the crane could not pass through the archway. The only way to remove the crane was to dismantle it at considerable cost and inconvenience to the site.

07

7.5.6 Wind

The lifting equipment supplier or manufacturer will be able to advise on the maximum in-service and out-of-service wind conditions for the specific model to be used. It should be remembered that this is a design maximum wind speed and the operator may decide to take the equipment out of service at a lower speed due to the type of load being lifted or difficulty in controlling the equipment.

The operator has the primary responsibility for making the decision, in conjunction with the competent person (lift planner) or lift (crane) supervisor.

 The operator's decision to take the equipment out of service should not be overridden by site management under any circumstances.

The wind forces exerted on both an item of lifting equipment and any load suspended from it may be quite large and affect both the strength and stability of the equipment, and safe handling of the load. It is not always appreciated that these forces are due to wind pressure, not wind speed, and consequently, if the wind speed doubles, the wind pressure increases by a factor of four. This means that a small increase in wind speed can have a significant effect on the safe operation of the lifting equipment.

Wind speeds should be monitored by either the anemometer installed on the equipment (such as tower cranes and large mobile cranes and MEWPs) or the use of hand-held anemometers, bearing in mind that wind speed increases with height and that the wind pressure on the load may increase as it is lifted.

All operating personnel should be aware of the maximum in-service wind speed for the particular equipment being used. This value may need to be significantly reduced when lifting loads with a large wind sail area.

Tower cranes normally have a maximum in-service design wind speed of 45 mph (20 m/s, 72 kph), but following a review of in-service wind speeds by the CPA Tower Crane Interest Group, the industry-recommended maximum wind speed at which tower cranes operating in the UK must be taken out of service is 38 mph (16.5 m/s, 60 kph). This takes into account the time required to take the crane out of service and the difficulty of lifting large area loads in high winds. This maximum wind speed would be reduced by the competent person (lift planner), depending on the surface area of the load and other factors relating to the operation.

For mobile cranes, the duty charts will specify the maximum wind speed at which the mobile crane must be taken out of service. This value will vary with the specific make and model of crane and also the duty on which it is rigged, but normally has a maximum value of 31 mph (14 m/s, 50 kph) and is frequently below this value.

 For further information on wind speeds and how they may be estimated by use of the Beaufort scale, refer to Appendix D.

 For specific guidance on the effect of loads with large wind sail areas on limiting wind speeds, refer to the Liebherr publication *Influence of wind on crane operation*, which can be downloaded from its website free of charge.

7.5.7 Noise

Some locations where lifting equipment is used may have restrictions on noise, particularly at night, and the competent person (lift planner) should ensure that any such restrictions are taken into account in the planning process.

7.5.8 Exhaust gas emissions

If lifting equipment powered by an internal combustion engine is to be used in a confined space the competent (appointed) person (lift planner) should consider the effect of vehicle exhaust emissions on persons in the vicinity and take appropriate measures (such as forced ventilation or the use of fume extraction ducts).

7.6 Lifting persons

Some items of lifting equipment (such as mobile elevating work platforms (MEWPs) or suspended cradles) are specifically designed to lift people.

The Approved Code of Practice to regulation 5 of LOLER says:

 The raising and lowering of people using work equipment, which is not specifically designed for the lifting of people, should only be undertaken in exceptional circumstances, when it is not practicable to gain access by less hazardous means. Where it is necessary to use such work equipment then you should ensure that all necessary precautions are taken to ensure safety, including appropriate supervision.

If people are being lifted by lifting equipment not specifically designed for the purpose (in exceptional circumstances only), steps must be taken to ensure the following.

● The carrier is constructed to prevent a person using it from being crushed, trapped or falling from the carrier, either during lifting or carrying out work from the carrier.

- Personal fall protection equipment (PFPE) is worn.

- The equipment contains suitable devices to prevent the carrier falling.

- A person trapped in a carrier is not exposed to danger and can be rescued in the event of the lifting equipment breaking down.

 For further guidance on MEWPs refer to Chapter C08 Lifting equipment.

 If a personnel carrying platform suspended from a crane is being used, BS 7121 Part 1 gives detailed advice.

MEWPs are specifically designed for lifting people

7.7   Control of lifting operations

When a lifting operation is undertaken it is essential that it is adequately controlled by suitably trained and competent people. Depending on the complexity of the lift the following roles may be involved.

Competent (appointed) person (lift planner). Although the competent (appointed) person (lift planner) has overall responsibility for the lift, they may choose to supervise the operation themselves or delegate the role to a lift (crane) supervisor.

Lift (crane) supervisor supervises the operation on behalf of the competent person (lift planner), working to the approved method statement or lift plan. If circumstances require any change to the method statement, this must be approved by the competent person (lift planner).

Operator operates the equipment within its permitted duties as per the method statement and as instructed by the lift (crane) supervisor.

Slinger/signaller connects lifting accessories to the load, initiates lifting by signalling to the operator, observes the path of the load to its destination, signals to the operator and detaches lifting accessories once the load is safely positioned.

7.7.1   Combination of roles

In certain circumstances it may be possible to combine some of the roles of members of the lifting team (illustrated in the following table). However, the table should not be taken as definitive for every circumstance. Role combination should only take place following review of the lifting operation by the competent person (lift planner).

It should be noted that a competent person (lift planner) is required to plan all lifting operations. It is good practice for them to be present on the site during a complex lift. In some circumstances it may be appropriate for the competent person (lift planner) to also assume other roles (such as lift (crane) supervisor, slinger/signaller or operator). The combination of roles requires that the person undertaking the combined role has achieved the necessary competence for each role.

Activity	Role	Lift category		
		Basic	**Intermediate**	**Complex**
Planning	Competent person (lift planner)	Required	Required	Required
Site visit	Competent person (lift planner)	Not essential	May be required	Required
Lifting operation	Competent person (lift planner)	Not essential	May be required	Required
	Lift (crane) supervisor	Roles may be combined	Roles may be combined	Required
	Operator			Required
	Slinger/signaller		Required	Required

Note: this table is for guidance. It is the competent person's (lift planner's) responsibility to determine the combination of roles for each lifting operation following a site-specific risk assessment that takes account of the load, the lifting equipment and the site environment.

7.7.2   Signalling methods

Communication between the people involved in the lifting operation should be clear and unambiguous. Communication can be by recognised hand signals *(refer to Appendix C)* or voice communication using portable radios. Signallers should be provided with distinctive PPE (such as fluorescent safety-helmet covers) so that they are immediately identifiable to the lifting equipment operator (Build UK sites have initiated the use of orange safety helmets for slinger/signallers and white for competent persons).

 All CPA publications, including TIN 017 *Radio communication for lifting operations,* can be downloaded free of charge.

7.7.3 Radio communication systems

Lifting equipment is often used on congested construction sites where the signaller is out of sight of the lifting equipment operator (blind lifts) and the standard hand signals cannot be used. As an alternative, hand-held VHF/UHF radios are often used.

This, however, can lead to a number of problems that may interfere with the clear communication vital for safe lifting operations.

Some examples are shown below.

● Loss of signal and thus communication, leading to loss of control of the lifting operation.

● Interference from radios on adjacent sites, which can lead to loss of communication to the lifting equipment operator.

● A misunderstanding between the lifting equipment operator and the signaller, leading to problems, such as a load being lifted before the slinger has their hands clear, loads colliding with a building and the load being lowered before people are clear of the landing area.

If communication is lost during a lifting operation, the operator must stop immediately until communication is regained.

The following points should be considered for the use of radio communication systems.

Radio specification: to avoid loss of signal and interference, select the correct radio equipment for the application.

Radio frequencies, channels, coverage, and license requirements: two types of radio system for two-way communication on construction sites are available. Low output power private mobile network (PMR) radios can be used without a licence; higher output power radios require a licence from Ofcom.

Recording of voice communications: it is recommended that radio systems used on tower cranes are provided with systems that record all voice communications. The information may be stored on a local computer, server or remotely in the 'cloud'. The recording of voice communications assists with the monitoring and training of radio users, and the investigation of incidents. It is essential that crane operators and signallers are told that the radio system will record all voice communications, and the reasons why the recordings are being made.

Radio protocol, call signs and standard commands: poor radio discipline and failure to follow protocols can lead to lifting incidents. To avoid misunderstandings between the crane operator and signaller, all radio users should be trained and familiar with the radios and communication protocols that they will be required to use.

7.8 Operation of lifting equipment

Lifting equipment should only be operated by people who have been trained and assessed as competent.

7.8.1 Manuals and signs

All operations should be carried out in accordance with the manufacturer's operating manual, a copy of which should be with the lifting equipment at all times.

Checks should be made by the supplier to ensure that the manual is the correct manual for the lifting equipment supplied, conveys information to the users in a simple and understandable format and is in a language (usually English) that is understood by the operator.

All signs, labels and decals (stickers) on the lifting equipment must be clear, legible and in a language (usually English) that is readily understood by the operator. A rated capacity chart for the specific lifting equipment must be available to the operator.

7.8.2 Pedestrian-operated lifting equipment

The operation of some types of lifting equipment (such as lorry loaders and self-erecting tower cranes) is frequently carried out by a pedestrian operator at ground level, using remote controls.

Whilst pedestrian control provides flexibility, with the possible combination of roles there are several potential disadvantages to consider when planning the lifting operations. Operators may:

● be at risk of tripping and falling when trying to move around the site over uneven ground, whilst concentrating on controlling the lifting equipment or handling the load. (Pedestrian-operated lifting equipment should only be controlled whilst the operator is stationary.)

● not have a good view of the load and any obstructions and consequently must always have the lifting equipment jib or boom and load in sight at all times, unless they are working under the direction of a signaller who has a clear view of the load and load path

● put themselves in a hazardous position, where they may be struck by the load or part of the lifting equipment.

The operator should have full view of the jib and load at all times

Operating lifting equipment with remote controls

Operators should always:

- check site rules to confirm that the use of a remote control is permitted
- use the belt/neck strap provided
- be aware of the working area, including their proximity to the load and vehicle
- use the remote control in accordance with the manufacturer's instructions
- ensure the remote control is deactivated when not in use
- store the control unit in a suitable place when not in use.

Operators should never:

- stand between the load and a fixed object (such as a vehicle or a wall)
- walk whilst operating the remote control.

7.8.3 Radio remote controls

To prevent unauthorised use, the operator of lifting equipment that is controlled by transmitted signals (such as radio signals) should retain the control station (transmitter) in their physical possession or remove the key from its key-lock switch and, for short periods, retain the key in their possession. For longer periods, or when the lifting equipment is not in use, the transmitter should be kept in secure storage.

When the transmitter is fitted with a belt or harness, the operator should be wearing the harness before switching on the transmitter so that accidental operation of the lifting equipment is prevented. The transmitter should only be switched on when operating the lifting equipment and should be switched off before removing the harness and when attaching loads.

7.8.4 Rated capacity

The rated capacity (SWL) of lifting equipment should not be exceeded, except when testing the lifting equipment under the supervision of a competent, authorised person (usually after installation). Care should be taken to prevent pendulum swinging of the load, by controlling the operating motions to match the swing of the load and to keep it under control at all times.

Rated capacities apply only to freely suspended loads. The hoisting, slewing, telescoping, or raising and lowering motions of lifting equipment should not be used to drag a load under any circumstances. Before lifting a load, the hook and hoist rope should be vertically above the centre of gravity of the load. Failure to observe these points can adversely affect the stability of the lifting equipment or introduce loadings (stresses) into the lifting equipment structure for which it has not been designed and, even with a rated capacity indicator/limiter fitted, a sudden structural failure or overturn can occur without warning.

It is essential that all lifting equipment is clearly marked to indicate its rated capacity (SWL). Where the rated capacity (SWL) depends on the lifting equipment's configuration (such as changing radius) it should be clearly marked to indicate its rated capacity (SWL) for each configuration. As an alternative, information that clearly indicates its rated capacity (SWL) for each configuration should be kept with the lifting equipment.

Equipment designed for lifting persons should be clearly marked to confirm that it is suitable for lifting persons. Equipment which might be used in error for lifting persons must be clearly marked to indicate that it is not for lifting persons.

Most lifting equipment with a rated capacity not less than 1,000 kg or an overturning moment not less than 40,000 Nm is fitted with a load control device that will sense when the rated capacity is being approached or has been exceeded and prevent further movement. These devices vary between different types of lifting equipment and on cranes are generally known as rated capacity limiters (RCL). Cranes are also fitted with rated capacity indicators (RCIs), which indicate approach to overload and overload.

 Effective lift planning should ensure that the rated capacity (SWL) of lifting equipment is never exceeded. The RCL or load control device should never be used to establish the weight of a load.

7.8.5 Lifting of loads near persons

When loads have to be lifted in the vicinity of persons, extreme care should be exercised and adequate clearances allowed. The route of the load should be planned to prevent lifting over persons. Operators and signallers should pay particular attention to possible dangers of persons working out of sight.

All persons should be instructed to stand clear of the load being lifted. When lifting from a stack, they should be instructed to stand away from the stack in case adjacent materials or objects are displaced. This also applies to the removal of part loads from the deck of a vehicle.

Where possible, lifting of loads over pavements, highways, railways, rivers, or other places to which the public have access, should be avoided. If this is not possible, permission should be obtained from the appropriate authority and the area kept clear of traffic and persons.

7.8.6   Multiple lifting

Multiple or tandem lifting (carrying out a lift with more than one piece of lifting equipment attached to the load) should always be planned and carried out with great care. A multiple lift is always classified as **complex**. Multiple lifts are generally only carried out with mobile cranes. Consequently, the term *crane* will be used here, rather than lifting equipment.

7.8.6.1   Weight of the load

The total weight of the load and its distribution should be either known or calculated. Where the information is taken from a drawing, allowance should be made for manufacturing tolerances.

7.8.6.2   Centre of gravity

Owing to the variable effect of manufacturing tolerances, variable density, and so on, the centre of gravity of the load might not be known accurately and the proportion of the load being carried by each machine could therefore be uncertain. If the centre of gravity is uncertain, the lift will be classed as a non-routine lifting operation and will require a more detailed lift plan.

7.8.6.3   Weight of the lifting accessories/attachments

The weight of the lifting accessories/attachments should be part of the calculated load on the cranes. When handling heavy or awkwardly shaped loads, the deduction from the rated capacity (SWL) of the lifting equipment to allow for the weight of the lifting accessories/attachments might be significant. The weight of the lifting accessories/attachments, and hook blocks, where appropriate, and its distribution should therefore be accurately known.

In cases where the hoist ropes are reeved around pulleys that are part of a specially designed lifting accessory/attachment (such as a lifting beam), the weight of the removed hook block and hook may be taken into consideration when determining the net weight of the lifting accessories/attachments.

7.8.6.4   Capacities of the lifting accessories/attachments

The distribution of the forces within the lifting accessories or attachments that arise during the lifting operation should be established. The lifting accessories/attachments used should, unless specially designed for the particular lifting operation, have a capacity margin well in excess of that needed for its proportioned load.

 Special lifting accessories/attachments might be necessary to suit the maximum variation in distribution and direction of application of loads or forces that can occur during multiple lifting.

7.8.6.5   Synchronisation of lifting equipment motions

If the variations in the direction and magnitude of the forces acting on the crane during the multiple lift are to be kept to a minimum, it is essential that the crane motions are synchronised.

Lifting equipment/cranes of equal capacity and similar characteristics should therefore be used whenever possible. In practice, there is always some variation due to differences in response to the activation of the control system.

The rated capacity of a crane is calculated on the assumption that the load is raised and lowered in a vertical plane. The crane structure is designed to withstand any lateral loads imposed by accelerations in the various crane motions, but it is unsafe to rely on this lateral strength to withstand horizontal components of 'out-of-vertical' lifts.

If the cranes have dissimilar characteristics, it is unlikely that the motions will be accurately synchronised. Therefore, an assessment should be made of the effect of variation in verticality of the hoist ropes that could arise from inequalities of speed, together with a determination of the means for keeping such inequalities to a minimum.

7.8.6.6   Instrumentation

Instruments are available that constantly monitor the angle of the load, verticality and the force in any hoist rope throughout the lifting operation. The use of such instruments and the restriction of the motion speeds, together with the strict use of one motion at any one time, can assist in the control of the loads on the cranes within the planned values.

7.8.6.7   Supervision

One competent person (lift planner) should be in attendance and in overall control of a multiple crane operation. Only this person should give instructions to personnel operating or driving machines, except in an emergency when a commonly recognised stop signal may be given by any person observing a situation leading to danger.

If all the necessary points cannot be observed from one position, other personnel should be positioned at various points to observe and report to the person in charge of the operation.

 It is essential that adequate means of signalling are provided between the person in charge of the operation, the operators of the cranes, and the slingers and signallers.

7.8.6.8   Recommended rated capacity during lifting

As all the factors cannot be accurately evaluated, an appropriate down-rating should be applied to all the cranes involved. The down-rating might need to be 20% or more.

7.9   Training and competence of personnel

As with all work activities on site, employers must ensure that the correct levels of training, competence and medical fitness of personnel are in place, and that maintenance and inspection regimes are carried out and recorded.

 For detailed information refer to Chapter C06 Mobile work equipment: 6.7 Training and competence of personnel, and 6.8 Maintenance, checks and inspections.

For further guidance on training and competence refer to BS 7121 Parts 1, 3, 4 and 5.

 For detailed guidance on medical fitness refer to the Strategic Forum for Construction Plant Safety Group's *Medical fitness to operate construction plant* (Good practice guide).

07

Appendix A – Definitions

Competent (appointed) person or lift planner. A person who has the competence, adequate training, authority and experience to take overall responsibility and control of a lifting operation, having been formally appointed in writing by the management of the organisation(s) that requires the load to be moved.

Competent person (equipment examination). (For the purposes of inspection and examination.) A person who has the practical and theoretical knowledge, together with actual experience of what they are to examine, so as to enable them to detect errors, defects, faults or weaknesses, which it is the purpose of the examination or inspection to discover; and to assess the importance of any such discovery.

Crane co-ordinator. A person who plans and directs the sequence of operations of cranes to ensure that they do not collide with other cranes, loads and other equipment (for example, concrete placing booms, telehandlers and piling rigs).

Lift (crane) supervisor. A person who controls the lifting operation and ensures that it is carried out in accordance with the appointed person's safe system of work (lift plan).

Crane operator. A person who operates the crane for the purpose of moving and positioning loads or erection of the crane.

Lifting accessory. A lifting beam or frame, chain sling, rope sling or similar gear, a ring, link, hook, interlocks, plate clamp, shackle, swivel or eyebolt, and any loose equipment that is used with lifting gear.

Lifting equipment. A piece of work equipment for lifting or lowering loads, including a crab, winch, pulley block or gin wheel (for raising or lowering), a hoist, crane, shearlegs, excavator, dragline, piling frame, aerial cable way, aerial ropeway or overhead runway, goods hoist, MEWP, scissor lift, vehicle hoist, ropes used for access, forklift truck, lorry loader and passenger lift.

Mobile crane. A crane capable of travelling under its own power, but does not include cranes that travel on a line of rails.

Plant and equipment. Any plant, equipment, gear, machinery, apparatus or appliance, or part thereof.

Rated capacity. The load that any item of lifting equipment (such as a crane or hoist) or any accessory for lifting is designed to lift for a given operating condition (such as configuration or position of load). Rated capacity was formerly known as safe working load (SWL).

 On certain types of crane (for example, mobile cranes), the rated capacity includes the weight of the hook block and all the lifting gear. The weight of these should be deducted from the declared rated capacity of the lifting equipment to obtain the net load that can be safely lifted.

Rated capacity indicator/limiter RCI/L. Device(s) that warns of the approach to overload and prevents the crane from being overloaded as described in BS EN 12077-2.

Thorough examination. An examination by a competent person (equipment examination) in such depth and detail as the competent person considers necessary to enable them to determine whether the equipment being examined is safe to continue in use.

Appendix B – Case study of lifting operation categorisation

Example activity – Lifting of a generating set and fuel tank with a lorry loader

Situation 1		Straightforward off-load on to level ground beside lorry.	
Environment – 1	Load – 1	Example hazards	Example control measures
Lift categorisation – Basic		Overturning of lorry loader or failure through overloading of the lorry loader attachment or lifting accessory.	■ Accurately assess the weight of the load. ■ Accurately assess the maximum radius at which the load can be lifted. ■ Correctly select the lorry loader and lifting accessories.
		Overturning of the lorry loader through ground bearing failure.	Assessment of ground conditions and use of spreader pads.
Lifting team ■ Competent person (lift planner) prepares generic risk assessment and method statement. ■ Operator takes the role of lift (crane) supervisor, slinger/signaller and operator.		**Planning requirements** ■ Generic risk assessment and method statement. ■ On-site review of risk assessment and method statement by lift (crane) supervisor.	

Situation 2		Lifting a generating set and fuel tank in a pedestrian area with narrow access and restricted view of load.	
Environment – 2	Load – 1	Example hazards	Example control measures
Lift categorisation – Intermediate		Overturning of lorry loader or failure through overloading of the lorry loader attachment or lifting accessory.	■ Accurately assess the weight of the load. ■ Accurately assess the maximum radius at which the load can be lifted. ■ Correctly select the lorry loader and lifting accessories.
		Overturning of the lorry loader through ground bearing failure.	Assessment of ground conditions and use of spreader pads.
		Operator has restricted view of load.	Use separate slinger/signaller (including use of two-way radio if required).
		Ingress of personnel. Lifting near or over persons.	■ Cordon area off with physical barriers. ■ Utilise site personnel to monitor the area. ■ Close area to public access. ■ Perform lift out of hours.
Lifting team ■ Competent person (lift planner) prepares task and/or site-specific risk assessment and method statement. ■ Operator takes the role of lift (crane) supervisor and operator. ■ Separate slinger/signaller.		**Planning requirements** ■ Task and/or site-specific risk assessment and method statement. ■ On-site review of risk assessment and method statement by lift (crane) supervisor. ■ Cordoning off of lift area by site manager. ■ Agreement between operator and site manager to fulfil duties of controlling cordoned off area.	

07

Situation 3	Lifting a generating set and fuel tank in an electrical sub-station with overhead cables and unpaved ground.		
Environment – 3	Load – 1	Example hazards	Example control measures
Lift categorisation – Complex		Overturning of lorry loader or failure through overloading of the lorry loader attachment or lifting accessory.	■ Accurately assess the weight of the load. ■ Accurately assess the maximum radius at which the load can be lifted. ■ Correctly select the lorry loader and lifting accessories.
		Overturning of the lorry loader through ground bearing failure.	Assessment of ground conditions and use of spreader pads.
		Ingress of personnel. Lifting near or over persons.	Cordon area off with physical barriers. Utilise site personnel to monitor the area.
		Electricity cables.	Have power switched off.
		Blind lift.	Dedicated slinger/signaller.

Lifting team

■ Competent person (lift planner) prepares site-specific risk assessment and method statement.

■ Separate lift (crane) supervisor oversees lifting operation.

■ Dedicated slinger/signaller required.

■ Operator takes the role of operator only.

Planning requirements

■ Site-specific risk assessment and method statement.

■ On-site review of risk assessment and method statement by lift (crane) supervisor.

■ Cordoning off of lift area by site manager.

■ Agreement between operator and site manager to fulfil duties of controlling cordoned off area.

07

Appendix C – Recognised hand signals

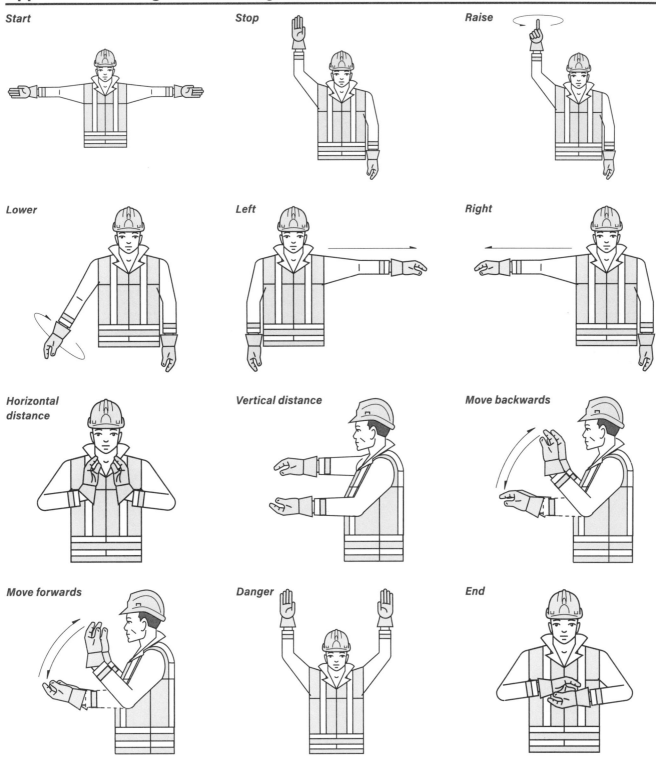

Start

Stop

Raise

Lower

Left

Right

Horizontal distance

Vertical distance

Move backwards

Move forwards

Danger

End

 The signaller should stand in a secure position, where they can see the load and can be seen clearly by the lifting equipment operator, and they should face the operator if possible. Each signal should be distinct and clear. These signals have been reproduced from BS 7121-1 *Safe use of cranes – General*.

 For further information refer to the HSE publication *Safety signs and signals. The Health and Safety (Safety Signs and Signals) Regulations 1996. Guidance on regulations (L64).*

(This appendix contains public sector information licensed under the Open Government Licence v2.0.)

Appendix D – Wind strengths and effects (Beaufort scale)

Wind force number	Description of wind	Wind effect locally	Speed (mph)	Speed (m/sec)
0	Calm	Calm, smoke rises vertically.	1	0–1
1	Light air	Direction of wind shown by smoke drift, but not by wind or weather vanes.	1–3	1–2
2	Light breeze	Wind felt on face. Leaves rustle. Wind or weather vanes move.	4–7	2–3
3	Gentle breeze	Leaves and small twigs in constant motion. Wind extends light flags.	8–12	3–5
4	Moderate breeze	Wind raises dust and loose paper. Small branches move.	13–18	5–8
5	Fresh breeze	Small trees in leaf begin to sway. Little crested wavelets form on inland waters.	19–24	8–11
6	Strong breeze	Large branches in motion. Umbrellas used with some difficulty.	25–31	11–14
7	Near gale	Whole trees in motion. Becoming difficult to walk against the wind.	32–38	14–17
8	Gale	Twigs break off trees. Progress is generally impeded.	39–46	17–21
9	Strong gale	Chimney pots, slates and tiles may be blown off. Other slight structural damage may be caused.	47–54	21–24

07

Lifting equipment

08

GT700 Toolbox talks / supporting checklists and forms

Toolbox talks on some of these topics are available in the GT700 publication. Supporting checklists and forms covering some of these topics are available on our companion website.

Supporting
INFORMATION

LIFTING EQUIPMENT

Overview

There are a number of serious accidents in the construction industry each year as a result of the failure of lifting equipment or accessories.

The majority of these accidents could be avoided through appropriate levels of planning, suitable selection, maintenance, inspection and thorough examination of equipment and comprehensive training, assessment, supervision and briefing of personnel.

This chapter outlines some of the different types of lifting equipment and lifting accessories and gives an overview of the requirements for installing, operating, checking, maintaining, inspecting and thoroughly examining them.

8.1   Introduction

Lifting equipment is any work equipment (such as mobile or static cranes, hoists, telehandlers and excavators) used for lifting or lowering loads (including people) and includes the attachments used for anchoring, fixing or supporting them, such as tie bars used for securing cranes to the cores of high-rise buildings.

Lifting equipment includes any lifting accessories that attach the load to the equipment, in addition to the equipment that carries out the actual lifting function.

Experience has shown that the use of lifting equipment can be a hazardous activity if not properly planned and carried out. The safe use of lifting equipment and accessories will depend upon the following.

● Thorough pre-planning of each lifting operation and the selection of suitable equipment and accessories.

● The availability of suitable lifting equipment and accessories, which are properly inspected and maintained.

● The provision of adequate information, instruction and training on the use of lifting equipment for everyone involved.

● The thorough examination of lifting equipment and accessories, in line with established safe systems of work.

This chapter is intended to provide advice to non-specialists on the implications that utilising lifting equipment and accessories on site will have for them. The content is therefore restricted to information considered relevant for site managers, project managers and others who may become involved in hiring lifting equipment or managing its safe use on site.

As a consequence, the inclusion of technical information on, for example, the technicalities of lifting equipment, its construction, maintenance, inspection and thorough examination, has been limited.

By way of illustration, whilst it is reasonable to expect a site manager to know when a piece of lifting equipment should be thoroughly examined, detail of the content of such examinations is beyond the scope of this chapter.

 Problems with lifting operations often occur because of poor equipment and accessory selection.

 The general principles of planning and carrying out lifting operations are covered in Chapter C07 Lifting operations.

8.2   Important points

● The rated capacity (safe working load (SWL)) of any item of lifting equipment or lifting accessory must never be exceeded.

● All lifting equipment and lifting accessories must be adequately maintained.

● All lifting equipment and lifting accessories must be subjected to a schedule of inspections and thorough examination.

● Detailed attention must be given to site features (such as overhead cables, unstable ground conditions and adjacent properties).

 The collapse, overturning or failure of any load-bearing part of a hoist, crane or other lifting equipment is a reportable dangerous occurrence, even if nobody is injured.

For further information refer to Chapter A13 Accident reporting and investigation.

08

8.3 Legislative requirements

A brief summary of the main legislative requirements for lifting equipment is listed below.

 For detailed information on legislation refer to Section A: *Legal and management* **and for other related legislation refer to Chapter C05 Work equipment and hand-held tools.**

8.3.1 Provision and Use of Work Equipment Regulations (PUWER)

PUWER are concerned with such matters as the selection of suitable work equipment, safeguarding of dangerous parts of machinery, provision of appropriate controls, training of operators, inspection and maintenance of work equipment, including lifting equipment and accessories. PUWER place duties on any person who has control to any extent of any of the following.

- Work equipment.

- A person who uses, manages use or supervises work equipment.

- The way in which work equipment is used at work (including maintenance).

PUWER apply to employers in respect of work equipment provided for, or used by, their employees, self-employed persons in respect of work equipment they use and other people (such as visitors).

 For further guidance on PUWER refer to the HSE's ACoP and guidance *Safe use of work equipment* **(L22).**

8.3.2 Lifting Operations and Lifting Equipment Regulations (LOLER)

LOLER deal with the specific risks arising from the use of lifting equipment. LOLER build upon PUWER in many areas and apply to all lifting operations, equipment and accessories. LOLER requirements are shown below.

- Specific requirements are applied to the lifting of people.

- Pre-use checks and inspections at appropriate intervals are carried out on lifting equipment.

- All operations are planned, supervised and carried out safely.

- Lifting equipment must be thoroughly examined by a competent (appointed) person on specified occasions and at specified intervals.

 For further guidance on LOLER refer to the HSE's ACoP and guidance *Safe use of lifting equipment* **(L113).**

8.4 Mobile cranes (wheeled and crawler mounted)

A mobile crane is a form of lifting equipment, mounted on a wheeled or crawler chassis, that can move under its own power between lifting positions.

- Wheeled mobile cranes are generally mounted on either truck crane chassis or all-terrain chassis. Truck cranes are generally restricted to travelling on metalled roads and well-compacted ground on site whilst all-terrain cranes can travel on public roads and over most site conditions. Some all-terrain wheeled cranes may have a limited ability to lift and travel with a load (pick and carry duties). Wheeled mobile cranes range in capacity between 25 tonnes and 1,200 tonnes.

- Crawler mobile cranes require transporting to site in component form or on a low loader. Once the crane has been rigged, it can travel around the site with ease and lift and travel with a load. Crawler mobile cranes range in capacity from 40 tonnes to 3,000 tonnes.

- Mini or compact cranes are generally mounted on small crawler or wheeled chassis and may be fitted with outriggers to provide stability. Some are fitted with cabs for the operator and have pick and carry duties. Mini crane capacity is generally in the range of one tonne to ten tonnes.

Crawler crane

08

LIFTING EQUIPMENT

8.4.1 Planning and use of mobile cranes

The planning and carrying out of lifting operations with mobile cranes should be carried out in accordance with Chapter C07.

 For further detailed guidance refer to the *Code of Practice for safe use of cranes – Part 3: Mobile cranes* (BS 7121-3).

8.4.2 Maintenance, checks and inspections of mobile cranes

 For further information on maintenance, checks and inspections refer to Appendix A.

When planning and carrying out maintenance work on mobile cranes, it should not be forgotten that when travelling on the road, the condition of the crane chassis (brakes, suspension, steering, lights, wheels, tyres, and so on) will have a significant effect on the safety of the crane driver, other road users and the public. The Road Vehicles (Construction and Use) Regulations (Reg. 100) require that they should:

 at all times be in such condition ... that no danger is caused or is likely to be caused to any person in or on the vehicle or on a road.

Because a mobile crane has the potential to cause as much damage in a road traffic accident as any other large vehicle, it is important to follow the recommendations set out in the manufacturer's service manual. These normally set maintenance intervals based on engine hours run and distance travelled, whereby the first parameter reached determines the need for maintenance. Failure to maintain the chassis of a mobile crane adequately may put the crane operator and other road users at risk from issues such as those listed below.

- Poor brake performance or failure leading to increased braking distances and an inability to stop in time.
- Insufficient tyre tread, reducing grip, leading to increased braking distances.
- Hydraulic fluid leaks from the suspension system creating hazardous road surfaces and potential loss of control for other road users.
- Tyre blow-outs leading to loss of control of the crane.
- Steering system failures leading to loss of control of the crane.
- Lighting failures leading to the operator not being able to see clearly and other road users not being able to see the crane.
- Wiper, washer and demister failures preventing the crane operator from seeing clearly.
- Failure of the vehicle suspension system.
- Failure of the crane chassis.
- Security of outrigger plates, covers, guards and other potentially loose items.

It is essential that the chassis of a mobile crane is effectively cleaned before maintenance and inspection is carried out, to ensure that defects can be detected.

For further detailed guidance on the maintenance, inspection and thorough examination of mobile cranes refer to the following.

- **Construction Plant-hire Association's *Maintenance, inspection and thorough examination of mobile cranes* (Best practice guide).**
- **Construction Plant-hire Association's *Annual roadworthiness inspection scheme for mobile cranes mounted on a non-standard chassis* (Good practice guide).**
- ***Code of Practice for the safe use of cranes – Inspection, maintenance and thorough examination – Mobile cranes.***

8.4.3 Thorough examination of mobile cranes

The Approved Code of Practice (ACoP) to LOLER states that any testing is required every six or 12 months or at the discretion of the competent (appointed) person carrying out a thorough examination and that the competent (appointed) person will decide on the nature of the test and the method of carrying it out.

Advice from the Health and Safety Executive (HSE) confirms that four yearly overload testing is no longer a legal requirement and repeated overload testing itself may be dangerous as it may create the conditions for additional faults or even failure during testing.

In the HSE's view, the most appropriate method of assessing the condition of a mobile crane is to adopt a defined scope for thorough examination. This is where a specific examination schedule is drawn up for the machine being examined by a competent (appointed) person, which details the parts of the crane that should be thoroughly examined and the supplementary reports and tests that should be carried out.

 For further information on thorough examination refer to Appendix B.

8.5 Tower cranes

Tower cranes fall into three main categories.

Top slew tower cranes, which are controlled from a cab at the top of the mast and are erected and dismantled using a suitably sized mobile crane, for which provision has to be made in terms of space and stable ground conditions. Top slew tower cranes are further subdivided into saddle jib and luffing jib types.

Self-erecting tower cranes, which are controlled from ground level, often using remote controls, and are self-erecting and folding.

Vehicle mounted tower cranes, which are often controlled remotely from the ground and should be treated as a mobile crane.

Two saddle jib cranes and a luffing jib crane

8.5.1 Tower crane installation

When contemplating the erection of a tower crane on site, the temporary works co-ordinator will be responsible, and the following points should be taken into account.

● All tower cranes require suitable foundations. For top slew tower cranes particularly, both static and travelling, the foundations will require careful design by a competent engineer.

● Some tower cranes are tied to an adjacent structure for support. The ties and their connections to the crane and the supporting structure will require careful design by a competent engineer.

● On sites where more than one tower crane is erected, there may be overlapping arcs of operation when slewing; anti-collision devices may be fitted or crash radios utilised. As a result, the cranes should be erected with their jibs at different heights and crane slewing operations will have to be co-ordinated.

● The required airspace must be confirmed with regard to the proximity of adjacent structures, overhead power lines or other obstructions.

● The requirement for airspace may need to be discussed with any local airport to establish that there will be no intrusion into, or unacceptably near to, aircraft flight paths.

● There may be a requirement for an aircraft warning light or beacon on the highest point of the crane; the colour intensity and whether it is on steady or flashes will depend upon the local rules for any flight path affected.

● Electrically-powered tower cranes will require a heavy-duty power supply and the crane must be effectively earthed to protect against electrical faults and lightning strikes, including earthing of the appropriate rails. The requirements of the Electricity at Work Regulations apply to all electrically powered tower cranes and their power supply.

08

8.5.1.1 Over-sailing

In many cases, the crane jib has the capacity to over-sail adjacent properties and areas to which the public have access. Over-sailing is classed as trespass.

Permissions have to be obtained from the respective landowner and a licensing agreement put in place. When drawing up a licensing agreement the following issues need to be addressed.

● What height will the crane operate at?

● Where will the crane be erected?

● What will the turning circle of the crane be?

● What fees will be payable for the consent?

● What times of day (24 hours) will the crane be in operation?

● What will the time frame of the licence be?

● How will the crane be erected and dismantled?

● What compliance is needed with applicable laws and regulations?

● What situations would incur termination of the licence?

● Where the right to over-sail adjacent property is not given, it may be necessary to:
  – rearrange siting of the tower crane(s)
  – review the type of crane required (for example, a luffing jib crane that has a smaller radius of operation might be the only solution).

 For detailed guidance on the design and installation of tower crane bases and ties refer to the Construction Industry Research and Information Association's *Tower crane foundation and tie design* (C761).

 For further detailed guidance on the erection, climbing and dismantling of tower cranes refer to the *Code of Practice for safe use of cranes – Part 5: Tower cranes* (BS 7121-5) and the Construction Plant-hire Association's *Climbing of tower cranes* (Best practice guide).

8.5.2 Tower crane operation

Detailed information for carrying out lifting operations with tower cranes can be found in Chapter C07.

In summary, the following points should be taken into account.

- High winds can temporarily stop tower crane operations; each crane should be fitted with an anemometer (wind-speed indicator).

- In high winds, tower cranes must be left in free slew with their hooks raised.

- A plan for rescue from height must be in place in the event of an accident or incident (for example, the operator becoming ill).

- The emergency services have no obligation to carry out these rescues and are often not able to assist because of the height of the rescue and because of restricted access for large vehicles (such as fire service turntable ladders).

- A system must be in place to control the operator hours, taking into consideration the need for operators to take regular breaks to maintain high levels of concentration. BS 7121 suggests the following number of operators.

  - One tower crane: two operators.

  - Two tower cranes: three operators.

  - Three tower cranes: five operators.

 For further detailed guidance refer to the Construction Plant-hire Association's *Good Practice Guide, TCIG 2101: Emergency Action Planning & Rescue From Height on Tower Cranes.*

Tower cranes must be secured against unauthorised access, including climbing the tower and unauthorised use.

A lifting plan, approved by the competent person (lift planner), must be in place.

For further detailed guidance on the safe use of tower cranes refer to:

- ***Code of Practice for safe use of cranes – Tower cranes* (BS 7121-5)**

 - **Construction Plant-hire Association's (Best practice guide):**
  - ***Safe use of top slew tower cranes* (TCIG 0701)**
  - ***Safe use of self-erecting tower cranes* (TCIG 0601)**
  - ***Tower crane operator's handbook.***

8.5.3 Maintenance, checks, inspections and thorough examination of tower cranes

 For further information refer to Appendices A and B.

 For further detailed guidance refer to the Construction Plant-hire Association's *Maintenance, inspection and thorough examination of tower cranes* (Best practice guide) and the *Code of Practice for the safe use of cranes – Inspection, maintenance and thorough examination – Tower cranes* (BS 7121-2-5).

8.6 Lorry loaders

Lorry loaders were originally designed to load and unload goods onto and off the body of the vehicle on which they were mounted so that deliveries and collections did not have to rely on other loading and unloading facilities.

In recent years lorry loaders have developed significantly and are now able to carry out many of the tasks traditionally undertaken by mobile and tower cranes.

When used safely they make a valuable contribution to lifting operations. However, it should not be forgotten that all lifting operations must be planned and executed to the same standard, irrespective of the type of lifting equipment being used.

Unfortunately, over the past few years there have been a significant number of accidents involving lorry loaders, which have included fatalities. These could have been prevented by correct planning, supervision, use and maintenance.

The cost in human suffering resulting from poor planning places a moral obligation on employers to improve safety performance. Even the smallest of accidents will also have a financial cost that will impact on the business.

 For further information refer to the Construction Plant-hire Association's *Work at height whilst loading and unloading transport* (Best practice guide).

08

8.6.1 Types of lorry loader

A lorry loader is a commercial vehicle or trailer fitted with a loader crane. Loader cranes have a column that slews about its base and a boom system that is attached to the top of the column.

Lorry loaders are rated in terms of load movement and are available in sizes from 0.5 metre tonne to 84 metre tonne.

The term metre tonne represents the capability of the lorry loader. For example, 10 metre tonne is represented by:

– 5 metre radius x 2 tonne safe work limit, or

– 10 metre radius x 1 tonne safe work limit.

When in use, the lorry loader is generally stabilised by two stabilisers mounted on the loader crane base. In the past loader crane controls were mounted and operated at the base of the column, but today they are normally portable, wireless units that give the operator greater flexibility of movement and help to keep the load in view.

Typical lorry loader

8.6.2 Planning and use of lorry loaders

The planning and carrying out of lifting operations with lorry loaders should be in accordance with the principles set out in Chapter C07.

8.6.3 Maintenance, checks, inspections and thorough examinations of lorry loaders

 For further information refer to Appendices A and B.

 For detailed guidance on the safe use of lorry loaders refer to the Construction Plant-hire Association's *The management of lifting operations with lorry loaders* (Best practice guide).

8.7 Mobile elevating work platforms

Mobile elevating work platforms (MEWPs) are designed to provide temporary working platforms which, when people are in the work platform, can be easily adjusted for height and outreach.

They can also be easily moved from one location to another, and are particularly suitable for tasks where the use of a ladder would be unsafe and the erection of a scaffolding platform too time-consuming or impracticable in relation to the job to be done.

Good management, planning and consultation with interested parties before and during any work close to overhead lines will reduce the risk of accidents. This applies whatever type of work is being planned or undertaken, even if the work is temporary or of short duration. Stop and consider the risks if the intended area to work in is within a distance of 10 m, measured at ground level horizontally from below the nearest wire.

Remove the risk. The most effective way to prevent contact with overhead lines is by not carrying out work where there is a risk of contact with, or close approach to, the wires. If this cannot be avoid and there is a risk of contact or close approach to the wires, consult the owner to find out if the line can be permanently diverted away from the work area or replaced with underground cables.

This will often be inappropriate for infrequent, short-duration or transitory work. If this cannot be done and there remains a risk of contact or close approach to the wires, find out if the overhead line can be temporarily switched off while the work is being done.

Sizes and capabilities of MEWPs vary considerably. Small, one-person machines are available, with a maximum rated capacity (SWL) of 120 kg, and working heights of a few metres, whilst at the other end of the scale, work platforms may be 4 m x 2 m or more and have a rated capacity (SWL) in excess of 1,000 kg.

Extending boom heights can exceed 100 m and the outreach of some units can approach 40 m.

8.7.1 Types of mobile elevating work platform

Common types of MEWP found on construction sites are listed below.

- Scissor lifts.
- Vertical lifts.
- Telescopic booms.
- Articulating and multi-boom articulated.

These types of MEWP may be mounted on chassis that are towable units, vehicles, self-propelled (wheeled or crawler) or pedestrian controlled.

8.7.1.1 Scissor lift

This type of MEWP gives a substantially vertical lift. The work platform may be fitted with a sliding extension that will give a small amount of outreach.

8.7.1.2 Vertical lift

This type of MEWP gives vertical lift only and is generally used for small, lightweight machines for indoor use only.

8.7.1.3 Telescopic boom

This type of MEWP gives both vertical height and outreach, and the telescoping function gives smooth and fine control near structures. The work platform may also be able to swivel in the horizontal plane and is mounted on a fly jib for additional manoeuvrability.

Boom-type MEWPs are sometimes known as cherry pickers. They generally have smaller baskets and lower lift capacities than scissor-type MEWPs, and their platforms can 'bounce' at height due to the boom structure flexing. This may make them less suitable to use for installing long or heavy materials, or bulky materials that may obstruct the control panel.

8.7.1.4 Articulating and multi-boom articulated

These types of MEWP may be mounted on a road-going vehicle chassis or a self-propelled wheeled or crawler chassis. They give a wide range of reach and height.

Vehicle-mounted MEWPs are nearly always equipped with outriggers and specialised types are available (for example, machines that enable access to the underside of bridge arches from the roadway above).

Units mounted on a self-propelled chassis have a 'travel while elevated' ability and may have four-wheel drive. Rough-terrain MEWPs have been specially developed for construction site work.

Scissor lift   Vertical lift

Telescopic boom

8.7.2   Planning and use of MEWPs

The planning and carrying out of lifting operations with MEWPs should be in accordance with the principles set out in Chapter C07. In addition the points below should be taken into account.

8.7.2.1   Entrapment of people on the platform

In certain circumstances (such as working at height amongst steelwork), there is an increased risk to people in the MEWP of becoming trapped and, in some cases, crushed between the platform and a fixed obstruction. There have been a number of such incidents in the UK over the past few years, several of which have resulted in fatalities. Job planning should consider this hazard and, where required, additional measures should be taken.

- Consideration of additional safety devices on the MEWP.

- Devising and implementing a rescue plan for people trapped at height.

- Briefing of operators and other people who will be working from the platform.

This issue has been highlighted by the HSE as a result of several accidents in which MEWP operators had become injured and immobilised and unable to release themselves, having become trapped between the machine (such as the top guard-rail or controls) and a fixed structure (often structural steelwork).

Articulating MEWP

For comprehensive guidance on avoiding entrapment refer to the Strategic Forum for Construction Plant Safety Group's *Avoiding trapping/crushing injuries to people in the platform: Best practice guidance for MEWPs* and the HSE's guidance Avoiding trapping/crushing injuries to people in the platform of mobile elevating work platforms (MEWPs).

8.7.2.2 Emergency controls

Most MEWPs can be controlled either at ground level or from within the platform.

Both of these controls and the emergency stop and emergency lowering controls should be checked as part of the pre-use inspection to ensure they are working correctly.

The operator, or their supervisor, should ensure that a responsible person, who is familiar with the emergency lowering system, is always in close proximity to the MEWP, to lower the work platform in the event that rescue is required.

 Auxiliary controls decal

This image can be used on MEWPs, in conjunction with existing manufacturer's symbols, to aid location of the emergency controls.

Even experienced operators sometimes have difficulty locating the auxiliary controls that every MEWP is fitted with.

This decal (sticker) is a practical visual aid and a prime example of an industry initiative to make access equipment even safer.

The decal should be positioned to clearly indicate the location of the auxiliary controls. Employers should ensure that somebody at ground level is properly trained on how to use the controls and can gain access to the controls in an emergency.

Personnel must never attempt to climb out of an elevated MEWP if the emergency back-up system fails to work, but should stay in the work platform until rescued by other means.

Decal for auxiliary controls for descent in an emergency

 This decal is available to download free from the IPAF website.

8.7.3 Overturning

- Check for soft ground, drains and other unsuitable ground conditions before deploying the outriggers or stabilisers; check for any hazards before siting the machine. These items should all be considered at the planning stage.

- Beware of overloading, especially if the work platform is being used at maximum outreach to remove fans, motors or other heavy loads. Always observe the rated capacity (SWL).

- Be careful when operating on a slope, even if the machine is properly levelled with the stabilisers or outriggers.

- Always check that the machine is stable before operating.

- Be careful when travelling with the work platform raised, especially on poor ground conditions. Check that the MEWP is designed to be moved in the elevated position.

- Never attempt to travel while the outriggers or stabilisers are deployed, unless the machine is designed for this purpose.

- Be careful not to collide with any obstruction or other vehicle.

Mobile boom

- Some modern machines are fitted with a tilt sensor, which, if activated, enables the work platform to only be lowered.

8.7.4 Fall protection

The following refers predominantly to the use of boom-type MEWPs although, in some circumstances, parts could also be relevant to the use of scissor or other vertical lifts. Personal fall protection systems come in two categories: work-restraint systems and fall-arrest systems. In most instances for MEWPs, the use of work restraint is preferable over fall arrest due to the impact that the forces resulting from a fall could have on the stability of the MEWP.

8.7.4.1 Work-restraint system

Work-restraint equipment prevents the fall from happening. The main feature of work-restraint equipment is that a shorter lanyard is used, which restricts the operator's limit of travel to the confines of the work platform. Lanyards should be carefully selected, taking into account the features of the machine on which they are to be used, to ensure that the user cannot get into a situation where a fall could occur. The lanyard must always be attached to a designated anchor point in the work platform. A work-restraint lanyard must **not** be used for fall arrest.

8.7.4.2 Fall-arrest system

Fall-arrest equipment allows a person to fall but arrests the fall before the person hits the surface below. Where a decision has been taken to rely on fall-arrest equipment as a means of preventing injury, it will be necessary for the operator to wear a full body harness and a lanyard equipped with an energy absorber. Vital considerations are shown below.

- The height at which work is being carried out must be such that it allows the energy absorber to deploy to arrest the fall before the wearer hits the surface below. A minimum working height of 6.75 m is recommended if fall arrest is to operate successfully.

- The anchor point on the machine must have been designed to withstand the shock-loading of arresting a fall. Many anchor points fitted to MEWPs are only rated for work restraint. If it is not marked with its rating, contact the manufacturer.

- Users of harnesses and lanyards must have been trained in their use, inspection and care.

IPAF recommends a full body harness with a short lanyard in boom type platforms

- In arresting a fall, a boom-type MEWP will flex, which could eject other occupants and materials out of the basket. This could also overturn the machine if it is operating at maximum outreach.

- A check must be made that the structure has no projecting features that the falling person would strike during the fall.

- Decide how the person who has fallen will be rescued after the fall has been arrested. This may be as simple as another operator gently lowering the boom of a MEWP using the ground level controls until the fallen person is at ground level.

An exception to wearing a harness whilst operating a MEWP is when the machine is working over, or near to, water where there is a risk of drowning. In these scenarios a lifejacket should be worn.

 Visit the IPAF website to download free Clip on! decal stickers.

 For advice on the inspection of harnesses and lanyards refer to the HSE information sheet *Inspecting fall arrest equipment made from webbing or rope* (INDG367).

8.7.5 Working over or near to water

There could be a danger of drowning where a MEWP, particularly an articulating boom (cherry picker), is being used over, or near to, water. It is possible that the work platform could come to rest underwater if it were to overturn. It is essential, therefore, that the occupants do **not** clip on to the anchorage point, and do wear appropriate personal flotation equipment (such as a lifejacket). In such circumstances:

- even though the machine toppling would have a traumatic effect on the user(s), they still might have a chance of being able to swim to, or scramble back onto, dry land

- a risk assessment must be carried out to determine and implement effective fall prevention measures that would normally be covered by wearing a harness and lanyard.

 For further information refer to Chapter F05 Working over or near to water.

8.7.6 Restricted or enclosed spaces

- Extra care is needed when working in, or manoeuvring into, restricted or confined spaces to avoid collisions and/or entrapment. Operators must have a full understanding of all controls.

- If the MEWP has an internal combustion engine, remember that the exhaust fumes will cause a hazard in any confined or enclosed space.

- Batteries for units should not be charged in enclosed spaces. There is a hazard of explosive hydrogen gases being given off.

- Liquefied petroleum gas (LPG) powered vehicles should not be refuelled in a confined space. Any spillage of fuel will quickly and dramatically expand into a large gas cloud. The gas will then accumulate at the lowest point and create an explosive hazard.

8.7.7 Interference with MEWPs in public places

- Whenever MEWPs are used in public places, additional precautions should be taken to ensure segregation between members of the public and the machine. This may be by the use of barriers or posting marshals around the machine.

- Additional interlocks or guards may be necessary to prevent operation of, or tampering with, ground level controls by unauthorised persons.

- Care should be taken against the risk of entrapment as a result of inquisitive people, and especially children, getting too close or underneath MEWPs. Scissor lifts are particularly hazardous.

For further detailed guidance on the planning and safe use of MEWPs refer to the:

- *Code of Practice for the safe use of MEWPs* (BS 8460)
- HSE information sheet *The selection, management and use of mobile elevating work platforms* (GEIS6)
- HSE's online construction safety topic *Mobile elevating work platforms (MEWPs).*

8.7.8 Maintenance, checks, inspections and thorough examinations of MEWPs

For further information refer to Appendices A, B and D.

8.8 Construction hoists

Hoists of various types are widely used on construction sites. These range from high-capacity passenger/goods hoists, goods-only hoists, transport platforms, and inclined hoists (often referred to as construction hoists, where the load is guided), to scaffold hoists and trestle/beam hoists and the humble gin wheel (where the load is not guided).

As pressure increases to become more efficient and reduce manual handling, hoists are an increasingly vital part of many construction sites. The smooth and rapid movement of persons and materials assists in efficient management of projects. Even where other methods of moving materials are to be used (for example, by tower crane), it is not unusual to find a hoist used solely to assist the scaffold erection process.

The number and type of scaffold hoists and trestle/beam hoists available for hire has increased significantly and their use will require a lifting plan (*refer to Chapter C07*) to be drawn up by a competent person (lift planner). This plan must consider possible exclusion zones around the hoist in the event of the load dropping, safe slinging methods, the appropriate lifting accessories, and so on. These are a different set of risks to loads being carried in the enclosed platform of a goods hoist.

Risks can arise from a late decision to use a hoist to solve a previously unforeseen problem during construction. For example, if planning to use a hoist tied to a scaffolding system that is already in place but which was not originally designed to take the additional loadings, there is a need for careful planning and discussions with the scaffold designer before simply allowing a hoist to be hired and fixed to the scaffold.

The requirement for a dedicated power supply to the hoist must also be considered (except for manually-operated hoists and any with an independent power supply). Most are electrically powered, so the Electricity at Work Regulations will apply. The electrical requirements may result in the need for generators, which must be of adequate capacity. This introduces potential noise, fumes, fuel storage and spillage issues.

8.8.1 Types of hoist

A wide range of hoists are used on construction sites. The main types are described below.

8.8.1.1 Passenger/goods hoists

- Have a rack-and-pinion drive mechanism.
- Are tied to an adjacent structure.
- Can be erected to lifting heights of up to 250 m.
- Can travel at up to 100 m per minute.
- Are operated from inside the cage.
- Available in a range of cage sizes, up to 1.5 m wide x 4.6 m long.
- Available with payloads of up to 3,200 kg.

Hoist operators carrying out pre-use checks on a passenger/goods hoist

8.8.1.2 Goods only hoists

- Generally have a rack-and-pinion drive mechanism.
- Are tied to an adjacent structure.
- Can be erected to lifting heights of up to 100 m.
- Can travel at up to 40 m per minute.
- Are operated from outside the cage.
- Available in a range of cage sizes, from 1.4 m wide x 0.8 m long, to 1.5 m wide x 6.0 m long.
- Are available with payloads from 200 kg up to 2,500 kg.

Pre-use checks should only be carried by authorised personnel on goods-only hoists

8.8.1.3 Transport platforms

Transport platforms are dual-purpose machines that either carry goods only, in which case they are operated from outside the platform, or carry passengers, in which case they are operated from inside the platform and are restricted to a speed of 12 m per minute.

 For detailed guidance on transport platforms refer to the Construction Plant-hire Association's *Safe use of transport platforms* (Good practice guide).

8.8.1.4 Inclined hoists

- Generally have a wire-rope drive mechanism.
- Are supported by an adjacent structure.
- Can be erected to lifting heights of up to 40 m.
- Can travel at up to 25 m per minute.
- Are operated from outside the platform.
- Have platforms of about 0.7 m x 0.8 m.
- Are available with payloads up to 250 kg.

8.8.1.5 Scaffold hoists

Scaffold hoists are not hoists in the true sense, in that the load is not guided, as is the case with a goods or passenger/goods hoist. They are in fact small cranes that are generally attached to scaffolding, and have a small swinging jib on which is mounted a wire rope winch. They:

- have a lifting capacity of up to 250 kg.
- have a standard lifting height of up to 50 m.
- can lift at up to 25 m per minute.

Equipment designed to carry goods only should be marked accordingly

Inclined hoists should be supported by the adjacent structure

Scaffold hoists should only be fixed to designated points on a scaffold

8.8.1.6 Trestle/beam hoists

Trestle/beam or gantry hoists consist of a runway beam mounted in a trestle structure, with a wire rope winch mounted on the beam. The beam is cantilevered over the edge of a building roof or floor, enabling materials to be lifted from ground level. They:

- have a lifting capacity of up to 1,000 kg.
- have a standard lifting height of up to 25 m.
- can lift at up to 20 m per minute.

8.8.2 Planning and installation of hoists

The installation and dismantling of hoists requires good planning and co-ordination and must be undertaken by competent individuals in compliance with legal requirements and relevant standards. Special attention must be given to ground conditions to ensure adequate support for the hoist. The forces imposed on the structure by the hoist, its loads and inclement weather, particularly high winds, must also be taken into account. Hoist operators must be adequately trained, competent and authorised and should be specifically responsible for ensuring that the hoist is not overloaded or otherwise misused.

8.8.2.1 Pre-planning (construction hoists)

When it has been decided (ideally at the tender stage) that a construction hoist will be needed, requirements must be quantified as follows.

- Consideration of the locations for siting the hoist.
- The loads to be carried in terms of size and weight and whether goods only or both goods and passengers are to be carried.
- The likely loading on the structure and whether any enabling work or structural changes are required.
- Any constraints in the position where the hoist can be erected and whether other features (such as scaffolds) must be modified to accommodate the hoist.
- The loading on the hoist's foundations.

At an appropriate point, the user of the hoist and the supplier of the hoist should assign a competent (appointed) person who must liaise with each other to ensure that all aspects of the hoist selection, delivery, erection and use are carried out safely. The user's competent (appointed) person may need to rely upon the experience and competence of the supplier's competent (appointed) person in order to fulfil their responsibilities. The detailed requirements of these roles, both of which require specific training and previous relevant experience, are considered to be outside the scope of this chapter.

 For further information refer to the *Code of Practice for the safe use of construction hoists* (BS 7212).

A full and detailed risk assessment should be carried out before a hoist is positioned. A method statement can then be developed, which must then be agreed with the user.

8.8.2.2 Site survey

Prior to delivery of the hoist it will be necessary for a competent person, representing the supplier, and the lift planner to visit the site to establish the practicalities of installing it. During the site survey the supplier's competent (appointed) person will determine the appropriate type of hoist required, based upon the criteria and information on intended usage of the hoist provided by the user's competent (appointed) person.

The findings of the survey will determine the optimum position for the hoist, based upon factors such as those listed below.

● Co-location with materials storage areas.

● Avoidance of hazardous features (such as overhead cables).

● The need for safe access at all levels.

● The need for safe access to the cage or platform at ground level.

● The need for foundations and drainage.

● Suitable locations on the building structure for the attachment of ties.

In selecting the most appropriate hoist, the supplier's competent (appointed) person will need to take into account factors such as those listed below.

● The space constraints of the area.

● Access implications relating to the size and weight of the hoist components.

● Ground conditions and suitable locations on the building structure for the attachment of ties.

● The proximity of site features (such as overhead power lines, railway tracks and adjacent public thoroughfares).

● Other work that will take place whilst the hoist is in place and how the site might change during this period.

● Foreseeable extremes in weather conditions.

8.8.2.3 Erecting, altering and dismantling hoists

Hoists that rest on the ground must only be erected on a firm base, adequately supported and secured. All materials supporting the hoist must be strong enough to support the weight of the completed hoist structure and its maximum load, and be free from defects.

The erection of the hoist must be carried out in accordance with the manufacturer's instructions and a method statement that has been discussed with and approved by the user, as the proposed method and timing may impact upon other site work.

 Refer to Chapter C07 Lifting operations.

In many ways, erection, alteration and dismantling are potentially the most hazardous work associated with hoists on site. Anyone not directly involved in erecting the hoist should be excluded from the area.

Planning how the hoist will be erected, and deciding who is responsible for what, are vital when implementing a safe system of work. This is particularly important where the hoist will be built in conjunction with the erection of a scaffold. It is essential that the erection and, later, the modification and dismantling of hoists are properly planned, adequately supervised and carried out in a safe manner by competent people.

Where the hoist is attached to and supported by a scaffold, the scaffold must be designed to take account of the imposed loadings. This becomes more important where the use of a larger capacity hoist is being considered. Hoists should only be erected by competent, authorised personnel who hold a relevant card.

8.8.2.4 Use of part-erected hoists

It is common practice for scaffolders to build three or four lifts of scaffold, raising the components by hand, followed by the hoist company erecting the hoist to the height of the scaffold. Further erection of the part-completed hoist is co-ordinated with the scaffold contractors, so that it can be used for hoisting scaffold components as it follows the scaffold up.

LIFTING EQUIPMENT

In such circumstances, normal safe working practices may not be practical. It is important that before any hoist is used to support scaffold erecting, users of the hoists/transport platforms required for transporting scaffolding materials must first ensure that the machine is designated as a lifting platform and thoroughly examined as such before being used for that purpose.

 The rules regarding the interlocking of landing gates cannot be applied when some of the gates have not been installed. Detailed guidance is available and it is strongly recommended that anyone faced with this situation on their site obtains and reads it.

The guidance is published jointly by the National Access and Scaffolding Federation and the Construction Plant-hire Association, and is available from both organisations.

 For further detailed guidance refer to the Construction Plant-hire Association's *Transporting scaffolding in construction hoists* (Best practice guide).

8.8.2.5 Work at height

Some work at height is unavoidable when carrying out the erection, maintenance, alteration or dismantling of hoists. Work at height must always be planned in accordance with the hierarchy set out in the Work at Height Regulations.

 For further detailed guidance refer to the Construction Plant-hire Association's *Work at height on construction hoists* (Best practice guide).

8.8.2.6 Alteration

Alteration of hoists (such as increasing or decreasing the height) should be planned and carried out in the same way as erection.

8.8.2.7 Dismantling

Dismantling operations should be planned and carried out in the same way as erection. Care should be taken to ensure that adequate time is allowed in the construction programme to ensure that dismantling can be carried out without time pressures on the dismantling team. Before dismantling starts it is essential to ensure that the hoist is in a satisfactory condition for safe dismantling.

8.8.3 Safety of hoistways, platforms and cages

Where necessary to prevent injury, hoistways and/or the hoisting machinery must be segregated by a substantial enclosure at ground level. Suitable barriers must be installed at all other access points, over the full height of travel, and wherever persons could be struck by any moving part, to prevent injury and/or falls. Consideration must be given to the area around the base of the hoist with regard to loading and unloading materials, and whether a ramp or pit is required to facilitate access to the cage or platform. The area between the cage or platform and the host structure (the threshold) must be suitably protected to prevent any person or material falling through the gap at each landing.

8.8.3.1 Landings and gates

Where access to a construction hoist is required at several levels, consideration must be given to the space requirements at each landing with regard to loading and unloading the hoist. It is essential that each landing and threshold (the area between the platform and landing) can withstand the loads that will be imposed, with particular emphasis on items, such as pallet trucks, which can impose significant point loading. The mechanical or electrical features of the hoist should ensure that the gates at any landing point cannot be opened unless the cage or platform is at that landing point, and the cage or platform cannot be set in motion unless all of the landing gates are closed and locked.

 For further detailed guidance on landing and gating requirements for goods hoists refer to the Construction Plant-hire Association's *Safeguarding requirements for landing gates on goods-only hoists* (Best practice guide).

8.8.3.2 Handover

Once erected, the hoist will be subjected to a thorough examination, after which the supplier's competent (appointed) person should arrange to formally hand over the hoist to the user's competent person (lift planner). The user's competent person (lift planner) should arrange for all trained operators to be present at the handover of the hoist to receive:

- familiarisation training on the use of the hoist in normal operations
- instruction on what to do in emergency situations
- instruction on how to carry out the daily, pre-use inspections and weekly inspections.

A handover report, containing details of the instruction given, should be passed to the user's competent (appointed) person.

 For detailed guidance on the planning and installation of construction hoists refer to the *Code of Practice for the safe use of construction hoists* (BS 7212).

8.8.4 Planning and use of construction hoists for lifting operations

The planning and carrying out of lifting operations with construction hoists should be in accordance with the principles set out in Chapter C07. In addition, the points below should be taken into account.

8.8.4.1 Operation of hoists

It is essential that only operators who have been trained in the use of the hoist are allowed to operate it. The operator should:

- know the rated capacity (SWL) of the hoist

- be able to accurately assess the weight and distribution of any load brought on to the hoist, and therefore identify if it is overloaded

- have access to accurate wind-speed figures and be aware of any limitations placed on the hoist

- be able to lower the hoist to the next landing in the event of a power failure (passenger carrying hoists only)

- carry out daily, pre-use checks and weekly inspections, and take the appropriate follow-up action as necessary. On some complex hoists, it may be necessary for the weekly inspection to be carried out by an employee of the hoist company.

Each hoist should only be capable of being operated from one position at any one time. Where, as in the case of a goods only hoist, the operator is not carried on the platform, they must have a clear view at all levels from the operating position or, if they have not, arrangements must be made for signals to be given to them at each level.

Whatever the system of signalling used, it must be distinct and clear to the operator.

It is reasonable to expect that the hoist operator and the person(s) giving signals are at least 18 years of age. It is not illegal for younger people to do this work but, under regulations, a specific risk assessment would need to be carried out to ensure that immaturity had been considered. Irrespective of their age, hoist operators must be trained and competent, unless under constant supervision by a competent person for the purpose of training. Competence can be evidenced via the relevant scheme (for example, the CPCS Hoist operator card).

8.8.4.2 Safety notices

The platform of a goods hoist must carry a notice stating:

- the rated capacity (SWL)

- that passengers must not ride on the hoist

- any restrictions regarding load position and concentration.

Cages for passenger hoists must carry a notice stating:

- the rated capacity (SWL)

- the maximum number of passengers that can be carried

- any restrictions regarding load position and concentration.

Landing gates for goods only hoists must carry a notice stating:

- 'Goods only hoist'

- 'No passengers'

- 'Keep gates closed'

- the rated capacity (SWL) in kg.

Landing gates for passenger/goods hoists must carry a notice stating:

- 'Keep gates closed'

- the rated capacity (SWL) in kg.

8.8.5 Carriage of persons in hoists

No person should be carried in a hoist, unless it is a designated passenger/goods hoist or transport platform and it is provided with the following.

- Gates that shut to prevent persons falling out or being trapped between the cage and any other part.

- An efficient interlocking device, which ensures that gates can only be operated when the cage is at the landing place, and that the cage cannot be moved until the gate is closed.

- An efficient automatic overrun device to ensure the cage will come to rest at its lowest and highest points of travel.

The construction of the cage or platform must be such as to protect passengers from falling objects. No person should be allowed to travel in a hoist that is designated a goods only hoist.

8.8.6 Security of loads

All loads must be secured to prevent any part from slipping and falling. Loose materials (for example, bricks and slates) must be lifted in a properly designed box or cage. The platform of a goods only hoist should have sides with a minimum height of 0.6 m, or 1.1 m high if persons can access the platform during loading or unloading.

 For detailed guidance on the planning and use of construction hoists refer to the *Code of Practice for the safe use of construction hoists* (BS 7212).

08

8.8.7 Maintenance, checks, inspections and thorough examinations of construction hoists

 For further information refer to Appendices A and B.

 For further detailed guidance refer to the Construction Plant-hire Association's *Maintenance, inspection and thorough examination of construction hoists* **(Best practice guide).**

8.8.8 Specific requirements for scaffold hoists, trestle/beam hoists, inclined hoists and gin wheels

Scaffold hoists, trestle/beam hoists and inclined hoists are now commonly used throughout the construction industry. These can be easily transported to the site, are quickly erected and require little operating space. They may be fitted with buckets, skips, platforms or cages. Different models allow for basic height variations of between 8 m and 30 m, although much greater heights can be reached with extensions. Load capacity varies with the model but lifting capacity of 500 kg is not uncommon. This equipment all comes within the scope of LOLER and, although free standing, is subject to the same provisions as construction hoists that are tied to a structure.

8.8.8.1 Scaffold cranes or barrow hoists

These are lifting equipment within the meaning of LOLER and must not be overloaded. The attachment of these to scaffolds is critical, and must be carried out in accordance with manufacturer instructions. They must only be attached to scaffolds made to take the loads imposed.

8.8.8.2 Trestle/beam hoists

These are classed as lifting equipment as defined by LOLER. They rely on counterweighting for stability, at the rear of the trestle frame, and supply of adequate counterweights is essential, often provided by filling bins attached to the frame with sand or gravel. Before use, checks should be made to ensure that sufficient material has been added to bins, and that they are in good condition so that ballast cannot leak out.

 For further information on maintenance, checks, inspections and thorough examinations of these two hoist types, refer to Appendices A and B.

8.8.8.3 Inclined hoists

These are lifting equipment as defined by LOLER. They are particularly useful for trades such as bricklaying and traditional roofing, and have the potential to eliminate a significant amount of manual handling. Inclined hoists are also known as roof tile or brick carriers.

New developments include telescopic and slewing functions. Load capacities go up to 250 kg and lateral extensions may be up to 35 m. They are specifically designed for use at angles between 10° and 85°, and may incorporate a hinged section to allow the hoist to follow the pitch of a roof. They provide flexible solutions to the problems of removing demolition waste from locations at height, utilising a conveyor-belt system, so care needs to be taken to ensure that the guards to the rollers are in place to ensure that fingers and/or clothing cannot be dragged in. Maintenance, inspection and thorough examination should follow the requirements for construction hoists.

8.8.8.4 Gin wheels

In many cases provision has to be made to raise tools and light materials manually with a rope and gin wheel or single block. Whilst these are still commonly used, modern variants have an automatic locking mechanism (inertia braked) to prevent the load from going into free-fall if the hoisting rope is accidentally released. The following requirements apply when connected to a scaffold.

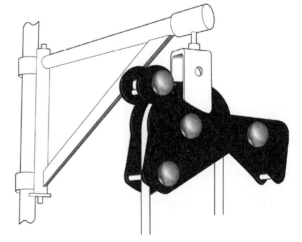

- Any scaffold tubes and hooks should be strong enough to take the load, and be properly secured to prevent movement.

- All ropes should comply with the relevant BS EN standards and fit the wheel correctly. They should be marked with a tag confirming their rated capacity (SWL).

- Preferably, the gin wheel should be suspended from a ring-type fitting passed over the end of the supporting tube and secured against lateral movement by scaffold fittings. If using a hook type, it should be properly lashed and moused.

- Any joints in standards should be made with sleeve couplers.

- Gin wheels should be suspended no more than 750 mm from the outer scaffold standard.

An inertia braked gin wheel utilising a purpose built bracket system. Inertia braked wheels are now more common and far safer than traditional gin wheels

- Hooks used for supporting materials should be safety hooks and spliced into the rope.

- The maximum load should be no more than 50 kg at 750 mm from the outer scaffold standard.

08

Whilst of simple construction, gin wheels are categorised as lifting equipment, so must be thoroughly examined before use and then at regular intervals, and the results recorded. As a guide, once weekly should be sufficient. Similarly, lifting accessories (such as the rope, hook and shackles) must be thoroughly examined before use and then at least every six months. Given the scope for the harsh treatment of this type of equipment, all parts of a gin wheel assembly should be thoroughly examined at least every six months. The extent of any thorough examination should reflect the risks that would arise from its failure.

8.9 Mast climbing work platforms

A mast climbing work platform (MCWP) is a form of temporary working platform giving variable height access to structures. They allow work to be carried out on the façade of buildings safely, efficiently and economically. MCWPs are commonly used during window replacement, lift shaft installation, curtain walling, bricklaying, cleaning and refurbishment.

They comprise a powered platform attached to one or more vertical masts, with mechanical drive units on the masts. Two or more units have to co-ordinate together to get to the required height.

 For further information on MCWPs refer to Chapter D02 Working at height.

8.9.1 Training

Training in the safe use of a MCWP on sites is available for mobile operators, demonstrators, installers and advanced installers. In addition, CPCS offers a category for mast climbing. Training is differentiated according to the following job categories and responsibilities.

Demonstrators are responsible for inducting users and ensuring that the equipment is used safely. They need to understand model-specific servicing and engineering details.

Installers, who install the platforms, must have detailed understanding and experience in erection and dismantling procedures for the models that they will be installing or dismantling.

Advanced installers are trained as managers or supervisors. They will have the ability to plan, carry out a risk assessment and method statement, and to configure special arrangements, including special tie and anchor specifications.

 Health and Safety Executive - Safety alert

The industry is alerted to a serious technical fault that HSE has found with MCWPs used widely across construction projects.

The problem

Following investigation, it has been discovered that some MCWPs that rely on two independent motor drive units per mast as the means to prevent falling with overspeed are not fitted with suitable and sufficient controls to manage this risk. This means platforms could fall from height where mechanical faults in drive units go undetected. If not rectified quickly, the fault could cause serious injury, or even death.

Failures in drive units can be such that neither the centrifugal brakes (intended to limit the speed of descent) nor the automatic brakes (intended to engage when powered travel is stopped) are able to have an effect.

Immediate action required

The installer must take immediate action as required, and check that necessary control measures are in place for all MCWPs in use or available for use on site. If measures are not in place, they need to withdraw MCWPs from use until those responsible for supply, installation, inspection, servicing, maintenance and for thorough examination of MCWPs ensure that the following are carried out.

- There is the means to identify a loss of mechanical integrity in each drive unit to prevent falling with overspeed.
- Each unit is fitted with a mechanical device (e.g. centrifugal brake) to automatically prevent an excessively quick descent.
- Damage to drive units due to platforms being powered onto buffers/base frames is prevented.
- Platforms and associated equipment are not damaged by physical overloading.
- Thorough examinations, inspections and tests, and visual and functional checks are appropriately planned and carried out.

For further information refer to:

- *HSE - Safety alert - Mast climbing work platforms: Failure to detect mechanical failure in drive units leading to uncontrolled fall of platforms*

 - *Lifting platforms – Mast climbing work platforms* **(BS EN 1495)**

- *Code of Practice for the installation, maintenance, thorough examination and safe use of mast climbing work platforms (MCWPs)* **(BS 7981)**

- **The Construction Plant-hire Association's** *Guidance on tying construction hoists and mast climbing work platforms to supporting structures.*

08

8.10　Telehandlers (telescopic handlers)

Telehandlers (also known as rough terrain telescopic handlers or variable reach trucks) make a valuable contribution to the construction process by enabling materials to be unloaded from delivery vehicles, transported around construction sites and placed at height (reach).

They are versatile machines that can be fitted with a wide range of attachments (such as buckets, skips, work platforms and crane jibs). The manufacturer's recommendations for the fitting and use of attachments should be followed. Unfortunately, there have been a significant number of accidents involving the use of telehandlers, which have tragically included a number of fatalities.

As with all lifting equipment the safe use of telehandlers requires selecting the right equipment, which has been adequately maintained, planning the operation effectively and having a trained and competent operator.

8.10.1　Types of telehandlers

Telehandlers fall into two broad categories, non-rotating and rotating.

8.10.1.1　Non-rotating

These machines comprise a powered wheeled chassis onto which is mounted a telescopic boom, pivoted on the chassis, which can be elevated from below the horizontal to an angle approaching the vertical.

The outer end of the boom is fitted with a fork carriage and forks for handling unit loads. Levelling of the forks in the longitudinal plane, as the boom elevation changes, is carried out automatically.

These machines are able to transport loads from one part of a site to another and place the load at height. On construction sites, the wheels are generally fitted with lug grip tyres to enable the chassis to negotiate rough uneven ground.

Various drive and steering configurations are available (such as two-wheeled drive, four-wheeled drive, pivot steer, rear-wheel steering and four-wheeled steering).

Many telehandlers are fitted with stabilisers that are deployed when the machine is stationary to provide additional stability and enhance the machine's lifting capacity.

Telehandlers are often fitted with a feature that allows the chassis to be levelled laterally, where appropriate, before the boom is raised, when the machine is standing on uneven ground.

Typical non-rotating telehandler

Typical rotating telehandler

8.10.1.2　Rotating

Rotating telehandlers have all of the features of the non-rotating type, but with the addition of a rotating or slewing superstructure on which the boom and operator's cab are mounted.

These machines also have outriggers fitted at either end of the chassis that enable the entire chassis to be lifted clear of the ground for maximum stability.

The main advantages of these machines over the non-rotating type is compact chassis size, enhanced lifting height, increased stability and ease of placing loads without moving the chassis.

8.10.2　Telehandler attachments

Telehandlers are versatile machines which, in addition to the lifting of unit loads on forks, can be fitted with a wide range of attachments. Some examples are shown below.

- Sideshift forks.
- Sweepers.
- Block grabs.
- Tipping skips.

- Crane hooks.
- Crane jibs.
- Buckets (general purpose and material handling).
- Integrated access platforms.

It is essential that all attachments are compatible with the telehandler with which they are to be used.

Where necessary, the telehandler manufacturer should be consulted where third-party attachments are to be used.

Planners and operators should be aware that attachments will alter the rated capacity (SWL) and centre of gravity of the machine.

8.10.3 Quick hitches

Some telehandlers are fitted with quick hitches or quick couplers, which enable attachments to be changed easily and rapidly. They fall into two types.

Mechanical quick hitch, where the hitch is engaged with the attachment, using the boom functions combined with fork carriage tilt. Once the quick hitch and attachment are engaged, a locking pin is inserted and secured with a retaining pin.

Hydraulic quick hitch, which is engaged in the same manner as the mechanical quick hitch but the locking pin is engaged hydraulically using the controls in the telehandler cab.

Both types of quick hitch can allow the attachment to become detached from the quick hitch if the manual locking pin is left out or the hydraulic locking pin fails to engage fully. There have been several serious injuries caused by falling attachments and misuse.

 It is essential that operators get out of the cab to physically ensure that all quick hitches are securely locked before starting work with a newly fixed attachment.

For further detailed guidance on quick hitches refer to the:

- **Strategic Forum for Construction Plant Safety Group's** *Safe use of quick hitches on excavators* **(Best practice guide)**
- **HSE's online construction safety topic** *Industry guidance on quick hitches.*

8.10.4 Planning and use of telehandlers

The planning and carrying out of lifting operations with telehandlers should be in accordance with the principles set out in Chapter C07. In addition, the points below should be taken into account.

8.10.4.1 Visibility

Restricted visibility when the boom is raised or when large loads are carried, as well as poor pedestrian segregation, have been identified as major causes of accidents involving pedestrians and telehandlers. Telehandlers are often fitted with aids to improve visibility and the operator's awareness of people in the vicinity of the telehandler.

These aids should be in good working order and properly adjusted. It is the operator's responsibility to check the condition of all secondary aids to visibility and **not to use the machine** if they are not present or not working correctly. It is the site manager's or supervisor's responsibility to fully support the operator in this action.

Some telehandler operations present particular challenges. A suspended load, for example, will clearly block some forward vision, but the raised boom may also obscure vision to the side. If a telehandler is to lift suspended loads on site, the physical dimensions of the loads and their effect upon visibility must form part of the risk assessment.

If a telehandler is used to load or unload a truck, the partially raised boom will obstruct vision to the forward offside and may block the wing mirror that gives visibility to the rear offside. The safest way of using a telehandler to load/off-load is to keep the machine stationary and use the telescopic facility of the boom, rather than using the wheels. The truck driver should remain in a designated safe location.

Whilst the principal contractor has the primary responsibility to ensure adequate segregation and the supervisor must ensure that it is enforced, it remains the operator's responsibility to look around and check for the absence of pedestrians before moving and whilst manoeuvring and travelling. If the operator cannot see clearly, they should seek assistance or leave the cab to look around to confirm it is safe to continue the procedure.

8.10.4.2 Travelling on inclines, slopes and gradients

The telehandler must only operate on slopes or gradients at a speed designated by the site, taking into account ground conditions, to ensure that the operator has full control at all times. Traffic routes should be on consolidated ground or temporary roadways giving equivalent safety.

 Consolidated ground is firm ground capable of accepting the mass of a loaded telehandler without significant deformation.

The slopes or gradients given in the table are to assist planners in the preparation of traffic routes. They are the maximum gradients on which a telehandler can travel while being operated when crossing sites **in the standard travelling mode and at walking speed**.

The standard travelling mode of a telehandler is with the boom retracted, the load/fork arms lowered to provide a clearance of 300 mm and not more than 500 mm (see manufacturer's instruction manual) from the ground to the upper faces of the fork arms, and the fork arms fully tilted rearwards. Operation on any traffic route with a greater slope or in a travelling mode different to the above should be subject to a site-specific risk assessment.

Slope	%	Gradient	Angle
Maximum down slope			
Maximum up slope	15%	1 in 6.66	8.5°
Maximum lateral slope			

08

8.10.4.3 Stability of the telehandler

The stability of telehandlers and loads are affected by the condition of the ground on which they travel or stand when loading or unloading.

The area selected by the planners as a static loading area must be large enough to accommodate all the wheels of the telehandler and stabilisers or outriggers when fitted. The area should be of consolidated firm ground or surfaces giving similar levels of safety. It should be capable of accepting the mass of the loaded telehandler without significant deformation and be substantially level in both planes to ensure lateral and longitudinal stability when lifting operations are being carried out. Substantially level ground is defined as ground with a gradient of ideally 1% (1 in 100 gradient, 0.6°) but not more than the standard drainage slope of 2.5% (1 in 40 gradient, 1.4°).

When determining the area to be used for the unloading of lorries and the storage of materials, care should be taken to ensure the ground is consolidated and level. The area provided must be large enough that the telehandler will not need to make tight turns with an elevated load. A telehandler may be used for loading/unloading operations in areas that are not level if they are used within their design capabilities. Where the achievement of a level loading or unloading area is not reasonably practicable, a risk assessment will be necessary.

 Standard telehandlers are normally fitted with load movement indicators (LMI) and, in some cases, load movement limiters (LML). These prevent components (such as the boom) from extending if an overload situation is indicated. The operator should never rely on the LMI as a way of checking whether the machine is safe to pick up a load. Refer to the lift plan and lift capacity charts of the machine at all times.

 Load movement indicator units only warn of longitudinal instability. They can become inaccurate and require resetting by a competent (appointed) person on a regular basis.

Telehandlers become less stable in a lateral or sideways direction as the boom and load are raised and, because telehandlers normally have freely oscillating rear axles, the tipping lines form a triangle, rather than the rectangle of machines supported on outriggers (such as rotating boom telehandlers and mobile cranes). These effects are shown in the following diagrams.

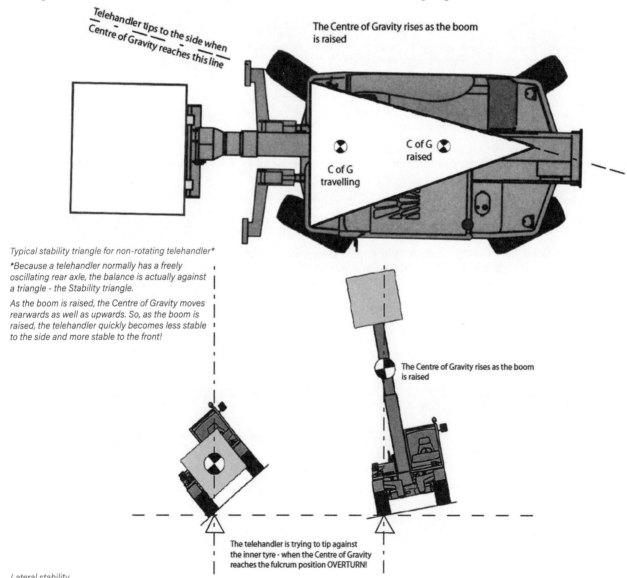

Typical stability triangle for non-rotating telehandler*

*Because a telehandler normally has a freely oscillating rear axle, the balance is actually against a triangle - the Stability triangle.

As the boom is raised, the Centre of Gravity moves rearwards as well as upwards. So, as the boom is raised, the telehandler quickly becomes less stable to the side and more stable to the front!

The Centre of Gravity rises as the boom is raised

The telehandler is trying to tip against the inner tyre - when the Centre of Gravity reaches the fulcrum position OVERTURN!

Lateral stability

When travelling with a load, the load should always be kept as near to the ground as possible.

Tyres play a vital part in the stability of telehandlers. Stability and load carrying capacity can be adversely affected by issues such as those shown below.

- Incorrect tyre pressures.
- Incorrect ply rating.
- Poor tyre repairs.
- Differences in diameter of tyres on the same axle due to differential wear.

- Tyres with identical nominal sizes being of different physical size.
- Use of tyres that are not of the required performance specification.

8.10.4.4 Wearing of seat belts

Telehandler cabs are provided with seat belts to restrain the operator and reduce the risk of serious injury in the event of a machine overturning. Machines should be fitted with green flashing lights indicating that the seat belt has been activated. A survey of telehandler accidents in the UK carried out by the HSE shows that in seven years there have been at least 72 lateral overturns of telehandlers.

In three cases, the operator was killed by being ejected from the cab and crushed; in a further two cases the operator was ejected from the cab and received serious crushing injuries. Had they been wearing seat belts, their deaths or injuries would probably have been avoided.

 It is vital that operators of telehandlers wear their seat belt at all times – it could save their lives.

8.10.4.5 Stability of the load

When using a telehandler for loading or unloading a vehicle or stack, care must be taken to ensure that the load on the vehicle or stack remains stable. Unless the correct sequence of loading or unloading is followed there is risk of the load becoming unstable with the potential for injury to persons in the vicinity.

- Loading should always be carried out with unloading in mind.
- Vehicles should always be loaded as directed by the vehicle driver, working from side to side and distributing the load evenly.
- Unloading should be carried out by reversing this sequence.
- When loading uncoupled articulated trailers, the first part of the load should be placed over the rear axle before loading from the front of the trailer.
- Care should also be taken to ensure that the part of the load on the vehicle or stack is not dislodged by contact with the telehandler carriage, forks or other attachments.
- During loading and unloading, measures (such as exclusion zones or barriers) should be put in place to ensure that personnel are kept clear as there is a greater potential for falling loads.
- Before lifting a load, it should be assessed to ensure that it will be stable and secure during lifting.
- The forks should always be evenly spaced on either side of the centre of gravity of the load.
- Long or irregularly shaped loads may have a centre of gravity that is close to the edges of the forks and may well result in the load falling during lifting.
- Long loads can be easier to control using a wider fork carriage. Personnel should be kept clear of the load and should **not** be asked to steady the load.

Use of a wider fork carriage

 The practice of undercutting, where the load is lifted on the ends of the forks, rather than back at the heel, closest to the fork carriage, is often used when the load is to be placed adjacent to a wall or another item. This practice will reduce the rated capacity of the telehandler and may affect the stability of the load as its centre of gravity may be near or beyond the end of the forks.

8.10.4.6 Use of lifting hooks or crane jibs for suspended loads

Lifting and travelling with suspended loads is not the primary purpose of telehandlers. When selecting equipment for this activity, first ensure that a telehandler is suitable for carrying out the task safely. Where other equipment is more suitable, it should be used.

08

LIFTING EQUIPMENT

Using a telehandler to lift and travel with a suspended load is generally more hazardous than lifting unit loads on the forks of a telehandler. The operation should be effectively planned and communicated to all those involved *(for further information refer to Planning of lifting operations in Chapter C07)*. The lifting of suspended loads should always be carried out with a telehandler that is fitted with a suitable lifting hook or attachment. If this can be shown to be not reasonably practicable, it is essential that any other method is justified by a robust risk assessment, taking account of the hierarchy of control.

Any lifting hook or crane jib should be marked with a rated capacity (SWL) that must not be exceeded; the rated capacity of the hook may be less than the rated capacity of the telehandler or vice versa. It is important that the lower of the two values is used to determine the rated capacity of the combination. When working out the total weight of the load to be lifted, the weight of the lifting hook or crane jib and any lifting accessories (shackles, slings, and so on) must be taken into account.

Telehandler manufacturers supplying lifting hooks and crane jibs for their own machines will generally provide reduced rated capacities where suspended loads are being lifted and carried. This is intended to reduce the risk of overload or overturn due to displacement of the load through travelling, boom movements or the effect of wind.

Extreme care should be taken when travelling with a suspended load, as any movement of the load will alter the load radius and may affect the stability of the telehandler. The signaller's position should also be considered, as they are at risk of being in close proximity.

 Basic telehandler operator training does not include lifting or travelling with suspended loads

If these tasks are to be carried out, the employer must ensure that the operator is suitably trained and assessed as competent. The majority of basic training courses only deal with fork-mounted unit loads. Only training providers who can demonstrate having appropriate expertise of suspended loads and lifting operations with telehanders or mobile cranes should be selected. Any training should also include an appropriate element of slinging and signalling.

 For further guidance on suspended loads refer to the Strategic Forum for Construction Plant Safety Group's *Lifting and travelling with suspended loads using telehandlers* (Good practice guide).

8.10.4.7 Use of telehandlers for the lifting of persons

Telehandlers can be used with working platforms to allow people to work at height. It is generally accepted that an integrated working platform provides a higher level of safety than a non-integrated type and can be used for the lifting of persons where a MEWP is not available.

 Non-integrated platform attachments must not be used for tasks on construction sites.

8.10.5 Maintenance, checks and inspections of telehandlers

 For further information on maintenance, checks and inspections refer to Appendix A.

In addition, the points below should be taken into account.

8.10.5.1 Tyre repair, replacement and maintenance

This section applies to pneumatic tyres only. Foam-filled tyres are not user serviceable.

Tyre pressure check

- Tyre pressures should be marked on the telehandler chassis adjacent to each wheel.

- Pressures should be checked daily when the tyres are cold.

- Tyre pressures should be the same for all tyres on the telehandler and should be within +5% and -0% of the manufacturer's specified pressure, unless a different tolerance is specified by the manufacturer.

  Note: *research undertaken by a major telehandler manufacturer indicates that -5% reduction in tyre pressure below the manufacturer's specified value can result in a 30% reduction in rated capacity at certain points on the load/height/radius curve.*

- Tyre pressure gauges should be of known accuracy (within +/- 1%).

- Where a tyre is found to be significantly under pressure, no attempt should be made to reinflate it and return the machine to use. It is essential that the cause is investigated by a competent tyre specialist, as this may be an indication of imminent tyre failure.

Tyre inflation applies to tyres fitted on single-piece wheels. Where multi-piece wheels are fitted or there is any doubt about the type of wheel, a competent tyre specialist must be consulted.

 For tyres fitted on multi-piece wheels refer to the BITA publication *Multi-piece pneumatic tyred wheels – Inspection, maintenance and repairs* (GN67).

- Provided the tyre has been checked and confirmed to be safe to inflate, air should be added, if required, inflating to the pressure specified in the manufacturer's manual.

- Before starting inflation a personnel exclusion zone of at least 3 m around the machine should be established by the use of barriers, cones, and so on *(refer to image below)*.

- Personnel inflating tyres should stand a minimum of 3 m away from the tyre and outside the likely explosion trajectory to avoid injury in the event of a failure. This will require at least 3 m of airline between the nozzle and the airline trigger mechanism *(refer to image below)*.

- Personnel should ensure that they stand on the other side of the telehandler when inflating *(refer to image below)*.

- Tyre valves should be checked to ensure that they are not leaking. Valve stem caps should always be replaced.

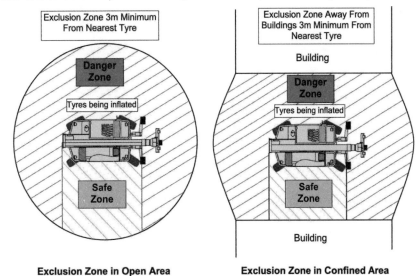

Exclusion Zone in Open Area   **Exclusion Zone in Confined Area**

Tyre inflation safe zones and exclusion zones

 For further detailed guidance on the safe inflation of tyres refer to the HSE publication *Safety during tyre inflation in motor vehicle repair* (INDG433).

e.g. A real-life example of tyre issues

A telehandler operator had been checking the tyre pressures on his machine. Having completed the checks, he was walking away from the machine when one of the tyres exploded. Subsequent investigation revealed that the tyre, which had recently been replaced, was 14 ply with a 3.5 tonne load rating rather than the manufacturer's specification of 16 ply with a 6 tonne rating. The contractor also found that the tyre had been ordered from an approved supplier by asking for a tyre for that model of telehandler, without any mention of ply or load rating. A subsequent check of other machines found that 30% were fitted with incorrect tyres.

Tyre damage. All tyres should be inspected daily. The tread and side walls should be checked for bulges, separation and cuts. For pneumatic tyres, when any cut, rip or tear is discovered that exposes sidewall or tread area cords in the tyre, measures must be taken to remove the product from service immediately. Arrangements must be made for replacement of the tyre or tyre assembly.

Tyre replacement. Telehandler manufacturers generally list a range of approved tyres in the parts manual for a specific machine. If not using an approved replacement tyre, consult with a competent tyre specialist and ensure replacement tyres have the following characteristics.

- Same physical size as the original.

- Equal or greater ply and load rating than the original.

- Tyre tread contact width equal or greater than original.

- Equivalent performance specification.

Unless specifically approved by the manufacturer, foam-filled or ballast-filled tyre assemblies must not be replaced with pneumatic tyres. When a tyre is being replaced it is essential that the condition of the other tyres is assessed by a competent tyre specialist and appropriate action taken. This may include moving partly worn tyres around, to ensure that the telehandler is substantially level when standing on a flat, level surface. If tyres on opposite sides are different sizes, the telehandler boom will not be vertical when the machine is standing on level ground. This will cause the combined centre of gravity of the telehandler and load to move sideways, which may lead to instability.

8.10.5.2 Wheel replacement

It is essential that replacement wheels have the same diameter, width and offset dimensions as the originals.

8.10.6 Thorough examination of telehandlers

 For further information on thorough examination refer to Appendix B.

 For further information refer to the Strategic Forum for Construction Plant Safety Group's *Safe use of telehandlers in construction* (Good practice guide).

08

8.11 Excavators used for lifting

The use of excavators for lifting operations, particularly on construction sites, has become more common over the last few years. Excavators and backhoes are primarily designed for earthmoving, not for lifting operations. When planning a lifting operation, consideration should be given as to whether an excavator is the most appropriate machine, taking into account the type of lift and the duration of the task.

The use of an excavator or backhoe for lifting creates additional hazards for personnel in the vicinity. Under normal circumstances, personnel are kept away from the working area around the bucket, as this is considered to be a hazardous area. Where the excavator is used for lifting, the slinger has to be in the danger area in order to hook the load onto the hooking device. This puts the slinger at risk of being struck by the load, bucket or excavator arm if the excavator moves without warning.

8.11.1 Planning and use of excavators used as cranes

The planning and carrying out of lifting operations with excavators should be in accordance with the principles set out in Chapter C07. In addition the following points should be taken into account.

8.11.1.1 Excavator requirements when used for lifting

The design of earthmoving machinery for lifting (object handling) is covered by BS EN 474 Parts 1, 3, 4 and 5. Any such machine designed for object handling should have a rated object-handling capacity table available inside the cab. If this is not available, then the machine should not be used for object handling.

 Handling attachments (for example, grab) that do not require the assistance of a person for hooking or guiding are considered to be part of normal earthmoving operations and do not require warning devices and a rated capacity (SWL) table.

An earthmoving machine used for lifting operations must be fitted with a load hooking device. If the device is a hook, then this should have a clip or other device that prevents a sling slipping off the hook. Many quick hitches provide a load hooking device in the hitch design. If the rated lifting capacity for an excavator or the backhoe portion of a backhoe/loader is greater than one tonne (or the overturning moment is greater than 40,000 Nm) then the machine must be fitted with the following.

- A boom-lowering control device on the raising boom cylinder(s) that meets the requirements of ISO 8643:2017.

- An acoustic/visual warning device that indicates when the object-handling capacity or corresponding load moment is reached.

A change in the definition of rated object-handling capacity, in the latest version of EN 474, affects excavators manufactured and CE marked after 29 December 2009 and UKCA marked on any equipment purchased from 1st January 2021. It requires any new excavator that has a rated capacity (SWL) of over one tonne, and which is going to be used for lifting, to be fitted with a rated capacity indicator (RCI) and check valves. Previously, some manufacturers had been marking the excavator for a rated **lifting capacity** of one tonne even though it had a **rated capacity** in excess of this. Excavators manufactured and CE marked before 29 December 2009 are not affected by these changes.

 - **Loaders and the loader portion of a backhoe/loader do not require a boom-lowering control device or acoustic/visual warning devices.**

- **Where a risk assessment shows that there is a significant risk of overloading and/or overturning on machines with a rated capacity (SWL) of one tonne or less, a rated capacity indicator may be required. (*Refer to LOLER ACoP and Guidance.*)**

Suitable slings must be available to attach the load to the excavator. Slings and other lifting accessories should be CE marked, or UKCA marked on any equipment purchased from 1st January 2021, and marked with the rated capacity (SWL).

Whilst BS 7121 (*Code of Practice for safe use of cranes*) may not specifically refer to excavators used as cranes, compliance with all the appropriate parts of BS 7121 would assist in the provision of safe systems of work, as required by Section 2(2) of the Health and Safety at Work etc. Act 1974.

8.11.1.2 Lifting of persons with excavators

Excavators should not be used under any circumstances for the lifting of persons, as they are primarily designed for excavating with a bucket and consequently are capable of operating speeds and movements that make them totally unsuitable for the lifting of persons.

8.11.1.3 Load attachment

Where the hooking device (the point on the machine designed for connection of the load) is not part of the bucket, the bucket should (where possible, and unless the manufacturer's instructions specify otherwise) be removed in order to improve visibility and reduce the weight being lifted. If the bucket is retained, then the weight of both the bucket and quick hitch has to be added to the load when determining whether the load is within the rated capacity.

 When attaching lifting slings to the hooking device or lifting point care should be taken to ensure that the slings and their attachments are able to hang free at all times.

Attachment using a shackle may limit rotation if, for example, a pipe suspended from the slings is to be turned end to end

Hitch tilted backwards with master link subject to bending

 If the quick hitch is tilted backwards and/or the dipper arm is raised, the master link of the sling and any attachments may bend or twist – possibly leading to damage or failure.

Hitch tilted backwards with master link subject to twisting

Using a swivel to overcome this problem

Good practice of chain and master link hanging freely without obstruction

 For further information on quick hitches refer to *Quick hitches* within Chapter C06 Mobile work equipment.

 It is essential that operators get out of the cab to physically ensure that all quick hitches are securely locked before starting work with a new attachment.

For further guidance on planning and carrying out lifting operations with excavators refer to the Construction Plant-hire Association's *Lifting operations in construction when using excavators* (Guidance).

 For further detailed guidance on quick hitches refer to the Strategic Forum for Construction Plant Safety Group's *Safe use of quick hitches on excavators* (Best practice guide).

08

8.11.2 Maintenance, checks, inspections and thorough examination of excavators used as cranes

 For further information refer to Appendices A and B.

In addition the following points should be taken into account.

8.11.2.1 Thorough examination of quick hitches

Quick hitches used for lifting fall under the thorough examination requirements of LOLER, whilst those not used for lifting fall under the inspection requirements of PUWER. The periodic examination and/or inspection of quick hitches forms a vital addition to planned preventive maintenance. It provides evidence of the adequacy of a maintenance regime and highlights any deficiencies, leading to improved reliability and safety of the hitch being used. The requirements for examination or inspection vary with the type of hitch, and consequently the type of examination/inspection and its frequency is a decision for the competent (appointed) person carrying out the examination/inspection.

 For information on the legal minimum requirements for quick hitches see the current version of the HSE - _Quick hitch devices on excavators 23.10.13_. In all cases, seek guidance from the competent (appointed) person regarding the most appropriate regime for a particular hitch.

 Quick hitches

The nature and extent of both LOLER thorough examinations and PUWER inspections are risk based and since the risks associated with quick hitch failure are similar for lifting and non-lifting duties, good practice requires that all quick hitches:

- that remain permanently fitted to a machine are thoroughly examined and/or inspected at the same time as the base machine
- suitable for lifting (fitted with a lifting eye), which are regularly removed from the machine (as interchangeable equipment), are subjected to a periodic thorough examination at intervals not exceeding six months.

All quick hitches subject to thorough examination must be permanently marked with a unique identification number. If a quick hitch does not have such a number, the owner/user must ensure that one is applied. Reports of thorough examination should contain the details required by Schedule 1 of LOLER.

 Refer to Appendix C for information on Schedule 1 of LOLER.

Thorough examinations should be carried out by competent (appointed) persons who have the genuine authority and independence to ensure that examinations are properly carried out and that the necessary recommendations arising from them are made impartially.

8.11.2.2 Thorough examination/inspection following major alteration, damage or incident

If the quick hitch has been subjected to major alteration, repair, damage or has been involved in an incident, it should be thoroughly examined/inspected before it is put back into service.

e.g. Major alterations

- Alteration of attachment mechanisms.
- Attachment of lifting eyes.
- Modification of pin bores.
- Application of heat.

8.12 Lifting accessories

Lifting accessories are items of equipment used for attaching the load to the lifting equipment (such as chains, ropes, slings, hooks, spreader-beams, shackles and eye bolts). All lifting accessories must also be:

- properly constructed and maintained
- free from any defect or damage likely to affect their strength
- regularly maintained and inspected
- thoroughly examined
- securely attached to the lifting equipment (for example, the crane) and the load
- used within their rated capacity (SWL).

Accessories used for lifting must be thoroughly examined at six monthly intervals, or more regularly if being used in harsh conditions with records kept as specified in Appendix B.

8.12.1 Marking

All lifting accessories must be clearly marked with their rated capacity (SWL) and carry an identifying mark. Where this is not possible then a coding system (such as a tag or colour code) should be used to allow the user to determine the rated capacity (SWL). A lifting accessory may also be marked with its own weight, which is a consideration when assessing the total load to be lifted.

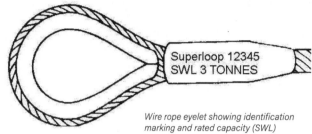

Wire rope eyelet showing identification marking and rated capacity (SWL)

Where the rated capacity (SWL) depends on the configuration of a lifting accessory (such as a two leg chain) then the rated capacity (SWL) for each configuration should be clearly marked on the equipment using a tag or by a chart available at the point of use.

8.12.2 Overloading

Lifting accessories must never be overloaded, except under test conditions authorised by an experienced and competent (appointed) person.

8.12.3 Preventing damage

The edges and corners of a load should be packed to prevent sharp edges damaging lifting ropes, chains or slings.

8.12.4 Hooks

All hooks used for lifting must be fitted with a safety catch, or otherwise shaped to prevent the sling eye or load coming off the hook.

8.12.5 Slings

Slings must be attached correctly to the lifting equipment by an approved method, either by securing the ring directly onto the hook if size permits, or by use of a suitable shackle, fitted with the pin of the shackle on the hook and the load suspended from the bow.

Open top swivel hook   *Hook with spring-loaded safety catch*   *Liverpool or 'C' hook*

The correct method of slinging will vary with the types of load, the different materials or the items lifted. It is essential to see that the load is secure. Care must be taken to see that slings are not damaged. Suspect or defective slings must be discarded.

Tag lines, securely attached to the end of the load, should be used when handling long or large loads, to direct the load into position and prevent it spinning. Tag lines should be as short as possible.

Multiple slings (two-legged, three-legged, and so on) must be connected by a ring or shackle and the load properly distributed so that no leg is overloaded. Chandelier lifting (using each leg to lift a load at different heights) must not be undertaken when using multi-legged slings as this would place the slinger in danger when detaching the load.

When the sling is in use, the angles between sling legs should be less than 90°. At angles greater than 90°, the strain on each leg increases rapidly to a point where they may break because of overloading.

With a simple two-legged parallel sling, the load on each leg is half the total load. As the angle between sling legs increases, the load on each sling leg increases to approximately double at an angle of 120°.

With a sling angle of 90°, the rated capacity (SWL) of the sling should be at least 43% greater than the nominal weight of the load.

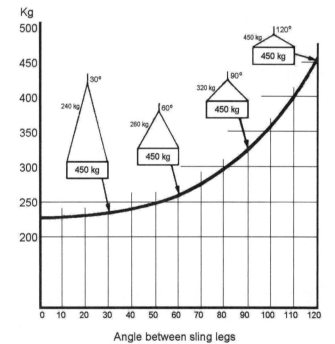

Good practice showing the load in each sling leg increasing as the angle between the sling legs is increased

8.12.6 Repaired lifting accessories

Any lifting accessory (chain, sling, and so on) that has been altered or repaired by welding must be thoroughly examined and may require testing before being put back into service. The record of thorough examination should be kept until at least the next scheduled thorough examination.

LIFTING EQUIPMENT

Knotted ropes, chains or slings and those that have been shortened or joined by nuts and bolts through the links must not be used.

Any lifting accessory that is thought to have suffered a loss of strength, been damaged or overloaded, or is otherwise defective, should be withdrawn from use and quarantined. The accessories should be disposed of or re-examined by a competent (appointed) person who will recommend that either it can be put back into service or must be disposed of.

8.12.7　Construction of slings

Slings are available in a wide range of styles made from many different materials to suit particular purposes.

Chain slings are made from various grades of steel. They can stretch and the links, rings or hooks may become distorted and fracture if subject to excess stress.

Chain slings should only be shortened by using the correct shortening clutches. Chains must not be knotted or joined by nuts and bolts. Hooks must be of the 'C' type or fitted with a safety latch. No chain sling should be used if the angle from the vertical exceeds 60°, as beyond this point the forces in the legs drastically increase.

Chain slings or lifting chains should **never** be used for towing a site vehicle horizontally.

Wire rope slings are made from drawn steel wire. Each leg of the sling will have an eye formed at either end. Wire rope slings may be damaged when kinked sharply or if put under stress when twisted. Steel wire rope may be damaged by corrosion through poor care and storage.

Wire rope slings must not be made up on site using bulldog grips.

Wire ropes and slings are supplied in many different types of construction, for different lifting applications. It is therefore important, when ordering an item, to specify the intended use.

Fibre rope slings might be made from natural fibres (manila, sisal or hemp) or synthetic fibres. Slings made from natural fibres can be prone to rotting. Only purpose-made slings, clearly marked with their rated capacity (SWL), should be used on site.

On no account should slings be fabricated from lengths of rope found lying around the site. Fibre rope slings are more easily cut or damaged, and should be visually examined by a competent person every time before use to ensure they are serviceable. Natural fibre ropes should not be used for making up slings on site.

Synthetic fibre ropes do not rot but can be affected by some chemicals. Care should be taken to avoid contamination with alkalis or acids. **Suspect or contaminated synthetic fibre ropes and slings must not be used.**

Flat lifting slings and strops are used where special lifting operations are required and afford a certain amount of protection to the load.

Flat and round slings may be made of woven synthetic materials (such as nylon, polyester, polypropylene and Terylene) with 'eyes' sewn in, or plastic-coated wire mesh, or formed by a series of plaited wire ropes (rope made from strands of high tensile wire) between two end fittings. These might also be covered with a plastic material. All woven materials are prone to damage and should be regularly checked for serviceability. Slings should be protected from sharp edges and placed evenly about the load, not twisted. Care must be taken to see that the rated capacity (SWL) is not reduced by having a sling angle greater than 90°.

8.12.8　Shackles

Two types of shackle are commonly used in lifting operations. They are the **dee type** shackle and **bow type** shackle, both of which are available with threaded or plain pins.

Only bow type shackles may be used to suspend a load from a hook. The shackle must be positioned with the pin across the hook and the load suspended from the bow. If necessary, spacers should be fitted over the pin to centralise the shackle on the hook.

Overloading, out-of-balance loads and misuse can distort shackles; they should be checked regularly for shape and wear.

Dee shackle

Bow shackle

8.12.9 Eyebolts

Eyebolts are made to screw into or through a load, and may be plain (dynamo) or have collars, with or without links. The plain eyebolt is good only for vertical loading. Even when a collared eyebolt is used, the rated capacity (SWL) is reduced if the load to which it is attached is initially lifted at an angle.

Collared eyebolts with links may be used providing the angle of load to the axis of eyebolt thread does not exceed 15°. Over 15°, rated capacity (SWL) must be derated in accordance with *Forged steel eyebolts Grade 4* (BS EN ISO 3266) for general lifting purposes. When installed, the collar must be at right angles to the hole, should be in full contact with the surface, and be properly tightened.

The load should always be applied in the plane of the eye, never in the other direction. If necessary, washers or shims should be inserted below the collar to ensure that the eye is correctly aligned when tight. Extreme care must be taken to ensure that metric threaded eyebolts are not inserted in imperial threaded holes. Although these might appear to match, it is an interference fit only, and the mechanical strength may be almost nothing.

8.12.10 Bulldog grips (wire rope grips)

Bulldog grips, if used properly to make an eye with a thimble, provide a simple and effective means of securing the ends of wire ropes instead of splicing or socketing. The final rated capacity (SWL) will be about 75% of that of the wire. It is essential that the correct size and type of grip is used, that the wire is clean and that the correct torque is applied when tightening the grips.

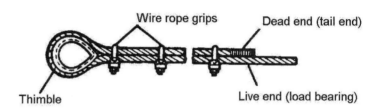

Correct method of fitting wire rope grips

Bulldog grips must be fitted with the 'U' bolt on the dead or tail end of the line (non-load-bearing end). There must be no deviation from this.

 The image of the wire rope grips shown above is for illustration purposes only. The number of wire rope grips will change depending on each specific set of requirements.

Wire rope grips meeting the requirements of BS EN 13411 are efficient when correctly installed by a competent person. In all cases, the manufacturer's recommendations should be closely followed, in addition to the advice given in the standard. The correct number of grips must be used and tightened to the correct level of torque.

The wire should be in good condition and all threads and nuts should be suitably greased. The first bulldog grip should be fitted as close as possible to the thimble and, thereafter, at a spacing of no greater than six times the rope diameter.

Nuts must be tightened to the relevant torque:

- when the rope is assembled
- when taken into use
- on the application of the load
- at periodic intervals when in continuous use.

If the above criteria are not followed, then the strength of the eye and thimble will be considerably reduced. If the criteria are neglected for an extended period, the eye and thimble may fail.

Wire rope grips must not be used to make lifting slings, long splices, or to join two wire ropes, other than with thimbles or eyes. For intermediate diameters of rope, the next-largest wire rope grip should be used, except as follows.

Maximum nominal rope diameter (mm)	Required number of wire rope grips	Tightening torque required (Nm)
5	3	2.0
6.5	3	3.5
8	4	6.0
10	4	9.0
12	4	20.0
14	4	33.0
16	4	49.0
19	4	68.0
22	5	107.0
26	5	147.0
30	6	212.0
34	6	296.0
40	6	363.0

- The 5 mm grip should only be used on a nominal 5 mm diameter rope.
- For 11 mm diameter rope, use four 10 mm rope grips tightened to a torque of 14 Nm.

8.12.11 Maintenance, checks, inspections and thorough examinations of lifting accessories

 For further information refer to Appendices A and B.

 For further guidance on the selection, use, maintenance, inspection and thorough examination of lifting accessories, and planning and carrying out lifting operations with excavators, refer to the Lifting Equipment Engineers Association *Code of Practice for the safe use of lifting equipment*.

Appendix A – Maintenance, checks and inspections

Maintenance, checks and inspections of lifting equipment are essential if the equipment is not to deteriorate over time, break down and ultimately fail. All maintenance should be carried out by a competent person who is familiar with the equipment and has the knowledge and experience to detect and repair existing or potential faults.

All work should be in accordance with the manufacturer's instructions and be carried out at the recommended intervals.

All lifting equipment should have a pre-use check carried out daily or at the start of each shift and any defects reported to a supervisor. This is normally undertaken by the operator who should be trained to carry out the checks.

In addition to pre-use checks, inspections should be carried out at appropriate intervals, either as part of the maintenance process or at more frequent intervals (such as the weekly inspection of mobile cranes).

The frequency of inspections will depend on assessment of the risk of failure of the lifting equipment and should be guided by the manufacturer's instructions.

Equipment (such as self-erecting tower cranes) often needs to be dismantled for routine inspection and maintenance to be carried out safely and effectively

 It is particularly important to ensure at frequent intervals that the load control device or rated capacity limiter on lifting equipment is functioning correctly.

The results of all checks and inspections should be recorded and there should be a system in place to ensure that all reported defects are rectified and recorded.

 Each item of lifting equipment should have a history file containing all records of maintenance, inspection and through examination. The records can be used to identify maintenance trends and protect against prosecution by demonstrating adequate maintenance in the event of an accident.

 For further guidance on maintenance and inspection refer to BS 7121 Part 2-1.

Appendix B - Thorough examination

Types of thorough examination

There are four situations where thorough examination is required by LOLER.

1. Before being put into use for the first time.

2. After installation on a new site, installation in a new location on the same site, or where significant changes have been made to the lifting equipment (such as an extension of a tower crane jib).

3. Periodically while in service.

4. After exceptional circumstances have occurred (for example, extreme weather or impact).

Frequency

LOLER place a duty on employers to ensure that all lifting equipment and lifting accessories are subjected to a thorough examination by a competent (appointed) person at intervals **not exceeding** six months for lifting equipment used for lifting persons and all lifting accessories, and 12 months for other lifting equipment.

The competent (appointed) person carrying out the thorough examination may, however, decide, for a variety of reasons, that the examination should be carried out more frequently (for example, every three months).

A thorough examination must also be carried out after any other event (such as damage or overloading) likely to have affected the safety of any lifting equipment or accessories or where the equipment has been out of use for a long period.

Furthermore, where the safety of lifting equipment depends upon the way it has been installed, as for the many items of temporary lifting equipment used on construction sites (such as hoists and tower cranes), it must be thoroughly examined after assembly and before being put into service at a new site, or a new location on the same site, or after alteration on the same site.

Competent (appointed) person

The competent (appointed) person carrying out thorough examinations must have sufficient practical and theoretical knowledge and experience of the lifting equipment to enable defects and weaknesses to be detected, and their importance in relation to the safety of the equipment to be assessed.

It is essential that the competent (appointed) person is sufficiently independent and impartial to allow objective decisions to be made. This does not mean that competent (appointed) persons must necessarily be employed from an external company. If employers and others within their own organisations have the necessary competence then they can use it.

However, if they do, they must ensure that their in-house examiners have the genuine authority and independence to ensure that examinations are properly carried out and that the necessary recommendations arising from them are made objectively.

This means that thorough examinations of lifting equipment should not be carried out by the person carrying out maintenance or installation of that lifting equipment.

In practice, lifting equipment where the consequence of failure is greatest (such as tower cranes, mobile cranes, MEWPs and hoists) are generally thoroughly examined by a third party.

Reporting

Once a thorough examination has been completed the competent (appointed) person must complete the following.

- Immediately inform both the user and the owner of the lifting equipment of any defect or risk to property or the environment, which in their opinion is, or could become, a danger to persons.

- As soon as is practicable make a report of the thorough examination in writing to both the user and the owner of the lifting equipment.

- Where there is, in their opinion, a defect in the lifting equipment involving an existing or imminent risk of serious personal injury, send a copy of the report as soon as is practicable to the relevant enforcing authority (generally the HSE for construction activities).

 Reports of thorough examinations must contain the information contained in Schedule 1 of LOLER, which is reproduced in Appendix C.

(Appendix B continues overleaf)

Retention of reports

LOLER require that reports of thorough examination are kept for minimum specified periods, depending on the type of thorough examination, as shown in the table below.

Type of equipment	Type of thorough examination	Retention period
Lifting equipment	Before first use	Until the user ceases to use the equipment
Lifting accessories	Before first use	Two years after the report is made
Lifting equipment	After installation at a new site	Until the equipment is removed from site
Lifting equipment and lifting accessories	Periodic	Until the next periodic thorough examination report is made or the expiration of two years, whichever is later
Lifting equipment and lifting accessories	Intermediate inspections	Until the next report is made

 Each item of lifting equipment should have a history file containing all records of maintenance, inspection and thorough examination, so that maintenance trends can be established and adequate maintenance demonstrated in the event of an accident.

Testing

LOLER specify that testing, including overload testing, may be considered as part of a thorough examination and should be carried out at the discretion of the competent (appointed) person.

The design of some lifting equipment and the use of high tensile materials mean that damage may be caused by conventional overload tests. Consequently, it is important that the competent (appointed) person carrying out the thorough examination or testing takes account of the manufacturer's instructions and, if necessary, consults the manufacturer before carrying out any test.

 Overload testing is not mandatory and is only carried out when required by the competent (appointed) person.

 For further guidance on thorough examination refer to BS 7121 Part 2-1 and the HSE document *Thorough examination of lifting equipment: a simple guide for employers* **(INDG422).**

08

Appendix C – Information to be contained in a report of thorough examination (Schedule 1 LOLER)

1. The name and address of the employer for whom the thorough examination was made.

2. The address of the premises at which the thorough examination was made.

3. Particulars sufficient to identify the lifting equipment including, where known, its date of manufacture.

4. The date of the last thorough examination.

5. The rated capacity (SWL) of the lifting equipment or (where its rated capacity (SWL) depends on the configuration of the lifting equipment) its rated capacity (SWL) for the last configuration in which it was thoroughly examined.

6. In relation to the first thorough examination of lifting equipment after installation or after assembly at a new site or in a new location:

   ● that it is such a thorough examination

   ● (if such be the case) that it has been installed correctly and would be safe to operate.

7. For a thorough examination of lifting equipment other than a thorough examination relating to the circumstances in 6 above:

   ● whether it is a thorough examination:
     - within an interval of six months under regulation 9(3)(a)(i)
     - within an interval of 12 months under regulation 9(3)(a)(ii)
     - in accordance with an examination scheme under regulation 9(3)(a)(iii)
     - after the occurrence of exceptional circumstances under regulation 9(3)(a)(iv)

   ● (if such be the case) that the lifting equipment would be safe to operate.

8. In relation to every thorough examination of lifting equipment:

   ● identification of any part found to have a defect, which is or could become a danger to persons, and a description of the defect

   ● particulars of any repair, renewal or alteration required to remedy a defect found to be a danger to persons

   ● in the case of a defect which is not yet but could become a danger to persons:
     - the time by which it could become such a danger
     - particulars of any repair, renewal or alteration required to remedy it

   ● the latest date by which the next thorough examination must be carried out

   ● where the thorough examination included testing, particulars of any test

   ● the date of the thorough examination.

9. The name, address and qualifications of the person making the report; whether they are self-employed or, if employed, the name and address of their employer.

10. The name and address of a person signing or authenticating the report on behalf of its author.

11. The date of the report.

08

Appendix D – MEWP handover and inspection report guidance

These guidance notes are provided to assist the people appointed by the site manager to complete reports.

The term *MEWP* covers pedestrian-controlled, self-propelled and power-operated mobile elevating work and access platforms. The types of plant typically covered by the MEWP handover report are as follows.

- Scissor lifts.
- Telescopic boom or jibs.
- Articulating and telescopic booms.

- Towable units.
- Vehicle mounted.
- Self-propelled, or pedestrian controlled.

In the case of plant provided by a plant hire company, at the site manager's discretion, a competent (appointed) person appointed by the plant hirer may conduct the inspection and complete the report. In all other cases the inspection must be carried out by the contractor's competent (appointed) person.

In the case of plant owned or hired by a contractor, a competent (appointed) person employed by the contractor may conduct the inspection and complete the report.

All completed MEWP handover reports shall be retained for inspection on site.

The report is produced in a checklist format for ease of use and is intended to provide a means by which the condition of all plant delivered to site can be checked by the competent (appointed) person. All questions shall record an answer, with a suitable comment or action included when necessary.

The competent (appointed) person is required to confirm the validity of relevant statutory documentation (such as test certificates) and thorough examination and inspection reports.

An aide-memoire is provided below to assist the competent (appointed) person on statutory requirements that apply to certain items of plant.

MEWP	Regime	Comments	Documentation
All types of mobile elevating work platform (MEWP).	Thorough examination: ■ current six monthly (LOLER) ■ after 1,000 operational hours or as stated in the manufacturer's guidance, if different ■ after major repair or modification ■ following an incident. **Note:** *conducted by a competent engineering surveyor/fitter, with reports kept for two years.*	■ Fitted with suitable devices to prevent persons being crushed, trapped, struck or from falling when riding or working from carrier. ■ Provision of suitable devices to prevent risk of a carrier failing. ■ Safe means of escape for persons trapped in a carrier.	Evidence of six-monthly thorough examination, including certification of a rated capacity (SWL).
	Weekly maintenance inspection conducted by a competent operator or fitter.		Evidence of weekly inspection.
	Daily (pre-use) visual inspection conducted by a competent operator.		Evidence of daily inspection.

 Following completion of the report at receipt of the MEWP on site, formal inspection must be recorded weekly in normal operating conditions or, under higher-risk conditions, daily.

CONTENTS

Frame erection

09

Supporting
INFORMATION

GT700 Toolbox talks / supporting checklists and forms

Toolbox talks on some of these topics are available in the GT700 publication. Supporting checklists and forms covering some of these topics are available on our companion website.

FRAME ERECTION

Overview

The erection of steel structures can be difficult and dangerous. The principal hazard and cause of injury is falling from height while working from, or gaining access to, working positions. Other hazards include structural instability during erection, lifting operations and the movement of mobile plant in work areas.

Reading this chapter will not give you the competence to erect structures. It will inform you of the common hazards and how, through practical measures, the risks can be effectively controlled, enabling the work to be carried out safely.

9.1   Introduction

The building and construction industry as a whole has an unacceptably high accident rate, and workers handling and erecting steelwork suffer one of the highest fatality and serious injury rates within the industry. The majority of fatal accidents during the erection of steel structures are as a result of falls from height. In addition, many serious accidents occur due to workers being struck by falling materials.

The British Constructional Steelwork Association (BCSA), the national organisation for the steel construction industry, has reported that the increased use of mobile elevating work platforms (MEWPs) has reduced the need to put operatives onto the steelwork, resulting in a significant reduction of falls and fall-arrest accidents reported to the Health and Safety Executive (HSE). The BCSA provides information, directories, resources and a free encyclopedia for UK steel construction information, containing freely-available information for all sectors of steel construction.

 For further information on BCSA visit its website.

Using a mobile elevating work platform (MEWP) in the erecting of framework

9.2   Important points

- Most projects involving erecting steelwork will also involve working at height and exposure to associated potential hazards.

- Designers should consider fitting steelwork with proprietary edge protection before it is lifted into place as a collective fall prevention measure.

- Designers should ensure that the erection of steelwork can be carried out safely (for example, designing-in lifting eye attachment points or specifying ground-level fabrication).

Duty holders must:
▪ avoid work at height where they can
▪ use work equipment or other measures to prevent falls where they cannot avoid working at height
▪ where they cannot eliminate the risk of a fall, use work equipment or other measures to minimise the distance and consequences of a fall, should one occur.

- A detailed schedule should be developed and implemented to ensure the safe erection and stability of the structure to completion.

- All steel erection work must be carried out in accordance with a safe system of work including risk assessments and method statements.

- The erection of steelwork should be carried out in such a way that those completing the work are on a stable working platform at all times, for example, a scaffold or a MEWP. Operatives having to go onto the steelwork should be a last resort.

- Ground conditions must be assessed to confirm suitability to take the weight of MEWPs, cranes and their loads.

- The erection of steelwork will usually involve extended crane operations, the use of MEWPs in and around the new structure, plant movements, steel laydown areas and possibly a vehicle park, all of which must be planned for when the site is first set up.

- All lifting operations, including the use of cranes and MEWPs, must be properly planned, carried out by, and under the control of, competent (appointed) persons (lift planner).

- The presence of overhead power cables, other overhead hazards and the possible need to manually align steelwork components for connection at height should be considered at the planning stage and controlled throughout the project.

 Falls from height are the biggest cause of fatal accidents during the erection of steel structures.

 For additional information and resources regarding work at height visit the HSE website.

09

9.3   Design and planning

Important items that should receive attention during design and planning include the following.

9.3.1   Structural stability

The structure must be stable at all times, from when the first piece of steelwork is put into position until it is completed.

Temporary supports (such as bracing, guys or stays) must be used during the erection of any structure that may be unstable or liable to collapse before it is completed. Additionally, where any work is carried out that is likely to adversely affect the foundations or stability of any existing building or structure (or one under construction), all practicable precautions (such as shoring) must be taken. This should be noted in a temporary works register, and a design brief should be developed.

9.3.2   Temporary structures

Any temporary structure must be of good construction, adequate strength and stability, made of sound materials, free from obvious defects and be properly maintained.

 For further information refer to Chapter C04 Temporary works.

9.3.3   Safe means of assembly or making connections

Assembly of steelwork components or making connections should be planned so that erectors can do as much of the work as possible at ground level.

Where erectors have to work at a height, provision must be made for safe means of access to the connecting points and any other working areas. Ideally, work will be carried out from MEWPs operating on a suitable surface. However, where this is not possible, designers should consider the following points.

- Is there adequate working space and a suitable work platform for a crane?
- Connections between steelwork components that are simple to make off site can be assembled or fabricated at ground level to reduce the need to work at height.
- The provision of fixed work platforms and ladders.
- The provision of designated anchorage points for safety nets, fall prevention and arrest devices.

9.3.4   Steelwork components

The size, weight and shape of individual steelwork components will influence safe handling and erecting. Designers will need to consider the following.

- Optimising the length of structural members in an attempt to reduce the number of connections at height.
- Identifying the positions where components should be lifted (marked with pen or paint).
- Identifying and indicating centres of gravity where these are not readily evident (marked with pen or paint).
- Marking components as an aid to identification (also to prevent costly mistakes).
- Calculating the weights of components to assist in ensuring safe crane capacities and the location of cranes.

9.3.5   Safe systems of work and method statements for erecting steelwork

Method statements, as part of the safe system of work, should be written for all steel erection projects. The amount of detail required in the method statement will depend on how complex the work is. The method statement should provide clear evidence that attention has been given to design and planning, as well as to ensuring that the project is completed without risks to health and safety.

A typical safe system of work should include the following information.

- Details of how the project will be managed and how health and safety risks will be eliminated, avoided or reduced.
- Details about the site, including any hazardous features (such as power lines or basements) and what effect these will have on the project.
- The required level of competence of the people undertaking the work.
- The safety precautions to prevent falls from height (for example, arranging for as much assembling as possible to be done at ground level, minimising the number of connections to be made at a height).
- How people will be protected from falling objects (for example, use of screens, fans and debris nets, installation of barriers, exclusion zones and warning notices at ground level).
- Details of plant requirements (such as cranes, MEWPs and other lifting equipment) and the competencies required to operate them.
- Arrangements for the safe receipt, off-loading, storage and handling of steelwork components on site.

09

FRAME ERECTION

- Details of where and how steelwork will be assembled prior to erection.

- The sequential method of erecting the structure and how stability will be ensured at all times.

- How work such as slinging, lifting, unslinging and the initial and final connecting of steelwork components will be carried out safely.

- The means of providing safe access and a safe place of work by methods such as mobile towers, temporary platforms and walkways.

- Details of the means of communication during lifting operations.

- Any requirement for safety nets, safety harnesses and fall-arrest devices (provisions for design features should be specified, for example, attachment points for ladders, safety nets and fall-arrest devices).

- A contingency plan for dealing with any problems that may arise, including emergencies and rescues.

 For further information refer to Chapter A05 Risk assessments, method statements and permits to work.

9.4   Site considerations

Potentially hazardous site conditions should be identified. Some typical examples include the following items.

9.4.1   Overhead power lines

If there are any overhead power lines near the proposed erection site, the local electricity supply company must be consulted. The power lines should be made dead, temporarily rerouted or other suitable precautions (such as overhead cable goalposts) taken to prevent any close approach to, or contact with, live overhead lines.

 For further information refer to Chapter D07 Underground and overhead services.

 For further information on working near overhead power lines and for additional resources visit the HSE website.

9.4.2   Other contractors and their work

Certain work or processes on, or adjacent to, the site may have the potential to adversely affect the health and safety of workers on site. For example, noxious gases, vapours or dusts may be given off from chimneys, stacks, tank vents and ventilation ducts. These may not cause a problem at ground level but may affect steelwork erectors working at height.

9.4.3   Access and egress

The contractor, or principal contractor on a project involving more than one contractor, should check that all of the vehicles associated with the erection or dismantling of steelwork can access and exit the site safely. It is envisaged that the vehicles will mainly be cranes, MEWPs and delivery vehicles (delivering steel and plant).

A safe location for delivery vehicles to park must be identified and communicated to the steelwork contractor if their vehicles need to wait to be admitted to the site to be unloaded. This area must not be immediately outside the site or on any access road, if being there would create an unacceptable obstruction or other hazards for passing traffic or pedestrians. On larger sites, space should be allocated as a dedicated lorry or trailer park.

On sites where there is no space to park large vehicles, appropriate arrangements (such as a road or lane closure) must be made for delivery vehicles (and possibly mobile cranes) to be parked on the public highway adjacent to the site boundary for the off-loading of steel.

Where there is a loading or unloading bay for only a single vehicle, a strict schedule of delivery times must be written, communicated to the steel delivery contractors and adhered to. In this instance, it is highly advisable to identify a vehicle holding area, to which vehicles that miss their slot can be sent pending the allocation of another unloading slot.

Every effort should be made to avoid the need for vehicles to reverse, particularly out of the site gate and back on to a public road. Where this is not possible, suitable precautions must be taken (for example, the use of one or more vehicle marshaller or an alternative traffic-control system). Separate routes must be provided for pedestrians and vehicles and, where possible, separate entrances.

 For more detail on delivery and transport management refer to Chapter C01 Site organisation.

9.4.4   Housekeeping

Construction sites must, so far as is reasonably practicable, be kept in good order and a reasonable state of cleanliness. Platforms, gangways, floors and other places must not be obstructed by waste or loose materials. Projecting nails or similar sharp objects in timber or other materials must be removed or knocked down to prevent injury. Materials must be stacked safely.

 For posters that can be used for guidance on preventing slip and trip hazards visit the HSE website.

9.4.5   Existing site features that require consideration

- Suitability of access and egress routes for vehicles and lifting equipment.
- Ground contamination from previous use of the land.
- Ground-bearing capacity for delivery vehicles, lifting equipment and storage of steelwork.
- Checks for underground services.
- Amount of space required for the safe handling and storage of steelwork.
- Adjacent land uses (for example, railway lines).
- Restricted (crane) oversailing rights.
- Restricted area(s) for vehicle movements.
- Any buildings close to the site that may affect the erection process.
- Any rights of access that may bring members of the public close to the erection site.

9.4.6   Lighting

The following areas must be adequately and suitably lit.

- Every place of work.
- Access to and exits from working places.
- Where lifting operations are in progress.
- All dangerous openings.

9.4.7   Protection from falling material

At any place where people work, steps must be taken to prevent them from being struck by any falling material.

Scaffold components, tools and other objects should be properly lowered to the ground and not thrown or tipped from a height which can cause injury.

9.4.8   Lifting and slinging

All lifting operations should be properly planned by a competent person (lift planner). The level of supervision should reflect the complexity of the operation. Appropriate precautions must be taken to ensure the stability of lifting appliances when used on soft, uneven or sloping ground. These could include measures such as ground levelling, use of mats or hard standing.

The load must not exceed the rated capacity (SWL) of the lifting equipment (allowance should be made for the weight of lifting slings, beams, and so on). Any load that approaches the rated capacity of a crane should be carefully raised a short distance and the operation stopped to check safety and stability before continuing.

If more than one lifting appliance is used to raise or lower a load, levels of supervision should be increased. All lifting appliances should be operated well within their rated capacities to ensure stability. Suitable packing should be used to prevent the edges of the load from damaging the slings.

Loads should be lifted and lowered slowly to avoid any shock loading. The use of tag lines, fixed near the ends of the load, will help to prevent the load spinning when being lifted or lowered. Loads should be lowered onto timber bearers or battens to protect slings and enable them to be removed easily.

For further information refer to:

- **Chapter C07 Lifting operations**
- **Chapter C08 Lifting equipment**
- **the Lifting Operations and Lifting Equipment Regulations.**

For further information and for additional resources refer to the HSE website and the *Code of practice for safe use of cranes – Part 1: General* (BS 7121-1).

9.4.9   Off-loading, stacking and storage of steelwork

A safe means of access and a safe workplace must be provided when off-loading components from delivery vehicles.

Two examples of recently developed safety systems are outlined below.

1. Tensioned steel wire running the length of the trailer, at above the head-height of anyone standing on the trailer. Each slinger wears a safety harness and a fall arrest lanyard, the free end of which is clipped to the tension steel wire. In the event of a trip or stumble, the slinger is prevented from falling from the trailer.

2. 'U' shaped inflatable airbags or beanbags that fit around the back and sides of the trailer to act as a soft-landing system, in case anyone falls off the trailer.

FRAME ERECTION

Many accidents have occurred during the off-loading of vehicles when releasing the load-securing mechanism. This is because the load was either not stable when loaded or because it moved and became unstable during the journey.

The stability of the load on the vehicle or in the stack must be ensured at all times. Suitable timber wedges or packing pieces can be used as an aid to stability. Precautions should be taken to prevent slingers being struck by the load (for example, taking up a safe position off the lorry before the load is lifted).

The stack must be constructed so that components can be removed without the risk of someone being trapped or struck. There may be an advantage in using a suitable transportable storage rack (stillage) for smaller components. Anyone not directly involved in the off-loading activity should not be allowed into the area.

 Pedestrians and vehicles should be kept apart where practicable.

 The HSE leaflet *Safety in the storage and handling of steel and other metal stock* (HSG246) offers practical advice to everyone involved in the delivery and unloading of steel stock.

9.4.10 Traffic routes and vehicles

Prior to, and during, steel erection, deliveries of steel on articulated transport will be a feature of many jobs. In the context of this chapter, Construction (Design and Management) Regulations 2015 (CDM) place a legal duty on the person in charge of the site to ensure the following.

- That pedestrians and vehicles can move safely and without risks to health, so far as is reasonably practicable.
- There are sufficient traffic routes, suitable for the vehicles using them.
- There is sufficient segregation between pedestrians and moving vehicles, but where this is not reasonably practicable:
  - other means of protection are provided, such as traffic marshals and exclusion zones
  - a means of warning pedestrians of the approach of vehicles, such as vehicle alarms, where the pedestrians would otherwise be at risk, is provided.
- That (vehicle) loading bays have one exit for the exclusive use of pedestrians.
- Appropriate signs are erected in the interests of health and safety.
- Steps are taken to prevent the unintentional movement of any vehicle.
- Each vehicle must be operated in a safe manner with its load arranged securely.
- Every vehicle is fitted with a means of warning people who may be at risk when the vehicle is moving.

9.5 Safe working

The safe system of work must ensure the safety of all operatives:

- whilst getting up to the place of work and down again
- during the period of time at high level before an operative is able to clip on to a means of fall arrest or fall prevention systems.

If access has to be made inside a structural steel box section or any configuration of steelwork where ventilation is poor, it should be treated as a confined space and appropriate precautions taken. The atmosphere should be tested by a competent person, before entry is made, to ensure that there is sufficient oxygen present. Continuous monitoring for oxygen deficiency will also be required.

Tests for flammable or toxic gases or vapours and oxygen enrichment should be carried out as appropriate, depending on the proposed work activity (for example, oxy-fuel cutting or burning may lead to a build up of toxic gases or toxic metal fumes).

 For further information refer to Chapter D08 Confined spaces.

All welding fume can cause lung cancer, so you must put controls in place. It can also cause asthma and many other health conditions. The HSE has issued a safety alert about the health risks of welding fume.

 For further information visit the HSE website *Welding fume: protect your workers.*

9.5.1 Stability of structures

Steel erection, by its definition, involves the assembly of structures which need to be stable at all times. In particular:

- all practicable steps must be taken to ensure that no person is put at risk by the collapse of any structure that may become unstable or weakened
- structures must not be loaded to an extent that they become unsafe

- any temporary means of supporting a permanent structure must be:
  - designed and maintained to withstand any stresses and strains that are put on it
  - only used for the purpose for which it was designed and installed
  - not overloaded so as to render it unsafe

- there may be a requirement for hold points and the use of permits to work.

9.5.2 Safe means of access and safe place of work

To comply with the Work at Height Regulations, consideration must be given to reducing the need to work at height, for example by:

- doing as much of the connecting work as possible at ground level, or from erected floor decks as the work progresses

- using a releasing device so that lifting gear can be released remotely

- ensuring that, wherever possible, inspection and testing is carried out at low level.

When people must work at height, consideration should be given to the following requirements.

- Installing permanent or temporary handrails, stairways, ladders, walkways and floor decking, so that these can be used by erectors as the work progresses.

- Providing hard standings or floor slabs so that mobile access platforms can be used.

- Providing temporary access and working platforms, including scaffolds, lightweight staging and purpose-built platforms with safe means of access.

- Working from MEWPs.

Whilst the increased use of MEWPs has brought about safer working at height, it has also created the need to ensure that MEWP operators are adequately trained and competent, and that ground conditions on the site are properly surveyed and prepared to enable the safe use of such heavy plant without the risk of sinking or overturning.

It may be appropriate in some circumstances to use other means of access to height, such as roped access techniques, which must be carried out by trained and competent persons.

Alternatively, access may be achieved by using a personnel carrying platform suspended from a crane.

There may be occasions when it is necessary to use fall arrest rather than work-restraint measures, with safety nets or other soft-landing systems being the preferred method of fall arrest.

The BCSA has stated that the increased use of safety nets has had a significant beneficial effect on the steel construction industry's accident rate.

Steel erection in progress using a mobile crane, two MEWPs and edge protection being attached to steelwork at ground level before being lifted into position

09

 For further information refer to Chapter D02 Working at height, and Chapter D05 Fall arrest and suspension equipment.

9.5.3 Edge protection

Traditionally, scaffolding was the main form of edge protection and could only be installed, modified or removed by trained scaffolders, after the steelwork was in place. However, the development of various types of system edge protection has provided opportunities for pre-installing edge protection before work at height commences.

The use of such systems can also eliminate the need for successive trades to install their own edge protection and then remove it when leaving site, only for it to be replaced by the next trade's edge protection. The elimination of such duplication has obvious safety benefits.

9.5.4 Beam straddling

There may be occasions where the work cannot be done from a MEWP or other platform and erectors may have to work from the steel frame. This is known as beam straddling.

This form of access should only be considered as a **last resort** and only where the beam is of I-beam section.

A full body harness with a twin-tailed lanyard system may be used. However, users must ensure that this system is used correctly and that the second tail is not attached to the user's harness, as this may interfere with the operation of the energy absorber.

Consideration must be made as to suitable anchor points to which the lanyard can be attached. The erector can sit astride the flange with the sole and heel of each foot resting on the bottom flange and with both hands able to grasp either side of the top flange.

Alternatively, proprietary beam-gliding devices are available to improve mobility. The risk assessment **must** consider how anyone carrying out this practice is going to be rescued following an emergency or a fall. The use of a safety harness or lanyard requires a minimum clearance below the high-level place of work to allow the lanyard to function properly in arresting a fall. Expert advice should be sought.

 For further information on safe working at height refer to Chapter D01 Work at Height Regulations and Code of practice for selection, use and maintenance of personal fall protection systems and equipment for use in the workplace (BS 8437:2005).

9.5.5 The weather

A regular weather forecast should be obtained by the person in charge of the erection programme. Weather conditions (such as wind speeds) should also be monitored throughout the work. Erection should not take place where weather conditions impose an adverse effect, for example, from ice, frost, snow, strong winds, rain, dew and poor visibility (such as fog, mist or glare).

If erection work is stopped, measures should be taken to ensure that the structure remains stable. After a stoppage due to the weather, stability of the structure should be checked by a trained and competent person before work is allowed to restart.

 This section provides an overview of the steel erecting sector and should not be read in isolation. For comprehensive understanding of the site manager's role it should be read in conjunction with all other sections A, B, C, D, E and F of GE700.

CONTENTS

Mobile workforce and driver safety

Supporting
INFORMATION

GT700 Toolbox talks / supporting checklists and forms

Toolbox talks on some of these topics are available in the GT700 publication. Supporting checklists and forms covering some of these topics are available on our companion website.

MOBILE WORKFORCE AND DRIVER SAFETY

Overview

The description of a mobile workforce covers a multitude of trades in many different situations from a lone worker called out to an emergency, with little knowledge and control, to a group of workers operating in an unfamiliar or hostile environment where customer or client control is minimal.

This chapter provides a general overview of the legal framework and some practical guidance on the management of health and safety at work for mobile, lone and out-of-hours workers. It includes information about the potential risks they may be exposed to, and practical advice on the management and control of their work.

10.1   Introduction

This chapter aims to provide employers and managers with general practical guidance on processes and controls that can be put in place to provide their workers with a safe place of work. This ranges from simply saying 'tell us where you are' to planned work that identifies mobile locations where permits may be required. Management preparation information, pre-job briefing, competence, self-discipline, control, awareness and training are also identified, all of which will form a package of safety for the mobile workforce.

Employers are responsible for the health, safety and welfare at work of all of their employees. These responsibilities cannot be transferred to any other person, including those people who work alone. It is the employer's duty to assess risks to lone workers and take steps to eliminate or control risks where necessary.

The types of workers covered within this chapter are mobile groups of workers, lone workers and out-of-hours workers.

Types of workers

- Mobile groups of workers.
  - A group of operatives working away from their home base, undertaking such work as domestic and small-scale commercial refurbishment. This can include painters and decorators, scaffolders and roof workers.
  - A group of workers undertaking minor road works *(refer to Chapter F01 Street works and road works)* and rail maintenance works *(refer to Chapter F02 Trackside safety)*.
  - Those working in areas accessed by the general public, completing work for utility companies (gas, electric, water and telecommunications).
- Lone workers.
  - This group will include maintenance workers (such as plumbers, electricians, lift engineers, water and gas specialists, domestic aerial installers, aerial and mast maintenance personnel, and many others).
- Out-of-hours workers.
  - Those identified as mobile groups of workers or lone workers may, in addition, be required to work out of normal working hours to ensure continuance of 24-hour operations or emergency response (for example, security guards or utility company workers – gas, water, electricity and telecommunications).

10.2   Important points

10.2.1   Groups of workers

- Assess the risks to the mobile workers for that particular environment and the tasks to be undertaken.
- Ensure ongoing consultation so that all relevant hazards can be identified.
- Employers with five or more employees have to record significant findings of risk assessments.
- Ensure there is a safe system of work in place prior to work commencing.
- Provide the workers with a means to undertake a dynamic risk assessment and update the risk assessment to create an 'at point of work risk assessment'.
- Confirm the workers have a suitable level of training and competency (such as CSCS, PASMA and trade qualifications).
- Decide on equipment needed. Are special transport arrangements required?

- Ensure that any vehicle being used is suitable for the number of personnel to be carried.

- Ensure the vehicle is appropriate if required to tow equipment (such as a mini digger, trailer or welfare unit).

- Ensure the vehicle is rated for the safe towing weight limit.

- Ensure the nominated driver is trained and qualified to tow.

- Consider safe access to the roof of the vehicle (such as mechanised roof access), if it is unavoidable that equipment will need to be carried (such as ladders and pipes).

- Avoid climbing on or off flatbed lorries during deliveries, consider use of pallets or pre-slung loads.

- Does the area need segregation from pedestrians or from other traffic during deliveries?

- Is temporary traffic lighting and street signage needed? *(Refer to Chapter F01 Street works and road works.)*

- Is a fire emergency plan in place, including details of actions to take, assembly point, audible warning device and fire extinguishers?

- Ensure the work area is secure, including storage of materials, suitable waste containers, and so on.

- Consider what welfare arrangements are needed for these works (for example, provision of an integral welfare unit that complies with Health and Safety Executive (HSE) requirements (refreshment/seating area, toilet, shower, clothes storage and drying, and generator), use of client's facilities (with written agreement) or public facilities within suitable proximity).

- Do the works require an emergency rescue plan – are they high risk, confined space, work at height or electrical?

- Has a first-aid kit been provided, suitable for the number of persons and risks present?

- Is a member of the group trained either as an appointed person, emergency first aider or fully qualified first aider, depending on the outcome of the first-aid needs assessment. *(Refer to Chapter B05 First aid.)*

- Have suitable containers been provided to store waste for removal to suitable disposal facilities?

10.2.2   Lone workers

 The HSE defines a *lone worker* as someone who works by themselves, without close or direct supervision.

Lone workers include people who:

- work from a fixed base but are alone on the premises (such as security guards)

- work separately from others on the same premises (for example, security staff), or work outside of normal hours

- work away from a fixed base (such as maintenance workers, health care workers and environment inspectors), work at home (home workers) and mobile workers (such as site managers dealing with multiple sites).

The following points are additional to the relevant items listed for groups of workers *(refer to 10.2.1)*.

- Does the lone worker require extra risk control measures (such as a personal alarm linked to a 24/7 alarm-receiving centre or mobile phone)?

- Has training been given in the completion of the dynamic or at point of work risk assessment?

- Does the workplace present a specific risk to the lone worker (such as vulnerable tenants or working at height)?

- Is there a safe way in and out of the premises for one person?

- Can any necessary temporary access equipment (such as portable ladders or trestles) be safely handled by one person?

- Can all the machinery and goods involved in the workplace be safely handled by one person?

- Are any chemicals or hazardous substances being used that may pose a risk to the worker?

- Does the work involve lifting objects too large for one person?

- Is more than one person needed to operate essential controls for the safe running of equipment or workplace transport?

- Is there a risk of abuse or violence?

- Are young, pregnant or disabled workers particularly at risk if they work alone and is a further specific risk assessment required?

- Are there any other reasons why the individual (for example, on medication) may be more vulnerable than others?

- Are emergency contact arrangements in place in case of an incident (such as regular reporting to supervisor, GPS systems/tracker, regular phone contact, monitoring of staff security systems and so on)?

 For further information on the risks of working alone refer to the HSE leaflet *Protecting lone workers - how to manage the risks of working alone* (INDG73).

10.2.3 Out-of-hours workers

Either lone workers or groups of workers may need to work out of hours, frequently at short notice. Therefore, the following points also apply, in addition to those above.

- Are arrangements made for emergency situations (such as who to contact and backup information)?
- Has a specific risk assessment been completed?
- Is a safe system of work in place and has the operative been provided with a method statement for the tasks to be undertaken?
- Do they have the correct equipment required, and can it be operated by the operative(s)?

10.3 Legislative requirements

Many pieces of legislation are applicable to these types of workers – some of these are listed below.

Health and Safety at Work etc. Act – the umbrella Act under which most health and safety regulations have evolved. For example, it details information regarding an employer's duties in the workplace; access and egress; provision and suitability of plant; information, instruction, supervision and training of personnel; an employee's duties and much more. *(For further information refer to Chapter A01 Health and safety law.)*

Management of Health and Safety at Work Regulations – provide guidance on risk assessments and controls, monitoring and review. *(For further information refer to Chapter A05 Risk assessments, method statements and permits to work.)*

Provision and Use of Work Equipment Regulations – provide testing and maintenance information (such as chainsaw, angle grinder and compressor). *(For further information refer to Chapter C05 Work equipment and hand-held tools.)*

Lifting Operations and Lifting Equipment Regulations – provide information on cranes, telehandlers, lorry-loaded cranes and lifting accessories, including testing and maintenance requirements. *(For further information refer to Chapter C07 Lifting operations and Chapter C08 Lifting equipment.)*

Construction (Design and Management) Regulations – provide guidance for welfare arrangements. *(For further information refer to Chapter A03 Construction (Design and Management) Regulations.)*

Work at Height Regulations – provide information on scaffolding, use of ladders and alternative means of working safely at height. *(For further information refer to Chapter D01 Work at Height Regulations.)*

Personal Protective Equipment at Work Regulations – information on legislative requirements, for example, types and uses of specific equipment (such as eye protection and respiratory protective equipment) in particular environments and training in the fitting of such items. *(For further information refer to Chapter B06 Personal protective equipment.)*

10.4 Risk assessment and control

 A risk assessment is an important step in protecting your workers and your business, as well as complying with the law. It helps you focus on the risks that really matter in your workplace – the ones with the potential to cause real harm.

Employers need to identify the potential hazards faced by workers and assess the risks involved both to these workers and to any people who may be affected by their work. Employers should ensure that measures are in place to avoid or control such risks. The risk assessment must also identify the level of supervision required. High-risk activities may require another person to be present (for example, if visiting a vulnerable tenant or for working on or near to live electrical equipment).

10.4.1 Employer responsibilities

- **Involve** staff or their representatives when undertaking the risk assessment process.
- Take steps to **check control measures** are in place (examples of control measures include exclusion zones, barriers, use of less hazardous substances and PPE, as well as training and supervision).
- **Review** risk assessments and method statements regularly. Most workplaces are subject to changes that can affect existing working practices and introduce new hazards. (Also refer to 10.4.2 Point of work risk assessments.)
- **Allow** lone working **only** where the risk assessment and method statement shows it is safe to do so.
- Where a lone worker is working at another employer's workplace, that employer should **inform the lone worker's employer** of any hazards and the required control measures.

 Refer to the HSE publication *Risk assessment – A brief guide to controlling risks in the workplace* **(INDG163).**

10.4.2 Point of work risk assessment

A risk assessment completed by the employer or supervisor should be provided to workers before any works commencing, where practicable.

However, there are many occasions (as in the examples below) when a point of work risk assessment will be required.

- To update the previously prepared risk assessment.
- As a result of changes to the working environment.
- As a result of changes to the works to be undertaken.
- For out-of-hours working, when each call out will require a specific risk assessment (for example, emergency maintenance (such as a serious water leak or flooding) or urgent utilities works (such as a gas leak or explosion)).
- For a maintenance worker who is undertaking a number of different calls in a day where generic information is available but needs to be tailored to a specific location or task.

On arrival at site report to the person on site, contact base to confirm arrival (lone worker safety protocol) and prepare a point of work risk assessment.

 Employers and supervisors must satisfy themselves that the workforce is competent to carry out a point of work risk assessment. Training should be provided that includes practical, on-site mentoring. If a site activity *cannot* be done safely, the workforce must know when *not to start*, and contact their supervisor for further advice.

Some examples of unsafe working areas and/or conditions are shown below.

- An unguarded excavation.
- Traffic not segregated.
- Permits to work and disconnections and isolations where certificates do not match.
- Scaffolding where inspection records are not present or the date has expired.
- Inadequate or incorrect equipment and lack of training on the equipment.
- No fire extinguisher.
- Incorrect tools.
- Inadequate and/or unsuitable personal protective equipment (PPE).

10.4.2.1 Filling in a point of work risk assessment

Part 1. Stop and ensure the area is safe with adequate access and egress. Complete items listed under this section. Seek advice from a supervisor if you answer **no** to any of them.

Part 2. Think about what hazards may be present and carry out a safety assessment of those identified. Determine if the existing controls are adequate. Provide brief details of your rescue plan for safe escape in the event of something going wrong. Make a note on the form of any hazards that are significant but without, or with insufficient, controls.

Part 3. Act. Detail additional hazards and control measures needed to manage the risk. Is the remaining risk acceptable for work to commence? If no, this needs input from your supervisor.

Part 4. Review, and inform your supervisor if the job created any additional hazards or if there are lessons to be learned.

10.4.3 Dynamic risk assessment

A dynamic risk assessment is a mental evaluation of the environment you are going into. For lone workers, this could be someone's home or a remote location. In these situations, the worker needs to be continually aware of any changes in their immediate environment, make judgments and take appropriate actions to stay safe.

This could include the assessment of people's aggressive behaviour or tone of voice, as well as dangerous physical issues (such as animals or changing weather conditions). This does not replace the need for a full risk assessment but is an important skill for lone workers to have.

10.5 Work-related violence

People who deal directly with the public may face aggressive or violent behaviour. They may be sworn at, threatened or even attacked.

 ***Violence at work* is defined as any incident in which a person is abused, threatened or assaulted in circumstances relating to their work.**

Lone workers are at greater risk of violence whilst at work. There were an estimated 688,000 incidents of violence at work, as noted in the HSE's report *Violence at work, 2019/20*.

10.5.1 People at risk

People who are employed in jobs (such as those below) that involve them dealing with the public can be at a greater risk from violence.

- Giving a service.
- Education.
- Delivery or collection.
- Controlling.
- Representing authority.

10

Both the employer and employees have an interest in reducing violence at work. For employers, violence can lead to poor morale and a poor image for the organisation, making it difficult to recruit and retain staff. It can also mean extra cost, with absenteeism, higher insurance premiums and compensation payments. For employees, violence can cause pain, distress and even disability or death.

Physical attacks are obviously dangerous but serious or persistent verbal abuse or threats can also damage employees' health and wellbeing through anxiety or stress.

10.5.2 Managing violence in the workplace

A straightforward, four-stage management process is listed below.

1. Find out if you have a problem.

2. Decide what action to take.

3. Take action.

4. Check what you have done.

 For further information on work-related violence visit the HSE website.

10.6 Welfare facilities for mobile workers

Health and safety legislation requires that welfare arrangements for projects of any size are prearranged prior to works commencing on site. For these circumstances there are two types to be considered.

1. Use of client's facilities – prearranged and confirmed in writing, or local public convenience. It should not be assumed that local commercial premises can be used without their permission.

2. Provision of an integrated hygiene unit, which complies with HSE requirements and includes a refreshment area, toilet, drying area and generator.

If local facilities or a portaloo are considered sufficient then van-mounted equipment could be used for washing and the preparation of food and refreshment, using a battery-powered inverter.

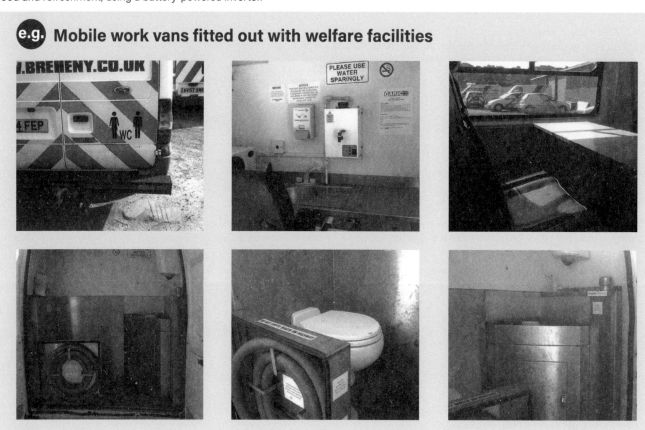

e.g. Mobile work vans fitted out with welfare facilities

 Visit the HSE website for further information about the provision of welfare facilities during construction work.

10.7   Waste storage and disposal

Waste that is created at a site must be disposed of appropriately. Hazardous waste will need to be stored in appropriate containers and removed by licensed contractors using a hazardous waste consignment note.

Non-hazardous waste generated during works undertaken by mobile groups of workers or lone workers can be transported to their base for sorting and transferring to suitable recycling facilities or landfill sites. The following points will need to be considered.

- Is the waste suitable for transporting? Is it hazardous or non-hazardous, and does it require special handling?

- Is the person removing it competent and authorised to do so? (This includes lone workers who are transporting the waste back to the depot for future disposal).

- Has the waste been segregated (for example, plasterboard separated from biodegradable waste)?

- Can the waste be segregated in the vehicle, by bagging or being placed in enclosed containers, or does it require collection from the location?

- Do the mobile workers have suitable containers to package the waste products?

- Can the waste be carried without exceeding the safe working load of the vehicle?

 If using a company vehicle to carry waste back to a depot or to a licensed waste treatment or disposal facility, then a waste carrier's licence may be required.

 For further information refer to Chapter E10 Waste and material management.

10.8   Driver safety

The nature of mobile working makes travel a necessity either between sites or operating plant. The HSE has made it clear that health and safety law applies to driving at work. Therefore, employers have a responsibility to ensure they have considered work-related road risks and implemented the necessary controls.

10.8.1   Fatigue

Another factor to consider is the effects of driving when drowsy. The vast majority of people believe that drowsy driving is unacceptable, yet the incidence of drowsy driving suggests there is a disconnect between what people say and what they do. Depending on which piece of research you read, between 20% and 40% of all accidents on the road are attributable to fatigue. Companies should encourage a healthy work-life balance and be alert to signs of driver fatigue.

Research has been undertaken to investigate the costs and understand the signs associated with drowsy driving, and to provide strategies to prevent it and explain how organisations can counter the problem.

 For further information visit the Third Pillar of Health website.

 Details of safe driving and work-related road risk can be downloaded from the Prospect website.

10

10

Index

INDEX

INDEX

CONTENTS

D High risk activities

i

CONTENTS

Work at Height Regulations

Supporting INFORMATION

GT700 Toolbox talks / supporting checklists and forms

Toolbox talks on some of these topics are available in the GT700 publication. Supporting checklists and forms covering some of these topics are available on our companion website.

WORK AT HEIGHT REGULATIONS

Overview

Falls while working at height remain the leading cause of fatal accidents and specified injuries in the construction industry. The majority of falls are from heights of less than 2 m.

Many accidents are caused by the poor selection of access equipment, by failures to provide fall prevention measures and by workers not using access equipment in a safe manner.

This chapter outlines what the Work at Height Regulations are about, what they require, what needs to be done and by whom.

1.1   Introduction

The purpose of the regulations is to reduce the number of deaths, injuries and personal suffering resulting from falls from height, and so improve the safety performance of the industry. The Work at Height Regulations came into force in 2005 and were amended in 2007.

The regulations cover all circumstances where a person is working at height, is gaining access to, or egress from, such a place of work, at, above or below ground level, where persons or objects could fall a distance liable to cause personal injury (that is, any distance whatsoever). These regulations do not apply to fixed staircases.

Common examples of tasks carried out within the construction industry, classified as work at height, are shown below.

- Working on a scaffold.
- Working from a mobile elevating work platform (MEWP).
- Standing on, or working from, the back of a lorry.
- Working close to an excavation's leading edge.

- Working on staging or trestles.
- Using a mobile access tower (MAT).
- Using ladders or stepladders.
- Working in an excavation or shaft.

Many other jobs in the construction industry also involve working at height and are covered by the Work at Height Regulations. Health and Safety Executive (HSE) evaluation reports of accidents that occurred during work at height show that common contributory factors include failures of the following.

- All parties to recognise that there was a problem.
- Management to provide adequate information, instruction, training or supervision
- Management to ensure that the safe system of work was followed.

- Management to provide a safe system of work (SSoW).
- The injured worker to use appropriate equipment.
- Management to provide safe plant and equipment.
- Collective protection to take priority over personal protection.

 Falls from height – 2021–22 statistics

- In 2021/22, 29 fatal injuries were due to falls from a height, accounting for 24% of all worker deaths over the year. While the number of fatal injuries has generally fallen over the past decade, the percentage of fatal injuries has not decreased.

 Falling from height

A timber company has been fined £80,000 after an employee fell through a stairwell while working on a barn conversion.

The 49-year-old driver and warehouse operative was working on the barn, which was being converted for rental use in May 2018.

He was trying to access the first floor of the barn from exterior scaffolding and jumped onto a piece of insulation which was covering a stairwell. The insulation gave way and the worker fractured two vertebrae in the fall.

An investigation by the HSE found the work was not properly planned, appropriately supervised, or carried out in a safe manner when the incident occurred. The company had a duty to control how the work was carried out, including staff supervision.

The timber company pleaded guilty to breaching Section 4 (1) of the Work at Height Regulations 2005, and was fined £80,000 and ordered to pay costs of £7,331 at the local Magistrates' Court. The company also ordered to pay a £170 victim surcharge.

Speaking after the hearing, a HSE inspector said: "This worker's injuries were serious. This incident could have been avoided if basic safeguards had been put in place. Falls from height remain one of the most common causes of work-related fatalities and injuries in this country and the risks associated with working at height are well-known."

 The HSE website has many resources, including a dedicated work at height section that includes information on the Work at Height Regulations, including *Working at height: a brief guide* (INDG401).

1.2   Important points

● Falls from height are the main cause of fatalities and specified injuries to construction workers.

● Falls from low heights (below 2 m) are the cause of many deaths and injuries.

● Working at height is defined as working at any height from which, if measures are not taken, a fall (of a person, materials or equipment) could occur and cause personal injury.

● Work at height must be carried out in accordance with the Work at Height Regulations, which require that such work is:

   – avoided if it is reasonably practicable to do the job another way

   – carried out using appropriate equipment to prevent falls

   – organised so that the distance and possible consequence of any fall are minimised

   – risk-assessment based

   – properly planned and supervised by a competent person(s)

   – carried out by competent operatives.

Duty holders must:
▪ avoid work at height where they can
▪ use work equipment or other measures to prevent falls where they cannot avoid working at height
▪ where they cannot eliminate the risk of a fall, use work equipment or other measures to minimise the distance and consequences of a fall should one occur

Collective protection for employees as a whole (for example, guard-rails) must take priority over personal protection (safety harnesses) at all times.

 Working at height **is defined as working at any height from which, if measures are not taken, a fall could occur and cause personal injury.**

 The Access Industry Forum website contains further information and guidance for work at height activities that can be downloaded upon request.

1.3   Requirements, interpretation and duties (Regulations 2 and 3)

1.3.1   Requirements of the regulations

The regulations require employers to ensure the following.

● Where it is reasonably practicable, the need to carry out work at height is avoided.

● Where such work cannot be avoided, the most appropriate equipment for the work and to prevent falls is selected.

● The distance of, and potential consequences of, any fall are reduced.

● The work is properly planned, including planning for emergencies and rescue. It must be risk-assessment based and carried out safely.

● The work is carried out by trained and competent persons who are adequately supervised.

The use of a ladder or stepladder is not prohibited by the regulations.

There are many situations where a ladder is the most suitable equipment for working at height.

A decision to use ladders must be justified by the findings of a risk assessment that clearly shows, given all of the circumstances, it is reasonable to use such equipment rather than safer types of access equipment and that any such work is short duration and low risk.

 For further information refer to the HSE guidance document *Safe use of ladders and stepladders – A brief guide* **(INDG455).**

Some clients, contractors and principal contractors are explicit in their views by not allowing ladders or stepladders on their sites.

They see this as importing an unnecessary risk where, with a small degree of planning, more suitable and ultimately safer equipment may be used.

The tendency of some contractors and sub-contractors to turn up at site with ladders without justifying why safer alternative equipment is not to be used, is being increasingly discouraged.

These regulations are a further stimulus to architects and designers to design out work at height for the construction and ongoing maintenance of buildings, or make safe working at height easier, to further contribute to safety in the industry.

01

1.3.2 Interpretation of the regulations (Regulation 2)

Below are the most important definitions from within the regulations.

Access and **egress** includes ascent and descent.

Fragile surface means a surface which would be liable to fail if any reasonable, foreseeable load were to be applied to it. This includes the weight of a person or any work equipment or materials.

Ladder includes any fixed ladder or stepladder.

Personal fall protection system means:

– a fall prevention, work restraint, work positioning, fall arrest or rescue system, other than a system in which the only safeguards are collective safeguards: or

– rope access and positioning systems.

Suitable means suitable in any respect, which it is reasonably foreseeable will affect the safety of any person, where, if the measures required by these regulations were not taken, a person could fall a distance liable to cause personal injury.

Work at height means work in any place, including a place at, below or above ground level, along with access to it and egress from it (except by a fixed staircase in a permanent workplace) where, if the measures required by these regulations were not taken, a person could fall a distance liable to cause personal injury.

Working platform:

– means any platform used as a place of work or as a means of access to, or egress from, a place of work

– includes any scaffold, suspended scaffold, cradle, mobile platform, trestle, gangway, gantry and stairway, which is used as a place of work.

 Reasonably practicable

The term *reasonably practicable* is used in the regulations. It has the same meaning as it does in the Health and Safety at Work etc. Act and elsewhere. Therefore, an employer can look at what the risks in a task involving work at height actually are, and what it would cost in terms of time, trouble and effort to avoid them. If it would cost a great deal of money or use of other resources to avoid a very small risk, then it may not be reasonably practicable to avoid it. However, the fact that falls from height often result in fatal or serious injuries should be a considerable factor when deciding what measures are reasonably practicable.

1.3.3 Application and duty of employer (Regulation 3)

The requirements of the regulations that are imposed:

● on an **employer** apply to work carried out by their employees or by any other person(s) under the employer's control, to the extent of that control

● apply to **self-employed** persons, together with persons under their control, to the extent of that control

● apply to persons who are **not self-employed**, in relation to work being carried out for them and under their control, to the extent of their control.

This last provision relates to clients and customers who are having work carried out for them, and the degree to which this duty applies. This depends upon the degree and extent of control that they have over the person(s) carrying out the work. A major client would obviously have more control over a contractor or sub-contractor than, for example, a domestic customer who is perhaps having a roof retiled or gutters cleaned.

1.3.4 Duties of employees

The regulations place a duty on employees, in that they have specific duties under Regulation 14. These duties are similar, and in addition to, their duties under other acts and regulations (such as Section 7 of the Health and Safety at Work etc. Act). In particular, in these regulations, employees must:

● report any activity or defect relating to work at height that they know is likely to endanger the safety of themselves or that of any other person

● use any work equipment or safety device provided for work at height in accordance with any training and/or instructions that they have received.

Given the legal status of health and safety regulations, failure by an employee to comply with the above requirements is an offence that could, in the appropriate circumstances, be dealt with in a court of law or by way of enforcement action.

Unsafe work at height – many factors could have led to these employees thinking this was an acceptable risk

1.4 Organisation and planning of work (Regulation 4)

It is the responsibility of every employer to ensure that all work at height is properly planned, appropriately supervised and carried out in a safe manner, taking into account weather conditions that could jeopardise the health and safety of employees and others that may be affected by the activity.

Planning must include the selection of appropriate work equipment, and planning for any emergencies or any rescue.

An employer will probably meet most of the requirements of this regulation if they have carried out and properly implemented the control measures identified within a suitable and sufficient risk assessment.

 For a work at height flowchart refer to Appendix A.

 Falling from height

A site supervisor was fined after a 24-year old temporary employee suffered multiple injuries and was left paralysed after falling 10 m from the roof of a warehouse. The temporary worker fell from an unprotected and fragile roof after the supervisor allowed workers who were removing cement sheets to go onto the roof, ignoring the company's safety policy.

The employer, who had a contract to remove asbestos cement roofs from a number of warehouses at the site, had identified them as fragile. The company had agreed a system of work where its employees would use scissor lifts to remove the roof sheets from the underside. However, when the task became difficult the supervisor did not bring the problem to the attention of the contracts manager, as required by the company procedure. Instead he allowed a change to the system of work, whereby he and other employees went onto the roof itself to carry out some of the work.

The HSE found the company's system of work was safe but by changing it the supervisor had sanctioned an unsafe system of work. The company was unaware of the changed way of working and the supervisor had failed to consult with them.

The supervisor pleaded guilty to breaching Regulation 4(1)(b) of the Work at Height Regulations, by failing to properly supervise work at height and make sure it was carried out safely. He was fined £1,000 and ordered to pay £9,765.88 costs.

The HSE inspector said: 'Those who supervise work at height have a responsibility to ensure that it is carried out in a manner that is safe and which guards against the risk of injury from a fall. Such injuries, if not fatal, may result in a lifelong disability for the injured person'.

 For further information on fragile roofs refer to Chapter D02 Working at height.

1.5 Competence (Regulation 5)

Employers must ensure that no person takes part in any work at height activity, including being involved in the organisation, planning and supervision of the work and work equipment, unless they are competent to do so or, if they are being trained, that they are being supervised by a competent person.

The level of supervision is important. The supervisor will need to be able to intervene, physically or by virtue of their authority, if an unsafe situation begins to develop, and rectify the situation or stop the work in progress.

The more inexperienced an employee is in relation to working at height, the greater the level of supervision required.

While there is no definition of *competence* in the regulations it may be taken to mean the following.

- A person who has practical and theoretical knowledge of the appropriate aspects of working at height, together with actual experience of what they are to do, which will enable them to ensure that all necessary planning and assessments have been prepared, and safety precautions taken, so that the work may be carried out safely, or that they may work safely. This person must also be able to understand and recognise their own personal limitations.

If they are involved in inspecting work equipment then *competence* may be taken to mean the following.

- A person who has practical and theoretical knowledge, together with actual experience of what they are to inspect, which will enable them to detect errors, defects, faults or weaknesses that it is the purpose of the inspection to discover and to assess the importance of any such discovery. This person must also know their limitations and must not put themselves or others at risk during the inspection of work equipment.

Training is an element of the competence necessary to work at height safely. Similarly, those who deliver such training must also be competent to do so.

 To assist trainers in this respect, British Standards publishes the *Code of Practice for the delivery of training and education for work at height and rescue* (BS 8454).

WORK AT HEIGHT REGULATIONS

1.6   Avoidance of risks from work at height (Regulation 6)

This is one of the main regulations and specifically requires employers to ensure that risk assessments take account of work carried out at height in accordance with Regulation 3 of the Management of Health and Safety at Work Regulations.

 For further information refer to Chapter A05 Risk assessments, method statements and permits to work.

In addition, the regulation requires that: 'every employer shall ensure that work is not carried out at height where it is reasonably practicable to carry out the work safely otherwise than at height'.

This clearly requires the employer to carry out a detailed study or assessment of all the ways in which the work could be carried out. If work can be carried out without the need to work at height, then the employer should do so, provided that it is reasonably practicable.

> **e.g. Eliminating the need to work at height**
>
> A good example of this was demonstrated during the construction of an over-bridge. The bridge deck was completed on flat ground before the spoil was excavated from below it. This virtually eliminated the need for working at height and reduced the height at which people had to work when constructing the upper parts of the structure.

Ground-level fabrication is another way of eliminating, or at least reducing, some tasks that have been traditionally carried out at height.

The fact that falls from height often result in fatal or serious injuries should factor heavily in any risk assessment when deciding if an alternative to working at height is reasonably practicable.

 When assessing risk or developing a safe system of work, the hierarchy for working at height should be followed.

1.6.1   Hierarchy for working at height

Any person planning work at height should always consider options at the top of the hierarchy before moving down.

Step 1. Avoid working at height
e.g. assemble on the ground and lift into position using a crane or by fixing guard-rails to structural steelwork on the ground before lifting and fixing at height

Step 2. Prevent falls from occurring
Use an existing safe place of work
e.g. parapet walls, defined access points, a flat roof with existing edge protection

Step 3. Prevent falls by providing *collective* protection
e.g. scaffolding, edge protection, handrails, podium steps, mobile towers, MEWPs

Step 4. Prevent falls by providing *personal* protection
e.g. using a work restraint (travel restriction) system that prevents a worker getting into a fall position

Step 5. Minimise the distance and/or consequences of a fall using *collective* protection
e.g. safety netting, airbags or soft-landing systems

Step 6. Minimise the distance and/or consequences of a fall using *personal* protection (The last resort)
e.g. industrial rope access (working on a building façade) or a fall-arrest system (safety harness and fall-arrest lanyard), using a suitable, high-level anchor point

 Ensure that people with sufficient skills, knowledge, training and experience are selected to perform any task. Any person being trained should be under full supervision at all times.

1.7 Selection of equipment for work at height (Regulation 7)

In selecting work equipment for use in work at height there is a requirement for the employer to consider work equipment or other measures that will give **collective protection** to employees as a whole, rather than just individual personal protection for one person. For example, a guard-rail will protect everyone (collective), whereas a safety harness and lanyard only protects the wearer (personal).

The Work at Height Regulations require that employers follow current industry good practice when selecting equipment for work at height. In particular, employers are required to take account of the following elements.

- Working conditions and risks to the safety of persons at their place of work.
- Access, egress and distances to be negotiated.
- Distance and consequences of any potential fall.
- Duration and frequency of use of the work equipment.
- Need for and ease of evacuation and rescue in any emergency.
- Any additional risks posed by the installation, use or removal of the work equipment, by any evacuation or by any rescue from it.
- Any other provisions of the regulations.

Any work equipment which is selected must meet the following requirements.

- Be appropriate for the work intended to be carried out and the foreseeable loadings.
- Allow the safe passage of persons and materials without risk.
- Be the most suitable equipment for avoiding risks while working at height.

Where a trade or occupation has historically used ladders, stepladders, trestles and other similar work equipment, the regulations do not prohibit their continued use, provided that the provisions of the Work at Height Regulations and the Management of Health and Safety at Work Regulations are fully considered and complied with.

In such circumstances employers will have to be in a position to demonstrate the following.

- The work at height has been properly planned and cannot be avoided or done any other way that is reasonably practicable.
- The most suitable work equipment is proposed to be used, and a risk assessment shows that the remaining risks are low.
- Appropriate steps have been taken to mitigate the effects of any fall, should one occur (for example, safety nets or safety harnesses).
- Employees are competent and properly supervised.

Risk assessments should be thorough but proportionate to the risks inherent in the work that is to be done.

It may, however, be the case that a client or contractor, or principal contractor where appointed, will not allow, or will control through a permit system, certain types of access equipment (such as ladders, stepladders or some types of trestles) on their premises or site.

This requirement may form part of the client's or contractor's own policies and procedures in relation to the use of this form of access equipment. It may mean that an alternative form of access equipment is used.

 The HSE has developed a brief step-by-step guide to help workers at height understand the key factors to consider when selecting the safest and most appropriate types of access equipment.

1.8 Requirements for particular work equipment (Regulation 8)

This regulation and Schedules 2 to 6 of the regulations cover the following provisions.

- Guard-rails, toe-boards, barriers and similar means of protection.
- Working platforms (such as scaffolds and trestles).
- Safety nets, airbags and other collective means of arresting falls.
- Personal fall protection systems.
- Work positioning systems.
- Rope access and positioning systems.
- Work restraint systems.
- Ladders.
- Fall-arrest systems.

In respect of guard-rails, the main guard-rail must be installed to at least 950 mm above the work surface or the edge from which a person may fall.

WORK AT HEIGHT REGULATIONS

Although there is no statutory minimum height for toe-boards, both BS EN 12811-1 and the current industry guidance, TG20:21, which relate to scaffolding good practice, recommend a minimum of 150 mm. They must be suitable and sufficient to prevent the fall of persons or materials. In line with current industry practice it is anticipated that scaffold boards on edges will continue to be used in most circumstances.

The maximum distance or gap between the top of a toe-board and the mid guard-rail, or between the mid guard-rail and the top guard-rail, is 470 mm.

Where brick guards or similar items are used as a means of protection, then they must meet the following criteria.

- Be placed so as to prevent the fall of persons or materials.

- Be of a suitable size and strength.

- Be placed or secured so that they do not become accidentally displaced.

- Be inspected at regular intervals.

Guard-rails may be removed on a temporary basis for the movement of materials, provided that suitable and effective alternative fall protection measures are put in place for the duration of the work, and that the guard-rails are replaced as soon as possible after the work is completed.

Members of the public should be protected from items falling from height

Gap between guard-rails no more than 470 mm

Top guard-rail at least 950 mm high

Toe-board at least 150 mm high

Guard-rail and toe-board dimensions

There is also provision in the regulations for danger areas (*refer to Regulation 11*). Where a workplace contains an area where there is a risk of injury to any person at work falling, or being struck by a falling object, measures should be taken to prevent unauthorised access and the danger area must be clearly indicated. This would generally mean the provision of an exclusion zone, supported by safety signage. The safety signage must comply with the Health and Safety (Safety Signs and Signals) Regulations.

Where employers can demonstrate that they are complying fully with current industry good practice and HSE Codes of Practice or guidance, then in the majority of situations they will meet most of the requirements of the Work at Height Regulations. Their risk assessments for working at height will then essentially be a comparison between what they are already doing to control the risks and what is regarded as good practice, then implementing further control measures if necessary.

1.8.1 Use of scaffolds

The current industry guidance is based on the content of the British Standard: *Temporary work equipment. Part 1. Scaffold – Performance requirements and general design* (BS EN 12811-1) and *The standards for temporary edge protection systems* (BS EN 13374).

Additional practical guidance is produced by the National Access and Scaffolding Confederation (NASC), which produces the *Guide to good practice for scaffolding with tubes and fittings* (TG20) and *Preventing falls in scaffolding* (SG4). Both documents are accepted by the scaffolding industry and the HSE as essential in ensuring that scaffolding is designed and erected in a safe manner, and in compliance with the Work at Height Regulations. Industry trade bodies, including the Scaffolding Association and system scaffold manufacturers, also publish advice, technical information and guidance for scaffolders and their clients, on industry standards, scaffold design and health and safety in scaffolding operations.

1.8.2 Use of ladders, stepladders and trestles

Ladders may be used for access to and egress from the place of work. Ladders, stepladders and trestles may be used to work from, provided that all of the requirements of the Work at Height Regulations are fully complied with.

The primary objective of the regulations is to eliminate work at height (and so the possibility of falls) and, where this is not possible, to ensure that all work at height is carried out safely and that the work equipment being used (such as a ladder or stepladder) is appropriate, suitable and safe for the work and the environment in which they are to be used.

In deciding to use a ladder for access or egress, or a ladder, stepladder or trestle for work at height, the employer must have carried out an assessment and found that it is not reasonably practicable to use any safer means, and that a risk assessment has shown that the risks from using the ladder, stepladder or trestle are low.

Ladders should be used in accordance with manufacturers' instructions. They must be the right ladder for the job, positioned at the correct angle, placed on a firm, level surface, and secured or otherwise prevented from slipping or moving. Users should face the ladder at all times when climbing up or down, have both hands free, and not be carrying anything that would interfere with their safety or balance.

Ladders may be used as a place of work, subject to the above, and if it is light work and of short duration (working on a ladder for no more than 30 minutes at a time). Users should be trained in how to safely erect and safely work on ladders (for example, not to overreach).

When stepladders are to be used to carry out work they should be of a suitable size and type. Generally, stepladders should be placed facing the work. They should not be used side-on to the work in any situation where a sideways load could be applied. Again, the work should be light and of short duration.

Pre-fabricated access equipment (such as podium steps) are a product that was developed as a result of the implementation of the Work at Height Regulations and, in simple terms, are a stepladder with a secure working platform with guard-rails and toe-boards in place. They are available in various sizes and heights and many are fitted with castors to make them more mobile. This type of access equipment provides a safe working platform and collective means of fall protection.

Trestles should be of sound construction, and properly set up on a surface that will bear their weight, as well as any loading of persons or materials. Trestle boards must be supported at a distance specified by the manufacturer. If they are adjustable, using telescopic adjustment, they should have high tensile pins in the adjusters. If they are fitted with wheels or castors, they should have brakes or other suitable locking devices on the wheels or castors. Employees who install and use trestles should be trained how to do so safely.

Trestles should be fitted with guard-rails and toe-boards, where appropriate.

 The Ladder Association, in consultation with the HSE, has produced risk assessment guides for ladders and stepladders.

 For further information on the use of ladders refer to Chapter D03 Common access equipment.

1.9 Fragile surfaces (Regulation 9)

The general requirement is that employers must ensure that no person passes across or near, or works on, from or near any fragile surface when it is reasonably practicable to carry out the work safely without their having to do so.

Where this requirement cannot be met, then the employer must:

- provide and ensure that there are suitable and sufficient platforms, coverings, guard-rails or other similar means of support or protection, which must be capable of supporting any foreseeable load or loading
- where the risk of a fall still remains, take suitable and sufficient steps to minimise the distance and consequences of any fall, should it occur
- place prominent warning notices at the approach(es) to any fragile material
- where such notices cannot be used, ensure that employees (and others as appropriate) are made aware of the fragile materials by other means.

1.10 Falling objects (Regulation 10)

The requirement in this regulation follows current good practice in that employers must take suitable and sufficient steps (including prohibiting the throwing down of materials) to prevent, so far as is reasonably practicable, the fall of any materials or objects that are likely to cause injury to any person. Suitable steps will include the use of brick guards, toe-boards and debris nets.

Where there is a residual likelihood of falling objects, or in the interests of safety, suitable and sufficient measures must be taken to prevent persons from being hit by falling objects or materials. This will cover the use of protective fans, boarded or roofed walkways and exclusion zones at ground level, which must all be supported with the appropriate level of safety signage.

Materials on scaffolds and working platforms must be stored so that they cannot fall or pose a risk of injury to anyone by their collapse, overturning or unintended movement.

1.11 Danger areas (Regulation 11)

Following from Regulation 10 and building on its requirements, in any workplace where there is a risk of any person falling or of persons being struck by falling objects, employers must take all reasonably practicable steps to prevent any unauthorised access to that area (such as putting up physical barriers and appropriate warning signs). Any signs must comply with the Health and Safety (Safety Signs and Signals) Regulations.

1.12 Inspection of work equipment (Regulation 12)

This regulation only applies to work equipment to which Regulation 8 and Schedules 2–6 apply, and closely follows the current requirements in the Provision and Use of Work Equipment Regulations (PUWER) as regards the inspection of work equipment.

Where the safety of equipment used for working at height (for example, a scaffold) depends upon how it has been installed or assembled, then it must be inspected by a competent person before being used.

 Throughout the regulations, *inspection* means any visual or more rigorous inspection, and any appropriate testing that a competent person decides is necessary.

All work equipment exposed to conditions causing deterioration that may result in dangerous situations must be inspected. This will ensure that it remains safe and that any deterioration can be detected and remedied.

WORK AT HEIGHT REGULATIONS

Inspections must take place at suitable intervals and after exceptional circumstances have occurred that are liable to have jeopardised the safety of the work equipment.

In addition to these requirements, any working platform that is used for construction work, and from which a person could fall more than 2 m, must not be used unless it has been inspected in that position within the previous **seven days**. A mobile working platform (such as a mobile scaffold tower or a MEWP) must have been inspected within the previous seven days.

Employers must ensure that work equipment (other than lifting equipment for which a similar provision applies under the Lifting Operations and Lifting Equipment Regulations (LOLER)), whether it is purchased, brought in or hired, is not used unless they have evidence that the inspection records are compliant with regulations and up to date (see 1.14.7 below).

If there is no evidence of the last inspection then the work equipment cannot be used on site until an inspection is carried out by a competent person. Formal inspection should not be regarded as a substitute for any routine pre-use checks that should be carried out by the user.

Inspection intervals should be decided by a competent person, based on the results of risk assessments, and then be reviewed in the light of experience.

The purpose of an inspection is to identify whether the work equipment is safe to use, and that any defect or deterioration is detected and repaired. If this is not possible, the work equipment should be removed from service before it becomes an unacceptable risk.

The results of every inspection must be recorded and kept on site until the construction work is completed, and after that they must be kept at one of the company offices for three months. The detail of the inspection must be recorded before the end of the working day, in accordance with the particulars given in Schedule 7, and the report delivered within 24 hours.

Lifting equipment that has had a thorough examination under the provisions of LOLER is treated as having had an inspection under these regulations.

Provided that the required information is recorded, and is readily available, then an employer may adopt their own recording system. Any computer-based system should be secure and cannot be interfered with. Systems may also be in the form of a register.

1.13   Inspection of places of work at height (Regulation 13)

So far as is reasonably practicable, every employer must ensure that the surface and every parapet, permanent rail or other such fall protection measure be inspected visually prior to each use. While there is no requirement to record such inspections, a simple record (a note in the site diary for example) would provide evidence that the risk has been identified and appropriate inspections carried out.

1.14   Schedules 1 to 8

There are eight schedules to the regulations. Much of the information contained in the schedules is virtually identical to current requirements and/or guidance. Therefore, if employers are actively working to current standards and guidance then there is little extra for them to do.

1.14.1   Schedule 1. Regulation 6(4)(a)

The requirement in this schedule is for existing places of work at height and means of access to or egress from such places to be stable, of sufficient size and strength and with suitable edge protection as necessary. Ladders, in particular, must rest on stable, strong surfaces.

A place of work is to be properly constructed, used and maintained so as to prevent the risk of tripping, slipping or being trapped between it and adjacent surfaces. It should have no gaps through which materials could fall and injure someone below.

1.14.2   Schedule 2. Regulation 8(a)

This covers the requirements for guard-rails, toe-boards, barriers or similar means of collective protection *(refer to Regulation 8)*. The remainder of the requirements are unchanged, other than the fact that the top guard-rail must now be at least 950 mm above the edge from which any person might fall (with the provision of 910 mm for fixed guard-rails that were in place at the time the Work at Height Regulations came into force), and the removal of any specific height above ground level at which guard-rails and toe-boards must be fitted.

1.14.3   Schedule 3. Regulation 8(b)

This covers the requirements for working platforms. Part 1 deals with requirements for all working platforms, and Part 2 covers the additional requirements for scaffolding.

Part 1. All working platforms must be erected and used so that components cannot become displaced and cause danger to anyone. They must be suitable for the work, and of sufficient strength and rigidity. If they are altered or modified (by a competent person) they must remain safe and stable.

A *supporting structure* means any structure used for the purpose of supporting a working platform and includes any plant used for that purpose. It must be suitable and of sufficient strength and stability while being erected, used or dismantled. It must be prevented from slipping or moving, and if it has wheels or castors, they must be capable of being locked or similar. Working platforms and supporting structures must not be overloaded.

Part 2. As regards the **additional requirements for scaffolding** strength and stability, calculations must be carried out unless it is being assembled in conformity with generally recognised standard configurations (for example, a TG20 compliant scaffold, erected in accordance with a TG20 compliance sheet).

If the scaffold is not a TG20 compliant scaffold then design calculations will need to be provided by the scaffolding contractor. Such calculations are usually supported by the provision of detailed drawings, to assist scaffolders during construction and inspection of the scaffold.

If prefabricated scaffolding materials are being used (for example, ladder beams and hop-up platforms), then the manufacturer's data will be required to confirm that these products may be used in conjunction with the scaffold in question.

Depending on the complexity of the scaffold, an assembly, use and dismantling plan (commonly referred to as a method statement) shall be drawn up by a competent person. This may be a standard or generic plan, supplemented with specific details, as appropriate.

A copy of the plan must be kept for the use of any persons concerned with the erection, use or dismantling of the scaffold.

The size and layout of the scaffold must be appropriate and suitable for the work to be performed, and it must also permit the work and passage of persons to happen safely. (The detailed design drawings or TG20 compliance sheet for the scaffold will give details on specific scaffold dimensions, layouts and load bearing capacities.)

When a scaffold is not available for use during erection, alteration and/or dismantlement, then warning signs in accordance with the Health and Safety (Safety Signs and Signals) Regulations need to be displayed (scaffold tagging systems are available that will help fulfil this requirement).

Physical barriers must also be put in place to prevent access to the scaffold, or any unsafe or incomplete parts of the scaffold.

 Scaffolding may only be assembled, dismantled or altered under the supervision of a competent person and by persons who have received appropriate and specific training.

 The Construction Industry Scaffolders Record Scheme (CISRS) has a card scheme in place for people working in the scaffolding industry, including scaffolders, trainee scaffolders, labourers, supervisors and inspectors.

1.14.4   Schedule 4. Regulation 8(c)

This schedule covers the requirements for collective safeguards for arresting falls. Collective safeguards include safety nets, airbags, landing mats and any similar devices or arrangements. All must be suitable and of sufficient strength to be able to safely arrest or cushion a fall and may only be used in the following situations.

- Where a risk assessment has shown that the work to be done can be carried out safely while the safeguard is being used, and without influencing its effectiveness.
- Where the use of safer work equipment is not reasonably practicable.
- If a sufficient number of employees (or others) have received adequate training specific to the safeguard, including rescue procedures.

An important requirement is that if the safeguard is designed to be attached to a building or a structure then the safeguard, the structure and all anchorages must be suitable and of sufficient strength for any foreseeable load that a fall might impose on it.

Airbags and landing mats must be suitable for the purpose intended, and they must be stable.

If a safeguard is designed to distort when arresting a fall, it must give sufficient clearance from the ground or adjacent structures to avoid injury to a person whose fall is being arrested.

1.14.5   Schedule 5. Regulation 8(d)

This schedule covers the requirements for personal fall protection systems (Part 1), work positioning systems (Part 2), rope access and positioning techniques (Part 3), fall-arrest systems (Part 4) and work restraint systems (Part 5).

 Much of the information in this schedule is technical in nature and it is of paramount importance that employees are fully trained in the use of any of the fall protection systems available to them. There is insufficient detail within this brief explanation of the schedule to train a person on the requirements, or for them to gain sufficient knowledge to be regarded as competent.

All safety harnesses, lanyards and other fall prevention or fall-arrest equipment must comply with the appropriate British and European standards.

Part 1 deals with the requirements for all personal fall protection systems. See 'Interpretation of the regulations' *(refer to 1.3.2)* for the definition of personal fall protection systems.

Current guidance is that the requirements set out in this schedule apply to all rope-based activities for work at height, including industrial rope systems and any other similar activity when carried out as a work activity.

WORK AT HEIGHT REGULATIONS

The following points are requirements for personal fall protection systems within the schedule.

● Shall only be used if a risk assessment has shown that the work can be done safely while it is being used, and that the use of other, safer work equipment is not reasonably practicable.

● The user and a sufficient number of others have been trained in its use and in rescue procedures.

● It shall be suitable and of sufficient strength for the purpose for which it is to be used and will withstand any foreseeable loading.

● It fits the wearer and is correctly fitted or worn.

● It is designed to minimise injury to the user in the event of a fall, and is such that the user will not fall or slip out of it should they fall.

● It is designed, installed and used so as to prevent unplanned or uncontrolled movement of the user.

Any anchorage point must be suitable and of sufficient strength to support any foreseeable loading. If designed to do so, the equipment must be securely attached to at least one such anchorage point when in use.

Part 2 deals with the additional requirements for work positioning systems. They may only be used in the following instances.

● If the system includes a suitable backup system for preventing or arresting a fall.

● If the system includes a line as a backup system and the user is connected to it.

● Where it is not reasonably practicable to do either of the above, then other suitable measures are taken to prevent or arrest a fall.

Part 3 deals with the additional requirements for rope access and positioning techniques, which may only be used in the following instances.

● If it has two separate lines: the working line and a safety line.

● If the user has a safety harness that is connected to both the working line and the safety line.

● When the working line has safe means of ascent and descent, and a self-locking device to prevent falling.

● When the safety line has a mobile fall protection system that is connected to, and travels with, the user.

● Subject to the type and duration of work, and the findings of a risk assessment, it has a seat with appropriate accessories. However, if a risk assessment has demonstrated that a second line would entail a higher risk to the user, then, provided that appropriate safety measures have been taken, a single rope may be used.

Part 4 deals with the additional requirements for fall-arrest systems. It requires that they must have a suitable energy absorber (often called a shock absorber and which is usually either a folded metal strip that deforms, or tear-away stitched webbing), or other suitable means of limiting the force applied to the user's body in the event of a fall. In addition, a fall-arrest system must not be used if there is any risk of a line (a rope or a lanyard) being cut, or where there is no safety zone or clear zone to allow for any swinging or pendulum effect after a fall, or in a way that hinders the system's safety performance or makes its use unsafe.

Part 5 deals with the additional requirements for work restraint systems (often a safety harness with a very short lanyard), and requires that they are designed so that they are used correctly to prevent the user from getting into a position where they could fall.

1.14.6   Schedule 6. Regulation 8(e)

This schedule contains a specific requirement on the use of ladders and stepladders for work at height. Employers and the self-employed must ensure that a ladder or stepladder is only used for work at height if a risk assessment has shown that the use of more suitable work equipment is not justified because of the low risk and the short duration of the work, or because of existing features on site that cannot be altered.

The remainder of the schedule is in line with current industry good practice. The requirements are shown in brief below.

● The surface on which a ladder rests must be stable and of sufficient strength.

● The ladder is strong enough for loads that may be put on it.

● The ladder is placed so that it is stable during use.

● A suspended ladder is attached in a secure manner so that it does not swing.

● Portable ladders are prevented from slipping by being secured at or near their top or bottom, or with anti-slip or stability devices, or other effective means.

● Access ladders are long enough to provide a handhold when getting off at the top, unless other suitable handholds have been provided.

● Sections on interlocking or extension ladders are prevented from moving while in use.

● Mobile ladders are prevented from moving before being stepped on.

● Where reasonably practicable, rest platforms are provided where a run of ladders rises a vertical distance of more than 9 m.

● Ladders are used in such a way that a secure handhold and secure support are always available to the user.

● The user can maintain a safe handhold while carrying a load.

This last point is qualified for stepladders in that:

 ... unless, in the case of a stepladder, the maintenance of a handhold is not practical when a load is carried, and a risk assessment has demonstrated that the use of a stepladder is justified because of the low risk and the short duration of the work.

 For advice on footing ladders, refer to Chapter D03 Common access equipment.

1.14.7   Schedule 7. Regulation 12(7)

This schedule states the details to be recorded in a work equipment inspection report (for example, scaffold inspection), as follows.

- The name and address of the person for whom the inspection was carried out.

- The location of the work equipment inspected.

- A description of the work equipment inspected.

- The date and time of the inspection.

- Details of any matter identified that could give rise to a risk to the health or safety of any person.

- Details of any action taken as a result of any matter identified in the point above.

- Details of any further actions considered necessary.

- The name and position of the person making the report.

Reports of inspection have to be kept on site until construction work is completed and then at the employer's offices for three months.

1.14.8   Schedule 8. Regulation 19

This schedule outlines various other regulations or parts of them that are revoked by the coming into force of the Work at Height Regulations.

Appendix A – Work at height flowchart

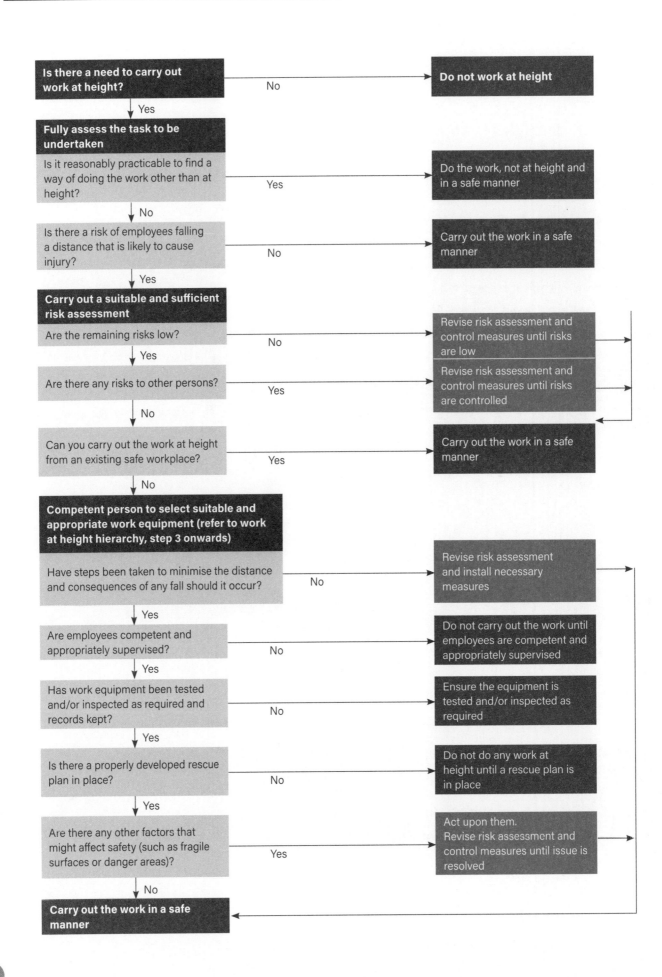

CONTENTS

Working at height

02

Supporting INFORMATION

GT700 Toolbox talks / supporting checklists and forms

Toolbox talks on some of these topics are available in the GT700 publication. Supporting checklists and forms covering some of these topics are available on our companion website.

02

Overview

There is no such thing as a safe height; anyone who is working at height is at risk of falling. This hazard exists on working platforms, scaffolds, ladders, flat and pitched roofs, open steelwork and any area where work is carried out near fragile materials, openings, holes and roof edges.

Ladders, stepladders and trestles (or lightweight staging) are among the most commonly used pieces of access equipment on site and, perhaps, the most misused. Most construction workers have used them at some point and it is essential that safe working practices should be followed if accidents are to be avoided.

2.1 Introduction

Before you read this chapter, it is strongly recommended that you familiarise yourself with Chapter D01 Work at Height Regulations. There have been a number of major improvements in safety standards and practices with regard to working at height. For example, the standard practice of profile roofing workers using safety nets on new build projects and steel workers using powered access have been significant steps forward in construction health and safety.

Every year, however, falls from height remain by far the largest cause of death in the construction industry. Roof work, in particular, including work on fragile roofing materials, gives rise to a substantial number of fatal and serious accidents. These invariably affect lives and livelihoods.

It needs to be emphasised that there is not just the actual roof working to be considered but the whole process: planning the job, creating a safe access, the safe storage of equipment and materials, and so on.

Various work at height solutions in practice, including proprietary edge protection mesh barriers and scaffold guard-rails

In many respects, working for domestic clients on maintenance or repair work may offer greater challenges to providing a safe working environment. The work is typically of shorter duration than new build, and often carried out directly for a client who may not be aware of the required standards. This does not lessen the need for safe working methods and compliance with the law for those undertaking the work.

Compliance with legislation and well-established codes of practice could save many lives and prevent many injuries. Most accidents could be avoided with provision of appropriate equipment and the adequate information, instruction, training and supervision of those who use it.

2.1.1 Planning, design, construction and maintenance of tall buildings

With the number of tall buildings within the United Kingdom, particularly in London, increasing rapidly, a working group was put together by the Construction Industry Advisory Committee (CONIAC) consisting of the Access Industry Forum, members of the construction industry, and those associated with it, all of whom have knowledge and experience of the planning, design, construction and maintenance of tall buildings. The group has worked together to produce a guidance book called 'Industry guidance for the planning, design, construction and maintenance of tall buildings'. This is freely available, and provides guidance on how to follow a 'risk management approach' to identify hazards and provide solutions to enable the design and safe construction of tall buildings.

 For further information and a link to download the guidance, please visit the Construction Industry Publications website.

Following the Grenfell Tower tragedy, a new regulatory framework was established for duty holders involved with the planning, design, construction and refurbishment of a building to ensure safety across the building's life cycle. The Building Safety Act 2022 sets out safety requirements for landlords of higher-risk buildings (buildings that are at least 18 m or seven storeys high, with two or more residential units). The Act has six parts, and contains provisions intended to secure the safety of people in or about buildings as well as improve building standards.

 For further information on the Building Safety Act 2022, visit the HSE website.

For additional information refer to:

- **Chapter D01 Work at Height Regulations**
- **Chapter D03 Common access equipment**
- **Chapter D04 Scaffolding**
- **Chapter D05 Fall arrest and suspension equipment**
- **Chapter F05 Working over or near to water.**

For further sources of information and guidance relating to roof work visit the following websites.

- **Advisory Committee for Roofsafety (ACR).**
- **National Federation of Roofing Contractors (NFRC).**
- **Access Industry Forum (AIF).**
- **National Access and Scaffolding Confederation (NASC).**
- **HSE.**
- **British Constructional Steelwork Association (BCSA).**

2.2   Important points

- Those who work on roofs are, by the nature of their work, at risk of falling if appropriate measures are not taken.

- Those who plan, supervise or carry out roof work must be competent to do so.

- A risk assessment and a method statement should be compiled for all such work.

- Integral features of roofs (such as a steep pitch, valleys, fragile cladding or roof lights) can increase the risk of falling.

- Falls through fragile roofing materials continue to be the cause of many deaths and injuries. Where such surfaces have been identified, proprietary covers (either temporary or permanent installations) prevent those passing or working nearby from falling through.

- Bad weather can have a significant impact on the risk control measures that have to be taken.

- Ideally, work will be carried out from a stable working platform, fitted with guard-rails and toe-boards, all of which comply with the requirements of the Work at Height Regulations.

- If safe working platforms cannot be provided, then safety harnesses with work restraint systems should be used to prevent falls.

- Where safety harnesses with work restraint systems cannot be used, effective fall-arrest measures must be put in place, ideally collective measures (such as safety nets or other soft-landing systems).

- People who work on roofs must consider the safety of anyone passing below to protect them from falling materials or tools.

- Access equipment (such as powered access (MEWPs), scaffolding, ladders, stepladders and lightweight stagings) are all easily transported means of access to work at height. They can all be used safely in certain conditions.

- Danger often occurs when access equipment is used for a job for which it is not suitable; this particularly applies to ladders and stepladders.

- All persons working at height must have received adequate training in systems of work and any equipment that they are planning to use for access.

- The nature and duration of the job will be significant factors in determining the most appropriate type of access equipment to use for work at height.

- The HSE's evaluation of accidents resulting from work at height shows that inappropriate access equipment, provided by management and used by workers, is a significant factor.

- Falls from low levels (such as a height below 2 m) are the cause of many injuries and fatalities.

- All openings and holes in floors must be protected with secured guard-rails, toe-boards, coverings or similar barriers and be clearly marked with warning signs.

2.3   Legislative requirements

2.3.1   Work at Height Regulations

The relevant requirements of these regulations with regard to roof work are considered to be as follows.

- Employers should ensure that work at height is planned, supervised and carried out in a safe manner by trained and competent persons.

- Work at height must be carried out using appropriate work equipment, particularly that which provides collective fall protection.

- Suitable and sufficient steps should be taken to prevent falling objects that are likely to cause injury to any person.

- Consideration needs to be given to the weather conditions.

- Plan for the emergency rescue of employees from height and where appropriate make specific arrangements for how to rescue someone who has fallen but is suspended.

- The method of rescue needs to be proportionate to the risk and should not rely on the emergency services.

- Where there is a risk of a person falling or being struck by a falling object, steps need to be taken to prevent unauthorised access into that area.

There are a number of trade associations for roofing companies (listed below) that could be consulted on, or that comment upon, queries about competence.

- National Federation of Roofing Contractors (NFRC).
- Flat Roofing Alliance (FRA).
- Single Ply Roofing Association (SPRA).
- Mastic Asphalt Council (MAC).
- Rural and Industrial Design and Building Association (RIDBA).

Whilst membership of these organisations by itself does not guarantee either good health and safety practices or quality, they do all vet members and operate a dispute resolution service, which may be a useful facility.

 The Advisory Committee for Roofsafety is a body dedicated to making working on roofs safer. It was established in 1998 and is made up of nominees from HSE, trade associations and organisations involved in roof work that provide many years of experience of involvement in working on roofs.

Visit the Access Industry Forum website for some useful online videos.

2.3.2 Construction (Design and Management) Regulations

The regulations place legal duties on duty holders, each of which has the potential to reduce the risks to health and safety during and after the construction phase.

 For additional information and resources visit the HSE website.

2.3.2.1 Designers

The definition of **designer** under CDM is broad. It can include architects, consulting engineers, quantity surveyors, interior designers, temporary work engineers, chartered surveyors, technicians or anyone who specifies or alters a design. Therefore, principal contractors, specialist contractors and individual tradespersons could also be designers. A common scenario would be where the client asks the contractor to sort out a leaking roof and the contractor designs the solution. A commercial client who becomes actively involved in designing their project may also be considered to be a designer.

Whoever prepares or modifies a design for a construction project (including temporary works) or instructs someone else to do so will be considered to be a designer. This is very important as all designers have a legal duty to consider health and safety issues in relation to not only carrying out the work, but also the maintenance, cleaning and eventual removal (demolition) of the roof.

In common with all aspects of design, the person carrying out the design should be sufficiently knowledgeable of the construction process to specify how the work can be carried out safely.

Roofers working on industrial type buildings are commonly faced with the problem of fragility. This may be because the roof itself is made of a fragile material (such as asbestos cement sheets) or because the roof lights are not load bearing. As the standard specification for roof lights is 10% by area, this represents a significant amount of fragile roof surface.

The HSE states quite categorically that stringent effort should be made by designers to ensure that fragile roof lights are not specified.

 The Advisory Committee for Roofsafety (ACR), which is the lead authority in the UK on roof work health and safety and represents all the relevant trade associations, has published jointly with the HSE definitive guidance on what constitutes fragile material: *Red book – Test for non-fragility of large element roofing assemblies* **(ACR[M] 001:2019).**

This book details tests that manufacturers should carry out on profiled roof sheets. Anyone who specifies this type of roofing must be aware of the contents of this book and ensure the materials they specify meet the standards, where possible.

When designing roofs, designers should also consider such things as ongoing maintenance work (for example, how roof lights and gutters can be cleaned safely) and whether the safe access for this type of work can be designed-in at the design stage.

2.3.2.2 Clients

Under the regulations the client has the main duty for providing relevant pre-construction information to each designer (including the principal designer) and contractor (including the principal contractor) being considered for the job, or already appointed to it, to enable the job to be planned so that it can be carried out safely. For projects involving more than one contractor the client can expect help from the appointed principal designer.

The main type of information that would be relevant for roof work would be the presence of asbestos, areas of damage, loading limitations of the roofing material, the existence of fall-restraint systems, the location of safe access routes where known, as-built drawings, where available, and so on.

It should be noted that the client may not be aware of such factors as damaged areas of the roof or the existence (or lack) of safe access routes. The client may assume that the job will be carried out by a method that is neither practical nor safe. They commonly expect roofing contractors to be able to access places and do tasks that they would simply not allow their employees to do.

2.4 Stages of a roofing project

The various stages of a roofing project are shown below.

- Design.
- Selection of contractors and staff.
- Planning.
- Carrying out the work.
- Post-completion information (at the end).

2.4.1 Stage 1. Design

Designers have duties under the Construction (Design and Management) Regulations 2015 (CDM) to eliminate, reduce or control foreseeable health and safety risks that may arise during construction, use and future maintenance of roof structures. Where residual hazards remain in the design, these should be communicated in the planning so that suitable precautions may be considered.

A designer must take all reasonable steps to provide, with the design, sufficient information about the design, construction or maintenance of the structure, to adequately assist the client, other designers and contractors to comply with their duties under these Regulations. This information will assist all duty holders, during design, construction and for the lifetime of the structure.

Designers should take into account the specification of materials and construction methods, including fragility. Particular consideration should be given to future requirements for maintenance, cleaning and access to the finished project. Discussing these requirements with those who will be carrying out this work is important. They may have established methods of working, or specific needs or suggestions, which will need to be considered in the design.

 Design includes drawings, design details, specifications and bills of quantities (including specification of articles or substances) relating to a structure, and calculations prepared for the purpose of a design.

 For further information refer to Chapter A03 Construction (Design and Management) Regulations.

2.4.2 Stage 2. Selection of contractors and staff

Where a company is using its own employees to carry out roof work, it is essential that several factors are taken into consideration. Operational work on roofs can be both hazardous and strenuous, often involving:

- work at considerable heights for long periods of time
- work outdoors, including adverse weather conditions (such as hot, cold or wet weather, high winds, snow, ice and fog)
- repetitive materials handling
- reaching, stretching and maintaining balance in awkward postures whilst carrying loads on varying roof terrains.

This means that fitness to work is particularly important and needs to be considered by the employers. The Advisory Committee for Roofsafety (ACR) suggests that it is vital that people working on roofs do not suffer from the following conditions.

- Any neurological condition likely to cause a seizure.
- Weakness of limbs.
- Loss of balance, including vertigo (dizziness from being at height).
- Any heart or lung condition likely to be aggravated by strenuous work.
- Any disability or impairment of limb function.
- Any other disease, disability or the effects of medication, alcohol, drugs or toxic substances (lead and so on) likely to impair mental or physical activity, especially at a height.
- Temporary ailments (such as influenza) or other conditions that may affect judgement.
- Uncorrected sight problems.
- A physique that would be unsuitable for the work.

Obviously an employer needs to be aware of the provisions of the Equality Act with regard to the above. It is strongly suggested that employers should establish a policy on fitness for work, and ideally that this should be implemented before taking on any new staff.

So-called fitness to work medicals are not new and many sectors already use them for their staff. Often a local GP or a specialist occupational health service provider can carry out these medicals.

 For further information refer to the ACR's *Black Book; Guidance note for competence and general fitness requirements to work on roofs.*

2.4.3 Stage 3. Planning

Planning the work should include consideration of the progression of the work with regard to the following.

- Site-specific hazards and risks.
- Weather conditions.
- Emergencies (including rescue).
- Safe means of access and egress.
- Materials handling and storage.
- Personnel involved, including competence and supervision.

2.4.3.1 Site-specific hazards and risks

Site-specific hazards could include the following.

- Working above public areas (such as shopping malls or public streets).
- The difficulties in delivering materials and transferring them to roof level.
- The presence of site traffic or road traffic on a public road.
- Awkward working environments (such as occupied houses or factories).
- Nesting birds that will aggressively defend their territory.
- The presence of accumulated pigeon droppings *(refer to Chapter B01 Management of health)*.
- Emergency situations (such as rescuing someone who has fallen and is suspended at high level in a safety harness or recovering an injured worker from height).
- Vent pipes that may suddenly shower unsuspecting roof workers with anything ranging from high pressure steam to noxious chemicals.

2.4.3.2 Weather conditions

The weather can have a significant impact upon the intention to carry out roof work and may ultimately be the reason for the start of a job being delayed, or suspended part-way through. Heavy rain, high winds, frost, snow or fog might make it unsafe to work at height.

 It is essential to monitor wind speeds on a regular basis at the relevant working height.

Wind speeds and temperatures quoted in weather forecasts can differ considerably at height (for example, if installing a glass atrium roof on top of a multistorey tower block). If a roofing job has started and the weather is forecast to be changeable, with perhaps extremes of conditions, it will be essential to monitor the forecast and conditions so that work can be halted before it becomes unsafe to continue.

Wind speeds in excess of 25 mph can create unsafe working conditions. Winds can funnel and eddy around buildings, causing turbulence, which again may make working places unsafe. In cold weather conditions, the wind will effectively lower the temperature considerably – this is known as the wind chill factor.

Work involving the handling of sheeting and cladding requires extra care in windy conditions, when a sheet may act like a sail, causing the person holding it to lose their balance. Guidance from the National Federation of Roofing Contractors (NFRC) suggests that the following work should cease when the average wind speeds shown are exceeded.

Typical hand-held wind meter (anemometer) (Image supplied by Kestrel Weather & Environmental Meters by NK)

17 mph – handling lightweight materials and any materials over 5 m long or rolls of felt.
23 mph – general roofing work.

The Beaufort wind scale for use on land (see below) provides indicators of prevailing wind conditions. Fixed or hand-held anemometers (wind velocity meters) should be used where additional accuracy is required.

Windforce number	Description of wind	Wind locally	Speed mph	Speed m/sec
0	Calm	Calm, smoke rises vertically.	1	0–1
1	Light air	Direction of wind shown by smoke drift, but not by wind or weather vanes.	1–3	1–2
2	Light breeze	Wind felt on face. Leaves rustle. Wind or weather vanes move.	4–7	2–3
3	Gentle breeze	Leaves and small twigs in constant motion. Wind extends light flags.	8–12	3–5
4	Moderate breeze	Wind raises dust and loose paper. Small branches move.	13–18	5–8
5	Fresh breeze	Small trees in leaf begin to sway. Little crested wavelets form on inland waters.	19–24	8–11
6	Strong breeze	Large branches in motion. Umbrellas used with some difficulty.	25–31	11–14
7	Near gale	Whole trees in motion. Becoming difficult to walk against the wind.	32–38	14–17
8	Gale	Twigs break off trees. Progress is generally impeded.	39–46	17–21
9	Strong gale	Chimney pots, slates and tiles may be blown off.	47–54	21–24

For detailed guidance on wind speed advice for different roof work refer to the HSE guidance *Health and safety in roof work* **(HSG33).**

For further information refer to the National Federation of Roofing Contractors' guidance booklet *Roofing and cladding in windy conditions.*

2.4.3.3 Emergencies (including rescue)

Emergencies (such as a fire or gas leak) could occur either at ground level or at height, which requires that an emergency evacuation of the whole site, or evacuation of the roof where work is taking place, is carried out. For this reason the planning stage must ensure that safe access and egress will be available at all times. Depending upon the nature of the job, it may be necessary to have more than one access and/or egress route.

If the nature of the work and site layout necessitates that an asphalt or bitumen boiler, or other forms of hot work, have to be sited on the roof, then this must be considered as part of the fire risk assessment, local hot-work procedure and emergency arrangements.

 For further information refer to the HSE guidance *Fire safety in construction* **(HSG168).**

It may be necessary to deal with medical emergencies where someone becomes incapacitated at height through illness or injury and is unable to make their way back to ground level. In such circumstances, the local fire and rescue service (FRS) may have to be involved to effect a safe rescue.

Consider emergency arrangements when selecting the method of roof access (for example, it may be easier to evacuate a casualty via a passenger hoist or stairway rather than ladder access).

Carrying out roof work will often involve the use of fall-arrest equipment (such as safety nets or safety harness and lanyard). Anyone who falls will have to be rescued promptly, particularly if they are suspended in a harness.

Where mobile elevating work platforms (MEWPs) are used to carry out the work it is essential that an effective emergency plan is produced, rehearsed and implemented. There must always be someone at ground level who is familiar with the ground controls and able to take action in the event of an emergency while a MEWP is in use.

The method of rescue needs to be proportionate to the risk and you should not rely on the emergency services.

 For further information refer to Chapter D05 Fall arrest and suspension equipment.

2.4.3.4 Safe means of access and egress

The means of gaining access to height and safely working there will depend upon many factors (such as the nature of the roof structure, whether there is room to erect a scaffold or bring in a MEWP, and even the length of time that the job is expected to take).

Some common means of gaining access to height or actually working at height are listed below.

- Ladders.
- Mobile access equipment.
- Fixed or mobile towers.
- Stair towers.
- Independent scaffolds.

Before using an existing access and working platform (such as a permanently installed ladder or stairway) it should be inspected by a competent person to ensure its stability.

Additional temporary measures may be necessary to meet the requirements of the Work at Height Regulations for working platforms (for example, a parapet wall less than 950 mm high would require additional guard-rails).

2.4.3.5 Materials handling and storage

The planning process will involve taking decisions on the following.

- What roofing materials are required and where they can be stored safely at ground level.
- A safe means of transferring roofing materials to height and in what quantities, pack size and load (weight).
- Avoiding the overloading of any part of the roof including the integrity of steelwork members. (Overloading can occur when materials are stacked on the roof prior to installation)
- The safe storage of sheet materials if they are to be stored for any length of time, particularly during windy weather.
- The safe distribution of materials around the roof during installation.
- The safe transfer of waste materials back to ground level.

Further notes on the safe stacking of materials on roofs are included later in this chapter. *(Refer to 2.9 Handling and storage of roofing materials.)*

2.4.4   Stage 4. Carrying out the work

To a large extent, the risks of doing the job, the risk-control measures that will be necessary and therefore the way in which the work is carried out will depend upon the type of roof and nature of work to be undertaken.

Short duration means a matter of minutes rather than hours (up to a maximum of 30 minutes). It includes jobs such as brief inspections or minor adjustments (for example, minor adjustments to slipped slates).

Work on a flat roof is still dangerous, even if it lasts a short time. Appropriate safety measures remain essential.

It may not be reasonable to provide full edge protection for short duration work but something will need to be provided in its place. The minimum requirements for short duration work on a roof are safe means of access to and egress from the roof level and safe means of working on the roof (such as a properly constructed and supported roof ladder for sloping roofs, or a fall-restraint system for flat roofs) that prevents the wearer reaching a position where they could fall.

Mobile access equipment (such as scaffold towers or MEWPs) or proprietary access systems can provide a suitable working platform for some short duration tasks.

2.4.5   Stage 5. Post-completion information

The principal designer must ensure a health and safety file is prepared, developed and reviewed as the project progresses.

At the end of the project the principal designer must pass the file to the client. If the principal designer's appointment finishes before the end of the project, they must pass the file to the principal contractor, who must take responsibility for making any additional amendments and the hand over to the client at the end of the project.

The purpose of the health and safety file is to provide useful health and safety related information for anyone who, at a later date, has to carry out subsequent work (such as maintenance, cleaning, refurbishment or demolition).

In accordance with CDM it will be necessary for the roofing contractor to provide the principal designer (or principal contractor) with relevant health and safety information about the roof structure and materials used, as requested, for inclusion in the health and safety file.

2.5   Types of roof work

2.5.1   Flat roofs

On flat roofs, falls most frequently occur:

- from the edge of a completed roof
- from the leading edge where work is being carried out
- through openings or gaps
- through fragile material.

 A *flat roof* is defined as any roof having a pitch of less than 10 degrees.

Flat roof with parapet wall barrier and skylight hazards

Safe access to the roof, and to any working place on that roof, must be provided and maintained. If there is no suitable parapet wall of 950 mm in height or similar barrier to stop anyone from falling, edge protection must be provided.

This may take the form of standard guard-rails and toe-boards or, providing nobody will approach the edge, a suitable physical barrier set back from the edge. All barriers should be positioned at least 2 m from a leading edge, to prevent workers from accessing danger areas where they would be exposed to a risk of falling. Barriers should also be secured to prevent them becoming displaced (such as in high winds). Warning signs should be displayed on the barriers.

Where works are to be undertaken that could result in materials or equipment falling onto people passing below, protective measures must be taken (for example, adding netting, close boarding or debris fans to scaffolds or establishing exclusion zones with fenced-off areas and warning signs to stop people from accessing the drop zone at critical times).

There could be circumstances when operatives need to work at exposed leading edges but it is not reasonably practicable to install guard-rails or other collective fall prevention measures. In these circumstances, it will be necessary to use personal work restraint systems or collective fall-arrest systems.

The most suitable type of fall-arrest system will be indicated by a risk assessment. Where safety nets, airbags or other soft-landing systems are used, they will provide collective fall protection for anyone working above them who falls.

The last resort would be the use of a personal fall-arrest system, such as a safety harness with a lanyard clipped to a suitable anchor point or a horizontal running line. The effectiveness of this system depends upon the training and personal discipline of operatives. Adequate supervision is required to ensure the system is effective (such as the operatives actually clipping on).

Employers should consider work restraint systems where the lanyard should be sufficiently short or can be adjusted so that it prevents the wearer from reaching a position from which they could fall.

When a safety harness and lanyard with an inertia reel device is used, consideration must be given to the position of the anchor point, which should be above the head-height of the user.

It is important to note that, when using this form of fall-arrest system, the anchor point and self-retracting lifeline (SRL) are as high as possible to ensure that the fall factor, which provides an indication of the length and severity of fall, is kept as low as possible.

As a guide, when using a 2 m length lanyard, the fall distance required (to provide adequate clearance to the fallen operative) is 5.2 m when attached above head height, 5.75 m when connected at shoulder height and 6.75 m when attached at foot level. Where the anchor point is at ankle level, for example, there will be more slack in the lanyard so the fall will be further before it is arrested.

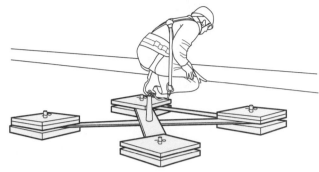

Temporary anchorage for a fall-restraint system (Photo © NASC)

Inertia reel blocks are designed to be used vertically with a restricted horizontal movement. If the inertia reel moves through angles it will become less effective. Users should refer to the manufacturer's instructions to ensure inertia reels are used correctly. If not, they can create a pendulum effect (swing fall risk) and, as well as not stopping the fall, they can expose the user to additional hazards.

The use of this type of equipment has become more common as it is not as restrictive as a fixed line system.

 For further information refer to Chapter D05 Fall arrest and suspension equipment.

Sometimes, guard-rails have to be moved or removed to enable work to be undertaken. Consider using proprietary edge protection systems that are designed to allow adjustments without compromising the guard-rail protection (for example, raising a guard-rail post to allow access to the roof surface). If temporary removal of a guard-rail is unavoidable then the following precautions should be followed.

● An equally effective safe system of work must be in place and maintained, which will prevent falls of persons or materials.

● The guard-rails must be replaced or re-erected as soon as practical.

Some flat roofing systems will involve the use of various chemicals or hot works and fumes or solvents may be present. Consideration to the Control of Substances Hazardous to Health (COSHH) Regulations and the manufacturer's information should be given as well as the significant possibility of fire, explosion or burns from hot bitumen.

2.5.2   Traditional pitched roofs

On traditional pitched (sloping) roofs, most falls occur:

● from the eaves or ridge, by slipping down then falling from the roof

● during truss erection (falling into the structure)

● from unprotected gable ends

● through fragile roofing materials, particularly fragile roof lights.

 A *pitched roof* is defined as any roof having a pitch of more than 10 degrees.

Work on pitched roofs should only be carried out in the following circumstances.

● By persons who are physically capable, trained and competent.

● Using roof ladders or a temporary work platform equipped with guard-rails and toe-boards, as necessary, and securely fixed to prevent it slipping. (The use of homemade or improvised roofing ladders should be prohibited.)

Traditional pitched roofs

● Providing that either a suitable catch barrier or a working platform with guard-rails is erected at the eaves and verge of the building.

These requirements apply to any work on a pitched roof, including access to, and egress from, other workplaces.

A steeper roof pitch increases the risk of slipping down the roof surface. The European Standard BS EN 13374 provides guidance and a specification for temporary edge protection depending upon the slope of the roof and potential fall distance.

Working platforms should be provided where the pitch of the roof prevents a secure foothold. Alternatively, work restraint systems or rope access techniques may need to be considered.

2.5.3 Curved roofs

Curved roof surfaces (such as a barrel-vault structure) may be used as a working platform, but this will depend upon the radius of the curve, as to whether a secure foothold can be safely maintained (similar to steeper pitched roofs). The more acute the curve the greater the risk of slipping and falling down the roof.

Therefore, it is often necessary to employ rope access techniques (such as work positioning or abseiling). It is essential that any such system incorporates lines secured to the apex or other suitable anchor point and a self-locking device to prevent the uncontrolled descent of anyone who loses their footing.

Additionally, proprietary rubber steps are available that follow the exact contour of a curved roof, with sections being joined to extend the overall length. These steps must be regarded as a foothold only, as they are not equipped with a handrail. They must therefore only be used in conjunction with another form of fall protection (such as a fall-arrest block).

Where there is a risk of falling through a curved roof, fall-arrest safety netting or similar protection should be installed. Special measures are required when rigging safety nets to curved type roofs.

2.5.4 Profiled roofs

These range from a single asbestos cement sheet on an outside toilet to the latest continuously extruded system formed in situ to cover large portal frame buildings. The systems will differ in complexity and range from single skin and multiple skin (build-up type) through to composite factory-produced sheeting units.

New build profiled installation will normally be carried out over a system of safety nets that provide fall protection.

 For further information refer to Chapter D05 Fall arrest and suspension equipment.

Other systems include temporary leading edge devices (such as stages with guard-rails) and trolley systems that are designed to run along purlins. However, installation, use and moving of these systems can be high risk and will normally require the use of additional fall protection measures (such as safety nets or a safety harness system). The HSE recommends that trolley systems should only be used where there is no safer option.

Designers who specify roofing materials should consider fragility and provide precise information on fixing configurations and load-bearing capacity, so that contractors can prepare safe systems of work.

Composite roof sheet systems are often immediately load bearing, independent of fixings. However, safe systems of work should be developed for handling these heavier sheets.

If a built-up roof system is being installed, the inner sheet or liner tray must be securely fixed before it can be stood on. Metal profile roof sheets are therefore still fragile until they have been fixed.

Edge protection on a steel structure

Furthermore, many roof-light assemblies, which are often installed as part of a profiled roof system, may also be fragile. This will necessitate proprietary work platforms (such as stagings) that are used to enable safe access and an additional means of fall protection (such as safety nets).

Edge protection should be provided in accordance with BS EN 13374 (practical method of providing temporary edge protection for working on roofs). Any working platform must comply with the Work at Height Regulations and be, ideally, a minimum of 600 mm wide with handrails on one or both sides, depending on whether a fall can occur.

2.5.5 Trussed roofs

The design of safe access into a roof truss system should be undertaken by the truss designer or architect, and this information passed to the contractor. This will then form part of the overall risk assessment.

A safe working platform around the roof perimeter should be erected and safe access provided where required within the trusses.

The most common fall protection systems typically used for internal falls when constructing a trussed roof include the following.

● Proprietary decking systems.

● Interior birdcage scaffolding.

● Boarding out the bottom chord of the trusses (as long as they are stable and capable of taking the imposed loads).

● Soft-landing systems (such as airbags or bean/foam bag types).

Safety nets can be used, providing that a safe clearance distance can be achieved below, and that there is suitable anchorage.

2.5.6   Solar panel installation and maintenance

The installation and maintenance of solar energy photovoltaic (PV) panels on roofs presents the same inherent risks to health and safety as roof work itself and, therefore, the same levels of protection need to be adopted. Consideration should be given to the following points.

- Safe access to the roof surface (such as scaffolding work platforms or edge protection) for fixing rails, brackets, PV panels, and so on, as a priority before resorting to personal fall protection (such as harnesses and work restraints).

- Working on or near fragile roofing materials.

- Raising and handling heavy PV panels at height.

- Future access for repairs or maintenance.

 For further information refer to *Solar panel installation* (GS001).

 Magistrates issue £250,000 fine following worker's fall from roof

A solar panel installation company was fined after failing to control risk and supervise work, resulting in a 49-year-old worker falling more than 3.5 m through a void in a roof at a school. The man suffered serious injuries, including bleeding on the brain, a ruptured spleen and fractured ribs.

A Magistrates' Court heard how he was one of several workers contracted by the solar panel installation company to undertake roof works. HSE investigations found that the company failed to ensure physical guarding was in place to prevent the worker and his colleagues from falling through voids in the roof. The inquiry also found that the company failed to appropriately supervise the work.

The solar panel installation company pleaded guilty to breaching Regulation 4(1) of the Work at Height Regulations 2005 and was fined £250,000 and ordered to pay costs of £12,073.14.

Speaking after the hearing, an HSE inspector said: 'The company failed to properly organise the work and make sure the workers knew what safety measures were needed, as well as providing appropriate supervision to ensure work was not undertaken without the measures being put in place. As a result, serious harm was caused to one worker and others were put at serious risk'.

(Source: HSE.)

2.6   Fragile roofs and surfaces

All roofs, once fixed, should be treated as fragile material until a competent person has confirmed otherwise.

 Falls through fragile surfaces account for over 20% of all fatal injuries of falls from height.

The following are likely to be fragile.

- Cement sheeting (non-reinforced sheets, irrespective of profile type, for example asbestos).

- Roof lights (difficult to see in certain light conditions or hidden when painted).

- Liner panels on built up sheet roofing.

- Metal sheets, where corroded.

- Glass, including wired glass.

- Chipboard or similar materials, where rotted or not sufficiently supported.

- Other materials, including wood wool slabs, slates and tiles.

The CITB video: Fragile roofs - Fragile lives *shows the devastating effects that falls can have*

As far as the strength of materials is concerned, the appearance of fragile roofs is often misleading. Surface coatings, dirt or moss may give a false appearance of soundness to glass, plastic, asbestos, and so on. Even if the roof is clad in a load-bearing material, roof lights can often be fragile. Asbestos and various plastic materials are particularly brittle and may shatter without warning.

 Falls from roofs

- A 50-year-old roofer was killed when he fell from the edge of a pitched roof. He was understood to have been carrying out extensive repair work following storm damage. There was no edge protection and the access ladder was not secured.

- A 60-year-old employee was killed when he fell through a fragile roof while installing a ventilation duct for a spray booth.

- A self-employed builder, aged 52, fell through a fragile roof light while trying to repair damage to the asbestos cement roof of an industrial unit.

WORKING AT HEIGHT

Effective precautions are required for all work on or near fragile surfaces, no matter how short the duration, whether the work concerns construction, maintenance, repair, cleaning or demolition.

Ideally, another way of carrying out the job that does not require anyone to work on or near to fragile roofing materials should be found.

Fragile materials should be protected when anyone passes by or works near to them. They should be securely covered and a warning notice displayed if people are working within 2 m of the area. Appropriate precautions should be taken when installing protection (such as the use of netting, birdcage scaffold or a harness system).

Sometimes it will not be reasonably practicable to provide such protection, usually if the proximity to fragile materials is irregular and of short duration (such as a matter of minutes).

Safety harnesses will usually be the most appropriate solution and may be used in conjunction with any permanently installed running line systems.

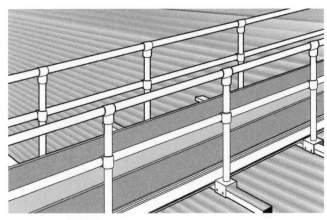

Temporary working platform

Boundaries can be established using barriers to identify safe areas within the workplace and routes to and from them. The safe area boundary should be at least 2 m from the nearest fragile material and leading edge.

It does not need to comply with full edge protection standards, but there should be a continuous physical barrier (a painted line or bunting is **not** acceptable), and discipline is essential to ensure that everyone stays inside the safe area at all times.

Where walkways with a handrail are not an integral part of the roof structure, a safe system of work must be devised.

If it is necessary to pass across a fragile roof, a roof-board complete with a guard-rail should be used to spread the weight and provide a good handhold. Depending upon the job, it may be necessary to use more than one roof-board: one to support the person, whilst the other is moved to a new position.

In such cases additional fall protection may be necessary (such as fall-arrest netting or a safety harness system) if there remains a risk of a fall through a fragile roof surface.

Walkways near fragile surfaces (in valleys, parapets, gutters or channels) must be provided with suitable guard-rails or, if not, the fragile surface should be overlaid with a load-bearing material to prevent the possibility of anyone falling through.

Warning signs should, so far as is reasonably practicable, be fixed at all approaches to roofs constructed with fragile materials. This is a requirement of the Work at Height Regulations. Such signs must comply with the Health and Safety (Safety Signs and Signals) Regulations.

Where such signs cannot be or are not fixed in place, it is essential that the presence of fragile material is identified in advance

Rooftop walkway with guard-rails preventing access to a leading edge of fragile materials (Image supplied by Kee Safety Ltd)

and those doing the job are made aware of it by other means, such as during risk assessment/method statement briefings, task safety briefings, or toolbox talks.

 Trying to walk the line of the bolts or purlins on a roof is dangerous and must not be attempted.

 Refer to the HSE publication *Health and safety in roof work* (HSG33) (paragraphs 170–202) and *Fragile roofs* (GEIS5) for details of the dangers presented by fragile surfaces.

 ## Fatal fall through a skylight

A scaffolding firm was ordered to pay more than £100,000 in fines and costs following the death of an employee who plunged 13 m through the roof of a warehouse.

The employee stepped onto a skylight, which broke and gave way. There were around 80 fragile skylights, each measuring 1 m x 2 m, on half of the roof.

However, the company failed to arrange for covers to be put on the skylight nearest to where the employees were working.

Things to consider

Avoidance. Plan and organise work to keep people away from fragile surfaces, so far as possible (for example, undertake work from below the surface in a MEWP).

Control. Working on or near fragile surfaces requires a combination of staging, guard-rails, fall restraints, fall arrests and safety nets slung beneath.

Communication. In addition to the controls, fix warning notices to the approach of any fragile surface. Workers must be trained, competent and instructed in the use of the precautions required.

Co-operation. On business premises contractors should work closely with the client and agree the arrangements for managing work.

2.7   Managing asbestos in roof work

Asbestos-containing materials have been widely used in UK roof construction for many years. It is a legal requirement of the Control of Asbestos Regulations (CAR) that anyone liable to disturb asbestos during their work, or who supervises such employees, receives the correct level of information, instruction and training. The level of training required will be determined by the type of work being carried out.

 The HSE maintains a list of accreditation bodies for training organisations that can deliver training of this nature.

The HSE has produced *Asbestos essentials*, a task manual for building, maintenance and allied trades on how to safely carry out non-licensed work involving asbestos.

The method statement must be written by someone who is deemed competent with regard to asbestos and who understands the requirements of CAR. All asbestos-containing materials removed from roofs will be classed as hazardous waste (special waste in Scotland) and will need to be disposed of by a registered waste carrier at a licensed facility under a hazardous waste consignment note.

Under CAR an employer must assume all materials are asbestos-containing unless they can prove otherwise (for example, by reference to the asbestos survey undertaken to meet the requirements of *Asbestos: the survey guide* (HSG264) and by extension of CAR). Whilst it is not difficult to recognise asbestos cement roof sheets, determining if roofing felt, soffits or insulation boards contain asbestos is normally more problematic.

All commercial clients have a duty to provide information about the presence of asbestos and should be able to give designers and contractors a copy of their asbestos register and/or asbestos survey report. Domestic clients have no such obligation, and it will be the contractor's responsibility, prior to work commencing, to identify any asbestos-containing materials present. This may require a survey in line with HSG264 (identified above). All asbestos removal work must be undertaken, in accordance with CAR, by those competent to do so.

 For further information refer to Chapter B09 Asbestos.

2.8   Access arrangements

2.8.1   Stair towers

Stair towers are an effective and safe means of access. They help speed up access, production and enable the workforce to carry materials and equipment far more safely than ladder access.

Many companies now default to stair towers, unless a risk assessment deems that ladder access is suitable for the situation (such as short or low-risk access).

2.8.2   Ladders

Ideally, access to a scaffold or roof will be via a purpose-built stair tower. However, where the decision is taken to use a ladder, the scaffold should be constructed to incorporate internal ladders and protected ladder traps.

If an external ladder is used it should be positioned along the face of the scaffold rather than at right-angles to it. Ladder gates should be installed at access points.

A typical site stairway tower (Photo © NASC)

External scaffold access with safety gate (Photo © NASC)

A ladder must not be used as access to, or egress from, a workplace unless it is reasonable to do so, taking into account the work being carried out, its duration and the risks to the safety of any person arising from the use of the ladder.

 Competence is vital

Demonstration of competence is a vital requirement of the Work at Height Regulations, and successful completion of the Ladder Association's industry standard training course contributes significantly to providing proof of competence when working with ladders and stepladders.

 For further information on this course, and the regulations, refer to the Ladder Association website and Schedule 6 of the Work at Height Regulations.

2.8.3   Landing areas (rest platforms)

Landing areas must be provided for ladders where the vertical height is over 9 m, must have adequate dimensions and must be provided at suitable intervals. All landing areas must be provided with the following.

● A guard-rail at a height of not less than 950 mm.

● An intermediate guard-rail.

● A toe-board.

● A gap not exceeding 470 mm between the toe-board and guard-rail, or between any two guard-rails.

2.8.4   Roof ladders

Personnel involved in roof work should not walk directly on slates or tiles on sloping roofs, as these do not normally provide a suitable foothold, especially when wet.

Roof ladders, designed for the purpose, should be secured by means of a ridge hook over the ridge tiles, bearing on the opposite roof pitch.

The ridge tile or gutter should not be used to support roof ladders, as they can become accidentally displaced.

2.8.5   Edge protection

Falls from the edge of the roof should be prevented by perimeter scaffolding or an edge protection system fixed to the building structure. Designers of new buildings should consider how edge protection may be secured to the building for construction and future maintenance.

Edge protection to prevent the fall of people and materials should be provided in accordance with the Work at Height Regulations and BS EN 13374 for construction and maintenance work. This British and European standard is not generally suitable for the public, other workers, vehicles or mobile plant equipment or bulk materials (such as packs of roofing materials). The classification of edge protection systems is primarily based on the gradient of the surface and the potential fall distance down the roof for which they are to provide protection.

The performance requirements for the various classes are detailed within the standard BS EN 13374. These requirements are briefly summarised below and in the images on the following page.

Class A provides protection to flat surfaces and slopes of generally up to 10 degrees. It provides resistance to static loads and is based on the requirements to support a person leaning against, walking beside, and possibly stumbling against the edge protection.

Class B provides protection to flat surfaces and slopes of generally up to 30 degrees, and to even steeper slopes with short slope lengths. It provides resistance to both static and low dynamic loads and is based on the requirements to support a person leaning against, walking beside, possibly stumbling against and sliding down a sloping surface towards the edge protection.

A proprietary roof ladder

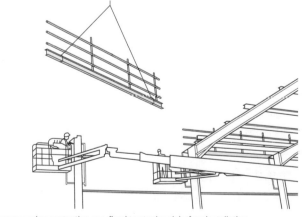

Temporary edge protection pre-fixed to steelwork before installation (Photo © NASC)

Class C provides protection to steeply sloping surfaces of generally up to 45 degrees, and up to 60 degrees for 5 m slopes. It provides resistance to high dynamic loads only and is based on the requirements to contain a person sliding down a steeply sloping surface. All edge protection systems should be adequately secured so that they cannot become accidentally displaced in their intended use (loading as per BS EN 13374 or, in the case of scaffolding, BS EN 12811).

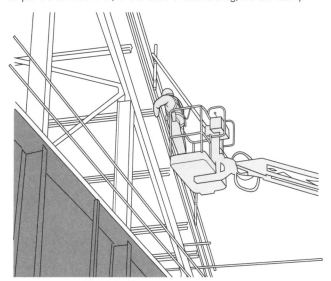

Scaffolding edge protection installed from a MEWP (Photo © NASC)

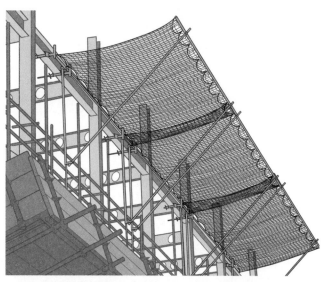

A proprietary safety net fan system provides fall protection, enabling perimeter guard-rails to be erected above without MEWP access (Photo © NASC)

Safe systems of work must be established for the installation and removal of temporary edge protection. Where possible, edge protection installed to the building structure should be accessed by a MEWP. Where MEWP access is not practical, collective fall-arrest fans or, as a last resort, fall-restraint systems should be used.

Where scaffolding is used with a working platform, guard-rails and toe-boards to provide roof edge protection, it should be positioned close to the eaves to minimise the potential fall distance to the platform. This should be ideally no more than 300-450 mm below the eaves or roof edge.

However, sometimes access may also be required to the eaves (for example, facia and soffit) where the fall distance may be slightly greater (up to 600 mm) but avoids unnecessary scaffold adaptations.

In such cases the increased risk of injury must be assessed so that the fall distance is minimised and consideration given for safe access to and egress from the roof surface and the possible need for an additional guard-rail for increased fall protection (for example, internal guard-rails to the eaves or an additional, third guard-rail above the main platform guard-rail).

Counterweight temporary edge protection (Image supplied by Kee Safety Ltd)

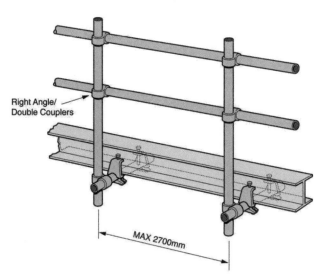

Right Angle/
Double Couplers

MAX 2700mm

Temporary edge protection on open steelwork (Class A)

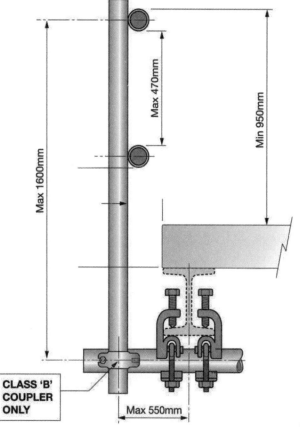

Max 1600mm

Max 470mm

Min 950mm

CLASS 'B'
COUPLER
ONLY

Max 550mm

It is recommended that the platform should be wide enough to provide a suitable catchment area should someone fall from a sloped roof. Ideally the platform should extend 2 m past the work area on the roof, or guard-rails should be installed on the roof to contain the workers within the protection offered by the scaffolding. Special consideration should be given in the following situations.

- When workers can encroach within 2 m of the verge, guard-rails or gable-end scaffolding may be required.

- If there is a risk of workers falling down the opposite side of a ridge and unprotected eaves. Edge protection to the opposite eaves should be provided or a work restraint system used.

- When workers can encroach within 2 m of an opening or fragile surface within the roof surface.

Edge protection on a sloping roof

2.8.6 Access to chimney stacks

Construction and maintenance of chimney stacks should always be undertaken from a properly constructed working platform with safe access. Traditionally, scaffolding to chimney stacks offers the safest option. However, risks involved during erection and dismantling also need to be considered.

There are various purpose-designed, lightweight stagings and access systems available for work on or around chimney stacks. MEWP access may also be a practical solution for short duration or inspection work before resorting to ladders. Consideration should be given to the roof structure and load imposed by the access equipment. If in doubt engineering advice should be sought.

 For further information on scaffolding refer to Chapter D04.

2.8.7 Powered access

Powered access covers a wide range of mechanical access equipment, such as those listed below.

Example of a chimney stack and access scaffold (Photo © NASC)

- Mobile elevating work platforms (MEWPs).
- Mast climbing work platforms (MCWPs).
- Suspended cradles.
- Personnel carrying platforms.

Mobile access platforms are often used as an alternative to ladders, scaffolds and cradles.

Each of these types of equipment can be suitable for carrying out particular types of roof work (for example, using a telescopic boom MEWP (also known as a cherry picker) might be a suitable and safe way of accessing a job that would otherwise require someone having to cross a fragile roof). This is particularly important for inspection or short duration maintenance work. Truck-mounted MEWPs now have sufficient reach to enable inspection of many building types to be made without having to directly access the roof. The use of drones is increasingly being used to carry out a range of activities including inspection and surveys for working at height.

 For further information on drones see Chapter C05.

2.8.7.1 Mobile elevating work platforms

- All MEWPs must conform to *Mobile elevating work platforms. Design calculations. Stability criteria. Construction. Safety. Examinations and tests* (BS EN 280).

- MEWPs must be operated by authorised and trained persons who hold the appropriate International Powered Access Federation (IPAF) powered access licence (PAL) for the type of MEWP to be used.

- Operators must be familiar with the model of MEWP and maintain a log book to record experience.

- Safety harnesses with fall restraint lanyards must be used in boom-type MEWPs (except when working over or near water), to prevent operatives from accessing a position where they could fall.

- Only use suitable anchor points, as specified by the manufacturer. Never use the guardrails as an anchor point.

- Fall restraint lanyards must be adjusted to the shortest practical length necessary for the platform, ideally no more than 1.5 m long.
  Note: adjustable or suitable length fall-arrest lanyards can be used in a fall restraint mode, as energy absorbers will not deploy until a load of 3 kN is applied.

- When working in a MEWP harnesses should not be used in a fall-arrest scenario as the dynamic loads imposed could be beyond the capacity of the MEWP and cause overturning or collapse.

- Never exceed the safe load rating of the MEWP. Specially designed devices are available for handling materials within a MEWP (such as cladding installation systems). Seek advice from the supplier.

- Never use a MEWP as a hoist, crane or prop, unless it is designed for the purpose.

- MEWPs must be used in accordance with the *Operators' safety guide* (IPAF) and *Safe use of MEWPs – Code of Practice* (BS 8460).

- Care should be taken to avoid trapping and crushing people in the platform.

- When operating a MEWP in a high-risk area of entrapment (such as near overhead steel beams), equipment that has a secondary guarding device installed must be selected.

- MEWPs must be inspected and maintained in accordance with the manufacturer's recommendations and subject to LOLER thorough examination every six months.

- Planning for emergencies must include how rescue and recovery from a MEWP is to be carried out, including the competence of the rescuer(s).

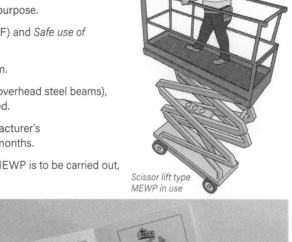

Scissor lift type MEWP in use

IPAF powered access licence

IPAF operators' safety guide

 For further information refer to the Strategic Forum Plant Safety Group *Best Practice Guidance for MEWPs - Avoiding trapping/crushing injuries to people in the platform*.

2.8.7.2 Mast climbing work platforms

Mast climbing work platforms (MCWPs) are not commonly used or suitable for roof access or edge protection; their primary function is to provide a movable façade access to buildings that, when repositioned, will leave the leading edge exposed. With this equipment, the platform or cradle rises up one or more static masts in a similar way to a hoist, providing a temporary work platform at height, usually on the side of a building. Some procedures to be observed in the erection of mast climbers are described below.

- Installers must be trained, in accordance with the manufacturer's instructions.

- Make sure there is a system in place to identify a loss of mechanical integrity in each drive unit. Check each unit is fitted with a mechanical device, such as a centrifugal brake.

- MCWPs should be operated by authorised and trained persons who hold the International Powered Access Federation (IPAF) powered access licence (PAL) special category for MCWPs.

- MCWPs must be inspected daily, before use, by the user.

- MCWPs must be regularly inspected by a competent person and records maintained of the inspection. They must be thoroughly examined every six months.

- The safe working load and the permitted number of persons allowed on the platform at each configuration must be clearly marked on the MCWP. They should not be used as a substitute for using stairs or a passenger lift for travelling to higher levels.

- Planning should consider the interface with building features that could impede the working envelope of the MCWP and present trapping or shear points to the users or residents of occupied buildings (such as opening windows and balconies).

- All MCWPs must conform to the *Code of Practice for the installation, maintenance, thorough examination and safe use of mast climbing work platforms* (BS 7981) and *Lifting platforms. Mast climbing work platforms* (BS EN 1495).

 For further information on MEWPs and MCWPs visit the International Powered Access Federation website.

02

2.8.7.3 Suspended cradles

This section covers suspended working platforms, commonly referred to as cradles. As with MCWPs, cradles are not commonly used or suitable for roof access or edge protection, as their primary function is for façade access.

- All proprietary cradle systems must conform to *Safety requirements for suspended access equipment. Design calculations, stability criteria, construction. Examinations and tests* (BS EN 1808).

- Temporary suspended cradles and scaffolds must conform to the *Code of Practice for the planning, design, setting up and use of temporary suspended access equipment* (BS 5974).

- The design, inspection, testing and use of suspended cradles must be in accordance with the Specialist Access Engineering and Maintenance Association (SAEMA) guidance.

- Installers of proprietary cradle systems must be trained in accordance with the manufacturer's instructions.

- Users of suspended cradles must use personal fall protection equipment and be attached to a designated anchor point within the cradle or line system.

- The use of permanently installed cradle systems for access during building construction, designed for future maintenance use, may be a practical option. However, consideration should be given to the nature of use and advice should be sought from the manufacturer.

Permanently installed cradle system for future building maintenance used during construction operations

For further information visit the Specialist Access Engineering and Maintenance Association website.

2.8.7.4 Personnel-carrying platforms

Personnel-carrying platforms (or baskets) are not powered access equipment. However, they are designed to be used with cranes or lift trucks and, when combined, provide a means of powered access. Consideration should be given to a MEWP, or similar purposely-designed access equipment, before resorting to personnel-carrying platforms.

The use of baskets with rough terrain or telescopic type lift trucks in construction increases the risks to users, and therefore safer alternatives (such as MEWPs) should always be considered first.

- Personnel carrying baskets provide specific hazards, as the user is reliant on the operator of the crane or lift truck. Therefore, there must be an effective means of communication and a signaller used, as per other lifting operations.

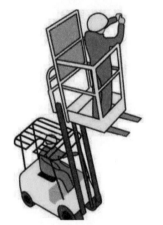

Lift truck mounted and crane slung personnel carrying platforms

- The use of a personnel carrying platform must be planned, managed and operated, the same as any lifting operations under the Lifting Operations and Lifting Equipment Regulations (LOLER).

- The type of personnel carrying platform must conform to *Cranes. Equipment for lifting of persons. Suspended baskets* (BS EN 14502).

- The lifting device (crane or lift truck) must be suitable and have the correct load rating.

- The personnel carrying platform must be slung and/or secured to the lifting device, as per the manufacturer's instructions.

- Passengers in the personnel carrying platform must use personal fall protection equipment and be attached to a designated anchor point within the platform or the lifting equipment (for example, a crane hook).

- Due consideration must be given to the thorough examination requirements of LOLER when mobile work equipment is used to lift people, including the accessory itself: six months for lifting equipment and any associated accessories used to lift people, and six months for all lifting accessories and 12 months for all other lifting equipment.

For further information refer to:

- **Chapter D05 Fall arrest and suspension equipment**
- **Chapter C05 Work equipment and hand-held tools**
- **Chapter C07 Lifting operations.**

2.8.8   Safety nets

For most industrial and commercial roofing and flooring construction, properly rigged fall-arrest safety nets and perimeter edge protection is the preferred solution. Nets provide workers with maximum freedom of movement, as long as they do not encroach beyond the protected area.

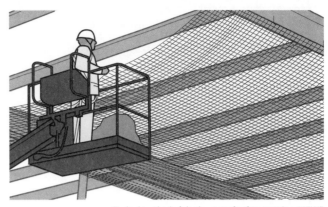

Typical method of rigging a roof safety net via a MEWP
(Photo © NASC)

● Nets must be supplied in accordance with BS EN 1263 Part 1 and rigged in accordance with BS EN 1263 Part 2 and BS 8411 (*Code of Practice for safety nets on construction sites and other works*).

● Prior to installation and use on site, **all** safety nets must have been patch tested within the previous 12 months (unless they are new, i.e. less than 12 months old).

● All nets must have a tag displaying:

  – the net's serial number

  – date tested

  – date of next test, and

  – confirmation that the net meets the minimum test criteria set by the manufacturer.

● Only competent and trained riggers are permitted to rig, alter or de-rig safety nets, ideally in accordance with the *Fall arrest safety equipment training* (FASET) scheme, or equivalent.

● Anchorage for safety nets must be capable of withstanding 6 kN of force. Therefore safety netting must be tied to a suitable structure. Never fix nets to scaffolding unless it has been designed for the purpose.

● Ensure the most suitable method of access is used for rigging and de-rigging safety nets, in accordance with the FASET safety guidance notes.

● Remote methods of rigging and de-rigging should be used wherever possible.

● Rescue plans must consider recovery of a casualty from the safety nets.

● Nets can be rigged with debris netting for light debris containment.

● Net repairs must be tagged by a competent person, in accordance with FASET recommendations.

● Never store materials below safety nets that reduce clearance distances.

● Nets must be inspected by a trained safety net rigger or inspector, before use, every seven days, and after any event likely to jeopardise the safe condition of the nets.

● Nets should have a further inspection by a competent person every seven days after handover, if the nets continue to be worked above.

● A safety net inspection register must be maintained.

For further information refer to the following:

● **FASET website**

● ***The Blue book – Recommended practice for the use of safety nets for roof work*, published by the Advisory Committee for Roofsafety.**

2.8.8.1   Working platform nets

Tensioned netting systems are being used more commonly within the construction industry for roofing operations and to enable access to difficult workplaces, for example under deck areas of structures such as bridges, piers, jetties and offshore platforms. Tensioned netting systems must be subject to a specific design scheme.

● Installation and use must be properly planned, risk assessed and a detailed method statement produced.

● They must be installed, inspected, used and maintained in accordance with FASET recommendations and specific design.

● The design must determine the maximum loading and the load imposed on the supporting structure.

● A methodology for the safe use must be established for the management of this work at height access system as part of the specific design of the scheme.

● As a minimum, working platform nets should be inspected to the same standard as fall-arrest safety nets.

2.9   Handling and storage of roofing materials

Care must be taken at all times when stacking bulk material on or at roof level. Attention should be given to the following points.

- Size of the load involved.

- Types of material involved.

- Methods of raising the load, whether manually or mechanically.

- Means of communication (signals) and the competence of the slinger or signaller.

- Position authorised for stacking materials.

- Distribution of the loads (loading plan).

- Maximum load or stack size.

- Loading limitations of the roof.

- Adequate support or packing to the truss.

- Provision of exclusion zones at ground level.

- Careful stacking of materials on roofs.

- Protection of the existing roof surface and any weatherproofing.

- Prevention of the displacement of loads that should be secured against:
  - the wind, especially split bundles and sheets
  - sliding down sloping roofs (sheet stop).

Manual handling of materials needs to be considered by roofing contractors as part of the risk assessment process, especially heavy or unwieldy sheeting materials and the increased risk associated with adverse weather conditions.

 For further information refer to *Health and safety in roof work* (HSG33) and the NFRC guidance for handling roofing sheets and recommended safe wind speeds.

Mechanical handling equipment should be used where possible for handling bulk materials. Specially strengthened sections of scaffolding or loading bays may be required.

Where roofing materials are being stripped from an existing roof and stored on a scaffold for reuse, they must be stacked safely, not overloading the structure, and there should be sufficient space for working and safe passage.

The risks from falling materials and other objects in roof work must be considered and suitable controls established to prevent and protect against this.

Where the risk of falling objects cannot be completely eliminated, the risk must be managed. Some precautions are shown below.

- Toe-boards on working platforms.

- The use of brick-guards.

- Protective fans *(refer to Chapter D04 Scaffolding)*.

- Containment sheeting and debris netting, including overlay debris netting for fall-arrest netting.

- Pedestrian gantries with crash decking.

- Debris chutes for removal of waste materials from the roof.

- Segregating the area below as a designated danger area and preventing unauthorised access with physical barriers and displaying appropriate warning signs.

Example of a brick-guard (Photo © NASC)

Example of a debris chute (Photo © NASC)

2.10   Other considerations

This section is primarily focused on roof work. However, work at height and associated risks are present in a wide range of construction, refurbishment and maintenance activities. Employers must ensure all work at height is properly planned and managed in accordance with the Work at Height Regulations.

2.10.1   Danger areas

Under the Work at Height Regulations there is a specific legal requirement to ensure the safety of those working at height (from falls), and others who may be working or passing below (from falling objects), by the creation of danger areas, either around the high-level workplace and/or below it.

This is achieved by preventing unauthorised access into any danger area, so far as is reasonably practicable, by the use of barriers and appropriate signs or in some cases designated personnel to control access in and around the danger zones.

Where designated personnel are used to control danger areas it is essential that an effective means of communication is established between themselves and those working at height.

2.10.2   Personal protective equipment

 In the context of roof work, *personal protective equipment* (PPE) includes items of fall-arrest equipment (such as safety harnesses and lanyards).

In deciding which type to issue, the employer must take into account the risk that the PPE is being used for, and also ensure that the PPE will fit the wearer and allow them to work comfortably.

The employer must ensure that employees have been given adequate and appropriate information, instruction and training to enable them to understand the risks, the purpose of the PPE and the manner in which it is to be used.

Whilst the employer must take reasonable steps to ensure that any PPE supplied is used, the employee, in turn, must use the PPE provided in accordance with instruction and training given and follow the procedures for reporting loss or defects to their employer.

2.10.3   Presence of bats

Bats commonly roost in roof spaces and it is therefore vital that contractors are aware of their obligations.

All species of bat and their breeding sites or resting places (roosts) are protected under the Conservation of Habitats and Species Regulations and the Wildlife and Countryside Act.

It is an offence for anyone intentionally to kill, injure or handle a bat, to possess a bat (whether live or dead), disturb a roosting bat, or sell or offer a bat for sale without a licence. It is also an offence to damage, destroy or obstruct access to any place used by bats for shelter, whether they are present or not.

 If bats are discovered during the course of the work, work in that area should be stopped and specialist advice sought. This should include consultation with the client.

 For further information refer to Chapter E05 Ecology.

2.10.4   Presence of pigeons

The accumulated droppings of pigeons, if disturbed into airborne dust and then inhaled, can cause severe respiratory problems as well as the possible risk of contracting an acute respiratory disease called Psittacosis. It typically causes flu-like symptoms (fever, headache and muscle aches) that usually appear five to 19 days after exposure, but can lead to severe pneumonia and non-respiratory health problems.

Salmonella may also be present in some bird droppings, and is a bacterial infection that can cause severe diarrhoea, fever and abdominal cramps. It is anticipated that the presence of pigeons will mainly be a problem during refurbishment and repair work, or demolition.

If, during early visits to site, it is evident that pigeons are present, or have been, then measures must be taken to clean up the droppings before work starts, using a safe system of work, and to discourage the return of the birds. Workers with a weakened immune system should not be directly involved in tasks involving bird droppings.

This should be considered as part of the risk assessment process.

Common access equipment

03

Supporting
INFORMATION

GT700 Toolbox talks / supporting checklists and forms

Toolbox talks on some of these topics are available in the GT700 publication. Supporting checklists and forms covering some of these topics are available on our companion website.

COMMON ACCESS EQUIPMENT

Overview

The purpose of this chapter is to give an understanding of the health and safety requirements when selecting and using common forms of access equipment (such as ladders, podium steps, mobile access towers and hop-ups).

While the chapter provides relevant information, formal and recognised training in the actual access equipment system to be used will be necessary before a person can be regarded as competent.

It is important that anyone reading this chapter has a good understanding of the requirements of the Work at Height Regulations.

3.1 Introduction

There is a huge range of access equipment and solutions available to meet every need of the construction industry.

Access equipment includes items such as hop-ups, stepladders, ladders, podium steps, lightweight stagings and trestle systems, powered access (mobile elevating work platforms) and scaffolding.

These can all provide an easily transported means of access to work at height and they can be used safely in certain conditions. Danger often occurs when access equipment is used for a job for which it is not suitable – this particularly applies to ladders and stepladders.

Access equipment should only be erected, altered, used, dismantled or operated by a competent person, who has received adequate training in systems of work and in any equipment that they are planning to use for access.

In accordance with the Work at Height Regulations, all work at height should be avoided, where possible.

When it cannot be avoided, falls should be prevented by selecting the most appropriate form of access equipment for the particular environment and circumstances.

 For information on the working at height hierarchy, refer to Chapter D01 Work at Height Regulations.

3.2 Important points

- When selecting suitable access equipment, the working at height hierarchy should be followed.

- Mobile towers and other forms of access equipment must be subject to a statutory inspection, with a report produced, where appropriate.

- All mobile towers must be properly erected. They must remain stable, be suitable for their purpose and be equipped with toe-boards and guard-rails on all working platforms.

- All personnel involved in the installation and dismantling of mobile towers and access equipment must have received appropriate training for the type of equipment in use.

- Installers and users should be familiar with, and refer to, the manufacturer's instruction manual.

 The HSE has developed a brief step-by-step guide.

This toolkit has been developed to help workers understand the key issues when working at height and the factors to consider when selecting the most appropriate and safest type of access equipment.

3.3 Ladders and stepladders

Traditionally, ladders and stepladders have been used as the way of getting up to or down from a place of work at height (for example, the means of access to a roof or scaffold).

However, under the Work at Height Regulations, a ladder or stepladder that is being used to carry out an activity (for example, painting a first-floor window) could now be considered as a place of work.

The Work at Height Regulations require that employers give adequate consideration to the safety of the user before selecting a ladder or stepladder as either a means of access to height or as a place of work at height.

In deciding whether or not a ladder or stepladder should be used, the employer must carry out a risk assessment and be able to demonstrate that it is not reasonably practicable to use an alternative, safer means of access and that the risks from using the ladder or stepladder are low.

HSE guidance is that ladders and stepladders should only be used as a place of work when the nature of the work meets the following criteria.

- Is of short duration (up to a maximum of 30 minutes).

- Is of a light (up to 10 kg) nature (requires no heavy lifting, carrying or a destabilising pressure applied by the user or equipment in carrying out the work – minimal manual handling).

- Allows one hand to be available at all times for holding on to the ladder or stepladder.

- Requires nothing to be carried that would cause instability of the ladder, stepladder or user.

Additionally, when stepladders are used as a place of work they should be positioned so that the user faces the work as the stepladder is climbed. A stepladder must not be positioned so that the user is side-on to the work, where the nature of the work would apply a sideways pressure and cause the stepladder to become unstable.

Ladders should:

- be set up at an angle of 75° (1 m out for every 4 m up – a ratio of 1:4)

- be positioned on a firm, level surface

- not be vulnerable to impact by pedestrians or traffic

- be used in accordance with the manufacturer's instructions

- be the right ladder for the job (remember that no single ladder will suit all applications)

- be inspected before use to ensure there are no defects

- ideally, be lashed at or near the upper point of rest by the stiles, not the rungs

- extend at least 1 m above the stepping-off place unless an alternative handhold is provided that enables a safe transfer between the ladder and stepping-off place

- be secured at the bottom or footed* if securing at the top is not possible

- not be rested against fragile or flexible items (such as plastic guttering); a ladder stay or stand-off device must be used, as necessary

- never be painted to an extent that the paint could conceal defects

- be subjected to a schedule of periodic inspections with written inspection reports kept, be individually identifiable and proof of inspection demonstrated

- be visually checked by the user for obvious defects before use and not used if found to be defective. If defective the ladder should be taken out of service and reported.

The working area should also be inspected for the presence of overhead hazards, including power cables.

HSE research has shown that, to be most effective, the person footing a ladder should stand with both feet on the bottom rung at all times. Even then, footing is not an effective method of stopping a long ladder from slipping sideways. Ideally a ladder will only be footed when it is climbed for the first time for the purpose of tying it off.

 Footing a ladder is the last resort and should be avoided, where reasonably practicable, by the use of other access equipment.

 For further information on the performance and effectiveness of ladder stability devices visit the HSE website.

3.3.1 Types of ladder

Standing ladders are a single stage ladder up to 6 m in length.

Pole ladders are a variant of standing ladders, but with the stiles having been made from a long, wooden pole cut centrally to give even strength and flexibility. Lengths can vary up to a maximum of 10 m.

The practice of shortening a pole ladder to fit a particular situation should be discouraged. Care must be taken to ensure that the fabric of the ladder remains stable if a tie wire is removed.

Extension ladders consist of two or three sections coupled together and extended by sliding over or inside each other. Longer multi-stage ladders are extended by means of a rope and pulley. The maximum reach of a single run ladder is 9 m. At this height and above, resting points must be provided.

Stepladders are of various types, have flat rectangular treads and are usually free standing.

Platform stepladders have a built in working platform, and newer models can have wheels for ease of movement, handrails and restraint chains. Due to the provision of a platform, these are usually a better option for work that is regularly carried out at the same height.

Roof ladders are ladders with a ridge hook on the top end for securing over the ridge on the opposite side of a roof (not hung on the actual ridge tiles).

Aluminium and steel ladders are available in various types. Their main advantage is that they are light and weather resistant. They can be prone to slipping at the base if the rubber feet are not properly maintained.

Telescopic ladders are a variation of leaning ladders, but they do not all work the same way. They should always be used, stored and transported with care and kept clean, and it is always important that you read and follow the user instructions provided by the manufacturer.

 The Ladder Association, a not-for-profit body dedicated to promoting safe ladder use, has produced a safety guide for users of telescopic ladders - an increasingly popular piece of equipment for working at height - following recent reports of unsafe products in the UK. Visit the Ladder Association website to download a free copy of the guidance.

3.3.2   Classes of ladder (BS EN 131)

Portable ladders, steps, trestles and lightweight staging are covered by BS EN 131.

A **duty rating** indicates their suitability of use.

EN 131 Trade and Industrial. Heavy duty and industrial use (for professional users).

EN 131 Domestic. (For non-professional users.)

In December 2017, the British Standards and regulations for ladders and steps changed to meet criteria set out by the recently-revised European standard for all ladders: BS EN 131 Trade and Industrial – heavy duty and industrial use (for professional users) and EN 131 Domestic (for non-professional users). The new standards ensure products are built with additional safety standards, such as wider bases and stabilisers on ladders over 3 m in height.

If your existing ladders conform to the previous BS 1129 or BS 2037 standards and are in good condition and inspected regularly then you can continue to use them – there is no need to scrap existing ladders and stepladders that are in good condition. As part of the inspection policy it is advisable to add a note referencing the change so that when new ladders need to be purchased they meet the new BS EN 131 standard.

 All ladders should be marked with a unique identification number and the class or duty rating. For more comprehensive guidance refer to LA455 Safe Use of Ladders and Stepladders - a brief guide, the new guidance jointly produced by the Ladder Association and the HSE. Released in July 2021, the guidance replaces the HSE Guidance Document INDG455 of the same name.

3.3.3   Inspection of ladders

Every ladder should be inspected on a regular basis and should carry an identification mark, as detailed above. A written record should be kept of all inspections, defects and repairs.

 The frequency of ladder inspections should be determined by considering the use, duration and environment in which they will be used. In addition to pre-use checks, it is common for ladders that are used regularly to be thoroughly inspected every three months.

Ladders should not be used if defective in any way and, if damaged beyond repair, they should be destroyed. Regulation 12 of the Work at Height Regulations requires work equipment (including ladders) to be inspected at regular intervals. It also recommends that all ladders are inspected prior to use. Laddertag systems are available that are in line with the Work at Height Regulations and BS EN 131. The safety tag inserts provide a location to record when the ladder was last checked. Each insert also has a checklist printed on the reverse side.

Some considerations for ladder inspections are shown below.

● There should not be any signs of splitting, cracking, splintering, warping or bruising.

● Metal ladders should not exhibit signs of mechanical damage or chemical attack.

● There must not be any undue wear or movement of the rungs.

● All rungs must be in place.

● Wedges and tie rods must be tight.

● Any metal reinforcements must be positioned correctly.

● Feet must not be split or frayed.

● Plastic inserts must be intact and not be excessively worn.

● There should not be any mud or grease on the rungs. Workers should check that their footwear is clear of mud.

● Wooden ladders should be free from rot.

● Locking mechanisms should be checked. If they are bent or the fixings are worn or damaged the ladder could collapse.

● Any locking bars should be engaged.

● Where repairs are not possible, the report should specify that the ladder should be scrapped.

The condition of any ropes and cords, along with pulleys, hinges and any other fittings, should be checked for fraying to ensure that they are all secure with no sign of damage.

3.3.4 Carrying a ladder

A short ladder may be carried comfortably by having it vertical against the shoulder and holding one of the lower rungs, using the other hand to hold the stile. Longer ladders should be carried horizontally by two people. Care should be taken in negotiating corners and obstacles.

Ladders must not be taken into the vicinity of overhead power lines (OHPL) unless a permit to work has been issued and/ or a physical barrier is present, to provide a clearance distance between the OHPL and ladder.

Where any doubt arises the electricity supply company should be contacted for further advice. This may include the installation of temporary, protective overhead line covering (also known as shrouding) or isolation of the OHPL. Even then, extreme care is still advised.

Timber ladders generally do not conduct electricity (unless wet) but aluminium ladders are extremely conductive and are dangerous to use in close proximity to OHPLs.

Carrying a ladder correctly

3.3.5 Erecting and lowering ladders

The procedure for erecting a ladder, when the ladder is flat on the ground, is as follows.

- Check there are no overhead obstructions in the vicinity.

- One person stands on the bottom rung while the other takes position at the head of the ladder and takes hold of the top rung, raising the ladder off the ground.

- Then, rung by rung, that person moves towards the foot of the ladder, lifting as they go. The person at the foot grasps the lower rungs as soon as possible and draws the ladder towards them, steadying it at the same time.

- The sequence is reversed when lowering.

- Short ladders may be raised by one person placing the foot of the ladder against a wall or fixture and pushing the ladder upwards, starting at the top, walking, under-running and raising the ladder as they go.

Extension ladders are raised one section at a time and slotted into position. The minimum recommended overlap on extension ladders is shown in the table below. Latching hooks must be properly engaged.

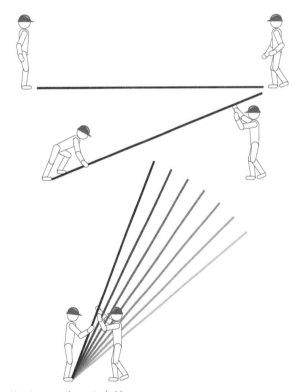

How to correctly erect a ladder

Closed length	Approximate no. of rungs	Overlap of rungs
Under 5 m	Under 18	2
5–6 m	18–23	3
Over 6 m	Over 23	4

 Ladders must never be lashed, tied or spliced together in an attempt to make an extension ladder.

Roof ladders should only be used when it has been established that the use of a safer alternative is not possible. Any work undertaken involving roof ladders must be of short duration and involve only low-risk work. Roof ladders should be erected as follows.

First, the work area must be assessed and, if necessary, an exclusion zone set up with barriers and appropriate safety signs. When all involved are satisfied that the area is segregated and safe, a standing ladder is erected for access to the eaves of the roof.

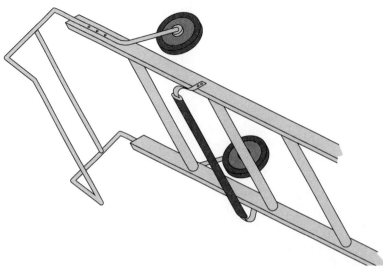

A roof ladder, with ridge/anchor hook (Credit: HSG33: Health and safety in roof work*)*

It should extend at least 1 m above the eaves of the roof and be properly secured, but not to the guttering, downpipes or any other plastic or fragile material. Proprietary ladder anchors are available and these should be used in preference to other methods.

Adopting good manual handling methods, the roof ladder should then be passed up by an individual at ground level, before being brought up and pushed up the roof on its wheels, with the anchor hook or ridge hook uppermost.

Once over the ridge, the ladder is turned over and the hook engaged. Where possible secure the roof ladder with a rope.

Ideally, where it is necessary to use a roof ladder, access to the lower end of it will be from a working platform at the eaves.

Where access is from a free-standing ladder, the points on ladder safety *(refer to 3.3 Ladders and stepladders)* must be observed.

Three points of contact should be maintained at all times when climbing the roof ladder.

Roof ladders must be:

● only used by persons who are competent to use them

● positioned to enable easy and safe transfer between:

– any other ladder used to get to the eaves and the roof ladder

– the roof ladder and the place of work

● designed for the purpose

● of good construction, strong enough to enable the planned work to be carried out and regularly inspected

● adequately supported to take the user's weight without damaging the roof

● securely fixed to the sloping part of the roof by means of a ridge hook placed over the ridge. Ridge hooks must not bear down on ridge tiles or capping tiles.

3.3.6 Storage of ladders

Ladders, especially if made of wood, deteriorate when exposed to the weather for prolonged periods. Where indoor storage is not available, they should be covered or stored in a protected, well-ventilated position. They should not be exposed to excessive heat, moisture or chemicals.

Ladders should be stored on racks, supported on the stiles only, with sufficient supports to prevent them from sagging. They must not be hung from the rungs or stiles. Aluminium ladders should be kept away from wet lime or cement, as the chemical composition may result in corrosion of metallic components.

Pulleys and hinges should be lubricated and the condition of ropes and cords checked. Any damage or deterioration should be noted and made good before use.

3.3.7 Stepladders

Many of the general rules for the safe use of ladders also apply to stepladders.

In addition, the following points should be considered.

● Stepladders are only to be used based upon a risk assessment confirming their suitability for the task.

● The treads (or steps), hinges, bolts, screws and fixings must all be sound and secure.

● Retaining cords or hinges should be of equal length and in good condition.

● The stepladder must be stable when open and standing on a level base.

- The legs of stepladders should be positioned as far apart as the restraining mechanism allows, with all four legs firmly and squarely on the ground.

- Wherever possible, the stepladder should be positioned so that the person climbing it is facing the work to avoid twisting and unnecessary movement that can create instability.

- Unless the design permits, the knees of the person using the stepladder should be kept below the top step.

- The user should not work from the top three steps of a stepladder (including a step forming the very top of the stepladder) unless there is a suitable handhold.

- Where provided, any gate or guard-rail barrier should be closed when the stepladder is in use.

If it is not practicable to maintain a handhold when a load is being carried, a risk assessment must demonstrate that the use of the stepladder is justified because of the low risk and short duration use of the stepladder.

3.4   Podium steps, mini mobile towers and pop-ups

Podium steps and **mini mobile towers** provide low-level height access, with adjustable height and guard-rails. The use of this type of equipment is preferred to stepladders in most circumstances as it provides a small but stable working platform, complete with guard-rails.

This type of access equipment has the advantage over a stepladder in that it allows the user to work in a safer manner, facing any side of the working platform without it becoming unstable, and it also provides collective means of fall protection.

Podium steps and **mini mobile towers** are lightweight in construction and some types will fold flat for ease of transportation. Specific models are designed to be wheeled through a standard-sized door. Some types of this form of access equipment can be fitted with outriggers to increase stability.

There are many differing types of podium steps and mini mobile towers with different arrangements of use. Some are just wheeled platforms and others have specific installation requirements.

Podium in use, correctly assembled and wheels locked

Example of a push around vertical (PAV)

The instructions for each individual podium or mini mobile tower must be available and understood by the user (for example, the manufacturer's instruction manual) and it is advised (through Regulation 5 of the Work at Height Regulations) that users of equipment of this nature are trained in its use.

The PASMA low-level access course is one example of suitable training. Users should also ensure equipment is manufactured to BS 8620.

Push around verticals, commonly called **pop-ups**, are an increasingly popular and versatile item of access equipment. These are a category covered by IPAF's PAL (powered access licence) card.

Whilst providing a high degree of safety in most situations, there are a number of specific hazards with the use of this type of equipment and the employer should ensure the following precautions are considered in selecting and using podium steps and mini mobile towers.

- The height of the working platform should be assessed: too low and the user will not reach; too high and the user may be inclined to work from the steps rather than the platform.

- Where adjustable height platforms are in use, ensure that the user is trained in how to adjust the platform and handrails to ensure protection.

- Brakes must be used whilst the platform is in use and users must not be permitted to pull themselves along (surfing) from the top of the podium or mini mobile tower, as this can cause equipment to tip over. Some podiums are fitted with anti-surfing features, intended to ensure users do not try to surf.

- Podium steps and mini mobile towers, like any other access equipment, must have an individual identifying mark and be subject to frequent inspection.

- The manufacturer's instruction leaflet or hire company information leaflet should be available during the inspection to check that the low-level access equipment has been erected in line with these requirements. It is good practice to laminate and attach this information to the item of low-level access equipment being used.

 For further information about low-level access equipment and training visit the PASMA website.

COMMON ACCESS EQUIPMENT

3.5 Lightweight staging and trestle scaffolds

Trestles can be used if the risk assessment shows that the risk of a person falling and injuring themselves is low and the work on top of the trestle is of short duration.

Guard-rails and toe-boards should be installed on all trestle equipment, as per requirements of the Work at Height Regulations.

More modern trestles are similar in many ways to system scaffolding, including the fact that guard-rails and toe-boards are an integral part of the working platform. The spacing of the supports is fixed by the system design, which enables platform boards to fit snugly without overhanging or overlapping.

All lightweight staging should be marked with the maximum permitted distributed loading. This can be done by either specifying the maximum number of persons, allowing for their tools and equipment, or by specifying the maximum safe weight.

The following guidelines should be met.

- Trestles must be set on a firm, level base.
- Only one working platform is installed.
- Guard-rails, barriers and toe-boards are required where a fall would cause a personal injury, as indicated by a risk assessment.
- Trestles should be installed according to manufacturer's recommendations for use. This information should be readily available.
- Scaffold boards used on trestles to form a working platform must be of a consistent length and of equal thickness.
- The trestle assembly must be completely stable when in use.
- A safe means of access to the working platform must be provided (for example, a ladder that is of sufficient length, properly positioned and securely lashed).
- Where locating pins are used, they should be of the correct size and type and not rebar off-cuts or other makeshift items.
- Trestle based working platforms should be subject to a pre-use check. They should also have a formally documented inspection, which can be recorded (for example, on a scafftag).

 The use of loose scaffold boards, supported on split-head trestles with no means of preventing falls that could cause an injury to the user, is totally unacceptable and should not be considered as an option for working at height.

3.6 Mobile access towers

The use of prefabricated aluminium mobile access towers (mobile towers) on construction sites is a popular alternative to the use of traditional tube and fitting scaffolding.

However, these systems have some limitations and should only be used when they can satisfy both legislative and general site requirements.

 Aluminium and thin-wall steel mobile towers are light, and can easily overturn if used incorrectly.

Five different items make up a basic mobile access tower.

- Frames.
- Braces.
- Platforms.
- Legs.
- Wheels or castors.

 For further information on tower scaffolds visit the HSE website.

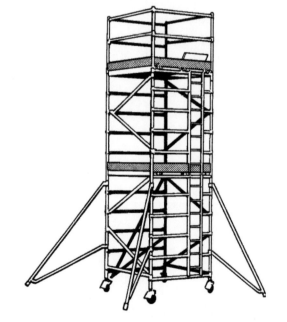

A prefabricated aluminium mobile access tower

3.6.1 General conditions and provisions

The same points that arise from the Work at Height Regulations in relation to the safe erection and use of system scaffolds apply to mobile access towers but, in addition, the following points should be particularly noted.

The Prefabricated Access Suppliers' and Manufacturers' Association (PASMA) has developed two methods of installing guard-rails that do not require the erector to stand on a working platform until the guard-rail frames have been installed.

These are the:

- Advanced guard-rail system.

- Through-the-trap (3T method).

The **advanced guard-rail** system involves the use of specially manufactured, hinged guard-rail frames that can be raised and slotted into position from below.

The progressive erection of guard-rails from a protected area at lower level ensures the operator is never exposed to the risk of falling from an unguarded platform.

The **3T method** involves the erector only passing through the platform trapdoor far enough to be able to locate the guard-rail frames in place.

In many cases, safe erection of the guard-rail sections can be achieved with the erector sitting on the platform with their legs through the trap and their feet supported on the ladder section below.

Both of these methods are accepted by the HSE.

 Fall protection equipment must not be attached to aluminium tower scaffolds.

3.6.2   Materials

Mobile access towers may be constructed from steel, but are principally aluminium.

All components must be free from any welding defects, dents, bends or distortion, or any corrosion that could prevent their safe use. Platform boards must be free from holes, cracks, splits or any delamination that would affect their safe use.

3.6.3   Competence

Any person erecting and dismantling a mobile access tower must be competent to do so, having received adequate training (such as that provided by PASMA). Always read and follow the manufacturer's instruction manual and never use the equipment beyond its limitations.

The tower must start off and remain vertical as it is built and used.

 For further information about training on the safe use of mobile towers visit the PASMA website.

3.6.4   Maintenance

Mobile access towers and their individual components are covered by the Provision and Use of Work Equipment Regulations (PUWER), and must be properly maintained and appropriate to each task.

3.6.5   Preparation and planning

A risk assessment should be carried out to determine whether or not a mobile aluminium tower scaffold is a suitable item of work equipment for the type of work that is to be carried out and the environment in which it is intended to be used.

Factors that should be considered when deciding whether or not it is safe to use a mobile tower are shown below.

3.6.5.1   Ground and surface conditions

Is the surface sufficiently level to use a mobile access tower, if there is no adjustment on the legs for levelling the tower? A mobile tower should not be erected if it cannot be levelled and therefore made stable.

Is the surface strong enough to take the loading? Mobile towers only have a small area of each wheel in contact with the ground and therefore each wheel imposes a high loading at each point of contact.

It may be possible to use sole boards on soft ground to effectively spread the load and allow a mobile tower to be used, providing that there is no chance of the tower sinking, tilting or otherwise becoming unstable.

Are there any features (such as voids, cellars, drain covers, inspection chambers, or signs of tracks or trenches with underground pipes or services) that may not be able to take the direct or indirect loading imposed by one or more wheels?

3.6.5.2   Weather (outdoor use)

Aluminium mobile towers are lightweight structures that can become unstable in moderately high winds.

- Has a check of the weather been made for the period that the mobile tower will be erected? Consider the use of an anemometer (instrument used to measure wind speed).

- Is it possible to tie-in the mobile tower to the structure against which it is to be erected?

- If any doubt exists on the limitations of the mobile tower in high winds, has the manufacturer's or supplier's information been consulted?

3.6.5.3 Overhead power lines

Before starting the job identify any lines that are close enough that make the use of a metal tower unsafe.

Remember, it is not necessary to touch a high-voltage cable to get a shock. Many overhead power lines are not insulated, and the electricity can arc through the air to an adjacent metal object.

Risks from electrocution need to be managed and controlled, especially if a live electrical cable is within a distance of 10 m from the working platform.

If in any doubt, do not erect a tower until such time that the electricity supply company has been contacted and its advice received in relation to clearance distances, shrouding or isolation of the power supply.

3.6.6 Pre-assembly inspection

The competent person who will erect a mobile tower should check that all the components are present and undamaged, are all from the same manufacturer or supplier and are for the same type of tower.

A check should be made that the castors and wheels rotate and swivel freely and that they have a functioning locking device (brake).

3.6.7 Safety during use

3.6.7.1 Stability

Due to their lightweight nature, aluminium mobile towers can have problems with stability – this increases the higher they are built.

Manufacturers provide specific guidance on height-to-base ratios, including circumstances where the installation of outriggers will be necessary. Such guidance should be available to the competent person erecting the tower.

As general guidance, it should be assumed that stabilisers will be required if an aluminium tower is to have a working platform higher than 3 m above ground level.

In addition there are several other factors that can affect stability.

Safe working on a mobile tower, with toe-boards and both guard-rails in position and wheels locked

- Ground conditions – bricks or building blocks should never be used to take the weight of any part of the tower.

- Sheeting (outside) – will increase the wind-loading on a mobile tower. In many instances it will not be acceptable to sheet a tower unless it can be tied-in to the structure.

- Overreaching by occupants of the scaffold – if this is so severe that the centre of gravity is moved to a point outside the tower's base area, the tower will overturn. It is far safer to move the tower scaffold.

- Work activity – any work that involves applying a sideways pressure to the adjacent structure (for example, water-jetting at a point that is high on the tower will create an equal and opposite pressure that may overturn the tower. In many cases, tying-in the tower to the adjacent structure may overcome this problem.

- Hoisting materials – if heavy items are hoisted up the outside of the tower, it could become unstable and overturn. Again, tying-in the tower to the adjacent structure may overcome this problem.

- Climbing the tower – access to the working platform should be gained by using the built-in stair or ladder sections. If a vertical ladder is built into an end frame of the tower, the person climbing the ladder must **always** do so on the inside of the tower. Climbing the outside could overturn the tower. Never gain access to the working platform by leaning a ladder against the tower.

 Mobile towers should never be erected to heights above those recommended by the manufacturer.

3.6.7.2 Tying-in a mobile tower

Only special couplers should be used to avoid causing damage to the aluminium tubing. Advice on the horizontal and vertical frequency of ties will be supplied by the manufacturer or supplier or, in the case of substantial or linked towers, the scaffold designer.

3.6.7.3 The working platform

The access hatch to the working platform must be closed as soon as everyone working from the tower is on the working platform.

The working platform must be fully boarded unless a design feature of the tower enables safe access and egress and effective guard-rails and toe-boards to be installed around a partially boarded platform.

The Work at Height Regulations state that a working platform must be of sufficient dimensions for the safe passage of people, plant and materials with due regard to the type of work being carried out. However, BS EN 12811-1 and BE EN 13374 recommend that working platforms on all types of scaffold should not be less than 600 mm wide.

3.6.7.4   Gaining extra height

Placing stepladders and ladders on the working platform of a mobile tower to gain additional height is dangerous and must be prohibited. Adjustable legs are only to be used for levelling, and not to gain additional height. If additional height is needed then a further lift should be added, providing this is within the manufacturer's guidelines relating to height limitations.

In some situations the original equipment might no longer be suitable for the task and an alternative form of equipment will be required.

3.6.7.5   Brakes

The wheel brakes must be locked in the ON position at all times when the tower is not being moved. The lightweight nature of aluminium towers presents the potential for unattended towers to be moved by the wind if the brakes are not applied, particularly where they are used on exposed floor slabs at height.

3.6.7.6   Moving a tower scaffold

The tower must not be moved whilst anyone is on the tower or the working platform. Any item that could fall or cause the tower to be unstable whilst being moved, taking into account the condition of the floor surface, must also be removed.

A tower must only be moved by pushing or pulling at the base. Movement should not take place in windy conditions and surfing is strictly prohibited. Towers in excess of 4 m high should not be moved.

The tower must never be moved by towing it with a vehicle or by a person who is on the platform pulling the tower along using an adjacent structure (surfing).

3.6.7.7   Avoiding collisions

Suitable barriers and warning signs should be erected to prevent people or vehicles from accidentally colliding with a tower, particularly where it is erected in a public place.

The size of safety zone around a tower may vary depending on the nature of the work being carried out above.

3.6.7.8   Loading capacity

The capacity of each platform and tower structure is often shown on labels attached to the frame of the mobile tower, or will be in the manufacturer's assembly guide. Never exceed the recommended loading levels.

3.6.7.9   Incomplete towers

When a tower is in an incomplete or unsafe state, it should not be left unattended without the display of a notice stating 'Scaffold incomplete. Do not use'.

A new inspection and report is not required every time a mobile tower is moved to a new location on the same site. However, if guard-rails or other components have to be removed, to enable the tower to move past an obstruction, then a pre-use check must be undertaken by a trained and competent person to ensure the tower has been reinstated correctly.

3.6.7.10   Protecting the public

Extra caution is required when towers are used in public places.

● Erect suitable barriers and warning signs at ground level to prevent people walking into the tower or the safety zone.

● Remove ladders and prevent access by using physical barriers to prevent unauthorised access if the tower is to remain in position unattended. If this is not practical, the tower should be dismantled.

3.6.7.11   Wind strength

Aluminium structures are vulnerable to the strength of the wind. It is recommended by many manufacturers that if the wind reaches a speed of 17 mph then all work should cease on the tower.

If the wind speed is likely to reach 25 mph, the tower should be tied-in to a rigid structure. If there is a possibility of the wind reaching speeds of 40 mph, the tower should be dismantled. The manufacturer's instructions should always be followed when using any tower in windy conditions.

Operators should be aware of the possibility of sudden high winds or gusty conditions in exposed areas. It must be remembered that wind speeds at high levels are often greater than at ground level. Wind speed can also increase as it funnels and eddies between buildings or other solid structures.

 For further information on the Beaufort wind scale refer to Chapter D02 Working at height.

3.6.8 Inspection and reporting

The purpose of an inspection is to identify whether the work equipment is safe to use, and to ensure that any defect or deterioration is detected and repaired. Where the tower constitutes a working platform, it must be inspected by a competent person, as shown below.

● After assembly but before being used for the first time.

● After any substantial addition, dismantling or other alteration and after any event that is likely to have affected its strength or stability.

● Towers with a platform at 2 m or more should be inspected at regular intervals not exceeding seven days since the last inspection.

● Towers with a platform at less than 2 m should be inspected at suitable intervals, depending on the frequency and conditions of use.

For towers with a platform at 2 m or more, a written record must be more than simply a scafftag system. A written report must be prepared by the competent person.

A copy of the report should be kept on site, and a further copy be retained, for a period of three months from the completion of the work, by the person on whose behalf the inspection was carried out.

3.6.9 Training

Training for any operation that involves working at height is a requirement of the Work at Height Regulations (Regulation 5 – Competence). Adequate training must be provided for those erecting, dismantling, modifying or inspecting any mobile tower equipment or other equipment used for work at height.

 Training courses are available from CITB, as well as from manufacturers and suppliers. Certificates should be provided as proof of training.

3.7 Other access equipment

There is a huge range of access equipment and solutions available to meet every need of the construction industry.

3.7.1 Proprietary access systems

Proprietary access systems are easy to transport between sites, quick to erect and provide good access.

They can be used as an alternative to fixed edge protection, where appropriate for the work being planned.

In some cases proprietary access systems can avoid the need for scaffolding. They are appropriate for short duration, minor work.

3.7.2 Hop-ups

Depending on the results of the risk assessment, hop-ups up to 600 mm high may be suitable for some applications, especially wet trades (such as plastering) that involve constant stepping up and down.

Other solutions with handrails are available, but it is important to balance the risk of falls against the risk of musculoskeletal injuries if other solutions restrict or make movement awkward.

An example of a hop-up

 Hop-up type platforms are for low-level access requirements.

3.7.3 Stilts

Fit out and finishing trades (such as dry lining, ceiling fixing and plastering) use professional stilts for low-level access.

These should be designed and manufactured for professional use. However, there is not currently a British or European Standard applicable to these products.

Stilts can be used providing the following requirements are met.

● Following a risk assessment and method statement, and once the system of work has been agreed with the site management team.

● They have been inspected before use and maintained in good order.

● They are used in accordance with the manufacturer's instructions.

● Operatives have received training and can demonstrate that they have the skills and competence to use the stilts safely.

● The floor surface is level and clear from obstructions.

3.8 Work at Height Regulations

These regulations govern all work carried out at height in all industrial sectors and the schedules of the Work at Height Regulations contain a number of important dimensional and prescriptive requirements.

The regulations state that suitable and sufficient measures must be implemented to prevent, so far as is reasonably practicable, any person falling a distance liable to cause personal injury.

 For more detailed information refer to Chapter D01 Work at Height Regulations.

3.9 Supporting information

There is a huge range of access equipment available to meet every need of the construction industry, and advice can be sought from a variety of means (such as the Access Industry Forum).

Members of the Access Industry Forum (AIF) are listed below.

- ATLAS – Association of Technical Lightning and Access Specialists.
- BSIF – British Safety Industry Federation.
- EPF – Edge Protection Federation.
- FASET – Fall Arrest Safety Equipment Training.
- IPAF – International Powered Access Federation.
- IRATA – Industrial Rope Access Trade Association.
- Ladder Association.
- NASC – National Access and Scaffolding Confederation.
- PASMA – Prefabricated Access Suppliers' and Manufacturers' Association.
- SA – Scaffolding Association.
- SAEMA – Specialist Access Engineering and Maintenance Association (Suspended access).
- WAHSA – Work at Height Safety Association (Fall protection).

No Falls Foundation

 The No Falls Foundation is the first and only UK-based charity devoted exclusively to the work at height sector. With stakeholders including the Ladder Association, the AIF and the HSE, the foundation is dedicated to preventing falls from height and helping people affected by the life-changing consequences of a fall.

For further information on risk assessment, selecting the right equipment and the importance of training, visit the No Falls Foundation website.

03

CONTENTS

Scaffolding

04

Supporting INFORMATION

GT700 Toolbox talks / supporting checklists and forms

Toolbox talks on some of these topics are available in the GT700 publication. Supporting checklists and forms covering some of these topics are available on our companion website.

SCAFFOLDING

Overview

The purpose of this chapter is to give individuals an understanding of the safety issues that relate to the use of scaffolding, particularly site management with a responsibility for managing and controlling sites where scaffolding operations take place.

While the chapter provides relevant basic information, training in the actual techniques of erecting, altering or dismantling any scaffolding will be necessary before a person can be regarded as competent.

4.1   Introduction

This chapter will provide you with a basic knowledge of what to look for in the scaffold contractors you employ and the scaffolds that are erected. It will not confer competence in scaffolding techniques or scaffold inspection. Current industry training standards and requirements for different levels and types of scaffolding training are detailed within this chapter.

4.1.1   British Standard and technical guidance

BS EN 12811 (Part 1) *Temporary works equipment. Scaffolds – Performance requirements and general design* is a standard that specifies performance requirements and methods of structural and general design for access and working scaffolds.

Although this chapter applies to tube and fitting scaffolding, it is important to note that all proprietary scaffolding equipment (for example, system scaffolds, beams, modular transom units and hop-up brackets) must be manufactured and tested to the relevant British and European Standards (for example, BS EN 12810). All such equipment must also be used in accordance with manufacturer's instructions.

 The British Standard can be accessed via the British Standards Institution (BSI) website.

Industry trade associations, including the Scaffolding Association (SA) and the National Access and Scaffolding Confederation (NASC), also publish advice, technical information and guidance for scaffolders and their clients on industry standards, scaffold design and health and safety in scaffolding operations. An example of this is the NASC publication *Good practice guidance for tube and fitting scaffolding* (TG20), which has been produced in response to the introduction of BS EN 12811 as a guide to good practice for all of those involved in the procurement, supply and use of tube and fitting scaffold. Although specifically for tube and fitting scaffolding, this guide can be used in the wider industry to increase awareness and make good practices accessible to all.

 Visit the SA and NASC websites for further information.

4.1.2   Training and competence

The term *competent person* is used in the Work at Height Regulations. However, although the regulations give no definition of competence, the Construction (Design and Management) Regulations 2015 (CDM) specify competence to be a combination of skills, knowledge, training and experience.

 Competent person (for the purposes of scaffold inspection)

A **competent person** may be defined as a person who has both practical and theoretical knowledge, scaffold inspection training and actual experience of what they are to examine, in respect of a scaffold, so as to enable them to identify errors, defects, faults or weaknesses and to assess the importance of any such discovery.

A competent person must understand and recognise their limitations.

 Competence (of individuals, for scaffold erection)

As regards the **competence** of individuals in relation to scaffold erection, competence may be taken to mean a person who has practical and theoretical knowledge, together with actual experience of scaffolding, and has acquired the recognised qualification in scaffolding.

This person must know their limitations and must not put themselves or others at risk.

The Work at Height Regulations require scaffolders to demonstrate specific training for the erection, alteration and dismantling of scaffolding.

Note: unless otherwise specified, all graphics are from TG20:21 with kind permission from the NASC.

4.1.3   Record schemes

4.1.3.1   Construction Industry Scaffolders Record Scheme

The CISRS record card scheme is managed and administered by CISRS Ltd. The scheme is the industry-recognised qualification for the scaffolding sector. All registered scaffolders are issued with an identification card that details the grade of their qualifications.

The card scheme categories include scaffolding labourer, trainee, scaffolder, advanced scaffolder, scaffolding supervisor and scaffold inspector (basic and advanced) qualifications. Scaffolding apprenticeships are also available for new entrant scaffolders. Options are available for tube and fitting scaffolding and system scaffolding. The system scaffold product training scheme (SSPTS) is for existing scaffolders who use specific proprietary system scaffolding products and can have their record card endorsed to demonstrate this. It is achieved by attending a two-day course on the type of system scaffold concerned.

The basic access systems erector (BASE) training is aimed at non-scaffolders who use system scaffold within a restricted scope of operation (for example, no public interface and a maximum height of 6 m). CISRS training makes it a requirement for any new entrant scaffolding trainee or scaffolding labourer to complete the CISRS construction operative training scheme (COTS) one-day course, before a card will be issued. Existing CISRS scaffolding labourer cardholders will be required to complete the COTS course upon expiry of their current card and prior to a new card being issued.

 The CISRS website provides further information on UK-recognised training schemes within the scaffolding industry.

4.1.3.2   Other scaffolding training

Employers must demonstrate supervision by a competent person(s) and specific training for the use of proprietary products not covered by the CISRS scheme (such as temporary roofs, public access stairways, falsework and formwork systems).

4.2   Important points

- Scaffolding must only be erected, altered or dismantled by operatives who have been trained to do so or are under the direct supervision of a competent scaffolder.

- Employers who employ the services of scaffold contractors should look for proof of competence via the CISRS scheme.

- The main piece of legislation that applies to scaffolding is the Work at Height Regulations.

- Scaffolds are subject to statutory inspections, with reports of inspections raised where appropriate.

- All scaffolds must be properly erected, stable, tied to the structure as appropriate, suitable for their purpose and equipped with toe-boards and guard-rails on all working platforms.

- The BS EN 12811 and BS EN 13374 series of standards are supported by manufacturer's instructions, industry guidance (such as TG20) and bespoke design information for some structures.

4.3   Planning and design

4.3.1   Planning and preparation for a scaffolding contract

When selecting a scaffolding contractor you should check that they are competent, and consider the following.

- The competence of their management and operatives for the type of work.

- That they have a proven track record for the type of work.

- Their arrangements for managing health and safety (such as a recognised and auditable safety management system).

- Their past health and safety performance.

- That they have a positive safety culture.

- That they will allocate sufficient physical and human resources to service the contract (for example, scaffolding equipment, transport, qualified scaffolders, supervision and designers).

- Whether they are members of a recognised trade organisation (such as the Scaffolding Association or NASC).

- Whether they have any third-party health and safety or environmental accreditations (for example, OHSAS 18001/45001/14001 or accreditation through a SSIP members scheme).

Before engaging a specialist scaffolding contractor, it is strongly advised that information is prepared on the intended use of the scaffolds for the contractor to take into account.

 For further information on engaging and appointing specialist contractors and pre-construction information refer to Chapter A03 Construction (Design and Management) Regulations.

SCAFFOLDING

Before the erection of any scaffold, the following points should be clearly defined.

- What is the scaffold going to be used for and how long will it be required?

- What dimensions are required for the scaffold?

- Is the scaffolding compliant with BS EN 12811 and BS EN 13374? Is there a TG20 compliance sheet for the scaffold or is it met through manufacturer's instructions or bespoke design?

- Exactly where is it to be erected? Consider environmental factors (such as interface with the public or wildlife) and other areas (such as railway lines and overhead power lines).

- Can safe access be provided for the erection and use of the scaffold?

- How many working platforms will there be and will more than one working platform be loaded at any one time?

- What loadings will be imposed upon the working platforms, and on the scaffold as a whole?

- Are the ground conditions where the scaffold is to be erected suitable and capable of withstanding the intended load?

- How and where can the scaffold be stabilised (for example, ties)?

- Will the scaffold be clad with sheeting, netting or other materials (such as advertising hoarding)?

A pre-contract site inspection should be completed to understand the nature of the site and as the first part of the risk assessment process to identify any significant hazards.

This will allow suitable and sufficient control measures to be implemented and will help to ensure the safe and successful completion of the works.

Trainee scaffolders under instruction during training

4.3.2 Scaffold design

The Work at Height Regulations require strength and stability calculations for all scaffolds unless constructed to a generally recognised standard configuration.

TG20 provides guidance and definitions for compliant tube and fitting scaffolds, designed using structural calculation to BS EN 12811 .

System scaffolding should be planned and constructed in accordance with manufacturer's instructions, to BS EN 12811 and BS EN 12810 along with BS EN 13374 *The standard for edge protection built with scaffold components*, otherwise the scaffold must be subject to bespoke design and calculation by a competent engineer.

Site management responsible for controlling scaffolding operations should seek assurance that the planned scaffolding conforms to a standard configuration or a bespoke design and that calculations have been prepared.

This can be achieved by the completion of a handover certificate, which will advise that the scaffold has been erected to the agreed specification, left in a condition suitable to perform the duty for which it is intended, and complies with all regulatory requirements.

The *Code of Practice for temporary works procedures and the permissible stress design of falsework* (BS 5975:2019) provides guidance on the procedural management of temporary structures, including scaffolding.

The TG20 design guide provides technical guidance for scaffolding design engineers on the application and interpretation of BS EN 12811 and related standards.

Scaffolding contractors and principal contractors should have suitable arrangements in place to manage and control the erection, alteration and commissioning of designed scaffolds (such as issuing drawings, managing variations to the design, inspection and handing over designed scaffolds).

For further information, including a list of scaffold structures where bespoke design is recommended, refer to the Health and Safety Executive (HSE) scaffold checklist.

4.3.3 TG20 compliant scaffolding

The TG20 operational guide contains a range of common scaffold configurations and scaffolding add-on features that do not require additional design. Any scaffold erected in accordance with TG20 is also in accordance with BS EN 12811 and BS EN 13374, and would not require a bespoke design.

A TG20 compliance sheet contains a brief summary of criteria that must be met in order for the scaffold to be considered compliant, and should be read alongside the operational guide. Types of TG20-compliant scaffolding used in the construction industry are shown below.

- Tied independent scaffolding.
- Freestanding independent scaffolding.
- Tied putlog scaffolding.
- Tower scaffolding, including lift shaft access.
- Interior access birdcage scaffolding.
- Cantilevered platforms and protection fans.
- Chimney-stack scaffolding.
- Loading bays.
- Ladder-access towers.
- Bridging with beams.
- Pavement lifts.
- Prefabricated transoms and hop-up brackets.

TG20 compliance sheets can be used for various purposes, including scaffold plans, risk assessments and method statements. They are not intended to replace the scaffolding handover certificate or permit to load; however, they can be appended to these documents issued by the scaffolding contractor.

4.3.4 Fall prevention in scaffolding

Falling from height whilst erecting, altering or dismantling scaffolding presents a significant risk to all scaffolders. The HSE-endorsed NASC safety guidance *Preventing falls in scaffolding operations* (SG4), is the accepted industry standard to which all scaffolding contractors should be working. It highlights basic requirements and principles of fall prevention and protection that should be taken by scaffolders. The guide provides practical steps to follow to ensure compliance with the hierarchy of control measures specified by the Work at Height Regulations.

 SG4 is free to download from the NASC website.

A range of collective fall protection methods and equipment are recommended in the SG4 guide (such as advanced guard-rail systems, step-ups and methods of working). These collective measures enable scaffolders to provide guard-rail protection in advance of erection and to maintain fall protection for alterations and dismantling. The use of temporary platforms with guard-rails should always take priority when establishing safe systems of work. SG4 refers to such temporary working platforms as the **scaffolders' safe zone**.

Such systems do not completely eliminate the risk of a fall in all circumstances and the guidance still recommends the use of personal fall protection equipment. SG4 recognises that personal fall protection equipment should be worn by scaffolders working at height and provides guidance for use as part of the systems of work, including the use of suitable anchor points.

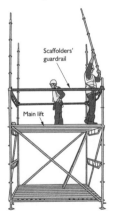

Examples of collective protection equipment and methods and use of personal protection. Guard-rail shown in red is an integral part of the scaffolders' safe zone (Photo © NASC)

Personal fall protection equipment used for scaffolding should be inspected at the following intervals.

- Before use, by the user.
- Thoroughly by a competent person every three months and recorded.
- Thoroughly at other specified intervals if the need is identified via a risk assessment.

 For further information on the management of fall protection equipment refer to Chapter D05 Fall arrest and suspension equipment.

SCAFFOLDING

4.3.5 Rescue planning

The Work at Height Regulations require employers to plan for emergencies and rescue for all work at height. These arrangements should not rely on the emergency services.

Scaffolding plans must also consider the rescue and recovery of a scaffolder suspended by their personal fall protection equipment.

A rescue and recovery plan must be prepared as part of the risk assessment for each job, and the details must be included in the risk assessment and method statement shared with the client.

To ensure compliance with the above requirements:

● scaffolders and their supervisors should be trained in the requirements of PGN03 (latest version) and the most up-to-date version of the site specific work at height rescue plan, including the correct use of any specialist rescue equipment and techniques required

● site managers and others who run construction sites should check that the scaffold contractors coming on to their sites have been adequately trained in the requirements of PGN03 and SG19 (latest versions).

For further information on rescue planning refer to:

● **the Work at Height Safety Association's practical guidance note** *Guidance on rescue during work at height* **(PGN03)**

● **the NASC's safety guidance note** *A guide to formulating a rescue plan* **(SG19).**

Specialist rescue equipment (Photo © NASC)

4.4 Basic independent scaffolding

This section provides basic guidelines for independent scaffolding commonly used in the construction industry.

For detailed guidance refer to the manufacturer's instructions for proprietary scaffolding equipment or TG20 guidance.

4.4.1 Common materials and components

4.4.1.1 Tubes

Tubes are made from cold formed high tensile steel and manufactured to British standard BS EN 39:2001, the technical standard for loose steel tubes for tube and coupler scaffolds.

Tubes come in two main types:

● Type 4 galvanised steel tubes or equivalent, 48.3 mm diameter with a 4 mm wall thickness.

● high tensile thinner wall 3.2 mm tubes made from hot or cold formed high tensile steel to BS EN 10210 (technical standard for hot finished structural hollow sections) or BS EN 10219 (technical standard for cold finished structural hollow sections). These standards set the minimum design load strengths for tubes.

An example of a galvanised steel tube (Photo © NASC)

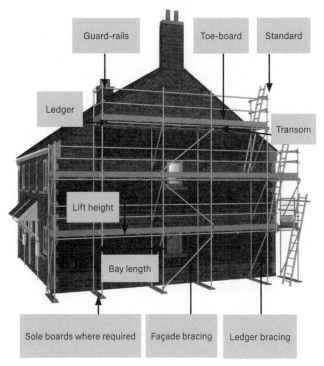

Guard-rails · Toe-board · Standard · Ledger · Transom · Lift height · Bay length · Sole boards where required · Façade bracing · Ledger bracing

Scaffolding terminology (Photo © NASC)

4.4.1.2 Fittings

- Couplers for tubes are manufactured to British standard BS EN 74-1:2005, the requirements and test procedures for couplers, spigot pins and baseplates for use in falsework and scaffolds.

- Old stocks of BS 1139 coupler can still be used. British standard BS 1139-2.2:2009(+A1:2015) provides the requirements and test methods for metal scaffolding, couplers and fittings (couplers and fittings outside the scope of BS EN 74).

Right-angle coupler (double) (Photo © NASC)

Swivel coupler (Photo © NASC)

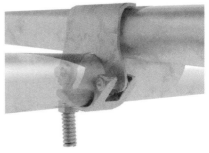
Putlog coupler (single) (Photo © NASC)

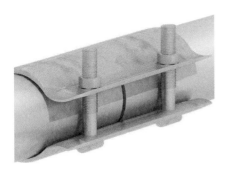
Sleeve coupler (Photo © NASC)

'Wedge' style right angle coupler (Photo © NASC)

Base plate (Photo © NASC)

4.4.1.3 Boards

- BS 2482 timber scaffold boards, 38 mm thickness, with a target span of at least 1.2 m.

- Laminated veneered lumber (LVL) or composite plastic decks may be used with a target span of 1.2 m and a unit weight not in excess of a 38 mm timber scaffold board.

  Note: *BS 2482 does not cover laminated or finger-jointed scaffold boards.*

38 mm timber board (with end-bands) (Photo © NASC)

38 mm timber board (with nail-plate option) (Photo © NASC)

4.4.1.4 Ladders

- Ladders used with scaffolding should conform to BS EN 131 *Trade and Industrial – heavy duty and industrial use (for professional users).*

- BS EN 131 replaces the British Standards for timber ladders (BS 1129) and aluminium ladders (BS 2037), which have been withdrawn. Ladders manufactured to these withdrawn standards may continue to be used, provided they are in good condition.

- Regulation 12 of the Work at Height Regulations 2005 requires work equipment to be inspected at regular intervals. When the ladder forms part of a scaffolding structure, the inspection should form part of the overall report for the scaffold.

External scaffold ladder access with safety gate (Photo © NASC)

A structural transom unit (Photo © NASC)

4.4.1.5   Transom units

Prefabricated transoms are manufactured with integrated end connections fixed to both the standards and ledgers. As these connections are typically stronger than those of tube and putlog (single) couplers, in many cases scaffolding with these transoms can be erected without ledger bracing.

They are available in a limited range of fixed lengths to accommodate the required number of scaffold boards and toe-boards between the standards.

Extending transom units are available in different width configurations. These components are adjustable, giving maximum on-site flexibility. They are designed for use as an intermediate board-bearing transom, which has an extendable section for inside board support. Many scaffolders value and benefit from the fast erection times, reduction in components and costs delivered through the use of these units.

An extended intermediate transom unit (Photo © NASC)

A standard for prefabricated transom units has not been published. The NASC has defined and published a minimum specification for their structural performance, and manufacturers and suppliers can certify their transom units as TG20-compliant. If this is the case, they may be used to erect scaffolding in conjunction with a suitable TG20 compliance sheet.

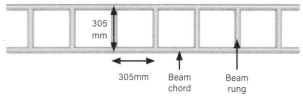

305 mm

305mm   Beam chord   Beam rung

Steel ladder beam (Photo © NASC)

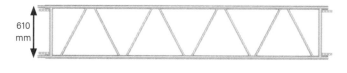

610 mm

Steel unit beam (Photo © NASC)

4.4.1.6   Beams

Scaffold beams are used with all types of scaffolding, to provide openings and bridges within a structure, to spread the load through the scaffold. A range of beam types is available, made from steel or aluminium (for example, ladder beams, lattice beams and X beams). Always check manufacturer's instructions when using beams with system scaffolding. Ensure the correct beams are used, as specified in bespoke designs or the TG20 compliance sheet provided for the work.

4.4.2   Foundations

The foundations for all scaffolds must be of adequate strength to support and disperse the applied load for the structure throughout its life. On hard surfaces (such as steel and concrete of sufficient strength and thickness) standards may be placed directly on the surface, although it is generally preferable to use a base plate that is 150 mm x 150 mm in size. Sheeting or a proprietary plastic spreader plate can also be used to protect sensitive floors from damage or marking. They also serve to highlight the base plate to pedestrians. When supported by a typical pavement, a TG20-compliant scaffold with a maximum leg load of 12kN can be supported by base plates and plastic plates.

Typical high-visibility plate (Photo © NASC)

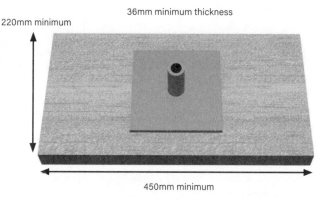

36mm minimum thickness

220mm minimum

450mm minimum

Minimum sole board dimensions (Photo © NASC)

On other surfaces, the load should be spread by using base plates and sole boards. The soil or ground beneath the sole board should be level and properly compacted. When a sole board is used on hard ground, the area beneath any one standard should be at least 0.1 m². If a timber sole board is used, it must be not less than 36 mm thick and a minimum dimension of 220 mm. Scaffold boards are typically used for this purpose. The scaffolding contractor should inform the client of the loads likely to be transmitted by the standards to the foundations, so that they may ensure that the ground or supporting structure is capable of supporting them.

The system scaffold instructions, bespoke design or TG20 compliance sheets should specify the requirements for scaffolding foundations. Planning should consider the loads likely to be imposed to any surface by scaffolding; this may include seeking specialist engineering advice. Planning should also include whether single or double sole boards are required and whether the scaffold requires double standards that may share sole boards.

For double standards a minimum sole board dimension of 750 x 225 x 75 mm is required, unless each standard has its own sole board.

A foot lift (also referred to as a foot tie) is considered good practice and helps the stability of the scaffold, although it is not strictly necessary for most TG20 compliant scaffolds. This varies for system scaffolding, so refer to the manufacturer's instructions. TG20 compliance sheets may also specify that a foot lift is required for taller scaffolds.

A foot lift is also recommended for sloping ground with a gradient of more than 1:10.

Double sole board (Photo © NASC)

Double standards sharing a sole board (Photo © NASC)

Foot lift example (Photo © NASC)

04

4.4.3   Bracing

For tube and fitting scaffolding the TG20 operational guide specifies the requirements for bracing the various types of TG20 compliant scaffolds and scaffolding features (for example, pavement lifts, bridging with beams and loading bays).

System scaffolding must be braced in accordance with the manufacturer's instructions. All other scaffold configurations must be braced in accordance with the bespoke design. The following examples are for basic tube and fitting tied independent scaffolds.

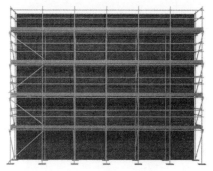

Single-bay façade brace (Photo © NASC)

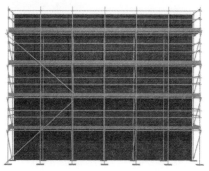

Double-bay façade brace (Photo © NASC)

Continuous façade brace (Photo © NASC)

4.4.3.1   Façade bracing

● Also referred to as sway bracing.

● Required between standards and ledgers on every elevation of scaffolding generally every sixth bay horizontally. (The six bay rule should be used as a guide because additional bracing is based on the number of bays, loading and sheeting requirements).

● Can be fixed as single-bay, double-bay or continuous.

4.4.3.2   Ledger bracing

● Connects the inner and outer ledgers, or standards, to help stiffen and stabilise the scaffold.

● The first (end) pairs of standards and alternate pairs should be ledger braced at all lifts.

4.4.3.3   Plan bracing

● Not routinely required for basic independent scaffolds, except in two cases: bridges over openings supported with beams to help stabilise the beams; and pavement lifts, which provide clear access for pedestrians by omitting the bracing below the first lift.

● Other than these cases, it may be needed when erecting scaffolding that has been specially designed by an engineer, if the design requires it.

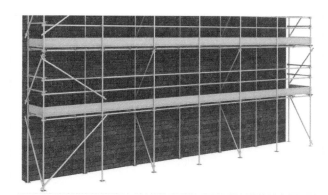

Ledger bracing (Photo © NASC)

Plan bracing at the underside of a lift (Photo © NASC)

SCAFFOLDING

4.4.4 Ties

A tie secures the scaffold to the supporting structure and is provided to resist inward (push) and outward (pull) movement, as well as to give some additional longitudinal stability (sway). Butting tubes may be required to provide sway resistance.

Ties are generally designated as moveable or non-moveable. Where possible, ties should be left undisturbed until the scaffold is dismantled. Where it is necessary for ties to be removed, even for a short period, the scaffold will be less stable and the fitting of additional temporary ties will be necessary, unless the initial tie-pattern was designed to allow for temporary removal.

Ties must not be removed by anyone other than a competent scaffolder or someone who is under the direct supervision of one. The removal of scaffold ties must be carried out in compliance with a safe system of work (such as a method statement and risk assessment).The manufacturer's information, scaffold design information (bespoke) or TG20 compliance sheets will provide details of the specification of ties to be used.

There are several methods of tying scaffolding to a building or other permanent structure, principally the assembly of tubes and fittings around structural features, or drilled or cast-in anchors to the building material. The capacity and load classes are stated in the TG20 operational guide. Refer to manufacturer's instructions for tying information of system scaffolding.

The specification, frequency and capacity must be determined from the TG20 compliance sheet for tube and fitting scaffolding, system scaffolding manufacturer's instruction manual or a design drawing. This will include the duty, frequency and maximum spacing of ties, which will vary due to the following factors.

- Location.
- Height.
- Load class.
- Lift height.
- Façade type.
- Cladding (brick guards, netting or sheeting).
- Seasonal variations.

At least 50% of ties should be fixed to ledger braced standards. Scaffolds erected around corners (returns) can provide stability and reduce the tying requirements. Refer to TG20 or the system manufacturer for details. Some typical methods are shown below.

4.4.4.1 Box ties

- Assemblies of tubes and fittings to form a square around a column or similar structural feature.
- Depending on its construction, it has variations that can be used for standard or heavy duty ties.

4.4.4.2 Through ties

- Fitted through windows or other façade openings.
- Suitable as a standard duty tie.
- Inner and outer tubes to resist movement and packing to protect the surfaces. If packing is used, it must be secured in position to prevent it falling and causing harm.

4.4.4.3 Lip ties

- Can be used if it is not possible to provide box or through ties.
- Suitable as a standard duty tie.

Box tie (Photo © NASC)

Through tie (Photo © NASC)

Lip tie (Photo © NASC)

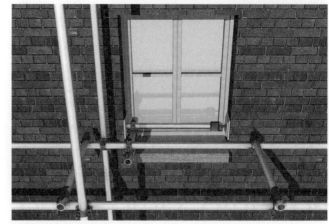
Reveal tie (Photo © NASC)

- Opposing lip ties, butting tubes and/or sway transoms should be used to resist movement.

4.4.4.4 Reveal ties

● Used where other forms of tie are not practical.

● Only suitable as a light duty tie.

● A maximum of 50% of ties in a façade may be reveal ties.

● Reveal pins should be proof tested with a calibrated meter and regularly checked throughout the life of the scaffold to ensure they remain secure.

4.4.4.5 Anchoring methods

● Drilled or cast into the building fabric.

● Several types and methods of assembly (such as self-tapping screws and expanding plugs and sockets).

● Careful planning, selection, installation and testing are required for the correct use of masonry anchors *(refer to the Code of Practice for the selection and installation of post-installed anchors in concrete and masonry (BS 8539:2012), NASC guidance (TG20 and TG4 Anchorage systems for scaffolding) and manufacturer's instructions).*

● Scaffolders installing and testing anchors must be trained to do so.

4.4.4.6 Girder couplers

● Used to tie scaffolding to structural steelwork.

● They must be used in opposing pairs.

● The tie duty will depend upon their application and manufacturer's specifications.

4.4.5 Anchor testing

TG20 requires two levels of testing.

● Preliminary testing – to check the suitability of the fixing for the tie load required.

● Proof testing – to check the installation and that the required tensile loads can be achieved.

The preliminary tests should be carried out with a sample of five anchors for each base material within the project. If all test anchors support the load without slipping by 1mm or more, the anchor may be used. For proof testing, a minimum of three ties must be tested and 5% (1 in 20) thereafter. If any anchor fails the test, the cause must be investigated and recorded. If more than two anchors fail then all of the ties (100%) must be tested. A test report should be provided with the test results as part of the handover process. The strength and pull-out capabilities of all cast or drilled anchorages must be confirmed before use.

4.4.6 Working platforms

The Work at Height Regulations and BS EN 12811, along with BS EN 13374 (the standard of temporary edge protection), set out minimum standards for working platforms for workers and users of scaffolding (Schedule 3 *Requirements for working platforms*). A higher standard is required for temporary scaffolding structures accessed by the general public and others (for example, temporary footbridge or fire escape) and specialist advice should be sought.

Working platforms should be assessed at planning stage to ensure there is sufficient space for access and working. BS 12811 stipulates a minimum width of 600 mm for work and 500 mm for access. TG20 recommends a minimum platform width of 800 mm for personnel and storage of materials.

Smaller diameter ring bolts into masonry (Photo © NASC)

Girder clamps (Photo © NASC)

Typical anchor testing rig (Photo © NASC)

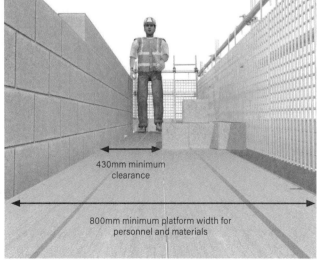

430mm minimum clearance

800mm minimum platform width for personnel and materials

Suggested minimum clearance in TG20 (Photo © NASC)

04

Where materials are stored on a working platform TG20 also recommends that a minimum clearance of 430 mm be maintained for access.

Platforms are generally constructed using scaffold boards (BS 2482 or equivalent). Decking should be correctly supported, as recommended by TG20, the system scaffolding manufacturer's instructions or the design drawing. The spacing of transoms beneath scaffold boards is referred to as the target span and varies depending on the load class of the scaffold and specification of the board (for example, visually graded BS 2482 board load Classes 1-3 are 1.2 m and load Class 4 is 0.9 m).

The ends of boards must be supported to allow for deflection and to avoid accidental tipping (known as trap ends). Transoms must be positioned a minimum of 50 mm and no more than 150 mm from the end of the boards.

Note: 33 mm LVL boards have a maximum overhang of 130 mm.

All short boards less than 2.13 m (7 ft) must be secured at both ends. Rope, wire lashings or proprietary board clamps should be used. Overlapping of boards should be avoided, except at corner returns. Where an overlap is unavoidable, the lapped board should be secured to prevent movement and, if necessary, bevelled pieces should be installed (known as a fillet).

Gaps in platforms should be avoided, where possible, unless measures have been taken to prevent people from falling and falling objects from injuring someone. Where standards protrude through the platform (for example, between inside boards and the main platform) there will be a gap of approximately 50 mm. This gap is normally acceptable in construction. However, it may need to be covered following a risk assessment. There are several methods to cover such gaps. A competent scaffolding contractor would be able to advise on site specific requirements.

The space between the inner edge of a working platform and the adjacent structure should be kept as small as possible to prevent falls. However, there can be circumstances in which this gap has to be wider. This is usually due to the nature of the work being carried out (for example, to enable the craning-in of sections of curtain wall between the scaffold and the building under construction or where there is only primary steelwork inside the scaffold). This is known as the service gap.

In such circumstances, suitable protection measures must be taken if there is a risk of people falling, or people being struck by falling objects. A competent scaffolding contractor would be able to advise on site specific requirements. It is recommended that where a service gap exceeds 225 mm and a person could fall or suffer injury, double guard-rails and toe-boards should be installed or other suitable compensatory measures used *(see examples below)*.

- Use of inner guard-rails and toe-boards.
- Segregation of the areas below the scaffold and post warning signs.
- Areas of the scaffold designated as danger areas, where access is restricted by guard-rails and warning signs.
- Use of personal fall protection equipment (work restraint or fall-arrest harnesses and suitable lanyards).

The space between scaffolding boards should be kept as small as possible and in any case should not exceed 25 mm.

Modern construction methods often require the use of inside boards to extend the width of the main platform. These inside platforms frequently need adapting to accommodate the construction work for various applications and trades (for example, they may require reducing to allow installation of the façade material). Inside boards can be supported by extending the main transoms, using telescopic transoms or using proprietary inside board brackets (known as hop-ups). Inside board brackets may be raised or lowered by up to 500 mm from the main platform. The inner board may need to be secured if there is a risk of accidental displacement.

Note: inside boards are generally rated as a lower load capacity to the main platform.

4.4.7 Guard-rails

All scaffolding working platforms must be protected with double guard-rails where there is a risk of a fall. The main or top guard-rail must be 950 mm above the edge (or above a working platform) from which any person is liable to fall.

An intermediate guard-rail (or mid guard-rail) must be placed approximately halfway between the top edge of the toe-board and the top guard-rail, so there is no gap larger than 470 mm between the guard-rails or the toe-board.

There will be occasions when it is possible to fall from the working platform into the structure under construction. In these cases, it will be necessary to consider installing guard-rails to the inner edge of working platforms or using other fall prevention or arrest measures.

Additional guard-rails may be required to maintain the minimum height of 950 mm for a raised inside board bracket and other

Work at Height Regulations guard-rail dimensions (Photo © NASC)

scenarios identified through a risk assessment. Where it is necessary to load out scaffolds with, for example, bulk materials, ideally there will be a purpose built loading bay with a lifting safety gate or similar. Where this is not the case, it is permissible to temporarily remove guard-rails and toe-boards in the following circumstances.

- Unless other work is stopped, other equally effective fall prevention or arrest measures are put in place (such as safety harnesses) whilst there is an exposed edge.
- Once the loading has been completed, the guard-rails and toe-boards are replaced immediately.

The removal and refitting of guard-rails and toe-boards must only be carried out by a competent scaffolder or someone who is under the direct supervision of a competent scaffolder.

 The removal and refitting of guard-rails and toe-boards must only be carried out by a competent scaffolder or someone who is under the direct supervision of a competent scaffolder.

4.4.8   Toe-boards

Toe-boards should be fitted to all boarded platforms where there is a risk of material or a person falling. The minimum height of a toe-board (as per BS EN 12811 and BS EN 13374) is 150 mm. In practice they are typically 225 mm scaffold boards, placed on edge and fixed inside the standard, at a minimum of two positions.

4.4.9   Brick guards

Brick guards should be installed where there is a possibility of materials toppling from working platforms and where materials will be stacked higher than the toe-boards. If using the common type of brick guard, intermediate guard-rails should also be fitted. The scaffold design or TG20 compliance sheets should take account of the use of brick guards and increased wind loading. Brick guards are now available in various materials and colours (for example, wire or plastic). Colour allows missing brick guards to be easily identified from the ground.

4.4.10 Loading

It is essential that scaffolds are not loaded beyond their maximum design load. Materials should be distributed as evenly as possible with heavy items (such as piles of bricks) positioned adjacent to standards. Overloading of working platforms can result in the failure of the boards or a scaffold collapse.

BS EN 12811 identifies six scaffold load classes, from 0.75 kN/m² to 6 kN/m². TG20 provides standard configurations for load Classes 1-4. Some system scaffolds may provide standard configurations for load Classes 5 and 6. A kilonewton (kN) is a unit of pressure, or force per area. 1 kN/m² = 100 kg/per square metre (approximately).

Regardless of how many lifts are boarded, only one lift may be fully loaded with personnel and material (100%) and one lift loaded to 50%. If it is necessary to simultaneously load more than two lifts, then a bespoke design is required.

TG20 states a load rating of 0.75 kN/m² for inside boards. Site managers should ensure that loading and use of scaffolding is properly controlled to prevent overloading. Where loading and storage of materials will exceed the load class, or it is to be loaded with mechanical handling equipment, then a specially strengthened section of the scaffold or a loading bay should be provided. Proprietary loading bays can be used in accordance with the manufacturer's instructions or TG20 compliance sheets for a compliant loading bay: otherwise, a bespoke design is required. The load rating and any special restrictions should be clearly displayed on the loading bay.

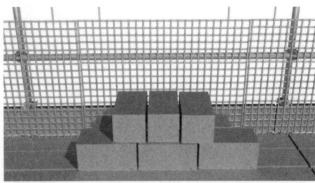
Wire brick guard with double guard-rails and toe-board (Photo © NASC)

TG20 loading bay (Photo © NASC)

4.4.11   System scaffolding

- Manufactured to BS EN 12811 and BS EN 12810.
- There are various types of system scaffolding available and these must be used in accordance with the manufacturer's instructions.

Pressing type (such as Kwikstage)

Cup type (such as Cuplok)

Rosette type (such as Layher)

SCAFFOLDING

All scaffolding material must be supplied in good condition and inspected before use. Scaffolding contractors should have systems in place to ensure scaffolding equipment is routinely inspected, serviced and, if necessary, repaired by a competent person.

4.4.12 Freestanding access scaffolds

Some scaffolds are designed to be used as freestanding structures, such as those listed below.

● Stationary freestanding towers.

● Chimneystack access scaffolding.

● Freestanding independent scaffolding (supported by rakers).

● Interior access birdcage scaffolding.

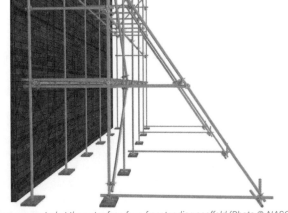

Freestanding access scaffolds or sections of scaffolds for modern methods of construction (such as timber-frame type structures) or demolition require calculations to be made for stability. These scaffolds would therefore be classed as special scaffolds and require bespoke design and calculations. Engineers can utilise alternative methods of achieving stability (such as buttressing, kentledge (ballast or counterweights), guys and ground anchors). Returns around corners, access towers and loading bays can also be taken into account by engineers when calculating stability.

Rakers connected at the outer face for a freestanding scaffold (Photo © NASC)

4.5 Methods of access

The **Work at Height Regulations** require employers to specify the use of existing structures as a means of access to height (for example, lifts or a permanent staircase) in preference to temporary measures (such as ladders). Whilst ladders have been the commonly used means of access to scaffolds, the use of other, safer means of access (such as stair towers) should now be considered in preference. This would also aid timely evacuation in the event of an emergency (such as a fire).

BS EN 12811 recommends that where extensive work is carried out, stairways should be provided for access, and for taller scaffolds consideration should be given to the use of a passenger hoist.

A typical site stairway (Photo © NASC)

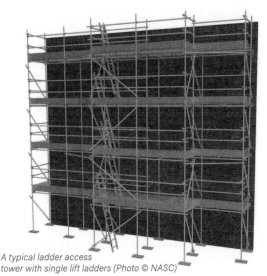

A typical ladder access tower with single lift ladders (Photo © NASC)

Where passenger hoists are used, additional non-mechanical access must also be provided in case of any breakdown or emergencies.

The following hierarchy of access is recommended for all scaffolds.

1. Staircases or lifts in permanent structures.

2. Mechanical hoists (for larger structures with additional emergency access).

3. Temporary stairways.

4. Ladder access towers with single lift ladders (to reduce the potential fall distance).

5. Ladder access bays with multiple lift ladders.

6. Internal ladder access with protected ladder traps.

7. External ladder using a safety gate.

Straight ladders used for access to a scaffold must meet the following requirements.

● Be manufactured to BS EN 131, BS1129 and BS2037 (see Section 4.4.14 for more detail).

● Not be defective in any way.

● Not be painted or treated in any way that might hide defects.

● Be placed on a firm footing, with each stile equally supported.

● Be so positioned that there is sufficient space at each rung to give an adequate foothold.

- Be positioned approximately at an angle of 75°; that is, one measure horizontal to four measures vertical.

- Be secured at the top using square lashings or a proprietary ladder clamp. For longer ladders, additional ladder supports (stays) can be used to prevent the ladder deflecting when used. The stay must not obstruct the rung of the ladder.

- Extend approximately 1 m above the working platform, unless there is another adequate handhold.

- Be provided with suitable rest platforms if rising more than 9 m.

- Be the right way up (tie wires or bars positioned under the rungs).

Shorter ladders, which provide access to only one lift, are recommended to reduce the potential fall risk, although the Work at Height Regulations allow a maximum vertical height of 9 m between rest platforms.

Where scaffolds are designed with internal ladders, working platforms must be provided with access holes for each ladder.

External access ladder and safety gate (Photo © NASC)

Such access holes should be at least 450 mm wide (across the platform) and not less than 600 mm in the other direction.

Typical ladder trapdoor (Photo © NASC)

An alternative ladder trap protection (Photo © NASC)

 The access hole should be protected with a ladder trapdoor or similar (such as guard-rails and a gate).

Lateral gaps in guard-rails and toe-boards for access and egress must be kept to a minimum and protected with a ladder safety gate.

4.6   Inspection and handover

All scaffolds and working platforms (together with all other protective measures) are work equipment for the purposes of the Work at Height Regulations and so the inspection requirements of the regulations apply, which state:

 ... every employer shall ensure that where the safety of work equipment depends on how it is installed or assembled, it is not used after installation or assembly in any position unless it has been inspected in that position.

Employers must ensure that working platforms used for construction and from which a person could fall more than 2 m are not used in any position unless they have been inspected in that position within the previous seven days. Additionally all scaffolding, working platforms and edge protection should be inspected before being used for the first time and following significant alteration

All scaffolding inspections should be carried out by a competent person whose combination of knowledge, training and experience is appropriate for the type and complexity of the scaffold. Competence may have been assessed under CISRS or an individual may have received training in inspecting a specific type of system scaffold from a manufacturer or supplier.

An employer may wish to have a commercial arrangement with a scaffolding contractor or independent consultant in order to carry out inspections.

 For further information about scaffold inspection qualifications refer to the CISRS scaffold inspection training scheme (SITS).

SCAFFOLDING

There is a further requirement that every employer must ensure that work equipment exposed to conditions that may cause any deterioration liable to result in dangerous situations is inspected at suitable intervals, and also when any exceptional circumstances that are liable to jeopardise the safety of the work equipment have occurred (such as severe weather conditions or vehicle impact).

It is common for proprietary inspection tags to be used to provide a status report for the scaffold. Where tags are used it is important that one is positioned at every access point to the scaffold.

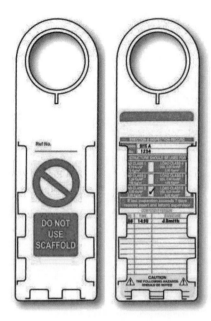

Typical scaffold tagging system

4.6.1 Inspection of places of work at height

An additional requirement as regards inspection (or checking) is that every employer must ensure, so far as it is reasonably practicable, that every surface, parapet, permanent rail or other such fall protection measure of every place of work at height are checked before each use. While there appears to be no requirement to record these checks, the prudent employer should do so to prove (for example, to the HSE or clients) that they have in fact been done.

4.6.2 Reports

Where an inspection has been carried out, a written report of the findings must be made before the end of the working period. The person who prepares the written report must provide a copy within 24 hours to the person on whose behalf the inspection was carried out. The report, or a copy of it, must be kept on the site where the inspection was carried out until the construction work is completed, and then kept at the company offices for three months. Employers are free to design their own inspection report forms or purchase pads of them from commercial suppliers. In either case, Schedule 7 of the Work at Height Regulations 2005 says they must include the following information.

- The name and address of the person for whom the inspection was carried out.
- Details of any matter identified that could risk the health or safety of any person.
- The location of the work equipment inspected.
- A description of the work equipment inspected.
- The date and time of the inspection.
- Details of any action taken as a result of any matter identified above.
- Details of any further actions considered necessary.
- The name and position of the person making the report.

When an inspection has been carried out, and it has been identified that the structure has been interfered with or is not safe, the first priority is to ensure the safety of anyone who may be working on, near to or intending to work on the structure. Everybody must be taken off the structure, by a safe means, and access to it must be restricted until it can be inspected again - and, if required, components replaced or defects rectified by competent operatives.

4.6.3 Handover

After completion or following a modification to the scaffolding, a competent person must carry out an inspection and complete a report.   It is good industry practice for scaffolding contractors to then complete a scaffold handover certificate and ensure that the client's representative receives a copy. Where a tagging system is used a green or red tag must be completed after each inspection and inserted into a holder at every access point of the scaffold. Some sites may require the report completed in the form of a site register.

Scaffolding contractors should include supporting documents (such as those listed below) with the handover certificate.

- TG20 compliance sheet(s).
- Bespoke design drawings and calculations.
- Anchor testing reports.

Good example of a warning incorporated into a physical barrier (Photo © NASC)

4.6.4 Incomplete scaffolding and danger areas

Where the erection of a scaffold has not been completed, physical measures must be taken to restrict access (for example, remove or board over the access ladder(s) and warn people of the fact that the scaffold is not safe to use). The method of warning is usually a 'Scaffold incomplete' sign at each point of access.

Warning and prohibition signs must conform to the requirements of the Health and Safety (Safety Signs and Signals) Regulations. Any scaffold structure, or part of (for example, during alterations to a scaffold when part of the structure remains in use), and a workplace where scaffolding operations are being undertaken, where there exists a risk of a fall

04

or a risk of a person being struck by a falling object, shall be defined as a danger area. Access to danger areas should be restricted and communicated effectively to all concerned (for example, by guard-rails or other suitable barriers and signs).

 For further information refer to *Access and egress from scaffolds* (SG25).

4.7 Other considerations

4.7.1 Hoists with scaffolding

Special goods and personnel hoists are often used with scaffolding. Ideally mechanical hoists should be fixed to the permanent structure unless the scaffold has been specifically designed for the purpose. NASC and the Construction Plant Association (CPA) have produced specific guidance for the use of hoists for transporting scaffolding materials during erection, alterations and dismantling *(for further information refer to SG26)*. Mechanical and non-mechanical winches are commonly used both for scaffolding operations and by the users of scaffolding (for example, gin wheels and ropes).

A selection of typical hoists and winches used with scaffolding

4.7.2 Protection of the public

Protection of the public and other persons against falling materials should be provided by the use of nets, brick guards, toe-boards, protective fans, and so on. The precautions to be adopted should be identified at the planning stage of the scaffold provision, including the risk assessment process.

Guidance on protection of the public **(SG34) provides general advice for scaffolds erected in the public domain, including the planning required and the range of precautions that should be considered to eliminate the likelihood of harm (for example, through falling material or transport accidents).**

 TG20 includes compliant scaffolding features (such as pavement lifts up to 2.7 m and light-duty protection fans).

Reference should also be made to the HSE guidance document *Protecting the public: Your next move* (HSG151).

A TG20-compliant protection fan (Photo © NASC) *TG20 pavement lift (Photo © NASC)*

Local Authority permission will normally be required for scaffolds to be built on the pavement or footpaths. Scaffolds can cause particular problems to people with physical and visual disabilities, unless adequate steps are taken to reduce contact hazards with items such as tube ends and threads on fittings.

The needs of children, the elderly and the disabled should be considered: for example, ramps for wheelchairs and tapping boards may be beneficial to warn visually-impaired people of the hazards.

This can usually be achieved by cladding the run of standards or binding the scaffold poles and fittings with suitable padding and/or brightly coloured bunting and tape (black and yellow are recommended for people who are sight impaired).

All joints should be wrapped to protect the public and other persons from sharp edges, and plastic protective cups should be placed in or over the ends of tubes. Both of these precautions should be carried out to a height of 2 m above the ground level, and Local Authority minimum clearances for the lift dimensions must be met.

It is not sufficient for employers to warn the public of the hazard just by placing safety signs on the scaffold, even if they meet the requirements of the Health and Safety (Safety Signs and Signals) Regulations. Employers must have acted to reduce the hazard as far as reasonably practicable.

To ensure the scaffold is not struck by vehicles, no part of it should be allowed to project into the roadway, unless appropriate measures are taken, such as traffic control or a road closure. The provision of lighting at night may also be necessary, as specified by the Local Authority.

Supplementary lights should be installed on the scaffold where it has been erected in a place to which the public has access (pedestrians or vehicles), unless the level of background lighting after dark is thought to be sufficient. Pavement gantries will require bespoke design and calculations.

4.7.3   Sheeting and netting

Sheeting, netting or hoarding should not be attached to scaffolding, unless the scaffold has been designed and calculated to resist the additional wind loading. Some proprietary scaffold sheeting includes sacrificial ties designed to break in tension at a certain load.

Planning for clad scaffolding needs to consider fire risk from sheeted scaffolding, particularly on occupied premises. Flame-resistant sheeting or netting should be specified and conform to the Loss Prevention Certification Board (LPCB) standard LPS1215, BS 5867-2, BS EN 13501 or equivalent.

4.7.4   Rubbish chutes

Rubbish chutes (also referred to as debris chutes) may be fixed to a scaffold. However, the scaffolding supporting the chute assembly is a non-standard scaffolding, and it therefore requires a design check for strength and stability. The chutes should be installed and inspected in accordance with the manufacturer's instructions.

Site managers should ensure that chutes are regularly checked for blockages as the increased load could affect the stability of the chute and the scaffolding.

4.7.5   Temporary edge protection (scaffolding)

Temporary edge protection constructed from scaffolding should comply with *Temporary edge protection systems* (BS EN 13374).

For further information refer to the HSE guidance *Health and safety in roof work* (HSG33), the Edge Protection Federation's *Code of Practice 2014 – A guide to the selection and use of temporary edge protection systems*, and NASC's TG1:22 *Temporary edge protection*.

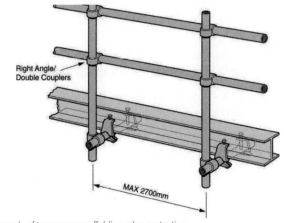

Right Angle/ Double Couplers

MAX 2700mm

Example of temporary scaffolding edge protection

4.7.6   Unauthorised modifications to scaffolds

4.7.6.1   Maintaining safe scaffold structures

The consequences of any unauthorised alterations or modifications to scaffolds could result in a fatality or serious injury to contractors, the general public or yourself and may result in damage to adjacent property. The modification of scaffolds by non-qualified scaffolding operatives (a practice also known as *interference*) is unacceptable under any circumstances and may lead to prosecution by the enforcing authorities.

Scaffolds should only be modified by competent scaffolders who have been authorised to do so by the scaffold contractor.

It is also unacceptable for the client and/or user to authorise alterations without prior consent from the scaffold contractor, as it may invalidate their insurance cover and could be an offence under Sections 7 and 8 of the Health and Safety at Work etc. Act 1974.

Most contractors and principal contractors now enforce a zero tolerance policy in regards to unauthorised scaffold interference by their contractors, and work closely with the scaffolding contractor to ensure it is applied.

The most common types of scaffold interference are the removal of scaffold structural ties by other trades, the removal of handrails and toe-boards to allow materials to be loaded directly onto the working platforms and the undermining of the scaffold foundations by utility contractors. Good planning and communication with all contractors will help prevent unauthorised scaffold modifications.

The guidance below will help the user in assuring that scaffold structures are, and remain, fit for purpose.

- All scaffolds shall be erected in accordance with statutory requirements and in accordance with the manufacturer's instructions when using system scaffolds.

- Employers must provide appropriate levels of supervision, taking into account the complexity of the work and the levels of training and competence of the scaffolders involved.

- Employees should be competent for the type of scaffolding work they are undertaking and should have received appropriate training relevant to the type and complexity of scaffolding they are working on.

- As a minimum requirement, every scaffold gang should contain a competent scaffolder who has received training for the type and complexity of the scaffold to be erected, altered or dismantled.

- Erection, alteration and dismantling of all scaffolding structures (basic or complex) should be carried out under the direct supervision of a competent person.

- All mobile tower scaffolds shall be erected by a competent person who is in the possession of a PASMA qualification or other recognised qualifications.

- All structures must be handed over, by a competent person, to the customer. In some cases a tag-type system is used at the ladder access points to clearly show the validity and suitability of the structure. Scaffolding should be inspected:
  - before it is put into use
  - at seven-day intervals until it is dismantled
  - after bad or excessively wet weather or high winds or another event likely to have affected its strength or stability
  - after any substantial additions or other alterations
  - after unauthorised interference.

- A written report must be prepared by the competent person. A copy of the report should be kept on site and a further copy be retained for a period of three months from the completion of the work with the person on whose behalf the inspection was carried out. If a scaffold fails inspection this must be reported by the person carrying out the inspection, to the person responsible for the scaffolding, as soon as possible.

04

4.7.6.2   How to identify unauthorised modifications

The following information is not an exhaustive list but should help you to recognise good practice before and whilst using scaffold structures.

- Check that the foundations have not been disturbed or undermined and the standards are on base plates and sole boards (as necessary).

- Check that guard-rails are not missing and they are installed on every lift in all areas in which falls could occur.

- Check that toe-boards have not been removed or displaced.

- Check that any scaffold boards have not been removed, displaced or damaged (such as disc cutter marks).

- Check that transoms are suitably placed to support the boards and that the maximum support span identified on the board end plate has not been exceeded.

- Check that scaffold ties have not been removed.

- Check that any bracing is not missing.

- Check that ladders are properly secured.

- Check that any brickguards and/or netting, where fitted, are still in place.

- Check that the structure is not being overloaded. The safe load should be clearly marked on the scaffold tag.

- Check for any other signs of unauthorised interference. If found, report them to the scaffold contractor immediately.

4.7.6.3   Action to be taken if concerned

If for any reason you identify that the structure has been interfered with, the first priority will be to ensure the safety of any contractors who may be working, or intending to work, on the structure.

All users must vacate the structure by a safe means and access to the scaffold should be restricted until such time that it has been inspected and, if required, the components replaced by competent scaffolding operatives.

SCAFFOLDING

Appendix A – Putlog scaffold inspection guidance

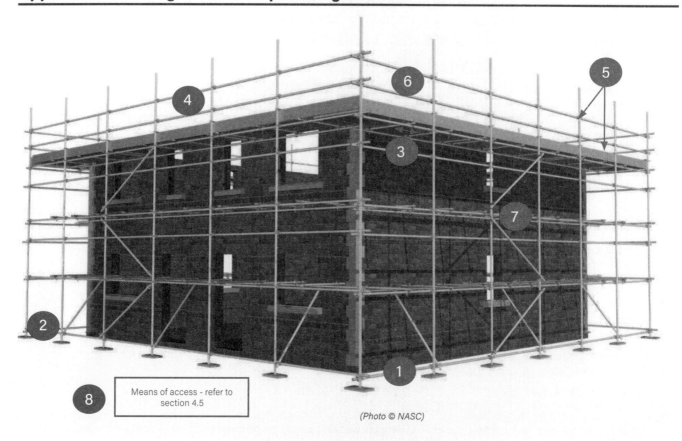

Means of access - refer to section 4.5

(Photo © NASC)

Safety checklist	
Check from the ground (see numbers above)	**Check from inside building or on the scaffold**
1. Base soundness; adequate spread of load; particularly as there is only one line of standards, avoidance of pavement lights, inspection chambers, and so on; no nearby excavations.	**9.** Spade end of putlog laid horizontally where possible, fully home (75 mm) in brickwork (bed joint).
2. Line of standards and ledgers. Standards vertical.	**10.** Ties, particularly on lift below working platform or, in early stages, rakers on alternate standards. Special attention to 'through' ties on large flank ends without windows. Load-bearing couplers to be used.
3. Spacing of putlogs.	**11.** Platform loading (not overloaded).
4. Working platform. Check line and even support of boards; overhang; lapped boards and fillets.	**12.** Security and correct use of all fittings (couplers), particularly on transoms and bracing.
5. Guard-rails and toe-boards.	**13.** Condition of tubes and fittings.
6. Security of boards, toe-boards and guard-rails.	**14.** Damage from falling material.
7. Longitudinal bracing.	**15.** Security of boards, toe-boards and guard-rails.
8. Means of access.	**16.** Security of stacked materials.
Internal edge protection has been omitted for clarity.	
Refer to Section 6b of TG20 for additional information on putlog scaffolds.	

Appendix B – Independent tied scaffold inspection guidance

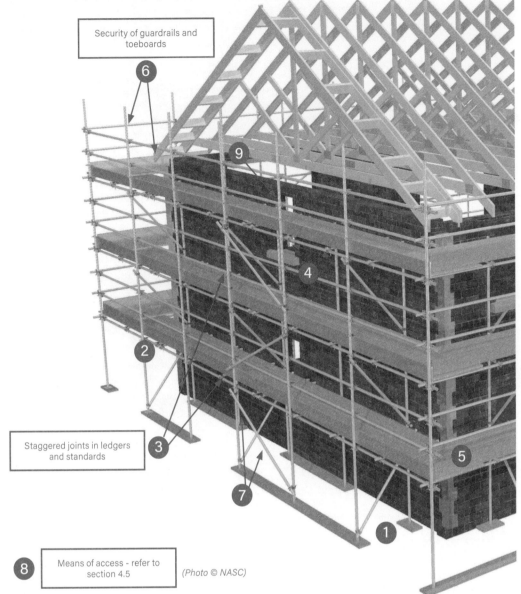

Security of guardrails and toeboards

Staggered joints in ledgers and standards

Means of access - refer to section 4.5

(Photo © NASC)

Safety checklist	
Check from the ground (see numbers above)	**Check from the scaffold**
1. Base soundness; adequate spread of load; avoidance of pavement lights, inspection chambers, and so on; no nearby excavations.	9. Ties, particularly on lift below working platform or, in early stages, rakers on alternate standards. Special attention to 'through' ties on large flank ends without windows. Load-bearing couplers to be used.
2. Line of standards and ledgers; standards vertical.	10. Special loadings by protective fans, wind sails, and similar; anchorage and spread of load.
3. Staggering of joints (vertical and horizontal).	11. Security of boards, toe-boards and guard-rails.
4. Spacing of transoms.	12. Security and correct use of all fittings (couplers), particularly on transoms and bracing.
5. Working platform. Check line and even support of boards; overhang; lapped boards and fillets.	13. Condition of tubes and fittings.
6. Security of guard-rails and toe-boards.	14. Damage by loads swinging from cranes or by falling material.
7. Longitudinal, ledger and plan bracing.	15. Overloading.
8. Means of access.	16. Security of stacked materials.
Refer to Section 6 of TG20 for additional information on independent tied scaffolds.	

Appendix C – Birdcage scaffold inspection guidance

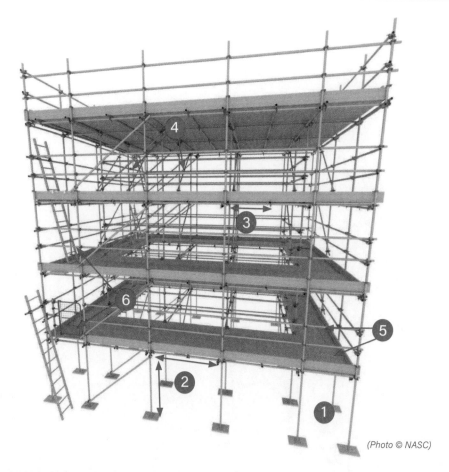

(Photo © NASC)

Safety checklist (1-6 above, 7-11 in section 4.4)	
1. Base.	**7.** Security and correct use of couplers and fittings.
2. Line of standards and ledgers.	**8.** Condition of tube and fittings.
3. Line and spacing of transoms.	**9.** Even spread of load on platform.
4. Diagonal bracing (in both directions).	**10.** Overloading.
5. Security of boards, toe-boards and guard-rails.	**11.** Security of stacked materials.
6. Means of access.	
Refer to Section 13 of TG20 for additional information on interior birdcage scaffolds.	

Appendix D - Case studies demonstrating the need for a good approach to scaffold management

 Independent tied perimeter scaffold collapse

An independent tied perimeter scaffold collapsed at a construction site in Milton Keynes. The collapse started on the west elevation, with a partial collapse of the north elevation. The scaffold collapse was contained within the site boundary. Three workers, who were on the scaffold, sustained multiple injuries. Sadly, one worker died three days later in hospital.

The HSE issued a safety alert to the construction industry following this incident. The warning aimed to alert those working on similar projects to the importance of their arrangements to provide and maintain stable scaffolds. The HSE recommended that those arrangements are reviewed regularly.

The HSE principal inspector said:

 It is totally unacceptable for companies to disregard the safety of their workers. If the scaffolding had been designed, erected and managed properly, this incident would never have happened.

04

 Near-fatal scaffold collapse

Three construction firms were fined a total of £40,000 following a near-fatal scaffold collapse on an Essex building site.

Workers at the former Riverside Centre in St John's Avenue, Braintree, were forced to leap to safety through open windows when the 40-metre long and five-storey high scaffolding fell.

Chelmsford Magistrates' Court heard how the CDM co-ordinator had not provided suitable advice to the builders, who then failed to implement the requirements of the construction phase plan and monitor the scaffolding works as they progressed.

The scaffolding firm admitted failing to plan the work or design the scaffold. They also failed to send trained and competent workers to the site and, in the weeks prior to the collapse, allowed a scaffolding labourer to act as the supervisor and oversee trainee scaffolders.

Following the collapse, the HSE served a Prohibition Notice which required that a scaffold design be provided, but the firm continued to send untrained scaffolders to the site and the principal contractor allowed them to continue to work.

The court was told that the principal contractor had received an inspection from the HSE at the same site several months before the collapse, when five enforcement notices were issued for other management failings. A Notification of Contravention was also issued on the CDM co-ordinator for failing to provide suitable and sufficient advice to the client.

The principal contractor pleaded guilty to breaching Regulation 22(1)(a) of the Construction (Design and Management) Regulations 2007. The contractor was fined £20,000 and ordered to pay costs of £2,893.

The scaffolding firm pleaded guilty to breaching Regulations 4(1)(a), 5 and 8(b) of the Work at Height Regulations. They were fined a total of £15,000 and ordered to pay costs of £1,981.

The CDM co-ordinator pleaded guilty to breaching Regulation 20(1)(a) & (b) of the Construction (Design and Management) Regulations 2007. They were fined a total of £5,000 and ordered to pay costs of £1,981.

After the hearing, a HSE inspector said:

 This collapse was entirely preventable and it is only by chance that multiple fatalities did not occur. It beggars belief that, following the collapse, no lessons were learnt and untrained people were still allowed to adapt the scaffold.

This case highlights the importance of ensuring those who undertake construction work have the relevant skills, knowledge, training and experience to do so.

Note: whilst every effort has been made to provide reliable and accurate information, we would welcome any corrections to information provided by the writer which may not be entirely accurate; therefore and for this reason, the NASC, or indeed the writer, cannot accept responsibility for any misinformation posted.

Fall arrest and suspension equipment

05

Supporting
INFORMATION

GT700 Toolbox talks / supporting checklists and forms

Toolbox talks on some of these topics are available in the GT700 publication. Supporting checklists and forms covering some of these topics are available on our companion website.

FALL ARREST AND SUSPENSION EQUIPMENT

Overview

Where a risk assessment has identified that the risk of falls from height cannot be eliminated by the installation of working platforms with barriers, guard-rails or other similar collective measures, the use of personal fall protection or fall-arrest equipment may then be the only option.

Safety nets or the use of other soft-landing systems are preferred to the use of safety harnesses and lines, as they provide a larger area and collective protection for persons working above them. They do not rely on individual workers wearing a safety harness and lanyard connected to a secure anchorage point.

5.1   Introduction

In situations where people and traffic pass below others working at height, in addition to exclusion zones (or danger areas), a safety net used in conjunction with a fine-mesh debris net will help to protect those below from falling objects and materials. It will also provide collective fall-arrest for the people working at height.

Where safety nets cannot be rigged for any reason, and it is not practical to use another form of soft-landing system, it may be necessary to resort to the use of a safety harness and lanyard.

In the first instance work or **fall restraint** should be considered (a technique used that positions the worker so a fall cannot occur). If the worker is required to move around an area where they have the potential to fall, then **fall arrest** should be used (a technique used to reduce the distance and mitigate the consequences of a fall).

● It is imperative that operatives have been trained in the use and care of the equipment provided and that they wear it correctly.

● When operatives are utilising fall-arrest equipment, consideration must be given to the clear space beneath the work area required to allow the energy absorber within the lanyard to operate effectively. A 2 m lanyard anchored at foot level will require approximately 6.75 m of clear space beneath the anchorage point to prevent injury. This distance is made up of the 2 m lanyard length, 1.75 m energy absorber maximum payout length, approximately 2 m body height and a 1 m safety margin.

● A secure, designated anchor point must be available.

● The person working at height must physically attach their personal fall protection equipment to a secure, designated anchor point.

Whichever system is used, whether it is safety nets, another soft-landing system or harness and lanyard, the system must be designed to provide a safe system of work, be installed by competent persons and maintained, inspected and adequately supervised to ensure it is used correctly.

For further information also refer to:

● **Chapter D01 Work at Height Regulations**

● **Chapter D03 Common access equipment**

● **Chapter D04 Scaffolding**

● **Chapter F05 Working over or near to water.**

In the first instance, where practicable, falls should be prevented by the use of collective control measures. These include the use of edge protection, parapets, scaffolding, temporary towers and mobile elevating work platforms (MEWPs) – all of which are preferable to the use of personal fall protection equipment.

5.2   Important points

● In situations where the prevention of falls from height cannot be guaranteed, it is essential that measures are put in place to ensure that any fall that does occur is arrested, without injury to the person who has suffered the fall.

● In many cases safety nets are the preferred method of arresting falls because:

– they provide what is termed *collective fall protec*tion (control measures that, once installed, require no input from those they protect and which can protect more than one user at a time)

– if rigged immediately below the work area, they reduce the fall distance and can make recovery of anyone who has fallen into the net easier. Recovery should be executed in accordance with the work at height rescue plan

– they are a soft-landing system that should cause no injury to the person who has fallen.

● The condition of safety nets will deteriorate over time so the requirement to carry out inspections to identify wear and tear will take on additional importance.

- Other forms of soft-landing systems (such as airbags or beanbags) also offer collective protection and may be appropriate in some circumstances.

- If fall protection is to be achieved using a safety harness and lanyard, the wearer must be trained in inspecting, fitting and adjusting the harness and selecting the appropriate lanyard (such as fall restraint or fall arrest) and secure anchor point.

- A harness and lanyard offer individual protection only and therefore require a high degree of personal discipline to ensure they are used correctly.

- Some items used in a fall protection application (for example, retrieval devices) may need a regime of inspections and servicing in accordance with manufacturer's instructions and possibly thorough examination under the Lifting Operations and Lifting Equipment Regulations (LOLER).

- It is imperative that any personal fall protection equipment is used only in the application for which it is intended. Inappropriate use can make some activities more hazardous and should be avoided at all costs.

- Personal suspension equipment (such as rope-access equipment) must only be used by people who have been trained and are competent. BS 7985 gives practical advice and recommendations for good practice to those who use specialist rope access methods for work at height and those who commission rope access work. Rope access training is available through the Industrial Rope Access Trade Association (IRATA).

 For further information visit the HSE website.

5.3 Safety nets

The use of nets has become widespread throughout the industry, particularly on new build steel frame structures. They have revolutionised safety in roof work. Figures quoted by the trade association FASET (Fall arrest safety equipment training) suggest that upwards of 50 falls per year are arrested by nets, borne out of the fact that the fatal accident rate in industrial roofing has been massively reduced in recent years as the use of nets increases.

It is important to note that the use of nets does not eradicate risk entirely. It is vital that site managers appreciate that they have an important role in the safe provision of nets on their sites; this is best done by making sure that the net provider is following guidance in British Standards and also guidance produced by the trade body for safety net installers (FASET).

Nets are an area where complying with good practice means testing, inspection, record keeping and storage facilities are required to ensure that the net itself is fit for use. It is important that the end users appreciate that a safe net is not simply about whether the net erectors have a training record card. Systems should also be in place to ensure that the net itself has been checked and inspected.

There are a number of British Standards relating to safety nets. Nets should be manufactured to the requirements of BS EN 1263-1 and erected in accordance with BS EN 1263-2. This latter standard gives information on the installation and use of safety nets.

Safety nets installed prior to roof works commencing

A further standard, BS 8411, contains construction-specific information and, more importantly, a list of duties for the parties usually involved in construction projects. This includes principal designers, designers, engineers, principal contractors, scaffold contractors and anyone having on-site responsibility for the integrity of safety net installations.

BS 8411 specifies that anyone who is planning the installation of a safety net system should take the following points into account.

- Experience and competence of the net erectors.

- Sequence and type of work being carried out during installation and removal.

- Sequence of construction work to be carried out whilst the nets are in position.

- Provision of effective anchorages.

- Means of access for erecting and removal.

- Access for inspection, debris removal and temporary repair.

- Clearance distances below the net.

- Protection of anyone below.

- Recovery of anyone who has fallen into the net.

FALL ARREST AND SUSPENSION EQUIPMENT

Modern safety nets are efficient at saving lives and preventing injury. They are an energy-absorbing system designed to minimise the consequences to the person who has fallen.

Safety nets should be erected as close as possible to the working level to minimise the height of any fall that may occur. The area in which they are installed should be free from obstruction (such as plant or machinery) that may injure a casualty falling into the net.

There are two types of net manufacture.

Knotless, which provide energy absorption by permanent plastic deformation (stretching) of the net material.

Knotted, which is generally a heavier and older type of net, providing energy absorption by tightening at the knots and permanently deforming.

Safety nets are manufactured in square or diamond mesh, with two mesh sizes: 60 mm and 100 mm. The 100 mm is the normal mesh size used in the UK.

All safety nets should carry an identification label. This includes the date of manufacture, the net type, class and size, and reference to BS EN 1263-1. It should also carry a unique serial number for record purposes and traceability.

Safety nets should have a tag showing their repair history and any net that is older than 12 months should have a tag showing that it has been tested within the last 12 months.

5.3.1 Fall heights

The positioning of a safety net system is critical to minimise the height of falls that may occur. Safety nets are designed for a maximum fall height of 6 m from the work position, which means that the maximum nominal fall height from the centre of gravity of a person is 7 m.

It should be noted that for safety nets less than 35 m² in total area, or with a side length less than 5 m, the maximum height an operative is allowed to work above a net is 2 m, as there is insufficient fabric area to absorb the energy of falls from a greater height.

However, in accordance with the Work at Height Regulations any fall distance into a safety net must be as little as is reasonably practicable, as the greater the fall distance into a net the greater the likelihood of injury.

 When nets are installed, the maximum amount of sag in the net should be no more than 10% of the bay width.

When a load or person falls into a correctly erected net, the net material will deform as it absorbs the energy from the fall. It is therefore critical to provide adequate clearance below the net, to allow the deformation to occur without the load or person striking the ground or another object below the netted area.

Guidance on minimum clearance below nets is available from FASET and the manufacturer's data (for example, if a person were to fall 2 m into a net between 5 m and 9 m wide, the total deformation, including the erection sag, may be between 2.6 m and 3.5 m, depending on the width of net).

It is essential to check the manufacturer's specification to ensure that there is adequate clearance below the planned net position.

 Where safety nets are rigged so that the fall distance is less than 6 m, the safety net must extend a minimum of 3 m beyond the leading edge where operatives are working. If the working area is inclined by more than 20° then there must always be 3 m minimum beyond the leading edge.

5.3.2 Competence

The way in which safety net systems are installed is critical. Not only must those installing the net system be trained and competent, so must the people who carry out the routine inspection of safety nets.

After rigging, the nets must be inspected before use by a competent person and a handover certificate should be issued.

The minimum competence someone requires to issue a handover certificate would be a safety net rigger who holds a blue, skilled worker Construction Skills Certification Scheme (CSCS) card, signifying that they have the appropriate experience and training.

 The CSCS safety net rigger card is the only evidence that an operative has undergone extensive training and assessment in the proficiency of fall arrest safety equipment training and has achieved the required industry standard.

Always receive a handover certificate from the riggers for each section of netting as it is completed.

There are industry-agreed standards and qualifications for training in the rigging and inspection of safety nets. The training of inspectors is aimed at site management staff as well as professionals within the industry.

 Information on netting training providers is available from FASET, the netting industry trade body.

5.3.3 FASET guidance

FASET's website contains the latest technical and safety information, guidance and bulletins for the selection, installation and use of safety nets. These are freely available on their website and should be consulted before selecting and installing nets (for example, understanding the maximum numbers of workers allowed above a safety net, and how to attach safety nets to temporary edge protection).

Items included in the guidance are shown below.

1.	Why specify a FASET member?	11.	Gathering and under-rolling.
2.	Safety net test records.	12.	Joining safety nets together.
3.	The testing of safety nets for ultraviolet (UV) light degradation.	13.	Testing requirements for safety net attachment devices.
4.	Safety net labels and record keeping.	14.	Drilled fixings.
5.	General arrangement for repairing both knotted and knotless safety nets.	15.	Incorrect safety net support clamps – single Gravlock.
6.	Repairs to a knotless safety net.	16.	Attaching safety nets to temporary edge protection.
7.	Repairs to a knotted safety net.	17.	Working above a safety net.
8.	Tagging of safety net repairs.	18.	Loading of safety nets.
9.	On-site safety net temporary repair.	19.	Temporary works.
10.	Maximum permissible gaps.	20.	Ground conditions.
		21.	Safety net handover and in-use inspections by a competent person.

 FASET's *The selection of access methods to install and dismantle safety netting* can be freely downloaded from its website and site managers should familiarise themselves with it in order to manage and monitor the activities of the installation team.

There are six methods of access currently recommended for rigging and de-rigging safety nets, which should be considered in the following order.

FASET recommended hierarchy for work at height	
1.	Rig/de-rig safety nets remotely (using remote attachment devices).
2.	Rig/de-rig using powered access (MEWPs).
3.	Rig/de-rig using ladders (recommended maximum height 4.5 m).
4.	FASET specialist rigger – employing industrial climbing access techniques.
5.	Rope access techniques – IRATA.
6.	Mobile access towers.

Site conditions often dictate that a combination of any or all of the above methods may be required.

 Rigging and de-rigging

FASET does not recommend the use of scaffold towers or hop-ups for the rigging and de-rigging of safety nets under normal rigging conditions. There may be rare and isolated occasions for specific work where towers may be appropriate, having taken due regard of the FASET *Good practice guide: the selection of access methods to install and dismantle safety netting* and the hierarchy set out within it. Where such occasions arise, the rigging contractor must prepare a suitable, specific risk assessment taking account of the rigging conditions and the additional control measures required. Towers must always be erected in accordance with the manufacturer's/supplier's instructions by trained personnel.

5.3.4 Periodic testing

Safety nets are typically manufactured from polypropylene or nylon, which are materials that are adversely affected by ultraviolet (UV) light. As such, safety nets must be tested to ascertain whether the safety net meets or exceeds the manufacturer's withdrawal from service level (minimum strength).

All safety nets that are in service must have been tested within the previous 12 months to ensure they meet or exceed this level. These tests typically include removal of a section of mesh and testing it to destruction, to ascertain its structural properties and to ensure the remainder of the net is in good condition.

FALL ARREST AND SUSPENSION EQUIPMENT

Test results must be maintained electronically and should include detail relating to the date, serial number, test result and manufacturer. If this information is not available, the net cannot be considered safe for use.

Nets that have been tested and are safe for use must be tagged, to include the following details.

- Testing company's name.
- Date of the test.
- Confirmation that the test was passed.
- Date the next test is due.
- Any additional information.

 For further information refer to FASET's *The testing of safety nets for UV degradation* (Bulletin no. 3).

5.3.5   Inspection

Safety nets are classed as *work equipment* by the Work at Height Regulations and therefore, in addition to pre-use or handover inspections, they should be inspected on a weekly basis by a competent person to ensure that they are still in a safe condition, fixed correctly and will provide the fall arrest capability if required.

Inspections should be carried out more frequently if circumstances indicate that the integrity of the net system is in doubt.

A net should also be inspected after a person or substantial load has fallen into it, to determine whether it should remain in service or be replaced. In some cases, it may be necessary to seek specialist advice.

It is recommended that the findings of all inspections are recorded.

 A safety net inspection sheet template is available from FASET upon request.

5.3.6   Care of nets

Care should be taken to reduce to a minimum unnecessary wear and mechanical damage likely to weaken the net.

Materials must not be stacked on it, and deliberate jumping into it or dropping of objects onto it must be prohibited, as permanent deformation may occur.

The following sources of damage or wear should be avoided as far as possible.

- Dragging the net over rough surfaces.
- Contact between the net and sharp edges.
- An accumulation of debris in the net.
- Any sparks from hot work, welding, grinding, burning operations, hot gases from blowlamps, or hot ash from chimneys or furnaces.
- Chemical attack.
- Any form of radiation.

Special care should be exercised and precautions taken to prevent the net and any supporting framework from being struck by loads on moving vehicles or by the vehicles themselves.

The net manufacturer should be consulted when there is any doubt about the suitability of nets for use in hazardous conditions, after any known contamination or when deformation has occurred.

If overhead power lines are present in the vicinity of an area where safety nets are required, they should not be installed (nor should any access to height be permitted) until such time that the electricity supply company has been contacted and it has been established that it is safe to do so.

5.3.7   Maintenance

Nets must always be thoroughly inspected after use and before being returned to storage to identify any damage and any required repairs.

If contaminated by acids or alkalis, nets should be thoroughly washed, preferably by hosing, and allowed to dry naturally away from heat.

If areas of damage are found, or chemical damage is suspected, contact the manufacturer to obtain a list of competent people able to repair or clean the nets.

5.3.8 Storage

- Nets should be stored away from heat, chemicals and out of direct light.

- Nets should be stored in dry conditions.

- Nets should be stored away from rodents to minimise damage.

- Wet nets should be dried naturally.

- Storage areas should be well ventilated.

- Nets should be turned periodically to allow air circulation.

- If stacked, nets should be packed up clear of the ground.

- Nets should be segregated into three distinguishable categories (for example, nets that are safe for use, nets that are awaiting repair and nets that are beyond economical repair).

5.3.9   Rescue from a net system

Where the net is erected as close as possible below the work area, many of the situations where persons enter a net will be minor, with a self-rescue being possible. On other occasions, a person may fall a considerable distance into a net. They may fall onto materials lying in the net, or strike their head or body on, for example, structural steelwork during the fall.

When such accidents occur, extreme care must be taken during the rescue of the person lying injured in the net. Due to the stretching nature of the net, it is possible that any rescuer entering it could inadvertently and unavoidably cause further injury to the victim.

It is therefore essential that companies using safety net systems have, as part of their risk assessment process, emergency procedures written for:

- treating first aid needs whilst the injured person is in the net

- emergency recovery from a rigged net system (an additional two people may enter the net in an emergency situation)

- gaining access to height to execute a prompt recovery of the casualty.

It must be recognised that procedures for the above must be robust and, where additional equipment is required (for example, MEWPs), this should be instantly available in the work area and suitable for the circumstances. Therefore, rescue must always be pre-planned and must consider the work activities and the changing site environment.

5.4   Other soft-landing systems

Soft-landing systems can provide an effective alternative to safety nets in some circumstances. They are essentially bags that are packed with polystyrene chippings or another energy-absorbing material, which serve to both cushion a fall and reduce the distance of that fall (by the depth of the bag). The bags are linked together with plastic snap clips to completely fill the area over which protection is required. They can also be used on the first or subsequent floors while trusses are being installed or in the roof space when fixing bracings.

An alternative system that may be considered in appropriate circumstances is the use of air-filled bags. Similar to the above, bags of varying sizes may be clipped together to completely fill the area over which fall-arrest protection is required. Airbags require an air compressor running all the time that fall arrest is required, to maintain the pressure in the airbag system. These devices work on the principle of a controlled rate of constant inflation and leakage so that the airbags will absorb the energy of someone falling onto them without bouncing. If air bags are used at first floor level measures must be put in place to prevent any person falling into the air bags from being catapulted out of open window reveals. This can occur if the bags are over inflated or packed too tightly against walls in the fall zone.

Whilst soft-landing systems do not prevent falls, they can be effective in eliminating injuries arising from low-level falls. However, care should be taken when selecting the particular system for use as maximum fall heights vary from product to product.

5.5   Personal fall protection equipment

- All personal fall protection equipment (PFPE) must be manufactured to the relevant British and European Standards.

- PFPE must only be selected if safer options cannot be justified.

- The use of PFPE must be justified by a risk assessment. (Methods of rescue must be considered.)

- All training must be carried out in accordance with BS 8454 (the *Code of Practice for the delivery of training and education for work at height and rescue*).

- All operatives using PFPE must be trained in the use and inspection of PFPE. Training must also include specialist equipment required for rescue.

FALL ARREST AND SUSPENSION EQUIPMENT

- All PFPE must be subject to a pre-use inspection by the operative, which must be included in the user training.

- Periodic examination of equipment must be carried out by a competent person who has received specific training.

- Contractors must compile and retain records of examination as recommended by HSE guidance INDG367.

- PFPE must be identified by its unique serial number or other means.

- Any PFPE found to be defective or damaged must be removed from service immediately and quarantined to prevent it from being used.

If fall prevention measures (for example, working platforms, barriers or guard-rails) or collective fall-arrest measures (such as safety nets or other soft-landing systems) are not practical, an alternative safe system of work must be employed. This safe system may require the use of safety harnesses and lanyards but, as with any item of PPE, it should be considered only as a last resort. Safety nets and other soft-landing systems are collective measures (in other words, they automatically provide protection for more than one person), whereas safety harness systems protect the user only. PFPE can be broadly grouped into the following four categories.

- Fall-restraint systems.

- Work positioning systems.

- Rope access systems.

- Fall-arrest systems.

Fall-restraint system (Photo © NASC)

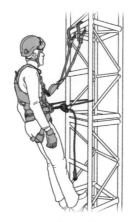

Work positioning system (Image supplied by PETZL)

Rope access system (Image supplied by PETZL)

Fall-arrest system (Photo © NASC)

5.5.1 Selection of equipment

It is important to recognise that few safety harnesses serve multiple purposes and they are often provided for use in a particular application. Examples include harnesses that arrest falls, harnesses that restrict movement of the individual to prevent access to the leading edge and harnesses that are used to facilitate the rescue of an individual from a dangerous situation (such as a confined space or vessel).

Anchor points and fall distances are critical considerations when planning to use a safety harness and lanyard. Consequently, individuals planning work of this nature should have a high degree of training and competence and the work activity will need to be closely supervised.

The type and nature of the safety harness to be used must be provided only after having given consideration to the individual who will be using it, the work activity to be carried out and other factors that may impact on the effectiveness of the equipment (for example, the ability of a lanyard to resist fraying or cutting from a sharp or abrasive edge in a fall, known as a running edge).

In addition to different types of harness, there are also several types of lanyard, with each being intended for a particular purpose. Some of these are discussed below.

5.5.1.1 Fall-arrest lanyards

Fall-arrest lanyards incorporate an energy-absorbing feature to reduce the shock loading on the body of the wearer.

5.5.1.2 Twin tailed lanyards

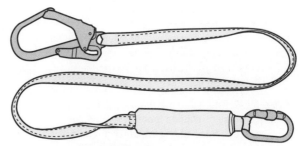

Fall-arrest lanyard (Photo © NASC)

Twin tailed lanyard (Photo © NASC)

Twin tailed lanyards are a type of fall-arrest lanyard. They allow greater mobility at height by enabling the repositioning of one tail at a time so that the user is constantly attached to an anchor point.

05

Users of this type of lanyard should note that if used incorrectly they can pose additional risks to safety. If only one tail is clipped to a secure anchorage and the second tail is not located correctly, then during a fall the second tail could loop over a fixed object and arrest the fall before the energy-absorber has deployed, which may cause severe personal injury.

The second tail must never be clipped back on to the user's harness, unless it is fitted with purpose fitted (sacrificial) parking points that will break away from the harness if the second tail comes under tension. Alternatively, the second tail can be either left to hang free or be simultaneously clipped to the same secure anchorage.

5.5.1.3   Restraint lanyards

Restraint lanyards are used as a means of limiting the range of movement of the wearer in order to stop them falling from an exposed edge. For example, when allowing maintenance to be carried out on a gutter on the edge of a roof, the worker can reach the gutter but the lanyard is not long enough to allow the worker to physically lose contact with the structure, thus preventing a fall from the roof.

These lanyards are not designed to arrest falls and have no energy-absorbing feature. Sometimes two of these may be worn at the same time, with each lanyard fixed to a clip on either side of the harness (EN 358) to make the harness what is termed a work positioning harness.

Adjustable buckle

Restraint lanyard (Photo © NASC)

Irrespective of the type of lanyard used, they are only effective if the free end is securely anchored to a suitable anchorage point.

5.5.2   Training

Any training should cover the selection, fitting, adjustment, maintenance and use of personal fall protection equipment and explain the choice and use of suitable anchorage points. Employees should not be permitted to use the equipment before adequate instruction has been given and they have been judged to be competent in its use.

5.5.3   Selecting the anchor point

When working in fall arrest, in order to limit the drop, the designated anchorage points should always be as high as possible above the person and as near to vertical as possible in order to avoid the pendulum effect (the casualty swinging from the point of work to the point of attachment).

Anchor points must be capable of withstanding the anticipated shock loading (*refer to Personal fall protection equipment. Anchor systems. System design, installation and inspection. Code of Practice (BS 7833) and other industry guidance*).

Consideration should also be given to how persons would be rescued following an arrested fall, particularly when work is from high structures.

Some harness manufacturers also produce rescue systems that enable a single rescuer to raise a suspended person back to the working platform or safely lower them to ground level, or self rescue for a person who is suspended but conscious and uninjured to safely lower themselves to ground level.

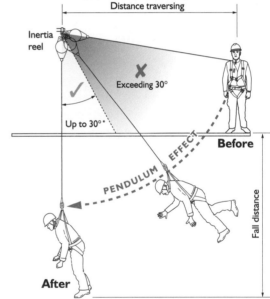

Pendulum effect

5.5.4   Arrester devices

These devices operate with a similar mechanism to the seat belts used in cars and snap to the locked position as a result of sudden movement.

Most inertia reel-type arresters are only designed to safely arrest someone who is working in and has fallen from a position that is almost directly vertical to the anchor point. As with lanyards, these devices will not counter the pendulum effect or swing fall.

Most equipment of this nature is not tested for over the edge type falls in which the retractable lanyard is pulled tight across the edge of a surface (for example, a roof sheet or floor slab) by the weight of the fallen person. In these circumstances, the abrasive action of webbing being pulled taut over an adjacent surface can have catastrophic effects in terms of the device's ability to successfully protect against falls.

If the proposed work method involves the equipment trailing over a running edge, it is unlikely to be a suitable method of work and advice must be taken from the manufacturer to ensure that the equipment is suitable for use in this application.

Other types of fall arrester are available, such as a traveller on a pre-tensioned vertical cable. There are also proprietary systems where the lanyard is attached to a traveller that moves along a pre-positioned and tensioned horizontal or vertical steel cable.

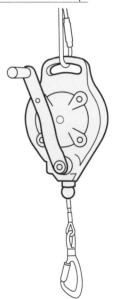

Typical arrester device (Photo © NASC)

FALL ARREST AND SUSPENSION EQUIPMENT

These systems can improve movement around corners and past obstacles without the need to unclip. Advice should be sought on the selection of the best type of equipment to be used for the job to be done. Refer to the manufacturer for information about inspection and maintenance of fall-arrest devices. Where the client provides this equipment, as is common in many cases, care still needs to be taken that it has been inspected and checked as required and that the users are trained and understand how it works.

5.5.5 Shock absorbers

If a person wearing a harness and shock-absorber lanyard falls, there is a considerable shock loading to the body impact force; the greater the fall distance, the greater the force that is applied.

The maximum distance a person can fall will depend on the height of their anchor point and length of lanyard. A higher anchor point essentially means the fall distance is reduced.

In a worst-case scenario, with a 2 m lanyard (the maximum permitted length under EN 354) anchored at foot level, the area of clear space beneath the person required is 6.75 m, made up from the following.

- 2 m lanyard length.
- 1.75 m energy absorber extension.
- 2 m body height.
- 1 m safety.

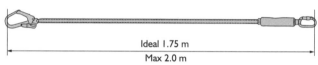

Ideal 1.75 m
Max 2.0 m

A shock-absorbing lanyard (Photo © NASC)

Shock absorbers in the form of tearaway stitching, stretch springs or a deforming metal strip are built into fall-arrest lanyards as a means of reducing the shock loading.

 A lanyard that has been used to arrest a fall should never be reused. It should be withdrawn from service immediately and destroyed or returned to the manufacturer.

5.5.6 Markings on fall protection equipment

Fall protection equipment must be clearly and indelibly marked or permanently labelled with the following.

- British or European Standard to which it conforms. (Check equipment is compliant to the current standards.)
- Name, trademark or other means of identification of the manufacturer.
- Year in which the fall protection equipment was manufactured. (These have a maximum working life of 5-10 years, depending on the manufacturer.)
- Type of fall protection equipment.
- Manufacturer's serial number.
- Company serial number, or other recognition system, for recording maintenance and inspections.

 The Work at Height Safety Association (WAHSA) has produced leaflets and information on the use and positioning of fall-arrest equipment for those working at height.

 Main performance standards

- *Code of Practice for selection, use and maintenance of personal fall protection systems and equipment for use in the workplace (BS 8437).*
- *Code of Practice for delivery of training and education for work at height and rescue (BS 8454).*
- *Personal fall protection equipment. Anchor systems. System design, installation and inspection. Code of Practice (BS 7883).*
- *Code of Practice for the use of rope access methods for industrial purposes (BS 7985).*
- *Inspecting fall-arrest equipment made from webbing or rope (HSE guidance INDG367).*
- WAHSA technical guidance notes.
- IRATA International Code of Practice.
- *Preventing falls in scaffolding operations (SG4).*

 For further information visit the HSE website.

5.5.7 Storage

When not in use, equipment should be stored in a cool, dry place and not be subjected to direct sunlight. The use of purpose-designed cabinets, which allow ventilation, is recommended. If fall protection equipment becomes wet it should be dried thoroughly by natural means.

The equipment should not be subjected to unnecessary strain or pressure and must be kept free from contact with sharp implements, corrosives and other possible causes of damage. Manufacturer's guidance is the best resource for checking usage, storage and maintenance requirements.

5.5.8 Inspection

 Reduction of a lanyard's strength

Research carried out for the HSE involving synthetic fibre webbing lanyards confirmed potential causes of degradation. A 1 mm cut in the edge of a lanyard was shown to result in up to a 40% loss of strength, depending on the make of lanyard being used for the test. Most users do not appreciate the possible loss of strength as they assume that there is a proportional strength-to-width relationship; so in their eyes a 1 mm nick on a 25 mm flat sling is not really significant.

A further study investigated the resistance of the webbing material (used to make harnesses and lanyards) to abrasion by various types of surface, including concrete and angle iron. The findings of this study revealed that severe abrasion of the material, and a significant reduction in its strength, occurred after a small number of cycles of abrading the material across concrete. Abrasion across angle iron also degraded the material but at a significantly slower rate.

05

The wearer must make a visual inspection of safety equipment **before use**. The equipment should be examined by a competent person at least once every six months and the results recorded. Equipment examination should be carried out at the following minimum frequencies.

- Every six months for normal use.
- Every three months for extreme conditions, environments or occupations.
- Interim examination, as determined through risk assessment.
- Installed systems (horizontal and vertical lines), according to the manufacturer's recommendations.

Many contractors have a weekly examination regime because of the rigorous conditions of use.

Harnesses and lanyards should be examined by a competent person after a fall or other circumstances in which the equipment has been deployed, before it is reissued for use. Any equipment found to be damaged should be removed from service immediately.

Safety belts, harnesses and lanyards should be taken out of use if found to be damaged or defective. Under most circumstances, knots in lanyards would be considered a significant problem. Typically, a knot is presumed to reduce the strength of a lanyard by 50%. Particular attention during inspection should be directed to the points below.

Webbing and leather. Examine for cuts, cracks, tears or abrasions, stretching and distortion, damage due to deterioration, contact with heat, acids or other corrosives and rot.

Snap hooks. Examine for damaged or distorted hooks, faulty springs, strained jaws, hairline cracks and corrosion.

Buckles. Carefully examine the shoulders of buckles; inspect for open or distorted rollers, undue wear, hairline cracks and corrosion.

Stitching. Examine for broken, cut or worn threads, open seams and failed or loose stitching.

Lanyards and ropes. Examine for damage or signs of wear, cuts, abrasions, flat spots, knots and permanent kinks. For kernmantle ropes (the variety often used in climbing and abseiling activities), also check for visible signs of the inner core.

Unauthorised modifications. Examine equipment for homemade attachments, repairs or adaptations. Impress on the wearers that their lives could depend on the continued efficiency and durability of their safety equipment and that, by frequent personal inspections, the possibility of equipment failure will be reduced to a minimum.

For webbing lanyards, specific attention should be given to the following.

- Cuts of 1 mm or more to the edge of the lanyard (for example, as a result of being choke-hitched around steelwork).
- Surface abrasions to surface or edges and damaged stitching.
- Knots in the lanyard.
- Results of chemical attack.
- Damaged or deformed fittings.
- Partially deployed energy-absorbers.
- UV degradation (identified by possible loss of colour and a powdery surface).

 For full details refer to the HSE publication *Inspecting fall arrest equipment made from webbing or rope* (INDG367).

5.5.9 Records

An inspection and maintenance record should be kept for each harness and lanyard. This should be used to document the life cycle of the equipment. It is imperative that each piece of equipment should be marked with an individual serial number for identification purposes. If the unique serial number is no longer visible, the item should be withdrawn from service and replaced.

5.5.10 Dead weight anchor devices (mobile person anchors)

The use of dead weight anchors in accordance with European and British Standards BS EN 795 and BS 7883 (Class E) has become an acceptable means of providing a safe fall protection system on flat roof surfaces, particularly where it is not possible to penetrate the roof surface. They can sometimes be used in both fall-restraint and fall-arrest applications, but are more commonly associated with fall restraint.

BS EN 795 requires these devices to be tested for capability to arrest falls due to the foreseeability of misuse, even for use in a restraint application (note that BS EN 795 applies only to single-user systems. Where multiple-user systems are required, PD CEN/TS 16415 will apply).

As with all other systems, deadweight anchors do have their limitations, as detailed below.

- Location distances of the anchor device from the edge of the surface they offer protection against.

- Their safe use is impacted by the presence of water as it will reduce the level of friction available between surfaces.

- They can be cumbersome to install.

- They are less suitable for heavier people (due to loading limitations).

- They are often unsuitable for use on surfaces with a slope in excess of five degrees.

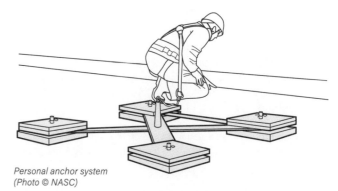

Personal anchor system
(Photo © NASC)

As with other items of fall protection equipment, deadweight anchor devices should be used only after thorough consideration of the task and reference to manufacturer's guidance has been made.

5.5.11 Suspension risk (syncope or fainting)

Many people who work in the fall protection and construction industries often talk about *suspension trauma* but HSE research (RR708) suggests the term *suspension trauma* is inappropriate because orthostasis, motionless vertical suspension is responsible, as opposed to physical injury (trauma), as was widely believed. For this reason, the terms *suspension syncope* or *fainting* are preferred.

Previous guidance recommended that rescued casualties should be placed into a sitting position, as opposed to the more common recovery position suggested by most medical guidance.

However, the HSE's research document states: 'there is no evidence to support assertions that, post-rescue, this position is physiologically superior or even equivalent to the horizontal position' and consequently the traditional lying-down recovery position is recommended.

In all situations, when a worker has fallen and their fall has been arrested by fall protection equipment, the individual should be retrieved as quickly as possible to prevent the onset of fainting. In many cases, the casualty may be able to assist either fully (self-rescue) or partially.

Casualties who are conscious and uninjured and are suspended by fall protection equipment are able to slow the onset of suspension syncope by moving their legs, by positioning their body in a horizontal or slight leg-high position or, in the presence of the appropriate equipment, using a proprietary suspension loop that will enable the casualty to stand up whilst suspended.

When rescued, the casualty should be referred to a medical practitioner for professional medical assessment, even if it seems there have been no harmful effects caused by the fall.

> **!** **Research suggests that if rescue is effected within 10 minutes, most people will not experience symptoms of pre-syncope (dizziness) or syncope (fainting).**

5.5.12 Harness fall recovery with specialist equipment

Many of the companies who manufacture and supply fall protection equipment also produce kits that are specifically designed to facilitate the rescue of those suspended at height.

Depending upon the design of the equipment, sometimes a single person is able to attach the rescue system to the D-ring of the fallen person's harness and either lower them to ground level or raise them back up on to the working platform in a controlled manner.

This type of rescue equipment is classified as lifting equipment under LOLER and therefore carries all of the training, examination and maintenance obligations that this brings.

5.6   Rope access (abseiling)

Rope access is often seen as a cost effective solution for certain work at height activities. However, due to the risk involved and high levels of skills and control required, it should only be selected after all other forms of collective protection have been considered.

It is generally suitable for inspection, cleaning and maintenance work, but is only used for construction activities in exceptional circumstances. An example might be the rigging of safety nets where it is not reasonably practicable to do it by using other means of access (such as a MEWP or another form of working platform).

General requirements for rope access are listed below.

● All personnel involved in rope access operations must be trained and assessed in accordance with the IRATA training scheme.

● Each working party (crew) must have at least one Level 3 technician who is responsible for the direct planning and supervision of the work.

● The team leader shall prepare an access permit before beginning rope access work. The access permit should include all salient aspects of the work to be undertaken, including detail of other workers involved, equipment to be used, associated hazards, PPE requirements, rescue arrangements and safety arrangements (safety line and back-up line), and so on.

● All work must be carried out in accordance with the following.
    – The *Code of Practice for the use of rope access methods for industrial purposes* (BS 7985).
    – *Personal equipment for protection against falls. Rope access systems. Fundamental principles for a system of work* (ISO 22846 Part 1).
    – The *Code of Practice. Personal equipment for protection against falls. Rope access systems* (ISO 22846 Part 2).

 The trade association that governs the rope access industry is the Industrial Rope Access Trade Association (IRATA).

A second group of specialists (steeplejacks and lightning conductor engineers) commonly use rope access, boatswain's chairs and bosun's seats. Steeplejacking is work at height and therefore the requirements of the Work at Height Regulations apply, as they would to any other work at height activity.

 The trade associations for the steeplejack industry are the Association of Technical Lightning and Access Specialists (ATLAS) and the Steeplejack and Lightning Protection Training Group (SLPTG).

5.7   Temporary suspended access equipment

Temporary suspended access equipment can refer to a wide range of equipment that is used to support or contain workers working at height.

It includes equipment such as a single suspended chair (for example, a boatswain's chair), usually suspended from the roof and suitable for one person carrying out light work (such as for window cleaning or working on the side of a building), and a platform, cradle or work cage, suspended from the roof, that can have a load rating of 1,000 kg (or more) and a span of more than 15 m, capable of carrying a number of persons.

These larger types of equipment are typically used in industrial and commercial construction projects (such as building, restoration, painting, sandblasting, waterproofing, window cleaning, inspections and general building maintenance).

The equipment is a temporary means of carrying out a specific task; the equipment is dismantled and removed from the work area upon completion of the task.

Temporary suspended access equipment is a specialist subject and is covered by the British Standard for ***Planning, design, setting up and use of temporary suspended access equipment – Code of Practice*** (BS 5974:2017).

The equipment is normally raised or lowered by means of a manually operated or powered hoist or climbing device that can be attached to the temporary suspended platform, work cage or suspended chair.

Permanently installed suspended access equipment is not covered here or within BS 5974:2017.

(For trade association information relating to subjects that do not fall under the temporary suspended access equipment standard (for example, rope access (IRATA), Steeplejack and Lightning Protection Training Group (SLPTG) and Association of technical lightning and access specialists (ATLAS) refer to 5.6.)

 For further information visit the Specialist Access Engineering and Maintenance Association (SAEMA) website.

05

FALL ARREST AND SUSPENSION EQUIPMENT

Appendix A – Inspection of webbing harnesses and lanyards

The Health and Safety Executive and other key industry stakeholders (including the British Safety Industry Federation, the Height Safety Group and the Working at Height Safety Association) recommend that a three-tier inspection regime (pre-use, detailed inspections and interim inspections) is implemented where webbing harnesses and lanyards are in use. The regime should be drawn up by a competent person and include the following information.

- The equipment to be inspected (including unique identification references).

- The frequency and type of inspection (pre-use checks, detailed inspection and, where appropriate, interim inspection).

- Designated competent persons to carry out the inspections.

- Action to be taken on finding defective equipment.

- Means of recording the inspections.

- Training of users.

- Means of monitoring the inspection regime to verify inspections are carried out accordingly.

All persons who carry out any inspection must have the independence and impartiality to make objective decisions, and sufficient authority to discard defective equipment.

 In the unlikely event of a fall, a webbing harness and lanyard that are worn out or damaged may not take the impact and stress of a person arresting, and fail. A harness, lanyard and secure anchor point are the last resort to a person falling – their sole purpose is to save lives.

The importance of pre-use checks and regular inspections cannot be overemphasised.

Inspection regime

Harnesses and lanyards should be subjected to the following checks and inspections.

Pre-use checks

These are visual and tactile inspections, carried out by slowly passing the lanyard or harness through the hands to detect small cuts in the edges, softening or hardening of the fibres and traces of contaminants. The inspection should only take a few minutes and should be carried out by the user prior to each period of use. These inspections do not need to be recorded.

Detailed inspections

These are more formal and in-depth inspections carried out at least every six months, and every three months for frequently used equipment, particularly where equipment is used in extreme conditions or environments (such as demolition, scaffolding and steel erection). They are normally carried out by a designated individual who is also responsible for recording the results and implementing the required action.

Interim inspections

These are in-depth, formal inspections, carried out when it is suspected that equipment has deteriorated and an inspection is needed before the next scheduled detailed inspection. Results of these inspections must also be recorded.

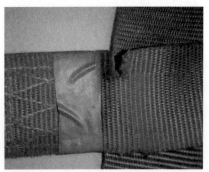  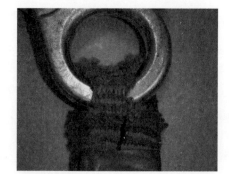

Examples of damaged equipment – the user should check for signs of tears, damage and wear

Appendix B – Fall arrest safety equipment training (FASET) top 10 dos and don'ts for safety net use

FASET top 10 dos and don'ts for safety net use
Do
✔ Ensure you use competent safety net rigging companies with relevant experience (such as FASET member companies).
✔ Ensure you use competent safety net riggers (those with a safety net rigger competency card).
✔ Ensure that methods of access for work at height have been properly assessed, and the safest method that is reasonably practicable has been chosen.
✔ Carry out a formal inspection if nets are in place for more than seven days, or subjected to extreme weather conditions. A visual user inspection should be carried out prior to working above the safety nets.
✔ Ensure that all materials are secure before lifting or craning above a safety net.
✔ Ensure that a handover certificate is completed prior to allowing works above a safety net.
✔ Ensure that nets are struck prior to any hot works being carried out above.
✔ Report any damage to a safety net.
✔ Ensure all falls into a safety net are reported to site management and call FASET. Ensure the supervision of the loaded net's removal from service.
✔ Ensure that the safety nets used conform to BS EN 1263-1:2014 and are rigged in accordance with BS EN 1263-2:2014.
Don't
✘ Allow the use of nets unless there is evidence of an appropriate inspection and maintenance regime and UV testing within the last 12 months.
✘ Allow the use of nets unless a competent person has verified there is sufficient clearance distance (rule of thumb: no less than 3 m).
✘ Allow work above nets without evidence that any repairs have been carried out by a competent person authorised by the manufacturer.
✘ Allow nets to be installed which don't have serial numbers or labels.
✘ Allow workers to use the nets as a means of access or working platform.
✘ Attach nets to any structure without first confirming it has the capacity to deal with a minimum 6 kN loading at a 45° angle.
✘ Allow gaps greater than 100 mm unless exceptional circumstances dictate otherwise (in these cases, not greater than 225 mm).
✘ Tamper with or adjust any nets and attachment points.
✘ Allow work above net systems that have been damaged or loaded.
✘ Allow work above the net if it is positioned greater than 2 m from the working level.

05

05

CONTENTS

Excavations

06

Supporting
INFORMATION

GT700 Toolbox talks / supporting checklists and forms

Toolbox talks on some of these topics are available in the GT700 publication. Supporting checklists and forms covering some of these topics are available on our companion website.

EXCAVATIONS

Overview

This chapter gives practical guidance on factors to be considered when planning excavations, setting up of the work and safe working within them. This includes elements to consider, such as soil composition, depth, support structures, access and egress, vehicles and plant, and guarding excavations.

Good planning and correct preparation for excavations are essential, as every year people are killed or seriously injured by collapses and falling materials while working in excavations.

6.1 Introduction

Most construction work will involve a form of excavation for foundations, sewers or drainage. These will vary in size and depth but are always a high-risk activity as they can be affected by diverse factors (such as rainwater, hot weather, adjoining structures, ground conditions and vibration).

Many accidents occur when the excavation appears to be in good condition, with its sides clean and self-supporting, and with no obvious hazards.

Some excavations may need to be classed as confined spaces, and will therefore need additional precautions. Excavations and excavation supports also require temporary works procedures to be followed. Some excavation and excavation support work may require specific design considerations and additional precautions.

 For further information refer to Chapter C05 *Temporary Works*.

 Neither the shallowness of an excavation nor the appearance of the ground should be taken as indicators of safety. Accident reports suggest that far too often such assumptions are made incorrectly.

 An unsafe excavation

The Health and Safety Executive (HSE) inspector served a prohibition notice for this excavation, which was 1.9 m deep and unsupported.

The contractor was fined £10,000 and the HSE was awarded £8,000 costs.

In addition, the supervisor was fined £1,000 and the HSE was awarded £800 costs.

The method of excavation must be specific to local conditions and may need to be different to an excavation nearby. Workers will often have to improvise and use their knowledge and skills to overcome unforeseen obstructions and different ground conditions. It is important that supervisors and their workers are trained and competent to ensure excavation work is completed in a safe way.

6.2 Important points

A **risk assessment** must be completed for any works that are to be undertaken, and this must be done by a competent person.

This risk assessment must take into consideration the potential for the sides to collapse, that someone may be injured and need first aid, a site-specific rescue plan, and the possible need for a support structure.

The risk assessment should eliminate or reduce the risk at source (such as using trenchless techniques or having the sides battered or stepped). Risks, from the following hazards, must also be considered.

● Collapse of the sides.

● Underground services.

● Contaminated ground.

- Fall of persons, materials, plant or equipment into the excavation.
- Confined spaces – poisonous or explosive atmospheres or lack of oxygen.
- Flooding.
- Overhead services.
- Moving plant – injury to persons.
- Lifting operations.
- Undermining adjacent structures, scaffolds, services or trees.
- Surcharging the excavation, meaning applying pressure to the sides (for example, vehicle routes or material storage areas too close to the excavation).

 For details on safety awareness for working around excavators refer to Appendix A.

Control measures described in the risk assessment should include the following.

- Protection of person(s) installing the support system.
- Identifying safe exposure and, if necessary, support of underground services.
- Safe access to and egress from the excavation.
- Adequate ventilation of the workspace.
- Arrangements to dewater the trench if necessary.
- Inspections of the excavation by a competent person.
- Consideration for the stability of adjacent structures or land.
- Arranging for appropriate signing, guarding and lighting and, where necessary, protection of non-employees (pedestrians and the public).

 A cubic metre of soil can weigh over a tonne.

06

 ## A collapse captured while taking site record photos

The excavation was 1.8 m deep and the collapse took less than two seconds. The method was to dig and pour concrete with no-one entering. Due to heavy rain, this method was abandoned and trench support installed. The section that broke away weighed about one tonne and it can be seen how easily a serious accident could happen.

 Information on the structural stability of excavations can be found on the construction pages of the HSE website.

6.3 Excavation support

There will always be water present during excavations, even if only moisture in the soil, and this is an additional hazard to be considered (as shown in the illustration on the right).

Soils that are akin to fine sand flow easily; however, those like stiff clay stick together more easily.

Do not rely on any soil, whatever its structure, to support its own weight. If it cannot be battered or stepped, then alternative support will be essential.

Loose and fractured rock will also need support.

Before commencing any excavation work consider what temporary support is required, and whether any equipment or special precautions are needed.

Clients must provide information to contractors before work begins. This should include relevant information on ground conditions, underground structures or watercourses and the location of existing services.

This information should be used during the planning of, and preparation for, excavation work. It will allow the contractor to choose the most suitable method to support the excavation.

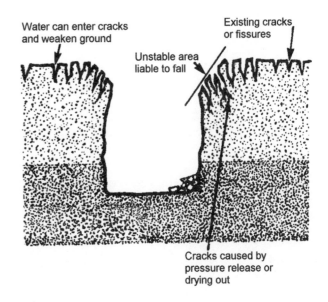

An excavation in firm or stiff clay-type ground

 Prevent collapse – shore, step or batter back. NEVER assume the ground will stand unsupported, even for a short time.

6.3.1 Trenchless techniques

Persons planning construction work should be aware of alternative techniques that may be able to partially or totally eliminate the need for excavations.

Examples of the trenchless techniques include boring, directional drilling and pipe jacking – some will need excavation pits at each end to launch and retrieve equipment and to make connections to pipework or jointing of cables.

6.3.2 Battering or stepping excavations

Battering back or stepping the sides of an excavation to a safe angle is an acceptable means of preventing instability and collapse. In many situations this is the safest and simplest way of ensuring stability and should be given due consideration.

The diagram (right) is an example of typical safe slope angles and should be used for guidance purposes only. If there is any doubt regarding soil conditions, the site engineer or the shoring provider should be consulted.

Battering or stepping excavations will depend on the nature of the soil, which could be one material or could be a mix of materials. Consideration will need to be given to the level of the water table and water content, and the increase or decrease of this while the excavation is open. A small percentage increase in water content can reduce the stability of the excavation sides.

The slope angles described in the diagram are known as the **angle of repose**. In granular soils the angle of slope should be less than the natural angle of repose of the material being excavated. This will prevent the granular material from *running*. In wet ground a considerably flatter slope will be required.

Plant, pedestrians, materials and equipment should be kept at a safe distance outside the angle of repose to prevent surcharge (vertical pressure or load that acts over the ground surface) on the sides of the excavation.

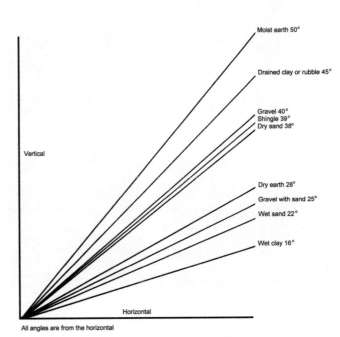

Typical safe slope angles. The vertical distance should not exceed 1.2 m

Stepped excavation – but showing Chapter 8-type barriers, which should not be used for edge protection

This image demonstrates bad practice.

It shows red, plastic- style barriers, which are not suitable for this type of excavation work, but which should be used for street works and road works on the public highway in accordance with the Code of Practice for roads and street works (Traffic signs manual, Chapter 8).

(Image supplied by Barconn Ltd/Paramount Health and Safety)

6.3.3   Trench supports

The type of support will depend on the following.

- The type of excavation.
- The nature of the ground.
- Groundwater conditions.
- Surcharge of the excavation sides.

Depending on the risk assessment the excavation may need to be supported.

A survey should be carried out for all but shallow trenches, to determine the type of soil and other ground conditions; this will then identify what support will be required. This survey must be carried out by a competent person. A specialist engineer will be required for large or complex excavations. In the more complex projects bespoke solutions will be required.

Equipment for support must be available before excavation work is started, and be of good quality and well maintained; they must also be fixed securely.

All erection, dismantling and alteration of any support must be under the supervision of a competent person.

6.3.3.1   Types of support systems

Timber shuttering, steel trench sheets and fixed or adjustable props may be used; the props can be mechanical or hydraulic.

A temporary framework of support of a protective box or cage type may be required to protect workers. This can be moved forward as timbering progresses.

 The Construction Plant-hire Association has produced guidance on the management of shoring in excavations, hazard identification for risk assessment, as well as selection of proprietary shoring equipment. The guidance is aimed at anyone involved in the planning, management, design and supervision of excavation works.

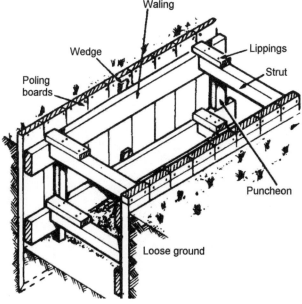

Close-boarded excavation

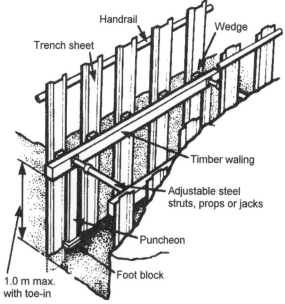

Open sheeting using steel sheets and jacks or acro props

EXCAVATIONS

Proprietary support systems are available and include the following.

Shields (drag boxes), which are two vertical plates that are braced permanently apart; they are intended as temporary localised protection for workers, and can be dragged along by the excavator as work progresses.

Trench boxes, which are modular and are lowered in, and form a permanent support for the trench sides; they can be extended in height and width.

Plate lining systems have metal plates that slide into position between vertical soldier posts at preset intervals; the posts counteract stress from trench sides.

You need to be aware that any of these support systems can cause problems when underground services cross the line of the trench being excavated. The use of a hydraulic waling frame may be better used in this case, as spaces can be left between the metal sheets once they are in position. Hydraulic frames are ideal when excavating pits and inspection chambers, as they can be extended in both length and width.

6.3.4   Inspection and maintenance of support systems

Excavations must be closely monitored when they are first opened and sides are unsupported. The Construction (Design and Management) Regulations 2015 (CDM) state the following.

- All practicable steps must be taken to prevent danger to any person, including, where necessary, the provision of supports or battering, to ensure that:
  - no excavation or part of an excavation collapses
  - no material forming the walls or roof of, or adjacent to, any excavation is dislodged or falls
  - no person is buried or trapped in an excavation by material which is dislodged or falls.
- Suitable and sufficient steps must be taken to prevent any person, work equipment or any accumulation of material from falling into any excavation.
- Suitable and sufficient steps must be taken, where necessary, to prevent any part of an excavation or ground adjacent to it from being overloaded by work equipment or material. All excavations must be inspected by a competent person at the start of the shift, after any event that may have affected the strength or stability of the excavation, or if material unintentionally falls or is dislodged. No work should be undertaken until the inspection has taken place and the excavation is safe *(for further information refer to 6.5 Inspections and reports).*

Small movements of 6–12 mm are usually the only sign of weakening in cohesive soils – be aware of them, as they can pass unnoticed but they mean something is wrong. Movement can be seen from slight distortion in the timbering, bowing of poling boards and walings, or signs of local crushing. The ground can also dry out and shrink, which loosens timbering. Timber can be displaced by the ground absorbing additional moisture.

- Avoid damage to struts or walings when moving loads into or out of the excavation.
- Check timber regularly – it can dry out, shrink or rot.
- In bad weather spoil heaps can slump and loose boulders or masonry can fall into the excavation.
- A guideline is that the distance from the edge of the trench and the bottom of the spoil heap must be equal to or greater than the depth of the excavation. For example, the bottom of a spoil heap should be a minimum of 1 m from the edge of a trench that is 1 m deep.
- Do not allow heavy vehicles near the edge of an excavation unless the support work has been designed to permit it.
- Take care not to affect the stability of any neighbouring structure or features.
- Take into account the Party Wall Act and any surveys, permissions or restrictions.
- Take precautions to protect workers (and others) before and during excavation works.

 An unsupported excavation

In the example pictured here to the right, this excavation was only about 650 mm deep, and it was left unsupported overnight.

There was heavy rain during the evening, and the team returned the following morning to find this collapse, which had put the existing cast-iron gas main at risk.

6.4   Excavation safety

6.4.1   Access and egress

There must be adequate and safe arrangements in place for getting into (access) and getting out of (egress) an excavation.

This is usually achieved with ladders, which need to be properly located and fixed with suitable overruns or other handholds. Adjustable, lightweight staircases or towers are becoming increasingly common, and are safer and quicker to use.

Under no circumstances should anyone use the side supports or underground services that cross or run along the trench as footholds to climb into or out of an excavation.

The risk assessment should also consider emergency escape and recovery of casualties. Ideally, provision should be made to have a hoist installed that is equipped with the capability to lift a stretcher from the base of the excavation.

First aid needs, provision of trained personnel and suitable equipment for the hazards that may be present must also be accounted for.

Safe access into a deep excavation, with all-round secure edge protection

 Climbing into or out of an excavation using walings, underground services or struts must be prohibited. This must be specifically covered in the safe system of work and/or method statement.

6.4.2   Guarding excavations

Suitable steps must be taken to prevent any person, vehicle, plant or equipment, or any accumulation of earth or other materials, from falling into an excavation. These include the following

- Robust physical barriers and toe boards. Barriers must be capable of resisting impact or the weight of a person leaning on them. They should be used to keep people safe and materials, plant and equipment away from the edges. (Pin-and-rope or rolls of orange plastic mesh are not suitable.)

- When barriers are removed to facilitate work, they should be replaced as soon as possible.

- The edges of an excavation should be lit during darkness, particularly if close to public roads and spaces.

- If excavation work is carried out on the highway, Local Authority approval is required and appropriate signing and guarding complying with the *Traffic signs manual*, Chapter 8, and the *Code of Practice for safety at street works and road works* must be utilised.

Excavation edge protection barriers

- Ensure adequate signs and hazard warning lights are used when it is dark or during foggy conditions.

 **If plastic Chapter 8-type barriers are used, such as during street works and road works on the public highway, they must be installed to be robust enough to stop a person who falls or leans against them from falling into the excavation.**

This is particularly important if the barriers are being used to protect the public.

For further information on guarding excavations refer to Chapter F01 Street works and road works.

A series of images presented on the next page demonstrate a number of safe excavation systems in practice, with features shown including edge protection, guarding, and access and egress.

EXCAVATIONS

e.g. Safe systems in practice

Deep inspection chamber excavation with good access and edge protection

Deep inspection chamber excavation with good access, edge protection and additional ladder

Protected excavation

Drag boxes with guard-rail attachments and ladder access is good practice. Plastic orange netting, which is not suitable guarding for this type of excavation work, is bad practice

Remote controlled trench compactor avoiding the need to enter the excavation

Designated bucket changing area

Fencing along utility trench

6.4.3 Vehicles and plant

Plan traffic routes so that no vehicles or plant go near excavations, other than those that need to complete the task at hand.

Be aware of surcharging when heavy items of construction plant are near to an excavation. Where this cannot be avoided, it must be considered in the design of the support system that will be installed.

Stop blocks must be used if vehicles are required to tip into an excavation. Ensure these are placed far enough away to avoid damage to the edge of the excavation.

Use a vehicle marshaller to give directions to the vehicle driver or plant operator.

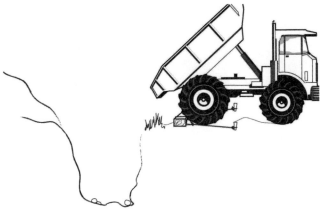

Stop blocks should be used, where appropriate

Safe segregation of excavation work and plant

 During 2016, a large number of incidents involving forward tipping dumpers resulted in many serious injuries and six fatalities in six months. These mainly involved the dumpers overturning and collisions with pedestrians. Many of the fatalities from overturns were a result of the operator not wearing the seat belt and attempting to jump clear, but becoming caught and crushed by the overturning machine.

 For further guidance refer to the HSE publications *The safe use of vehicles on construction sites* (HSG144) and *Construction site transport safety: Safe use of site dumpers* (CIS52) which can be downloaded free from the HSE website.

 For further information refer to Chapter C06 Mobile work equipment.

6.4.4 Site lighting

There must be suitable and sufficient lighting at every workplace, the approaches to it and on traffic routes. During hours of darkness or other periods of reduced natural light, excavations and the guarding surrounding them will need to be illuminated, particularly if the public have access to those areas.

You must pay particular attention to ensuring there is adequate lighting for access points, openings and lifting operations. The workforce should be wearing suitable high-visibility clothing. It is important to clean and maintain high-visibility clothing so that it remains effective in low light or during the hours of darkness.

6.4.5 Ventilation

Excavations must be kept clear of suffocating, toxic or explosive gases. Gases can seep through the soil and accumulate in the bottom of the excavation.

Naturally-occurring gases include hydrogen sulphide, as one example: a colourless, toxic gas that can be created by the decomposition of organic matter such as rotting vegetation or sewage, which if in inhaled can cause convulsions and cardiac arrhythmias.

Gases that are heavier than air (such as plant exhaust emissions) can leak or roll into an excavation and displace the air, which can lead to asphyxiation.

Leakage of propane and butane from liquefied petroleum gas (LPG) cylinders is potentially dangerous; any gas leak will sink to the lowest point and form an explosive concentration that cannot disperse naturally.

The excavation will need to be checked and continuously monitored for the presence of gases and purged before entry by workers if these are found.

 For further information on ventilation refer to Chapter B07 Control of substances hazardous to health.

6.4.6 Confined spaces

An excavation could be designated as a confined space due to any of the following hazards being present.

- Risk of engulfment, drowning or entrapment by a free-flowing solid (such as sand and fine soils) or a sudden rush of groundwater or rainwater.

- Nature of the excavation (deep and narrow) and the ground in which it is dug, which could result in the accumulation of a naturally occurring gas, such as hydrogen sulphide (H_2S).

EXCAVATIONS

- Risk of asphyxia due to the nature of the ground. Peaty soils absorb oxygen from the atmosphere so the bottom of a trench dug in peat is unlikely to have a sufficient level of oxygen. The action of chemicals in the soil on brownfield sites can also alter the oxygen content in an excavation. Soil which is high in limestone can produce carbon dioxide if it is contaminated with acidic rainwater.

- Substances used (such as LPG), which are heavier than air.

- Presence of carbon monoxide (CO) from internal combustion engines within the excavation. Though slightly lighter than air, CO may build up in the excavation and take time to dissipate (clear).

- Nature of the substances released from any underground services that have to be broken into.

- Extremes of temperature leading to hypothermia or heat exhaustion.

- Dust and fumes from mechanical cutting equipment or welding.

All of these factors can potentially reduce the percentage of oxygen in the air and/or introduce toxic, flammable or explosive gases into the air. Control measures on the risk assessment may include forced fresh-air ventilation or, as a last resort, appropriate RPE.

 For further information refer to Chapter D08 Confined spaces.

If an excavation is classified as a confined space, tests for toxic gas or oxygen depletion must be carried out before work starts and continuously as work progresses.

It is also recommended that the work should be subject to the issue of a permit to work certificate, and that the first consideration should always be what measures can be taken to enable the work to be carried out without the need to enter the confined space.

6.4.7   Underground cables and services

Before any excavation works take place, you must ensure underground services (such as gas, electricity, water and telecommunications) have been identified. Many injuries each year are caused by accidental contact with underground services. You must have controls in place to reduce the risk of injury from underground cables or other underground services.

 For further information refer to Chapter D07 Underground and overhead services.

6.5   Inspections and reports

An inspection of an excavation must be carried out by a competent person at the following intervals.

- At the start of each shift during which work is to be carried out.

- After an event that is likely to have affected the stability of the structure.

- After the accidental fall or dislodgement of any material.

The competent person must be satisfied that work can be carried out safely and a report, containing the following information, must be prepared.

- Name and address of the person on whose behalf the inspection was carried out.

- Location of the work being inspected.

- Description of the place of work, or part of that place of work inspection, including plant and equipment or materials.

- Date and time of the inspection.

- Details of any issues identified that could give risk to the health and safety of any person.

- Details of any action taken as a result of any issues identified.

- Details of any further actions considered necessary.

- Name and position of the person making the report.

If, following inspection, the competent person is not satisfied that work can be carried out safely then no work should be carried out until the matter has been satisfactorily remedied. All reports must be completed and written by the competent person, and a copy provided within 24 hours to the person on whose behalf it was undertaken.

A copy of the report must be kept on site until the work is completed and for three months, generally at the company head office, from the date of completion. You do not need to do more than one written report in any period of seven days. However, it is advisable that a daily record of inspection is kept (for example, in the site diary). There is no statutory form for inspections and information can be kept electronically. However, you must be able to produce a hard copy for an HSE inspector, if so requested.

6.6 Excavators used as cranes

Excavators are classed as mobile work equipment and are therefore subject to the requirements of the Provision and Use of Work Equipment Regulations (PUWER) and, when being used for lifting operations, the Lifting Operations and Lifting Equipment Regulations (LOLER).

Excavators and backhoes are principally designed for earth-moving operations and not lifting operations as a main function. The planning for a lifting operation using excavators should primarily consider whether these machines are suitable for the required lifting activity. As a lifting operation, it is subject to suitable and sufficient planning by a competent person, including a risk assessment and a safe system of work, that takes into account the capabilities of the excavator for the selected task.

The risk assessment and method statement should take into account that when an excavator is in the object handling mode (being used as a crane), it will be necessary for the slinger to approach the machine to attach or detach the lifting accessories. They will then be within a hazardous area (the slewing arc of the boom and dipper) and be at risk of being struck by the load, bucket or excavator arm.

Excavator operators and slingers must be made aware of these dangers; effective communication and constant vigilance are essential.

 When the slinger is within the slewing arc of the machine's boom to attach or remove lifting accessories, the operating controls of the machine must be isolated.

The weight of the bucket (if still fitted), plus the quick hitch coupler must be added to the weight of the load to establish if the machine will be working within its safe working load (or rated capacity).

The bucket should be removed to improve the excavator operator's visibility. If a quick hitch coupler is fitted, the operator must ensure that the link is facing downwards (operating ram extended) so that any part of the lifting accessory will not foul the coupler, allowing the accessory to hang free at all times.

The risk assessment must also address the following.

- The need for the lifting operation to be ideally segregated from other work activities taking place in the vicinity, particularly where it is necessary for the machine to travel with a suspended load.

- Ground conditions, particularly where an excavator will carry out the lifting operation, which should be on level, firm terrain. Where a pick and carry operation is required, the intended travel route must be checked (for both tracked and wheeled types) so that there are no voids, it is clear of trenches, is on firm, level ground, has no obstructions and personnel are safely segregated from the travel route.

A rated object handling capacity table must be available in the cab. If the rated lifting capacity for an excavator (or the backhoe of a backhoe loader) is greater than 1 tonne (or the overturning moment is greater than 40,000 Nm), the machine must be fitted with the following.

- A boom lowering control device on the raising boom cylinder(s) (a safety check valve), which meets the requirements of BS ISO 8643 (*Earth-moving machinery. Hydraulic excavator and backhoe loader lowering control device. Requirements and tests*).

- An acoustic or visual warning device, which indicates to the operator when the object handling capacity or corresponding load movement is reached.

Where the upper structure of a 360° excavator needs to slew, the machine's lifting capacity is reduced when slewing away from the front or rear of the tracks or axles. This is because the track or wheel width is less than the track length or wheel base.

Chains or slings for lifting must not be placed around or on the teeth of the bucket. Accessories for lifting must only be attached to a purpose-made point on the machine.

Lifting points are manufactured with the machine. Unofficial ad-hoc additions (such as after-market hooks or points welded onto machines) are highly dangerous and not acceptable.

Where the risk assessment shows that there is a significant risk of overloading or overturning of the excavator, the fitment of a rated capacity indicator may be required.

 For further guidance refer to the CPA document *Guidance on lifting operations with 180° and 360° excavators*.

 For further detailed guidance refer to Chapter C08 Lifting equipment.

06

Appendix A - Safety awareness around excavators

This information covers basic safety rules that should be followed by the operator, vehicle plant marshaller (VPM) and others working around both tracked and wheeled excavators to reduce the risk of injury and allow everyone to go home safely. Plant operating and plant movements are a significant risk for everyone on site, not just those working directly around the excavator.

 Accidents involving moving plant result in many serious injuries and fatalities every year in the construction industry.

If work is not managed safely people working around excavators are at high risk of sustaining serious life changing injuries or death. In confined work areas or where more than one piece of plant is in use, near misses, collisions and plant damage are also highly likely.

Technical advances in machinery (such as a remote operated cut-off switch) and familiarisation periods for new machines coming on to site help to reduce incidents and accidents.

Communication and risk assessment

 Before beginning any activity, a pre-task briefing should be carried out to ensure everyone involved is familiar with the task, and is aware of any risks and the control measures required. Any interface between different tasks should also be discussed to co-ordinate activities.

A risk assessment of the task should reflect the hierarchy of risk control to eliminate, reduce, isolate, control and, as a last resort, provide personal protective equipment (PPE).

- Does the workforce need to be working around the excavator?
- Where personnel are close to plant, are exclusion zones in place and are the required safety critical devices fitted to the excavator fully functional?
- Are vehicle plant marshals (VPM) required for the safe system of work?
- Is everyone wearing appropriate high-visibility clothing, which is in good order?

Safety zones

 When working around an excavator it is important to be aware of the operator's limited all-round vision and the safety zones for the machine.

Where a risk assessment has identified the need for a competent VPM to manage the excavator movements then all instructions by the VPM must be followed. A VPM is responsible for managing the movement of people and vehicles safely around the excavator.

A vehicle marshaller carries out a separate role and supervises the general movement of vehicles on site (for example, deliveries).

Before entering the radius of the excavator, wait in an area of safety and acknowledge the machine operator or, where provided, VPM. The VPM will then instruct the excavator to stop, power down the engine, apply the hydraulic isolation lever and turn the engine off. Once the operator has acknowledged you it is then safe to approach.

 Approach the excavator cabin in the operator's clear line of sight.

You should only approach the excavator cabin in the operator's clear line of sight. Approaching the excavator from any other angle should be avoided (Zone 1 in the illustration). Where this is not possible (such as when an excavator is working near to a pedestrian route) the machine operator or VPM must acknowledge your need to approach and the correct shut-off procedure must be followed, as described above, before personnel enter the exclusion zone.

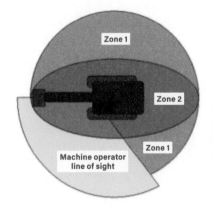

The machine operator should only restart the machine once they have seen you leave the exclusion zone or the VPM has confirmed that it is safe to do so.

Pedestrians often still approach an excavator from the operator's blind side, assuming the operator is unlikely to move or that they can be seen by the operator. It is important that all personnel on site are aware of the restricted visibility in excavators. An appreciation of this can be achieved by allowing non-excavator operators to sit in the cab in controlled conditions to experience the restrictions for themselves. Stickers on the machine can be used as a reminder.

 Danger! You are approaching on my blind side. I cannot see you.

It should not be necessary to enter the area directly around the machine or underneath the boom (Zone 2 in the illustration). Any tasks where this is unavoidable should be individually considered and have a site and task specific safe system of work put in place. These activities may include the following.

- Drainage or pipe laying.

- Archaeology.

- Piling.

- Earth moving.

- Bearing tests.

- Lifting operations.

- Plant maintenance.

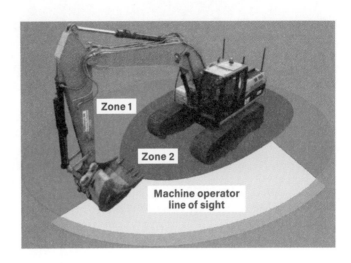

 Always gain permission from the vehicle plant marshall before entering an excavator's working area.

Safety zones

Using the safety zones guidance, spot what is wrong in this example.

- Supervisor and workforce are on the blind side of the plant operator.

- No exclusion zone is visible if operatives are to be excluded from the works area.

- No visible control of excavator. No eye contact with operator, and no VPM present.

- No-one is taking the decision to work safely or not at all.

06

Appendix B – Case study – Excavation collapses after dangers are ignored

 ### Director and excavator operator jailed

A 52-year-old director of a house building company (working as the site manager at the time of the accident) was convicted of gross negligence manslaughter following the death of a worker on a construction project. The conviction followed a nine-week trial at Northampton Crown Court into the death of a 33-year-old father-of-five whilst he was employed as a ground worker at a building site in Collyweston, Northants.

The court heard evidence of how the worker had been standing next to a deep trench, which had been incorrectly excavated by the excavator driver, when a wall of the trench collapsed and buried him beneath the collapsed material. Despite the efforts of fellow workers he was pronounced dead at the scene after his body was recovered. Northamptonshire Police and HSE investigators found that the sides of the trench had not been properly or adequately secured and that the site manager (the company director) and excavator driver both ignored basic safety measures.

Northampton Crown Court convicted the defendants, as follows.

- The site manager and director of the company was found guilty of gross negligence manslaughter and received a four-year sentence. He will spend two years in custody and two years on license. He was also ordered to pay costs of £90,500.

- The self-employed excavator driver, who traded as a demolition contractor, was found guilty of a failure as a self-employed person to discharge his duty to ensure the health and safety of persons not in his employment, contrary to Section 3(1a) of the Health and Safety at Work etc. Act 1974. He was also found guilty of failing to take all practicable steps to prevent danger, contrary to Regulation 31 of the Construction (Design and Management) Regulations 2007. He was given a 12-month sentence and will spend six months in custody and six months on license. He was ordered to pay £20,000 towards costs.

Speaking after the verdict a detective superintendent from Northamptonshire Police said: 'This was a tragic loss of a young life that could so easily have been avoided. The defendants were both experienced in ground works and failed to show even the most basic safety measures to prevent harm to workers – such as the young father who lost his life. He leaves behind five young children who are now being cared for by his parents. They were in court throughout the trial and have shown true dignity and strength despite listening to harrowing evidence. This has been a very lengthy and complex investigation and I would like to thank the jurors for their dedication and attention to detail during this long trial'.

Appendix C – Case study – Building contractor jailed after house collapse

 ### Structural integrity of house undermined, leading to collapse

In April 2018 a building contractor was sentenced to seven months' imprisonment following an incident in February 2015 in which a house in Brighton partially collapsed.

Hove Crown Court heard how the builder undermined the structural integrity of the house by digging out the basement. He then failed to act on the advice of a structural engineer on how to remedy the situation, resulting in the gable wall partially collapsing and the ground floor collapsing into the basement. Adjacent properties had to be evacuated and the area cordoned off due to concerns that members of the public living nearby and passing through the area were at risk.

An investigation carried out by the HSE found that the property had bungeroosh walls, common to buildings built in the mid-18th to 19th century in the Brighton area. They are constructed with a mixture of rubble, timber, pebbles, stones, lumps of chalk, pieces of flint and anything else at hand, in a lime mix mortar set between shuttering. It has been described by some construction experts as 'the worst construction material in the world'. The porous composite is susceptible to rot and can become friable in either excessively damp or dry conditions.

The HSE said the builder did not have sufficient knowledge of bungaroosh and that those working on properties made from the legacy material 'must fully understand what they are dealing with' because the buildings are 'more challenging in terms of structural stability'.

The investigation also found that the builder failed to report the incident to the HSE as a dangerous occurrence, in accordance with the Reporting of Injuries, Diseases and Dangerous Occurrences Regulations (RIDDOR) 2013.

The builder, of Woodingdean, Brighton, pleaded guilty to breaching Regulation 25(1) of CDM 2007 and Regulation 7 of RIDDOR 2013. The defendant was sentenced to five months' imprisonment for count one and two months' imprisonment for count two, to run concurrently. He was also ordered to pay costs of £7,000.

The HSE principal inspector said: 'Basement work must be properly planned to ensure the structural integrity of the building throughout the construction work. When this type of work is done badly, workers and members of the public are at significant risk of serious injury or death. In addition, we cannot underestimate the impact on the homeowners when their properties are extensively damaged'.

(Source: HSE.)

CONTENTS

Underground and overhead services

Supporting
INFORMATION

GT700 Toolbox talks / supporting checklists and forms

Toolbox talks on some of these topics are available in the GT700 publication. Supporting checklists and forms covering some of these topics are available on our companion website.

UNDERGROUND AND OVERHEAD SERVICES

Overview

This chapter provides practical guidance on factors to be considered when preparing to work with, or near to, underground and overhead services.

On the majority of occasions a licensed utility company will carry out this type of work. However, existing services, whether known or unknown, remain a risk on nearly all projects.

Always bear in mind that location drawings for services are not always accurate. Therefore, locations may not be correct and there may even be some services that have not been recorded.

This chapter also includes practical guidance for dealing with the hazards and the subsequent risks of working, or coming into contact, with overhead power lines.

7.1 Introduction

Underground services are, to a great extent, out of sight and out of mind until, perhaps, there is a fault or another reason to excavate. Every year people are injured and some killed due to accidental contact with underground services, such as electricity cables and gas pipes.

In every case, damage and injury could have been avoided if the proper procedures had been followed. The statistic of 70,000 instances of damage and 400 injuries per year as a result of coming into contact with overhead and underground electricity cables shows that there is considerable room for improvement.

Coming into contact with overhead services also includes the power lines serving the railway network.

 For further information refer to Chapter F02 Trackside safety.

This chapter makes reference to plant or equipment (for example, cranes, excavators, MEWPs and scaffold poles) that may come into contact with overhead power lines (OHPLs).

 The construction phase plan will provide information about hazards specific to a site, and must include locations and types of underground and overhead services that can be found in the area.

7.2 Important points

PLAN the work.

LOCATE the underground services.

DIG using a safe method of work.

7.2.1 Underground services

- Before doing anything yourself, check with the utility providers for existing services in the area that you are planning to work in.
- Ensure existing service routes are clearly marked on your plans.
- Use paint, tape or markers to identify existing services. Do not use metal spikes, which might penetrate a cable or pipe.
- Absence of marker posts is not evidence that there are no underground services.
- Damage to gas pipes can cause leaks, which can result in fire and/or explosion.
- The most common injury is from contact with electrical cables. These often carry high voltages and can result in death or major burns.

 The exact position of a service will only be known once the service is uncovered.

7.2.2 Overhead services

- Where work cannot be avoided near to overhead services you must consult the local electricity supplier or distribution network operator (DNO) for advice before any work begins.
- A safe system of work must be planned and implemented for all work on or near to overhead electrical works.
- Ensure power lines are dead, or suitable precautions are taken.

- Contact with overhead power lines can give an electric shock, burn or **kill**.

- Injury can also occur when a person or object gets too close to a line and a flashover (arcing) occurs.

- Establish a safe zone under and around the overhead power lines before any work starts. Ensure no materials or machinery are stored nearby.

- It is not only high voltage cables that are dangerous. Voltages lower than 230 volts can kill people.

7.3 Underground services

7.3.1 Risks and costs of damage

Damage to gas pipes can happen even when their location is known (such as contact by an excavator bucket).

Damage to water pipes and telephone cables is often less evident but still potentially serious, affecting local businesses, schools, hospitals and emergency services that are dependent on those services.

If plant damages a fibre optic cable, this could result in a long section needing to be replaced, in most cases costing tens of thousands of pounds. In some cases, fibre optic cable strikes have cost up to £250,000.

All utility companies take cable strikes and damage very seriously. Not only because of the risks to the lives of their employees but also because of the financial costs and negative impacts on future business.

Some utility companies have problems with retaining liability insurance if they have a poor record of utility strikes. Multi-million pound organisations have gone out of business as a result of being unable to obtain liability insurance.

Most investigations into cable strikes reveal human error, where procedures for locating, identifying, supporting and working safely around services are not followed or shortcuts have been taken.

Such errors and omissions have resulted in many fatalities and life-altering injuries to individuals, and the dismissal of persons involved.

In the event of a gas leak, suspected gas leak or any other emergency relating to gas, immediately phone the National Grid gas emergency service on 0800 111 999.

In the event of an electrical emergency, phone the National Grid 24-hour electrical emergency service on 0800 404 090.

The guidance document *Avoiding danger from underground services* (HSG47) can be downloaded from the HSE website.

7.3.2 Types of underground services

The most commonly encountered underground services are gas, water, electricity and telecommunications, but drains and sewers will also need to be located as they are underground services too.

There are other services that may not be known about or detected other than through investigation before digging or excavation is started; these include cable television, hydraulics, private telecommunications and street lighting cables.

In some cases, depending on the location, it may be necessary to investigate for petroleum and fuel oils (large bore pipelines linking major installations – the majority of these pipelines are buried deep, although some may have reduced cover and be shallower in certain situations).

If work in the vicinity of gas transmission pipelines is being considered, the local gas company will be able to provide details of suitable procedures.

For further information on types of underground services refer to Chapter C03 Electrical safety and Chapter F01 Street works and road works.

7.3.3 Colour coding of underground services

There is national agreement between the utility groups for colour coding of services.

Full information can be obtained from the NJUG guidelines on the *Positioning and colour coding of underground utilities' apparatus.*

You will, however, need to bear in mind that large numbers of pipes and services have been laid over the last 100 years, in a mixture of materials and colours.

07

UNDERGROUND AND OVERHEAD SERVICES

Note: *The table below identifies that water and electricity can use different coloured pipes.*

Recommended colour coding for underground utility apparatus	
Service(s)	**Duct, pipe or cable**
Electricity, water, oil, fuel pipelines and telecoms	Black PVC
Water	Blue PVC
Water and telecoms	Grey PVC
Electricity	Red PVC
Telecoms	Natural clay (terracotta), or grey, white, green, black or purple PVC
Gas	Yellow PVC

Note: *all plastic, polyethylene (PE), and polyvinylchloride pipes are shown above as PVC.*

Pipe or cable material used by the different services	
Pipe or cable	**Service(s)**
Cast iron	Gas and water
Steel	Gas and water
Braided steel	Electricity
Yellow steel	Gas
Copper	Water
Lead or lead covered	Electricity and water
Asbestos	Water
Hessian wrapped	Electricity

(The information in the table above is for guidance purposes only.)

 ## Considerations when identifying underground services

- The coal authority has laid some yellow PVC electric cable.
- Black PVC must always be assumed to be live electricity until proved otherwise.
- All cast iron and steel must be assumed to be carrying gas until proved otherwise.
- Ducts may contain any one of the services, irrespective of type or colour of the duct.

7.4 Plan

7.4.1 Checking for underground services

Before carrying out any work, check with all public and private utilities for existence of services in the area that work is planned for and ensure these service routes are clearly marked on the plans.

 The local electricity or gas company will give advice by telephone. BT operates a similar type of service and those wishing to make such enquiries should phone and select the option 'dial before you dig'.

Be careful when reading plans; reference points may have been moved, surfaces regraded (increasing or reducing the depths of cover), services moved without authority and not all connections may be shown.

On old brownfield sites there may be abandoned services and underground metallic items (such as tram lines and cast iron pipes); these can distort survey results, as can depth, certain ground conditions and concrete slabs.

Once routes have been identified, mark them with paint, tape or markers but **not** metal spikes, which might penetrate a cable or pipe.

Remember that the exact position will only be known when the underground service is uncovered.

Changes in colour of the surface material (sometimes known as tracks) may indicate where a service trench can be found. Absence of marker posts is not evidence that there are no underground services.

Shallow service

 An electricity cable was damaged by the floor saw used to cut the road prior to excavating a new service trench. Although a cable avoidance tool (CAT) survey had located the cable, it was discovered that it was directly under the asphalt sub-base, which was 270 mm thick.

Never assume that services have been installed at the recommended depth – they are often shallower. Never assume that a located service is the only one; there may be others adjacent to, above or underneath it.

Beware of services encased in concrete bases or structures, or in the concrete backing to kerbs.

Beware of services rising over obstructions, culverts, bridges, and so on. They are often much shallower in these locations.

Services leading to buildings and properties often also rise near to the point of entry to the building, due to the building foundations.

The presence of the following items indicates that underground services exist.

- Lamp posts (street lighting).

- Illuminated traffic signs.

- Telephone boxes.

- Concrete or steel inspection chamber covers.

- Hydrant and valve pit covers.

- Steel cabinets in the footway (set back) or in a verge.

Types of marker posts commonly found to indicate the location of underground services

 The Utility Strike Avoidance Group (USAG) has a free online toolkit, *Best practice in avoiding underground services.*

The toolkit has been prepared by a working group made up of contractors, asset owners and utility service providers. The aim is to improve the risk management of work on and around underground services and to reduce the number and severity of utility strikes.

7.5   Locate

7.5.1   Using cable and pipe locators

Be aware that the cable avoidance tool (CAT) and signal generator should be used together, to provide the full picture. Equipment should be regularly serviced and calibrated, at intervals not exceeding 12 months.

All equipment of this type must have valid calibration certificates. Users should receive formal training in the make and model of the location equipment being used.

 Recent developments in technology include depth read-outs and some models include GPS for accurately mapping the location of services.

Power frequency. A CAT will find most electricity cables whilst power is flowing through them, but it may not work in the following situations.

- If the cable has been disconnected.

- When the loading on a three-phase supply is evenly distributed.

- If the current is so small it is beyond the detection capability of the tool.

- If no current is flowing as the device is inactive (such as street lighting in the daytime).

Radio frequency can be used to detect electricity cables that have not been found by power detection, but its limitations can be geographical and it can also pick up other metal objects.

Radio frequency can be used to detect telecommunications cables of certain frequencies, but may not work on fibre optic cables.

A cable avoidance tool

The **transmitter and receiver** (inductive or conductive) mode is the most suitable when there is no current in the services being sought.

 Conventional cable locators will not find plastic pipes.

A **generator** (genny), when attached to an exposed part of a pipe or cable, will provide a signal for a CAT to track; it is important to continue to use the locator as the excavation progresses.

Metal detectors can detect hidden flat metal covers, joint boxes, and so on, but can miss cables or pipes. The deeper these objects are buried, the less chance of detection.

Ground penetrating radar is a portable transmitter that can sweep the area of land where there are thought to be underground services.

UNDERGROUND AND OVERHEAD SERVICES

The transmitter will display variations in the materials below the surface and can show where ground has been disturbed.

An operative properly trained in the use of radar equipment can detect the majority of underground services.

Whichever locating equipment you are using you must always compare your findings with existing plans to identify any differences between the supposed and actual locations.

Information on all cables and pipes detected should be recorded and passed to the principal designer for inclusion in the client's health and safety file.

Ensure that co-ordinates, lines and levels of newly installed services are included.

7.6   Dig – excavating

7.6.1   Permit to work and permit to dig

Where necessary, a formal permit to work system should be employed. A permit system will show the precautions that must be taken, what has been done and what is required. The permit to work also enables the person in charge to check that all the conditions have been met before work commences.

 Some sites operate a system where a copy of the permit to dig is held by the worker in an armband. This allows site management and supervisors to monitor that excavation work is being undertaken under a permit.

7.6.2   Digging methods

Depending upon the potential hazards, it may be necessary to use a permit to work system before commencing any digging. On some sites a specific permit to dig system is used prior to breaking the ground.

*Deep excavation with sheet piling (**Note:** black sleeving on white cable indicating repair to strike damage)*

Hand digging near live services

Trial holes should be dug by hand to establish the exact location and depth of the service; **never** assume the service runs in a direct line or at the same depth between two trial holes.

Do not use power tools or excavators within 500 mm of services. Hand digging must be adopted using insulated tools (such as spades or shovels). Excavate alongside the service rather than directly above it.

Final exposure of the service by horizontal digging is recommended, as the force applied to hand tools can be controlled more effectively.

Power tools can be used to break paved surfaces, but be careful to avoid over-penetration as services near buildings may be much closer to the surface than the recommended minimum depth.

Do not use power tools directly over an indicated line of a cable unless it has been made dead or actions have been taken to ensure safety and avoid damage.

Where excavations are supported with shuttering or trench boxes, the sides must be designed to accommodate any services that pass through the excavation.

Services may need to be supported in these surroundings.

 Never assume that a service is dead – always treat it as live until confirmed otherwise.

Checklist – prior to and during excavation

- Check with all utilities providers and landowners before starting work.

- Assume the presence of services when digging, even if nothing is shown on plans.

- Use detection devices and keep a close watch for signs of underground services (such as marker tape or tiles).

- Don't assume the services will be at the recommended minimum depths, they may be closer to the surface than normal, especially in the vicinity of works, structures or other services.

- Check that markers (such as plastic tape, tiles, slabs or battens) actually indicate the exact location of the underground service. Markers may have been displaced and will not necessarily be accurate.

- Some electric cables and water pipes look alike, as do some gas pipes and water pipes. Ensure each pipe is properly identified before starting work on them.

- Take additional care and use insulated spades and shovels when working near to services that can be easily damaged by a fork or a pick axe forced into the ground.

- Depending upon the risk assessment, those that are likely to encounter live services on a regular basis should wear flame resistant clothing, gloves and suitable eye protection for the task.

- Carefully lever out rocks, stones and boulders.

- Avoid over-penetration of the ground or surface with hand-held power tools as this is a common cause of accidents.

- If an excavator or digger has to be used near any service, the task will need to be specifically risk assessed to prevent accidental damage. Where possible, no-one should be near the digger bucket while it is digging.

- Ensure the excavator operator and others excavating are informed of the presence of suspected services.

- If the service is embedded in concrete or paving material, the owner may be able to de-energise it. Otherwise, make it safe or approve a safe system of work before it is broken out.

- Always assume closed, capped, sealed, loose or pot-ended services are live or charged, not dead or abandoned, until proved otherwise.

- Follow the guidelines and advice issued by the electricity, gas, water and telecommunication industries.

- Where possible, carry out the final exposure of underground services in a way that prevents any damage (such as using a vacuum excavator or compressed air lance).

07

 For further information refer to Chapter D06 Excavations.

7.6.3   Piling and drilling

A safe system of work must be devised and implemented before any piling or drilling takes place. If it is possible that there are services nearby, surveys should be carried out and their position must be exposed by hand digging first.

 For further information and guidance on recommended good practices and safety in piling operations, visit the Federation of Piling Specialists website.

7.6.4   Exposure and protection

If a service in a trench is exposed, protect it with wood or other suitable materials to prevent any damage to the service. Services crossing trenches need support to avoid stress. Seek advice from the relevant utility company, if necessary. **Never** use services crossing in a trench as footholds, anchorage or climbing points.

 For information on working adjacent to underground pipelines and the location of underground pipelines around the UK visit the Linewatch and Linesearch websites.

7.6.5   Backfilling

When backfilling a trench **do not** place hard core, surplus concrete, rock, rubble and flint onto a service pipe or cable, as it may damage it. **Do not** use wet spoil or any perishable materials for backfill. Use suitable material and ensure it is compacted with care to avoid shocking the service pipe or cable. Warning tape should then be placed approximately 300 mm above the service. If gas service pipes have been exposed, advice on backfilling should be obtained from the local gas company.

UNDERGROUND AND OVERHEAD SERVICES

7.6.6 Emergency works

Emergency works often mean there is no time to contact the utility companies. However, this work can be carried out safely if:

- the area is marked out carefully
- detectors are used correctly
- trial holes are dug by hand
- the practice of safe digging is followed.

7.6.7 Working in the roadway

Only licensed utility companies may carry out work in the footway, carriageway or any verge. When working in the roadway, ensure compliance with the New Roads and Street Works Act.

 For further information refer to Chapter F01 Street works and road works.

7.7 Damage to underground services

Damage to underground services **must** be reported to the owner and/or occupier immediately. When such damage causes an emergency situation, call the **police**, **fire** and/or **ambulance** services as necessary.

7.7.1 Gas

 In the event of a gas leak, suspected gas leak or any other emergency relating to gas, immediately phone the National Grid gas emergency service on 0800 111 999. This and all other emergency contact numbers and details should be readily accessible on site.

If a gas leak is suspected, contact the police, fire brigade and gas supply company immediately. If there is a dangerous situation and the emergency services have not arrived, try to evacuate the immediate area including, if necessary, the occupants of nearby properties to an upwind position.

As far as possible, prevent anyone from smoking and keep traffic clear of the area.

 If the gas escape catches fire, do not attempt to extinguish the flames.

The normal minimum depth of cover for gas mains operating in the low and medium pressure ranges is:

- 600 mm in footways or verges
- 750 mm in carriageways.

These figures may vary since each gas company can have its own standards for certain situations.

Where service pipes serve as connections from mains services that run from the road as a supply to a building, they may be shallower, especially when near to any property or structure.

7.7.2 Electricity

 In the event of an electrical emergency, phone the National Grid 24-hour electrical emergency service on 0800 404 090.

Avoid contact with any damaged cable or apparatus. If operating a machine, do not attempt to disentangle any equipment. If safe and if possible, jump clear of the machine, ensuring that contact is not made with the vehicle and ground at the same time.

Do not return to the machine. If this is not possible, stay exactly where you are. Shout for help. As far as possible, do not touch any metallic part of the vehicle, such as steel parts of the cab or door. If possible, inform the electricity company or ask someone else to. Keep people away.

The depth at which electricity cables or ducts are usually installed in the ground is decided by the need to avoid undue interference or damage. Depending on the type of cable and the power that it may be carrying, the depth of cover may vary from 450–900 mm.

However, existing services can be found at any depth. It is not uncommon for them to have as little as 50 mm cover. In all cases where the depth of cover is likely to increase or decrease, the service owner must be consulted.

7.7.3 Other services

Leave a damaged service well alone and inform the owner.

 Some cables are automatically re-energised by the local sub-station after a short time following the supply tripping out due to damage. Do not assume that a damaged cable will remain dead.

07

7.8   Overhead services

Every year people are killed or seriously injured when they come into contact with overhead electricity power lines. Incidents occur when working activities are not properly planned and result in contact with power lines (for example, contact with tipping trailers, cranes, scaffold tubes and ladders).

If there is contact with, or even if a piece of equipment gets too close to a power line, the electricity can be conducted to earth, which can cause fire, an explosion and shock or burns to anyone touching the machine or equipment. Overhead lines can be difficult to spot, particularly in foggy or dull conditions. Often, people just fail to look up.

Electricity supplies above 33,000 volts are usually routed overhead. Supplies below this voltage may be either overhead or underground. There is a legal minimum height above ground level for overhead power lines that varies according to voltage carried, shown below.

Voltage carried	400 kV	275 kV	132 kV	33 kV-low voltage
Legal minimum height above ground level	7.3 m	7.0 m	6.7 m	5.2 m. except for roads where the minimum is 5.8 m

 The law requires that work may only be carried out in close proximity to live overhead lines when there is no alternative, and only when the risks are acceptable and can be properly controlled.

Where work cannot be avoided, consult the local electricity company or distribution network operator (DNO) **before** any work is started; a safe system of work must be planned and implemented. Power lines should be isolated and made **dead** or suitable precautions taken to prevent danger before any work takes place. There may be other suppliers who have to be notified (such as Local Authorities, National Grid and other electricity companies). Where necessary, wait for the supplier to isolate or re-route the cable to enable the work to take place.

Take practical steps to prevent danger from any live cable or apparatus. This should include the placing of substantial and highly visible barriers. A barrier is only required one side if access is only possible from one side of the overhead power line (i.e. at the edge of the site), but if the line crosses the site, barriers will need to be placed on both sides. If there is a danger to people with scaffold poles or other conducting objects then the barriers should exclude people and mobile plant.

 Electricity travels at the speed of light – more than 186,000 miles per second. The people you are responsible for don't.

7.8.1   Working near but not underneath overhead lines and the use of barriers

Where there will be no work or passage of machinery or equipment under the power lines, ground level barriers can be erected to establish a **safety zone**. This area should not be used to store materials or machinery. Suitable barriers can be constructed out of large, steel drums filled with rubble, concrete blocks, wire fence, earthed at both ends, or earth banks marked with posts.

- If steel drums are used, highlight them by painting them with, for example, red and white horizontal stripes.

- Make sure the barriers can be seen at night, perhaps by using white or fluorescent paint or attaching reflective strips.

- The safety zone should extend at least 6 m horizontally from the nearest wire or apparatus on either side of the overhead line. You may need to increase this on the advice of the line owner, or to allow for the possibility of a jib or other moving part encroaching into the safety zone. The electricity supplier will give specific, on-site advice on the position of safety zones.

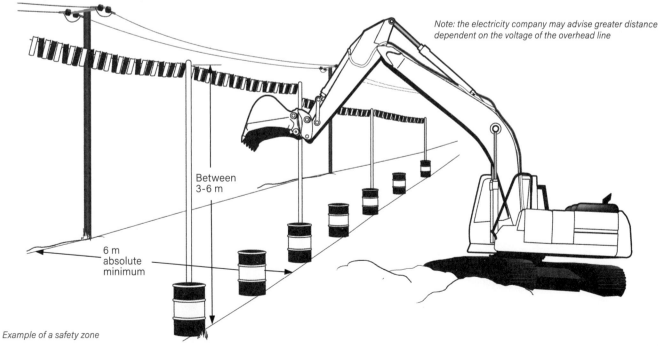

Note: the electricity company may advise greater distance dependent on the voltage of the overhead line

Between 3-6 m

6 m absolute minimum

Example of a safety zone

Where plant (such as a crane) is operating in the area, additional high-level indication should be erected to warn operators. A line of coloured, plastic flags or bunting, mounted 3-6 m above ground level over the barriers, is suitable.

Extreme caution must be exercised when erecting bunting and flags to avoid contact or arcing with the wires. The electricity supplier will give specific, on-site advice on the positioning of high level indicators.

 It must be assumed that all overhead lines and cables are live unless advised otherwise by the electricity company.

7.8.2   Safe working when passing underneath overhead lines

If equipment or machinery capable of breaching the safety zone has to pass underneath the overhead line, you will need to create a passageway through the barriers. In this situation you should ensure the following.

● The number of passageways is kept to a minimum.

● The route of the passageway is defined using fences, and goalposts are erected at each end to act as gateways using a rigid, non-conducting material (such as timber or plastic pipe) highlighted with, for example, red and white stripes.

● If a passageway is too wide to be spanned by a rigid, non-conducting goalpost, you may have to use tensioned steel wire, earthed at each end, or plastic ropes with bunting attached. These should be positioned further away from the overhead line to prevent them being stretched and the safety clearances being reduced by plant moving towards the line.

● The surface of the passageway is levelled, formed up and well maintained to prevent undue tilting or bouncing of the equipment.

● Warning notices are displayed at either side of the passageway, on or near the goalposts and on approaches to the crossing, giving the crossbar clearance height and instructing drivers to lower jibs, booms, tipper bodies, and so on, and to keep below this height while crossing.

● Notices and crossbars are illuminated at night or in poor weather, as required, to make sure they are visible.

● The barriers and goalposts are maintained.

Ensure arrangements have been made for the passage of tall plant at specific times where overhead power lines have been made dead.

 Working on or near live conductors

Regulation 14 of the Electricity at Work Regulations for work on or near live conductors states:

● no person shall be engaged in any work activity on or so near any live conductor (other than one suitably covered with insulating material so as to prevent danger) that danger may arise unless:

– it is unreasonable in all circumstances for it to be dead

– it is reasonable in all circumstances for a person to work on or near it while it is live

– suitable precautions (including where necessary the provision of suitable protective equipment) are taken to prevent injury.

7.8.3   Working underneath overhead lines

Exclusion zones should be set up around the line and any other equipment that may be fitted to the pole or pylon. If you cannot avoid transitory or short duration, ground-level work where there is a risk of contact from, for example, the upward movement of cranes or people carrying tools and equipment, you should carefully assess the risks and precautionary measures.

The minimum extent of these zones varies according to the voltage of the line, as follows.

● 1 m from low-voltage lines.

● 3 m from 11 kV and 33 kV lines.

● 6 m from 132 kV lines.

● 7 m from 275 kV and 400 kV lines.

 For detailed advice about the line voltage or use of exclusion zones you should always consult the owner of the overhead line.

● Arrange for the work to be directly supervised by someone who is familiar with the risks and can make sure that the required safety precautions are observed.

● Make sure that workers, including any contractors, understand the risks and are provided with instructions about the risk prevention measures.

● Poles and hand tools should not be able to encroach within these zones. Allow for uncertainty in measuring the distances and for the possibility of unexpected movement of the equipment due, for example, to wind conditions.

● Carry long objects horizontally and close to the ground and position vehicles so that no part can reach into the exclusion zone, even when fully extended. Machinery (such as cranes and excavators) should be modified by adding physical restraints to prevent them reaching into the exclusion zone.

- Insulating guards and/or proximity warning devices fitted to the plant without other safety precautions are not considered adequate protection on their own.

- Machinery (such as cranes and excavators) should be modified by adding physical restraints to prevent them reaching into the exclusion zone.

Work should not take place close to or under an overhead line during darkness or poor visibility conditions. Dazzle from portable or vehicle lighting can obscure rather than illuminate power lines.

 Electricity can kill. The correct information, instruction, training and supervision can help to keep workers, and others, alive.

 Worker receives fatal electric shock from overhead power line

A trainee scaffolder received a fatal electric shock whilst handling a 6.4 m long scaffold tube that came into contact with an 11,000 volt overhead power line. No site-specific risk assessment had been carried out, only generic ones at the office.

The company employing the worker was prosecuted under the Health and Safety at Work etc. Act, Section 2(1), and fined.

The company should have:

- closely supervised the trainee until he was able to demonstrate competence in a wide range of work situations

- undertaken a risk assessment for that site and informed all workers of the outcome

- taken action to reduce the risks from contact with overhead power lines (for example, requesting that the electricity distributor made the overhead power line dead during the work).

For further information refer to the HSE guidance note *Avoiding danger from overhead power lines* (GS6).

07

CONTENTS

Confined spaces

08

Supporting
INFORMATION

GT700 Toolbox talks / supporting checklists and forms

Toolbox talks on some of these topics are available in the GT700 publication. Supporting checklists and forms covering some of these topics are available on our companion website.

CONFINED SPACES

Overview

Every entry into a confined space is potentially hazardous. Accidents in confined spaces cause deaths at work, killing several people each year in a wide range of industries, including construction.

Some confined spaces are easy to identify (such as closed tanks, vessels and sewers). Others are less obvious but may be equally dangerous, including basement-level boiler rooms, toilets, lofts and attics, as well as open-topped tanks, vats, silos or other structures and excavations that become confined spaces during their construction, installation or manufacture.

8.1   Introduction

A confined space is a place which is both substantially or largely enclosed (though not always entirely), and where serious injury can occur from hazardous substances or conditions (such as lack of oxygen) within that space or nearby. It may be small and restrictive for the worker (like a loft space or inspection chamber) or it could be a far larger space (such as a basement or site storage silo with a capacity of hundreds of cubic metres).

Accidents in confined spaces are caused by a combination of factors arising from a lack of awareness, inadequate supervision and a lack of training. The situation is often made worse by heroic but ill-conceived rescue attempts, founded on insufficient planning and knowledge, which may lead to multiple fatalities. It is essential, therefore, to be able to identify confined spaces and the hazards associated with entering and working in them.

 A *confined space* is any place, including any chamber, tank, vat, silo, pit, trench, pipe, sewer, flue, well or other similar space in which, by virtue of its enclosed nature, there arises a reasonably foreseeable *specified risk*.

In every situation, the planning of the work must first consider what measures could be taken to enable the work to be carried out properly without the need to enter the confined space.

If entry to a confined space is required the work must be properly planned to avoid any of the following specified risks.

- Injury to any person arising from a fire or explosion.
- Loss of consciousness of any person at work arising from an increase in body temperature.
- Loss of consciousness or asphyxiation of any person at work arising from gas, fumes, vapour or the lack of oxygen.
- Drowning of any person at work arising from an increase in the level of liquid.
- Asphyxiation of any person at work arising from a free-flowing solid or the inability to reach a respirable environment due to entrapment by a free flowing solid.

Places not usually considered to be confined spaces may become confined spaces because of a change in the condition inside or a change in the degree of enclosure or confinement.

Application of the Confined Spaces Regulations in any of these places will depend on the presence of a reasonably foreseeable risk of serious injury from a hazardous substance or condition within the space or nearby.

Below are some examples of confined spaces that may be encountered during construction work.

- Cellars, small bathrooms or an inadequately ventilated basement room.
- Boilers, boiler flues or chimneys.
- Inspection chambers, sewers, drains, excavations or deep trenches.
- Ceiling voids or ducts.
- Caissons or cofferdams.
- Loft spaces or plant rooms.
- Any room or enclosed space with poor ventilation, as these can become a confined space (for example, paint spraying in a room or power floating in a large hanger using petrol-powered equipment).

There are many more examples of confined spaces and the hazards will vary with the location, the type of work being carried out and the equipment or substances used.

Care must be taken when entering a confined space

8.2   Important points

- Working in confined spaces has the potential to be hazardous unless the appropriate controls are put in place.

- Many people have died as a result of work in confined spaces not being adequately planned, organised or safely carried out; many of them were would-be rescuers.

- Confined spaces are not just sewers and ducts; under the regulations many other work areas could also be classified as confined spaces.

- Always consider options to carry out the work without anyone having to enter a confined space.

If working in a confined space cannot be avoided:

- A risk assessment must be carried out for all work in a confined space.

- Where the findings of the risk assessment reveal significant risks to health or safety, they should be recorded in a method statement and safe system of work and included in all briefings.

- Entry to a confined space should be controlled by a permit to work and, where considered necessary, a separate permit to enter.

- Any plan of the work must consider the method of communication from inside to outside, raising the alarm and safely rescuing the people in the confined space should the situation become unsafe.

- Any training may need to be specific for the type of confined space (for example, a sewer entry course may not be appropriate for someone who has to work in a hot roof space). Training should extend not only to those entering confined spaces but also to managers, supervisors and emergency personnel.

- Where possible, the confined space should be certified as safe to work in without the need for respiratory protective equipment (RPE). If the risk assessment identifies the need for RPE, it must be suitable for the hazards present and compatible with other personal protective equipment (PPE). (Wearing RPE and PPE can result in an increase in respiration and heat stress, and preventative measures may be required to reduce the risks of heat stress and dehydration.)

Unplanned or poorly planned work in confined spaces has the potential to kill – reading and understanding this chapter is not a substitute for adequate training and experience.

 Take great care identifying what is and what could be a confined space. Many confined space accidents occur in work areas that have simply not been identified as potential confined spaces.

8.3   Hazards in confined spaces

8.3.1   Oxygen deprivation and suffocation

The air that we breathe contains around 21% oxygen and, at that level, people can work without difficulty. A falling level of oxygen will create an increasingly serious situation if breathing apparatus is not worn. Generally, the symptoms referred to in the table *(below)* are experienced at the corresponding level of oxygen depletion.

Oxygen deprivation may be the result of any of the following.

- The displacement of oxygen by gas leaking in from elsewhere, or the deliberate introduction of purge gas (for example, nitrogen or argon).

- The displacement of oxygen by a naturally occurring gas (such as methane).

- Oxidisation, rusting or bacterial growth using up the oxygen in the air.

- Oxygen being consumed by people working and breathing, or by any process of combustion.

- Welding and other hot works.

- The discharge of a fire extinguisher containing carbon dioxide or other asphyxiating gas.

- Paint spraying or using chemicals for cleaning.

Oxygen depletion	Symptoms
19%	Tiredness (this is the normal acceptable minimum level for working).
17%	Judgement (decision making) is affected.
12%	Respiration is affected and fatigue experienced.
10%	Light-headedness and increasing breathing difficulties.
8%	Nausea and possible collapse.
6%	Respiration stops and death follows within minutes.

8.3.2   Hazards of excess oxygen

An oxygen-enriched atmosphere is a major hazard. Organic materials (such as oil and wood) become highly combustible, and ordinary materials (such as paper and clothing) will burn with exceptional ferocity.

An increase of only 4% oxygen is sufficient to create a hazard and this may occur inadvertently. In oxyacetylene and oxypropane processes, sometimes not all of the oxygen supplied to a cutting torch is consumed. Some may be released, increasing the atmospheric oxygen above the normal 21%.

CONFINED SPACES

 The oxygen enrichment of the atmosphere in a confined space also results from the practice of using oxygen to sweeten or enrich the atmosphere when it has become oppressive, stale, hot, fume-filled or otherwise unpleasant. This is a dangerous practice and must be prohibited.

Another way in which the atmosphere may become oxygen-enriched is through leakage from torches or hoses that may go unnoticed (such as during meal breaks or overnight). For this reason, they should be removed and properly isolated at each breaktime. The deliberate kinking or nipping of an oxygen hose while changing a torch does not cut off the supply completely and can result in the release of substantial quantities of oxygen.

If excess oxygen is discovered, the space must be quickly evacuated and ventilated until normal levels of oxygen are regained.

8.3.3   Toxic atmospheres

However much oxygen is present in the atmosphere, if there is also a toxic gas present in sufficient quantity it will create a hazard.

Below are some of the many toxic gases that may be encountered.

● Hydrogen sulphide, usually from sewage or decaying vegetation, which can smell like rotten eggs.

● Carbon monoxide, from internal combustion engines, or any incomplete combustion, especially of liquefied petroleum gases (LPG).

● Carbon dioxide, from any fermentation, or being naturally found in soil and rocks, or coming from the combustion of LPG.

● Fumes and vapours, from chemicals such as ammonia, chlorine, sodium, and from petrol and solvents.

Whenever a toxic gas (or any gas, fume or vapour that may be hazardous to health) is thought to be (or known to be) present, then an assessment of the risk to health must be made under the provisions of the **Control of Substances Hazardous to Health (COSHH) Regulations** and the appropriate control measures must be put into place to eliminate the hazard or control the risks.

Petrol and diesel engines create carbon monoxide, which is an extremely toxic gas.

Liquid petroleum gas-powered engines create an excess of carbon dioxide, which is a suffocating hazard.

The use of any form of internal combustion engine within a confined space must be prohibited, unless a specifically dedicated exhaust extraction system is in operation.

 Carbon dioxide and carbon monoxide are colourless, odourless and tasteless. Both can cause loss of consciousness and death in a very short time. Acute exposure to high concentrations of hydrogen sulphide can result in collapse (knockdown), respiratory paralysis, cyanosis, convulsions, coma, cardiac arrhythmias and death within minutes.

8.3.4   Flammable and explosive atmospheres

Some gases and vapours need only be present in small quantities to create a hazard. Examples of major sources of explosive and flammable hazards are shown below.

● Petrol or LPG, propane, butane and acetylene. These are explosive in the range of 2% upwards in air. The hazard is normally created by a spill or leak.

● Methane and hydrogen sulphide, which are naturally evolved from sewage or decaying organic matter. These are explosive in the range of 5-15% in air for methane and 4-44% in air for hydrogen sulphide.

● Solvents, acetone, toluene, white spirit, alcohol, benzene, thinners, and so on. These are explosive in the range of 2% upwards in air. The hazard generally results from process plants and/or spillage.

● Hydrogen and other gases that are created from processes such as battery charging.

In an explosive or flammable atmosphere, a toxic or suffocating hazard may also exist.

8.3.5   Hostile environments

Apart from the hazards dealt with above, other dangers may arise from the use of electrical and mechanical equipment, from chemicals, process gases and liquids, dust, paint fumes, welding and cutting fumes.

Extremes of heat and cold can have adverse effects and may be intensified in a confined space. Consideration must be given to the timing of what would otherwise be considered standard work. During hot weather, roof spaces and other types of confined spaces may reach temperatures that will lead to a dangerous increase in body temperature.

If work cannot be planned to avoid this (for example, by starting early) then physical measures (such as cooling and reducing the time spent working in the confined space) must be introduced following an assessment by a competent person.

 For further information and guidance on heat stress in the workplace, visit the HSE website.

Further dangers exist in the sheer difficulty of getting into or out of, and working in, a confined space. The potential hazards of an inrush of water, gas or sludge due to a failure of walls or barriers, or leakage from valves, flanges or blanks, must all be considered at the risk assessment stage.

8.4 Confined Spaces Regulations

These require employers to plan work so that entry to confined spaces is avoided so far as is reasonably practicable (for example, by doing the work from outside). They also require a safe system of work to be developed and implemented if entry to a confined space is unavoidable, and adequate emergency arrangements, which will also safeguard rescuers, to be put in place before work starts.

Duties to comply with the regulations are placed on:

● employers in respect of work carried out by their own employees and work carried out by any person (for example, a contractor) insofar as work is, to any extent, under the employer's control

● the self-employed in respect of work carried out by any other person insofar as work is, to any extent, under the control of the
self-employed person.

The main duty under Regulation 4 is a complete prohibition of any person entering a confined space to carry out any work for any purpose whatsoever, where it is reasonably practicable to carry out the work by any other means.

Depending upon the work activity, any space can become a confined space, including lofts, lifts or inspection pits, service risers and unventilated rooms, even if they are large spaces

If entry into a confined space is necessary then a risk assessment by a competent person, under the **Management of Health and Safety at Work Regulations**, is required. If your company does not have a competent person employed they must engage the services of a competent person from outside the company. The outcome of the risk assessment will then provide the basis for the development of a full and effective safe system of work, including rescue arrangements.

These regulations are supported and explained by an Approved Code of Practice (ACoP) and guidance notes. The competent person responsible for carrying out the risk assessment, or otherwise planning work in a confined space, should be familiar with all aspects of the regulations, including the ACoP and guidance material. If you follow the advice in the ACoP you will be doing enough to comply with the law in respect of those specific matters on which the Code gives advice.

 For the definition of *reasonably practicable* refer to Chapter A01 Health and safety law.

 The complete regulations and the ACoP and guidance notes, which includes a flowchart to help in the decision-making process, can be downloaded for free from the HSE website.

8.5 Information, instruction and training

The need for comprehensive training prior to any involvement in confined space working cannot be stressed too highly. The number of deaths in confined spaces in recent years is testimony to the extreme hazards that can be present in confined spaces.

The information, instruction and training given to employees must enable them to carry out work safely and without risks to their health. The extent of training needed will vary according to circumstances and the type of space being entered. Any entry into a confined space requiring the use of breathing apparatus would require a full breathing apparatus and rescue training course.

However, training to enter a bund around a large diesel tank where the risks are less significant (such as fumes and possible drowning in diesel) would not require such an intensive course, and indeed adopting the use of breathing apparatus in this instance may be entirely inappropriate. Training should involve demonstrations and practical exercises. It is important that trainees are familiar with both equipment and procedures before working for the first time in confined spaces.

Practical refresher training should be organised and available. The frequency with which refresher training is provided will depend upon the length of time since the type of work was last carried out, or if there have been changes to methods of work, safety procedures or equipment.

The training needs for confined space working should be considered for each of the four categories of employee.

● Supervisors.

● Employees entering confined spaces.

● People employed as attendants outside of confined spaces.

● Rescue teams.

CONFINED SPACES

Some of the roles identified may be carried out by the same person.

There is currently no legal requirement to have obtained a specific standard of training prior to working in a confined space. However, there has been discussion between the utility companies, who are the clients for much of the sewer-entry work, with regard to recognising each other's training standards.

 No person should enter a confined space unless they are trained and competent to do so safely.

 Tunnelling offers more specific challenges. For the latest updates on training standards visit the Pipe Jacking Association and the British Tunnelling Society websites.

8.6 Safe working

If you cannot avoid entry into a confined space a safe system of work must be implemented. This can be achieved by the use of a permit to work system, in which each step is planned and all foreseeable hazards are taken into account. Such a system, backed up by adequate rescue facilities, should enable work to be carried out safely.

At the planning stage it will be necessary for the following information to be determined.

● Whether an entry into the confined space is required, or whether there is an alternative method of doing the work.

● If an entry is necessary, whether it can be carried out without the use of breathing apparatus.

● Whether the entry must be made with the use of breathing apparatus.

It should be emphasised that entry into a confined space using breathing apparatus should not be made routinely or undertaken as a matter of convenience, where the use of isolation and mechanical or forced ventilation would achieve a safe atmosphere.

If it is decided that the work can be done without anyone entering the confined space, provided that a safe system of work exists and the confined space has been isolated from potential sources of hazard, the work can proceed.

It is important to avoid systems or plant being re-energised while work is proceeding and everyone involved should be advised accordingly.

Once it has been decided that people must enter a confined space, a preliminary meeting should be held with all concerned, and effective lines of authority and communication established to minimise any risk of subsequent misunderstanding.

The exact routine to be followed will vary, depending on the type of confined space to be entered. The provisions and precautions required for entry into a large, empty surface water tank will obviously be different from those needed for entry into a narrow service duct containing pipes and valves, but the fundamental principle of a safe system of work applies to all cases.

The risk assessment, as mentioned previously, will have identified many of the above points and should be used as the basis for developing the safe system of work.

It is stressed that all PPE in general, and RPE in particular, must have been specified by a competent person who fully understands the circumstances surrounding its use, and that the persons wearing it are trained and competent in its use.

Employers must put in place adequate emergency arrangements before the work starts. No person must enter a confined space until suitable and sufficient procedures are in place to facilitate a rescue in the event of an emergency. Reliance on the emergency services alone will not be sufficient to comply with the regulations.

If the fire and rescue service forms a part of the rescue plan, they must be given a warning that a confined space entry is to be made. This will give them the opportunity to assess the risks to their own staff and identify any equipment they might need.

8.6.1 Supervision

The level of supervision will be determined by the findings of the risk assessment. In most cases the level of risk will require the presence of a competent person to supervise the activities and remain present from start to finish. Supervisors should be given responsibility to ensure that the necessary precautions are taken to check safety at each stage.

8.6.2 Isolation

The confined space must be isolated from all possible external sources of danger to persons entering it. It is good practice to use **positive isolations** for confined space entries – this means complete separation of the plant or equipment to be worked on from other parts of the system. If complete isolation is not possible, an approved system must be in place to ensure an alternative isolation is effective and remains so.

A full permit to work system should be used to record the location and types of isolation, and the hazards being guarded against.

Electrical isolation must never rely on a switch or fuse. The switch gear or fuse holder must be locked off and a warning notice applied *(for further information refer to 8.6.15 Permits)*.

Mechanical isolation of pipework should not rely on a single valve or on a non-return valve; these may leak and create a hazard. Whenever possible, a section of pipe should be removed or a blank or spade should be put into a flange between the valve and the confined space and a warning notice displayed.

Isolation from mechanical and electrical equipment will often include locking off the switch and formally securing the key in accordance with a permit to work, until it is no longer necessary to control access. Lock-and-tag systems can be useful here, where each operator has their own lock and key giving self-assurance of the inactivated mechanism or system. Check there is no stored energy of any kind left in the system that could activate the equipment inadvertently.

Paddles, stirrers or agitators, whether electrically or mechanically operated, should be physically disconnected by the removal of an operating arm, and a warning notice displayed.

8.6.3 Cleaning

There is a variety of methods of cleaning the inside of confined spaces to remove hazardous solids, liquids or gases. Cold water washing, hot water washing and steaming will remove many contaminants, while solvents or neutralising agents may be necessary for others. If hot water or steam is used, with or without a solvent, care must be taken to ensure that adequate ventilation exists for steam pressure and that condensation does not build up to unacceptable levels.

If steam is used or water is boiled in a confined space, account must be taken of the vacuum that can be created on cooling. When steam or solvents are used, these may create a toxic, suffocating or flammable hazard. Even though a space has been well cleaned, it must not be entered until the atmosphere has been tested and is confirmed to be safe. Great care must be taken if encountering any sludge or heavy deposits that may release toxic gases if disturbed.

8.6.4 Purging and ventilation

Air purging and ventilation can be carried out by removing covers, opening inspection doors, or similar, and allowing ordinary air circulation, or by the introduction of compressed air via an air line. However, higher rates of air exchange can be achieved by the use of air movers, induction fans or extractor fans.

It is especially important that when an inert gas (such as nitrogen) has been used to purge or render inert a flammable atmosphere, the inert gas itself is properly purged with air. When air purging is taking place, the flow of air should be of a sufficient volume and velocity to ensure that no pockets or layers of gas remain undisturbed. This also needs to be constantly monitored.

8.6.5 Atmospheric monitoring

Depending on the circumstances, as a result of the assessment made under the COSHH Regulations, or the risk assessment made under the Management of Health and Safety at Work Regulations, continuous atmospheric monitoring may well be necessary when any work is to be done that would expose employees to any substance hazardous to health.

Before an entry is made into such a confined space, tests must be carried out to establish the levels of oxygen, toxic gas or flammable gas in the atmosphere.

The external atmosphere around the opening should be monitored first and, if the results are satisfactory, internal monitoring should be carried out by extending or lowering a gas monitor into the confined space before it is occupied. This may be necessary at different levels or points, depending on the size, height or depth of the space.

Atmospheric testing prior to entry

If entry into the confined space is necessary to carry out the tests, breathing apparatus or other RPE must be worn.

Suitably trained and competent personnel may use simple, reliable instruments to measure oxygen and flammable gas levels.

 The accuracy of the instruments must be assured by periodic calibration.

A satisfactory oxygen content must not in itself be relied on to indicate safety since flammable, explosive or toxic gas may exist alongside oxygen and need only be present in minute quantities to create a serious hazard.

The tests applied should take account of what the space is known to have contained, including any inert gas used to purge a flammable atmosphere, which may itself produce toxic hazards or the risk of asphyxiation. Account must also be taken of hazards arising from other sources (such as materials used for cleaning). Methane, hydrogen sulphide and carbon dioxide can all evolve naturally due to the decomposition of organic matter or, in some cases, by the effect of rainwater percolating through certain types of ground. It is necessary to test the atmosphere of a confined space at both high and low level as well as in any corners where pockets of gas may exist.

 Instances have occurred of carbon dioxide displacing oxygen at lower levels while a normal oxygen level continues to exist at higher levels of the same confined space.

The sense of smell must never be relied upon to detect gases. Some are odourless, and hydrogen sulphide, in particular, can paralyse the sense of smell to such an extent that even fatally high concentrations of the gas cannot be detected. The sense of smell varies from person to person and deteriorates with age.

8.6.6 Monitoring and testing equipment

Providing that the specific contaminant is known, tests can be carried out by competent persons using the individual detector tubes available for the detection of specific toxic and asphyxiant, flammable or explosive fumes or gases.

The tubes have a wide range of tolerance, so readings close to an occupational exposure limit should not be acted upon until the test has been repeated and the manufacturer's standard of accuracy applied.

A wide range of portable gas detection equipment is available for flammable and toxic gases; some are specific to one gas (for example, hydrogen sulphide), while others can sample a range of different gases. Such instruments need to be properly calibrated.

8.6.6.1 Continuous monitoring

Close-up of a monitor   *A monitor with individual detector tubes*

The initial monitoring and testing must establish that the confined space is safe to enter. Monitoring should then be carried out at intervals to ensure the continued safety of personnel. Tests should be repeated after any breaks (such as lunch or overnight) or after the time limit set out in a permit to work has expired.

It may be necessary to issue individual monitors to people working in a confined space to give them an instant warning of low oxygen, or toxic or flammable gas hazards.

8.6.6.2 Competence of monitors

All atmospheric monitoring must be carried out by persons who are trained and competent to use the instruments and interpret the results. They must have sufficient practical and theoretical knowledge to enable them to make a valid judgement based on the results. They must be fully aware of their responsibilities in permitting entry into a confined space.

8.6.7 Selection of personnel

Care is required in selecting the right people to work in confined spaces, since conditions can be difficult. They must be physically fit, agile and, most importantly, not be claustrophobic (fear of confined spaces). People who suffer from asthma, bronchitis or other respiratory conditions, or whose immune system has been suppressed, must be assessed by a medical practitioner as to their suitability to work in confined spaces.

Other health conditions that might indicate that a person is not suitable for working in a confined space, or that further checks need to be made before it is allowed, are listed below.

- High blood pressure.
- Partial or complete deafness.
- Lack of mobility through joint problems.
- Diabetes.

- Stress, depression or other mental ill health.
- Defective eyesight (which is not corrected by wearing glasses).
- Sensitivity of the skin to some substances.
- Taking some types of medication.

Stamina is also required. The wearing of any form of respiratory protection tends to lead to an increase in respiration and a higher use of energy; the amount of work that can be done in confined spaces is less than that expected under normal conditions.

When respiratory protection is to be used, it should be remembered that facial hair and spectacles often prevent a respirator from fitting properly and thus achieving the assumed degree of protection. Face-fit testing must be carried out to ensure that the chosen mask fits the wearer. As people come in all sorts of shapes and sizes, it is unlikely that one particular type or size of RPE face-piece will fit everyone.

Fit testing of individuals will ensure that the equipment selected is suitable for the wearer. This can be achieved quantitatively using a 'portacount' for half or full face masks or qualitatively using bitter/sweet solutions for half or disposable masks.

 For more detail information on fit testing RPE, go to the HSE website to read or download their publication *Guidance on respiratory protective equipment (RPE) fit testing* INDG479.

8.6.8 Communications

Adequate and effective communications must exist between those inside and those outside of the confined space, so that, in the event of an incident, a warning can be given and the space safely evacuated or those inside safely rescued. The system needs to be fail-safe, ensuring that, if a reply is not received or a scheduled call not made, the procedure for rescue starts immediately.

When a confined space is relatively small, so that the person entering it cannot move far from the entry point and there are no other factors that could hinder effective communication, the method of communication may be relatively simple (such as a prearranged system of tugs on the safety rope, which must be fully understood by all involved). However, if the nature of the confined space, the job to be carried out and other factors necessitate the person travelling some distance from the entry point, a more elaborate communication system might be required.

The following factors could hinder effective communication and may need to be considered in the risk assessment.

● Level of noise inside or outside of the confined space, which may or may not be associated with the confined space work.

● Physical nature of the confined space or the presence of substances that could reduce visibility.

● Distance between the point of entry and the place of work.

● Presence of workers with little or no understanding of English.

Depending upon the findings of the risk assessment, prior communication with the emergency services regarding the location and nature of the work might be considered necessary. This will allow the emergency services to comment on the rescue plan and also prepare for any eventuality. All types of respiratory protection affect verbal communication to some degree and, whatever method of communication is chosen, it should be tested and proved outside the confined space before entry is made.

8.6.9 Work equipment

Due to the potential for a flammable or explosive atmosphere in confined spaces, selecting tools and other work equipment with which the work can be carried out safely is essential.

If there is any possibility of flammable gas existing in a confined space, even below the lower explosive limit (LEL), all tools must be of a non-sparking material (for example, non-ferrous materials such as brass, bronze or copper-aluminum alloys – these softer materials greatly reduce the risk of producing ignitable sparks) and all lighting and electrical equipment should be extra low voltage (less than 25V) and must carry British Approvals Service for Electrical Equipment in Flammable Atmospheres (BASEEFA) approval.

Smoking and naked lights must be strictly prohibited, and care must be taken to avoid the generation of static electricity with the consequent risk of sparks.

8.6.10 Fire safety

Hot works must not be carried out in a confined space unless atmospheric testing has confirmed that flammable or explosive gases are not present and the findings of a risk assessment show that it is safe to do so.

Where there is still a residual risk of fire, appropriate fire extinguishers may need to be kept in the confined space at the entry point. Operatives must be suitably trained in the selection and use of appropriate fire extinguishers.

Where hot works are being carried out inside a confined space, the operative carrying out the work must also have a suitable and serviceable fire extinguisher at the place of work. In the event of a fire, the local fire service should be called in case the fire cannot be contained or extinguished.

8.6.11 First aid

Appropriate first-aid equipment and suitably trained first aiders should be provided and available for emergencies and to provide first aid until professional medical help arrives. First-aid training should cover incidents that may occur as a result of the hazards present in the confined space.

8.6.12 Rescue

The arrangements for the rescue of persons in the event of an emergency, both in terms of trained persons and equipment, need to be carefully planned and practised. The rescue plan must be able to be implemented swiftly in an emergency and understood by all involved. The arrangements must be in place and all equipment checked before any person enters or works in a confined space.

In some circumstances (for example, where there are prolonged operations in confined spaces and the risks justify it) there may be advantage in prior notification to the local emergency services (for example, local fire or ambulance service) before the work is undertaken.

However, reliance on the emergency services alone will not be sufficient to comply with the regulations. Employers must put in place adequate emergency arrangements before the work starts. Proper and effective rescue training is quite hard and arduous, and is not to be undertaken lightly. Persons selected for such training need to be physically fit and able to adapt to situations as they arise during a rescue.

 Injury and collapse

If a person is **injured** in a confined space that has been certified safe to enter without respiratory protection, an entry can be made to rescue and remove them straight away.

If a person **collapses** in a confined space and the cause is not known, irrespective of whether or not the confined space was certified fit for entry without respiratory protection, no-one must enter unless they are wearing breathing apparatus. The collapse may have been due to deterioration in the atmosphere within the confined space. The first duty of any rescuer is to ensure that they do not become a casualty themselves.

CONFINED SPACES

Each year, would-be rescuers who are insufficiently trained or equipped die by going into confined spaces where a person has collapsed.

This point is illustrated in the following two case studies.

 Open-topped inspection shaft fatalities

At Carsington Reservoir, four men, all aged between 20 and 30 and physically fit, died in an open-topped inspection shaft. Naturally evolved carbon dioxide had displaced the oxygen. No tests were made before entry. The first man down collapsed and the three other men climbed down to their deaths in futile attempts to rescue him.

An HM Inspector of Factories working in the Public Utilities National Industry Group of the Health and Safety Executive (HSE) wrote about this major accident and stressed: 'It should be manifestly obvious that confined spaces working is one activity where shortcuts in safety cannot be permitted. The deaths of these four men will be more tragic if the lessons of this incident are not fully learnt'.

 Fatalities in a sewer

When an engineer collapsed in a sewer, a rescuer entered without breathing apparatus and was overcome. A second person made a similarly vain attempt to reach the victims. When the rescue team from the fire and rescue service arrived they had to remove the bodies of the two would-be rescuers before they could get to the engineer. By then it was too late and he had died. Had everyone waited for the fire and rescue service, the engineer might have lived and the rescuers would not have needlessly died.

8.6.13 Rescue equipment

Every person entering a confined space wearing breathing apparatus must also wear a rescue safety harness. The harness must be attached to a lifeline, attended by a person outside the confined space.

The harness must be one that is suitable for confined space rescue, in that it must enable an unconscious person to remain in an upright position whilst being hoisted.

An unsuitable harness will allow the unconscious person to bend at the waist, making recovery through a narrow opening difficult or impossible.

This equipment forms part of a safe system of work for any entry into a confined space. Properly used, it may enable a rescue to be carried out successfully without the need for a rescuer to enter the confined space.

Rescue equipment must include some means of lifting or pulling a person up from a confined space, since it is virtually impossible for the average person to achieve this solely by muscular effort. There are a variety of tripods, winches, blocks and tackles which, when used in conjunction with a safety harness, enable a person to be lifted quickly and safely out of a confined space.

If any lifting equipment or accessories are to be used, then the equipment and accessories will be subject to the Lifting Operations and Lifting Equipment Regulations (LOLER). This would mean testing and inspection in accordance with the schedule drawn up by the competent person.

In practice, harnesses, lines and accessories (such as carabiners) should be subjected to a formal, thorough examination by a competent person every six months and be checked by the user weekly and before each use. Tripods, hoists and other lifting devices need to be load tested every six months, as part of the thorough examination, in the same way that a scissor lift used for lifting people would.

Dependent on circumstances, rescue equipment may have to include first-aid equipment, oxygen or resuscitation packs and rescue breathing apparatus. A secure line of communication to the emergency services may also be required.

8.6.14 Respiratory protective equipment

RPE is provided in addition to engineering controls and safe systems of work. If it is identified in the risk assessment that RPE is required, the RPE must be selected by a competent person, be CE marked and be suitable for the type of hazard against which it is to protect the wearer.

A wide range of RPE is available from various manufacturers and PPE suppliers. There are two main types of RPE for use in confined spaces work, which are outlined below.

8.6.14.1 Respirators – Purifying the air breathed

The air inhaled is drawn through a filter or medium that removes the harmful substance or pollutant. The nature of the filtering agent depends on the type of pollutant to be dealt with. These types are commonly called *respirators*.

The simplest form of respirator is the dust mask, a preformed cup made of filtering material that fits over the nose and mouth to filter out nuisance dust. These masks give no protection against harmful or toxic gases or fumes and the protection factor of the mask may not offer adequate protection against the level of airborne dust that can be experienced in a confined space.

More complex types have filter cartridges that may be suitable for various types of dust or fume, or are specific to a particular substance.

8.6.14.2 Breathing apparatus – Supplying clean air

The air can be supplied straight through an air line via a pump or compressor or, alternatively, the person may carry compressed air in cylinders. These types are known as *breathing apparatus*.

An alternative type of breathing equipment is the escape breathing apparatus or self-rescue set. These can consist of a small, compressed air bottle, the necessary hoses and valves and a facepiece. Self-rescue sets can be carried by operatives who enter confined spaces where the air is initially safe to breathe.

Should the air quality deteriorate, the facepiece is placed over the nose and mouth and the air valve opened. The air bottle supplies fresh air to the operative whilst an escape from the confined space is made. The air bottle of a self-rescue set has a duration of typically 15-20 minutes.

Other devices can supply oxygen via a chemical reaction. Some types can provide up to 60 minutes of rescue oxygen.

Rescue training with dead weight rescue dummy and rescue sets

 Care must be taken to select the correct type of protection for the conditions. Respirators (as opposed to breathing apparatus) do not protect against oxygen-deficient atmospheres and should not be used in any atmosphere dangerous to life.

RPE should not be used unless all other methods of control or protection have been examined and it is established that the use of RPE is the only reasonably practicable solution.

www **The HSE publication *Respiratory protective equipment at work – A practical guide* (HSG53) sets out the nominal protection factor for each type of respirator and describes their limitations; it should be carefully consulted in cases of doubt.**

Respirators can only be used for protection against the gases or dusts for which they are specifically intended. It is important to note that all forms of RPE will have a limited period of usage before becoming saturated with the contaminant. They may also have a limited shelf life, indicated by a use-by date.

8.6.15 Permits

8.6.15.1 Permit to work

A permit to work ensures a formal check is undertaken to make sure all the elements of a safe system of work are in place before people are allowed to enter or work in the confined space.

It is also a means of communication between site management, supervisors and those carrying out the hazardous work.

Entries into a confined space can be made under a permit to work, whereby a competent person must be satisfied that all necessary precautions have been taken and provisions made to secure the safety of those entering the confined space, before signing the permit to work. The signed permit thus gives an assurance that work may safely take place.

Permits should only be issued by named, authorised persons, who must sign them. Such persons must be competent, have authority and possess sufficient practical and theoretical knowledge and actual experience of working conditions to enable them to judge whether everything necessary has been done to ensure the safety of personnel.

It is quite common for several authorised persons to sign a permit to work, each certifying that they have taken the necessary actions with regard to their own area of responsibility (for example, electrical isolation and atmospheric testing).

Where a permit to work system involves the use of padlocks and keys (for example, for locking-off electrical isolators or other sources of energy) the keys must stay with authorised persons until such time as the permit is returned for cancellation, either when the task is completed or when any time limits stated on the permit have been reached (such as at the end of a shift).

Essential features of a permit to work are listed below.

- Clear identification of who may authorise particular jobs (and any limits to their authority) and who is responsible for specifying the necessary precautions (for example, isolation, air testing and emergency arrangements).

- Making sure that contractors engaged to carry out work are included.

- Training and instruction in the issue of permits.

- Monitoring and auditing to make sure that the permit to work system works as intended.

08

127

8.6.15.2 Permit to enter

Depending upon the nature of the confined space and the inherent risks of carrying out the work, some companies may choose to run a separate permit to enter system. An example of when such a system might be used is where all preparatory work is carried out to meet the requirements of the permit to work and then the permit to enter is issued when final pre-entry checks of the atmosphere have been carried out.

Such a system would cover situations where a single permit to work covers the duration of the whole job, but successive shifts of workers are each authorised to enter the confined space under a newly raised permit to enter.

8.6.15.3 Access and egress

A safe way in and out of the confined space should be provided and, wherever possible, allow quick, unobstructed and ready access (such as a fixed, vertical ladder inside an underground chamber that terminates just below the entry/exit point at ground level).

The means of escape must be suitable for use by the number of individuals who enter the confined space so that, ideally, they can quickly escape in an emergency. However, it must be accepted that in many cases the entry/exit point will be of a restricted size that will not necessarily allow an easy escape route in an emergency, particularly if the person who is escaping is wearing a compressed air cylinder. The means of achieving a prompt escape or rescue must be considered in the risk assessment.

Suitable means to prevent access (for example, a locked hatch) should also be in place when there is no need for access to the confined space. There should be a safety sign that is clear and conspicuous to prohibit unauthorised entry alongside openings that allow for safe access.

8.6.16   Conclusion

For work to be done safely in a confined space, great care has to be taken over the detail of each step of the procedure. Common causes of accidents are shown below.

- Failing to identify work areas as confined spaces.
- Failing to identify activities or processes that can affect the atmosphere of a safe area, resulting in it becoming an unplanned confined space.
- Inadequate risk assessments.
- Poorly trained and equipped workers.
- Failing to put in place adequate emergency arrangements before work starts.
- Failing to set up a safe system of work, including continuous air monitoring, based around a permit to work system.

- Failing to carry out an initial check of air quality.
- Failing to follow an established safe system of work.
- Deviations in conditions rendering the risk assessment or safe system invalid.
- Incorrectly using RPE.
- Using the wrong type of RPE.
- Failing to use safety harnesses and lifelines.
- Ill-conceived and badly executed rescue attempts.

All such accidents are avoidable. If an accident does occur, it demonstrates that a breakdown has occurred in the supposed safe system of work.

8.7   Legislative requirements

In addition to the **Confined Spaces Regulations** and the **Management of Health and Safety at Work Regulations** the following legislation may also apply.

8.7.1   Construction (Design and Management) Regulations 2015

These regulations place a legal duty on designers, when preparing designs, to design out risk, so far as it is reasonably practicable.

In the context of this chapter, designers should carry out their design work so that no-one has to enter a confined space during construction work, maintenance or cleaning of the structure or during its demolition.

The regulations place a duty on the designer, when preparing their designs, to consider the users of any finished structure that will be a workplace.

Also, within the context of this chapter, these regulations place legal duties on contractors and principal contractors, where applicable, with regard to the following.

- Safe places of work.
- Cofferdams and caissons.
- Excavations.
- Prevention of drowning.

- Prevention of risk from fire, explosion, flooding and asphyxiation.
- Emergency procedures.
- Fresh air.

 For further information refer to Chapter A03 Construction (Design and Management) Regulations.

8.7.2 Provision and Use of Work Equipment Regulations

These regulations require that an employer only supplies work equipment that is correct and suitable for the task and work environment. PUWER require that the equipment is inspected, maintained and kept in good working order. Where the use of the equipment involves a specific risk to the health and safety of employees, the use of the equipment must be restricted to specified trained and authorised workers.

8.7.3 Personal Protective Equipment at Work Regulations

These regulations require that, where a risk has been identified by a risk assessment and it cannot be adequately controlled by other means, which are equally or more effective, then the employer must provide and ensure that suitable PPE is used by employees.

In essence, PPE may only be used as a last resort after all other means of eliminating or controlling the risk have been considered and are found to be not reasonably practicable to implement. In practice, however, unless it is possible to carry out the work without entry into the confined space, the wearing of PPE will usually be necessary.

In deciding which type to issue, the employer must take into account the risk that the PPE is being used to protect against, and ensure that the PPE will fit the wearer and allow them to work safely. Where the use of RPE is necessary, face-fit testing to establish the suitability of the RPE for the wearer is required. If more than one item of PPE is being used, the employer must make sure that individual items of PPE are compatible and suitable for the task that is to be undertaken.

Whenever PPE is to be issued, the employer must ensure that employees have been given adequate and appropriate information, instruction and training to enable them to understand the risks being protected against, the purpose of the PPE and the manner in which it is to be used.

Whilst the employer must ensure that PPE is supplied and used, the employee has a duty to properly use the equipment provided, follow the information, instruction and training that they have been given, and know the procedures for reporting losses or defects to their employer. In the context of this chapter, in addition to the more commonly used PPE, confined space working will often require the use of appropriate RPE and rescue equipment (such as a safety harness and line).

 For further information on the Personal Protective Equipment at Work Regulations refer to Chapter B06 Personal protective equipment.

8.7.4 Lifting Operations and Lifting Equipment Regulations

Access to and egress from many confined spaces is made by lowering or raising a person vertically through the entry or exit point, including during practice or actual rescues. In these circumstances:

- safety harnesses and rescue lines must be regarded as lifting accessories
- the tripod hoist or other type of winch must be regarded as lifting equipment used for lifting persons and, as such, requires thorough examination on a six monthly basis under LOLER.

However, if the rescue involves a sideways or inclined drag (for example, along a duct) then there would be no lifting and LOLER would not apply, although the Provision and Use of Work Equipment Regulations (PUWER) would.

 For further information on LOLER refer to Chapter C07 Lifting operations.

8.7.5 Other legislation

The following legislation can also have an impact upon how work in confined spaces is planned, organised and carried out.

- Health and Safety (First Aid) Regulations *(refer to Chapter B05 First aid)*.
- Control of Substances Hazardous to Health Regulations *(refer to Chapter B07 Control of substances hazardous to health)*.
- Work at Height Regulations *(refer to Chapter D01 Work at Height Regulations)*.
- Dangerous Substances and Explosive Atmospheres Regulations *(refer to Chapter D09 Dangerous substances)*.
- Regulatory Reform (Fire Safety) Order (RRFSO) (England and Wales only) *(refer to Chapter C02 Fire prevention and control)*.

08

CONFINED SPACES

CONTENTS

Dangerous substances

Supporting
INFORMATION

GT700 Toolbox talks / supporting checklists and forms

Toolbox talks on some of these topics are available in the GT700 publication. Supporting checklists and forms covering some of these topics are available on our companion website.

DANGEROUS SUBSTANCES

Overview

Dangerous substances are widely used on construction sites. The main hazards are fire and explosion, and everything possible must be done to lessen the risks.

Safety is divided into three main areas: the storage of substances, the safe handling and transport of substances and the uses to which substances are put.

9.1   Introduction

This chapter does not cover the storage of explosives, which may be used in the demolition and civil engineering sectors. There are specific requirements under the **Explosive Regulations**. The regulations are supported by guidance which is available from the Health and Safety Executive (HSE).

In most cases, the HSE enforces fire safety legislation on construction sites, under the Construction (Design and Management) Regulations 2015 (CDM) and the Management of Health and Safety at Work Regulations, although they also have enforcement powers under the Regulatory Reform (Fire Safety) Order or in Scotland under the Fire (Scotland) Act. In Scotland requirements on general fire safety are covered in Part 3 of the Fire (Scotland) Act. The Fire Safety Regulations (Northern Ireland) apply in Northern Ireland.

Local Authority environmental health officers are likely to have a similar role where the work is carried out on a construction project in a premises that they enforce.

The local fire and rescue service (FRS) has responsibilities for the enforcement of fire safety in some circumstances.

 Dangerous substances and explosive atmospheres

Dangerous substances. Any substance or mixture of substances that can put people's health or safety at risk from fire and explosion.

Explosive atmospheres. Any substance or mixture of air and one or more hazardous substances in the form of a gas, vapour, mist or dust, which will explode after ignition has occurred.

9.2   Important points

- A risk assessment must be carried out before dangerous substances are stored, transported or used. In some cases, a method statement and/or a permit to work will also be required.

- Important pieces of legislation relating to this chapter are the:
  - Dangerous Substances and Explosive Atmospheres Regulations (DSEAR)
  - CDM
  - Regulatory Reform (Fire Safety) Order (England and Wales only)
  - Fire (Scotland) Act
  - Fire Safety (Employees' Capabilities) (England) Regulations
  - Fire Safety Regulations (Northern Ireland) 2010
  - Carriage of Dangerous Goods and Use of Transportable Pressure Equipment Regulations (CDG).

- DSEAR covers the flammable or explosive properties of dangerous substances used in the workplace.

- There may also be health issues that are covered by the Control of Substances Hazardous to Health (COSHH) Regulations.

- Fire safety legislation will be enforced by the HSE or the local FRS, generally depending upon the location where dangerous substances are stored and used.

- People who use dangerous substances must be fully aware of their hazardous properties, adopt methods of controlling the risks and be trained in the selection and use of portable fire extinguishers.

- Electrical apparatus and naked flames should not be used near flammable or explosive dangerous substances, particularly if they are being sprayed.

Uncontrolled use or storage of explosive materials can have fatal consequences

- Good ventilation is essential wherever flammable or explosive dangerous substances are used or stored.

- Non-smoking policies and waste disposal policies must be established and diligently monitored.

- Liquefied petroleum gas (LPG) cylinders are fitted with a spring loaded safety relief valve that will lift and vent gas into the atmosphere if the internal gas (head) pressure valve reaches 26 bar.

 Start by identifying dangerous substances on site and quantities. Use the material safety data sheets and labels to identify these hazards. Also consider processes that may generate dangerous forms of substances.

9.3 Dangerous Substances and Explosive Atmospheres Regulations (2002)

9.3.1 Principles of the regulations

The Dangerous Substances and Explosive Atmospheres Regulations (DSEAR) (2002) require employers to control the risks to safety from fire and explosions.

The regulations apply at all places of work where a dangerous substance is present (or is liable to be present) or if the dangerous substance could be a risk to the safety of people as a result of fires, explosions or similar energetic events.

Dangerous substances are:

- a substance or mixture of substances that is classified as explosive, oxidising, extremely flammable, highly flammable or flammable

- any dust, whether in the form of solid particles or fibrous materials, which can form an explosive mixture in air.

In the construction industry, many dangerous substances are used, or created by work. Some examples are shown below.

- The storage and use of solvents, adhesives and paints.

- The storage and use of flammable gases (such as oxygen and acetylene) during cutting and welding.

- The storage and use of LPG for work processes, heating or cooking.

- The creation of large quantities of airborne dust (for example, as a result of wood-machining or sanding) and the handling and storage of bulk waste dust.

- The storage and decanting of vehicle fuels and lubricants.

- The storage and handling of liquid flammable wastes (such as fuel oils).

- Many tasks that involve hot works (such as the hot-cutting of tanks and drums that have contained flammable materials).

 For further guidance on DSEAR visit the HSE website.

9.3.2 Employers' duties under DSEAR

09

DSEAR place duties on employers (and the self-employed, who are considered employers for the purposes of the regulations) to assess and eliminate or reduce risks from dangerous substances.

Complying with DSEAR involves the responsibilities shown below.

9.3.2.1 Assessing risks

Where a dangerous substance is, or is liable to be, present at the workplace, employers must assess the fire and explosion risks that may be caused by dangerous substances. This should be an identification and careful examination and as a minimum should:

- identify and determine the hazardous properties of the dangerous substance(s)

- identify those different groups of workers and people who may be harmed, and the likelihood and severity of the consequences

- consider any employees who may be at increased risk because of lack of awareness, such as inexperienced trainees and those under 18

- consider others, including workers of another employer in the workplace or nearby, members of the public and other visitors, both on and off site

- be satisfied that, where a 'model' risk assessment is being used from somewhere else that uses similar processes, in each case, the model:

  – reflects the core hazards

  – is adapted to the details of the particular situation

  – is appropriate to the type of work.

DANGEROUS SUBSTANCES

The purpose is to help employers to decide what they need to do to eliminate or reduce the risks from dangerous substances. If there is no risk to safety from fires and explosions, or the risk is low, no further action is needed. If there are risks then employers must consider what else needs to be done to comply fully with the requirements of DSEAR. If an employer has five or more employees, the employer must record the significant findings of the risk assessment. This is the same risk assessment required under the Management of Health and Safety at Work Regulations. There is no requirement to carry out two risk assessments, as long as the requirements of both sets of regulations are met.

The assessment (including the recording of significant findings) enables employers to demonstrate to themselves, and to others who may have an interest (such as HSE inspectors, principal contractors and employees' representatives), that they have followed a structured and thorough approach in considering the risks to the safety of employees and the control measures that are needed. The persons carrying out the assessment should have the skills, knowledge, experience and training (competence) to do so.

9.3.2.2 Preventing or controlling risks

Employers must put control measures in place to eliminate risks from dangerous substances, or reduce them as far as is reasonably practicable. Where it is not possible to eliminate the risk completely employers must take measures to control risks and reduce the severity of the effects of fire or explosion.

The best solution is to eliminate the risk by replacing the dangerous substance with a less dangerous substance, or using a different work process. In DSEAR, this is called substitution.

In practice, this may be difficult to achieve. However, it may be possible to reduce the risk by using a less dangerous substance (for example, by replacing a low flashpoint liquid with a high flashpoint liquid). In other situations, it may not be possible to replace the dangerous substance. For example, it would not be practical to replace petrol with another substance at a filling station.

9.3.2.3 Control measures

Where the risk cannot be eliminated, DSEAR require control measures to be applied in the following priority order.

1.	Reduce the quantity of dangerous substances to a minimum.
2.	Avoid or minimise releases of dangerous substances.
3.	Control releases of dangerous substances at source.
4.	Prevent the formation of a dangerous atmosphere, including the application of appropriate ventilation.
5.	Collect, contain and remove any releases to a place that is safe or is otherwise rendered safe (for example, through ventilation).
6.	Avoid ignition sources.
7.	Avoid adverse conditions (for example, exceeding the limits of temperature or control settings) that could lead to danger.
8.	Keep incompatible dangerous substances apart.

These control measures should be proportionate to the degree of risk as highlighted in the risk assessment and be appropriate to the nature of the activity or operation.

 Worker suffers severe burns during equipment refuelling

A company specialising in spray foam insulation services has been fined after an inexperienced worker suffered severe burns during the refuelling of petrol powered equipment.

Southwark Crown Court heard how workers were spraying insulation into a ceiling cavity of a retail outlet. The foam spraying equipment was installed in a van parked outside of the premises. The worker entered the van to refuel the equipment from a jerry can container fixed with straps, within the compartment containing a petrol powered compressor/generator. When the jerry can was opened, petrol sprayed over the worker and the vapour ignited immediately, thereby covering him in flames. He was in a coma for three months and spent over a year in hospital.

HSE investigators found that the company had failed to ensure that risk from petrol was either eliminated or reduced so far as is reasonably practicable. Reasonably practicable actions, which the HSE argued could have been taken, included using diesel powered spray foam equipment or reducing the frequency of refuelling by installing a larger fuel tank or tanks. Refuelling could then have been reduced to once a day and could have taken place at the beginning of the day when the equipment was cool and not in operation. The potential for petrol spillage could have been reduced by storing it away from sources of heat and confining it to smaller containers, or by using a non-spilling fuel delivery nozzle.

The insulation company from Birmingham pleaded guilty to breaching Regulation 6 of the Dangerous Substances and Explosive Atmospheres Regulations (DSEAR) 2002. The company was fined £40,000 and ordered to pay costs of £11,779.

Speaking after the hearing an HSE inspector said: 'This was the worker's second day on the job. He suffered horrific injuries due to the company's failure to adequately consider the risks from refuelling and implementing safer alternatives to the system of work requiring refuelling petrol powered equipment every two hours'.

(Source: HSE.)

9.3.2.4 Mitigation

In addition to control measures, DSEAR require employers to put mitigation measures in place. These measures should be consistent with the risk assessment and appropriate to the nature of the activity or operation, and include the following.

- Reducing the number of employees exposed to the risk.

- Providing explosion-resistant plant.

- Providing explosion suppression equipment.

- Providing explosion pressure relief arrangements.

- Taking measures to control or minimise the spread of fires or explosions.

- Providing suitable PPE.

9.3.2.5 Preparing emergency plans and procedures

Arrangements must be made to deal with emergencies. These plans and procedures should cover escape routes, safety drills, first aid and suitable communication and warning systems, and should be in proportion to the risks. Where possible visual or audible warnings should be initiated so employees can be withdrawn before explosion conditions are reached. If an emergency occurs only workers essential to carrying out repairs must be allowed into the area and they must be provided with the appropriate PPE and equipment and plant to allow them to carry out this work safely.

The information in the emergency plans and procedures must be made available to the emergency services to allow them to develop their own plans if necessary.

9.3.2.6 Providing information, instruction and training for employees

Employees must be provided, in an appropriate manner, with relevant information, instruction and training, which will include the following.

- The dangerous substances present in the workplace and the risks they present, including access to any relevant safety data sheets and information on any other legislation that applies to the dangerous substance.

- The findings of the risk assessment and the control measures put in place as a result, including their purpose and how to follow and use them.

- Emergency procedures.

Information, instruction and training need only be provided to other people (non-employees) where it is required to ensure their safety. It should be in proportion to the level and type of risk.

The information, instruction and training provided should be appropriate to the
level of understanding and experience of the employees. It should be provided in a form which takes account of any language difficulties or disabilities. Information can be provided in whatever form is most suitable in the circumstances, as long as it can be understood by everyone.

In practical terms, the information must include the following.

- How and where the dangerous substance is to be used in the specific site activities in addition to the general information in the safety data sheet.

- The precautions and actions required. The information for employees should include the control and mitigation measures adopted, including methods of work, the reasons behind them, and how to use them properly.

- Training and instruction, which should include the reasoning (theory) behind the practice. Training in the use and application of control measures and equipment should be carried out, taking into account recommendations and instructions supplied by the manufacturer.

- Any procedures for dealing with accidents, emergencies and incidents. This ranges from smaller unplanned incidents (including dealing with faults and clearing blockages) to larger emergencies and should prepare staff for how to react if and when foreseeable events happen.

- Any further relevant information resulting from a review of the risk assessment, why it has been done and how any changes will affect the way employees do the work in the future.

Employers may need to make special arrangements for employees with little or no understanding of English, or those who cannot read English. This could include providing translation, using interpreters or replacing written notes with clearly understood symbols or diagrams.

Employers also need to take account of the needs of people other than employees who may be present on site, such as contractors, visitors or members of the public. While it may not always be practical to provide formal training in these circumstances, employers should consider what other information or instruction may be needed at site inductions to reduce risks.

For example, this could include pictorial signs for infrequent visitors to the site or for those whose first language is not English (which might be the case for delivery drivers and other staff or visitors), notices explaining hazards (warning notices, no smoking signs and so on) and copies of emergency and evacuation procedures.

The contents of pipes and containers must be identifiable to alert employees and others to the presence of dangerous substances, so that they can take the necessary precautions. It can also avoid incorrect mixing of contents.

09

DANGEROUS SUBSTANCES

9.3.2.7   Places where explosive atmospheres may occur

DSEAR places additional duties on employers where potentially explosive atmospheres may occur in the workplace. In relation to construction site work, this could include bottled gas, petrol or fuel storage areas. These duties include the following.

- Identifying and classifying (zoning) areas where potentially explosive atmospheres may occur.

- Avoiding ignition sources in zoned areas, in particular those from electrical and mechanical equipment.

- Where necessary, identifying the entrances to zoned areas by the display of signs.

- Providing appropriate anti-static clothing for employees.

- Before they come into operation, verifying the overall explosion-protection safety of areas where explosive atmospheres may occur.

Decisions on the zoning of areas and the appropriate actions to take must be made by someone who has been trained and is competent to do so.

(The above summary of DSEAR is reproduced from the HSE website under licence from The Controller of Her Majesty's Stationery Office.)

Whilst the employer must, as far as possible, ensure that any PPE supplied must be worn, the employee in turn must ensure that they wear and use the equipment provided correctly and know the procedures for replacing and reporting loss or defects to the employer.

In the context of this chapter, the relevance of these regulations includes the prevention of:

- inhalation of fumes and vapour given off by dangerous substances

- skin contact with dangerous substances

- eye injuries resulting from splashes of dangerous substances.

 For further information on the Personal Protective Equipment at Work Regulations refer to Chapter B06 Personal protective equipment.

9.4   Carriage of Dangerous Goods and Use of Transportable Pressure Equipment Regulations (CDG), and the European agreement

The CDG and the European agreement (ADR) are highly prescriptive and deal with the carriage of dangerous goods and their purpose to protect everyone, either those directly involved (such as consignors or carriers) or those who might be harmed (such as members of the public or the emergency services).

Note: ADR comes from the French abbreviation Accord Européen relatif au transport international des marchandises Dangereuses par Route.

Dangerous goods are liquid or solid substances, and the articles containing them, that have been tested, assessed and given a classification. Dangerous goods are given different classes depending on their predominant hazard. Goods being carried by rail or road are dangerous if there is a risk of spillage leading to fire, explosion, chemical burn or environmental damage following an incident. The regulations place duties upon everyone involved in the carriage of dangerous goods to ensure they know what they have to do to minimise the risk of incidents and guarantee effective responses.

 Many duty holders will need to appoint a dangerous goods safety adviser.

9.4.1   Carriage of Dangerous Goods and Use of Transportable Pressure Equipment Regulations 2009

These regulations were substantially restructured in 2009, with direct referencing to ADR for the main duties, with amending regulations made in 2011. CDG now cross-references almost totally to ADR; it is ADR that contains the detailed requirements. CDG sets the legal framework in the UK; ADR has no provision for enforcement. CDG includes a number of exemptions and make substantial changes to ADR requirements for the domestic (within the UK) carriage of many explosives.

Note: At the time of publication, the current CDG regulations are undergoing review and amendments by the UK Government, to meet the requirements of the UK's withdrawal from the EU.

9.4.2   ADR structure

Each part of ADR is sub-divided into chapters, with each chapter further divided into sections and paragraphs.

Part number	Description
1.	Introduction – setting out high-level aims and duties, together with exemptions. This part includes the need for a dangerous goods safety adviser.
2.	Classification.
3.	The dangerous goods list (including special provisions and exemptions related to limited quantities).

09

Part number	Description
4.	Packing and tank provisions.
5.	Consignment procedures, including documentation and vehicle marking.
6.	Construction and testing of packages, intermediate bulk containers, large packages and tanks.
7.	Carriage – loading, unloading and handling.
8.	Vehicle crews, equipment, operation and documentation (including driver training).
9.	Construction and approval of vehicles.

 For further information on the requirements of CDG and ADR visit the HSE website.

9.5 Control of Substances Hazardous to Health Regulations

The Control of Substances Hazardous to Health (COSHH) Regulations only apply to dangerous explosive or flammable substances where they also possess other hazardous properties. This would be identified as part of the COSHH assessment carried out on the substance.

 For further information refer to Chapter B07 Control of substances hazardous to health.

9.6 Storage of dangerous substances

On most construction sites, dangerous substances will be used at some time during the construction phase.

Depending upon the nature of the work it may be necessary to store bulk quantities of dangerous substances. Where site conditions allow this should be in an external, secure, purpose-built compound, or where this is not possible in a suitable, secure internal storeroom.

Alternatively, small quantities (for example, 200 ml containers upwards) will often be taken to the place of work by the person doing the job.

Where small quantities of dangerous substances for daily use are required in the workplace, metal lockable bins may be used.

Safe and secure storage

9.6.1 Storage in the open air

Where it is necessary to store dangerous substances in bulk, a store should be built to the following requirements.

- On a concrete sloping pad with a sump to catch any leaks or spills.

- With a low sill to create a bund with the capacity equal to 110% of the contents of the largest can or drum being stored.

- Surrounded by a 1.8 m high wire fence.

- So that it is protected against direct sunlight.

- At least 2 m away from nearby buildings or boundaries, except that, where the boundary of the store forms part of a solid wall, cans or drums may be stacked up against that wall up to 1 m from the top.

Cans or drums should be stored so that their contents can be easily identified and removed in the event of any leak or damage. They must also be stored on their sides and chocked to prevent movement.

Stores or bins must be kept locked and only sufficient amounts for each day's requirements should be removed, as and when needed.

They may be marked with suitable signs, such as 'Flammable liquid' or 'Flammable gas'.

Additionally, if an assessment under DSEAR shows that an explosive atmosphere may be present in a particular area, appropriate numbers of the illustrated sign must be displayed.

Examples of suitable warning signs

DANGEROUS SUBSTANCES

The sign comprises a yellow background and black graphics. Signs must conform to the Health and Safety (Safety Signs and Signals) Regulations and *Safety signs* (BS 5499). All signs purchased from reputable suppliers will be to these specifications.

Naked flames, smoking, matches or lighters must not be allowed in the area of the store, and proper prohibition signs must be clearly displayed, as well as other signs already indicated.

Any lighting within a store must be flameproof to the appropriate standard, and under no circumstances should electrical sockets be permitted.

Where there is a need for electrical apparatus (other than lighting) within a store, the supply must be permanently wired in using intrinsically safe equipment. Non-intrinsically or explosive safe-rated electronic devices (such as mobile phones, walkie talkies and torches) must not be allowed in the area of the store, and proper prohibition signs must be clearly displayed in addition to the other signs already indicated.

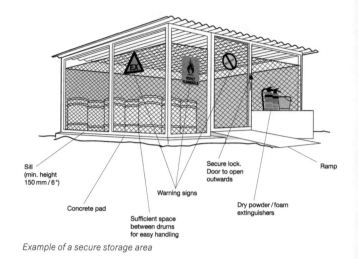

Example of a secure storage area

Other points to be noted.

- Stores should not be built below ground level because the vapours from spills and leaks will not be able to disperse (they are heavier than air).

- Stores must be located away from any emergency exit routes.

- Adequate cross-ventilation at both high and low level is necessary.

- The store should always be kept locked when unattended.

- A door sill of approximately 150 mm in height should be provided to catch any leaks or spills in order to retain the liquids inside the building.

- A sufficient quantity of absorbent material, to soak up any spilt liquids, and suitable containers for the collection and safe disposal of the contaminated absorbent, should be provided at the store.

- The use of mobile phones in or immediately adjacent to the store should be prohibited. Notices to this effect should be provided and prominently displayed.

- Any shelves or racking in the store should be of a non-ferrous metal or other non-combustible construction.

9.6.2 Storage inside a building

A separate building should be provided, if possible, solely for the storage of dangerous substances where security or protection from the weather is required. Ideally, it will be constructed from fire-resisting materials and it should be at least 2 m away from other buildings or boundaries.

A risk assessment should be carried out to determine whether the risks of storing dangerous substances in such a location are acceptable. If not, either additional control measures must be put in place or alternative arrangements made for storing the substances.

Where a separate building cannot be provided, and the store forms part of an existing structure, the surrounding walls and roof of the store must be fire-resisting and the door should be of the fire-resisting type and open outwards.

It is recommended that the maximum quantities that may be stored in cabinets and bins are no more than 50 litres for highly flammable liquids (and flammable liquids with a flashpoint below the maximum ambient temperature of the workroom/working area) and no more than 250 litres for other flammable liquids with a higher flashpoint of up to 55°C.

Other points to be considered.

- Stores should not be built below ground level, because the vapours from spillages and leaks will not be able to disperse.

- Adequate cross-ventilation at both high and low level is necessary.

- The store should always be kept locked when unattended.

- When not in use, containers of flammable liquids needed for current work should be kept closed and stored in suitable cabinets or bins of fire-resisting construction, which are designed to retain spills (110% volume of the largest vessel normally stored in it).

- A sufficient quantity of absorbent material, to soak up any spilt liquids, and suitable containers for the collection and safe disposal of the contaminated absorbent, should be provided at the store.

- Signs should be positioned on or near the store stating, for example, 'Highly flammable' or 'Flashpoint below 32°C'. All signs should conform to the Health and Safety (Safety Signs and Signals) Regulations and *Safety signs* (BS 5499).

- Naked flames, smoking, matches or lighters must not be allowed in the store, and signs stating this must be clearly displayed.

- The use of mobile phones in, or adjacent to, the store should be prohibited. Notices to this effect should be provided and prominently displayed.

- Any lighting or other electrical apparatus must conform to BS EN 60079-14.

- Any shelves or racking in the store should be of a non-ferrous metal or other non-combustible construction.

9.7   Handling and use of dangerous substances

The use of any dangerous substance, including decanting small quantities for daily use from bulk containers, must be the subject of a risk assessment.

The findings of the risk assessment will indicate the maximum quantity of the dangerous substance that can be taken to the place of work and the safe working practices to be observed once it is there and being used.

Generally, only enough of the dangerous substance to enable the work in hand to be carried out should be taken to the place where it is to be used.

 The HSE recommends that only the minimum quantity needed for frequently occurring work, or that required for use during a half day or one shift, should be present in the workroom/working area.

Clearly, actual quantities will depend on the work activity and also the organisational arrangements for controlling the fire risks in the workroom/working area.

Decanting, mixing or sampling should not be carried out in a store. It should be done in the open air or in a separate room constructed of fire-resisting materials.

Funnels or pumped nozzles with automatic cut off should be used to prevent spillage whilst decanting is taking place and drip trays should be used to catch any spillage that may inadvertently occur.

Any spillage should be soaked up using proprietary absorbents, dry earth or dry sand.

Metal bins with lids should be provided for any used absorbents to be placed in and these should be clearly identifiable with signs or colour coding and emptied regularly and carefully.

Handle flammable liquids with care

Consideration must be given to the disposal of any waste as it may well be classified as hazardous waste. Such waste must be transported by a registered carrier to a licensed landfill site. Depending on how much waste is produced, the relevant regulator may need to be notified: the Environment Agency (England), Natural Resources Wales, Northern Ireland Environment Agency or the Scottish Environment Protection Agency.

In general, where work involves the use of a dangerous substance that has the potential to create an explosive atmosphere inside a room, all electrical power should be turned off unless all electrical fittings are intrinsically safe by design. If space heating is needed, it should be flameproof and incapable of causing the ignition of any vapours present in the atmosphere.

The build-up of concentrations of vapours must be avoided and dispersed, if necessary, by natural or mechanical ventilation. If mechanical ventilation is necessary, a flameproof motor, not in the ventilation trunking, should be used.

Other points to be considered.

- Naked flames, welding and heating torches, and smoking materials should be prohibited in any area where an explosive atmosphere may be present.

- Metal bins with lids must be provided for offcuts, waste or rags, and should be emptied regularly.

- A suitable container with a lid should be used for any brushes or scrapers that require soaking to remove residues of dangerous substances. This should be placed in a safe area well away from any possible source of ignition.

9.7.1   Spraying of dangerous substances

New covering materials (such as paints, varnishes and lacquers), and the techniques for applying them, have been developed, and extensive use of spray painting equipment can now be seen on construction sites.

Using a spray gun for spraying dangerous substances is most likely to introduce an airborne explosive mist into the workplace, creating a hazard both to the user and to other workers in the area. Such work must only be undertaken by fully trained and competent employees and in a situation where all appropriate precautionary measures are in place.

A risk assessment must be carried out and other controls, including permits to work and/or permits to enter (for those people involved in the job, by implication, excluding all others), implemented as necessary.

09

DANGEROUS SUBSTANCES

Other points to be considered:

- Identify the material carefully and always follow the manufacturer's instructions on preparation, use and application.

- Always use the correct type of spraying equipment. Never make do, just because the proper equipment is not immediately to hand.

- If alternative control measures are not available or adequate, protective clothing and respiratory protective equipment (RPE) must be used.

- Always use the hygiene and washing facilities provided.

- Do not introduce ignition sources into the working area.

- Do not smoke or use naked flames in the working area.

- Always place warning signs in approaches to the area where the work is being carried out, and at entrance points to areas where dangerous substances are being used. Use physical barriers to stop unauthorised persons entering the area.

9.7.2 Empty tanks and containers

Do not cut or heat any empty tanks, containers or drums unless they have been certificated as being free of flammable vapours that could explode. Current opinion recommends reducing the length of time that such certification is valid for. Under most circumstances, the cutting work should be planned to start as soon as the gas-free certificate is issued.

Special care is necessary when demolishing or dismantling disused bulk tanks. By disturbing the tank or heating the residues left inside, you may cause an explosive concentration of vapours. It is important to be aware that even cold-cutting techniques (such as hydraulic shears) may cause sparks that lead to explosion.

Entry into any disused tank or vessel that may be regarded as a confined space should be avoided by doing the work from outside, if possible. Often, there will be a need to clean residues and if entry to a confined space is unavoidable, a safe system of work must be followed and the work carried out under a permit to work system.

Further advice on permit to work systems and entry into confined spaces is contained in the Approved Code of Practice (ACoP) and guidance notes that support the Confined Spaces Regulations (L101) and HSE leaflet *Confined spaces: a brief guide to working safely* (INDG258).

There are a number of factors to consider when the work involves large tanks. The first would be what the contents were. Oil storage tanks may have held so-called heavy fuel oil and these will undoubtedly have been insulated. It is quite likely that the insulation system will have been asbestos.

If the tanks once held petrol, it may have been leaded fuel. This means that exposure to asbestos fibres or lead fumes during cutting should be considered and suitable precautions taken in relation to the presence of asbestos or lead.

It is normal for large tanks, whether above or below ground, to be emptied and cleaned by a specialist contractor before dismantling. The contents are generally removed by a large vacuum tanker and then the inside of the tank is steam cleaned. Most of this work can be carried out from the outside and it is only to carry out the final clean that entry is required.

Operatives carrying out this final clean must be trained in confined space working and be provided with all the normal gas detector, rescue equipment and personal protective equipment (PPE) that would be expected for confined space working.

Having been cleaned, the tank is tested and a gas-free certificate issued. It should then be cut up as soon as possible. The risk of not doing so is that it is practically impossible to completely clean a tank, particularly where its construction incorporates internal ribs, welds and other internal features that could harbour residue of the content.

These residues may become fumes, and if the concentration becomes high enough then the atmosphere inside the tank may become explosive if ignited.

9.7.3 Industrial gas cylinder colours

While the cylinder label is the primary means of identifying the properties of the gas in a cylinder, the colour coding of the cylinder body provides a further guide.

The colour applied to the shoulder, or curved part at the top of the cylinder, signifies the European Standard colour coding.

The aim of the new standard (EN 1089-3) was to replace the old cylinder colour scheme (BS 349), to help improve safety standards within the gases industry.

 ***Gas cylinder identification. Label and colour coding requirements* (TIS6) can be downloaded for free from the British Compressed Gases Association website.**

 Operators should obtain a cylinder identification chart from their supplier, as different gas suppliers may paint the body of a cylinder different colours. For example, a BOC oxygen gas cylinder has a black body with a white shoulder whilst an air products cylinder has a grey body with a white shoulder.

9.8   Liquefied petroleum gas

LPG is a mixture of hydrocarbons that are a gas or vapour under normal conditions of temperature and pressure, but can be turned into a liquid by either the application of pressure or the reduction of temperature.

LPG can be found in numerous locations, in various sizes of cylinder, and can be put to a variety of uses on building and construction sites. Uses range from the heating of bitumen boilers, site huts and offices to providing a fuel for hand tools and cutting equipment.

If used properly and safely, LPG is a convenient and valuable source of energy. Misuse or carelessness can cause serious accidents.

 LPG and commercial butane and propane

Liquefied petroleum gas. Means any commercial butane, commercial propane or a mixture of the two.

Commercial butane. This is usually stored in blue cylinders. It consists mainly of butane and butane isomers. The remaining components are predominantly propane and propane isomers, pentane and pentane isomers. Because of the low vapour pressure, butane cylinders are not generally used outside.

Commercial propane. This is usually stored in vessels or in red cylinders. It consists mainly of propane and propane isomers. The remaining components are predominantly butane and butane isomers, ethane and ethane isomers.

 Important points about LPG

- In some cases, the Regulatory Reform (Fire Safety) Order will only be relevant where LPG is stored off site (for example, at company premises and builders' yards). However, it will also apply to some construction sites where LPG is used in conjunction with a work process.

- LPG is normally found as a compressed liquid, usually of commercial butane or propane.

- LPG is a colourless, odourless liquid that floats on water but vaporises to form a gas that is heavier than air. A stenching agent is normally added.

- A release or spillage of LPG can form a large vapour cloud of flammable gas capable of ignition from some distance.

- LPG is stored on site in fixed tanks, refillable cylinders or non-refillable disposable cylinders (cartridges).

- Storage should be in secure, non-combustible, well ventilated areas away from other risks and sources of ignition.

- There are special requirements for vehicles and drivers covering the transportation of LPG.

- In site huts all LPG cylinders and regulators for use with fixed heaters, cookers and lighting must be kept outside and piped in using rigid copper piping.

- Staff who work with LPG must be suitably trained in the hazards and use of LPG (such as not rolling cylinders).

- In the event of a leak, do not attempt to operate electrical apparatus or switches.

- If a fire breaks out that involves LPG cylinders:
    - immediately inform the Fire and Rescue Service of the whereabouts of all cylinders on site, including details of whether they are full or empty
    - if in any doubt as to the safety of the overall situation, evacuate the site and put a security cordon in place.

09

9.8.1   Properties

As a liquid, LPG is lighter than water and will float before evaporating.

As a gas, it is approximately twice as heavy as air and will sink and flow into sumps and underground excavations or workings. It will also sink into drains but, because its density is approximately half that of water, it will not flow through drains that are water-trapped.

As a gas, it is capable of ignition at some distance from the original leak. The resulting flame can travel back to the source of the leak.

Any release of liquid under pressure into the atmosphere results in its rapid conversion to gas. This gas has a volume of about 230 (butane) and 270 (propane) times that of the liquid.

The expansion, during a rapid release of pressure, results in a rapid drop of temperature, which for propane can approach its boiling point of -45°C. Leakage of liquid LPG will result in the release of large volumes of highly flammable gases.

Property	Commercial butane	Commercial propane
Density in comparison to water.	0.57	0.5
Density in comparison to air.	2	1.5
Litres per tonne.	1,745	1,995
Boiling point.	-2°C	-45°C
Pressure at 15°C.	1.5 bar	7.0 bar
Expansion ratio.	1:230	1:270
Levels of flammability.	1.9%–8.5%	2.0%–10.9%

DANGEROUS SUBSTANCES

For example, one litre of liquid propane spilt in a workplace will evaporate to make approximately 270 litres of gas. If it is diluted with air to 2%, this will give 13,750 cubic litres of an explosive gas/air mixture – enough to fill a room 3 m x 2.3 m x 2 m.

The use of LPG equipment in confined spaces, and small, poorly ventilated spaces (such as basement and sub-basement boiler houses, toilets, site cabins and kitchens) can give rise to a highly flammable or explosive atmosphere, if the equipment should leak.

9.8.2   Flammability

Following mechanical failure of LPG equipment, or any other event that causes the release of LPG, the resulting gas will form a flammable mixture with air at gas concentrations between approximately 2% and 10%.

Ignition of released LPG, where the concentration exceeds 2%, can result in fire or, if confined, an explosion. If a leak does not ignite immediately, and the LPG and air mixture drifts from the point of release, it will gradually become more diluted.

However, should the concentration still exceed 2% and ignition occur, this could cause a flash or cloud-fire back to the point of release.

A leak of LPG may sometimes be noticed either by the smell or the noise of the gas escaping. There may also be condensation or frosting on the outside of the cylinder.

All LPG systems must be leak tested each time prior to use. An approved leak detection fluid (not soapy water) should be applied to all joints and connections. The presence of bubbles indicates that the system is not gas tight and should not be used. If a leak is discovered the system should be shut down, safely de-pressured and the leak rectified. LPG leaks must never be traced with a lighted match or flame.

 If it is suspected that LPG has leaked inside a building, no attempt should be made to touch any electrical apparatus. Do not turn light switches, sockets or any other electrical appliance either on or off. Open all doors and windows, if it is safe to do so, and leave immediately. Do not re-enter the building until advice has been sought and you are told that it is safe to do so.

9.8.3   Health issues

9.8.3.1   Workplace exposure limits

The maximum levels of exposure, as stated in EH40/2005 workplace exposure limits under the heading LPG, are:

- 1,000 ppm (0.1%) for long-term exposure (reference period eight hours)
- 1,250 ppm (0.125%) for short-term exposure (reference period 15 minutes).

During any maintenance work involving release of pressure, especially in confined spaces, care must be taken that these exposure limits are not exceeded.

9.8.3.2   Inhalation

LPG gas is not toxic, but at concentration levels above about 10,000 ppm (1%) in air, propane becomes a slight narcotic. At higher levels, it becomes an asphyxiant by displacing oxygen.

In a sufficiently high concentration, a person will suffocate and die.

9.8.3.3   Cold burns

The release of liquid propane onto unprotected skin will cause cold burns. This is due to the rapid vaporisation of the liquid, withdrawing heat from the affected area of the body.

The release of liquid, or significant amounts of gas at vessel pressure, can also cause the adjacent fittings to cool. This may be sufficient to cause cold burns if the fittings are touched by unprotected hands.

Suitable skin and eye protection must be worn whenever there is the possibility of a release of liquid LPG.

 In the event of a cold burn, treat as for a burn from a hot object. The burn area should be placed under cool running water for 20 minutes and you should seek first aid or professional medical help (call 999). Be aware, shock may occur due to intense pain.

9.8.4   Environmental hazards

A small, unignited release of LPG would not pose a serious danger to the environment.

The gas, being heavier than air, will roll and sink to the lowest point (such as a basement or excavation). LPG vapours can travel large distances and this may result in a fire or explosion, even if the source of ignition is a considerable distance from the original leak.

A fire and explosion would be instantaneous on ignition and would be limited to immediate damage. The fire might devour only escaping LPG and then the danger will have passed with no lasting environmental damage.

The fire will burn fast and the explosion will be intense, but both may be over very quickly.

9.8.5 Storage

LPG can be stored on construction sites in one of three ways.

- Fixed storage tanks.
- Refillable cylinders.
- Non-refillable cylinders (that is, disposable cylinders).

9.8.5.1 Fixed storage tanks

Whilst most LPG used on construction sites can be found in cylinders, on some larger sites there may be a need for bulk storage. In view of the large capacity, it is essential that the positioning of any storage tank is carefully planned and discussed with the local fire prevention officer and the HSE.

LPG tanks should be positioned on a level concrete base to provide a stable foundation. For short-term installations it may be satisfactory to stand the tank on concrete slabs, but advice must be sought from the tank or gas suppliers. Consideration also needs to be given to any pipework that may run from the tank to the application.

Tanks should not be sited close to any ditches, cellars or drains, and delivery and emergency vehicles must easily reach them.

If the bulk tank is used as a supply vessel for filling LPG cylinders on site then reference should be made as to how this procedure can be undertaken safely.

All access roads must be clear of obstruction and the entire area kept free from weeds and other vegetation.

Tanks over 2,250 litres liquid capacity should be electrically bonded and earthed.

All bulk storage tanks must have good, all-round ventilation. On non-secure sites, tanks should be protected against vandalism by a chainlink fence at least 2 m high.

Motorway-type crash barriers should surround the installation to minimise damage by motor vehicles.

 Installations must be clearly labelled 'Highly flammable LPG. No smoking or naked lights'.

Signs must conform to the Health and Safety (Safety Signs and Signals) Regulations and *Safety signs* (BS 5499). Signs purchased from reputable suppliers will be to these specifications.

Adequate separation must be maintained between bulk storage tanks and adjacent buildings or boundaries. As a guide, the separation distances for bulk LPG tanks, detailed in the table on the right, should be followed.

Where possible, LPG storage areas should not be positioned under power cables. Where this is unavoidable, the **minimum** distances between the extremities of the vessel or cylinders to the nearest cable should be:

- up to 1 kV – 1.5 m
- 1 kV or above – 10 m.

Gas capacity	Water capacity		Minimum distance*
Tonnes	Litres	Gallons	Metres
Under 0.2	450	99	2.5
0.2-1.0	451-2,250	100-495	3
1.1-4.0	2,251-9,000	496-1,980	7.5

* Minimum distance from boundaries, buildings or sources of ignition.

 The above figures are for guidance only. Advice should always be sought from the power supply company before any work takes place in the vicinity of overhead power cables.

9.8.5.2 Refillable cylinders

A level base of compacted earth, concrete or paving slabs should be provided and surrounded by a secure chainlink fence at least 2 m high. A hard standing should be provided for the delivery and dispatch of cylinders. The area should be kept weed and vegetation free.

If the compound is more than 12 m square, two exits should be provided in opposite corners of the compound. The emergency exits should be fitted with a panic bar so that they can be easily opened in an emergency. If it is less than 12 m square, one gate will suffice.

Gates should open outwards and always be left unlocked when someone is in the compound. There should be sufficient shelter to prevent cylinders from being exposed to extremes of weather.

Signs must be clearly displayed indicating the presence of LPG, and prohibiting smoking and the use of any naked flame in the area of the store.

LPG cylinders must be stored with their valves uppermost. They must be stored away from oxygen, highly flammable liquids, oxidisers, toxic or corrosive gases or substances. A distance of at least 3 m must be kept between LPG cylinders and other such substances, although they may be kept in the same compound.

09

DANGEROUS SUBSTANCES

Any store for refillable LPG cylinders must be located away from boundaries, buildings, fixed sources of ignition or electrical equipment by at least the distances detailed in the table below.

LPG storage (including empties)	Separation from building/boundary
Below 50 kg	1 m
50–1,000 kg	3 m
1,001–4,000 kg	4 m

The store must be sited at least 3 m away from any cellars, drains or other excavations into which a leak of gas would collect. If only a small compound is used (3 m² for example) cylinders may be stored against the inside of the compound fencing, providing this fence is not within 3 m of any boundary.

Empty cylinders must be stored with their valves securely closed to prevent any residue of gas escaping, or air being drawn into the cylinder. Full and part-used cylinders must be stored separately from empty cylinders in properly identified areas.

Stocks should be grouped in batches of not more than 1,000 kg and batches separated by a minimum 1.5 m gangway. However, if there is less than 50 kg of LPG these may be stored with other gases. Where lighting is necessary, it should be mounted well above ground level and not less than 2 m above the cylinders.

Any equipment not in use (such as portable hand-held equipment) should be isolated so as not to be easy to get to for trespassers. Any cylinders not required should be returned to the storage compound or other secure position.

9.8.5.3   Non-refillable cylinders

Non-refillable LPG cylinders for use with small portable equipment (such as blowlamps) may be stored in a clearly identified, lockable, metal container, adequately ventilated, to prevent a build up of LPG gas. Care should be taken when changing cylinders to ensure that connections are correctly made and that there are no leaks. Always dispose of empty containers safely and in accordance with the manufacturer's recommendations. Do not, under any circumstances, puncture or throw empty cylinders onto a fire.

Small refillable cylinders (for example, primus) should also be stored in the same way as non-refillable cylinders. Although only containing small quantities of gas, they must not be stored in occupied site huts. They should be kept in a secure, non-combustible, well-ventilated external enclosure. The store should have warning signs 'Highly flammable – LPG', and prohibition signs 'No smoking/naked lights'.

The disposal of cartridges after use requires care as they still contain gas. Under no circumstances should cartridges be thrown in general waste skips or on fires. All empty cartridges and non-refillable cylinders should be disposed of by a specialist waste contractor. Small refillable cylinders should be kept and returned to the supplier when empty.

9.8.6   Cylinders

9.8.6.1   Handling

Care must be taken when moving cylinders around the site, especially by hand or on rough ground. A full 47 kg cylinder has a total mass of about 90 kg and, before moving by hand, requires an assessment under the Manual Handling Operations Regulations of the method to be used. Cylinders must not be rolled, even when empty.

Cylinders should be handled with care and, wherever reasonably practicable, moved using suitable equipment. They should not be moved unprotected in dumper trucks or on forklift trucks. The valve on a cylinder should not be used for lifting or to lever the cylinder into position. Damage to the valve can result in a non-controllable release of LPG under high pressure. Throwing cylinders from any height or dropping them is prohibited, as in such circumstances damage to the valve, shroud and cylinders is even more likely.

9.8.6.2   Damaged cylinders

Before use, cylinders should be examined. Any damaged or faulty cylinder should **not** be used. The cylinder should be labelled and the supplier immediately requested to collect the cylinder. If a cylinder is found to be leaking (usually from the valve) and the leak cannot be stopped, the cylinder should be carefully removed to a well-ventilated, open space, free from sources of ignition. It should be left with the leak uppermost, marked faulty, and notices displayed prohibiting smoking or other naked lights.

The area where the leaking cylinder is situated should be cordoned off with barriers to prohibit access. The supplier of the cylinder and, if necessary, the FRS, should be informed immediately. If it is necessary to inform the FRS, it may be good practice to evacuate any personnel to a place of safety, away from the leaking cylinder.

Under no circumstances should attempts be made to dismantle or repair defective cylinders.

9.8.6.3   Orphaned compressed gas cylinders

Whilst this advice applies to abandoned LPG cylinders, it is also valid for compressed gas cylinders that have held other gases.

Empty compressed gas cylinders may still contain some of their original content. They are abandoned for a variety of reasons and then appear at metal recyclers or council waste disposal sites, neither of which welcomes their presence.

It is thought that cylinders are often abandoned for the following reasons.

- They are empty and too troublesome to return to the supplier.
- They are damaged and therefore not returnable.
- The owner or supplier cannot be identified.
- They are at the end of their useful life.

Within the UK there is a cylinder retrieval system co-ordinated by the Liquid Petroleum Gas Association. Four major companies own around 90% of all UK compressed gas cylinders. Each company has arrangements in place to collect their own cylinders.

 For details of collection companies refer to Appendix A.

9.8.7 Carriage of dangerous goods

This section details the requirements of legislation for people who occasionally carry LPG cylinders in a van, truck or similar vehicle. This is covered by the CDG which implements the European agreement on carriage of dangerous substances by road, hereafter referred to as 'ADR' (from the French abbreviation *Accord Européen relatif au transport international des marchandises Dangereuses par Route*).

9.8.7.1 Transportation

Acetylene, LPG and other gases are commonly carried by tradespersons (such as welders, plumbers and motor vehicle repair technicians). Flammable gases are in transport Category 2. Oxygen and gases (such as carbon dioxide and argon) are in transport Category 3. Usually small load threshold exemptions will apply. The parts of ADR which apply are shown below.

- The driver will have received general awareness, function-specific and safety training (ADR 1.3). A record of such training must be kept.
- The vehicle must be equipped with at least one 2 kg dry powder fire extinguisher, which is kept in good working order.
- The load must be properly stowed.

Note that special provisions CV 9, 10 and 36 all apply in the case of these gases. In particular, CV 36 specifies:

 ... packages shall preferably be loaded in open or ventilated vehicles or open or ventilated containers. If this is not feasible and packages are carried in other closed vehicles or containers, the cargo doors of the vehicles or containers shall be marked with the following, in letters not less than 25 mm high: 'WARNING: NO VENTILATION, OPEN WITH CAUTION'.

 The HSE has published a leaflet *Working safely with acetylene* (INDG327) and the British Compressed Gases Association (BCGA) has a useful leaflet *Carriage of small quantities of gas cylinders on vehicles* as well as a wider range of publications that may be helpful.

9.8.7.2 Small load exemptions (ADR 1.1.3.6)

Small load exemptions relate to the total quantity of dangerous goods carried in packages by the transport unit (usually the van or lorry, but also any trailer). It is the transport category (TC) that determines the load limits (thresholds). Many substances are assigned a packing group, but these are not synonymous in all cases with the TC. The TC is given in Column 15 of Table A in ADR (Chapter 3.2). If this is not available, the table at ADR Part 1.1.3.6.3 needs to be consulted. References to load limits for the different transport categories are given in the table below. For convenience this has been amended in accordance with Regulation 19 but it needs to be used with care.

Vehicle/load	Driver training	ADR reference
All vehicles except those carrying packages under the load limit.	General training plus ADR training certificate. The certificate may be endorsed for different classes of dangerous goods or different modes (in tanks or other than tanks).	8.2.1
Any vehicle carrying packaged dangerous goods under the small load limit.	General training.	8.2.3 *(refers to Chapter 1.3)*. ADR 1.1.3.6
Vehicle with small tank (up to 1 m³).	General training.	8.2.1.3 8.2.3

If a vehicle is carrying dangerous goods under the small load threshold, many of the requirements of ADR are not applicable. Some care needs to be taken, as 'what is not exempted is still required'. In most cases the remaining obligations are as follows.

- General training for driver (ADR 1.3.2). A record of the training should be kept (ADR 1.3.3).
- Carry at least one 2 kg dry powder fire extinguisher or equivalent (ADR 8.1.4.2).
- Stow the dangerous goods properly (ADR 7.5.7).

Note that use of these exemptions is optional. For example, a carrier may choose to display the orange plates as long as the vehicle is carrying dangerous goods. All vehicle marks (orange plates) must be removed when dangerous goods are not being carried. An important aspect is that packaging has to comply with the relevant standards.

Small load application

- LPG. This is in transport Category 2. The small load threshold is 333 kg and LPG is LQ0. (Limited quantity (LQ) exemptions mainly apply to small receptacles, typically of the sort that go into the retail distribution chain, which are packed in boxes or on shrink-wrapped trays.) The result is that all cylinders count towards the load limit, but if that is less than 333 kg, the minimum ADR requirements apply.

- Section 8.2 of the ADR details mandatory training for drivers. There should be a record of their training, which must be carried at all times. The level of training required depends upon the load.

9.8.7.3 General transportation of LPG cylinders

When loaded onto vehicles, cylinders must be kept upright and secured. Vehicles must be equipped with two dry powder extinguishers (nominally a 6 kg and a 2 kg) and a first-aid kit, and must also display warning notices. LPG should not be carried with other flammable substances (such as paints and solvents). If this is unavoidable, such materials should be kept in a steel chest away from the cylinders.

Drivers carrying more than two LPG cylinders must have received training in what to do in an emergency and carry a transport emergency card containing details of the load carried. If a cylinder leaks during a journey, close the valve immediately. If this is not possible, move the vehicle to open ground, away from buildings and people, and inform the emergency services.

www **For information on fire extinguisher requirements when carrying dangerous goods refer to the HSE guidance.**

9.8.8 Safe use and handling of LPG

Everyone with any responsibility for the storage and transportation of LPG must understand the characteristics and hazards of the LPG product they are using. They should be suitably trained and understand the fundamentals of fire-fighting and control of leakages. They should also have knowledge of the procedures for dealing with emergencies. It is not possible to cover all aspects of the use and application of LPG, but the notes below (which should not be regarded as exhaustive) give the main points for its safe use and handling.

 Safe use and handling of LPG

- Never use or store a gas cylinder on its side, unless it is a special cylinder for use on LPG-fuelled plant and vehicles. Liquefied gas may escape, causing concentrations of gas, and operatives may suffer frostbite because of the low temperature of escaping liquid.

- Propane cylinders must never be stored indoors because any leakage will lead to large concentrations of explosive mixtures.

- Only hoses suitable for use with LPG installations or appliances should be used and these should be inspected frequently for wear. Hoses fitted with worm drive screws should not be used.

- Cylinders must not be dropped during handling, nor brought into violent contact with other cylinders or adjacent objects.

- After use, valve protection caps and plastic thread caps or plugs should be fitted to prevent accidental leakage.

- LPG cylinders should not be used below ground level as any leakage of gas will collect at the lowest point and will not disperse.

- Regulators must be handled with care, and should not be used if damaged, but replaced or sent for specialist repair. The regulator should be labelled for the type of gas it is designed for. It should be CE marked, comply with European Standards and be in date.

- Hoses and fittings should be examined before use. Damaged items must be replaced.

- LPG cylinders are fitted with a left-hand thread or push-on connection. Union nuts and couplers have grooves on the outside corners of the nuts confirming this. Always use the correct size spanner to tighten or loosen connections. Hand-tight connections will permit leaks. Over-tightening will damage threads and cause leaks.

- Checks for leaks should be carried out using a proprietary leakage detector. **Never use a match or other naked flame.**

- Before connecting any LPG cylinder to equipment, it is essential that all fires, flames or other potential ignition sources, including smoking materials, are extinguished. Where reasonably practicable to do so, cylinders should be changed in the open air.

- If a leak is found, the gas supply must be turned off at the cylinder immediately.

- Flexible hoses should be in good condition and protected or steel braided if they are likely to be subjected to damage by abrasion. Hoses must conform to BS EN 16436, *Rubber and plastics hoses, tubing and assemblies for use with propane and butane.*

- Before use, inspections should be carried out on all LPG appliances and equipment. The inspection should cover testing for leaks and the cleaning, adjusting and checking of hoses, hose clips and ferrules.

- Empty cylinders should always be treated with the same caution as new ones and be returned to a properly designated central storage area for collection. Under no circumstances should an LPG cylinder, either full or empty, be left around the site or buried during site operations.

09

9.8.9 Regulators

LPG regulators should be suitable for the equipment with which they are to be used. They should be suitable for either propane or butane and be set to the correct pressure. They should be capable of passing the correct flow capacity. It is dangerous to use regulators set at the incorrect pressure. Cylinders should not be transported with regulators and hoses attached, unless on a purpose designed trolley or carrier.

Before assembling regulators and fittings ensure that the cylinder valve outlet is clean, dry and free from damage and dirt. This will help to prevent the ignition of components. Oxygen regulators should be kept free from oil or grease and be suitable for the maximum cylinder pressure being used. Oxygen cylinder valves should be opened slowly.

Before attaching a regulator to a cylinder the following checks should be made.

- The regulator is within its expiry date. (All regulators have a lifespan, on expiry of which they require either replacement or refurbishment.)

- The gas inside the cylinder is correctly identified and the regulator is suitable for that specific gas.

- The maximum cylinder pressure is identified.

- The regulator is suitable for the maximum cylinder pressure (regulator inlet pressure).

- The regulator has a suitable outlet pressure for the application.

- The regulator is in a serviceable condition.

- The gauges are not damaged and do not show signs of over pressurisation.

- The cylinder valve outlet thread is mechanically compatible with the regulator inlet connection and is clean and free of dirt. A lint free cloth can be used to clean the outlet.

- The regulator outlet thread is in good condition.

- The regulator has the manufacturer's or supplier's name clearly visible.

- The regulator can be fitted at a suitable orientation.

- The regulator pressure adjusting screw is set to zero pressure position by turning the control knob fully anti-clockwise.

- The correct sized spanner is available for securing the regulator.

- The inlet connection should be inspected for damage. If an 'O' ring is fitted to the inlet, check for damage and replace, if necessary, with an 'O' ring recommended by the regulator manufacturer.

 Jointing paste or tape should never be used between the regulator and cylinder valve.

9.8.10 Bitumen boilers and cauldrons

Work with a bitumen boiler should always be supervised by a competent person.

The majority of boilers or cauldrons are fuelled by LPG to melt the block bitumen. Such a boiler or cauldron must be sited on a level, non-flammable base, away from pedestrian routes and areas where site traffic may damage hoses or gas cylinders. If avoidable, bitumen boilers should not be taken onto roofs.

Ensure that any LPG cylinder is at least 3 m away from the boiler or cauldron to which it is attached. Full cylinders, not attached, should be kept at least 6 m away from the boiler or cauldron and protected from heat. Supply hoses should be checked for crushing, damage to the metal braiding or impregnation with bitumen. Any unserviceable hose must be replaced.

Sequence for lighting	
1.	Remove the burner from the boiler or cauldron.
2.	Have the source of ignition ready before turning on the gas.
3.	Light the burner, ensuring that the gas is on slowly.
4.	Replace the burner beneath the boiler or cauldron.

In some circumstances (for example, due to levels of atmospheric humidity (climate conditions) and when using gas rapidly) frost, condensation or ice can form on gas bottles and/or gas regulators. The propane itself would not freeze, as that would require temperatures below the freezing point of -188°C.

If you are running a boiler or cauldron and frost forms on the outside of the cylinder, it may indicate that the gas flow rate is too high. Either use a smaller burner, to regulate the flow, or couple two or more cylinders together, by means of a manifold, to supply the larger burner at a suitable flow rate. Never leave a bitumen boiler or cauldron unattended when the burner is alight, and never move a bitumen boiler or cauldron with the burner alight. Always ensure the boiler or cauldron and bitumen has fully cooled before attempting to move it.

If a bitumen boiler or cauldron is overfilled, overflows or boils over, the LPG cylinder valves must be turned off immediately. Any spillage should be contained using dry sand or earth and then left until cool. No attempt should be made to remove or recover any spillage of hot bitumen. Where bitumen boilers are located at ground level, additional protection measures must be in place to prevent the public from gaining access to the boiler. If boilers are located on scaffolds they must offer protection to the public from spilt bitumen. This can be achieved with additional boards and edge protection. A dry powder extinguisher, of a minimum 4.5 kg in size, should be provided whenever a bitumen boiler or cauldron is used.

09

9.8.11 Gas-operated hand tools and equipment

There are two types of LPG cylinder available for use with portable tools: disposable and refillable.

These cylinders come in various shapes, sizes and colours, depending on the manufacturer. They range in size from small (0.5 kg) to large (47 kg).

All LPG cylinders used with portable equipment should be positioned upright and secured (if possible). Cylinders used with cutting equipment should always be placed on purpose-made trolleys.

- Before changing a cylinder, always make sure that all valves are closed.
- Hoses must never be kinked to try to shut off gas when changing torches. It does not work and can lead to a gas escape.
- Always replace valve protection caps and plastic thread caps.
- Flames from portable tools must not be allowed to play on LPG cylinders.
- When work has been completed, turn off the cylinder valves and allow the flame from the portable torch to burn out.
- Closure of torch valves rather than cylinder valves will retain gas in hoses which, if damaged, will allow gas to escape.
- Hoses and torches must never be put into site toolboxes while still attached to the cylinder.
- Manufacturers' operating pressures must be strictly observed and must never be exceeded.
- Do not interfere with preset pressure regulators.

9.8.12 Gas-powered fixing tools

Many of the principles for the safe use of cartridge-operated tools also apply to gas-powered fixing tools, which use a canister of pressurised gas (a fuel cell) as a propellant.

Generally, gas-powered fixing tools are used for firing fixings into softer materials (such as timber). However, in untrained hands they can be as dangerous as cartridge-operated tools.

The implications of a misfire when using a gas-powered fixing tool are not as serious as when using a cartridge-operated tool and it is usually safe after a misfire to attempt to make the next fixing immediately. The battery and fuel cell must be removed prior to attempting to remove a blockage.

However, it is important to store and dispose of canisters safely. *(Refer to 9.6 Storage of dangerous substances.)*

9.8.13 LPG for use in site huts and other small buildings

All LPG cylinders and regulators for use with fixed heaters, cookers and lighting within site huts must be kept outside and the gas supply piped in using rigid copper piping.

The use of flexible hosing is permitted only between the cylinders and changeover valves or manifolds, and for the final connection to appliances, but this must be kept as short as possible.

All pipework should be exposed and easy to get to for inspection, but located to prevent accidental damage. Any work on LPG pipework or other parts of a fixed installation, including testing, must only be carried out by appropriately trained (Gas Safe registered) persons.

Ventilation for heaters and cookers must be permanent and adequate. It should be divided equally between vents at high and low level.

A two-burner cooker in a site hut needs approximately 150 mm x 150 mm ventilation. A 3 kW convector heater needs approximately 225 mm x 225 mm ventilation.

Inspections of all appliances must be carried out before use. If soot forms or smells occur do not use or allow the appliance to be used. Find out the reasons for the problem and ensure that it is corrected.

9.8.14 Enclosed spaces

Before using LPG equipment in an enclosed space, it is essential to carry out a risk assessment under the Management of Health and Safety at Work Regulations.

It is essential to ensure that there is adequate ventilation, which may have to be forced. This is necessary to ensure full combustion and also to make certain that the products of combustion, other fumes and excess oxygen from any cutting apparatus are removed. Proper safety precautions and atmospheric monitoring should be considered.

Wherever practicable, cylinders used with operations in confined spaces should be located in a safe area, preferably in the open air. The supply pressure should be reduced to the lowest practicable level on leaving the source of supply.

Where cylinders are used below ground level, the number must be kept as small as possible.

All cylinders and hoses should be removed as soon as work has finished or if it is interrupted for a substantial period (for example, overnight).

LPG cylinders must not be taken into confined spaces, as defined in the Confined Spaces Regulations, unless exceptional safety precautions are taken.

9.9   Fire

Fires involving flammable liquids usually fall into one of two categories.

- Flowing liquid fires.
- Contained liquid fires.

Powder extinguishers are the most suitable type for tackling a flowing liquid fire. The use of foam or carbon dioxide extinguishers may be effective on a small, flowing liquid fire.

Foam extinguishers are the most suitable type for use on contained liquid fires. Powder or carbon dioxide extinguishers may also be used, but operators should be aware of the short duration of small carbon dioxide extinguishers and the possibility of reignition of any residual vapours being given off when an ignition source is still present.

 Do not use a water extinguisher for any fire involving flammable liquids. The water will not extinguish the fire, but will cause a violent reaction resulting in the burning liquid spreading around much faster. This could spread and intensify the fire.

Suitable portable fire extinguishers should, wherever possible, be sited in pairs (so as to minimise the risk of failure) and in strategic positions adjacent to the store.

9.9.1   Colour of fire extinguishers

With the introduction of the British Standard *Portable fire extinguishers* (BS EN 3) there are now two colour coding systems for portable fire extinguishers.

It is important that staff who may be called upon to use a fire extinguisher have a clear understanding of the colour coding.

This standard states that the body of all fire extinguishers should be red with zones of colour covering not more than 5% of the surface area of the extinguisher, fixed to the extinguisher body and denoting the extinguishing agent or medium it contains.

Colour coding by agent or medium (see right) enables a trained person to rapidly identify the type of extinguisher needed in an emergency.

Other information concerning its use may also be displayed on the body of the extinguisher.

Extinguishing medium	Colour of panel
Water	Red
Foam	Cream
Powder (all types)	Blue
Carbon dioxide	Black
Wet chemical	Yellow

The requirements of the standard are not retrospective. Fire extinguishers conforming to the older standard, BS 5423, which has been withdrawn, will continue to be found on premises and they can remain in use and be refilled until they need to be replaced. When replaced, the new extinguishers must conform to BS EN 3.

The full body colour coding of the older extinguishers is the same as is listed in the table above. In addition, a small number of extinguishers are bright silver or self-coloured metal with a designated panel stating the medium they contain. The colour coding of the panel is the same as the above.

Training in selecting the correct type of extinguisher to use and the safe way to operate fire-fighting equipment is essential and should be undertaken by all staff who work with dangerous substances. The use of the wrong extinguisher in the wrong way would have serious consequences.

 Advice on training can be obtained from extinguisher manufacturers or the local fire station.

9.9.2   Enforcement of fire safety legislation

The responsibility for the enforcement of fire safety legislation is split between the following organisations.

- HSE, or possibly the Local Authority on small sites, either of which would usually take enforcement action under CDM or the Management of Health and Safety at Work Regulations (MHSWR). However, the HSE also has enforcement powers under the Regulatory Reform (Fire Safety) Order.

- FRS, which would enforce their powers under the Regulatory Reform (Fire Safety) Order (England and Wales), the Fire (Scotland) Act or the Fire Safety Regulations (Northern Ireland).

In most circumstances, fire safety legislation will be enforced by the following organisations.

- HSE on construction sites, including on-site offices and other on-site accommodation.

- FRS where work other than construction is taking place, for example where:
  - one floor of an office block is being refurbished but the other floors remain occupied
  - part of a department store sales floor is a cordoned-off construction site but the public have access to the sales floor outside of the hoarding.

09

DANGEROUS SUBSTANCES

In the two circumstances described above it is usual for the HSE to enforce fire safety legislation within the confines of the site and the FRS to enforce it outside the hoardings. However, the responsibility for the enforcement of fire safety legislation may not always be as clear cut as this. For example, the FRS is likely to take an interest in any construction site where there is a significant fire loading or there are other factors that significantly increase personal risk. Some examples are shown below.

- Where the flammable nature of the partly finished structure is considered to pose a significant risk should it catch fire.

- The flammable (or highly flammable) nature and quantities of materials and substances stored and used on the site (for example, LPG).

- The vulnerability of adjacent premises should a fire start on site.

- If there is a large on-site multi-floor administrative complex housing technical staff and welfare facilities.

This aspect of fire safety is considered to be particularly relevant to this chapter if significant quantities of flammable or highly flammable substances are stored on site.

 For further information on legislation and other resources, including guidance and incident reports, visit the HSE website.

9.9.3 Liquefied petroleum gas

9.9.3.1 Action in an emergency

Instructions for dealing with incidents involving LPG will vary for each situation. The most important thing is to avoid endangering anyone's life. The following actions should be taken by anyone discovering a fire in the vicinity of LPG cylinders.

- In case of fire, **no matter how small**, call the FRS.

- Whilst waiting for the FRS to arrive, (if it can be done safely) turn off all cylinder valves to cut off the fuel supply and remove the cylinders from the area.

- If this action cannot be completed safely evacuate the site and impose a cordon to stop anyone inadvertently entering the area.

- General advice is to leave tackling any fire involving cylinders or tanks to the FRS unless it is judged that the fire can be put out without endangering anyone.

- Training in the correct type of fire-fighting equipment to use, and the safe way to operate it, should be undertaken by all staff who work with LPG. These staff must be trained to recognise when the situation is getting out of control and know when to evacuate the area.

- When the FRS arrives, inform the fire officer of the situation including:
  - the location and contents of all cylinders
  - details of any security cordon that you have implemented
  - confirmation that all people who were known to be in the area have been accounted for or details of anyone that is unaccounted for
  - if possible and required, offer them the data information sheet relating to the cylinder(s) involved.

9.9.3.2 Remember

- Cylinders fitted with pressure relief valves can produce gas jets that will extend a considerable distance.

- If cylinders are exposed to a severe fire or are engulfed in flames, no attempt should be made to fight the fire. **Evacuate everyone from the area.**

- Where a flame from a leaking gas cylinder is extinguished but the valve is still open, gas will continue to escape and there will be a danger of a gas cloud forming and the risk of an explosion.

- Any cylinder involved in a fire should be clearly labelled that it has been involved in a fire and removed from the area to a safe place. Telephone the suppliers – they will give advice and arrange for the cylinder(s) to be collected.

Instructions concerning emergency procedures should be clearly displayed and employers should ensure that all employees fully understand them. Emergency procedure drills should be practised regularly. Data information sheets are available from product manufacturers giving advice in case of an accident involving LPG cylinders. A copy of each sheet should be available for inspection and those sheets relating to the cylinders involved should be given to the fire officer.

9.9.4 Fire-fighting equipment

Employees who work with LPG should be identified and trained in the selection and use of fire-fighting equipment. Portable extinguishers should be used as a tool to preserve life where it is at risk, or a means to help you safely escape a dangerous situation. They should not be used as a tool to actively approach and fight an LPG fire. Advice on the training of staff can be obtained from the LPG supplier or the FRS.

Portable extinguishers, sited in pairs to minimise the risk of failure, should be positioned at strategic points wherever LPG is stored or used. As a guide, no fewer than two 4.5 kg dry powder extinguishers or equivalent should be provided for every 20 large (47 kg) cylinders stored.

9.9.5 Training

Most accidents involving LPG are due to ignorance of basic safety precautions. All persons using LPG cylinders, tools or equipment should be suitably instructed in the hazards associated with LPG, and the precautions to be taken in its use.

9.10   Legislative requirements

9.10.1   Construction (Design and Management) Regulations 2015

These regulations specify the measures to be taken to prevent the risk from fire, explosion or any substance likely to cause asphyxiation and include the measures that should be taken to detect and fight fires, which could occur on a construction site.

In practice, the HSE is likely to use this legislation for any enforcement action relating to the risks mentioned above.

 For further information refer to Chapter A03 Construction (Design and Management) Regulations.

9.10.2   ATEX and explosive atmospheres

ATEX is the name commonly given to the two European Directives for controlling explosive atmospheres.

1. Directive 99/92/EC (also known as ATEX 137 or the ATEX Workplace Directive) on minimum requirements for improving the health and safety protection of workers potentially at risk from explosive atmospheres.

2. Directive 2014/34/EU reflects the laws relating to equipment and protective systems intended for use in potentially explosive atmospheres.

In Great Britain the requirements of Directive 99/92/EC were put into effect through Regulations 7 and 11 of the Dangerous Substances and Explosive Atmospheres Regulations (DSEAR).

The aim of Directive 2014/34/EU is to allow the free trade of ATEX equipment and protective systems within the EU by removing the need for separate testing and documentation for each member state.

In Great Britain, the requirements of the directive were put into effect through the Equipment and Protective Systems Intended for Use in Potentially Explosive Atmospheres Regulations (SI 1996/192).

The regulations apply to all equipment intended for use in explosive atmospheres, whether electrical or mechanical, and also to protective systems.

Manufacturers or suppliers (or importers, if the manufacturers are outside the EU) must ensure that their products meet essential health and safety requirements and undergo appropriate conformity procedures.

This usually involves testing and certification by a third-party certification body (known as a notified body) but manufacturers or suppliers can self-certify equipment intended to be used in less hazardous explosive atmospheres. Once certified, the equipment is marked by the 'EX' symbol to identify it as such.

Note: *As from 1st January 2022, only UKCA-issued 'EX' certificates will be accepted in the UK for products that previously required ATEX Notified Body Certification.*

Certification ensures that the equipment or protective system is fit for its intended purpose and that adequate information is supplied with it to ensure that it can be used safely.

The UKCA mark

9.10.3   Competence and training

All the above sets of regulations stipulate the need for a degree of competence (skills, knowledge, training and experience) in assessing certain workplace situations. In most cases it will be necessary for the employer to provide employees with adequate information, instruction, training and supervision to enable them to carry out any work task safely and without risk to their health.

Appendix A – Retrieval of orphaned compressed gas cylinders

The cylinder retrieval arrangements in place for the major national companies are listed below.

Parent company	Collection company	Contact
Calor Gas	CylinderCare	www.wastecare.co.uk/services/cylindercare Tel: 0800 091 0000
BP	Synergy Recycling	www.synergy-recycling.co.uk/ Tel: 0800 083 9652
Flogas	In-house collection by own staff	www.flogas.co.uk/gas-bottles/returns Tel: 0800 574 574
BOC	In-house collection by own staff	www.boconline.co.uk/en/index Tel: 0800 111 333

 Orphaned cylinders

1. If a cylinder is no longer needed, it should be returned to the local dealer of the company owning the cylinder.

2. Where the original owner of a compressed gas cylinder cannot be identified, contact CylinderCare.

3. Until such time as they are collected, orphaned cylinders should be stored in a safe and secure manner.

4. If it is not known which company owns an LPG cylinder, the table of LPG cylinder fillers should be viewed in the 'who knows who' guidance table (available online).

5. In extreme circumstances, where all attempts to trace the owner of a cylinder have failed, the Local Authority waste disposal sites may offer a disposal service.

Index

INDEX

INDEX

INDEX

CONTENTS

Environment

CONTENTS

Sustainable construction and the environment

SUSTAINABLE CONSTRUCTION AND THE ENVIRONMENT

Summary of sustainable construction legislation and guidance

This list is not exhaustive and only includes legislation mentioned in this section of GE700.

Legislation and guidance	Enforcement agencies*						
	CIRIA	EA	HSE	LA	NIEA	NRW	SEPA
Acts (primary legislation)							
Climate Change Act		✓			✓	✓	
Climate Change (Scotland) Act							✓
Environmental Protection Act		✓			✓	✓	✓
Regulations (secondary legislation)							
COSHH Regulations			✓				
UK Building Regulations				✓			
Guidance							
ISO 14001 Environmental Management Systems							
ISO 20400 Sustainable Procurement							
ISO 26000 Social Responsibility							
ISO 50001 Energy Management							
Low Carbon Construction Action Plan and Routemap							
Waste Resources Action Programme (WRAP)	✓						
Working with substances hazardous to health: A brief guide to COSHH			✓				
Organisations that have information and guidance on their websites	✓	✓	✓	✓	✓	✓	✓

*Key

CIRIA	Construction Industry Research and Information Association
EA	Environment Agency
HSE	Health and Safety Executive
LA	Local Authorities
NIEA	Northern Ireland Environment Agency
NRW	Natural Resources Wales
SEPA	Scottish Environment Protection Agency

Overview

Environmental pressures are amongst the most serious issues facing the human race. Climate change, greenhouse gases, food production, loss of biodiversity and the harmful effects of plastics and chemicals are constantly in the news. Slowly, the global community is realising the damaging effects of these issues and the accelerating consequences of an increasing world population.

The construction industry can affect the environment in a number of ways. It therefore has a major role to play in protecting natural resources and ensuring that they are passed on to future generations, in good order, for their enjoyment.

This chapter gives a general introduction to the environment. It explains how the environment is defined, what local and global impacts put pressure on the environment and how these link with the overall concept of sustainable development. It also gives a general overview of the legal framework for the regulation of the environment and government environmental targets. It explains how the construction industry is responding to the environmental agenda by using fewer resources, less energy and promoting sustainable development.

1.1   Introduction

Rapid population growth and an ever-increasing demand for resources from economic development are placing huge pressures on our planet. In turn, this has led to an increase in all types of pollution and an acceleration of environmental damage. If everyone in the world lived as we do in Europe, we would need three planets to support us because we consume resources at a much faster rate than the planet can replenish them.

People, consumption, production and the environment are all linked and have a major impact on each other. It is therefore important to consider how construction's contribution to future development can be achieved without causing any further damage. Sustainable living is about respecting the earth's environmental limits.

The terms *sustainability* and *sustainable development* were first established in the paper *Our common future*, released by the Brundtland Commission in 1987 for the World Commission on Environment and Development. Sustainable development is the kind of development that meets the needs of the present generation without compromising the ability of future generations to meet their own needs. The main goal is to integrate the three pillars of sustainability that contribute to the achievement of sustainable development.

Environment. Protection and enhancement of natural resources.

Society. The wellbeing of people.

Economy. Sustainable consumption and production.

Most people now recognise that economic activity cannot take place without considering the environmental impacts. For example, the extraction of aggregates for new development has a significant effect on the local environment, which must be taken into account.

The Government's 25-year environmental plan (25YEP) was launched in 2018, and set out an ambition to become the 'first generation to leave the environment in a better state than we found it for our children, and our children's children'. The 25YEP set out a comprehensive delivery plan for the approach to halting and then reversing the decline in nature. Setting out a vision for a 'quarter-of-a-century of action' to help the natural world regain and retain good health, the plan has now started to deliver, and the following is evidence of this delivery in action.

● Wildlife habitats the size of Dorset have been created or restored.

● More than £750 million has been invested in the environment through the Nature for Climate Fund (NCF).

● The UK became the first major economy in the world to commit in law to Net Zero Strategy for the decarbonising of all sectors of the UK economy by 2050 and led international efforts to tackle climate change through our presidency of UN Climate Summit COP26.

● The UK is a world leader in its ambition to work with other nations to address environmental challenges the world is facing, which include the interlinked threat of climate change and biodiversity loss.

● The UK was first to co-design an agricultural programme to help sustainable food production to improve, not just protect the environment.

● A network of marine protected areas across 35,000 square miles of English waters has been established.

● Under the UK's Presidency of the UN Climate Summit COP26, 145 countries (representing over 90 per cent of the world's forests) signed a pledge to halt deforestation and land degeneration by 2030.

● The UK agreed to a new global deal for nature at the UN Nature Summit COP15, which set out a framework for restoring environments.

● The UK has sent a strong global message due to its long-term environmental targets, international leadership on climate and nature, and has evidenced that it takes environmental matters as seriously as Net Zero.

SUSTAINABLE CONSTRUCTION AND THE ENVIRONMENT

The 25YEP has now been refreshed, a commitment which was set into law in the Environment Act 2021 stating it would be reviewed and revised, if needed, every five years to ensure continued progress against the 10 goals of 25YEP. The Environment Act 2021 required government to set a suite of legally binding targets for environmental improvement in air quality, biodiversity, water, resource efficiency and waste reduction. These targets are meaningful, ambitious and advised by experts.

To achieve its vision, the 25YEP identified 10 complementary environmental goals, along with specific targets and commitments made in relation to each goal to ensure continual delivery of these targets and the overarching goals. These goals have been used to form the Environmental Improvement Plan 2023 (EIP23), and are laid down as follows:

Goal 1: thriving plants and wildlife

Goal 2: clean air

Goal 3: clean and plentiful water

Goal 4: managing exposure to chemicals and pesticides

Goal 5: maximise our resources, minimise our waste

Goal 6: using resources from nature sustainability

Goal 7: mitigating and adapting to climate change

Goal 8: reduced risk of harm from environmental hazards

Goal 9: enhancing biosecurity

Goal 10: enhanced beauty, heritage, and engagement with the natural environment

The EIP23 addresses how the Government will:

- create and restore at least 500,000 hectares of new wildlife habitats, starting with 70 new wildlife projects including 25 new or expanded National Nature Reserves and 19 further Nature Recovery Projects

- deliver a clean and plentiful supply of water for people and nature into the future, by tackling leaks, publishing a roadmap to boost household water efficiency, and enabling greater sources of supply

- challenge councils to improve air quality more quickly and tackle key hotspots

- transform the management of 70% of our countryside by incentivising farmers to adopt nature-friendly practices

- boost green growth and create new jobs – from foresters and farmers to roles in green finance and research and development.

 For further information on the ambitious roadmap for a cleaner, greener country and the EIP23, visit the Government website.

1.2   Changes on the horizon

1.2.1 'Biodiversity Net Gain' to be introduced for new developments in November 2023

The Government has announced that new housing, commercial and infrastructure developments are set to be 'nature positive' from November 2023. The plans are backed by £16m of funding for Local Planning Authorities and guidance to support the new approach. Developers in England will be required to deliver 10% 'Biodiversity Net Gain' when building new housing, industrial or commercial developments so there is a "positive benefit for nature". This means benefitting nature by making sure that the habitat for wildlife is in a better state than it was before development: either by trying to avoid a loss of habitat, or if unable to do so, then by creating habitats either on site or off site.

1.2.2 Cross-government plan to speed up delivery of major infrastructure projects

The Department for Levelling Up, Housing and Communities (DLUHC) has published an Action Plan for Nationally Significant Infrastructure Projects. The intended plan will streamline the planning process for large-scale infrastructure projects, speeding up the delivery of major infrastructure, such as off-shore wind, to support economic growth, improve connectivity across the country, bolster energy security for the future and deliver Net Zero. A new fast track process will be piloted, with powers for the Secretary of State to set shorter timelines for certain projects.

1.3   Important points

The construction industry has a major role in ensuring that the built environment is shaped in a way that delivers a sustainable future and reduces the environmental pressures on our planet from impacts such as climate change, resource depletion and biodiversity loss. For any construction project there will be a number of stakeholders who will have an interest in ensuring that the environmental requirements are being met: investors, clients, neighbours and regulators, to name a few. Effective environmental management will support your own legal compliance with environmental legislation and should ensure your stakeholder requirements are met. The environmental issues associated with construction are highly regulated. Environment Agencies and Local Authorities across the UK are responsible for ensuring that regulations are being complied with, and impacts that can cause pollution, reduce water supply or create nuisance (such as noise, dust and vibration) are minimised.

1.4   Sustainable construction

There are many reasons for the construction industry to work towards achieving these sustainable development priorities, including:

- The output of the construction industry is enormous; it is worth in excess of £100 billion per year.

- The construction industry accounts for around 6.5% of GDP, employs over 2 million people and supports 280,000 businesses.

- Buildings are responsible for almost 50% of UK carbon emissions, 50% of water consumption, about 30% of landfill waste and 25% of all raw materials used in the UK economy.

In the shift towards a Future Buildings Standard, the UK Government introduced a range of changes to the Building Regulations, including a mandatory 30% cut in carbon emissions for all new homes. These came into force in June 2022, with a one-year transition period to allow for planning applications underway at that time.

The changes included amendments to current Approved Documents (ADs) for ventilation (Part F) and conservation of fuel and power (Part L), and new ADs covering overheating (Part O) and infrastructure for charging electric vehicles (Part S). The majority of these changes are aligned to the roadmap and interim measures in the Government's Future Homes Standard and Future Buildings Standard, planned for 2025. A pivotal part is ensuring that all new builds are capable of being net zero in terms of operational carbon.

The Building Regulations will focus on reducing the need to heat and power buildings, and ensure that the UK is reaching its carbon zero goals.

e.g. ### Government and construction industry response to improving sustainability in construction

- Establishment of the UK Green Building Council (UKGBC) in 2008. Their most recent resources (housing standards playbook and social value in new development) offer guidance for developers and Local Authorities to support sustainable development.

- Improvements that support environmental protection through Parts L and F of the Building Regulations *Conservation of fuel and power* (amended 2022), by the DLUHC Future Buildings Standard, with a new Part O covering overheating in relation to building energy performance, air tightness and water efficiency.

- Establishment of the Waste Resources Action Programme (WRAP), operated between 2000 and 2015; Halving waste to landfill (HWL), and the Built Environment Commitment for clients, contractors, designers and waste contractors.
  Note: *this knowledge base has now been transferred to the Construction Industry Research and Information Association (CIRIA).*

- All new buildings on the central government estate must achieve a Building Research Establishment's Environmental Assessment Method (BREEAM) rating of *excellent (refer to 1.9.1 for further details on BREEAM).*

- Establishment of the Green Construction Board (GCB) as the sustainability workstream for the Construction Leadership Council. The GCB's priority and main focus is to advise on the regulatory, policy and technical framework required to overcome key barriers to the delivery of a zero carbon and zero waste built environment (both buildings and infrastructure), as well as to identify the commercial, jobs and export opportunities that such a clean growth, zero carbon and zero waste economy requires. Following the Infrastructure Carbon Review in 2013, it was identified that infrastructure is responsible for over 50% of the UK's carbon emissions: therefore, PAS 2080 was designed to specifically address the management of carbon in infrastructure. It looks at the whole life cycle of the carbon used on projects, and promotes reduced carbon, reduced cost infrastructure delivery, and a culture of challenge in the infrastructure value chain where innovation can be fostered.

- ISO 20400:2017 (sustainable procurement guidance) provides guidance to organisations on meeting their sustainability responsibilities, by providing an understanding of what sustainable procurement is; what the sustainability impacts and considerations are across various aspects of procurement (such as policy, strategy, organisation and process); and how to successfully implement sustainability within procurement.

- Establishment of the Government Construction Strategy 2016-20, committed to and identifying robust measurements and analysis of sustainability indicators.

- ISO 26000 Social Responsibility provides guidance on how businesses and organisations can operate in a socially responsible, ethical way.

- The Government is committed to the United Nations' sustainable development goals, which have wider reaching objectives beyond construction but also have, at their core, fundamental aims that impact on construction activity.

- The Clean Growth Strategy outlines the aims of the UK Government's vision of a low carbon future that supports reductions in greenhouse gases whilst promoting economic growth through increased efficiencies and innovative solutions.

For further information on ISO 20400 visit the ISO website.

For further information on PAS 2080 visit the Carbon Trust website.

SUSTAINABLE CONSTRUCTION AND THE ENVIRONMENT

1.5   Defining the environment

In its simplest terms, and according to the World Commission on Environment and Development, the **environment** is where we all live. More specifically, it can be defined as any physical surroundings consisting of air, water and land, natural resources, flora, fauna, humans and their interrelation.

1.6   Local and global environmental issues

Construction work can affect the environment in a number of ways, most noticeably at a local level where impacts are generally instantly evident. However, it also contributes to wider regional or global issues. The end result of any negative impact on the atmosphere, water or land is usually described as *pollution* or *contamination*. The surroundings in which a construction project operates includes air, water, land, natural resources, flora, fauna, humans, and their interrelationship, all of which can be impacted by construction activities if not controlled responsibly.

The use of energy, water and natural resources impacts the environment at a local and global level. Construction dust, noise, odours, site lighting and the inconvenience of traffic can each create nuisance, and can all have a significant effect on the neighbourhood and community.

1.6.1   Local environmental issues

The table below provides a summary of typical pollutants that cause local environmental impacts.

Atmosphere	Land	Water
■ Dust	■ Oils and fuels	■ Silt
■ Exhaust emissions	■ Chemicals	■ Chemicals
■ Gases or vapours	■ Lead	■ Concrete
■ Odours	■ Waste and litter	■ Contaminated water
■ Noise	■ Spillage of materials	■ Run-off
■ Vibration	■ Concrete	■ Effluent
■ Light or visual amenity	■ Asbestos	■ Oils and fuels
■ Smoke		■ Hazardous solid matter
■ Radiation		■ Slurry
■ Asbestos		

 One solution to environmental pollution must not divert the problem to another area (for example, a solution to air pollution should not lead to water contamination).

1.6.2   Global environmental issues

1.6.2.1   Climate change

Certain gases in the atmosphere (principally carbon dioxide, methane, nitrous oxide and chlorofluorocarbons (CFCs)) form an insulating blanket around the planet. This allows the sun's rays through, but prevents some of the heat radiated back from the earth escaping, which warms the planet. This can be likened to the role of glass in a greenhouse, hence the term *greenhouse effect*. Climate change brings various risks for construction, the most obvious of these being higher temperatures and erratic weather patterns, including flooding. It is important to ensure that buildings are designed to adapt to these risks and to mitigate further impacts through energy efficiency and the use of renewable energy.

Over the past century or so, CO_2 levels have risen by 40% since the 1800s, mainly as a result of burning fossil fuels. Although some CO_2 dissolves into the sea, the majority ends up in the atmosphere. Increased levels of CO_2 (and other gases) means that the Earth does not lose all the heat that it absorbs, and therefore the temperature rises. Over the last 100 years, records show that average temperatures have risen by 1°C. As a result of this temperature rise, the air is able to hold more water vapour, now 4% higher than 100 years ago. Increased water vapour has resulted in an increase in the energy stored in the atmosphere, which affects the world's weather patterns.

There have been many indications of climate change occurring from natural disasters, such as:

● the major storm conditions that resulted in severe flooding in New Orleans, USA in 2009

● the hottest average world temperatures were recorded in 2010, and again in 2012, 2014, 2015, 2016, 2020 and 2022

● severe flooding around the world (Australia, India and the UK) in 2011, along with the largest ever number of hurricanes in North America.

What could be the future of climate change? Temperatures could rise by 4% by 2100. Severe weather events in the UK are expected to increase by 30% by the end of the current century. The world's climate is a very complex system, and what might happen is by no means certain. Nothing is certain, but we cannot afford to just wait and see, we have to act now.

1.6.2.2   Acid rain

Acid rain is a collection of loosely related environmental problems involving acid substances and hydrocarbons. Burning fossil fuels, especially coal and oil (mainly in power stations and motor vehicles) produces acid gases (sulphur and nitrogen oxides). The presence of ozone in the lower atmosphere (harmful at this height), formed by the interaction of nitrogen oxides and hydrocarbons, also contributes to acid rain.

1.6.2.3   Deforestation

Deforestation, also known as forest degradation, is the cutting down of trees and forests. With 31% of the world covered in trees, deforestation is a threat to ecosystems around the globe.

The world's forests are being rapidly depleted by logging, slash-and-burn agriculture, development projects (such as businesses, homes, factories, roads, mines and dams), farmland and farm-related industries, and creation of pastures for livestock; forests are also being burned and destroyed by wildfire.

In the 1950s, forests covered about a quarter of the Earth's surface. At the turn of the 21st century, the figure was only one sixth. At our current rate, all rainforests will be gone in 77 years. The Amazon rainforest now emits more carbon dioxide than it absorbs.

According to the World Resources Institute, deforestation increased 12% globally in 2020. Even though the rest of the world pulled back during the global COVID-19 pandemic and the world economy shrunk by around 3.5% in 2020, the destruction of environmentally-sensitive rainforests was on the rise.

Without trees, many endangered species become even more vulnerable, and other animals are forced to find new homes. The atmosphere is plagued with higher levels of greenhouse gases that would have otherwise been stored by the trees as a carbon sink. Deforestation is having a detrimental impact on our planet.

Around 200,000 acres of rainforest are cut down or burned each day. That is an area equal to 120 football pitches lost every two minutes of every day, and 28 million acres lost every year.

50,000 species are lost each year as a result of deforestation, while 25% of Western drugs and pharmaceuticals come from rainforest sources, and 25% of all cancer-fighting drugs come from rainforests.

75% of tropical rainforests have lost the ability to properly recover from wildfires and drought, and 15 billion trees are chopped down every year. This equals every person on the planet having 3,000 rolls of toilet paper!

Forests are essential for a healthy world. They play an important role in regulating the global climate by locking up large amounts of carbon dioxide during photosynthesis. Trees prevent erosion, flooding and the formation of deserts.

Forests contain over half the world's plant and animal species and provide a home, fuel and food to many of the world's 150 million indigenous people. They also provide the basis for most medicines and cures discovered to date.

The construction industry uses a large amount of timber and is increasingly aware of the need to use this resource sustainably, hence why certification schemes such as the Forestry Stewardship Council (FSC) and the Programme for the Endorsement of Forest Certification (PEFC) have been established.

The world's forests are being rapidly depleted

1.6.2.4   Biodiversity loss

An ecosystem is made of plants, animals, micro-organisms, soil, rocks, minerals, water sources and local atmosphere interacting with, and over a given period of time sustaining, each other.

The clearing of natural ecosystems, which is usually a result of logging, agricultural or industrial development, or a consequence of war, causes great local disruption to the natural environment.

One major concern about the wholesale destruction of any natural habitat, particularly tropical forest, is that many species may become extinct as the ecosystem disappears.

On a wider scale, migratory species that use a particular habitat during one season (such as the breeding season) might also become extinct. Loss of biodiversity has a serious impact on the processes of nature. A wide range of biodiversity is an important

The loss of natural habitat threatens many invertebrates

element for a healthy planet. Animals, plants, trees and micro-organisms offer eco-services that help to purify the water and air, pollinate our crops for food and break down wastes naturally.

The destruction of habitats found in other ecosystems (such as wetlands, oceans and grasslands) has the same consequences as deforestation. Irresponsible construction can have a devastating impact on biodiversity.

In recognition, UK legislators have put planning processes in place to effectively manage this issue.

1.6.2.5 Resource depletion

The world's finite resources (such as coal, natural gas, oil, minerals, soil and metals) are rapidly being depleted. These resources have to be managed in a sustainable way because they are not renewable. Hydrocarbons (oil-based fuels and products) are finite resources because it takes millions of years for them to form: they cannot be replaced naturally within human timescales. Metals are also a finite resource; the amount of any available, as well as chemical and physical usability, is reflected in prices. Forests are a resource that can be regrown, but are currently being depleted *(refer to 1.6.2.3 Deforestation)*.

Large scale quarrying of finite resources

Water, especially clean drinking water, is being depleted and even in areas of Europe with regular rainfall this resource becomes limited after a short period of low rainfall. Construction is wholly dependent on the use of resources; without them, development could not happen. The drive for sustainable consumption and production will inevitably increase the costs for scarce resources and lead to technological improvements in the reuse and recycling of existing materials.

1.6.2.6 Ozone layer depletion

The ozone layer is a thin concentration of gas in the upper atmosphere. It protects the planet by filtering out harmful ultra-violet rays from the sun. These can cause skin cancer, eye cataracts, and restrict the growth of plants and other organisms. The layer has been depleted, especially above the North and South Poles, by artificial gases that destroy ozone molecules. The main offender was CFCs, which were used in industry and household goods but have now been banned. Worldwide action on ozone-depleting substances has significantly reduced this issue, with scientists estimating that a full recovery will have been reached by the middle of the 21st century.

1.7   Environmental stakeholders

Environmental management terminology often refers to *stakeholders* who, in simple terms, are interested parties who have either a direct involvement in a construction project or who may be affected by its work. Typical environmental stakeholders for a construction project could include the following.

Stakeholder	Potential interest
Investors	Ensure that the project's sustainable credentials increase value.
Non-governmental organisations (NGOs) (for example, Greenpeace, Friends of the Earth and the Green Building Council)	Publicise environmental practices, both good and bad.
Client or client's representative	Set the project environmental requirements.
Designer	Ensure that the client's environmental aspirations are reflected in the project design.
Planning authority	Approve the design, including relevant environmental requirements and set relevant planning conditions.
Local Authority	Ensure that the works comply with statutory requirements for local air pollution control, including noise and dust, and issue relevant permits.
Environment regulators (for example, Environment Agencies and Local Authorities)	Act as a statutory consultee in the planning process and issue relevant permits and licences for the works (such as discharge consents).
Staff and contractors	Ensure that the project environmental requirements are met and lead by example.
Government funded support organisations (for example, WRAP, the Carbon Trust and charities)	Provide support, advice and good practice and drive environmental improvement.
Residents and community representatives	Participate in the planning and consultation process and ensure that the works bring positive benefits to an area and are carried out without causing nuisance from noise, dust, light and traffic congestion.

Early identification of all relevant stakeholders, together with regular communication and liaison, is important to avoid delays, legal intervention or causing a nuisance to the local community.

 Identify all stakeholders and regularly communicate with them on relevant environmental issues.

 For further information refer to the community liaison section in Chapter E06 Statutory nuisance.

1.8   Regulatory framework for the environment

Construction sites have a number of legal obligations, many of which relate to protection of the environment. Environmental policy and law is based on guiding principles that define the content of any rules and regulations, and are firmly embedded within legal frameworks.

Prevention is better than cure, so policy measures are introduced to prevent environmental harm rather than remediate environmental problems once they have occurred.

Precaution. Where there is uncertainty over the environmental science of an urgent problem, environmental protection must be prioritised rather than risk an impact occurring.

Polluter pays principle requires that those causing (or potentially responsible for) environmental damage bear the financial costs of any remediation actions. For example, this payment may be made through remediation of contamination, investment in pollution abatement technology and clean production plant, or through environmental taxation and charges.

Legal obligations do not only originate from the UK Government, or its devolved administrations. There are many sources of environmental law, starting at the international level, which are then transposed into UK law. In fact, most environmental law in the UK currently comes from regulations made in Europe.

In the UK there are two general types of law.

Civil law is concerned with the compensation of people who have had harm done to them through no fault of their own.

Criminal law is concerned with the punishment of companies or individuals who have broken the law.

The two relevant sources of law are statute law, which is made by Parliament and implemented in the form of Acts, Regulations and Orders; and common law, which is established by custom and practice by judges through their decisions and the precedents that they set.

In the UK there are three levels of regulation relevant to criminal law.

Statutes or Acts of Parliament are laws that have been agreed by both houses of Parliament in the form of a Bill and have received royal assent. Acts of Parliament are also known as 'primary legislation' because they do not depend on other legislative authority. These Acts are enabling legislation, as they allow for the creation of regulations. The Climate Change Act 2008 is a statute.

Delegated (or secondary) legislation can take different forms.
- Statutory instruments (SIs) add detail to the Acts, through which the Secretary of State can issue specific regulations.
- Orders issuing specific rules relating to a statute or part of a statute (for example, the Carbon Reduction Commitment Energy Efficiency Scheme Order issued under the Climate Change Act).
- Byelaws, which are made by the various tiers of local government, and can cover such matters as the establishment of internal drainage boards.

Guidance. For some pieces of legislation the relevant Government department or regulator will issue guidance (such as those below) on the interpretation and implementation of the regulations.
- **Statutory guidance**, typically in the form of an Approved Code of Practice (ACoP) that sets out how to comply with the law, and gives a clear indication of what is expected.
- **Non-statutory guidance**, typically a circular from a Government department, or technical guidance from either Government or the regulator (for example, Defra *Non-statutory guidance*).

1.8.1   Government policy-making departments

The main Government departments involved in developing and implementing environmental policy and legislation are outlined below. They work with the devolved administrations of Wales, Scotland and Northern Ireland.

Department for Energy Security and Net Zero (DESNZ) is responsible for the mission to replace energy with cheaper, cleaner and renewable domestic sources to enable the UK to become a net zero economy by 2050.

Department for Environment, Food and Rural Affairs (Defra) is responsible for making policy and legislation, and works with others to deliver policies in the natural environment, biodiversity, plants and animals; sustainable development and the green economy; food, farming and fisheries; animal health and welfare; environmental protection and pollution control; and rural communities and issues.

Department for Business, Energy and Industrial Strategy (BEIS) is responsible for ensuring that the UK remains at the leading edge of strategies for industry, business, science, innovation, energy and climate change. Responsibilities include the development and delivery of a comprehensive industrial strategy and leading the Government's relationship with business, whilst ensuring the country has secure energy supplies that are reliable, affordable and clean through the Government's Clean Growth Strategy.

Department for Levelling Up, Housing and Communities (DLHC) is responsible for implementing planning policy, Building Regulations and building-related environmental standards (energy performance certificates and display energy certificates).

Construction Leadership Council (CLC) has been established to own and oversee industrial strategy for construction. Membership is composed of senior business people representing the main industry bodies and senior representatives of Government departments. The CLC will concentrate on achieving the following joint industry and government commitments from the construction strategy.

- 33% reduction in both the initial cost of construction and the whole-life cost of assets.
- 50% reduction in the time from the outset to completion for new build and refurbished assets.

- 50% reduction in greenhouse gas emissions in the built environment.

- 50% reduction in the trade gap between total exports and total imports for construction products and materials.

Green Construction Board is the sustainability workstream of the Construction Leadership Council, and its priority and main focus is to advise on the regulatory, policy and technical framework required to overcome key barriers to the delivery of a zero carbon and zero waste built environment – as well as to identify the commercial, jobs and export opportunities that such a clean growth, zero carbon and zero waste economy requires. It was established to ensure a sustained, high-level conversation and to develop and implement a long-term strategic framework for the promotion of innovation and sustainable growth. The board owns and monitors the implementation, and will build on the Low Carbon Construction Action Plan and Routemap.

 Further information on these departments can be found on the Government and Northern Ireland Department of Environment (DOE) websites.

1.8.1.1 Powering Up Britain

This plan is the first to come from DESNZ. Powering Up Britain sets out the department's approach for Britain to be powered by renewables including wind, solar, hydrogen, power with carbon capture, usage and storage (CCUS) and new nuclear plants, and is an introduction to the complementary Energy Security Plan and the Net Zero Growth Plan.

The Energy Security Plan sets out steps to transform the energy system in the UK to make sure the UK is energy independent, secure and resilient and to double Britain's electricity generation capacity by the late 2030s. The Net Zero Growth Plan sets out the actions to be taken to ensure the UK remains a leader in the transition to net zero by:

- driving investment into industries like offshore wind, CCUS and nuclear

- acting as the annual update against the Net Zero Strategy

- responding to the Climate Change Committee's Annual Progress report

- setting out the package of policies and proposals to meet the carbon budgets up to 2037.

 Further information on Powering Up Britain can be found on the Government website.

1.8.2 Environment Agencies

England. The Environment Agency (EA).

Northern Ireland. The Northern Ireland Environment Agency with the Department of Agriculture, Environment and Rural Affairs.

Scotland. The Scottish Environment Protection Agency.

Wales. Natural Resources Wales, linking with the Forestry Commission and Countryside Council for Wales.

The environment agencies exist to provide high-quality environmental protection and improvement. This is achieved by an emphasis on prevention, education and vigorous enforcement wherever necessary.

The aim of protecting and enhancing the whole environment is to contribute to the targets of global sustainable development.

The **enforcement powers** of the environment agencies are set out in their enforcement and sanctions statement and guidance, which outlines the circumstances under which they will normally prosecute. Enforcement powers available to the agencies will vary according to the nature and severity of the environmental offence, but could include the following.

- A formal warning.

- A formal caution.

- Enforcement notices and works notices (where contravention can be prevented or needs to be remedied).

- Prohibition notices (where there is an imminent risk of serious environmental damage).

- Suspension or revocation of environmental permits and licences.

- Variation of permit conditions.

- Injunctions.

- Remedial works (where it carries out remedial works, it will seek to recover the full costs incurred from those responsible).

- Criminal sanctions, including fines, prosecution and imprisonment.

- Civil sanctions, including financial penalties.

The environment agencies can authorise officers to enter premises, including any land, vehicle, vessel or mobile plant. The occupier may need to be notified in advance (other than in the case of an emergency) and entry may only be permitted at reasonable times. Officers must abide by and not go beyond the instructions within the authorisation. In the case of emergencies under Section 108 of the Environment Act persons authorised by the environment agencies have the authority to enter any premises, by force, at any time with or without a warrant, and to:

- take any equipment or materials necessary as evidence

- make any examination or investigation

- direct that the premises are left undisturbed while being examined

- take samples and photographs

- require the production of records to demonstrate and confirm evidence of compliance

- instruct any relevant person to answer questions and to declare the truth of the answers given.

Environment agencies can also carry out formal interviews under caution in accordance with the Police and Criminal Evidence (PACE) Act. The EA's *Offence response options* document sets out the options available to every offence that the EA regulates.

 For further information on EA sanctions and offences visit the Government website.

1.8.3   Local Authorities

Local Authorities are responsible for various environmental pollution control functions, including those listed below.

Air quality. Local Authorities are responsible for the management and assessment of local air quality, including the establishment of air monitoring zones, smoke control areas and the prohibition of dark smoke from chimneys under the Clean Air Act.

Contaminated land. Under the Contaminated Land Regime, Local Authorities have a duty to inspect their land, to formally classify it as contaminated land, and require it to be cleaned up by the owner/occupier. Land can be designated as a **special site** under certain criteria (for example, land seriously affecting drinking water, owned or occupied by the Ministry of Defence or used for certain industrial activity). In these circumstances the land will be regulated by the environment agencies.

Local Authority Air Pollution Control (LAAPC). For less polluting processes requiring an environmental permit (in England, Northern Ireland and Wales) or authorisation (in Scotland), the control of emissions to air alone is exercised by Local Authorities. Local Authorities have a duty to give prior written authorisation for processes under their control. This includes, for example, permits for mobile crushing and screening equipment and concrete batching plants.

Nuisance. Complaints of statutory nuisance (such as noise, dust and odour) are dealt with by Local Authorities. They may serve an abatement notice where they are satisfied that a statutory nuisance exists or is deemed likely to occur or recur *(for further information refer to Chapter E06 Statutory nuisance)*.

Planning. Local Authorities have the responsibility of implementing and regulating national planning policy, including environmental impact assessments, tree preservation orders (TPOs) and authorisations for hedge removal. In many cases other regulators will be a statutory consultee, as part of the planning process.

Waste controls. Local Authorities have some powers under waste legislation to stop and search waste carriers and confiscate (and, in some instances, crush) vehicles suspected of waste crime *(for further information refer to Chapter E10 Waste and material management)*.

1.8.4   Other regulatory organisations that support the protection of the environment

There are a number of other regulatory bodies (shown below) that have specific regulatory and advisory responsibilities that are relevant to construction sites.

Water companies. The composition and quantity of industrial discharges to sewers are controlled primarily by the regional water companies (frequently referred to as sewerage undertakers) *(for further information refer to discharge consents in Chapter E07 Water management and pollution control)*.

Lead Local Flood Authorities. On 6 April 2012, when a further phase of the Flood and Water Management Act was implemented, responsibility for regulating work on ordinary watercourses in most areas of England and Wales transferred from the EA to Lead Local Flood Authorities (LLFAs). These are unitary authorities where they exist, and county councils elsewhere.

Canal and River Trust. British Waterways ceased to exist in England and Wales and in its place the Canal and River Trust was set up in July 2012 to care for 2,000 miles of historic waterways. In Scotland, British Waterways continues to exist as a public body caring for the canals, operating as Scottish Canals.

Cadw is the historic environment service of the Welsh Assembly Government, having responsibility for designated archaeological and heritage sites in Wales.

Historic England is responsible for protecting historic buildings, landscapes and archaeological sites.

Health and Safety Executive (HSE). There is an overlap between environmental legislation and health and safety legislation, which is regulated by the HSE, including the COSHH Regulations and the Control of Major Accident Hazards (COMAH).

Internal Drainage Boards have powers under the Land Drainage Act (as amended) to undertake works on any watercourse within their district other than a main river. A board's district is defined on a sealed map prepared by the EA and approved by the relevant ministry. In addition, boards can undertake works on watercourses outside their drainage district in order to benefit the district.

Natural England is responsible for conservation of wildlife and geology, including sites of special scientific interest (SSSI) and prevention of damage to habitats.

Scottish Natural Heritage is responsible for designated ecological sites, geological and geomorphological sites, and protected species.

Historic Environment Scotland is an executive agency of the Scottish Government and is charged with safeguarding Scotland's historic environment and promoting its understanding and enjoyment.

Department for Communities is responsible for the historic environment in Northern Ireland.

SUSTAINABLE CONSTRUCTION AND THE ENVIRONMENT

1.9   UK environmental targets

The UK and EU environmental targets are identified in a large number of strategies for each environmental policy area.

The list below provides a summary of the main construction targets for each of these policy areas.

Policy area	Target(s)
Waste	To achieve a target of 50% for the reuse and recycling of waste materials (such as paper, metal and glass) by 2020; the target for non-hazardous construction and demolition waste is 70%. The latest figures suggest that these targets have already been met, with more than 80% of waste now being recycled. The target for landfill set out in the *Strategy for sustainable construction* was to halve waste sent to landfill by 2012. The Government's environment plan: *A green future: our 25 year plan to improve the environment*, published in 2018, sets an ambitious target to work towards eliminating all avoidable waste by 2050 (including all avoidable plastic waste by 2042).
Energy	To reduce carbon emissions by 80% (from 1990 levels) by 2050, with intermediate targets of 34% by 2020 and 57% by 2032. The UK also has a target to provide 15% of all energy from renewable sources by 2020. Revisions to Part L of the Building Regulations aim to reduce carbon emissions further, with the ultimate goal of zero emissions. With the cancellation of zero carbon policy in July 2015, the EU nearly zero energy buildings 2020 target may initiate further improvements in building regulations for energy efficiency standards. *Construction 2025* has a target to achieve a 50% reduction in greenhouse gas emissions in the built environment by 2025. From April 2018 new regulations were enacted in England and Wales for any privately rented properties to have a minimum energy performance rating of E and be validated by an energy performance certificate (EPC).
Water	To reduce the consumption of water through cost effective measures, to an average of 130 litres per person per day by 2030, or possibly even 120 litres per person per day depending on new technological developments and innovation. Water quality standards are also set out in the Water Framework Directive. Part G (water efficiency) of the Building Regulations sets requirements for new properties of 125 litres per person per day (with an optional 110 litres per person per day).
Air quality	Objectives and target values for the protection of human health and for the protection of vegetation and ecosystems are set out in the Clean Air Strategy 2019. It specifies objectives for reducing emissions from transport, homes, farming and industry.
Biodiversity	The UK is a signatory to the Convention on Biological Diversity (CBD) and is committed to the new biodiversity goals and targets (the Aichi targets) agreed in 2010 and set out in the strategic plan for biodiversity 2011-2020. The UK has put in place a set of indicators to measure its progress towards meeting these targets annually: *UK biodiversity indicators*. A new global biodiversity framework to 2030 is being negotiated under the Convention on Biological Diversity.

 For further information on *UK biodiversity indicators,* visit the Joint Nature Conservation Committee website.

1.10   Construction sustainability assessment tools

Building Research Establishment's Environmental Assessment Method (BREEAM) and BREEAM Infrastructure (formerly the Civil Engineering Environmental Quality Assessment and Award Scheme (CEEQUAL)) are assessment methods used by the construction and civil engineering industry to measure and improve the sustainability of projects.

Clients are increasingly making achievement of these standards part of the project obligations. Many of the assessment standards are directly linked to the objectives and targets set out in the Government's *Strategy for sustainable construction* discussed above.

1.10.1   The Building Research Establishment Environmental Assessment Method (BREEAM)

BREEAM is the world's leading science-based suite of validation and certification systems for sustainable built environment. Since 1990, its third-party certified standards have helped improve asset performance at every stage, from design through construction, to use and refurbishment.

BREEAM is a voluntary green building sustainability rating system established in the UK, and assesses the performances of buildings over a wide range of environmental issues to produce a rating of either Pass, Good, Very Good, Excellent or Outstanding.

A BREEAM assessment uses recognised measures of performance categories and criteria (which cover a range of areas associated with any development, ranging from energy to ecology) set against established benchmarks in order to evaluate a building's specification, design, construction and use.

BREEAM assessments are conducted by assessors who score a building or project based on 10 sustainability categories. Each category has a number of credits allocated to it and the overall score is a sum of these.

These 10 distinct BREEAM assessment categories gauge a building's sustainability as comprehensively as possible, and are as follows:

1. **Energy:** How energy efficient is a building? How much energy usage or wastage is there?

2. **Management:** How well is a building or project managed? Are there sustainability focused management policies in place?

3. **Water:** How much water does a construction project require? How much water does the building require to remain operational?

4. **Waste:** How much waste is produced by a construction project? Where does the waste end up?

5. **Pollution:** How much pollution results from the building? How can pollution be limited or removed entirely?

6. **Health and Wellbeing:** What health and safety measures are in place? Is there adequate ventilation and lighting?

7. **Materials:** Which materials are used to construct a building? Where are they sourced? Are they sustainable?

8. **Transport:** How accessible is a building to those who live or work there? Is the building easily connected to existing public transport?

9. **Land usage:** Is this a brownfield or a greenfield site? How is the surrounding environment and wildlife impacted?

10. **Innovation:** How innovative is the design? How innovative are the building's sustainability policies?

For a building to achieve the highest possible score it must achieve credits in all BREEAM Assessment categories.

The overall score for the assessment will be the percentage of credits achieved in each of the 10 categories, which are then weighted to provide an overall percentage score. The total score will determine the BREEAM rating, as shown on the right.

Assessment	Credits achieved
Outstanding	Minimum 85%
Excellent	Minimum 70%
Very good	Minimum 55%
Good	Minimum 45%
Pass	Minimum 30%
Unclassified	Less than 30%

To ensure that performance against fundamental environmental issues is not overlooked in pursuit of a particular rating, BREEAM sets minimum standards of performance in important areas (such as energy, water and waste).

It is important to bear in mind that these are minimum acceptable levels of performance and, in that respect, they should not necessarily be viewed as levels that are representative of good practice for a BREEAM rating level. To achieve a particular BREEAM rating, the minimum overall percentage score must be achieved and the minimum standards, applicable to that rating level, complied with.

BREEAM third-party certification involves the checking – by impartial experts – of the assessment of a building or project by a qualified and licensed BREEAM assessor to ensure that it meets the quality and performance standards of the scheme. Fees are charged for this service.

 For further information visit the BRE Group website.

1.10.2 BREEAM Infrastructure

BREEAM Infrastructure (formerly CEEQUAL) is the recognised industry leader for sustainability assessment tools for infrastructure and civil engineering projects. Its eight categories relate to different areas of sustainability against which the performance of a project is assessed. Projects are awarded a score for each category, and are combined to provide an overall sustainability assessment final rating.

There are six rating levels:

1. Unclassified

2. Pass

3. Good

4. Very good

5. Excellent

6. Outstanding.

Management · Resilience · Communities & stakeholders · Land use & ecology · Landscape & historic environment · Pollution

Resources · Transport

The eight BREEAM infrastructure categories

Competent BREEAM Infrastructure assessors (usually a member of the project team who influences and encourages the team to consider sustainability issues at appropriate times) and external verifiers are central to the assessment process. Assessors drive the process and verifiers provide third-party verification of the final rating. The fee scale is dependent on many factors such as project contract value or works, client's or engineer's estimates, and assessment type.

 For further information visit the BRE Group website.

1.10.3 Leadership in Energy and Environmental Design

Launched by the US Green Building Council (GBC) in 1998, the Leadership in Energy and Environmental Design (LEED) standard has become widely used both within the US and around the world. In recent years, UK based client groups have begun to ask for LEED certification alongside BREEAM.

 Around 2.8 million square feet of buildings around the world are LEED certified every day.

Like BREEAM, LEED is voluntary and it can be applied to any building type and any building life cycle phase. It promotes a whole-building approach to sustainability by recognising performance in important areas of energy and water efficiency, CO_2 emissions, indoor environmental quality and sustainable use of resources.

LEED credits are weighted differently, depending on their potential impact. The greatest weighting is placed on energy and atmosphere, with sustainable sites and materials and resources also receiving a high weighting. A total of 100 base points are available with, additionally, six possible innovation in design points and four regional priority points. There are four levels of achievement: certified (40-49), silver (50-59), gold (60-79) and platinum (80 and over).

There are five different rating systems to cover different types of project, including new construction, LEED for existing buildings, LEED for commercial interiors, LEED for retail, LEED for schools and LEED for core and shell. Most building types are included in one or more of these systems. LEED differs from BREEAM in a number of areas, and contractors should review requirements fully. Some differences are shown below.

● There is no need for an accredited assessor, as the US Green Building Council assesses applications (although an extra credit is available where an assessor is used).

● Design requirements are linked to the American ASHRAE standards whereas BREEAM relates to UK Building Regulations.

● Some credits are calculated using US specific outputs (such as US dollars saved for credits relating to energy).

● Regional priority credits can only be obtained in the US.

In 2018 the Building Research Establishment and the US Green Building Council entered into partnership to raise sustainability standards and deliver greater value.

 For further information visit the US Green Building Council website.

1.10.4 RICS SKA rating online assessment tool

In 2005, Skansen initiated a research project with the Royal Institute of Chartered Surveyors (RICS) and AECOM to establish whether it was possible to measure either the environmental impact of fit-outs, or measure or codify good environmental practice on fit-out projects, in order to remove the ambiguity prevalent in the fitting out and refurbishment industry. The result of this was SKA rating, and this assessment tool allows property and construction professionals and SKA assessors to design, specify, rate and certify non-domestic fit-out projects for environmental impact, using the SKA rating fit-out benchmark system. Use of the tool is free and open to all. Projects can be certified by qualified assessors for an additional fee. The SKA assessment process is broken down into three stages.

1. Design/planning.   **2.** Delivery/construction.   **3.** Occupancy stage assessment.

 For further information visit the RICS website.

1.11 Sustainable use of materials, energy and water – resource efficiency

Materials, water and energy (including transport) are all forms of resource, where efficiency of use has a considerable influence on construction schedules, costs and environmental impact.

Construction projects that use materials efficiently will often have lower construction times and lower costs. Clearly this will lead to greater competitiveness, more repeat business and greater customer satisfaction. It also reduces the amount of resources that are taken from the planet and the amount of waste that the planet receives via landfill from construction work.

Inefficient projects can be costly, late, use excessive resources, produce too much waste, and are bad for the corporate image and lead to reduced client satisfaction.

The Government's *Construction 2025* places a top priority on resource-efficient, low carbon construction. To achieve this outcome the project leadership must lead by example and communicate the correct behaviours, at all levels of the project, to emphasise the importance of resource efficiency.

 For further guidance on energy management, water management and resource efficiency refer to Chapters E03, E07 and E08 respectively.

CONTENTS

Site environment management systems

GT700 Toolbox talks / supporting checklists and forms

Toolbox talks on some of these topics are available in the GT700 publication. Supporting checklists and forms covering some of these topics are available on our companion website.

SITE ENVIRONMENT MANAGEMENT SYSTEMS

Overview

This chapter provides an introduction to environmental management systems, how they can be applied to construction projects and guidance on the environmental documents and records that should be maintained on a construction site.

In many respects these are the systems that capture all of the required detail identified in each chapter of *Construction site health and safety E: Environment* (GE700E).

2.1   Introduction

An environmental management system (EMS) provides an organised, systematic and consistent approach, allowing organisations to address environmental concerns through allocation of resources, assignment of responsibilities, and provision and continuous monitoring and evaluation of procedures, systems and processes.

They help companies reduce their environmental impact, achieve cost savings, comply with legislation and demonstrate their commitment to continual improvement in environmental performance. Being able to demonstrate that their company understands and is managing its environmental impact is an important prerequisite for construction companies when tendering for new business.

It is recognised that adopting standard environmental management policies and practices not only helps in protecting the environment but also brings business benefits in terms of reduction of waste, energy use and improved efficiency.

It also reduces the risk of causing incidents that may result in enforcement action, which could lead to prosecution.

Managing the environment, or environmental impact, is not just for one person in an organisation. It is a process of change for all involved.

An EMS can help all types and sizes of company meet their own environmental and sustainability targets as well as contribute to national targets on climate change, sustainable development, waste, water, emissions, energy, resource efficiency and other environmental issues.

An EMS has a number of important functions.

Help a company understand its environmental impact. It should be a practical tool to identify and describe a company's impact on the environment, manage and reduce these impacts and evaluate and improve performance. An EMS can help with identifying compliance obligations and managing risks and opportunities.

Secure positive environmental outcomes. It should not only document procedures and processes but also focus on improving environmental performance and complying with legal and client requirements.

Improve cost control and improve efficiency. An EMS can also help conformity with customer requirements in the supply chain, enable sustainable procurement policies, enhance a company's reputation, help Improve communication with and confidence of employees, regulators, investors and other stakeholders, and improve market positioning, waste minimisation and energy efficiency savings.

To fully contribute to improved environmental performance, a good EMS should include the detail below.

● Be implemented at a senior level and integrated into company plans and policies (top-level leadership and commitment is essential so that senior management understand their role in ensuring the success of an EMS).

● Identify the company's aspects (activities that impact on the environment) and set clear objectives and targets to improve its management of these impacts and the company's overall environmental performance. This also ensures the correct allocation of resources, such as money and staff time.

● Be designed to deliver and manage the organisation's compliance with environmental laws and regulations on an ongoing basis. This will quickly instigate corrective and preventative action in cases of legal non-compliance.

● Deliver good resource management and financial benefits.

● Incorporate performance indicators that demonstrate the effectiveness of the above and can be communicated in a transparent way in annual reports.

● Provide the workforce with ownership of environmental management.

● Enable the identification and correction of any issues, to facilitate continual improvement.

● Be integrated into the entire organisation.

 Demonstrating to clients that you have policies and arrangements in place to manage and improve environmental performance will enhance your company's reputation and contribute to obtaining future work.

Whilst larger construction companies will want to demonstrate that they have a robust EMS through certification to a formal standard (such as ISO 14001 *(refer to 2.3)*), smaller companies should consider implementing an EMS as this will help identify their environmental risks and put in place controls to manage them. This will also improve their opportunities in winning future work.

2.2   Important points

An effective EMS helps companies manage their environmental risks, reduce their exposure to potential legal action and improve performance.

This leads to other benefits, such as cost and efficiency savings and improved customer relationships. An EMS can also help companies demonstrate that they have policies, objectives and programmes in place to meet their own sustainability targets, as well as contribute towards wider Government targets.

Important aspects for delivering an effective EMS on site are shown below.

- Identifying the environmental and legal obligations for a project from a review of client documents. This is including, but is not limited to, planning consents and conditions, environmental statements, remediation statements, archaeological statements and ecological management plans.

- Identifying relevant environmental aspects (such as discharges to land, air and water) and meeting these obligations and their associated impacts. This should also include considering emergency situations (such as leaks and spillages).

- Putting the appropriate responsibilities in place to manage and reduce the impact associated with the project environmental obligations and risks.

- Creating an EMS plan that sets out what actions need to be taken, who is responsible for those actions, and identifying the appropriate records that need to be maintained.

- Putting an appropriate inspection, monitoring and audit regime in place to ensure that the project's environmental obligations and their associated risks are being managed effectively.

- Maintaining and retaining appropriate documented information to demonstrate that legal, client and company requirements associated with the project are being met and can be retrieved, if required, for any purpose.

2.3   Types of environmental management system

There are three main recognised standards or schemes.

ISO 14001 is the international standard for EMS, which specifies the components necessary to help organisations systematically identify, evaluate, manage and improve the environmental impacts of their work, products and services. It helps organisations become greener by putting a system of continual improvements in place. It is a framework for establishing performance targets alongside the procedures, systems and reviews that help ensure sustainable business operations.

ISO 14001 requires organisations to meet the following requirements.

- Identify interested parties relevant to the EMS and their needs and expectations.

- Ensure that top management demonstrate leadership and commitment with respect to the EMS.

- Establish an environmental policy relevant to the organisation.

- Identify the environmental aspects associated with the organisation's work and determine the significant environmental impacts.

- Identify applicable compliance obligations associated with the organisation's environmental impact.

- Identify priorities and set appropriate environmental objectives.

- Identify and provide the necessary resources for establishment, implementation, maintenance and continual improvement of the EMS.

- Establish a structure and programme(s) to implement the policy and achieve environmental objectives.

- Implement planning, control, monitoring, preventive and corrective actions, auditing and reviewing procedures to ensure that the policy is complied with and that the EMS remains appropriate, and is capable of adapting to changing circumstances.

EMAS (the EU Eco-management and audit scheme) is a voluntary EU-wide environmental registration scheme that requires organisations to produce a public statement about their performance against targets and objectives, and incorporates the international standard ISO 14001. Refer to the European Commission Environment website for guidance regarding ongoing EMAS registration now that the UK has left the EU.

BS 8555 is a British Standard, updated in 2016, which breaks down the implementation process for ISO 14001 or EMAS into stages, making implementation much easier, especially for smaller companies. The Institute of Environmental Management and Assessment (IEMA) has developed the IEMA Acorn scheme, which enables companies to gain United Kingdom Accreditation Service (UKAS) accredited recognition for achievements at each stage as they work towards ISO 14001 or EMAS. This allows for early recognition of progress against indicators, and can be used effectively to enhance supply chain management by setting agreed levels of performance, certified to a national standard, which have been checked by an independent auditor. Organisations who complete each stage of the scheme are entered on a public Acorn register.

 For further information and a guide to environmental management systems visit the WRAP website.

 For further details of the ESOS scheme, which is relevant to larger companies, refer to Chapter E03 Energy management.

SITE ENVIRONMENT MANAGEMENT SYSTEMS

2.4   Policy, objectives and targets

Requirements for a basic EMS policy are shown below.

- Be appropriate to the organisation, for its size and type of work.

- Be dynamic, flexible and simple so that it is easy to adapt and change, and easy to understand.

- Form part of a balanced overall management system, and be able to interact with other management systems.

- Establish a framework for setting and reviewing environmental objectives.

- Commit to comply with current legislation and other environmental requirements or obligations.

- Commit to pollution prevention and continual improvement.

- Be documented, implemented and maintained.

- Be readily available for employees and other interested parties.

The policy should be endorsed by someone of authority within the organisation, either a director or someone of equal seniority.

Setting targets is vital to a successful EMS and demonstrates the commitment of the business to reduce its impacts and set the path for a programme of continual improvement.

An initial baseline assessment of where the organisation is in terms of its current management of the environment will identify areas for improvement.

The following areas could be considered.

- Measuring and reducing the amount of waste produced.

- Improving recycling rates for different waste streams.

- Monitoring water use, setting reduction targets and implementing and sharing measures.

- Monitoring energy use (electricity and fuel), setting reduction targets and implementing and sharing measures.

- Purchasing services and materials from sustainable sources and/or with recycled content.

- Assisting and improving supply chain knowledge on environmental matters.

- Existing organisational environmental management practices and procedures.

- Industry best practices.

- Legal requirements.

Regular measurement and reporting against company targets will highlight whether they are being met and where future action needs to be focused.

This will allow the company to continually improve its environmental performance and demonstrate to clients, staff and the general public that it is taking its environmental responsibilities seriously.

2.5   Implementing environmental management on site

A company's EMS will define what plans and procedures, together with the appropriate documents, will need to be completed at a site level in what is known as a construction environmental management plan (CEMP). Whatever documents are used to achieve this, there are some clearly defined steps in order to deliver effective environmental management on site. The following five steps should be followed.

2.5.1   Step 1. Identify the project environmental obligations

The first important step in managing project environmental issues is to identify the environmental obligations. An obligation is a requirement to take a course of action, whether legal or moral. In the case of environmental obligations there are a number of potential sources.

- The first of these is legal obligations where individuals and organisations have to follow legal requirements or face prosecution (for example, duty of care under waste law or the protection of wildlife).

- The next concerns contractual obligations and these might relate to performance requirements that a client specifies (for example, BREEAM). Where these are not met a client can resort to a civil action to recover costs for the damages incurred.

- Another type of obligation arises from businesses' corporate and social responsibility and their duty to act in a way that recognises the interests and views of other stakeholders, in relation to the environment. Failure to recognise corporate and social responsibility can result in damage to corporate reputation.

A review of the project's contractual documentation, including any associated planning conditions, also known as Section 106 agreements, should be undertaken to identify the project-specific environmental obligations.

It is essential to have processes in place to identify potential obligations that might arise from different emergency scenarios that could have environmental impacts, and have an effective response plan in place that is regularly tested to mitigate effects if they occur.

2.5.2 Step 2. Identify the project environmental aspects and risks

Following the identification of the project environmental obligations the next step is to identify the associated environmental aspects and risks, together with any relevant opportunities.

Environmental aspects and risks can be present on a specific project wherever there is an interaction with the environment, arising from either raw material inputs or emissions and other outputs to the environment.

The goal of a good environmental management system is to identify what these aspects, risks and opportunities are and to put in place the necessary controls to manage them to within acceptable limits to achieve the desired objective.

- An **aspect** is an element of an organisation's activities, products or services that can interact with the environment. What that means is that you need to look at your activities, products and services that may have an impact on the environment.

- The **impact** is the consequence of not doing something correctly. It is any change to the environment, whether adverse or beneficial, wholly or partially resulting from an organisation's activities, products or services.

e.g. Aspect and impact

Illegally disposing of waste is the aspect, and the associated impact is it being disposed of incorrectly, such as at an unlicensed waste disposal facility.

Discharging water into a drain is the aspect; the impact is discharging water without consent or the discharged water polluting a connected river.

Another common aspect is storing fuel; the impact can be that fuel leaks into the ground and pollutes the ground or an underground drinking water aquifer.

The minimum level of performance is compliance with legal and other requirements. Organisations may also decide that they want to work to good practices where risks are minimised as far as reasonably practicable.

The best way of managing environmental risks is in a systematic way and ISO 14001 *Environmental management systems* provides an internationally recognised framework for doing this.

The production of a project environmental aspects register, identifying the obligations, together with the associated risks and control measures (including emergency situations or possible worst case scenarios), will be an important tool for communicating these issues to contractors and site personnel.

Environmental risks and opportunities should be assessed during the pre-construction phase of a project to ensure that environmental management is properly integrated within the project with respect to these issues.

Environmental risks are identified in the pre-construction phase through a number of sources, including ecology surveys, desk top studies and ground investigations. The client may also be able to provide information on existing environmental issues.

All new surveys and existing information must be included in the pre-construction information and passed to the designers and contractors to enable them to carry out their duties.

2.5.3 Step 3. Identify the environmental responsibilities

Having defined the project environmental obligations and associated risks and opportunities, it will be necessary to identify the main responsibilities for their control.

An environmental management system can involve every person on a project or within an organisation. Certain people within the management system will have specific responsibilities, and it is important that these are clearly defined and set out.

Successful implementation requires involvement from all employees and ownership of individual roles and responsibilities. Examples of functions and positions with specific responsibilities are shown below.

- Directors.
- Environmental co-ordinators.
- Architects and designers.
- Noise specialists.
- Waste co-ordinators.
- Sub-contractors.
- Suppliers.
- Community liaison staff.

It is important to ensure that the necessary lines of communication are defined between those individuals that have prepared the construction environmental management plan and site personnel.

Responsibilities of an environmental manager on a large construction project

- Implementing the requirements of the company EMS.

- Liaising with site teams, the client, stakeholders and a wider environmental team.

- Ensuring that relevant environmental policies are displayed and communicated to all project staff and personnel.

- Ensuring that a project assessment is carried out to identify the main types of work and the associated aspects.

- Ensuring that a construction environmental management plan (CEMP) is developed and maintained to identify the specific environmental requirements and responsibilities and includes legal, client and other relevant issues.

- Ensuring that a waste management plan is developed and maintained to manage waste and includes appropriate responsibilities, waste targets and legal compliance information.

- Ensuring that, as well as waste targets, relevant environmental objectives are set, implemented and monitored in line with the project construction programme or establishment requirements.

- Ensuring that the environmental requirements and objectives are included in inductions, toolbox talks and briefings, and records are maintained.

- Ensuring that specific activity method statements, including those of suppliers, are reviewed to include the relevant project environmental and waste requirements.

- Ensuring that appropriate inspections and monitoring arrangements are put in place to meet the environmental requirements (such as weekly supervisors' inspections).

- Ensuring that appropriate environmental emergency arrangements are identified, implemented and tested, as appropriate.

- Planning and implementing management reviews and audits of the status, adequacy and effectiveness of the project CEMP.

- Managing environmental non-conformances and subsequent corrective actions.

- Reviewing advised changes to environmental legislation and other requirements and taking the appropriate action.

- Ensuring that an environmental management file (EMF) is established to contain appropriate records of the above and is sufficient to meet the environmental requirements.

2.5.4   Step 4. Create a construction environmental management plan

A project construction environmental management plan (CEMP) is a working document that details how a project will mitigate the potential impacts of its construction activities on the environment and the local community.

It is vital for setting out what actions need to be taken and who is responsible for them. It will contain information including method statements, legislation, performance requirements and environmental risks. The CEMP is usually compiled by an environmental specialist, and the typical contents of a project CEMP will reflect the organisation's internal policies and environmental culture, as well as providing a practical set of guidelines for project processes during construction.

It may include, but is not limited to, the following:

- Environmental policies and EMS requirements.
- Project environmental objectives and targets.
- Environmental roles and responsibilities.
- Environmental risk assessments.
- Development of method statements.
- Site waste management plan.
- Environmental emergency response/action plans.

- Consultation.
- Environmental inductions, training and awareness.
- Environmental monitoring, measuring, inspections and audits.
- Environmental incident and investigation reports.
- Project environmental records.
- Compliance with current legislation.

2.5.5   Step 5. Monitor and inspect

After implementing a project CEMP a robust monitoring and inspection regime should be put in place to ensure that the identified risks and opportunities are being managed and that legal and contractual requirements are being met. Examples of monitoring and inspection work for risk management and compliance include the following.

- Noise level testing.
- Water sampling and analysis.
- Air monitoring.
- Dust monitoring.

- Duty of care checks.
- Soil testing.
- Microbial monitoring.

Monitoring and inspection can also take place to assess performance delivery and the achievement of performance objectives that have been set by a project. This may include monitoring and inspection of energy, carbon, water, resources and material use efficiency.

Monitoring and inspection work can include the following.

- Director tours.
- Site management tours.
- Supervisor tours.
- Internal audits.
- External audits.

- Supplier audits.
- Water monitoring.
- Energy usage.
- Resource use measurement.

2.5.6   Environmental performance improvement

Environmental performance improvement is vital to successful construction projects. Efficient use of energy, carbon, water, raw materials and waste reduction will bring multiple benefits to projects and contribute to cost savings. To achieve performance improvement requires a well-planned and structured management system, the right leadership and a mindset across the project that results in behaviours that are focused towards resource efficiency.

Regular project reviews involving all site personnel that are identified in the project CEMP, including sub-contractors and suppliers, will provide the opportunity to discuss environmental issues and how to improve performance. These reviews need not be separate, formal meetings and could be an agenda item of standard management meetings.

2.6   Environmental documentation

The project environmental requirements will dictate what environmental documentation is required to demonstrate compliance.

It is likely that a company will have a standard project recording system and it would be good practice to ensure a section of this is reserved for environmental records.

 Some likely documents that will need to be retained on site

- Initial review and identification of project environmental obligations.
- CEMP, including schedule of aspects, risks and details of their control.
- Waste management plan.
- Details of emergency environmental arrangements, including drainage plans and location of inspection chambers.
- Copies of environmental licences and consents, which could include, for example, the following.
    - Waste carrier licences.
    - Environmental permits for waste transfer stations.
    - Hazardous waste site registration.
    - Environmental permits for the operation of mobile crushing equipment.
    - Environmental permits for the operation of mobile soil treatment equipment.
    - Environmental permit exemptions for the reuse of construction waste.
    - Environmental permits for discharge.
- Waste transfer documentation.
- Environmental inductions, briefings and toolbox talks.
- Environmental consultations, including meetings and formal correspondence with regulators.
- Environmental incident reports and non-conformance reports and breaches.
- Environmental work instructions and operational procedures.
- Environmental monitoring and inspection records, which could include, for example, the following.
    - Weekly site inspection records.
    - Audit reports.
    - Water sampling records.
    - Soil and waste sampling records.
    - Dust and air quality monitoring, including visual inspections.
    - Visual records of sensitive area protection, including fencing.
    - Records associated with the achievement of project environmental objectives and key performance indicators.

SITE ENVIRONMENT MANAGEMENT SYSTEMS

A number of these documents will need to be retained for legal purposes, such as waste transfer documentation, which must be retained and accessible for:

- two years for non-hazardous waste
- two years for season tickets (tickets that can be set up for multiple transfers of the same type of waste over a 12 month period)
- three years for hazardous waste transfer notes, and hazardous waste consignment notes (different retention periods apply for consignees (receivers) of hazardous waste; refer to further detail in the hazardous waste guidance)
- six years if you are a landfill operator for non-hazardous waste (for landfill tax purposes)
- the lifetime of your permit if you are a landfill operator for hazardous waste
- the lifetime of an environmental permit (when the permit is surrendered, the regulator often requires a history of the types of waste received).

CONTENTS

Energy management

03

Supporting
INFORMATION

GT700 Toolbox talks / supporting checklists and forms

Toolbox talks on some of these topics are available in the GT700 publication. Supporting checklists and forms covering some of these topics are available on our companion website.

Summary of energy management legislation and guidance

This list is not exhaustive and only includes legislation mentioned in this section of GE700.

Legislation and guidance	Enforcement agencies*				
	EA	LA	NIEA	NRW	SEPA
Acts (primary legislation)					
Climate Change Act	✓		✓	✓	
Climate Change (Scotland) Act					✓
Environmental Protection Act	✓		✓	✓	✓
Regulations (secondary legislation)					
Building Regulations (Parts F, L and O)		✓			
Building (Scotland) Regulations					✓
Energy Performance of Buildings Regulations	✓		✓	✓	✓
Energy Savings Opportunity Scheme (ESOS) Regulations	✓		✓	✓	✓
EU Energy Efficiency Directive					
Streamlined Energy and Carbon Reporting Framework	✓		✓	✓	✓
Guidance					
Building Research Establishment publications and guidance					
Building Standards Technical Handbook		✓			
Net Regs Environmental guidance					
Information and guidance on websites	✓	✓	✓	✓	✓

*Key

EA	Environment Agency
LA	Local Authorities
NIEA	Northern Ireland Environment Agency
NRW	Natural Resources Wales
SEPA	Scottish Environment Protection Agency

Overview

Global warming and climate change have come to the fore as sustainability issues. Current energy production through the use of fossil fuels is a main contributor to UK carbon dioxide (CO_2) emissions. Reducing the reliance on fossil fuels, and the subsequent production of CO_2, is a growing concern for governments and many other organisations around the world. The construction industry as a whole needs to adapt its design and construction processes to meet clients' expectations and to prevent further environmental impacts, now and in the future.

This chapter gives a general overview of the UK's legally binding energy and carbon reduction targets. It provides guidance on actions that help construction companies to measure and reduce energy consumption and the associated carbon footprint during both the construction process and the occupation of the buildings and infrastructure on completion.

3.1   Introduction

Climate change is now seen as the defining challenge of this era. It is recognised that human activity (through the burning of fossil fuels in energy production, manufacturing and use in buildings and transport) and the generating of waste create greenhouse gases that contribute to global warming and climate change. Buildings, and the construction activity to produce them, contribute a significant amount to the overall carbon footprint from emissions. Carbon dioxide accounts for about 76% of all emissions from the seven main greenhouse gases. Almost half of these emissions are associated with buildings. The construction industry has a major role to play in improving energy efficiency and reducing greenhouse gases and costs.

Action to address the problem of global warming started in 1988, when the intergovernmental panel on climate change (IPCC) was established. The United Nations Earth Summit at Rio de Janeiro in 1992 was, however, the turning point in the fight against climate change. In the intervening years policies have evolved between developed countries around the globe, agreeing to make legally binding cuts in seven greenhouse gases, including carbon dioxide.

The UK has implemented the Climate Change Act 2008, which commits the UK government by law to reduce greenhouse gas emissions by at least 100% of 1990 levels (net zero) by 2050. This includes reducing emissions from the devolved administrations (Scotland, Wales and Northern Ireland) which currently account for about 20% of the UK's emissions.

In addition, in 2009 the UK set a target for 15% of all energy to be generated from renewable sources by 2020 from agreement at a European level. Recent Government figures indicate that these targets will be exceeded, with 2017 figures for reduction in greenhouse gases being reported at 43% (9% above the 2020 target) and renewable sources of energy being exceeded by almost 100% with figures of 28.1% being reported in 2018.

In 2019 greenhouse gas emissions from electricity generation were down 12% on 2018 levels and 71% lower than 1990 levels, the share of low-carbon electricity generation has risen to 59.3% in 2020 with renewables at 43.1%. In 2021 the UK Government introduced the Net Zero Strategy, which set further targets including a commitment to fully decarbonise our power system by 2035.

The UK Government's *Construction 2025: industrial strategy for construction*, published in July 2013, and the more recent Clean Growth Strategy set out an aspiration for a reduction in greenhouse gas emissions in the built environment of 50% by 2025, and 80% by 2050. Alongside this, the Green Construction Board has developed the Low Carbon Routemap enabling customers to understand the policies, actions and key decision points required to achieve the UK's 80% reduction target, to develop market and technology-based plans to secure the jobs and growth opportunities from driving carbon out of the built environment, led by the Green Construction Board.

 For further details about Construction 2025 and the Clean Growth Strategy, visit the Government website.

3.2   Important points

Energy is a valuable resource. Reducing the amount used and developing more efficient methods of generating energy can provide significant savings and reduce the emission of greenhouse gases, which contribute to climate change. A construction project can save energy in two main ways. First, by managing the energy used for the construction phase and second, by constructing the project in a way that ensures the completed structure achieves its optimum energy performance for its lifetime use *(for more information refer to 3.6.1.2 Quality and workmanship later in this chapter)*. The following site practices should be employed to reduce energy consumption and greenhouse gas emissions.

- Engage with distribution network operators and energy suppliers as early as possible to obtain a connection to the site to avoid the use of petrol or diesel generators.

- Ensure that all plant and equipment is switched off when not required. Reinforce through monitoring and inspections.

- Ensure that all plant and equipment is regularly maintained.

- Put an efficient transport policy and logistics plan in place, to reduce the need for lorry movements and double handling.

- Consider energy efficiency technologies for site accommodation (for example, LED lighting, PIR sensors and double glazing).

- Monitor and regularly report site energy and fuel use, and positively reinforce reductions through awareness and toolbox talk sessions..

- Use more sustainable materials. Ensure eco-friendly building materials (such as cork or sheep's wool insulation) are identified at the planning and design stages.

- Eliminate wastage by reusing building materials and components.

- Replace high-emission materials with sustainable timber.

- Use low-carbon concrete instead of traditional cement.

- Switch to electric, hydrogen and hybrid-powered plant and machinery from those powered by fossil fuels.

Construction detailing and quality of workmanship on site can have a major impact on the performance of the building in use. Gaps in insulation at junctions between windows and doors can cause cold bridging, reduced air tightness, increased heat loss and subsequent energy use. Building performance can also be supported and optimised through effective handover and commissioning processes called *soft landings*. Follow up and seasonal commissioning, including the appropriate training of operational staff in the use of the building's control systems, can also significantly improve the performance of a building in use.

3.3 Government incentive and certification schemes

Many mandatory and voluntary initiatives have been introduced by the UK and local governments, as well as the European Union, in response to the risk posed by climate change.

 Examples include the climate change levy on fossil fuels, revisions to Part L of the Building Regulations, the Energy Performance of Buildings Directive, the EU Emissions Trading Scheme (ETS), the Renewable Heat Incentive, the Carbon Reduction Commitment (CRC) Energy Efficiency Scheme, Energy Savings Opportunity Scheme (ESOS) and the Low Carbon Construction report.

3.3.1 Streamlined energy and carbon reporting framework

The *Streamlined energy and carbon reporting* (SECR) framework was introduced by the Department for Business, Energy and Industrial Strategy in April 2019, making mandatory energy and carbon reporting easier and aims to incentivise energy efficiency and cut emissions in large energy users in the UK's public and private sectors.

The framework applies to circa 11,000 companies across England, Northern Ireland, Scotland and Wales. It requires companies to measure and report their carbon emissions and to purchase carbon allowances in line with their carbon footprint. It applies to all quoted companies (those listed on the public exchange), and to larger UK incorporated unquoted companies with at least 250 employees, or an annual turnover greater than £36m and an annual balance sheet greater than £18m.

However, organisations that use a low level of energy (40MWh over the reporting period), public sector organisations and those undertaking public activities such as charities, universities, hospitals and academies are not required to submit SECR reporting. The government is encouraging voluntary participation to support transparent ESG reporting for these currently exempt organisations.

 For comprehensive guidance on the *Streamlined energy and carbon reporting* framework visit the Government website.

3.3.2 Energy Savings Opportunity Scheme Regulations

ESOS is a mandatory energy assessment scheme for organisations in the UK that meet the qualification criteria of being a large undertaking, in line with one or both of the following conditions.

- Employing 250 or more people.

- Having an annual turnover in excess of 50 million euros (£44,845,000) and an annual balance sheet total in excess of 43 million euros (£38,566,700).

The Environment Agency is the UK scheme administrator. ESOS applies to large UK undertakings and their corporate groups. It mainly affects businesses but can also apply to not-for-profit bodies and any other non-public sector undertakings large enough to meet the criteria.

Organisations that qualify for ESOS must carry out assessments every four years. These are audits of the energy used by their buildings, industrial processes and transport to identify cost-effective energy saving measures.

Qualifying organisations must notify the Environment Agency by a set deadline that they have complied with ESOS obligations. Various penalties apply for a breach of these regulations. In particular, in relation to providing a false or misleading statement, and to a failure to:

- notify
- maintain records

- carry out an energy audit
- comply with a notice.

Organisations caught under the ESOS Regulations can now demonstrate compliance by implementing ISO 50001. If this route is chosen, early action is advised as it often takes well over a year for companies to achieve certification.

 For further details of ESOS and qualification criteria refer to the Department for Business, Energy and Industrial Strategy and the Environment Agency.

3.3.3 PAS 2080 Carbon management in infrastructure

PAS 2080 *Carbon management in infrastructure* is a standard for managing whole-life carbon in infrastructure and introduces a joined up approach to the way industry evaluates and manages whole-life carbon emissions to reduce carbon and reduce costs. It aims to overcome disconnects in the value chain, embed effective whole-life carbon management approaches and encourage the right behaviours and approaches from clients, contractors, designers and product suppliers to deliver reduced carbon and reduced cost infrastructure.

3.4 Managing energy on site

Conserving energy during any construction activity is an ideal way to cut costs and save money. The main areas for action include on-site construction (energy use, plant and equipment) and site accommodation, transport associated with the delivery of materials and removal of waste, business travel and corporate offices. There are a number of measures that can be undertaken by companies to help reduce their energy use and carbon emissions.

- Ensuring sites connect to the electricity supply as early as possible to prevent lots of equipment running on fuel-driven generators.
- Using hybrid generators that switch off diesel generators when the power load is low to reduce fuel consumption and pull energy from internal storage batteries.
- Using sustainable or recycled products for site set up, logistics and enabling works.
- Using products with a lower carbon footprint.
- Installing eco-friendly site accommodation (for example: double glazing; door closers; waterless urinals; energy-efficient lighting (such as LEDs) and heating (controlled wirelessly); daylight controls; mechanical heat recovery ventilation; solar thermal heating systems; solar photovoltaics; passive ventilation; air-source and ground-source heat pumps; and green roofs).
- Efficient use of construction plant and equipment through induction and training (such as turning off when not required and keeping plant well maintained).
- Good practice energy management on site (for example, festoon low-energy light bulbs and turning task lighting off when not in use).
- Using off-site consolidation areas to facilitate smaller loads being combined and loaded onto larger vehicles (reducing the number of vehicle movements to and from site).
- Sharing transport to reduce the number of vehicle movements to and from site. Vehicle sharing can be planned by site staff, and project suppliers may permit the use of their parking areas as car-pooling points.
- Switch to electric, hydrogen and hybrid-powered plant and machinery rather than fossil fuels.
- Provision of electric charge points for encouraging the use of electric vehicles.
- Fuel-efficient driving through driver training.
- Good practice energy management in company offices.

Meter for monitoring electricity use and cost

Standards have been introduced to manage environmental issues, and ISO 50001 is specific to energy management. It provides a practical way to improve energy use, through the development of an energy management system, to meet the following.

- Develop a policy for more efficient use of energy.
- Fix targets and objectives to meet the policy.
- Use data to better understand and make decisions concerning energy use and consumption.
- Measure the results.
- Review the effectiveness of the policy.
- Continually improve energy management.

ISO 50001 certification can be used to comply with ESOS, as this is sufficient to constitute an ESOS assessment *(refer to 3.3.2)*.

ENERGY MANAGEMENT

3.5   Measuring energy and carbon

Measuring overall energy usage and being able to identify where energy is being used, and in what form, is a prerequisite to starting an energy and carbon management programme. To do so will require the use of meters to measure energy usage, and on large sites this may involve sub-meters. Sites may be required to measure journeys to and from the project associated with deliveries and business travel and measure the embodied energy associated for the materials they are using.

Embodied energy is an accounting methodology that aims to find the sum total of the energy necessary for an entire product life cycle. This life cycle includes raw material extraction, transport, manufacture, assembly, installation, disassembly, deconstruction and/or decomposition.

To measure the carbon footprint associated with energy use will require the use of conversion factors for each energy type. Different methodologies produce different understandings of the scale and scope of application and the type of energy embodied. Some methodologies account for the energy embodied in terms of the carbon that supports economic processes. Three levels of assessment are currently being used.

Scope 1 are the emissions from sources under the immediate control of the company.

Scope 2 are the off-site emissions from the purchase of electricity.

Scope 3 are the off-site emissions from the company's supply chain or from products sold by the company.

 The Greenhouse Gas Protocol developed by the World Business Council for Sustainable Development (WBCSD) and the World Resources Institute (WRI) is the global standard for the measurement and reporting of Scope 1, 2 and 3 carbon emissions.

The Environment Agency has a carbon calculator for construction work, which is hosted on the Government website. This calculates the final carbon impact of different material and transport options, and the footprint of an overall project. It also considers personal travel, site energy use and waste management. The tool has a number of benefits, some of which are shown below.

- Helping to assess and compare the sustainability of different designs, in carbon dioxide (CO_2) terms, and influencing design selection at the options appraisal stage.

- Helping to highlight where big carbon savings on specific construction projects can be made.

- Calculating the total carbon footprint from construction and helping to reduce it.

The tool was developed by the Environment Agency for its own construction work (predominantly river and coastal construction projects). However, other construction clients, contractors and consultants may find it useful when assessing their own work.

 For carbon reduction case studies refer to Appendix A.

Measuring and reporting of site energy use is also a requirement under the management credits of BREEAM. The BREEAM Industrial assessment scheme requires both energy and carbon assessments.

The European Network of Construction Companies for Research and Development (ENCORD) has established a *Carbon measurement protocol* to assist in the reduction of emissions from current and future construction work and operations. The document identifies the intended users of the protocol, the sources of emissions over which a construction company may have influence, and the method of measuring these emissions. Guidance is also provided on reporting methods at a company and project level, with a view that companies will report their emissions publicly.

As the energy supply becomes greener, the proportion of energy locked up in building materials increases. The greatest carbon use in the life cycle of a building is during use. Therefore, designers need to think about both embodied and operational energy of the building.

 ## Cleaner construction machinery for London: a low emission zone for non-road mobile machinery (NRMM)

For projects in London an inventory of all NRMM should be kept on-site, stating the emission limits for all equipment. All machinery should be regularly serviced and service logs kept on site for inspection. This documentation should be made available to local authority officers as required.

The NRMM register is an online inventory and details of all NRMM with a net power between 37 kW and 560 kW should be recorded, along with an indication of the proposed duration of use, no matter how short or long this may be, when the machinery is delivered to the site. NRMM is currently only active in Greater London but there are plans to expand it to other cities. From 1st January 2040, only zero-emission machinery will be allowed to operate within this zone.

The NRMM is part of London's Supplementary Planning guidance, detailed in *The control of dust and emissions from construction and demolition*.

 For further information visit the NRMM webpage.

3.6   Delivering energy performance in buildings

When considering energy use and emission reduction, this chapter has so far focused on construction site activities. Equally, there are important contributions that can be made to ensure completed buildings are energy efficient: warm in winter and cool in summer, with excellent indoor air quality, low energy bills and low carbon emissions. Every building will consume energy and may create emissions throughout its operational life. It is therefore important that buildings and projects are completed to ensure optimum energy performance and that clients help to reduce the costs and carbon emissions associated with this energy use.

3.6.1   Improving performance

3.6.1.1   Low carbon renewable energy

Transitioning from a high to low carbon construction project can be achieved by strategies focusing on:

- good quality of workmanship on site
- promotion of good practice
- waste reduction
- use of low-embodied energy, local products and materials
- use of recycled and recyclable products and materials
- designing for deconstruction
- on-site energy generation and storage
- reducing the use of vehicles and switching to electric
- high levels of insulation
- low infiltration rates
- low water and power-consuming appliances
- carbon capture and storage
- passive design techniques
- using alternatives to on-site diesel, such as bio-diesel.

The following types of low carbon renewable energy are increasingly being used on construction projects.

Renewable sources of electricity

- Solar photovoltaic (PV).
- Wind.
- Hydro-electricity, including tidal energy.
- Electricity generated from anaerobic digestion (AD).
- Electricity generated from combined heat and power (CHP).

Renewable sources of heat

- Biomass heating.
- Solar thermal hot water.
- Ground-source heat pumps.
- Air-source heat pumps.
- Heating generated from biomass-fuelled CHP.

In addition to renewable energy, a concept known as *district heating* or *heat networks* is increasingly being utilised. It works on the principle of supplying a number of homes and/or public buildings from one centralised location, with the heat being transferred through highly insulated pipes to each building.

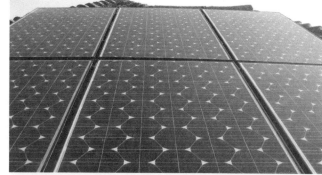

Photovoltaic power

Biomass heating

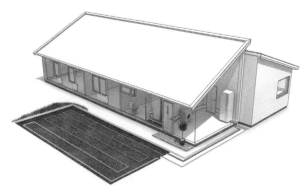

Ground source heat pump

Renewable energy reduces the overall carbon emissions of the building or project. However, the correct way to use the technology is to first consider energy reduction approaches (such as more insulation, better performing windows and glazing, or more efficient building services and domestic appliances).

Renewable energy can then be used to further reduce emissions and costs from the remaining energy needed. Renewable energy will, however, be a vital element of achieving zero or near zero carbon energy requirements set out in improved standards, such as the Building Regulations and BREEAM.

ENERGY MANAGEMENT

3.6.1.2 Quality and workmanship

As building regulations and air tightness standards for new and refurbished buildings become more demanding, the quality of materials and the workmanship, skills, knowledge, training and experience of the workforce required to install them have a significant impact on energy efficiency. It is therefore important that all site personnel understand how energy-efficient construction can be achieved, to deliver good energy performance in reality.

Incorrect detailing and substituting materials for inferior alternatives (which may look the same but have lower thermal performance) result in buildings that will not meet the expectations of design and thus perform poorly throughout their lifespan, resulting in a significant increase in energy use and running costs.

Insulation quality. Poorly-fitted insulation causes cold bridging (an area where there is a gap in the insulation which is colder than the main areas in a building) and heat loss (the term used to describe the measure of heat escaping from the inside to the outside of a building). This can have a significant negative impact on a building's energy performance. Poorly-fitted cavity wall insulation board has been measured as creating a 300% greater heat loss than designed values.

Air tightness. Air gaps, caused by poor detailing, unsealed service penetrations and poorly fitted doors and windows, allow more air infiltration than the designed values. These gaps will increase heat loss or heat gain, leading to a higher demand for additional energy for heating or cooling.

The lower the air tightness testing result in $m^3/(hr.m^2)$, the lower the unintended heat loss or gain will be (for example, an air tightness testing result of 1 $m^3/(hr.m^2)$ equates to a lower unintended heat loss or gain than a result of 10 $m^3/(hr.m^2)$ would).Performance greater than 10 times the Building Regulations' minimum standard has been achieved on many UK construction projects.

Cold bridging. Significant heat loss can be caused through cold bridges, produced by poor design, changes in the design details or poor workmanship. This heat loss can create condensation problems and damp when the building is in use. Installing insulation to provide a continuous barrier, particularly at junctions of walls, roofs, floors and around windows, is important in avoiding this.

3.6.2 Achieving energy efficiency

Buildings should work as an energy system in which heat gains and losses are always in balance. The higher the loss or gain from the building fabric, the more energy is needed to heat or cool it. Buildings lose heat through the external envelope in two ways: firstly, by a complex mix of conduction, convection and radiation through the materials and air spaces in the construction, and secondly via direct air leakage from inside to outside. This means that the design of the building envelope is critical.

An example of poorly-fitted cavity wall insulation board (Image supplied by Willmott Dixon)

Testing for air tightness (Image supplied by Willmott Dixon)

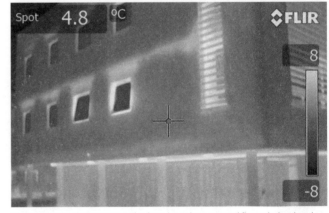
Thermal image showing excessive heat loss above second floor window heads, indicative of poor continuity of thermal insulation (Image supplied by Willmott Dixon)

Insulation layers and the detailing at junctions need to be designed and constructed with considerable care, based on a good understanding of the heat loss mechanisms involved. In addition, heating or cooling equipment needs to be correctly sized, energy efficient and the whole service system designed, installed, commissioned and operated to achieve maximum overall efficiency.

 Passivhaus

Passivhaus is an international design standard which delivers high standards of comfort and health, and minimises the energy use of buildings. Passivhaus buildings use very little energy whilst providing excellent air quality and high levels of comfort for the occupants. Attention to detail in design and construction are guided by principles developed by the Passivhaus Institute in Germany. Buildings designed and built using these exacting standards can be certified through a quality assurance process.

 For further information visit the Passivhaus Trust website.

3.6.3   Closing the performance gap

There is substantial evidence to suggest that there is a huge gap between how much energy a building is designed or predicted to use and its actual energy use, which is often much higher – in some cases it can be five to 10 times higher than compliance energy consumption calculations conducted during the design stage. The difference between anticipated and actual performance is referred to as the performance gap.

Although some of this can be attributable to variations in use, which is difficult to predict, a large element is related to the technical under-performance of construction materials and services due to design and construction failings; this is referred to as the *performance gap*. One of the important contributors to the performance gap is a lack of understanding of energy efficiency within the built environment workforce.

It is now common for building performance to be either measured during construction (for example, air tightness tests) or after the building is complete, to identify how it performs whilst in use, rather than just relying on a statement of the design intent.

 For further information and a copy of the *Sustainable building training guide* visit the Construction Leadership Council's website.

3.6.4   Understanding performance

Measuring a building's performance is achieved by using the Building Regulations Part L, or Building Standards in Scotland, and carrying out a standard assessment procedure (SAP) calculation. In Scotland a heat loss calculation may also be utilised. The SAP calculation generates the information that informs at what grade the energy performance certificate (EPC) will be issued. EPCs are issued using a grading system from A-G, to reflect the building's energy performance in operation, with A being the most efficient. Certification processes (such as BREEAM and LEED) are also useful in performance measurement.

All of these systems indicate how the energy efficiency of the design and construction of the project should perform **on paper**. Understanding how buildings are actually performing during occupation or operation is the first step in the improvement process.

An important factor is the regulations' methodology for checking how sustainable designs and performance promises work out **in reality**. There are many ways that this can be measured for buildings, but one of the most common in the UK for public buildings is the display energy certificate (DEC). The DEC evaluates how much energy the building actually uses during 12 months of occupation, and compares this performance with the typical use for buildings of a similar type.

The way that projects are actually performing is not always known to the contractors building them, creating a risk of them becoming disconnected. Research has shown that actual performance differs from clients' expectations of the regulation levels by a significant degree. This is known as the ***performance gap***.

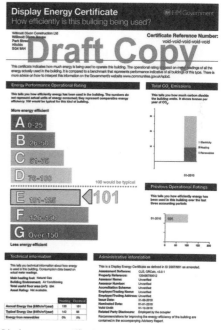

Display energy certificate
(Image supplied by Willmott Dixon)

Industry bodies (such as the UK Green Building Council and Zero Carbon Hub) have published numerous case studies explaining these issues in detail. The important point for the industry is to know how it can act to improve the energy performance of a building at design, construction, commissioning and handover stages of the project. The Building Performance Network (BPN) is an initiative that was established to improve a building's performance whilst in operation, to address in-use performance. The BPN brings together individuals and organisations who have an interest in improving building performance in operation.

3.6.5   Commissioning, handover and aftercare

Making sure that a building and its mechanical and electrical services are working properly and are handed over to the client in an effective way are vital steps to ensure it operates as it was intended to, and that energy consumption in use is minimised. The process, known as *soft landings*, is a step-by-step approach to ensuring that this is achieved as part of the project, includes a building performance evaluation, and is integral to targeting net zero carbon.

This approach is based on structured collaboration between designers, clients, future occupants and operators of a building to ensure that buildings being handed over are comfortable, easy to use and have systems in place to minimise energy use and maintenance costs. The soft landings process will contribute towards achieving net zero carbon buildings by helping to close the performance gap.

Midlands Primary School - Energy Data

8.3% below design usage

17.5% below design usage

Energy efficiency improvements following POE actions
(Image supplied by Willmott Dixon)

ENERGY MANAGEMENT

The soft landings' six-phase approach is as follows.

Phase 1: Inception and briefing. This establishes client requirements and success criteria, commits all participants to complete the project after handover and allocates responsibilities.

Phase 2: Design. Brings the project team together to review previous comparable projects, detail how the building will work for both the manager and the individual users. Agreeing the energy, the metering and monitoring strategies and the approach to commissioning.

Phase 3: Construction. Ensure that the project team is fully aware of the project's success criteria. Ensure that the facilities manager and the end user are closely involved in the overall project and decisions which affect operation and management of the delivered building

Phase 4: Pre-handover. Scaled handover enables operators to spend time understanding interfaces and systems before occupation. Ensure the building management system is set up the way the client intended including energy data reconciliation, data storage and the energy monitoring software. The metering must be checked to ensure it's working properly and will deliver real world insights into the energy use.

Phase 5: Initial aftercare. Project team should be on site for a period of time to spot emerging problems and issues, and to check that they meet the occupants' expectations and actual requirements.

Phase 6: Years 1-3 extended aftercare and POE. This is a period of longer term, less intrusive monitoring and support. Ensure that the energy monitoring is set up and working well and conduct systematic post-occupancy evaluation (POE) after 12 months, with a final project review at month 36.

 For further details of the soft landings approach and free guidance visit the BSRIA website.

 UK construction is already delivering quality projects every day, on time and on budget. Focusing on these issues will make 'on performance' the next major achievement.

3.6.6 Designed to Perform: An Illustrated Guide to Delivering Energy Efficient Homes

An illustrated and informative practical design guide to delivering better energy performance in all types of new-build homes, *Designed to Perform: An Illustrated Guide to Delivering Energy Efficient Homes* addresses construction quality and performance of new homes.

The performance gap between predicted and actual energy use in new homes has been identified as a key problem by the government and industry experts. This guide introduces the concept of the performance gap and highlights clear issues and solutions to help architects improve their detailing at design stage.

The guide has annotated details with photos taken from live construction sites.

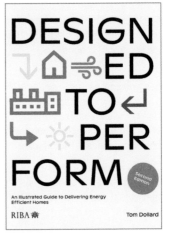

The Designed to Perform book

Appendix A – Carbon reduction case studies

 To access the *Construction carbon calculator*, referred to in some of the case studies below, visit the Government website.

03

Sandford bridge

Background. The Sandford bridge project (£380,000) spans the Sandford lock bypass channel on the River Thames. The bridge is primarily used for access to the lock house and the lock structure, but additionally there is a 3 m wide roadway spanning 40 m across the river. The aim of the bridge refurbishment was to increase the carrying capacity from 3 to 18 tonnes.

Reducing the carbon footprint. The design team were interested in minimising the environmental impact and maximising carbon savings throughout the duration of the project. Overall the team saved 62 tonnes of CO_2 (from 125 tonnes of CO_2 to 63 tonnes of CO_2).

The ideal solution was to reuse the existing sub-structure, replace the old deck with a new one and construct a new vehicle restrain parapet. The original bridge deck, constructed from large, longitudinal concrete slabs, was removed to install a new deck made from a steel frame and comparatively smaller pre-cast concrete slabs. The benefit of the latter was the requirement for a smaller crane for lifting and positioning, which reduced the carbon emissions from 48 tonnes of CO_2 to eight tonnes of CO_2.

The old deck material was crushed on site then reused to reinstate the car park, saving two tonnes of CO_2 by avoiding waste off site and import of aggregates.

The design of the vehicle parapet height was reduced from 1.5 m to 1 m. This was mainly for aesthetic purposes but it saved two tonnes of CO_2 from the amount of steel required and transportation.

Instead of using a sheet pile wall to separate the bank from the river the existing scour pile in the right-bank of the bridge was reused, instead of removing it, saving 18 tonnes of CO_2 in materials and transport.

The learning curve. The Sandford access bridge case study provides an example of a project seeking to maximise the reuse of existing site materials, which has led to a reduction in embodied CO_2 emissions, as well as making wider environmental gains and cost savings.

(Reproduced with permission from the Environment Agency – Case study IEM/2012/002.)

Weybridge 24-hour moorings

Background. Weybridge 24-hour moorings in Surrey was a £375,000 project to build a 120 m long river level footpath with access to moorings. The original design was based on the construction of an in-situ concrete wall supported by steel sheet piling. However, a design review was undertaken (primarily due to cost constraints and to meet a completion date).

The design was changed to utilise less costly and (overall) lower carbon materials whilst maintaining the same operational life.

Reducing the carbon footprint. The post construction emission was reduced by 169 tonnes of CO_2 compared with the original design (from 255 tonnes of CO_2 to 86 tonnes of CO_2).

Mesh filled concrete. The most significant CO_2 saving was from the 75% reduction in concrete used in the wall. A mesh filled with concrete was used instead of precast concrete blocks. This saved 173 tonnes of CO_2 (59 tonnes of CO_2 compared to 232 tonnes of CO_2 for precast concrete blocks). Originally a cast in-situ concrete wall was planned, which involved considerably more material.

Use of plastic piles. Further carbon savings were achieved through the innovative use of plastic piles (89.5% recycled) instead of steel sheet piles. The carbon footprint of the plastic piling was determined to be 8.6 tonnes of CO_2 compared to 17 tonnes of CO_2 for steel sheet piles.

Weybridge 24-hour moorings (continued)

Form liner. Using a dense foam form liner saved considerable time and cost compared to an authentic alternative. A brickwork finish was achieved to fit the surroundings using a reusable rubber form liner. This added four tonnes of CO_2 to the project.

Concrete specification. The concrete specification/grade was changed from exposure class XC3 to XC4 to increase the speed of the construction to meet a completion deadline. The carbon footprint increased by 27 tonnes, from 228 tonnes to 255 tonnes of CO_2 due to the time constraints.

The learning curve. The project was delivered on time and under budget. Overall the project team saved approximately £40,000 compared to the original design, with the same design life. Although the drivers for the fresh look at the design and consideration of innovative materials and approaches were predominantly cost and time, the carbon footprint reduced overall by 50%. This shows that innovation can have multiple benefits. It is well worth having a fresh look even without constraints being imposed.

(Reproduced with permission from the Environment Agency – Case study IEM/2012/001.)

 ## Nottingham left bank

Background. Nottingham left bank is a £51 million scheme that will protect 16,000 homes and businesses from flooding. The project spans a 27 km reach of the River Trent and comprises flood defences with a mixture of earth bunds, concrete walls and sheet piling.

Due to constraints from working next to a railway and nature reserve, and the requirement to prevent groundwater seepage through the underlying sands and gravels, the project team came up with an innovative method that also lowered the total project carbon footprint.

Reducing the carbon footprint. Using the *Construction carbon calculator,* the total carbon footprint of the Nottingham project was 11,800 tonnes. The most significant contributions were from steel, concrete and material transport. The project team implemented many innovative changes to reduce the carbon footprint of the project. One of these examples resulted in changing the material and method of construction, which saved approximately 2,500 tonnes of CO_2 during this section of the works.

Use of TrenchMix. Sheet piles are traditionally used to form a cut-off to protect against groundwater seepage through defences, but on this project a large section of piling was replaced by the use of TrenchMix.

This process involves the mixing of the soil with cement; this cementitious material then sets, forming a barrier with a greatly reduced permeability. The soil and cement are mixed by a modified drainage trenching machine (*see photo*).

By using this method the team reduced the amount of steel used on the project by two-thirds, saving around 1,876 tonnes of CO_2.

Another benefit of the reduction in steel is the reduced carbon cost of transportation, saving around 700 tonnes of CO_2. The raw materials (cement) and plant emissions from the operation have a footprint of 330 tonnes of CO_2.

The learning curve. Even when taking into account the footprint of the materials and emissions from the TrenchMix method, it is still carbon beneficial by about 70% compared to the sheet pile option. Other advantages include less noise and vibration than sheet piling. This could be useful when working near sensitive areas, such as nature reserves and residential properties.

(Reproduced with permission from the Environment Agency – Case study IEM01/2011/002.)

03

Burrowbridge bank

Background. The Burrowbridge bank is a £270,000 project to repair a failing asset. This bank is part of the Parrett tidal reach and had suffered erosion, lost many of its timber piles that provided protection and had been affected by landslides. The project trimmed the riverside slope to a more suitable profile while maintaining crest width by filling at the rear. The embankment's toe was also protected by new timber piles and stone while a soft engineering solution was used for the bank slope.

Reducing the carbon footprint. Using the *Construction carbon calculator*, the predicted total carbon footprint of the Burrowbridge project was 140 tonnes. The most significant contributions are from import of clay and timber materials to site and export of trimmed arisings off site.

Reuse of material. The project team challenged the specification for re-profiling of the rear slope of the bund. This meant that material trimmed from the riverside slope could be reused on the land side of the bank. This saved having to import 550 tonnes of clay, reducing the number of lorry movements by 30 and saving around 15 tonnes of CO_2. It also reduced the transport of similar volumes of arisings off site, while providing cost savings of £5,500.

Reducing material used. Access to the site was challenging. Instead of using a traditional stone access track, the team hired in a temporary trackway, which allowed the team to go past the Burrow Mump (scheduled ancient monument) with minimum disruption. Using this trackway saved the need to import 1,500 tonnes of quarried material, which saved 20 tonnes of CO_2 and reduced an additional 100 lorry movements.

Recycled materials. Recycled hardwood timber piles were sourced from a local wharf being demolished, which saved approximately £35,000 and 26 tonnes of CO_2 (compared to using virgin hardwood).

The learning curve. This relatively small project reduced its total footprint by 60 tonnes of CO_2 – a reduction of over 40% of the predicted footprint. This project team proved that by looking at material selection and challenging the specification, large savings can be made not only in carbon and project costs.

(Reproduced with permission from the Environment Agency.)

Radcot weir

Background. The Radcot weir project is one of five sites in the Paddle and Rymer package. The main construction work at Radcot involves removing the existing Paddle and Rymer structure and replacing it with a dipping radial gated weir. This will benefit operators of the weir through the removal of health and safety risk, easier operation and standardisation of the weir. In addition the project will provide a new bypass channel to allow upstream and downstream movement of fish and provide recreational use for canoeists.

Using the *Construction carbon calculator*, the total carbon footprint of the Radcot weir project is 600 tonnes. The most significant contributions are from concrete and steel. The project team, by looking at material selection, have saved around 50 tonnes of CO_2 during the first phase of works.

Reducing the carbon footprint. Use of granular ground blast furnace slag (ggbs) in concrete; 50% ggbs replacement was used in the base and 70% in the rest of the structure. This saved around 40 tonnes of CO_2 (a saving of over 60% when compared to a CEM1 concrete).

Reuse of material. The old structure was demolished and then crushed on site. This material was then used underneath the blinding instead of a primary aggregate, saving both the cost and carbon of disposal of the material and the import of primary aggregate. This saved around 5.2 tonnes of CO_2, resulted in 40 less lorry movements and saved £10,000.

Avoiding waste. The team cast the coping stones for the structure on site by using the leftover concrete from the back end of the concrete pours, which would normally be wasted. The coping stones were produced over time meaning that no extra concrete was ordered for their production, saving around 1.2 tonnes of CO_2 and around £2,000 to £3,000.

Radcot weir (continued)

Additional benefits. The big win from the project was the use of GGBS (ground granulated blast-furnace slag) as a replacement in the concrete. This also has many other benefits, apart from the saving in CO_2, including lighter colour (desirable in this case), lower early thermal cracking, higher strength development over time, increased durability and increased workability. A potential disadvantage was noted as slower, early strength development/longer striking time, which can increase the construction programme, hence only 50% replacement being used in the base, but in this case the concrete typically achieved a strength of 30 N/mm^2 at seven days.

These reductions are from only half of the project; the second phase, which was due to start later, is estimated to save at least an equivalent amount resulting in a final saving of around 100 tonnes, which is almost 20% of the estimated project footprint, as well as potentially £25,000 in costs. For future projects, the team is looking at saving further CO_2 by potentially reducing the criteria for crack control steel reinforcement.

(Reproduced with permission from the Environment Agency – Case study IEM01/2010/002.)

03

CONTENTS

Archaeology and heritage

04

Supporting
INFORMATION

GT700 Toolbox talks / supporting checklists and forms

Toolbox talks on some of these topics are available in the GT700 publication. Supporting checklists and forms covering some of these topics are available on our companion website.

ARCHAEOLOGY AND HERITAGE

Summary of archaeology and heritage legislation and guidance

This list is not exhaustive and only includes legislation mentioned in this section of GE700.

Legislation and guidance	Enforcement agencies*				
	CADW	HE	HES	LA	NIEA
Acts (primary legislation)					
Ancient Monuments and Archaeological Areas Act	✓	✓	✓		
Burial Act	✓	✓	✓		✓
Disused Burial Grounds Act	✓	✓			
Planning (Listed Buildings and Conservation Areas) Act	✓	✓			
Planning (Listed Buildings and Conservation Areas) (Scotland) Act			✓		
Protection of Military Remains Act	✓	✓	✓		✓
Protection of Wrecks Act	✓	✓	✓		✓
Regulations (secondary legislation)					
Listed Building Consent				✓	
Planning (Listed Buildings and Conservation Areas) (Heritage Partnership Agreements) Regulations		✓			
Scheduled Monument Consent	✓	✓	✓		✓
Town and Country Planning (Historic Environment Scotland) Amendment Regulations			✓		
Guidance					
Conserving and enhancing the historic environment	Department for Levelling up, Housing and Communities				
National planning policy framework					
Net Regs Environmental guidance					
Organisations providing information and guidance on their websites	✓	✓	✓	✓	✓

*Key

CADW	The Welsh Government's historic environment service
HE	Historic England
HES	Historic Environment Scotland
LA	Local Authorities
NIEA	Northern Ireland Environment Agency

Overview

The heritage environment is a precious resource bringing millions of tourists to the UK to enjoy our rich, cultural past. Archaeology is a major factor in construction and development and an estimated £218m is spent by developers on archaeology in the UK each year. Heritage is important, as it records the past and provides a sense of place.

This chapter gives a general overview of the legal framework for the protection and management of historic buildings, monuments, archaeological sites and remains. It identifies what constitutes the historic environment, how this environment's features are protected in law and where to obtain consent to carry out works on or near to them.

The chapter also gives guidance on the measures to be taken to protect historic and archaeological features during the works and the actions to take if an unexpected archaeological discovery is made.

04

4.1 Introduction

Archaeology is often underestimated as a business or project risk so is often not considered early enough in the feasibility or design stages of projects, leading to unexpected or unplanned consequences.

Archaeological remains and the historic environment provide a valuable and irreplaceable part of a nation's history and identity. The use of local and traditional materials in buildings creates a sense of place and attachment for the population. For these reasons archaeology and built heritage form an important element of planning policy and must be considered early in any construction project.

Today, archaeology is a significant element of construction and development, and all parties (developers, archaeologists, conservation officers and the regulatory authorities) should aim to ensure that good practice is applied.

The main reasons why the construction sector should address archaeology and the historic environment are shown below.

Planning law, heritage law and planning policy. Archaeological remains and historic buildings are an important part of our cultural heritage. They are a fragile, finite and irreplaceable resource that needs to be protected. This is recognised within the UK planning process and by national legislation and guidance. Whilst some archaeological sites are protected by law, all archaeological remains affected by development are treated as material considerations in the planning process. Local Authorities should maintain historic environment records and use these as a database to inform planning applications.

Education and new knowledge. Archaeology and the historic environment make a significant contribution to education, social cohesion and the economy and bring wide public benefits and knowledge through archaeological and historical education in schools and universities.

Economy and society. Archaeology, historic buildings and landscapes underpin the UK tourism and heritage industries and create jobs. They also play an important role in regeneration by invoking a sense of place, belonging and cultural identity for new developments.

Sustainability. Developers can demonstrate their commitment to sustainability and responsible development through a proactive approach to archaeology and the historic environment, and also a recognition that archaeological remains are a non-renewable resource that need environmental protection and management.

An early, positive and proactive approach to archaeological remains and historic buildings can:

- minimise the impacts
- provide early effective risk management in the planning phase, minimising the risk of unexpected archaeological finds, which would have significantly higher costs attached if found during the construction phase
- heighten a sense of place for new developments
- provide opportunities for involving the community, leading to positive publicity for the construction project.

4.2 Important points

A heritage statement (as part of an overall environmental statement or environmental impact assessment) may be required to support a planning application and may also require some intrusive works on the site. The heritage statement will identify the significance of heritage assets and the effects the proposed development will have on them.

The level of detail required within the statement will depend upon the significance of the asset (for example, a Grade 1 building will require more detail than Grade 2). Additional planning requirements will include a heritage management plan to identify the controls that are required during the works.

A professional archaeologist may be required, as a condition of any planning consent, to supervise the works as they proceed and to ensure that suitable protection measures are put in place and maintained.

An archaeologist may also be required to excavate and record remains that are due to be removed.

ARCHAEOLOGY AND HERITAGE

Suitable controls to manage archaeology and historic sites should be included in the project as early as possible for the following reasons.

- To comply with legal requirements relating to scheduled monuments, listed buildings and protection of the historic environment.

- To ensure buildings are designed to avoid the disturbance of remains and to preserve historic features.

- To enable designers to incorporate historic features of the site in the final development.

- To avoid disturbance during the construction process itself by the following means.
  - Ensuring all archaeological works are segregated from the main works with authorised entry.
  - Identifying existing underground services that might have an impact on archaeology.
  - Ensuring archaeological excavations are suitably protected during the works.
  - Avoiding dewatering work in the vicinity of archaeological remains.

- For guidance for working on projects in the UK set against or within the heritage environment, the following organisations should be contacted.
  - Historic England.
  - Department for Communities in Northern Ireland.
  - Historic Environment Scotland.
  - Cadw in Wales.

4.3 Protected monuments, buildings and sites

Heritage assets range from sites and buildings of local historic value to World Heritage sites that have the highest significance of international value.

Each asset is an irreplaceable resource and should be conserved so that they can be enjoyed by existing and future generations.

The main guidance in the UK is found in the following documents.

- National Planning Policy Framework (NPPF) (England).

- Strategic Planning Policy Statement for Northern Ireland.

- Scottish Planning Policy and the National Planning Framework.

- Planning Policy Wales.

 Historic England has *Good practice advice in planning* (Note 3) and *The setting of heritage assets* available on its website.

Guide to the conservation of historic buildings (BS 7913) provides information on the principles of conservation and restoration of historic buildings for architects, designers, surveyors and contractors.

It outlines the importance of using appropriate materials for maintenance and the principles behind honest repairs (work that is clearly identifiable as being a repair and is not disguised to look like part of the original building or structure).

It also explains how traditional buildings perform differently to modern buildings and highlights the damaging effects that the retrofitting of energy efficiency measures can have on a building.

 For further guidance on planning in England, Northern Ireland, Scotland and Wales visit the relevant website.

4.3.1 UNESCO World Heritage sites

World Heritage site status is the most significant form of protection. It is awarded by the United Nations Educational, Scientific and Cultural Organisation (UNESCO) to places or buildings that have been judged to be of outstanding universal value and are the best examples of the world's culture and/or natural heritage.

Some examples from the UK are given below.

- Stonehenge, an archaeological site in England.

- Giant's Causeway, natural environment in Northern Ireland.

- Edinburgh, a cultural city in Scotland.

- Blaenavon, an industrial landscape in Wales.

Stonehenge is a well known scheduled ancient monument

4.3.2 Scheduled monuments

The word *monument* covers a range of archaeological sites. The term *scheduled ancient monuments* (SAMs) is often used (however, not all scheduled monuments are ancient). Further, scheduled monuments are not always visible above ground or well known (for example, wells and wartime gun emplacements).

Nationally important sites, buildings and monuments are given legal protection by being placed on a schedule for monuments. The UK heritage bodies identify sites that should be placed on the schedule by the respective government.

The Ancient Monuments and Archaeological Areas Act supports a formal system of scheduled monument consents for any works to a designated monument.

All work to a monument that is scheduled as an ancient monument requires scheduled monument consent, as do any works to the grounds that surround it.

Some scheduled monuments are not visible in the landscape, such as this medieval well under the Doncaster market

The following are criminal offences, potentially leading to fines or imprisonment.

● Carrying out unauthorised works on a scheduled monument without consent.

● Causing damage to a scheduled monument.

● Failing to adhere to the terms of a consent.

Development or construction works that affect a scheduled monument require formal permission (scheduled monument consent).

The granting of scheduled monument consent does not imply planning permission, or vice versa.

Applications for scheduled monument consent are made:

● in England, to the Department of Culture, Media and Sport, through Historic England

● in Northern Ireland, to the Department for Communities

● in Scotland, to Historic Environment Scotland

● in Wales, to Cadw.

4.3.3 Listed buildings

A listed building has statutory protection against unauthorised demolition, alteration and extension.

The grades of listed building are shown in the table below (Grades I and A/Category A being the highest level of protection).

England and Wales	Scotland	Northern Ireland
Grade I is the highest grade, reserved for buildings of exceptional interest	**Category A** buildings are of 'national or international architectural or historic importance'	**Grade A** buildings display excellent architecture of a particular period or style
Grade II* buildings are special interest, and carry more significance than Grade II alone	**Category B** buildings have a regional significance	**Grade B+** are high quality buildings, but fall short of Grade A due to an impairment
Grade II listed buildings account for over 90% of all listed buildings	**Category C** buildings are of local importance, and are usually simple buildings	**Grade B1** buildings are a good example of a particular period or style
		Grade B2 buildings qualify by virtue of only a few attributes

Any works to be undertaken to a listed building that would affect its character, or the character of any building or structure in its curtilage (area of land attached to a building), require a listed building consent.

It is a criminal offence to demolish, alter or extend a listed building without consent. Where work has been carried out without consent, and the character and appearance of the building are affected, a listed building enforcement notice may be served. This will require reinstatement of the building back to its original condition or in keeping with the building's criteria of listing prior to works being carried out. If this is not feasible a fine, sentence or both may be served.

It should be noted that Planning Authorities and National Park Authorities have the power to serve a building preservation notice on the owner of a building that is not listed, but which they consider is of special architectural or historic interest. The building is then protected for six months, like a listed building, in which time the Secretary of State must decide whether to list the building.

4.3.4 Conservation areas

 A *conservation area* is defined as an area that has special architectural or historic character that is desirable to preserve or enhance. Every Local Authority in England has at least one conservation area, and there are over 11,000 across the UK.

 Local Planning Authorities are responsible for conservation area designation and policy, both of which seek to protect the character of the whole area, including open spaces, not just individual buildings.

Conservation areas are given greater protection by the Local Authority, which has extra control over demolition, minor developments and the protection of trees. In the past, conservation area consent from the local Planning Authority was required prior to works being carried out in the designated area.

The requirement for conservation area consent, however, was abolished in the Enterprise and Regulatory Reform Act and replaced with a requirement for planning permission for demolition of, or alterations to, a building in a conservation area.

4.3.5 Parks and gardens

Historic parks and gardens can be registered, which means inclusion on the register of parks and gardens of special historic interest. Alterations to parks and gardens generally do not require statutory consent unless a planning application is required or it affects a tree covered by a tree preservation order.

It should be noted that local Planning Authorities are encouraged to include policies in their development plans for the protection of registered historic parks and gardens.

4.3.6 Designated wrecks

Section 1 of the Protection of Wrecks Act provides protection to some 60 wrecks around the UK, designated for their archaeological and historical significance. In Northern Ireland these are regulated under the Historic Monuments and Archaeological Objects (Northern Ireland) Order.

The administration of this Act and the issue of licences allowing diving, survey, collection of objects or excavation on these sites is the responsibility of the following organisations.

- Historic England.
- Department for Communities in Northern Ireland.
- Historic Environment Scotland.
- Cadw in Wales.

4.3.7 Designated vessels and controlled sites

Certain military aircraft crash sites and military shipwrecks are designated and protected under the Protection of Military Remains Act. These sites are administered by the Ministry of Defence.

4.3.8 Burial grounds and human remains

In England and Wales, authorisation to disturb human remains may be granted by Act of Parliament, Home Office licence (through the Ministry of Justice) or Church of England Faculty. Under Scottish law there is no such system.

In England, disturbance of human remains may be allowed by an Act of Parliament that authorises a specific major project, but otherwise the following legislation applies.

- Town and Country Planning (Churches, Places of Religious Worship and Burial Grounds) Regulations.
- Disused Burial Grounds Act 1884.
- Disused Burial Grounds (Amendment) Act 1981.
- Burial Act 1857.

If any form of construction work is to take place on a disused burial ground, then the Disused Burial Grounds (Amendment) Act stipulates that human remains should be removed before work begins. However, if planned works will leave human remains undisturbed, then dispensation can be obtained from the Home Office authorising that the burials remain in situ.

4.3.9 Treasure

Under the Treasure Act (England, Wales and Northern Ireland), certain finds are deemed as treasure. These must be reported to the coroner for the district within 14 days, who will advise on the course of action to be taken. Under the Act, the following finds would be classed as treasure:

● Coins that are at least 300 years old (coins are usually only treasure if there are 10 or more, or if they are with other items that meet the treasure definition).

● Objects that contain at least 10% of gold or silver and are at least 300 years old.

● Any object that is found in the near vicinity of known treasure.

● Base metal deposits of prehistoric date.

In Scotland any treasure finds are controlled by a system called Treasure Trove. The role of Treasure Trove is to ensure that objects of cultural significance from Scotland's past are protected for the benefit of the nation and preserved in museums across the country.

 At the time of publication, the definition of treasure was being consulted upon in Parliament.

04

Proposed changes will help protect thousands more objects of exceptional archaeological, historical and cultural importance. This will ensure that more new discoveries can go on public display in museums across the country for the public to see and enjoy in England, Wales and Northern Ireland.

The proposed new criteria will apply to the most exceptional finds over 200 years old – regardless of the type of metal of which they are made, so long as they provide an important insight into the country's heritage. This includes rare objects, those which provide a special insight into a particular person or event, or those which can shed new light on important regional histories. Discoveries of treasure meeting these new criteria will be assessed by a coroner, and will go through a formal process in which they can be acquired by a museum and go on display to the public.

 The statutory instrument to widen the definition was laid before Parliament on Monday 20 February 2023. If Parliament approves the change, it will come into force four months after signing.

4.4 Managing archaeology

In project terms, archaeological remains should be considered as risks which, if not properly identified and mitigated, may cause an adverse effect on a development.

Typical archaeological risks faced by development include:

● planning constraints and potential for spot listing and scheduling of remains

● unforeseen or unexpected archaeological remains affecting design, implementation programme and profit margins.

The environmental statement and planning conditions for the project, provided by the client, should identify any obligations for the management and protection of archaeology and historic buildings, monuments or sites. These requirements should be incorporated into the project environmental management plan (EMP) in a sub-section for heritage management. In some cases it will be a condition of the planning consent to prepare an archaeological management plan.

Where this is the case, it is good practice to employ a qualified archaeologist to plan, recommend actions and identify areas of responsibility in relation to the following.

● What planning policy and legislation authorities will consider when deciding how to treat any archaeological remains.

● The types of archaeological site and range of features that may occur.

● The range of non-intrusive and intrusive techniques that archaeologists will use to assess and evaluate archaeological remains.

● The main roles of the client, archaeological consultant, contractor and curator.

It is often best to deal with archaeological issues (including excavation) in advance of the main construction phase.

 All field evaluation work should be completed and an agreed mitigation strategy (if required) should be in place before construction or groundwork starts.

It will also be important to agree the appropriate method of working adjacent to sensitive areas as vibration from operations (such as excavation or tunnelling) may cause damage.

ARCHAEOLOGY AND HERITAGE

There may be an obligation to provide vibration monitoring of the works to ensure that vibration levels are not exceeded.

It may also be a requirement of the planning consent to employ a qualified archaeologist to carry out a watching brief during construction works (such as for excavations or dismantling works). All areas of known archaeological or historic interest should be protected with suitable fencing to prevent damage or encroachment, with access to site traffic and personnel carefully controlled. This is a legal requirement for scheduled sites.

In respect to health and safety, any excavations for archaeological works should be treated as usual and protected to avoid inadvertent access by personnel or site equipment. The location of underground services should also be identified, as these could cross sites where archaeological excavation is planned. Consideration should be given to the possibility of the presence of materials that can be harmful to health (such as lead paints, asbestos-containing materials and horse-hair plaster, which may contain anthrax spores).

Many archaeological excavations will also take place on brownfield sites that have been contaminated. If there is reason to believe that the ground is contaminated, arrangements should be made to undertake sampling and testing before archaeological work starts on site.

Dewatering schemes can have a negative impact on archaeological features as they could cause differential settlement or damage to materials that have previously been protected by being waterlogged. Appropriate methods of dewatering should be agreed in advance of the works taking place.

4.5   Unexpected discovery

If suspected archaeological objects or remains are found during the construction works without an archaeologist on site, certain procedures should be followed. The archaeological finds should be protected and not be disturbed any further before any specialist investigation and advice has been obtained.

Advice should be sought by contacting the Local Authority archaeological officer on how to proceed.

 Accidental discovery

In the case of accidental discovery of archaeological finds or human remains, the following sequence of actions are considered good practice.

- Stop work in the area of the discovery.
- Leave the find in situ and undisturbed.
- Control access to the area to authorised persons only.
- Stop vehicle traffic entering the area.
- Report the find to the site manager.
- Take specialist advice as appropriate.
- Report human remains, treasure and other archaeological finds to the appropriate statutory authority (usually the coroner).
- Report the find to the appropriate local planning authority or other curator.

Under the Burials Act there is a requirement to report unexpected discoveries of human remains to a coroner.

If there is any possibility that the remains are recent (for example, less than 100 years old) the local police should be contacted to determine whether the remains are ancient or not.

For authorisation to continue, approval will need to be given by the Home Office.

CONTENTS

Ecology

05

Supporting
INFORMATION

GT700 Toolbox talks / supporting checklists and forms

Toolbox talks on some of these topics are available in the GT700 publication. Supporting checklists and forms covering some of these topics are available on our companion website.

Summary of ecology legislation and guidance

This list is not exhaustive and only includes legislation mentioned in this section of GE700.

Legislation and guidance	Enforcement agencies*				
	LA	NE	NIEA	NRW	SNH
Acts (primary legislation)					
Amenity Lands Act (Northern Ireland)			✓		
Conservation (Natural Habitats etc.) (Amendment) Regulations (Northern Ireland)			✓		
Countryside Act – England and Wales		✓		✓	
Countryside and Rights of Way Act		✓	✓	✓	✓
Countryside (Scotland) Act					✓
Environmental Protection Act		✓		✓	✓
National Parks and Access to the Countryside Act	✓	✓	✓	✓	✓
Pesticides Act	✓	✓	✓	✓	✓
Planning (Northern Ireland) Order			✓		
Protection of Badgers Act		✓		✓	✓
Town and Country Planning Act	✓	✓		✓	
Town and Country Planning (Scotland) Act					✓
Tree Preservation Orders	✓				
Weeds Act		✓		✓	✓
Wildlife and Countryside (Amendment) Act (England, Scotland and Wales)		✓		✓	✓
Wildlife and Natural Environment Act (Northern Ireland)			✓		
Wildlife (Amendment) (Northern Ireland) Order			✓		
Regulations (secondary legislation)					
Conservation of Habitats and Species Regulations	✓	✓	✓	✓	✓
Control of Pesticides Regulations		✓	✓	✓	✓
Environmental Permitting Regulations		✓		✓	
Hazardous Waste Regulations		✓		✓	
Hedgerows Regulations (England and Wales only)	✓				
Town and Country Planning (Environmental Impact Assessment) Regulations		✓	✓	✓	✓
Guidance					
CIRIA publication *Working with wildlife: guidance for the construction industry*					
INNSA Code of Practice *Managing Japanese knotweed*					
Net Regs Environmental guidance					
Organisations providing information and guidance on their websites	✓	✓	✓	✓	✓

*Key

CIRIA	Construction Research and Information Association
INNSA	Invasive Non-Native Specialists Association
LA	Local Authorities
NE	Natural England
NIEA	Northern Ireland Environment Agency
NRW	Natural Resources Wales
SNH	Scottish Natural Heritage

Overview

A high level of protection is given to wildlife, plants, trees and hedgerows through legal controls and contract conditions.

This chapter gives a general overview of the legal framework for the protection of wildlife and their habitats. It highlights endangered and protected species (animals and plants) and designated sites for their protection.

This chapter also gives an overview of the legal framework for the regulation of invasive species.

5.1   Introduction

Ecology refers to the relationships between plants, animals, people and their environments, and to the interaction within these relationships. An ecosystem is made up of plants, animals, micro-organisms, soil, rocks, minerals, water sources and the local atmosphere interacting as well as sustaining one another over a certain period of time.

The identification and management of wildlife needs to be undertaken early in the planning stage of a project to avoid costly delays to the programme and possible loss of reputation if damage takes place. Damaging, disturbing or removing protected species can result in prosecution under a range of environmental legislation, and wildlife is also held in high regard by the public.

Construction work (such as demolition, site clearance and dewatering) potentially impacts plants and wildlife in the following ways.

● Removal and fragmentation of habitats.

● Disturbance to aquatic wildlife and water quality.

● Disturbance to wildlife from noise and vibration.

● Damage to trees and hedgerows.

● Changes in lighting conditions.

 Refer to Appendix C for a list of construction work and its potential adverse effects on wildlife.

When making a planning application, developers must produce an ecological impact assessment identifying intended mitigation measures before, during and after construction work.

5.2   Important points

 The following practices should be employed to avoid damage to wildlife and its habitats

Plan in order to mitigate for ecological issues, before the work starts

● Employ a qualified ecologist to carry out a preliminary ecological appraisal (also known as Phase 1 habitat survey). The appraisal will identify wildlife features and ecologically important areas prior to works commencing and designate them as protected areas (for example, fence them off). The contract documentation should identify sensitive areas that will require protection and management. The appraisal will:
  – gather baseline ecological data using Phase 1 habitat survey guidelines (JNCC 2010)
  – make recommendations for detailed surveys, where required
  – identify key constraints to the project and make recommendations for design options to avoid significant impact on important ecological features
  – identify any necessary mitigation measures
  – identify enhancement opportunities
  – aid site management plans by mapping out ecological features
  – inform any BREEAM (land use and ecology credits) reports.

● Liaise with statutory bodies and local groups to explain any mitigation measures to be used.

● Where there is a need to take, disturb or relocate protected species, consents should be obtained from the relevant regulatory body and competent licensed ecologists used to carry out the work *(refer to 5.5)*.

● Plan site clearance or demolition works to avoid any nesting, hibernation or breeding seasons.
(Refer to Appendix A for a yearly ecology planner that identifies the constraints and best times for dealing with the main groups of protected species.)

● Inform site personnel of any protected areas and explain the consequences of any damage to these areas.

ECOLOGY

The following practices should be employed to avoid damage to wildlife and its habitats (continued)

During construction

- Regularly check the condition of fencing of any designated protected areas.

- Refer to the ecology year planner *(Appendix A)* to be aware of differing seasons and constraints.

- Ensure watercourses are free from contaminated run-off or any other forms of pollution.

- Confirm compliance against method statements, the construction environmental management plan and any environmental contractual requirements.

- In the event of any unexpected ecological finds, stop work and then consult with the site ecologist (if relevant) and statutory bodies.

5.3   Designated sites

The UK has a responsibility to ensure the protection of species and their habitats from both a national and international perspective. One approach to achieving this is to establish designated sites that are legally protected, as detailed below.

Areas of Outstanding Natural Beauty (AONBs). In England, Northern Ireland and Wales, the primary purpose of the AONB designation is to conserve natural beauty. This, by statute, includes wildlife, physiographic features and cultural heritage, as well as the more conventional concepts of landscape and scenery. Account is taken of the need to safeguard agriculture, forestry and other rural industries and the economic and social needs of local communities. AONBs have equivalent status to National Parks as far as conservation is concerned.

AONBs are designated under the National Parks and Access to the Countryside Act amended in the Environment Act. The Countryside and Rights of Way Act clarifies the procedure and purpose of designating AONBs. Originally designated in Northern Ireland under the Amenity Lands Act (Northern Ireland), AONBs are now designated under the Nature Conservation and Amenity Lands Order (Northern Ireland). In Scotland, National Scenic Areas are broadly equivalent to AONBs.

Areas of Special Protection for birds (AOSPs) (England and Wales) and **wildlife refuges** (Northern Ireland) are established under the Wildlife and Countryside (Amendment) Act and the Wildlife (Northern Ireland) Order. The purpose of such orders is normally to provide sanctuary to particularly vulnerable groups of birds. In Scotland these areas of protection are called Special Protection Areas (SPAs).

Biogenetic reserve. A number of National Nature Reserves (NNRs) and some important Sites of Special Scientific Interest (SSSIs) have been identified as biogenetic reserves under a Council of Europe programme for the conservation of heathlands and dry grasslands.

Country parks are statutorily declared and managed by Local Authorities in England and Wales under the Countryside Act and in Scotland under the Countryside (Scotland) Act. In Northern Ireland they exist as a non-statutory designation. Country parks are primarily intended for recreation and leisure opportunities close to population centres and do not necessarily have any nature conservation importance. Nevertheless, many are in areas of semi-natural habitat and so form a valuable network of locations at which informal recreation and the natural environment coexist.

Local Nature Reserves (LNRs) (England, Scotland and Wales) and **Local Authority Nature Reserves (LANRs)** (Northern Ireland) may be established by Local Authorities under Section 21 of the National Parks and Access to the Countryside Act. These habitats of local significance can make a useful contribution to nature conservation and public amenity.

Marine Nature Reserves (MNRs) are designated under the Wildlife and Countryside (Amendment) Act (England, Scotland and Wales) to conserve marine flora or fauna, geological or physiographical features, or to allow study of such features. In Northern Ireland they are designated under the Nature Conservation and Amenity Lands (Northern Ireland) Order.

National Nature Reserves (NNRs) are areas of national, and sometimes international, importance that are owned, leased or approved by the relevant regulatory authority (such as Natural England or Natural Resources Wales), or are managed in accordance with nature reserve agreements between the regulatory authorities and landowners and occupiers. The essential characteristic of NNRs is that they are primarily used for nature conservation.

Ramsar sites. The Ramsar convention requires the protection of wetlands that are of international importance, particularly as waterfowl habitats.

Sites of Special Scientific Interest (SSSIs) (England, Scotland and Wales) and **Areas of Special Scientific Interest (ASSIs)** (Northern Ireland). All sites of national and international importance on land, including National Nature Reserves (NNRs), Nature Conservation Review (NCR), Geological Conservation Review (GCR) (England, Scotland and Wales), Earth Science Conservation Review (ESCR) (Northern Ireland), Special Protection Areas (SPAs), Special Areas of Conservation (SACs) and Ramsar sites, are notified as SSSIs (England, Scotland and Wales) or ASSIs (Northern Ireland).

Owners and occupiers are required to notify the relevant regulatory authority of potentially damaging operations and may not undertake them for four months unless they are in accordance with the terms of a management agreement with consent of the relevant regulatory authority.

As protection, the Secretary of State may make a nature conservation order to protect any sites of national or international importance. SSSIs are classed as such under the Wildlife and Countryside (Amendment) Act. In Northern Ireland the law relating to ASSIs is contained in the Environment (Northern Ireland) Order.

Local planning authorities are required to consult with the statutory bodies (Natural England, Natural Resources Wales, Northern Ireland Environment Agency and Scottish Natural Heritage) prior to allowing any development to proceed that may affect an SSSI or ASSI. Water, gas and electricity companies must also do the same.

Special Protection Areas (SPAs) and **Special Areas of Conservation (SACs)** are intended to protect the habitats of threatened species of wildlife. SACs are strictly protected sites under the EC Habitats Directive. This states the requirement to establish a European network of important, high-quality conservation sites. SPAs are strictly protected sites classified in accordance with Article 4 of the EC Birds Directive on the conservation of wild birds (79/409/EEC). They are classified for rare and vulnerable birds, listed in Annex I to the Birds Directive, and for regularly occurring migratory species.

5.4   Promoting biodiversity

 Biodiversity **is defined as the variety of plant and animal life in the world or in a particular region or ecosystem. A high level of biodiversity is considered to be important and desirable for the survival of ecosystems and species.**

The objective of the Conversation of Habitats and Species Regulations is to protect biodiversity. The regulations ensure that the deliberate introduction into the wild of any species which is not native to their territory is regulated so it does not negatively impact natural habitats within their natural range or the wild native fauna and flora and, if necessary, prohibit such introduction.

Working together and following good design principles, planners, developers and clients should aim to minimise the impact of the project on ecological factors (such as habitat destruction, fragmentation and species isolation). Opportunities to promote biodiversity and support ecosystem services should be identified and, wherever possible, should actively seek to rebuild local ecological networks. This can be achieved through the actions set out below.

Enhance the overall ecological quality of the site and the surrounding ecological network by creating new habitats, buffer areas and landscape features that are of importance for wildlife. Focus should be made:

- in areas where the most important, fragile and/or threatened habitats and species are known to occur

- where there are species requiring large ranges (land areas required for them to exist), which have particularly suffered as a result of their habitats becoming reduced in size and isolated

- on species with low reproductive capacity (most large mammals), species highly sensitive to disturbance (most birds of prey) and species subject to recovery programmes (the focus of local biodiversity action plan targets).

Local biodiversity action plans, species action plans and habitat action plans should be used as a guide to the relevant priorities for such positive measures at the local level. These may include rehabilitation of degraded habitats or the creation of new habitats within and adjacent to development sites. Bird boxes, swift bricks, bat boxes, bat bricks, green roofs, green walls and habitat creation are examples where enhancement can be achieved on construction projects.

Avoid developing sites, and locations within sites, where existing habitats, important species, buffer areas and other landscape features of major importance for wildlife would:

- suffer direct impact resulting in the reduction or complete loss of habitat and/or diversity of species present

- suffer an indirect impact from nearby development through increased ecological disturbance and stress, thereby reducing the site's capacity to support the wildlife present

- suffer a reduction in ecological quality, so that the site is unable to support migration, dispersal or genetic exchange of wild species

- be further fragmented from other similar features by development that causes a barrier effect in the landscape between fragments.

Restore and, where possible, link and connect existing habitats and landscape features, which could potentially be of major importance for wildlife, enhancing their ability to support migration, dispersal and genetic exchange.

Retain and incorporate within the development site existing habitats, important species, buffer areas and landscape features of major importance for wildlife – making sure that the site retains at least the same capacity to support the diversity, abundance, migration, dispersal and genetic exchange of wildlife as it did prior to development.

Compensate for features lost to development through the following.

- Re-creation, as nearby as possible, of features and landforms capable of maintaining the same quality of habitats and species as would otherwise be lost or displaced through the development.

- Restoration and enhancement of surrounding or nearby features unaffected by development.

- Creation of new or additional buffer areas to reduce impacts.

- Translocation of habitats and species that would otherwise be lost.

 For further information on local biodiversity action plans visit the Joint Nature Conservation Committee (JNCC) website.

For practical advice visit the CIRIA website for its *Working with wildlife* mobile app.

05

ECOLOGY

5.5   Regulatory bodies for nature conservation

Organisations with responsibility for nature conservation in each of the devolved administrations are shown in the table below.

Area	Responsible organisation
England	Natural England
Northern Ireland	Northern Ireland Environment Agency
Scotland	Scottish Natural Heritage
Wales	Natural Resources Wales

The regulatory bodies' remit includes providing ecological advice, consultation during the planning process, promoting biodiversity, and protecting designated ecological sites and protected species. The Joint Nature and Conservation Committee (JNCC) is the main public body that advises the UK Government and devolved administrations on UK-wide and international nature conservation.

JNCC is led by the Joint Committee, which brings together members from the nature conservation bodies for England, Northern Ireland, Scotland and Wales and independent members appointed by the Secretary of State for the Environment, Food and Rural Affairs under an independent chairperson. There are many other organisations, national and regional, involved in the protection and enhancement of plants and wildlife across the UK. Below are a few examples of the more prominent organisations.

- The National Trust.
- The Royal Society for the Protection of Birds.
- The Wildlife Trust.
- National parks.

5.6   Endangered species

Nature is humanity's life support system, and underpins all life on Earth. The natural world slowly changes over thousands of years, during which time new species evolve and some species decline and may ultimately become extinct. Human activity can have a dramatic impact on these natural cycles by putting significant pressure on ecosystems through vegetation clearance, deforestation and habitat fragmentation caused by agricultural development, road building and other infrastructure projects. This can lead to an accelerated decline in species and the habitats that support them.

The responsible management of wildlife and its habitat is critical if we want to maintain a healthy, sustainable planet and ensure its renewable resources are passed on to future generations.

At an international level, the International Union for Conservation of Nature (IUCN) is recognised for its work in publishing the *Red list of threatened species*, which is the definitive international standard for species extinction risk. The *Red list* is regularly updated with new information about the status of endangered species. Estimates based on the IUCN Red list indicate that one million species are currently threatened with extinction. However, it is not too late to reverse these trends.

In the UK, priority species and habitats are those that have been identified as being the most threatened and requiring conservation action. Section 41 of the Natural Environment and Rural Communities Act identifies priority species and habitats at risk of human-induced extinction.

COP 15, the international biodiversity conference held under the United Nations Convention on Biological Diversity (CBD) implemented a new set of international goals for biodiversity known as the Kunming-Montreal Global Biodiversity Framework (GBF). 188 governments, including the UK, agreed to the GBF and committed to addressing the ongoing loss of terrestrial and marine biodiversity. The GBF contains four main goals and 23 targets.

The four global goals set out a vision to address ongoing biodiversity loss by 2050:

Goal A. Substantially increase the area of natural ecosystems by maintaining, enhancing or restoring the integrity, connectivity and resilience of all ecosystems. Reduce by tenfold the extinction rate and risk of all species and increase the abundance of native wild species. Maintain the genetic diversity of wild and domesticated species and safeguard their adaptive potential.

Goal B. Ensure nature's contributions to people are valued, maintained and enhanced, with those contributions currently in decline being restored.

Goal C. Share the monetary and non-monetary benefits of the utilisation of genetic resources, digital sequence information on genetic resources, and traditional knowledge associated with genetic resources with Indigenous people and local communities. Additionally, ensure traditional knowledge associated with genetic resources is appropriately protected.

Goal D. Ensure all parties (specifically developing countries) have adequate means to implement the GBF. This includes financial resources, capacity building, technical and scientific cooperation, and access to technology.

The 23 global targets for 2030 include:

- Effective conservation and management of at least 30% of the world's lands, inland waters, coastal areas and oceans, with emphasis on areas of particular importance for biodiversity and ecosystem functioning and services. This has been informally referred to as the '30 by 30' deal.
- Reduce global food waste by half and significantly reduce over-consumption and waste generation.

- Reduce by half both excess nutrients and the overall risk posed by pesticides and highly hazardous chemicals.

- Progressively phase out or reform subsidies that harm biodiversity by at least $500 billion per year, whilst scaling up positive incentives for biodiversity conservation.

- Encourage at least $200 billion per year in domestic and international biodiversity-related funding from public and private sources.

- Increase international financial flows from developed to developing countries by at least $20 billion per year by 2025, and to at least $30 billion per year by 2030.

- Require transnational companies and financial institutions to monitor, assess and disclose the impact on biodiversity of their operations, supply chains and portfolios.

The GBF is not legally binding, but it does require countries to monitor and report their progress against the goals and targets every five years, or earlier. The UK's Biodiversity Indicators are undergoing a comprehensive review (during 2022/23) to ensure that the best possible data is available, and in response to the development of the new post-2020 global biodiversity framework, agreed through COP15 of the Convention on Biological Diversity. The review is due for publication in the spring of 2023.

 For more information, visit the Government website.

The UK lists of priority species and habitats remain important and are valuable reference sources. They were used to help draw up statutory lists of priorities in England, Northern Ireland, Scotland and Wales. These UK priority species were identified as being the most threatened and requiring conservation action. The list of UK priority species and habitats represents the most comprehensive analysis of such information ever undertaken in the UK, and now contains **1,149 species** and **67 habitats**. Species were assessed according to four criteria, as shown below.

05

- Threatened internationally.

- International responsibility and a 25% decline in the UK.

- More than 50% decline in the UK.

- Other important factors, where data on decline was lacking but there is other evidence of extreme threat.

Examples of **priority species** in the UK are shown below.

Birds	Terrestrial mammals	Herptiles
▪ Common starling.	▪ Brown long-eared bat.	▪ Adder.
▪ House sparrow.	▪ Dormouse.	▪ Common lizard.
▪ Lesser spotted woodpecker.	▪ Otter.	▪ Common toad.
▪ Scottish crossbill.	▪ Red squirrel.	▪ Great crested newt.
▪ Skylark.	▪ Water vole.	▪ Natterjack toad.
Lesser spotted woodpecker	*Red squirrel*	*Great crested newt*

5.7 Protected species and habitats

Several hundred species of birds, wild creatures, insects and plants are protected under the Wildlife and Countryside (Amendment) Act and the Wildlife (Amendment) (Northern Ireland) Order and are listed in various schedules to the Act, for example:

- Schedule 1: Birds
- Schedule 8: Plants.
- Schedule 5: Animals

Under the Conservation of Habitats and Species Regulations, a person guilty of an offence under the regulations is liable for summary conviction to imprisonment for a term not exceeding six months, or a fine, or both.

ECOLOGY

The habitat regulations include the following.

- Protection of certain species of animals, Schedule 2 (such as the great crested newt, dormouse, bat, otter and large blue butterfly).

- Protection of species of plants, Schedule 4 (such as the fen orchid and early gentian).

- Designation of Special Areas of Conservation (SACs) and Special Protection Areas (SPAs), which are intended to protect the habitats of threatened species of wildlife.

Local planning authorities will, in consultation with Natural England, Natural Resources Wales, Northern Ireland Environment Agency or Scottish Natural Heritage, consider SPAs to protect birds from the effects of disturbance, shooting, egg collecting or other work.

 Under the Conservation of Habitats and Species Regulations, a person guilty of an offence is liable on summary conviction to imprisonment for a term not exceeding six months, or a fine, or both.

5.7.1   Badgers

The Protection of Badgers Act is provided to protect badgers from deliberate harm, injury or baiting. It is an offence to:

- disturb a badger when it is occupying a sett
- interfere with, damage or destroy a sett
- dig for a badger
- cause a dog to enter a badger sett
- obstruct access to, or entrance to, a sett
- wilfully kill, injure, entrap or ill-treat a badger.

Failure to comply with the legislation can lead to six months' imprisonment and an unlimited fine. A licence must be obtained from the relevant conservation body for any work that may cause disturbance to a badger or involves the damage or destruction of a sett. What constitutes disturbance depends on the nature of the activity proposed. As a rule, a licence is normally required for any work within 30 m of a badger sett. However, this distance may increase for more disruptive activities, such as blasting or pile driving.

Licences are not normally issued during the breeding season, and cannot be issued retrospectively. February is the peak month of the badger mating season, but they can mate any time of the year. It mainly occurs during two periods – one being January to May, and another being July to August. Activities that involve disturbance should therefore be programmed to take place outside of this period.

If a badger sett is discovered after works have started, it is essential to stop work immediately and seek expert advice.

Badgers

Artificial badger sett being built as part of mitigation

The following animals are all protected under the Wildlife and Countryside (Amendment) Act (England, Scotland and Wales) or the Wildlife (Amendment) (Northern Ireland) Order.

5.7.2   Great crested newts

Great crested newts are fully protected by law. It is an offence to:

- capture, kill, disturb or injure great crested newts deliberately
- damage or destroy a breeding or resting place
- take great crested newt eggs
- possess, sell, control or transport live or dead newts, or parts of them
- obstruct access to their resting or sheltering places (deliberately or by not taking enough care).

Each offence could result in an unlimited fine and imprisonment for up to six months.

Great crested newts rely on water bodies for breeding, but otherwise they spend much of their lives on land. They spend winter on land, normally hibernating underground, and emerge soon after the first frost-free days in January or February to begin the migration to breeding ponds (within 500 m). Initial surveys for great crested newts (by an ecological consultant) are required by the local planning authority and Natural England where water bodies are within 500 m of any proposed development. Four surveys must be made to determine presence or absence, with three surveys conducted between mid-April and mid-May.

Ideally, it is best if great crested newts and their habitats are protected before planning permission has been given for development of a site. If a known or suspected great crested newt site is threatened by a development, the local planning authority and the local office of the statutory nature conservation organisation (SNCO) should be informed as far in advance as possible and the appropriate mitigation scheme approved as part of the planning permission.

Any mitigation proposals will need the submission of a licence application to Natural England, Natural Resources Wales, Northern Ireland Environment Agency or Scottish Natural Heritage. It requires a report that sets out survey results, impacts and a mitigation scheme. The application will take up to 40 days to determine.

---

e.g. Mitigation for great crested newts

Minor impact – on site mitigation.

- Small scale relocation and exclusion.
- Fence erecting and traps set up to exclude newts from works (between March and October). Survey for 30 days minimum.
- Habitat creation (such as creation of refuges and hibernacula – piles of rubble/logs buried beneath the surface of the ground).

Major impact – translocation of newts away from site.

- Fence erecting and traps set up (between March and April). Survey for 60 days minimum.
- Translocation of newts to an area providing equivalent or better habitat (receptor site).
- Habitat creation and restoration prior to translocation (such as areas of coarse grassland, hedgerows and ponds).
- Creation of refuges and hibernaculas.

Great crested newt fencing

Great crested newt fencing and mitigation pond

5.7.3 Bats

All bat species, along with their breeding sites and resting places, are fully protected by law. Bats roost in a number of locations; some examples are shown below.

- Disused buildings and structures.
- Under bridges.
- Holes and cracks in trees.
- Roofs and walls of buildings.
- Caves.

Man-made bat house to encourage alternative roosting during construction works

Bats hibernate between October and April and breed between May and September. If it is suspected that bats may be present then a bat survey should be carried out by a qualified specialist to establish the size and location of any roost.

It is illegal to:

- deliberately capture, injure or kill bats
- damage or destroy a breeding or roosting place (even if it is unoccupied at the time)
- obstruct access to their roosting or sheltering places
- possess, sell, control or transport live or dead bats, or parts of them
- intentionally or recklessly disturb a bat while it's in a structure or place of shelter or protection.

Each offence could result in an unlimited fine and imprisonment for up to six months. Personnel holding a bat licence are legally allowed to enter a bat roost or to capture, handle or relocate bats.

5.7.4   Nesting birds

All birds, their nests and eggs are protected by law. It is illegal to:

- intentionally kill, injure or take wild birds
- intentionally take, damage or destroy a wild bird's nest while it's being used or built
- intentionally take or destroy a wild bird's egg

- possess, control or transport live or dead wild birds, or parts of them, or their eggs
- sell wild birds or put them on display for sale
- use prohibited methods to kill or take wild birds.

Some birds, for example barn owls, have additional legal protection. For these bird species, it is also an offence to:

- intentionally, or by not taking enough care, disturbing them while they're nesting, building a nest, in or near a nest that contains their young
- disturb their dependent young.

Each offence could result in an unlimited fine and imprisonment for up to six months.

If any type of bird is nesting in vegetation such as a tree or hedge, then it is legally protected, so long as the nest is still in use. This prohibits certain types of tree pruning or removal until the nesting season is over. Furthermore, removing dense hedges or substantially reducing them is illegal, but annual trimming may be acceptable.

The nesting season is in the spring and summer, generally from the beginning of March until the end of July. However, certain wild bird species such as crossbills may lay their eggs as early as January to coincide with food availability (such as pine seeds), while pigeons and doves nest all year round.

It is essential that construction is carefully planned to avoid any works in areas during the nesting period. If work cannot be avoided during the nesting period, areas must be fenced off to avoid damage or disturbance. There is also a risk of finding birds nesting in dry stone walls and occasionally on pieces of equipment (such as dumpers or cranes) during the construction phase.

Good awareness is important, and site personnel should be made aware of these risks through induction and toolbox talks, along with necessary actions to take.

5.7.5   Trees and hedgerows

Under Part 8 of the Town and Country Planning Act, the Town and Country Planning (Trees) Regulations and the Planning (Northern Ireland) Order, tree preservation orders (TPOs) can be put in place by the Local Planning Authority to prohibit the cutting down, uprooting, pollarding, topping, lopping, wilful damage or destruction of trees without the local planning authority's consent.

It is illegal to cut down or alter any tree under a TPO. All trees within a designated conservation area are protected.

The Local Authority Planning Department should be contacted well in advance of any work on any trees with a TPO. To work on a tree with a TPO, permission must be sought from the Local Planning Authority by submitting a standard application form. The form is available from the Planning Portal or the authority.

The information on the form must make clear what the proposed work is, and provide adequate information to support the application. The Local Authority has up to two months to make a decision.

Bad practice: tree damage caused by inappropriate storage of construction waste within the protection zone

Under the Hedgerows Regulations (England and Wales only), a hedgerow removal notice is required from the Local Authority if the hedgerow is older than 30 years and meets at least one of the criteria listed in Part 2 of Schedule 1.

These criteria focus on the length, location and importance of the hedgerow. The removal of a hedgerow longer than 20 m requires planning permission.

During the planning of a project you should make contact with the Local Authority to ensure that any trees or hedgerows identified for removal are discussed and their removal is avoided, where possible.

Translocation of mature or ancient hedgerows should also be considered. Works on trees and hedgerows are confined to certain times of the year due to nesting birds and bats, which are protected species.

All trees should be protected in accordance with *Trees in relation to design, demolition and construction* (BS 5837:2012)

The key requirements are as follows.

The roots of a tree help keep it healthy and upright. Roots tend to be found in the top 600mm of soil, and usually grow out further than the height of the tree.

If roots are damaged, this can cause irreversible harm and lead to the tree's death.

There are three **tree protection zones** surrounding a tree where certain rules apply to help prevent root damage.

The **prohibited zone** is located 1 m away from the trunk. Unless a full consideration with the Local Authority's tree officer has taken place, no excavations can be carried out in this zone. Materials, plant and spoil must not be stored here.

Good tree protection measures

The **precautionary zone** is four times the tree's circumference. If excavations must be undertaken in this zone, mechanical excavation is not allowed. If there are any exposed roots, then precautions must be taken to protect them. Materials, plant and spoil must not be stored here.

The **permitted zone** is any area beyond the precautionary zone. Excavation work can be carried out here, but with caution and limited use of mechanical plant. Any exposed roots must be protected.

BS 5837 recommends additional control measures relating to construction activities, and that the following practices should be followed when construction work is being carried out to protect trees.

Protected zones — a fenced-off area around the tree should be established to eliminate damage during construction, and the rules for each zone must be applied.

Avoid compaction of soil — soil compaction destroys the soil's pore structure, making it hard for trees to absorb water. This can be caused by storage of equipment, materials, machinery and soil, and by using the area as a thoroughfare by people and vehicles, as well as for welfare accommodation.

Considered excavation — when excavating for foundations and utilities, the welfare of root systems must be considered. It is a common misconception that the root system of a tree extends in a narrow, deep band directly below the trunk. In reality, the roots extend a large distance laterally at a shallow depth, at approximately 60cm.

Shallow foundations therefore impact root systems. The closer the excavation is to a tree, the more likely the chance of damage. Construction therefore should not take place within the protected zone. This also benefits the building as roots can damage foundations. Where foundations are to be located near major roots they should be carefully bridged.

Ground level change — tree root locations should be acknowledged. Increases in ground level could cause compaction, consequently suffocating shallow and fragile roots. Reduction in ground level can cause severance of roots and altered drainage rates, affecting water availability.

Machinery impact — torn branches, damaged bark and general wounds to the trunk can lead to disease and parasites causing decay of the tree.

Contamination of soil — leakage of chemicals from construction materials needs to be avoided through correct and secure storage. The storage of such substances must not be kept within the protection zone and should be downhill from the tree, ideally 10 m from the protection zone to allow for leaching of materials through the soil.

Tree surgery — consent could be required if the tree is protected or is within a conservation area. Any surgery or necessary felling needs to be detailed in the planning application and should be undertaken prior to the commencement of construction activities. It is easier to conduct surgery without unavoidable construction obstacles. Restrictions on surgery and felling must be considered during the bird nesting season.

 The National Joint Utilities Group (NJUG) has published *Street works UK guidelines for the planning, installation and maintenance of utility apparatus in proximity to trees*. The document provides details for the establishment of a tree protection zone, and precautions that should be taken for any works within it.

ECOLOGY

Tree protection zone

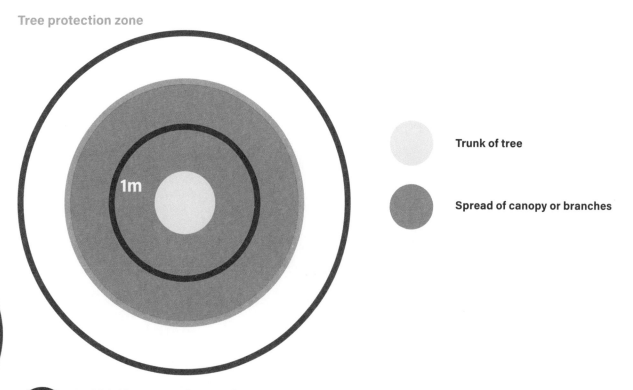

Trunk of tree

Spread of canopy or branches

1m

Prohibited zone – 1 m from trunk

Excavations of any kind must not be undertaken within this zone, unless full consideration with the Local Authority tree officer is undertaken. Materials, plant and spoil must not be stored within this zone.

Precautionary zone – four times tree circumference

Where excavations must be undertaken within this zone the use of mechanical excavation plant should be prohibited. Precautions should be undertaken to protect any exposed roots. Materials, plant and spoil should not be stored within this zone. Consult with the Local Authority tree officer if in any doubt.

Permitted zone – outside of precautionary zone

Excavation works may be undertaken within this zone. However, caution must be applied and the use of mechanical plant limited. Any exposed roots should be protected.

5.8   Invasive species

An invasive species is an organism that is not indigenous, or native, to a particular area, and can cause significant environmental and economic harm. These can have a damaging impact on British plants, animals and ecosystems by spreading disease, competing for habitat and direct predation (killing of another species for food).

The contract documentation or environmental statement for a project will highlight any invasive species of concern. Identifying invasive species early is key, and if present, advice should be sought from specialists on the best way to treat and dispose of them. Control measures should be included within the project environmental management plan, together with method statements that may need to be agreed with the relevant agencies before commencement of work.

It is possible that construction can impact invasive species, most likely by accidental dispersal. It is an offence under Section 14 of the Wildlife and Countryside (Amendment) Act (England, Scotland or Wales) or under Article 15 of the Wildlife (Northern Ireland) Order to deliberately permit the spread of an invasive species by releasing it into the wild.

One example is the American signal crayfish, which is driving the native white-clawed crayfish to extinction and causing diversity declines in aquatic communities. Commercial fisheries have been affected by egg predation and competition between crayfish and salmon for refuges. Burrowing can cause riverbank erosion and destabilise structures built at the river edges.

 Details of invasive species are available on the Government website, including a leaflet on how to manage non-native species.

Section 14 of the Wildlife and Countryside (Amendment) Act and Article 15 of the Wildlife (Amendment) (Northern Ireland) Order makes it an offence to plant or otherwise cause to grow any of the plants listed in Schedule 9. Some common examples include the following.

- Giant hogweed.
- Giant kelp.
- Japanese knotweed.

- Japanese seaweed.
- Himalayan balsam.
- Rhododendron.

- Floating pennywort.

- Australian swamp stonecrop.

- Parrot's feather.

Of these examples, the most common are Giant hogweed, Japanese knotweed and Himalayan balsam.

 Refer to Appendix B for details on how to deal with Japanese knotweed.

Giant hogweed   *Japanese knotweed (image by Bridget Plowright)*   *Himalayan balsam*

05

There are other pieces of legislation that relate to preventing the spread of invasive species in the UK, which can include both native and non-native species (for example, the native species ragwort is one of the species controlled under the Weeds Act).

 Practices to be employed for effective management of invasive plants

Before work starts

- Review the environmental statement and conduct a site survey to identify and confirm the location of any non-native invasive species.

- Liaise with landowners and statutory bodies on the appropriate treatment techniques where invasive species have been identified.

- Demarcate and fence off any areas found to contain non-native invasive species.

During construction

- Ensure that workers are made aware of invasive species at site inductions, using maps, and reinforce this via toolbox talks.

- Implement bio-security measures to ensure the work does not contribute to the spread of the non-native invasive species.

- Maintain fenced areas to restrict access and to prevent spread across the site.

- Any use of herbicides near or in watercourses needs to be approved by the environment agencies. Ensure that treatment companies hold appropriate certificates of competence.

- Ensure that any chemical containers or materials contaminated with herbicides are disposed of in accordance with the duty of care and Hazardous Waste Regulations waste treatment facility.

- Ensure that soils contaminated with invasive plants or roots are removed to an appropriately authorised landfill site.

Management of invasive species will often generate waste in the form of plant material, soil, contaminated water and sediment, or dead animals. This needs to be dealt with carefully to ensure that it complies with the relevant waste legislation. For example, when Japanese knotweed is dug up, the soil will contain rhizome (underground root-like stems) from which it can regenerate. This is likely to be classified as controlled waste under the Environmental Protection Act, and can only be transferred by an authorised person (such as a registered waste carrier) and taken to an appropriately-authorised landfill site for specialised disposal.

 For further information on waste management refer to Chapter E10 Waste and material management.

 Pesticides Act and Control of Pesticides Regulations

In many cases, management of invasive plants will involve the use of herbicides, which are controlled under the Pesticides Act and the Control of Pesticides Regulations. These place strict controls on the supply, storage and use of all pesticides, including herbicides used in the control of invasive species, and make it obligatory for those giving advice on the use of pesticide products (such as salespeople, advisers, managers and those who draft contracts) to hold a certificate of competence recognised by Defra. The only qualifications recognised by Defra are issued by the British Agrochemical Supply Industry Scheme (BASIS). Permission is also required from the relevant environment agency if spraying in or near watercourses.

Appendix A – Wildlife year planner

Traditionally, environmental issues are not considered at an early stage in project planning. The year planners below show the appropriate times of year to deal with specific issues. These are only a guide, and you must always consult a competent ecologist before carrying out any activity that might disturb these species. You can check this with the Chartered Institute of Ecology and Environment Management (CIEEM). Ecologists should also follow the biodiversity code of practice for planning and development (BS 42020:2013).

Badgers

Task	Jan	Feb	Mar	Apr	May	June	July	Aug	Sept	Oct	Nov	Dec
1		*	*	*					*	*	*	
2	*				*	*	*	*				*
3	*	*					**	**	**	**	*	*
4		*	*	*								
5							*	*	*	*	*	

1. **Badger surveys** are best carried out when the vegetation is low and field signs are easier to identify.

2. **Badger surveys** can continue but become less reliable as the vegetation becomes denser.

3. Artificial badger sett construction between July and October will require a licence to install, and this must be in place for six months before the original sett is closed.

4. Badger territorial bait marking surveys. Territorial marking is at its peak between February and April and the vegetation is low enough to identify latrines. This is the only time of year when bait marking is effective.

5. **Badger licensing season: Between 1 July and 30 November.** Nature conservancy councils will normally only issue disturbance and exclusion licences outside this time period in cases of proven urgency.

Water voles

Task	Jan	Feb	Mar	Apr	May	June	July	Aug	Sept	Oct	Nov	Dec
1			*	*	*	*	*	*	*			
2		*	*	*					*	*		

1. **Water vole surveys** need to be carried out during the summer breeding season (two survey visits are usually required).

2. Water vole exclusions. Excluding and trapping are recommended from 15th February to 15th April, before the breeding season, or 15th September to 31st October, after the end of the breeding season.

Otters

Task	Jan	Feb	Mar	Apr	May	June	July	Aug	Sept	Oct	Nov	Dec
1	*	*	*	*	*	*	*	*	*	*	*	*
2	*	*	*	*	*	*	*	*	*	*	*	*

1. **Otter surveys** can be carried out throughout the year, although surveys are easier to carry out during periods of low vegetation.

2. **Otter mitigation** can be carried out throughout the year but may be restricted if evidence of breeding is identified.

Great crested newts

Task	Jan	Feb	Mar	Apr	May	June	July	Aug	Sept	Oct	Nov	Dec
1			*	*	*	*						
2			*	*	*	*	*	*	*	*		

1. **Great crested newts breeding pond surveys** are the only way to effectively establish presence or absence and to quantify populations. These are best carried out between March and June.

2. **Terrestrial searches** are least effective but can be carried out from March to October, depending upon weather conditions. Surveys should be carried out when night temperatures are above five degrees centigrade and when the ground is moist.

Bats

Task	Jan	Feb	Mar	Apr	May	June	July	Aug	Sept	Oct	Nov	Dec
1				*	*	*	*	*	*	*		
2					*	*	*	*	*			
3	*	*	*									*
4					*	*	*	*	*	*		

1. **Flight surveys** that involve identification of bats in flight by observation or echolocation can be carried out between April and October, although the optimum time for the surveys is April to September. Surveys of this type can be carried out without a licence as they are non-intrusive.

2. **Dusk emergence and dawn swarming surveys** can be carried out between May and October although the optimum time for the surveys is between May and September.

3. **Hibernation roost surveys** can only be carried out between December and March when the bats are hibernating. These surveys are very difficult to carry out as bats hibernate deep in cracks and crevices and are therefore difficult to identify.

4. **Habitat surveys** can only be effectively carried out between April and October when the bats are active.

Crayfish

Task	Jan	Feb	Mar	Apr	May	June	July	Aug	Sept	Oct	Nov	Dec
1							*	*	*			
2					*	*						
3	*	*	*								*	*

1. **Crayfish surveys** are best carried out between July and September, although it is possible to carry out surveys during April.

2. **Crayfish releasing young surveys** should **not** be carried out during May and June because crayfish could still be carrying their newly hatched young.

3. **Crayfish reduced activity surveys** should **not** be carried out during the winter months due to reduced levels of activity.

Nesting birds

Task	Jan	Feb	Mar	Apr	May	June	July	Aug	Sept	Oct	Nov	Dec
1			*	*	*	*	*	*	*			
2	*	*								*	*	*

1. **Nesting bird season.** No vegetation clearance work should be carried out during the nesting bird season unless immediately preceded by a thorough nesting bird survey.

2. **Vegetation clearance work** is best carried out at these times of year when birds are not nesting, although work must stop if nests are found.

Reptiles

Task	Jan	Feb	Mar	Apr	May	June	July	Aug	Sept	Oct	Nov	Dec
1			*	*	*	*	*	*	*			
2				*	*	*	*	*	*	*		
3	*	*								*	*	*

1. **Reptile surveys** can only be carried out between March and October when reptiles are active, with the peak times April to May and September. During the winter months reptiles are in hibernation, therefore it is not suitable to carry out surveys.

2. **Reptile capture and release programmes** can only be carried out between April and October when reptiles are active.

3. **Scrub clearance** work can be carried out from October to February, when the reptiles are hibernating.

05

Appendix B – Dealing with Japanese knotweed

Japanese knotweed can cause structural damage. It can grow up to 20 mm a day and is strong enough to penetrate foundations. It is an offence under the Wildlife and Countryside (Amendment) Act (England, Scotland and Wales) and the Wildlife (Northern Ireland) Order to encourage the spread of Japanese knotweed. It is often found along railways, riverbanks, roads and derelict sites. Any known areas of Japanese knotweed will be highlighted within the environmental statement for the project. These areas must be cordoned off to prevent inadvertent spread. Extreme care must be taken to ensure that all equipment used on site is free of Japanese knotweed material before leaving the site, to avoid contamination.

If works are required in areas of known Japanese knotweed strands, control methods must be applied; the particular method to be employed will be dependent on site conditions. Where possible, excavation should be avoided and the plant should be treated in its original position.

Japanese knotweed can grow up to 20 mm a day
(Image supplied by Bridget Plowright)

Japanese knotweed in flower

 The Japanese knotweed rhizome system (root zone) may extend to, and beyond, a depth of at least 2 m and extend 7 m laterally from a parent plant.

Chemical control

Chemical control usually takes a minimum of three years to totally eradicate Japanese knotweed. Wherever there is a risk of contamination to a watercourse, choice of herbicide is limited to formulations of Glyphosate and 2, 4-D Amine that are approved for use in or near water. Use of herbicides in or near water requires formal consultation with the relevant environment agency. Spraying both the top and underside of leaves improves control. Plants respond best when actively growing. The most effective time to apply herbicide is from July to September.

Non-chemical controls

Cutting. Use a simple scythe method of cutting to prevent stem fragmentation. Continue cutting every 2–4 weeks to reduce both above and below-ground biomass (this will only control the knotweed, not eradicate it).

Burning. Controlled burning of stem and crown material may be used as part of the control programme. Such burning must take into account the potential for nuisance or pollution that may occur as a result of the activity. Burning in the open may be undertaken in accordance with a registered D7 exemption from the Local Authority, in accordance with the Environmental Permitting Regulations.

Burial. Soil containing knotweed material and burnt remains of knotweed may be buried on the site of production. On-site burial must be performed to a depth of at least 5 m. Knotweed material should be covered with root barrier membrane consisting of a geotextile layer or a heavy gauge polythene sheet prior to infilling. It is strongly advised to record the burial site location, and to inform any future owners of its position.

Excavation. Only consider excavating as a last resort, unless this is part of an on-site treatment method. When using excavation for off-site disposal, take great care to avoid excess waste and make sure the excavated material does not contaminate surplus soil.

Off-site disposal. Where the option for on-site disposal or treatment is not available, as a last resort in terms of sustainability, material contaminated with Japanese knotweed must be disposed of at an approved disposal facility, having informed the site operator of the presence of viable knotweed within the material.

To ensure compliance with the Wildlife and Countryside (Amendment) Act and to reduce the risk of spreading knotweed, any such on-site burial and any controlled burning must be done in accordance with the new Code of Practice developed by the Invasive Non-Native Specialist Association (INNSA).

 For further information on the INNSA Code of Practice visit the INNSA website.

 Failure to appropriately dispose of any material containing Japanese knotweed may lead to prosecution under Section 33 and 34 of the Environmental Protection Act and Section 14 of the Wildlife and Countryside (Amendment) Act.

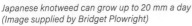

Appendix C – Construction work and its potential adverse effects on wildlife

Construction work and its potential adverse effects on wildlife		
Construction activity	**Implication**	**Examples of effect on wildlife**
Site clearance	Removal of trees and shrubs	■ Loss of important species or specimens of tree or shrub that may be protected by a tree preservation order (TPO) ■ Loss of bird nests or bat roosts ■ Loss of habitat for protected species ■ Loss of important invertebrates, including those that may require deadwood habitat (such as stag beetles)
	Removal of ground vegetation	■ Loss of habitat for protected species ■ Loss of rare plants ■ Loss of bird nests ■ Killing or injury of reptiles or amphibians ■ Killing or injury of small mammals ■ Loss of invertebrates and their breeding habitat
	Removal of soil	■ Loss of habitat for protected species ■ Loss of seed bank ■ Loss of water vole burrows ■ Loss of invertebrates and their breeding habitat ■ Destruction of badger setts
	Demolition of buildings and structures	■ Loss of bird nesting or bat roosting areas
	Removal of rubble and other materials	■ Loss of reptile and amphibian habitat
Site set up	Location of site offices and compounds	■ Disturbance of breeding animals
	Storage areas	■ Potential pollution of important watercourses, wetlands or other water bodies, including coastal waters, through spillage or dust
Establishment of haul roads	Rubble or concrete temporary roads constructed	■ Fragmentation of habitats ■ Road kills ■ Destruction of badger setts ■ Contamination of adjoining habitats by dust ■ Noise or light pollution may disturb nesting birds or other animals ■ Change of pH through leaching
Groundworks	Ground investigations Foundations Excavations and piling Temporary earthworks Tunnelling	■ Impacts on surface and groundwater, which may have secondary impacts on important wetlands both on and off site ■ Noise or light pollution may disturb nesting birds or other animals ■ Destruction of badger setts ■ Run-off and erosion, which may damage important habitats ■ Potential to introduce or spread invasive plants (such as Japanese knotweed)
Construction	Concrete pours and other wet trades	■ Silt run-off and wind blown dust create nuisance pollution, including loss of photosynthesis potential for plants, siltation of watercourses and adverse effects on hydro ecology, such as reduced photosynthesis and harm to filter feeders and fish gills, etc. ■ Contamination of wetlands ■ Change of soil pH through run-off

ECOLOGY

05

CONTENTS

Statutory nuisance

06

Supporting
INFORMATION

GT700 Toolbox talks / supporting checklists and forms

Toolbox talks on some of these topics are available in the GT700 publication. Supporting checklists and forms covering some of these topics are available on our companion website.

STATUTORY NUISANCE

Summary of statutory nuisance legislation and guidance

This list is not exhaustive and only includes legislation mentioned in this section of GE700.

Legislation and guidance	Enforcement agencies*				
	EA	LA	NIEA	NRW	SEPA
Acts (primary legislation)					
Clean Air Act	✓	✓		✓	✓
Clean Air (Northern Ireland) Order			✓		
Clean Neighbourhoods and Environment Act	✓		✓	✓	
Control of Pollution Act	✓		✓	✓	✓
Environmental Protection Act	✓		✓	✓	✓
Highways Act		✓			
Pollution Control and Local Government (Northern Ireland) Order			✓		
Pollution Prevention Control Act in Scotland					✓
Regulations (secondary legislation)					
Dark Smoke (Permitted Periods) Regulations	✓			✓	✓
Environmental Permitting (England and Wales) Regulations	✓			✓	
Pollution Prevention and Control (Industrial Emissions) Regulations in Northern Ireland			✓		
Pollution Prevention and Control (Scotland) Amendment Regulations					✓
Guidance					
Considerate Constructors Scheme – Code of considerate practice					
Evaluation and measurement for vibration in buildings (BS 7385-2)					
Net Regs Environmental guidance					
Noise and vibration (BS 5228)					
Process guidance note PG 3/16 for crushing work					
Organisations providing information and guidance on their websites	✓	✓	✓	✓	✓

*Key

EA	Environment Agency
LA	Local Authorities
NIEA	Northern Ireland Environment Agency
NRW	Natural Resources Wales
SEPA	Scottish Environment Protection Agency

Overview

Construction sites are inherently noisy. Noise is the largest single source of complaint but consideration should also be given to the effects of certain factors on the local communities neighbouring construction sites, including: lighting; dust; toxic generation; air, water and visual pollution; vibration; bad odours; traffic movements; and operations around vegetation that emit hazardous emissions.

This chapter identifies construction processes that could cause nuisance, provides an overview of the legal framework for their control and provides guidance on mitigating and managing these nuisances on site.

6.1   Introduction

 ***Nuisance* is something which is unreasonable that causes substantial interference with people's use and enjoyment of a local environment. It is much more than just an annoyance or being aware of something.**

Construction sites (which generate dust, noise, fumes, vibration, heavy traffic movements and artificial light) have the potential to cause nuisance to neighbours. This must be managed effectively to avoid Local Authority or individual intervention, with the potential of delaying or stopping the works.

There are three types of nuisance: statutory nuisance, where a particular nuisance has been recognised in statute law, and public and private nuisance, which are within common law based on precedent (rulings on similar previous cases).

6.2   Important points

Effective planning of site activities should take place to ensure that certain construction activities are limited, so that potential nuisances are minimised and do not cause annoyance to neighbours or impact on wildlife, trees or plants. To avoid causing complaints, sites should adopt the following practices.

- Identify sensitive receptors (people, wildlife, trees, plants and the environment), liaise with Local Authorities on any nuisance that is likely to occur and agree the appropriate mitigation measures.

- Plan all transport activities, both on and off site, to avoid dust, noise, fumes and disruption on local roads.

- Carry out regular dampening down of haul routes and cleaning of the public highway.

- Locate any crushing or cutting equipment away from sensitive areas and dampen down, as appropriate.

- Store dusty materials under cover.

- Consider alternative methods of construction to reduce dust and noise.

- Where noise could be an issue, apply to the Local Authority for a Section 61 prior consent to agree construction methods and noise levels.

- Locate noisy equipment away from sensitive receptors and/or use screening, where necessary.

- Ensure that plant and equipment meet current emission standards and are regularly maintained and kept in good working order.

- Ensure that a monitoring and inspection regime is in place to quickly identify and rectify problems.

- Prepare and communicate the process and responsibilities for dealing with and responding to environmental complaints.

6.3   Legislation

Current legislation for statutory nuisance in England, Scotland and Wales is contained in Part III of the Environmental Protection Act, and is enforced by Local Authorities with controls on various types of noise nuisance regulated under the Control of Pollution Act.

Section 79 of the Environmental Protection Act includes the following statutory nuisances.

- Premises in such a state as to be prejudicial to health.

- Smoke emissions that are prejudicial to health, or a nuisance.

- Fumes or gases emitted from premises so as to be prejudicial to health, or a nuisance.

- Any dust, steam, odour or other waste that is prejudicial to health, or a nuisance.

- Any accumulation or deposit that is prejudicial to health, or a nuisance.

- Artificial light emitted from premises so as to be prejudicial to health, or a nuisance.

- Noise emitted from premises that may be prejudicial to health, or a nuisance.

- Noise emitted from, or caused by, a vehicle, machinery or equipment on a street or road.

- Any water covering land, or land covered with water, that is in such a state as to be prejudicial to health or a nuisance (Scotland only).

Local Authorities have a duty to inspect their areas from time to time to detect whether a nuisance exists and investigate all complaints of statutory nuisances. Under Section 80 of the Environmental Protection Act, a Local Authority officer can serve an abatement notice, compelling the nuisance to be stopped. Failure to comply with the notice is a criminal offence.

If someone does not comply with an abatement notice, they can be prosecuted and fined:

- a lump sum (the amount is set by the court)

- further fines for each day that they fail to comply (the amount is set by the court).

Councils can also take action to stop or restrict the nuisance by:

- carrying out works and making the person given the notice pay for them (this can include seizure and confiscation of equipment)

- applying to the High Court for an injunction (if a prosecution is not adequate).

Prosecution does not always have to be initiated by the Local Authority. Under Section 82 of the Environmental Protection Act, individuals can also take action through the Magistrates' Court.

All employers should ensure that **best practical means** have been used to prevent, or to counteract the effects of, the nuisance.

 Best practical means

Best practical means is defined as taking the following points into account.

- Current technical knowledge.

- The design, construction and maintenance of buildings and enclosures.

- Design, installation, maintenance and periods of operation of plant.

- Financial implications.

- Local conditions.

6.3.1 Airborne dust, emissions and odours

A variety of air pollutants have known or suspected harmful effects on human health and the environment and can create a statutory nuisance. The UK Government has made provisions to ensure that air quality standards for certain pollutants are set centrally through the national air quality strategy.

Local Authorities have a responsibility to carry out and review air quality in their area. Where air quality is found not to meet the national air quality objectives they must declare an air quality management area. The Local Authority must then put together a management plan (called a local air quality action plan) to improve the air quality.

Local Authorities regulate the smaller, less polluting, installations and processes (such as batching plants, crushing work or paint spraying activities). For smaller activities of short duration you may have to apply for a T7 exemption (mobile crushing and screening). For the more polluting processes (such as landfill sites and asphalt plants) air emissions are regulated by the Environment Agency (England), Natural Resources Wales, the Northern Ireland Environment Agency and the Scottish Environment Protection Agency.

6.3.1.1 Controls under the Clean Air Act

The Clean Air Act provides a comprehensive control mechanism for the protection of the environment from smoke, dust, grit and fumes from all fires and furnaces, with the Local Authority as the relevant environmental regulator who can impose limits on dust, emissions and odours generated from a site.

Under Section 1 of Part 1 of the Clean Air Act, it is an offence to emit dark smoke from the chimney of any building on any day unless these occur within the permitted periods, as specified in the Dark Smoke (Permitted Periods) Regulations.

6.3.1.2 Controls under Environmental Permitting Regulations or Pollution Prevention Control Act

The provisions of the Clean Air Act do not apply to processes that are controlled under the Environmental Permitting Regulations in England and Wales, the Pollution Prevention and Control (Industrial Emissions) Regulations in Northern Ireland or the Pollution Prevention Control Act in Scotland. Permits are issued for three different types of installation categorised as Part A1, Part A2 and Part B installations. Part A1 installations are regulated by the environment agencies and are for more complex industrial activities. Part A2 and Part B installations are regulated by the Local Authority. From a construction perspective the activities will mainly be classed as Part B installations. These include, but are not limited to, installations such as batching plants, crushing work, waste transfer stations and landfill sites. Businesses which operate these types of premises must have a Part B permit.

The standard conditions for a Part B permit for mobile crushing plant require that no dust must cross the site boundary and the Local Authority must be informed if it does. In addition, visual inspections of dust must be made three times daily.

6.3.1.3 Controls under Highway Regulations

Under the Highways Act, Sections 161 and 161A, a person will be guilty of an offence if, without lawful authority, they light a fire on or above a highway, within 50 feet of the centre of the highway, and if they allow mud or other offensive matter to run onto the highway and a user of the highway is injured, interrupted or endangered. Those found responsible for such actions will be liable to a fine, unless reasonable attempts were made to prevent such actions from occurring.

6.4   Dust and emissions

Pollution from dust and emissions can cause problems of nuisance for the local community, businesses and the environment. It can also affect water ecology, such as streams, lakes and ponds; can cause groundwater pollution; and can affect local wildlife and plants.

 Managing dust and emissions

Before work starts, an assessment should be made to identify the risk of dust and emissions causing nuisance or environmental damage. The level of risk to local receptors will depend on the following.

- Activities being carried out (for example, demolition, number of vehicles and plant, and types of materials involved in the demolition).
- Duration.
- Size of the site.
- Local weather conditions (for example, wind speed, direction of wind and rainfall).
- Location of receptors to the activities.
- Sensitivity of the receptors to dust and emissions.

If appropriate, liaison with the Local Authority should take place to agree monitoring and control measures where there is a risk that nuisances could occur.

Fine water mist being sprayed to reduce airborne dust clouds

Control measures to mitigate any negative dust impacts could include the following.

- Dampening down of haul routes with water.
- Ensuring public highways are regularly swept.
- Installing wheel-washing equipment at site exits where appropriate.
- Ensuring that bulk materials leaving site are securely covered.
- Installing dust screens (for airborne dust) or silt fencing (for watercourses) to prevent dust spreading.
- Using mist cannons in dust suppression *(as shown in the image)* and water suppression in cutting and grinding work.
- Ensuring that bulk materials likely to cause dust are covered where appropriate.

 For further guidance on the assessment and mitigation of construction dust visit the Institute of Air Quality Management (IAQM) website.

6.4.1   Measuring and monitoring dust

All demolition and construction sites should be monitored for air pollution where there is a risk of nuisance or environmental damage. Monitoring and controlling dust levels on construction sites is crucial to the health and wellbeing of all workers, local residents and the local environment. Fine particles of dust can be carried from sites even in light winds. To mitigate the spread of this potentially hazardous substance, a proactive approach is needed.

The need for monitoring will generally depend on existing air quality, air pollution risks from the site, technical practicalities and the financial implications of such monitoring. Deploying best practical means will minimise dust and harmful emissions, which will in turn reduce the need for extensive monitoring.

Although deposited dust is one of the main causes of complaints about air pollution, there are no national UK standards or guidance currently in place. Defra's *Process guidance note PG 3/16* for crushing work does not specify any limits but simply refers to the avoidance of visible emissions crossing the site boundary. This correctly suggests that visual assessment of dust is a main indicator as to whether dust may cause a statutory nuisance. For more accurate assessment, reference is made in unofficial guidelines to a benchmark of 200 mg/m²/day as a value for the threshold for statutory nuisance.

 For further guidance from Defra on air pollution and control visit the Government website.

6.4.2 Silica dust

Silica is a natural substance found in varying amounts in most rocks, sand and clay. Sandstone contains more than 70% silica, and granite contains 15 to 30%. Silica is also a major ingredient of construction materials such as bricks, tiles, concrete and mortar.

Silica is the biggest risk to construction workers after asbestos. Heavy or prolonged exposure to silica dust is harmful to health, as it can cause serious respiratory diseases such as silicosis and chronic obstructive pulmonary disease.

Many common construction activities generate dust from these materials, including drilling, scabbling, chasing, cutting, grinding, polishing and blasting. The fine dust created is respirable crystalline silica (RCS), and is invisible to the naked eye. This does not remain within the boundaries of the construction site. It will migrate and contaminate the environment on the periphery of the site.

 For further information on the health risks associated with silica dust refer to Chapter B10 Dust and fumes (Respiratory hazards).

6.4.3 Diesel exhaust emissions

Most of the air pollution coming from construction sites is related to the burning of diesel fuel. Heavy-duty vehicles, cranes, excavators, generators, and many other types of equipment consume diesel, and discharge emissions into the atmosphere.

The sector's reliance on diesel fuel is due to the absence of grid power at construction sites, specifically in remote geographical locations. Carbon dioxide (CO_2), carbon monoxide (CO), sulphur, nitrogen compounds (NOx) and hydrocarbons are also present in diesel emissions.

The following actions can be taken to minimise the extent of pollution.

- Limit use of road vehicles or other internal combustion engines.
- Ensure that vehicles are switched off when not required.
- Ensure that haul routes are planned with minimum distances.
- Have a planned and preventative maintenance programme or modify existing engines to produce less pollution.
- Use fuels designed to cause less pollution.
- Consider using electrical equipment rather than internal combustion engines.
- Liaise with electricity suppliers early in a project so that equipment can be connected to the grid as early as possible rather than running off generators.
- Use a hybrid solution involving smaller diesel generators and energy storage systems (ESSs) that incorporate Lithium-ion battery technology.
- Use green products such as battery light towers and electric light towers, submersible pumps and mobile compressors.
- Install solar panels to use solar energy to charge tool stations.

Supplementary Planning guidance released by Greater London Authority on *The control of dust and emissions from construction and demolition* contains information outlining the new engine emission standards for non-road mobile machinery (NRMM) in London (under Chapter 7, Cleaner construction machinery for London: a low emission zone for non-road mobile machinery).

These are enhanced standards for monitoring air quality, and are being expanded to other cities in the UK.

 For further guidance on processes and procedures related to NRMM visit the NRMM webpage.

6.4.4 Vapours and fumes

Many materials or products (such as sealants or resins) release vapours, fumes or odours. These can damage the environment and be hazardous to the health of workers or other people.

The likelihood of such hazards must be assessed, and adequate control measures designed and implemented that include appropriate monitoring arrangements.

The controls should eliminate the risks, where possible, or otherwise minimise them. Consider selecting less hazardous products to avoid the risks during application and dispose of any used packaging, which will be classed as hazardous waste, appropriately.

6.5   Transport

Vehicle movements and the transport of materials and people represent energy resources being used. It is important that vehicle movements are handled, programmed and managed in an efficient way, as this will lead to greater resource efficiency and reduced costs.

Good logistics, with prompt arrivals and departures and materials being off-loaded in the right locations, will result in multiple benefits. Perhaps the key amongst these will be reduced fuel use and therefore lower carbon emissions, which brings associated cost savings.

Crucially there is also less potential for double handling and wastage of materials.

- There will be less time when noise is being generated. Effective vehicle sequencing will also prevent traffic build-up noise being generated from multiple sources.

- There will be less time when vehicles are on site, with fewer vehicles sitting with idling engines, resulting in lower exhaust emissions. This will reduce the potential adverse impact on air quality.

- Vehicle arrivals and departures that are sequenced in the right way will have less of an impact on local traffic flows and help to prevent local congestion.

- Effective traffic management will result in less dust and mud being produced. This will reduce the amount of road sweeping and dampening down having to be incorporated into the traffic management plan.

The flow of vehicles, materials and resources onto a site needs to be properly sequenced and planned.

This process needs to be undertaken with familiarity with the local environment, such as traffic flows, public road restrictions, wildlife, how the site will be accessed, the size of the site, and adjacent facilities such as schools.

A lack of understanding will result in nuisance to local residents, congestion, delays in material delivery and a variety of negative impacts occurring.

Traffic to and from a site, in relation to materials delivery and people, is one of the main areas of interaction with the local community.

A well thought-out traffic management plan and effective communication of the arrangements will demonstrate consideration and support good public relations with the surrounding community, leading to trust and appreciation in return from local residents.

Depending on where the actual work will take place on streets or roads, registration for a Local Authority lane rental or permit scheme may be needed. Requirements of the permit may push work into off-peak times during the night to reduce the impact on traffic at the busiest times.

This could, however, increase the possibility of creating a nuisance for local residents.

 A good traffic management plan will give consideration to the following set of factors:

- Local traffic conditions, peak flows and congestion hot spots.
- Delivery and departure sequencing and times for all site vehicles to minimise traffic movement.
- Off-site delivery and departure routes for all site vehicles.
- Signage and directions on site.
- Hold areas for vehicles waiting to off-load or depart.
- Communication between vehicles and the logistics manager on and off site.
- Wheel-wash locations, dust suppression and mud sweeping.
- Receiving and responding to complaints.
- Consultation processes with emergency services, local residents, schools, public facilities and businesses.
- Properly maintained plant and vehicles to ensure efficiency of operation.
- Consolidation areas and sharing of transport: the use of off-site consolidation areas and the sharing of transport will reduce the number of vehicle movements to and from site. Vehicle sharing can be planned by site staff. Project suppliers may permit the use of their parking areas as car-pooling points.

A good traffic management plan will give consideration to the following factors (continued)

- Demarcated traffic routes and pedestrian exclusion zones.

- Secured areas where heavy duty plant and vehicles are operating.

- Integrating a traffic turning circle, or a one-way road system, to eliminate reversing of delivery vehicles.

- Ensuring that all worker and visitors are aware of the traffic management plan, and are abiding by the instructions.

- Clearly identified parking and lay down areas.
    - On-site parking for staff, contractors and visitors.
    - Delivery vehicle and waste removal parking.
    - Vehicle off-loading and lay down areas.

- On-site traffic management (safe routes, dust and wheel wash).
    - Use wheel washes to prevent mud and any contaminated materials getting onto local roads.
    - Water bowsers can be used for dust suppression.
    - Road sweepers can be used to remove any mud or dust accumulations.

- Promotion of opportunities and arrangements for green travel for site personnel and visitors.

6.5.1   Construction logistics and community safety

Construction logistics and community safety (CLOCS) is a national standard brought about by the direct collaboration between the construction and fleet sectors. The mission of CLOCS is to ensure safe construction vehicle journeys, and to meet the following goals.

- Zero collisions between construction vehicles and local residents.

- Fewer vehicle journeys.

- Improved air quality and reduced emissions.

- Reduced reputational risk.

Construction vehicles continue to be significantly and disproportionately involved in life-changing road collisions with cyclists, pedestrians and the community as a whole. Every construction client and contractor should know their incident data on site, but perhaps do not know how many fatal or serious injury collisions occur on journeys outside of the site's perimeter fence associated with their projects.

In line with Regulation 4 of CDM, clients and principal contractors have a duty to ensure that the construction work they procure is carried out, so far as is reasonably practicable, without risk to the health and safety of any person affected by the project, including the wider community and all vulnerable road users.

 For further information visit the CLOCS website.

6.6   Noise, including consent requirements

Construction and demolition sites are inherently noisy and are often located in residential areas that are normally quiet. They have the potential to create a statutory nuisance in the form of noise and vibration. Excess vibration results in loud noises, which not only affect the quality of life of local residents, but also impact the local wildlife. Noise pollution can drive wildlife species, such as birds and small mammals, out of the area, seriously compromising the health of the local ecosystem.

It can also cause structural damage to nearby buildings and utilities, and create health and wellbeing risks for everyone working on or visiting the site, as well as the general public. Local Authorities may place restrictions on the person responsible for a construction site to observe specified controls designed to minimise noise and vibration nuisance.

The Control of Pollution Act, Section 60, gives Local Authorities the power to serve notices that specify the following.

- The maximum levels of noise that may be emitted from any particular point.

- Provisions for any change in circumstances.

- The type of plant or machinery that may, or may not, be used.

- The working hours when noise may be made.

BS 5228, which deals with noise and vibration control on construction sites, includes good practice to ensure that a Section 60 notice is avoided. It is in five parts, with Part 1 being a Code of Practice for basic information and procedures for noise and vibration control. The Control of Pollution Act and BS 5228 do not specify any limits for construction noise on the basis that a Local Authority knows its area best and should have the best understanding of suitable noise limits.

6.6.1   Application for Section 61 noise consent (prior consent)

Where it is possible that a noise or vibration nuisance will be created, the person responsible for the site should make an application to the Local Authority for prior consent to start work. Such consent applications should, where possible, be made at the same time as planning applications, or as soon as it is known the nuisance cannot be avoided (such as power-floating at night). The Local Authority has 28 days to approve the application.

Applications should contain particulars of the following points.

● The work to be undertaken.

● Location of the works.

● Working hours.

● Proposed methods, and the plant and machinery to be used.

● Proposed steps for minimising noise and vibration.

● Predicted noise levels.

The Local Authority, in granting consent for the works to begin, may:

● attach any conditions they wish to the consent

● limit or qualify a consent

● limit the duration of consent for the works to be carried out

● specify maximum boundary noise level, permitted hours of work, and plant and equipment that may or may not be used.

In the case of works that overrun for legitimate engineering or health and safety issues, you should advise the Local Authority as soon as is reasonably practicable of the reasons for the overrun, and the likely duration of such works. Where there are minor variations in the works featured in the consent application, and where the works to be rescheduled are of a critical nature, you may apply for a variation. This procedure may also be used for minor additional work that was not included in the original application and does not materially affect the predicted noise levels.

The Local Authority should receive applications for a variation within seven days, where practicable, but at least two working days ahead of the start of the works for which the application is made. Where the operation methods for proposed works have to be changed from the terms agreed in the original consent, you must apply for a dispensation at least 14 days in advance of the proposed operation, submitting the following.

● Details of the operation in question.

● Reasons why the operation cannot be carried out within the terms of the consent.

● Proposed working hours.

● Predicted noise and vibration levels at relevant locations.

● Proposed steps taken to reduce noise and/or vibration to a minimum.

 It is far better to apply for a Section 61 consent notice and work with the Local Authority to agree how the work will be carried out, than to be stopped following a complaint and have to comply with a Section 60 notice. Once a Section 61 consent has been given, the contractor is protected from action on noise grounds taken by the Local Authority as long as the conditions of the consent are complied with.

6.6.2   Managing noise on site

Before works commence on site the contract documentation needs to be reviewed to determine whether specific noise limits at various locations from the site boundary have been specified.

Where this is the case, it is likely that monitoring of noise levels will be required and may also be a requirement of a Section 61 noise consent, where this has been applied for.

The main objective of a noise survey is to gain an informed understanding of the main sources of noise, by using a dosimeter to measure noise levels around the site. Noise and vibration may be excessive both in terms of the amount of noise generated, and the duration of the proposed activities on the site. When carrying out a noise survey on site, BS 4142-approved methods should be followed.

Periodic noise survey

STATUTORY NUISANCE

The control of noise on construction sites can be achieved by controlling and reducing the noise at source.

Methods for **controlling and/or reducing noise at source** include the following.

Consider if the loud noise can be removed altogether. If this is not possible, then it must be controlled at source.

Selection of low noise method. Where possible, methods should be employed to reduce the amount of noise generated in the first place (for example, off-site fabrication of concrete panels would avoid the need for scabbling of concrete and the use of vibrating pokers).

Use engineering controls. This could include, for example, using damping to reduce the vibration of machine panels. Use anti-vibration mounts or flexible couplings, avoid metal-on-metal impact by lining chutes with abrasion-resistant rubber, fit silencers to air exhausts, and ensure the better fitting of guards on machinery.

Working hours. Adapt working hours to restrict noisy activity to certain periods of the day. Arrange delivery times to suit the area. Limit the time spent in noisy areas to reduce noise exposure.

Selection of quieter processes or low noise equipment. For some noisy operations (such as piling) there are alternative methods available (for example, drop hammer piling could be replaced by hydraulic jack if ground conditions are suitable). Many power tools are now available that can be operated using electricity or compressed air rather than petrol or diesel engines. Introduce a 'buy-quiet' purchasing policy for machinery and equipment.

Layout and design of the working environment. Design the workflow to ensure that noisy machinery is kept out of areas where workers spend most of their time, and away from quieter areas. Use absorptive materials (such as mineral wool or open cell foam) to reduce the reflected sound. For outside areas, use noise reduction landscaping such as plants and trees. Sound is absorbed by all parts of the plant or tree, such as leaves, branches, twigs and bark.

Provision of acoustic enclosures. Most modern equipment (such as compressors or generators) will come with its own hood or door. These should always be kept closed and in good order. Alter the direct path of the sound through the erection of enclosures around machinery, the use of barriers and screening to block the sound, and positioning noise sources away from workers.

Methods for **screening noise** to create a sound attenuation barrier include the following.

- Site hoarding.
- Purpose-built screens, barriers or walls.
- Placement of material storage areas.
- Bunding.
- Use of existing structures.

The screening should be placed close to either the source or the receptor. Other general measures that can be employed to reduce noise levels are shown below.

- Planning site haul routes to avoid vehicles reversing.
- Planning delivery times and routes to suit local conditions.
- Maintaining haul routes in good order to prevent vehicle noise caused by potholes or uneven surfaces.
- Minimising drop heights of materials into lorries and dumpers.
- Shutting down plant when not required.
- Using only plant conforming with relevant standards and directives on emissions.
- Maintaining plant in good order, including compressor air lines.
- Placing material handling areas away from sensitive receptors.
- Making use of noise-reducing equipment (such as jackets, shrouds, hoods and doors) and ensuring that they remain closed when the equipment is in use.

Site hoarding that acts as an acoustic barrier

- Ensuring all viewing openings in site hoardings are glazed with Perspex.
- Hold regular toolbox talks to provide and obtain feedback from workers on the effectiveness of current noise controls.
- Raise awareness of noise via targeted bulletins and good practice guides.
- Regular maintenance and lubrication of plant, equipment and machinery.
- Replace worn, loose or unbalanced machine parts.
- Provision and monitoring of training to relevant workers.
- Continual monitoring of personal protective equipment to make sure it is adequate and being worn and maintained correctly.

6.7 Vibration

Vibration is caused by the motion of mechanical equipment or sound waves travelling through solid material rather than through air. High levels of vibration can cause damage to buildings, disturb wildlife and disturb neighbours. With regard to statutory nuisance, in the UK, vibration is considered in the same manner as noise.

The most commonly used standard for environmental vibration assessment for disturbance is BS 6472 *Evaluation of human exposure to vibration in buildings [1 Hz to 80 Hz]*. The British Standard suggests that levels of vibration from 0.1 to 0.2 mm/s (at night) and below in residential buildings would have a low probability of adverse comment.

BS 7385: Part 2 *Evaluation and measurement for vibration in buildings* gives guidance on the levels of vibration above which building structures could be damaged. The standard states that there is a major difference between the sensitivity of people in feeling vibration and the onset of levels of vibration that damage the structure. For residential buildings, the standard states that, for cosmetic damage (such as cracking in plaster work) to occur, a peak particle velocity of some 15 mm/s is necessary at a vibration frequency of 4 Hz; this rises to 20 mm/sec at 15 Hz, and thereafter the limit rises to 50 mm/s at 40 Hz and above.

The potential for vibration is dependent on a number of factors, particularly the distance of the receptor from the source, together with the ground conditions and features within the ground (such as sewers). Piling, vibrating rollers, tunnelling and boring are important work that has the potential to cause vibration. Consideration should be given to the methods used to establish the solution with the least vibration risk. These types of activity should be considered carefully when working near to known archaeological features.

Important questions to be considered when planning the works are listed below.

- Can the activity be done using a different technique that results in lower vibration levels (for example, hydraulic pressed sheet piling rather than impact piling or vibrating methods)?

- Because high frequency vibration causes less damage than low frequency vibration, can the plant be operated in a way that generates less low frequency vibration?

- Can the equipment be isolated from the transfer medium (for example, putting generators on timber mats rather than directly on the ground)?

Before starting work, all sensitive structures and buildings should be identified and surveyed. Checks should be made to see if the work is covered under the Party Wall etc. Act. The survey should include photographic and written records of any of the following existing issues.

- Cracks and their width.

- Levels and verticality of tilting walls and bulges in walls.

- Damage, including broken bricks, tiles, pipework or plaster.

Hydraulic pressed sheet piling

06

Where some vibration cannot be avoided you should adopt a good neighbour policy and inform local residents and the local environmental health officer. Vibration levels should be monitored during the works using competent, trained staff with the appropriate equipment. Following the works, the same survey should be carried out to confirm that no damage has occurred.

6.8 Light pollution

Light pollution is artificial light that illuminates or intrudes upon areas not intended to be lit. There are a variety of sources of light pollution from construction sites, including lighting towers, offices and access or security lighting.

 Light pollution disrupts the natural habitats of wildlife, has negative impacts on human health and compromises the aesthetic beauty of the environment.

In England, Northern Ireland, Scotland and Wales light pollution can be a statutory nuisance and Local Authorities have powers to apply an abatement notice. If this is not complied with the matter may then go to a Magistrates' Court. In Scotland the Public Health etc. (Scotland) Act introduced measures covering light nuisance that were implemented by amendment to the Environmental Protection Act.

Light pollution can be really disruptive in a number of ways

Similarly, light nuisance provisions were introduced in Northern Ireland by the Neighbourhoods and Environment Act (Northern Ireland). Certain areas of the UK are given 'dark skies' status. Often located in national parks or near to observatories, their purpose is generally to promote astronomy. Additional mitigation actions must be taken to minimise light pollution if work is being carried out in these areas.

6.9   Community liaison

A good neighbour has consideration for those around them and takes an active interest in their wellbeing. Construction sites may have many different types of neighbour (such as householders, businesses, sports clubs, pubs and shops) and construction work will affect neighbours in various ways.

Construction projects need to take a proactive approach to community liaison and ensure that the right processes are in place for engaging with the local community. It is important to inform neighbours of what may affect them before it happens so that people can prepare and have a chance to have their say.

There are a number of ways in which this can happen.

- Involving the community (such as local residents, businesses and schools) at the planning and design stage.

- Letter drops to local residents and businesses.

- Visiting owners or occupiers of sensitive homes and businesses.

- Attending local interest group meetings.

- Articles in local publications and newspapers.

Local school children get involved in designing their school play areas

- Displaying contact boards with relevant contact details so that interested parties can comment – this is a requirement of the Considerate Constructors Scheme.

- Establishing a complaint system via email or a website.

It is also important that an effective complaints system is in place that provides a rapid and effective response to issues that have been raised. Being a good neighbour will result in a good relationship with the local community and will avoid complaints and damage to reputation.

The **Considerate Constructors Scheme** (CCS) has supported and driven positive change in the construction industry for the past three decades. The Code of Considerate Practice helps drive forward improved conduct and high standards across construction activities and focuses on three key areas:

1. Respecting the community.

2. Caring for the environment.

3. Valuing the workforce.

There are many organisations that collaborate with the scheme ranging from industry bodies, non-profit/charities and commercial organisations.

The CCS registration has different registration options, and is open to all types of construction activity. All registered site activities are visited periodically by a monitor, whose role is to assess conformance against the scheme's Code of Considerate Practice and give guidance on delivering continual improvements.

The monitor also identifies any measures being taken by a company or its sites that are above and beyond these requirements. Following every monitoring visit, a site or organisation will receive a detailed report capturing findings and highlighting good practice and areas that have been identified for improvement. A Certificate of Performance is also issued, so that achievements against the three areas of the Code of Considerate Practice can be highlighted. Bonus points are available for demonstrating leadership and industry collaboration in regard to the development and implementation of innovations and best practices.

For further information visit the Considerate Constructors Scheme website.

CONTENTS

Water management and pollution control

Supporting
INFORMATION

GT700 Toolbox talks / supporting checklists and forms

Toolbox talks on some of these topics are available in the GT700
publication. Supporting checklists and forms covering some of these
topics are available on our companion website.

Summary of water management and pollution control legislation and guidance

This list is not exhaustive and only includes legislation mentioned in this section of GE700.

Legislation and guidance	Enforcement agencies*				
	EA	LA	NIEA	NRW	SEPA
Acts (primary legislation)					
Environmental Protection Act	✓		✓	✓	✓
Flood and Water Management Act	Lead Local Flood Authorities				
Water Act	✓		✓	✓	✓
Water and Sewerage Services (Northern Ireland) Order			✓		
Water Environment and Water Services (Scotland) Act					✓
Water Industry Act	✓			✓	✓
Water (Northern Ireland) Order			✓		
Water Resources Act	✓			✓	
Water Resources (Scotland) Act					✓
Regulations (secondary legislation)					
Environmental Permitting (England and Wales) Regulations	✓			✓	
Groundwater (Amendment) Regulations (Northern Ireland)			✓		
Groundwater (England and Wales) Regulations	✓			✓	
Water Abstraction and Impounding (Exemptions) Regulations	✓			✓	
Water Abstraction and Impoundment (Licensing) Regulations (Northern Ireland)			✓		
Water Environment (Controlled Activities) (Scotland) Regulations					✓
Water Environment (Miscellaneous) (Scotland) Regulations					✓
Guidance					
Net Regs Environmental guidance for Scotland and Northern Ireland					
Sustainable drainage systems (SuDS): non-statutory technical standards					
The SuDS manual (C753)					
Organisations providing information and guidance on their websites	✓	✓	✓	✓	✓

*Key

EA	Environment Agency
LA	Local Authorities
NIEA	Northern Ireland Environment Agency
NRW	Natural Resources Wales
SEPA	Scottish Environment Protection Agency

Overview

Water is one of our most valuable natural resources and is vital for our survival, our social and economic wellbeing and to maintain precious habitats.

Despite the renewal cycle of water resources, its supply is not endless. Therefore, we have a duty to ensure that it is protected and managed effectively.

This chapter gives a general overview of the legal framework for the protection of natural water resources, including the permit and licence requirements needed for making discharges to foul and surface water drainage systems.

This chapter also provides practical advice for the prevention of pollution to surface and groundwater and implementing an incident response plan should an accidental spillage occur as a result of construction work.

7.1 Introduction

Construction work can cause serious harm to watercourses. Pollution can contaminate drinking water, suffocate fish (by removing essential oxygen from the water) and kill plants, animals and insects living in the water.

A construction site does not need to be next to a watercourse to cause a problem; any pollutants entering a surface water drain can end up in a watercourse miles away.

Pollution by silt can result in the suffocation of fish, destruction of spawning sites and the blocking of drains, which in turn can lead to flooding. Silt pollution can be caused by dewatering, over-pumping, rainwater run-off from uncovered stockpiles of material exposed during earthworks, tunnelling operations, cleaning of ditches and drains, and processes such as wheel washing.

Oil pollution reduces the levels of oxygen in water and can be toxic to aquatic wildlife. It coats plants, animals and birds. Oil pollution is mainly caused through spillages, often from refuelling, but it can be caused by accidental spills, vandalism or the overfilling of equipment.

 Oil spreads rapidly: one gallon of oil can completely cover an area of water the size of two football pitches.

Cement and concrete are probably the most common materials used in construction. If either is allowed to enter a watercourse it can have a devastating impact on wildlife.

Cement is highly alkaline and can alter the pH of the water, which can be toxic to aquatic wildlife and contaminate water supplies. Cement and concrete pollution is mainly caused by the cleaning out of equipment and shuttering failure.

Chemical pollution can have a wide range of impacts, including killing fish and plants, destroying habitats and contaminating drinking water. Chemical pollution can be caused by spillages, the leaking of containers or incorrectly-bunded areas.

Sewage pollution can be unpleasant, unsightly and smelly, and can decrease the amount of oxygen in the water. Sewage pollution often occurs when drains are blocked, damaged or wrongly connected.

The **Environmental Protection Act** makes reference to controlling the entry of polluting matter and effluents into any place that may ultimately affect a watercourse.

The **Water Resources Act** makes it an offence to contaminate water in a way that may poison or injure fish, spawn, fish food or spawning grounds, or knowingly cause or permit the pollution of controlled waters (such as those listed below).

- Rivers, streams, ditches, ponds, swales, underground streams, canals, lakes and reservoirs.
- Groundwater, wells, aquifers, boreholes or water in underground strata.

It is also an offence to deliberately or accidentally discharge trade effluents into public sewers without the relevant consent. Trade effluents are any liquids produced as part of a trade or industrial activity, excluding domestic sewage.

Trade effluents include the water or slurry from vehicle wheel washes, core drilling, brick/concrete/stone cutting machines, dewatering trenches, pumping out of excavations, concrete washout, pipework cleaning and commissioning, and any similar work.

Mitigation and monitoring processes are essential components to ensure watercourses are protected. Mitigation takes the form of having the necessary preventative measures in place. Monitoring ensures that these measures are working efficiently.

Monitoring must be undertaken on a regular basis to take account of changing site conditions or work methods and inform improvements. In periods of heavy rain, monitoring should be more frequent.

 Just half a teaspoon of soil in a bath full of water would be comparable to water quality that could kill fish and smother plants in a watercourse.

7.2   Important points

- Before any work starts on site it is essential to identify all existing site drainage systems and clearly mark them on site plans. Distinguish which are surface water, foul water and combined systems (foul and surface water in the same sewer).

- Seek to install permanent drainage systems as early as possible, as these can then be used to avoid temporary discharges to surface water.

- All drains should be covered or protected to prevent accidental ingress from mud and silt.

- All stockpiled materials should be stored away from drainage systems and watercourses and protected using geotextile silt fencing or cut-off ditches where appropriate.

- The abstraction of water from surface water or piped mains (using a standpipe) will require consent from the Environment Agency (EA) in England, Natural Resources Wales (NRW), the Northern Ireland Environment Agency (NIEA), the Scottish Environment Protection Agency (SEPA), or the relevant water authority respectively.

- All discharges to foul water drainage systems require permission from the local water authority and the consent conditions must be strictly complied with.

- All discharges of effluent to surface water systems will require an environmental permit from the relevant environment agency and the permit conditions must be strictly complied with.

- In England and Wales, temporary (less than three months) discharges from dewatering excavations can be carried out without the need for an environmental permit but strict conditions have to be complied with.

- Where septic tanks are designed to discharge to ground the liquid effluent must pass through a drainage field; you cannot use a soakaway. This will require an environmental permit for groundwater work. Discharges from small domestic septic tanks (that discharge less than 2,000 litres per day) are exempt, providing they meet the EA's general binding rules (England). In Wales the exemption should be registered with NRW and in Scotland SEPA. It is advisable to make contact with the relevant EA to check that your septic tank is not located near a designated sensitive area, and to find out whether you require a permit.

- Before any discharges are made to surface water systems, the water must be unpolluted and free from silt. Silts can be removed through a variety of techniques, as listed below.
  - Settlement tanks.
  - Lagoons.
  - Filtration systems, including the use of gravels, geotextiles or straw bales.
  - Use of flocculants.

- All fuels and chemicals should be stored on impervious material away from drains and watercourses. They should be suitably bunded to prevent pollution in the event of leakage or spillage. Refuelling should also be carried out at designated locations with impermeable surfaces away from drains or watercourses.

- All water from vehicle and boot washing facilities should be removed to foul water drainage systems (with the consent of the water authority) or taken away by tanker (waste duty of care must be complied with).

- Concrete and cement washout should be carried out in designated areas. The waste water should not be allowed to enter surface water systems (further details on the disposal options for concrete washwater and the Environmental Permitting (England and Wales) Regulations are covered later in this chapter).

- Monitoring of all permitted discharges should be made on a regular basis to ensure that consent conditions (quality and quantity) are being complied with. Oil and chemical storage facilities should also be inspected.

- Site and public roads should be regularly swept to reduce silt and mud entering surface water drainage systems.

- An incident response plan should be implemented identifying the following.
  - Type and location of drainage systems.
  - Type and location of spill kits.
  - Responsibilities for site personnel.
  - Awareness of environmental issues via training and induction.
  - Arrangements for spill kit replenishment.
  - Arrangements for disposal for contaminated materials from used spill kits.

07

7.3   Groundwater

Groundwater is the largest available reservoir of fresh water and accumulates underground in gaps in the rocks called aquifers. Groundwater provides a third of our drinking water in England and Wales and also maintains the flow in many of our rivers. In some areas of southern England, groundwater supplies up to 80% of drinking water through the taps.

The Water Resources Act gives the EA or NRW a duty to protect the quality of groundwater and to protect it as a valuable water resource. The Environmental Permitting (England and Wales) Regulations and the Groundwater Regulations implement the requirements of the EU Groundwater Directives. Similar legislation is in place in Scotland and Northern Ireland.

A groundwater protection position statement is available from the EA, offering guidance to stakeholders (such as developers, planners, environmental permit holders and water abstractors).

Groundwater sources are one of the largest water sources

As the regulator, the EA has established groundwater vulnerability maps and source protection zones (SPZs) for 2,000 groundwater sources (such as wells, boreholes and springs) used for public drinking water supply. There are four levels of SPZs (shown below). The shape and size of a zone depends upon ground conditions, how the groundwater is removed and other environmental factors.

Inner zone (SPZ1). This zone includes the 50-day travel time of pollutants to source, with a 50 m default minimum radius.

Outer zone (SPZ2). This zone includes the 400-day travel time of pollutants to source, with a 250 or 500 m minimum radius around the source, depending on the amount of water taken.

Total catchment zone (SPZ3). This is the area around a supply source within which all the groundwater ends up at the abstraction point, or where the water is taken. This could extend some distance from the source point.

Extended zones beneath protective cover. Some zones are extended to include areas where there is protective geology cover, such as clay. This is because activities below the surface, such as deep drilling, could create pathways for pollutants to enter the groundwater. They are indicated on the EA's 'MagicMap' as zones 1c, 2c and 3c.

Zone of special interest (SPZ4). This zone is where local conditions require additional protection.

Groundwater can be polluted by a range of construction materials, including fuels, chemicals, solvents, paints and other liquids. Pollution of groundwater will lead to prosecution. A small quantity of a pollutant has the potential to affect large volumes of groundwater. Remediating large volumes of groundwater is expensive and can take a long time.

Run-off from rainfall has the potential to pick up contaminants as it moves across a construction site. Contaminants may include particulates as well as hydrocarbons and chemicals. Run-off can penetrate permeable surfaces and infiltrate into groundwater.

Every effort must be made to prevent groundwater pollution, including the following.

- Secure materials storage with bunds protecting liquids stores.
- Suitable spill kits and competent spill teams with regular training.
- Storing materials on impermeable surfaces.
- Use of interceptor drains to catch run-off before it reaches permeable surfaces.
- Cover up all drains.
- Keep the road and footpath to the site clean at all times.
- Monitor and improve the management and disposal of site waste.
- Correctly collect and treat any wastewater that is produced.

 The unauthorised discharge of chemicals or sewage to groundwater without a permit is an offence and could lead to prosecution. Spills of diesel fuel and oil can penetrate underground plastic water pipes, contaminating the water and giving rise to odours and taints.

07

WATER MANAGEMENT AND POLLUTION CONTROL

7.4   Abstraction

Water is often taken from natural sources or water mains to reduce dust on haul roads or to reduce dust during cutting operations. Section 24 of the Water Resources Act states that:

 ... no person shall abstract water from any source of supply or cause or permit any other person to abstract any water, except in pursuance of a licence granted by the authority.

You should therefore not take water from groundwater, watercourses, lakes, streams or water mains without the permission of the relevant authority. The EA, NRW, NIEA and SEPA are responsible for licensing abstractions from groundwater and watercourses. The local water supply company will be responsible for licensing water that is taken from water mains. For guidance on the need for, and process in, obtaining a licence before abstracting any water, the relevant agency should be contacted (i.e. the EA, NIEA or NRW).

In England, Northern Ireland and Wales, if you plan to take more than 20 m³ (20,000 litres) per day, you are likely to need an abstraction licence from the EA. In Scotland, abstractions of less than 10 m³ (10,000 litres) per day do not require an application for authorisation, as they should be carried out in accordance with the relevant binding rules. Water volumes abstracted should be monitored on a daily basis to ensure that the conditions of any abstraction licence are complied with. This will also allow you to check whether there are any leaks in the system.

7.4.1   Dewatering excavations

Construction dewatering is the temporary lowering of groundwater levels by pumping from wells or sumps to provide stable conditions for excavations below the natural groundwater level. The water being removed may require the appropriate consent for discharge into either the foul water system or controlled waters. Dewatering points must be sited to avoid other pollutants or water of a different chemical composition from entering a body of groundwater.

If, as part of the works, you are dewatering or pumping groundwater that has gathered in an excavation, it does not require an abstraction licence if the water is to be disposed of solely to prevent interference with building operations and does not exceed 100 m³ per day, lasts for less than six months and there is no intervening use between the abstraction and discharge. **Where the abstraction is undertaken within 500 m of a conservation area or within 200 m of a spring, well or borehole the limit is 50 m³ per day.**

The dewatering of surface water from excavations does not have an exemption limit but must not cause damage to a protected site or protected species and must be immediately discharged downstream of the building and engineering works. If, however, you intend to use water from a dewatering operation for dust suppression or pressure testing on site, this will be classed as intervening use and you may require an abstraction licence. You must contact the appropriate Environment Agency if your discharge to surface water is going to be more than 10% of the dry weather flow (Q95 low flow) rate of the surface water and dilution is low, as this may increase the risk of flooding.

Geothermal heating and cooling systems that use groundwater to heat or cool buildings can have an impact on water resources. If you are installing an open-loop groundwater or surface water system you may need consent, a permit and a licence from the appropriate Environment Agency. Closed-loop systems will not require permissions.

7.5   Consents

7.5.1   Discharge consents

Where there is a requirement to discharge effluent from any construction activity to drainage systems, watercourses or rivers and streams, an application for consent to discharge must be made to the relevant authority. The issuing authority will depend on where the discharge is made. For example, discharges to foul sewers are usually regulated by the local water company under the provisions of the Water Industry Act. Here, a discharge consent from the appropriate water company is required, except where all discharges are regulated under an environmental permit (England and Wales) or integration pollution prevention and control (IPPC) authorisation (Scotland). Any discharges to surface watercourses, rivers, lakes or ponds would be regulated by the EA, NRW, NIEA or SEPA.

In England and Wales, consents to discharge to surface water systems are regulated under Schedule 21 of the Environmental Permitting (England and Wales) Regulations. The works covered by these regulations includes discharge or entry to surface waters that are controlled (but not to groundwater) of any poisonous, noxious, polluting or waste matter, or trade or sewage effluent. The term *water discharge activities* also includes any work that results in deposits that can be carried away in water (such as cleaning the bottom of a river channel).

As highlighted earlier, temporary discharge from dewatering excavations does not require an application for an environmental permit provided that all of the following apply:

● discharge is temporary, for an overall period of less than three consecutive months

● discharge is made directly to a surface water (such as a river, stream or the sea)

● discharge does not pollute the surface water or adversely affect aquatic life

● discharge location is more than 500 m upstream of a river, a European marine site or a Site of Special Scientific Interest (SSSI), and is not within a site designated for nature conservation (such as National Nature Reserves (NNRs), Local Nature Reserves (LNRs) and local wildlife sites)

● discharge does not cause flooding from the surface water

● discharge does not cause erosion of the banks or bed of the surface water.

Before starting work on site you must:

- plan how to minimise the level of contaminants (such as silt) entering the excavation

- plan how to dispose of water that enters the excavation

- plan not to use machinery in excavations while dewatering is taking place

- minimise water entering the excavation (for example, from rainfall, run-off, groundwater ingress or high water table)

- consider using sustainable drainage construction methods.

Discharges of uncontaminated surface waters are not classed as a water discharge activity. However, you should discuss any proposed discharge of surface water with the regulator before any work takes place.

Make sure contaminated water is contained

Water discharge activities that meet certain conditions are exempt from requiring a permit. Some of these are shown below.

- A small sewage treatment plant discharging 5 m^3 or less of effluent per day and subject to meeting other stringent requirements.

- A septic tank discharging 2 m^3 or less of effluent per day.

- Vegetation management activities.

Low-risk sewage discharges that meet the relevant conditions can be regulated under an exemption or standard permit. However, all other applications for a discharge permit will be regulated under a bespoke permit.

An application for a **discharge permit** must include, but not be limited to the following.

- The place at which the discharge will take place.

- The nature and composition of the material to be discharged.

- The maximum amount of material that is likely to be discharged in any one day.

- The time period over which the discharge will take place.

- Details of any monitoring and testing arrangements.

In Scotland, discharge consents to surface and groundwaters are regulated through the Water Environment (Controlled Activities) (Scotland) Regulations (as amended) (CAR).

CAR introduces three levels of authorisations proportionate to the type of risk for the activity.

1. General binding rules.

2. Registrations.

3. Licences.

General binding rules (GBRs), set out in Schedule 3 of CAR, represent the lowest level of control and cover specific low-risk work. Work complying with the rules does not require an application to be made to SEPA, as compliance with a GBR is considered to be authorisation. Since the operator is not required to contact SEPA, there are no associated charges. SEPA has prepared a practical guide to implementing CAR. In addition SEPA is also insisting that a pollution prevention plan must be submitted to them for approval prior to any work commencing.

In Northern Ireland, discharge consents are managed by the Northern Ireland Water Management Unit under the Water (Northern Ireland) Order.

7.5.2   Works consents

Responsibility for regulating work on ordinary watercourses in most areas of England and Wales is controlled by Lead Local Flood Authorities (LLFAs).

These are unitary authorities who lead in managing local flood risks (i.e. risks of flooding from surface water, groundwater and ordinary (smaller) watercourses). They also ensure co-operation between the risk management authorities in their area.

In England and Wales a flood defence consent is required from the LLFA before building a flow control structure (such as a culvert or weir) on an ordinary watercourse. For consent to carry out any works within 10 m of a watercourse, an application must include plans, sections and details including any environmental mitigation measures.

From April 2016 the requirement to have flood risk consent on a statutory main river in England and Wales was transferred to the Environmental Permitting Regulations. You will require an environmental permit or exemption for flood risk activities from the EA or NRW to carry out any work in, under, over or adjacent to a statutory main river.

If you are currently still working under a flood defence consent, it should automatically be covered as an environmental permit, but it is worth checking with the EA to confirm.

07

WATER MANAGEMENT AND POLLUTION CONTROL

In Northern Ireland works consent is required from the Rivers Agency, which is part of the Department of Agriculture and Rural Development. In Scotland, as with discharge consents, if you carry out building and engineering work that significantly affects the water environment, this is regulated through CAR and you must comply with one of the following three levels of control:

- comply with certain GBRs that apply to low-risk work
- register your work with SEPA
- get a licence from SEPA.

7.5.3   Septic tanks

The discharge of any sewage from a septic tank to the ground will require an environmental permit for groundwater work unless it is a small domestic discharge, then it may be exempt. In Wales it should be registered under an exemption with NRW. Septic tanks with discharges of less than 2 m³ per day are exempt from environmental permitting as highlighted above.

If any part of the building your septic tank serves is within 30 m of a public sewer, the EA will not allow you to start a new discharge from a septic tank or small sewage treatment plant under the general binding rules.

7.6   Disposal

Drains on site should be clearly identifiable as surface water drains (marked blue), foul water drains (marked red) or combined sewers (marked red 'C'). Surface water drains carry uncontaminated rainwater directly to a stream, river or soakaway. Foul water drains carry foul water directly to a sewage works for treatment before being discharged to a watercourse.

7.6.1   Disposal of contaminated water from dewatering excavations

Water may enter an excavation from either surface water inflows or inflows of groundwater. The inflows may already be polluted or they may pick up pollutants contained within the excavation. The amount of water that is pumped out from an excavation can be reduced by reducing inflows of both surface and groundwater. Edge drains connected to sumps can intercept surface water flows. Cut-off ditches and well dewatering will reduce groundwater inflows.

Any pumping out into a trade effluent system (such as a sewer) will require consent from the water company. An environmental permit from the EA, NRW or NIEA will be required for a discharge to controlled waters (such as rivers, streams or lakes).

Water being pumped to two blue silt traps (top left) allowing silt to settle prior to disposal

However, in England and Wales you do not need an environmental permit for temporary water discharge if the discharge is for less than three months and if you can meet the requirements of the regulator's position statement (or, in Scotland, the general binding rules) for *Temporary water discharges from excavations*.

The regulator's position statement is extensive and highlights issues relating to the water being uncontaminated, measures required to avoid pollution occurring, reducing the amount of water entering excavations and ensuring that the discharge is not near to sensitive protected areas.

For detailed guidance on temporary dewatering from excavations to surface water visit the Government website.

If you need a permit to discharge to a watercourse, it can take up to four months to obtain from the EA or NRW *(for further details of consent requirements refer to 7.5)*. Treatment of water before discharge will reduce the potential impact that it has.

Some forms of treatment are shown below.

- Pumping to grassland or other soakaway well away from excavations to avoid recirculation. (This option is only suitable for unpolluted water containing only silt.)
- Pumping to a settlement tank or lagoon, maximising retention time.
- Using a sump at the base of an excavation, wrapping the end of the pump in aggregates and keeping it off the excavation floor.
- Passing through a filtration system (such as aggregates, geotextile or straw bales).
- Using flocculants (chemicals used to aid solids removal) in conjunction with a settlement tank. Consultation with the regulators should take place first as adding chemicals could make things worse.

Where there is no alternative, water may also be taken and treated off site as waste and will therefore need to be controlled in accordance with the waste duty of care, together with the completion of waste transfer documentation.

7.6.2   Concrete and cement washout

Concrete and cement washout is highly alkaline and can cause severe pollution. Effluent produced from washing out any concrete mixing plant or ready-mix concrete lorries must not be allowed to flow into any drain, watercourse or to ground.

Washout areas must be situated at least 10 m away from watercourses, storm drain inlets, open drainage facilities and trees (roots absorb water), but as close to the works as possible to minimise the risk of spills and drips into the ground.

A lined skip can be used to place waste concrete and effluent, with the water being pumped to a foul sewer or taken away by tanker. Consideration should be given to recycling the concrete washout for reuse in the works.

A clearly designated washout area

7.6.3   Disposal of sewage

The provision of welfare facilities at fixed and transitional construction sites requires that disposal of sewage must be considered. Where possible, disposal may be made by direct connection to a foul sewer. Direct connection to the foul sewer will require consent from the maintaining authority.

On greenfield sites or sites remote from live foul sewers there may be no opportunity to connect to a local foul sewer, in which case a septic tank should be provided that can be regularly pumped out by a liquid waste disposal company. Where sewage waste is taken from site then the waste duty of care must be complied with, and waste transfer documentation completed. Both the location and design of the septic tank are important considerations to avoid raw sewage from entering groundwater or watercourses.

Where effluent from septic tanks is designed to be discharged to ground, an environmental permit will be required. The use of portable toilet facilities should be discouraged wherever possible.

7.6.4   Disposal from vehicle and boot washing

Site boot cleaning facilities

Vehicle wheels being inspected and washed before leaving site

Where wheel-wash facilities are provided on site, the resultant water will be contaminated with silt and possibly oil from vehicle bodies. This must not be discharged to surface water systems, and should be removed to foul sewers with the consent of the local water authority. Modern wheel-wash facilities will allow the wash water to be recycled and recovery of the silts to be separately removed as waste. Where the water is contaminated it may be removed by tanker.

Facilities should also be provided to allow site personnel to clean their boots before leaving site or entering site accommodation. The silty water from these facilities should be dealt with in the same way as the vehicle washing effluent.

7.7   Pollution prevention

A number of measures may be implemented to prevent spillages and reduce the risk of a pollution incident. The EA has a dedicated area on its website to assist in the identification and management of issues of pollution risk in construction and other industry areas. Guidance for pollution prevention provides environmental good practice guidance for the UK, and environmental regulatory guidance directly to Northern Ireland, Scotland and Wales.

For access to EA pollution prevention guidance for businesses visit the Government website.

For guidance on pollution prevention measures in Scotland refer to *Sector specific guidance: Construction sites* (WAT-SG-75) on the SEPA website.

WATER MANAGEMENT AND POLLUTION CONTROL

7.7.1   Site establishment

When planning the site set-up, the following should be considered.

- Whether the site is in a sensitive area (for example, near to a watercourse or in a site of special scientific interest). If so, restrictions are likely to be placed on the site (such as limited fuel/oil storage).

- Potential drainage on site (such as land drains, foul sewers, surface water drains and soakaways).

- The location of plant and materials away from drains and watercourses, especially fuel storage, top soil storage and waste disposal areas.

- Consider construction of gullies or ditches alongside haul roads and around the perimeter of the working area to collect and channel surface water.

- Whether the environmental regulator (EA, NRW, NIEA or SEPA) or relevant body has given permission to any consents or licences required.

- The placing of stockpiles and spoil heaps, which must be away from drains and watercourses (use geotextile silt fencing or cut-off ditches to avoid silt run-off where appropriate).

When planning or undertaking construction work, consideration needs to be given to the previous use and history of the site and the surrounding areas.

The site on which construction work is to be undertaken may be in the path of ground contamination seepage from an adjacent factory, chemical store, buried waste or other process that may result in pollution.

Records of water pollution may exist, which will give an indication of possible health problems for workers. Obtain all available historical records, as any subsequent pollution may be attributed to the construction company and not to the originators of the pollution.

You should also check if there is any sewage discharge upstream as this may cause issues if you are pumping that water.

Cut-off ditch

7.7.2   Silt management

Good surface water management during construction is essential to prevent sediment pollution, and to minimise the risk of prosecution, which can result in large financial penalties and damaged reputation.

It is essential for the protection of sensitive environmental receptors such as aquatic life in rivers, streams and lakes.

Silt pollution is easily identified by discolouration or cloudy water. Good practices to prevent pollution from happening in the first place include the following.

- Only stripping the minimum amount of land required.

- Use of cut-off ditches and geotechnical silt fences.

- Diverting clean water away from bare ground.

- Not pumping silty water directly into a watercourse.

- Diverting silty water away from drains and watercourses using sand bags, for example.

- Planning for the treatment of silty water when pumping out excavations or managing surface water run-off.

- Having a thorough understanding of site drainage in order to plan how to prevent clean water from entering site as well as how to manage silty water produced on site.

- Retaining vegetation cover, minimise soil stripping and establish new vegetation on bare ground as soon as is realistically possible.

Silt trap using straw bales and geotextile

- Identify key areas on site that need protection, such as haul roads, site welfare areas, entrances to drains, at river crossings, in drainage channels, and on slopes.

Silt can be removed by using silt traps, settlement tanks, ponds or lagoons, by allowing silty water to infiltrate through large areas of grassy ground, geotextiles filters or straw bales.

(For further information on disposal, refer to 7.6.)

7.7.3 Oil and fuel storage

The storage of potentially-polluting materials and the refuelling of mobile plant near watercourses or bodies of water (within 30 m) should be prohibited as far as practicable, and must not be placed where they could be damaged by impact, such as on vehicle turning circles or plant routes. Alternatively, barriers or bollards must be placed around the tank to protect from impact.

Storage should be within an impervious bund with a capacity greater than 110% of the total potential stored contents (for multi-tank bunds, the capacity must be 110% of the capacity of the largest tank or 25% of the total tank capacity, whichever is the greater). The maximum holding capacity should be painted on the side. All level gauges, filling valves and vents and filling nozzles (when not in use) should remain within the bund. All valves should be kept locked when not in use, and available only to authorised and competent persons.

Examples of safe storage for oil

 For further information about oil storage facilities visit the GOV.UK website.

The transportation of fuel across site in drums or other containers should be avoided as far as possible. All mobile plant, including but not limited to cranes, compressors, generators, and so on, should be maintained and operated such that all leaks and spills of oil or fuel are minimised. Oil and fuel storage facilities and storage tanks should be regularly inspected for integrity. Consideration should be given to the actions to take in the event of a spill. Necessary arrangements should be in place and incident response training will be required.

 Further information on oil storage and pollution prevention regulations can be accessed online.

7.7.4 Chemical storage

The floor area used for storing or decanting chemicals must be impermeable. Old or corroded drums will cause more problems than those in good condition. The following measures can be taken to minimise the risk of contamination.

- Start with an up-to-date chemical inventory and Safety Data Sheets, to know what hazards are posed.

- Undertake a COSHH risk assessment and supply it, alongside the Safety Data Sheet, so as to have the correct information for safe storage, use, disposal and what to do in the event of a spillage.

- Purchase chemicals in the appropriate-sized containers to avoid the need for decanting.

- Where decanting is necessary, have safe procedures to avoid any spillage.

- Provide relevant information, instruction, training and supervision to employees.

- Have a proper process for the disposal of all products.

An illustration of a chemical storage container

- Provide clear procedures and training for operatives to deal with all types of potential pollution spillages.

- Regularly check for any leaks and arrange immediate repair.

- Have set procedures for the refuelling or replenishing of plant so that any spillage cannot permeate into the ground.

- Install bunding around all storage areas, even temporary fuel stores on construction sites.

- Maintain equipment or storage vessels in good condition.

- Only store or use products that are needed, and in areas with impermeable floors and without drain gullies.

- Maintain good housekeeping procedures and avoid the accumulation of litter or rubbish.

- Ensure chemicals are segregated according to specific hazards.

- Keep containers closed when not in use.

- Shelves in storage cabinets should be level, stable and secured.

- Store chemicals away from direct sunlight, sources of heat, and egress pathways.

- Store hazardous chemicals below eye level.

- Do not store chemicals on the floor, or on window ledges etc.

- Ensure drip trays are in place.

- Label containers clearly.

- Use rated storage cabinets.

An emergency and incident response plan, appropriate to the size of the site and chemicals being used, should be in place in case of any spillages or pollution alerts *(refer to 7.8 for further details)*.

7.7.5   Mud

Mud from construction work has the potential to damage the environment. In wet weather it can enter surface watercourses and drains. In dry weather it can dry out and become airborne, in the form of dust, with the potential to be carried some distance and cause nuisance and pollution. Mud can be controlled using road sweepers and wheel washes, and dust can be minimised by dampening down during dry weather.

7.8   Pollution incident response plans (PIRPs)

Emergency planning is a key requirement of an environmental management system, and is necessary under certain legislation. If there is an occurence of pollution, the polluter pays for the clean up. Pollution clean-up is expensive, especially where immediate action has not been taken to mitigate the effects of the pollution immediately after it occurs. The clean-up costs of contamination could far outweigh those imposed by the courts, as a lot of these costs are hidden, such as:

● Replacement or repair to damaged, ruined plant and materials.

● Prosecution costs, e.g. fines and legal costs.

● Costs of civil claims for losses suffered by third parties.

● Loss of reputation, resulting in loss of repeat business.

Prompt action is needed to protect people and the environmental receptors. Incident readiness and response begins with considering what emergency scenarios and incidents (source) may occur on a construction site, on what pathways the pollution can travel and what in the surrounding environment may be impacted by them (receptor).

Types of incident include fires, spills and leaks. For each type of incident several different parts of the environment may be affected. For example, a fire will release products of combustion into the atmosphere, not only damaging the premises but potentially affecting neighbouring properties, the local community and the environment. Water used for fire-fighting may enter surface watercourses and sewers and permeate the ground.

An effective pollution incident response plan should include the following.

● Emergency contact numbers.

● Training of site personnel in the emergency response plans, and their specific roles and responsibilities.

● Practicing the incident response plans, so that staff have a clear understanding and expectation of what is required of them.

● Systems in place to be occasionally practiced to evaluate effectiveness, so that areas for improvement and necessary corrective actions can be identified.

● Easy access to site plans, which show the locations of site drainage, foul, surface water and natural run-off, as well as where materials are stored, the locations of permitted discharge points, bunded storage and secondary containment areas, and equipment emergency shut-down control panels.

● The use of containment equipment (such as drip trays, bunds and booms) to capture and avoid spread of the spillage.

● The location of spill kits and any other emergency equipment around the site, including designated refuelling areas.

● Arrangements and responsibilities for spill kit replenishment after an incident.

● Arrangements for the safe disposal of used spill kit equipment and contaminated materials.

● A relatively safe location from where to control the emergency situation with good sources of communication.

● Specific training for plant and equipment operatives, so that they recognise potentially hazardous situations and can take the necessary actions to mitigate the risks from the environmental hazard.

● For the incident response plans to operate smoothly and efficiently, it is essential that processes and responsibilities are laid down and understood by both internal (relevant company personnel) and external (fire, police, ambulance, HSE, local companies, local or national enforcement bodies) in line with an established environmental reporting procedure.

● Ensuring that a suitable and sufficient record of the incident is recorded and identified actions taken.

● Ensuring that the correct equipment is in place to deal with spills, such as absorbent materials (loose to deal with small spillages,in bags of various sizes to contain spills); flotation tubes to deploy into water sources to contain oil and fuel spillages; sand bags or similar to block drains and divert flows of potentially hazardous substances to containment areas; and temporary portable bunds to stand leaking containers in.

● Access to an up-to-date substance inventory, which should include any innocuous substances that could be environmentally damaging if they escaped, such as tanker milk spilled into a watercourse that will destroy the ecosystem.

● Guidelines on handling the press and media. This should be done by a competent person who has been thoroughly briefed and has knowledge of the organisation and environmental issues. This will ensure that reasoned and accurate responses are given to press and media questions.

A review of the incident response plans after an incident is vital, and processes need to be in place to ensure that this is carried out. Shortfalls in the current arrangements can be identified, and measures put in place to prevent or minimise the consequences of any foreseeable future incidents. This would form part of a management review within the Plan-Do-Check-Act cycle.

It is a requirement of the ISO 14001 standard to strive for continual improvement.

For each type of incident a plan must be put in place setting out the response needed. The basic process of **stop – contain – notify – clean up** must be followed. In the event of a spillage it is essential that a competent spill response team is deployed with the right spill clean-up materials. The team has to respond quickly for the spill to be controlled before it causes any environmental damage.

7.8.1   Booms

If work is to be carried out adjacent to a watercourse or river then arrangements should be put in place to ensure that a boom, which prevents the surface spread of oils and chemicals, can be deployed quickly to contain the spillage. The boom should be long enough to span the full width of the river.

If the work is carried out on navigable waterways then the appropriate authority should be notified before the boom is installed.

7.8.2   Drip trays

Where drip trays are used they should be used in conjunction with absorbent mats so that the contamination can be easily removed. Drip trays should not be left to fill with rainwater, as the resulting contaminated water will be more of a problem to dispose of and could cause contamination of the ground, drains and watercourses if left to overflow. Plant nappies are also available and allow water to pass through while absorbing any oils.

7.8.3   Spill kits

The type and quantity of spill kits deployed around a site will be dictated by the nature of the works and whether they are carried out on land or water. The type of spill kit will also depend on the type and quantity of oils and chemicals that are being used on the site. Typical spill kit equipment could include, but is not limited to, the items below.

- Absorbent booms.

- Absorbent granules.

- Drain covers.

- Heavy-duty plastic bags.

- Absorbent pads.

- Shovel.

- Gloves.

Spill kit deployed

There are multiple types of spill kits used in the construction work environment.

Oil spill kits are used for the clean-up of grease and oil-based liquids. They absorb oil and reject water.

Chemical spill kits are used for common hazardous liquid spills, as they soak up and hold chemicals. They can be used for outside and indoor spills, leaks and drips of corrosive chemicals and hazardous liquids.

General purpose spill kits are suitable for smaller and non-aggressive liquid spills. These are commonly used to absorb water, solvents, coolants, paint, blood, fluids, degreasers and less-damaging chemicals.

Anti-static spill kits are used for the clean up of highly flammable or explosive liquids.

The correct spill kit must be chosen to reflect the potential source of contamination, and this will be determined from the environmental risk assessment, both in terms of type and how many kits will be needed.

Spill kits should be clearly marked and located at signposted locations around the site. Arrangements for the replenishment of the contents should be kept on the inside lid of the spill kit.

Equipment contaminated with oils and chemicals is likely to be hazardous waste and should be stored separately and disposed of in accordance with the duty of care and Hazardous Waste Regulations.

Spill response training and simulated tests should be carried out on a regular basis to evaluate the effectiveness of incident response plans. According to the success of the response, improvements may be needed to the system.

After any incident, management must conduct a post-incident investigation to examine and determine what improvements are needed to prevent the incident from happening again.

 For more information, visit the Government website.

07

CONTENTS

Resource efficiency

08

Supporting
INFORMATION

GT700 Toolbox talks / supporting checklists and forms

Toolbox talks on some of these topics are available in the GT700 publication. Supporting checklists and forms covering some of these topics are available on our companion website.

RESOURCE EFFICIENCY

Summary of resource efficiency legislation and guidance

This list is not exhaustive and only includes legislation mentioned in this section of GE700.

Legislation and guidance	Enforcement agencies*				
	EA	LA	NIEA	NRW	SEPA
Acts (primary legislation)					
Climate Change Act	✓		✓	✓	
Climate Change (Scotland) Act					✓
Environmental Protection Act	✓		✓	✓	✓
Environment Act 2021	✓				
Regulations (secondary legislation)					
EU Timber Regulation	✓		✓	✓	✓
Guidance					
ISO 5001 Energy management					
ISO 14001 Environmental management systems					
ISO 20400 Sustainable procurement guidance					
Organisations with information and guidance on their websites	✓	✓	✓	✓	✓

*Key

EA	Environment Agency
LA	Local Authorities
NIEA	Northern Ireland Environment Agency
NRW	Natural Resources Wales
SEPA	Scottish Environment Protection Agency

 Refer to Chapters E03, E07 and E10 for specific legislation on energy, water and waste topics, which link into resource efficiency.

Overview

The construction sector is the largest consumer of materials in the UK, and the largest producer of waste. More efficient use of materials would make a major contribution to reducing costs and the environmental impacts of construction, including carbon emissions, landfill and the depletion of natural resources.

This chapter provides a brief introduction to the environmental and economic benefits of improved material efficiency and waste reduction. It provides guidance on the responsible sourcing of materials, chain of custody for timber and life cycle analysis, and highlights the benefits of reusing and recycling materials.

8.1   Introduction

Construction uses vast amounts of natural resources and raw materials. Historically, it has been an inherently inefficient process, arising from the bespoke nature of on-site construction. This not only wastes a lot of money, it also produces high levels of waste materials and causes excess material extraction to replace those that have been lost through inefficient use. Resource efficiency ensures that fewer materials are used (reducing waste outputs) to build or renovate buildings and infrastructure, while still achieving the same – or better – overall functionality. To be resource efficient, the industry needs to use the planet's limited resources in a sustainable way, and at the same time minimise impacts on the environment.

The Design for Manufacture and Assembly (DfMA) engineering methodology is an example of resource efficiency that enables a building to be designed and constructed much more quickly, efficiently and sustainably. It increases construction efficiency by using a manufacturing environment to create elements of a building off site, rather than on site. Standard designs and specifications are used to ensure that design and construction quality are not compromised. DfMA has the potential to create buildings that can be easily disassembled and re-assembled at other locations. This adds to the life cycle possibilities of a building and increases recycling, with the potential to achieve zero waste. It provides both short and long-term benefits such as improved health and safety, increased productivity and quality control, higher resource utilisation, shorter time to market, reduced product development, labour costs and wastage, and greater product reliability.

8.2   Important points

Clients, designers, manufacturers, suppliers, contractors and installers have an important role in ensuring that the materials and products that form a construction project are both sourced and used with sustainability in mind. This is a pre-requisite of meeting certification to standards such as the Building Research Establishment Environmental Assessment Method (BREEAM).

 For further details on sustainable construction standards refer to Chapter E01 Sustainable construction and the environment.

 ## Practical ways for improving resource efficiency and reducing waste

- Design.
  - Specifying materials from sustainable sources; recycled and locally sourced.
  - Designing the project to suit standard product sizes and to avoid site cutting.
  - Designing for off site, pre-assembly and ensuring that products are responsibly sourced.
  - Designing to allow a cut/fill balance and by utilising surplus materials in site features (such as landscaping).
  - Looking for opportunities to source excess materials from other projects (for example, utilising the CL:AIRE register of materials and services).
  - Specifying non-hazardous, low-impact materials with low embodied carbon.
  - Designing to allow for disassembly so components can be recovered and used elsewhere.
- Procurement.
  - Buying construction products from sustainable sources from suppliers with a good environmental track record.
  - Requiring sub-contractors to have a waste management policy and source sustainable products.
  - Not over-ordering materials.
  - Reducing the amount of packaging.
  - Ordering materials at the size required, to avoid off-cuts.
- Construction.
  - Avoiding over-excavation.
  - Storing materials to avoid damage, theft, contamination and double handling.
  - Segregating surplus materials for reuse elsewhere.
  - Crushing existing demolition waste for reuse in the works to avoid the need for virgin materials.

RESOURCE EFFICIENCY

8.2.1   Life cycle assessment (cradle to cradle)

Life cycle assessment (LCA) is a process of evaluating the effects that a product has on the environment over the entire period of its lifetime, thereby increasing resource-use efficiency and decreasing liabilities. A good LCA will identify where in the life of a product the main impacts occur and identify what can be done to reduce or mitigate these impacts. In construction LCA is applied to both the building itself and also to the products that go into that building.

The stages in the life of a building are material extraction, processing into a product, combination of products into the building, use of the building, end of life deconstruction and material recycling. Efficient recycling of materials at end of life has now given rise to the term *cradle to cradle*, while *circular economy* (CE) has gained traction, with many construction companies using the notion to operate in a way that minimises waste.

The CE system is based on the reuse and regeneration of materials or products, as a means of continuing production in a sustainable or environmentally-friendly manner. Unlike a linear economy of make-use-dispose, the aims of CE encompass all the LCA and cradle to cradle criteria with the intention of keeping materials, components and products at their highest utility and value. CE has beneficial impacts on the three pillars of sustainability: **environment**, **economy** and **society**.

 For further information on the circular economy visit the Green Construction Board's online resources contained on the Construction Leadership Council's website.

The EMS Standard ISO 14001:2015 requires organisations to adopt a life cycle perspective (Clauses 6.1.2 and 8.1 refer). Annex A to the standard also provides guidance on this approach. ISO 14001:2015 has also introduced the idea of looking for opportunities to reduce environmental impact. Improving resource efficiency is one way of demonstrating this.

 For further details refer to Chapter E02 Site environment management systems.

Life cycle costing is a narrower assessment of the overall economic impacts of an asset, whereas the use of environmental costs in a whole-life analysis allows a true comparison between options, particularly where they are quoted as 'good' for the environment. For a major project (such as the construction of a nuclear power station) it is possible to calculate the environmental impact of making the concrete containment, the water required for refining the copper for the power plants and all the other components. Only by undertaking such an analysis is it possible to determine whether one solution carries a lower or higher environmental cost than another.

PAS 2050, Specification for the assessment of the life cycle greenhouse gas emissions of goods and services, produced by the British Standards Institute, is a publicly available specification that provides a consistent method for assessing the life cycle greenhouse gas emissions of goods and services.

8.3   Sustainable and responsible sourcing of materials

With the increasing focus on sustainable development, many construction companies are recognising the need to prove that their buildings are built with sustainability in mind. One element of this is in the responsible sourcing of products used in their construction, and the onus of proof is increasingly being passed back to the manufacturers of those construction products.

BREEAM awards credits based on the environmental impact of materials and for materials responsibly sourced. The aim is to encourage the use of materials with lower environmental impacts over their life cycle and to recognise and encourage the specification of responsibly sourced materials for basic building and finishing components.

The Building Research Establishment (BRE) standard BES 6001 has been published to enable construction product manufacturers to ensure and then prove that their products have been made with constituent materials that have been responsibly sourced. The standard describes a framework for the organisational governance, supply chain management and environmental and social aspects that must be addressed in order to ensure the responsible sourcing of construction products.

Independent, third-party assessment and certification against the requirements of BES 6001 then give the organisation the ability to prove that an effective system for ensuring responsible sourcing exists and adds credibility to any claims made. BES 6001 is also aligned to BREEAM so that products from manufacturers certified against this standard are able to score points against the responsible sourcing credits.

The BRE *Green guide to specification* provides guidance on how to make the best environmental choices when selecting construction materials and components. The guide presents information on the environmental impacts of building elements and specifications by ranking them on an A+ to E rating scale, where A+ represents the best environmental performance. These environmental rankings are based on LCAs using an environmental profile methodology. They are generic rankings that illustrate a range of typical materials.

BS 8902 provides a framework and gives requirements for the management, development, content and operation of sector certification schemes for the responsible sourcing and supply of construction products.

For manufacturers and suppliers, having certification to the environmental management systems (EMS) standard (ISO 14001) provides some evidence that the company is measuring, and improving, the environmental impacts of their products. Relevant products assessed under the responsible sourcing elements of BREEAM are able to score points against credits where the certified EMS covers the main processes or main supply chain processes.

For example, the responsible sourcing of bricks would need to demonstrate that the certified EMS covers manufacture (main process) and clay extraction (main supply chain process) to obtain maximum points.

8.3.1 Water efficiency

Water is a precious global resource, critical for life in all its forms. As the world's population increases, there will be an ever-rising demand on what is a finite resource. Future climate change and resulting changing patterns of rainfall will make water supply increasingly challenging through the ageing water supply infrastructure.

Water is an expensive item with costs on both the supply side and the waste water treatment side. Given these pressures water will become a more expensive resource. What this means within construction is that water efficiency will become a higher priority at all stages in a building's life cycle. Materials with high embodied water content (such as high water usage during manufacture or use) will inevitably increase costs to take account of this priority. The increasing importance of embodied water is recognised in the Building Research Establishment Environmental Assessment Method for Infrastructure (BREEAM Infrastructure).

8.3.2 Water scarcity

Water scarcity is both a natural and a human-made problem. There is enough fresh water on the planet for six billion people but it is distributed unevenly and too much of it is wasted, polluted and unsustainably managed. Water scarcity is among the main problems to be faced by many societies in the world. Water use has been growing at more than twice the rate of population increase in the last century, and, although there is no global water scarcity as such, an increasing number of regions are chronically short of water.

 Water scarcity is defined as the point at which the total impact of all users affects the supply or quality of water under existing arrangements to the extent that the demand by all sectors, including the environment, cannot be fully met.

Water scarcity can occur at any level of supply or demand and may be caused by human behaviour or the consequence of altered supply patterns (for example, from climate change). Scientists typically measure scarcity by looking at the total amount of water available per person. An area is experiencing water stress when annual water supplies drop below 1,700 m³ per person. When annual water supplies drop below 1,000 m³ per person, the population faces water scarcity, and below 500 m³ is absolute scarcity.

Water scarcity already affects every continent. Four billion people – almost two thirds of the world's population – experience severe water scarcity for at least one month each year. Over two billion people live in countries where water supply is inadequate. Half of the world's population could be living in areas facing water scarcity by as early as 2025, and some 700 million people could be displaced by intense water scarcity by 2030. By 2040, roughly one in four children worldwide will be living in areas of extremely high water stress.

The UK's population is forecast to rise to 75 million by 2050. Most of this population growth is expected to be in geographical locations already experiencing water stress; mainly London and the South East of England. The Environment Agency has warned that within 25 years, the UK will not have sufficient water to meet demand due to climate change *(for further information on water efficiency and minimisation refer to 8.3.1)*.

8.3.3 Using and conserving water during site works

On larger construction projects, where high volumes of water are being used, the first action is to establish an approach to measuring and monitoring water usage so that it can be managed. This may involve the use of water meters at appropriate locations and the use of water balances to account for water usage. Water reduction targets can be set based on known volumes of water usage and progress monitored. Collecting data on water consumption during the construction process will provide the following benefits.

- Understanding and managing costs.

- Reducing environmental impact of overuse.

- Benchmarking and improving performance.

- Obtaining credits under BREEAM.

- Demonstrating continual improvement in accordance with ISO 14001/EMAS.

- Demonstrating good practice and meeting customer expectations.

Significant savings can be made by using rainwater harvesting systems to collect rainwater from roofs and other flat surfaces, or other impervious surfaces, so that it can be stored for later use. Early installation of suitable run-off collection systems would need to be investigated at the design stage and payback times calculated for the expected volume of water use. Harvested water can be used for dust suppression, avoiding the need to draw water from the mains or abstraction.

Collecting rainwater for reuse

RESOURCE EFFICIENCY

Water usage should be monitored and any obvious leaks and running hoses identified and dealt with. The use of triggers on hoses will prevent hoses from running whilst unattended.

Vehicle wheel-wash equipment is now available with water recycling and recirculation systems fitted. These will reduce the volume of water used and have the potential to save money. These systems work by providing a solids settling area combined with the use of flocculants to further precipitate solids out. The solids collected can be periodically removed.

Site welfare facilities can be fitted with waterless urinals, push taps and rainwater harvesting for toilet flushes.

Waterless urinals

 A roof area of 400 square metres will collect over 12,000 litres of water after 25 mm of rainfall.

8.3.4 Sustainable drainage system (SuDS)

Sustainable drainage systems (SuDS) offer a process of managing rainfall that minimises the negative envornmental impacts on the quantity and quality of run-off water, whilst maximising the benefits of amenity and biodiversity for people and the environment. The philosophy of implementing SuDS on a proposed development has four key pillars:

1. Water quality.
2. Water quantity.
3. Amenity.
4. Biodiversity.

SuDS can be used to manage surface water run-off from large areas (such as part of a housing estate, major roads or business parks). They provide a natural approach to managing drainage in and around developments. SuDS work by slowing down and holding back the run-off from a site, allowing natural processes to break down pollution.

They deal with run-off close to the source rather than transporting it elsewhere. They are designed to attenuate (storing and slowly releasing) surface water from developments in a manner that will provide a more sustainable approach than the previous, conventional practice of routing run-off through a pipe into a watercourse. They are also a tool for preventing flooding. (Early engagement with the lead local flood authority is advisable at the planning stage.)

Facilities for SuDS include the following.

- Permeable surfaces.
- Filter strips.
- Filter and infiltration trenches.
- Swales.
- Detention basins.
- Underground storage.
- Wetlands.
- Ponds.

Other facilities exist (such as hydraulic controls or silt traps).

In **England** the National Planning Policy Framework (NPF) is in place, and is currently being updated in order to develop policy to support levelling up, as well as how national planning policy is currently accessed by users. Currently, under the NPF all major developments and housing projects of 10 houses or more should incorporate SuDS, unless there is clear evidence that it would be inappropriate.

In Scotland, Wales and Northern Ireland the rules are considerably different. In Scotland, SuDS are a legal requirement for all developments except single dwellings that drain to the water environment, unless they discharge to coastal waters.

The Scottish Environment Protection Agency (SEPA) is the statutory agency responsible for protecting the water environment, and therefore requires the use of effective, appropriate SuDS features in new developments.

In Wales, all new developments of more than one dwelling house, or where the construction area is 100 square metres or more, will require SuDS for surface water. In Northern Ireland, there is currently only a requirement in the planning process to demonstrate that SuDS have been considered..

Whilst the benefits of SuDS are clear, conditions will be required by the planning authority to ensure that plans are in place and responsibilities allocated for the ongoing maintenance of SuDS for the lifetime of the development. The plans should cover general maintenance of litter clearing, vegetation control and more long-term repairs and/or dredging.

8.4   Timber and chain of custody

Chain of custody (COC) is a process that provides assurance about where timber has been sourced from. This is done by certifying timber from the forest to the final point of purchase and requires an effective audit process.

The process tracks timber through each stage of the supply chain, from forest and logging, through sawmill, factory and distributor, to timber merchant and contractor. This provides transparency and traceability to guarantee compliance with demands for ethically sourced timber products.

Construction uses large amounts of timber, so it is important that timber is sourced from forests that are managed in a sustainable and ethical way. Illegal logging results in soil erosion, loss of biodiversity and uncontrolled development. It is therefore important to know where timber has been sourced from.

The Timber and Timber Products Placing on the Market Regulations (UKTR) and UK FLEGT (Forest Law Enforcement Governance and Trade) Regulations give operators and traders an important role in ensuring that timber is sourced and supplied from legal and verifiable sources. This also applies to virgin wood products used for renewable heat installations (such as biomass boilers).

To combat illegal logging, which has serious environmental, economic and social consequences, timber imported from countries that have implemented a voluntary partnership agreement (VPAs) with the UK must be accompanied by a FLEGT licence. Under this agreement, the timber producing country agrees to control and license its timber exports to ensure that the timber products come from a legal source. These agreements are underpinned by strong systems for ensuring timber legality.

Contractors and suppliers working for the UK Government have to comply with the timber procurement policy (TPP). The policy sets rules that all products derived from timber and wood must be from independently verifiable, legal and sustainable sources, or FLEGT-licensed timber or equivalent sources.

The crucial point that clients and contractors need to know is that any timber used on site for construction or timber hoardings must be legally sourced. The most easily identifiable way of doing this is the **Forest Stewardship Council (FSC)** label, as this indicates that there is a traceable trail of where the timber has come from.

The UK Government has approved the FSC and the **Programme for the Endorsement of Forest Certification (PEFC)**, the two largest international forest certification programmes, as timber certification schemes that meet the central point of expertise on timber (CPET) requirements.

Around 10 million hectares of forest are lost each year, an area the size of Portugal

Timber and chain of custody certificate number

PEFC UK forms part of a global network of forest certification schemes

The FSC and their global certification scheme allows consumers to identify, purchase and use timber and forest products produced from well managed forests. FSC UK is a national office of the FSC, which is an international non-governmental organisation dedicated to promoting responsible management of the world's forest.

In the UK, FSC forest management certification is based on UKWAS, a national standard which is consistent with FSC principles and criteria whilst at the same time reflecting local ecological, social and economic circumstances.

PFEC UK is part of the global network for the assessment and mutual recognition of national forest certification schemes developed by the PEFC Council. PEFC UK's certification scheme for sustainable forest management incorporates the UK Woodland Assurance Standard as the certification standard to be used for assessing whether a woodland is managed sustainably.

 For further information on the FSC and PEFC visit the respective websites.

The BRE put responsible sourcing of timber at the top of its agenda in the development of BREEAM, making it a mandatory element within any BREEAM assessment. It also recognises FSC certification as an indicator of responsibly-sourced materials, and has adopted CPET requirements for the purpose of demonstrating responsible sourcing of timber. This should be high on the agenda for any project team involved in a BREEAM assessed project. Some large construction projects have adopted a chain of custody certification scheme themselves as good practice.

08

RESOURCE EFFICIENCY

8.5   Reuse and recycling of materials

Maximising the reuse of materials on site can significantly reduce the amount of waste generated. For example, careful cut and fill analysis can ensure that soils excavated from cuttings can be used as fill material elsewhere (such as within embankments) so that no waste is sent to landfill and the need to procure fill is removed.

Not only can demolition materials be processed for aggregates and fill materials, designers should aim to use other materials (such as reclaimed bricks, timber and steel sections).

Other materials that may incorporate recycled content include plastics, aluminium, steel and steel reinforcement. Eco-reinforcement is a trademark for responsibly sourced reinforcing steel. It is a third-party certification scheme developed by the reinforcing steel industry to comply with BRE's Framework Standard Responsible Sourcing of Construction Products (BES 6001).

Using construction materials that have been recycled and are low impact offers a number of environmental and business benefits.

- Demonstrating performance against corporate and sustainability policies.
- Reducing material costs (where locally reprocessed demolition materials are cheaper than virgin materials).
- Supporting sustainability goals, to meet the requirements of clients and planning authorities.
- Providing a competitive edge through differentiation.
- Complementing other aspects of sustainable design.
- Conserving finite natural resources by reducing the demand for raw materials.
- Conserving energy and water, as recycled materials require less processing than extracting raw materials.
- Reducing air and water pollution, since manufacturing from recycled materials is generally a cleaner process and uses less energy.
- Reducing the amount of material that would otherwise go to landfill.

Designers should follow the principles of the circular economy, incorporating opportunities to reuse or recycle materials at the end of a product's life (for example, designing for dismantling and reuse of building components).

8.5.1   Demolition and refurbishment information data sheets (DRIDs)

The demolition and refurbishment information data sheets (DRIDS) have been developed to help identify waste streams and explain how they can be reused and recycled. They have been developed by the demolition industry, by giving consideration to knowledge and information available on materials they currently manage, or will be required to manage, in the future.

The design and construction of buildings, structures and infrastructures are now governed by tighter regulation and legislation. Therefore, the use of DRIDS allows users to be better informed about the types of materials and products they will encounter and how best to maximise environmental and economic gain.

There are 13 **DRIDS groups** plus a miscellaneous group, each with their own distinct shape, colour and code, to ease recognition. Each group contains a number of DRIDS, depending on their material or product make-up. For example, the wood group includes DRIDS that are generally one product, such as plywood, chipboard or dimensional timbers. However, wood furniture or wood framed glass panel systems may be in the composites group.

The colours have been chosen to reflect those used by BRE, WRAP, Institution of Civil Engineers (ICE) and Zero Waste Scotland. The groups include the following:

Composite (C1)	Metal (M1, M2, M5)
Electrical	Organic matter
Flooring (F1, F2)	Packaging
Hazardous (H2)	Plasterboard (G1)
Inert (I1, I2, I3)	Plastic (P1)
Insulation (Z1)	Wood (W1, W2, W3)
Miscellaneous	

 DRIDS are a useful resource for the wider construction industry.

 For further information on DRIDS visit the National Federation of Demolition Contractors website or download the latest app.

08

8.5.2   CL:AIRE Development Industry Code of Practice

CL:AIRE (Contaminated Land: Applications in Real Environments) works with its members to raise awareness and pursue shared objectives in land, water and environmental management by collecting strategic industry information and developing initiatives that improve efficiency and save money. It has developed a Definition of Waste Code of Practice (DoW CoP) for dealing with the waste management aspects of contaminated land, which provides a clear, consistent and efficient process that enables the reuse of excavated materials on site, or their movement between sites. It has extended the scope significantly to further allow sustainable remediation and development of land, and to ensure that the industry uses materials sustainably within a robust technical and regulatory framework. Scenarios covered are shown below.

- Reuse of excavated materials on the site of production (contaminated and uncontaminated).

- Direct transfer of clean, naturally occurring soils between sites.

- Reuse of naturally elevated substances in soils (such as arsenic and lead).

- Cluster projects (multiple reuse at different development sites within a similar timeframe).

- Brownfield to brownfield transfers.

- Fixed soil treatment facilities allowing the release of treated materials to the market place.

The main purpose of the DoW CoP is to achieve good practice across the development industry to:

- assess whether materials are waste or not

- determine when treated waste ceases to become waste

- provide an auditable trail to demonstrate that the DoW CoP has been complied with on each site.

The DoW CoP specifies the implementation of a **materials management plan** (MMP), together with a declaration from a competent qualified person, before the commencement of the works. By complying with this DoW CoP, it may be possible to avoid the need to apply for a waste permitting exemption for the use of construction waste (U1). It also allows the direct transfer of uncontaminated natural excavation materials between projects without the need for a permit.

 Further advice should be sought from CL:AIRE with reference to the DoW CoP and for further information on the register of materials and services.

 Flowcharts providing further guidance on how the CL:AIRE CoP links with environmental permitting in regard to the use or reuse of soils can be found in Chapter E10 Waste and material management.

 CL:AIRE Code of Practice

Galliford Try – Ingsbeck flood alleviation scheme

Background

The voluntary DoW CoP developed by CL:AIRE in conjunction with the EA helps determine whether materials are classed as waste. The DoW CoP has recently been updated (CL:AIRE CoPv2) to allow the direct transfer of naturally-occurring soil materials.

Ingsbeck flood alleviation scheme is a £11 million development in Wakefield. It is spread across a number of areas and comprises the construction of new flood defence walls, channels, embankments and flood storage areas. Part of the construction involved building a new clay flood defence embankment around residential houses, which was valued at approximately £180,000. This required approximately 4,000 tonnes of clay. By applying the DoW CoP, a materials management plan (MMP) was produced to enable the reuse of this material, which had a number of benefits, shown below.

Reduced operational costs

A large volume of waste material would require the use of a standard rules environmental permit, which takes approximately four months in application and incurs costs of around £6,000 for application, subsistence and surrender, as well as the use of a technically competent manager. However, the MMP took three weeks from production to sign off and only cost £500. This benefited the project by reducing programme time and cost, which significantly decreased the overall project cost by £60,000, approximately 33% of the project value.

Reduced landfill costs

The surplus material would have been destined for landfill as there was no further use on the donor site. By utilising the MMP, 4,000 tonnes of material was diverted from landfill (avoiding a £10,000 landfill gate fee for importing inert material) and further benefiting from an 80 tonne embodied carbon saving.

Reduced use of natural resources

By utilising a recycled material, this avoided having to excavate a finite material from a quarry.

Reduced regulatory effort

The use of the MMP does not require any direct involvement from the EA and NRW regulator. This frees up its resources for deployment on other tasks and allows self-regulation for the industry, whilst minimising impact and protecting the environment.

08

8.5.3   Recycled aggregates

Recycled aggregates are materials developed from reprocessing of materials that were originally used in construction, including sand, gravel, concrete, stone, bricks asphalt, blast furnace and steel furnace slag, and, more recently, geosynthetic aggregates and recycled glass. Using recycled aggregates is cost effective, eco friendly and versatile. Benefits include lowering embodied energy and reducing transport if recycled on brownfield sites where the aggregates were produced.

 The extraction of virgin aggregates has a wide range of impacts upon the environment, including noise, vibration, vehicle emissions, visual impact on the landscape and hydrogeology (the impact on the movement of groundwater in soil and rocks). Where a site with existing buildings is being redeveloped there is the potential to recycle materials from the buildings that are reaching their end of life status. Good planning can facilitate making them available as new construction materials or processing them into recycled aggregates.

On-site processing of demolition materials into aggregates is classed as a waste operation and will require an environmental permit or exemption for the treatment and reuse of the material. The WRAP (Waste and Resources Action Programme) quality protocol for the production of aggregates from inert waste *(refer to 8.5.3.1)* explains the requirements for ensuring that the processed materials meet end-of-waste status. You have a responsibility to check that all relevant supplier documentation is correct to confirm that the protocol requirements have been met or that the relevant permit or exemptions that may apply are in place.

 For further information on the *Quality protocol: aggregates from inert waste* visit the Government website.

 For further details on reducing waste and permitting requirements associated with the treatment of demolition waste and contaminated soils refer to Chapter E10 Waste and material management.

8.5.3.1   WRAP quality protocol for the production of aggregates from inert waste

This protocol is published by WRAP and has been produced by the Quarry Products Association (QPA), the Highways Agency (HA) and WRAP as a formalised quality control procedure for the production of aggregates from recovered inert waste. These are referred to in the document as *Recovered aggregates*. The document has two main purposes.

1. To assist in identifying the point at which the inert waste used to produce recovered aggregates has been fully recovered, ceases to be a waste and becomes a product.

2. To give adequate assurance that recovered aggregate products conform to standards common to both recovered and primary aggregates.

You have a responsibility to check that all relevant documentation is correct to confirm that the protocol requirements have been met.

 For further information visit the WRAP website.

 For flowcharts providing further guidance on how the WRAP quality protocol links with environmental permitting for the reuse of aggregates refer to Chapter E10 Waste and material management.

8.5.4   Reuse of excavated soils

Soil is a vulnerable and essentially a non-renewable resource because it can take more than 500 years to form a 2 cm thickness.

Topsoils contain living organisms that provide essential ecosystem services, supporting the production of food, and the creation of environments for wildlife and human recreational activity (such as parks and sports fields).

Soil management is increasingly seen as an essential part of any project. If planned and designed carefully soil can be re-incorporated into the project, avoiding the need to remove it from site. Even soils with contamination from other materials can be processed to make them suitable for reuse.

Re-incorporating soil into the project is an efficient use of resources

 For further information refer to Chapter E09 Soil management and contamination control.

Soil management and contamination control

09

Supporting
INFORMATION

GT700 Toolbox talks / supporting checklists and forms

Toolbox talks on some of these topics are available in the GT700 publication. Supporting checklists and forms covering some of these topics are available on our companion website.

SOIL MANAGEMENT AND CONTAMINATION CONTROL

Summary of soil management and contamination control legislation and guidance

This list is not exhaustive and only includes legislation mentioned in this section of GE700.

Legislation and guidance	Enforcement agencies*				
	EA	LA	NIEA	NRW	SEPA
Acts (primary legislation)					
Environment Act	✓			✓	✓
Environmental Protection Act	✓	✓	✓	✓	✓
Waste and Contaminated Land (Amendment) Act (Northern Ireland)			✓		
Regulations (secondary legislation)					
Contaminated Land (England) Regulations	✓				
Contaminated Land (Scotland) Regulations					✓
Contaminated Land (Wales) Regulations				✓	
Control of Asbestos (Amendment) Regulations (Northern Ireland)			✓		
Control of Asbestos Regulations	✓			✓	✓
Environmental Liability (Prevention and Remediation) (Amendment) Regulations (Northern Ireland)			✓		
Environmental Liability (Scotland) Regulations					✓
Radioactive Contaminated Land (Modification of Enactments) (England) Regulations	✓				
Radioactive Contaminated Land (Modification of Enactments) (Wales) Regulations				✓	
Radioactive Contaminated Land (Scotland) Regulations					✓
Surface Waters (Fishlife) (Classification) (Scotland) Amendment Regulations					✓
Guidance					
CL:AIRE CAR-SOIL™ *Asbestos in soil and construction and demolition materials*					
Code of Practice for the design of protective measures for methane and carbon dioxide ground cases for new buildings (BS 8485)					
Construction Code of Practice for the sustainable use of soils on construction sites (Defra)					
Investigation of potentially contaminated sites (BS 10175)					
Model procedures for the management of land contamination (CL:AIRE and Defra)					
Net Regs Environmental guidance					
The CL:AIRE *Definition of waste: Development industry Code of Practice*					
Organisations with information and guidance on their websites	✓	✓	✓	✓	✓

*Key

CL:AIRE	Contaminated Land: Applications in Real Environments
Defra	Department for Environment, Food and Rural Affairs
EA	Environment Agency
LA	Local Authorities
NIEA	Northern Ireland Environment Agency
NRW	Natural Resources Wales
SEPA	Scottish Environment Protection Agency

09

Overview

This chapter gives a general overview of the legal framework for the management of soil before and during construction and the definition, regulation and management of contaminated land.

The chapter identifies the processes involved with soil management and the assessment and remediation of contaminated land, the licences that will be required for its treatment or disposal and guidance for the prevention of pollution. It will also identify the main health and safety considerations when dealing with contaminated land.

9.1   Introduction

Building and construction works take place in many different environments but general descriptions of greenfield and brownfield are commonly used. Greenfield land (a site located in a rural area not previously built on) is more likely to require effective management of soils and subsoils due to the rural environment. Increasingly, though, the redevelopment of brownfield land, previously used for commercial or industrial activities, has grown in recognition of the importance of conserving our rural environment. Bringing these brownfield sites back into use is also considered a more sustainable option than using greenfield land.

The UK's extensive industrial past has, however, left a legacy of contamination on many sites and this needs to be managed to ensure the sites are suitable for their new purpose. Both the surface and the ground beneath may be contaminated by materials that have been worked, stored, spilt, buried, dumped or abandoned on the land in previous years. This list will also include the residue, waste or by-products from some industrial processes and the ashes from fires. Both solid and liquid waste may have permeated the ground to a considerable depth.

Sites that have had previous industrial occupation should be assumed to be polluted, and tests undertaken to ascertain the types of pollutant and their levels of concentration.

Everyone involved in work on both greenfield and brownfield land must be made aware of the importance of soil management and the possibility of contamination. They must make an assessment of the potential risks to the project and the negative impacts to human health and the environment, and implement management and mitigation processes.

 Contaminated land

For the purpose of the regulations ***contaminated land*** is defined as any land that appears to be in such a condition, by reason of substances in, on or under the land, that significant harm or significant pollution of controlled waters is being caused or there is a significant possibility of such harm or pollution being caused.

9.2   Important points

- There are two main Codes of Practice that support soil and contaminated land management.
  1. The *Code of Practice for the sustainable use of soils on construction sites* is used to protect soils and ensure adequate soil function (for example, plant growth, water attenuation and biodiversity) during and after construction.
  2. The *Definition of waste: development industry Code of Practice* (DoW CoP) to provide a clear and concise process to determine whether excavated materials on a development site constitute waste in the first instance, and to identify the point when treated waste can no longer be considered as waste.

- Soils have a range of characteristics and it is important to understand the different properties and the advantages and disadvantages they offer with regards to drainage and growing mediums.

- Storage of soils must be carefully planned to avoid negative effects of compaction from stockpiles being too big and excessive traffic movements.

- Different classifications of soil should be stockpiled separately to avoid cross-contamination.

- The contract documentation and planning conditions for a project will identify known contamination of the site and the agreed methods for dealing with it. These should be referred to, and their requirements included, in the construction environmental management plan.

- Where a contaminated land assessment needs to be undertaken, this will be carried out in accordance with a systematic process of investigation, testing and appraisal to identify the most appropriate method for its treatment. The agreed method should be approved by the regulators before works commence.

- The testing of contaminated land must be carried out by certified, competent professionals in accordance with standard field testing and laboratory procedures approved by the regulators.

- All contaminated areas of the site must be fenced off and have clear exclusion signs to avoid unauthorised access and accidental spread of contamination across the site.

09

SOIL MANAGEMENT AND CONTAMINATION CONTROL

- The use of mobile plant for remediation of contaminated soils will require an environmental permit for the equipment and the need to complete a site deployment form detailing the work and management of the risks at each specific location.

- Where, following treatment, materials are still classed as waste, then their use will also require an environmental permit or registered exemption. The Contaminated Land: Applications in Real Environments (CL:AIRE) development industry Code of Practice can be used to ensure that contaminated materials are treated and managed so that they achieve an end of waste status. This will require the implementation of a materials management plan and a declaration by a qualified person that all requirements have been complied with.

- The stockpiling of contaminated soils should be avoided. Where stockpiling is unavoidable, material should be placed on impervious ground to avoid contaminates seeping into the ground and it should be covered to avoid wind-blown contamination and run-off to drainage systems and watercourses.

- Any removal of waste off site for treatment elsewhere or disposal should comply with the duty of care, including the provision of waste transfer or consignment documentation.

- All vehicles carrying contaminated materials off site should be appropriately sheeted and should pass through a wheel-wash facility to avoid contamination of the public highway.

- All personnel involved in the treatment of contaminated land should be aware of the relevant risks associated with the particular contaminants and wear the appropriate protective clothing, gloves and boots. Depending on the level of risk, a decontamination unit may need to be employed to prevent the spread of contaminants to clean areas of the site.

9.3   The importance of soil

Soil is vulnerable and because it can take more than 500 years to form a 2 cm thickness it is, in practical terms, non-renewable. One hectare of topsoil, the most productive soil layer, can contain up to 5 tonnes of living organisms. The importance of soil should not be overlooked. It is a resource that impacts on social, economic and environmental sustainability. It supports natural service to society, including the following.

- Food and fibre production.
- Environmental interaction (with water and air).
- Supporting ecological habitats and biodiversity.
- Supporting the landscape.

- Protecting cultural heritage.
- Providing raw materials.
- Providing a platform for construction.
- Supporting important eco-services (pollination and purification).

9.3.1   Planning for effective soil management

Soil, if planned and managed carefully, can be re-incorporated into the project, without the need to remove it from site because of poor design or contamination from other materials. Careful planning can help protect the quality and availability of topsoils. Make sure that you avoid the following construction activities that create negative impacts.

- Covering soil with impermeable materials, effectively sealing it and resulting in significant detrimental impacts on the soil's physical, chemical and biological properties, including drainage characteristics.

- Accidentally contaminating soil as a result of spillage or the use of chemicals.

- Over-compacting soil through the use of heavy machinery or the storage of construction materials.

- Reducing soil quality by mixing topsoil with subsoil.

- Mixing soil with construction waste or contaminated materials, which have to be treated before reuse or (as a last resort) sent to landfill.

The Department for Environment, Food and Rural Affairs (Defra), in support with the Waste and Resources Action Programme (WRAP), publishes a construction Code of Practice (CoP) for the sustainable use of soils on construction sites. Defra acknowledges that the publication has not been updated since 2009, but they still believe that it is a useful, relevant guidance document that can be used for reference purposes. Whilst the CoP is not legally binding, following it will help you to achieve the following.

- Protecting and enhancing soil resources on site and providing wider environmental benefits.

- Cost savings for your business.

- Supporting achievement of your business sustainability targets.

- Meeting your legal obligations regarding waste controls.

The CoP provides guidance on the various stages of site development where soil should be considered and contains ten sections to provide practical advice on different aspects of using soil sustainably on construction sites. Defra has partnered with CL:AIRE to review this document.

1. Knowing what soils are on site.
2. On-site soil management.
3. Topsoil stripping.
4. Subsoil stripping.
5. Soil stockpiling.

6. Soil placement.
7. Sourcing and importing topsoil.
8. Topsoil manufacture.
9. Soil aftercare.
10. Uses for surplus topsoil.

 For further information on the *CoP for the sustainable use of soils on construction sites* visit the Defra website.

9.3.2 Business benefits of good soil protection

Good soil management can identify opportunities for the reuse of topsoil on site, leading to cost savings, reuse of surplus subsoils, which might normally be sent to landfill, which in turn reduces the traffic movements to and from site to remove or import soils.

The identification of different types of soil will inform good storage processes and avoid cross-contamination between different soil types.

To facilitate the actions above, a soil resource plan should be undertaken.

The soil resource plan will set out in detail the methods, equipment, location, volumes and programme for the recovery, storage and reuse of all site topsoil and subsoil.

9.3.3 Protection measures for soil during construction

- Prepare a soil resource plan showing the areas and type of topsoil and subsoil to be stripped, haul routes, methods to be used, the location, type and management of each soil stockpile and named individuals responsible for soil management on site.

- When stripping, stockpiling or placing soil, do so in the driest conditions possible and use tracked equipment where possible to reduce compaction. If there is a sustained period of heavy rainfall (for example, >10 mm in 24 hours) stop work and only restart after the ground has had one full drying day or agreed criteria for the soil composition has been met.

- Confine traffic movement to designated routes.

- Keep soil storage periods as short as possible.

- Clearly define stockpiles of different soil materials.

Topsoils come with a wide range of different characteristics making them suitable for different landscapes and plants (for example, turfing, tree pits, wildflowers and grassland).

To ensure that the topsoil is suitable for the intended purpose, it is important to have the soil independently assessed against a topsoil specification.

The most functional specifications are those that list which properties the topsoil should possess prior to planting, turfing or seeding.

These normally include the following.

- Visual examination (for example, soil structure, consistency and foreign matter).

- Particle size analysis (texture) and stone content.

- pH and salinity values.

- Content of major plant nutrients.

- Organic matter content.

- Maximum levels of potential contaminants (for example, heavy metals, hydrocarbons, cyanide and phenols).

9.4 Regulatory bodies involved in contaminated land

Various organisations (as listed below) will be involved in granting approval for the treatment and the redevelopment of contaminated sites.

- The Local Authority, which has a statutory duty to inspect its land and identify any sites that are formally designated as contaminated.

- The Local Authority, before granting planning permission, will approve the remediation strategy to ensure that the ground is suitable for the proposed development.

- The Environment Agency (EA) for England, Natural Resources Wales (NRW) for Wales, the Northern Ireland Environment Agency (NIEA) for Northern Ireland and the Scottish Environment Protection Agency (SEPA) for Scotland, for issuing an environmental permit for the use of mobile treatment plant to treat contaminated soils or for the reuse of construction and demolition waste.

- The Local Authority for issuing an environmental permit for crushing equipment and for granting an exemption for the crushing and screening of demolition materials.

- The relevant environment agency for regulating the disposal of waste under the duty of care.

- The relevant environment agency for regulating contaminated sites that are deemed to be special sites (for example, areas that could seriously damage surface or groundwater supplies, or defence sites or radioactive sites).

- The Local Authority environmental health officers for dealing with any complaints regarding dust that crosses the site boundary.

- The water companies and the relevant environment agency for the disposal of polluted water from contaminated sites.

Effective contact with each of these authorities is essential, and must be established early in the project.

Any contaminated site must be totally fenced off and adequate warning notices must be prominently posted, advising all members of the public that the site is dangerous and to refrain from entering.

 For further information on waste management refer to Chapter E10 Waste and material management.

09

SOIL MANAGEMENT AND CONTAMINATION CONTROL

9.5 Contaminated Land Regulations

Part IIA of the Environmental Protection Act (EPA) provides the legal framework for dealing with contaminated land in the UK.

It is implemented in each of the devolved administrations through the following regulations.

9.5.1 England

- Contaminated Land (England) Regulations.
- Radioactive Contaminated Land (Modification of Enactments) (England) Regulations, which extend controls on contaminated land to radioactive contaminated land.

9.5.2 Northern Ireland

- The Contaminated Land Regime, which is set out in Part 3 of the Waste and Contaminated Land (Northern Ireland) Order.

This regime is very similar to that provided in Part IIA of the Environmental Protection Act in England, Scotland and Wales. The District Councils will be the primary regulators for the regime. Initial activity will focus on the preparation of site inspection strategies, which are to be completed within 12 months of the regime being in place.

9.5.3 Scotland

- The Contaminated Land (Scotland) Regulations, SSI 2007/178, and statutory guidance were brought into force in 2000 and are similar to the regulations that apply in England and Wales.
- Radioactive Contaminated Land (Scotland) Regulations.

9.5.4 Wales

- Contaminated Land (Wales) Regulations.
- Radioactive Contaminated Land (Modification of Enactments) (Wales) Regulations, which extend controls on contaminated land to radioactive contaminated land.

The Local Authority (or relevant environment agency in the case of a special site) has a statutory duty to ensure the remediation of contaminated land is paid for by an appropriate person(s).

The appropriate person(s) will be the person(s) who knowingly permitted the pollution or, if they cannot be found, the responsibility will fall to the owner or occupier of the site.

To enforce the remediation works the regulatory authority will serve a remediation notice on the appropriate person(s) specifying what needs to be done and by when.

There is a close relationship between the contaminated land regime under EPA Part IIA above and planning controls.

The National Planning Policy Framework confirms that planning policies and decisions should ensure the following.

- The site is suitable for its proposed use, taking account of ground conditions and any risks arising from land instability and contamination. This includes risks arising from natural hazards or former activities (such as mining) and any proposals for mitigation including land remediation (as well as potential impacts on the natural environment arising from that remediation).
- After remediation, as a minimum, land should not be capable of being determined as contaminated land under Part IIA of the Environmental Protection Act.
- Adequate site investigation information, prepared by a competent person, is presented.

Planning conditions should ensure appropriate investigation, remediation, monitoring and record keeping. Where contamination is suspected, the developer is responsible for investigating the land to determine what remedial measures are necessary and the actual remediation work to ensure its safety and suitability for its intended purpose. There is a significant emphasis on voluntary remediation by the developer to avoid a formal remediation notice being issued by the regulating authority.

Where there is a requirement to treat or dispose of contaminated material, then waste controls and the duty of care will apply (refer to 9.7 Managing contaminated land).

9.6 Brownfield sites

The definition of a brownfield site generally relates to land that has had some form of previous development.

Many brownfield sites will be land that is affected by contamination but not to an extent that it automatically falls within the definition set out in the Contaminated Land Regulations above. Previously published estimates of the extent of land affected by contamination vary widely, from 50,000 to 300,000 hectares, amounting to as many as 100,000 sites.

The Environment Agency estimates that, of these, 5,000 to 20,000 may be expected to be problem sites that require action to ensure that unacceptable risks to human health and the environment are avoided.

09

Some brownfield sites are affected by land contamination because of the previous industrial uses of the site, which has led to the deliberate or accidental release of chemicals onto the land. The following are examples of chemicals associated with four industrial processes.

Oil refineries (fuel, oil, lubricants, bitumen, alcohols, organic acids, polychlorinated biphenyls (PCBs), cyanides, sulphur and vanadium).

Lead works (lead, arsenic, cadmium, sulphides, sulphates, chlorides, sulphuric acid and sodium hydroxide).

Pesticide manufacturing (dichloromethane, fluorobenzene, acetone, methanol, benzene, arsenic, copper sulphate and thallium).

Textile and dye works (aluminium, cadmium, mercury, bromides, fluorides, ammonium salts, trichloroethene and polyvinyl chloride).

Sites with previous industrial occupation should be assumed to be polluted

9.7 Managing contaminated land

Managing land affected by contamination involves the identification of risks and then putting in the appropriate control measures to reduce those risks to an acceptable level so that the land is suitable for its intended use. Dealing with land contamination and regeneration helps towards making the environment clean and safe, enhances individual's health and wellbeing, and improves the economic, ecological and amenity value of the area.

The Environment Agency expects sites to follow the *Land contamination risk management* (LCRM) guidance when managing the risks associated with land contamination (applicable to England, Northern Ireland and Wales). This guidance can be used in Wales, but must also be used in conjunction with *Land contamination: our role in managing and dealing with land contamination* for differing requirements. For Northern Ireland, reference must also be made to the Department of Agriculture, Environment and Rural Affairs *Practice guide – redeveloping land affected by contamination*. Local authorities and other regulators may also provide additional guidance.

The LCRM can be used in a range of regulatory and management contexts, and helps with:

- identification and assessment of unacceptable risk.
- assessment of suitable remediation options to manage the risk.
- planning and carrying out remediation works.
- verifying that the remediation has been successful.

The LCRM consists of four guides:

1. LCRM: Before you start.
2. LCRM: Risk assessment.
3. LCRM: Options appraisal.
4. LCRM: Remediation and verification.

A staged risk-based approach is used, consisting of three stages. Each is broken down into tiers or steps.

 For further information on the LCRM guidance, visit the Government website.

9.7.1 Stage 1: Risk assessment

This stage has three tiers that are applied to approaching a risk assessment:

1. **Preliminary risk assessments** are the first tier of risk assessment, and develop the initial conceptual site model to establish whether there are any potentially unacceptable risks.

2. **Generic quantitative risk assessments** use generic assessment criteria and assumptions to estimate risk.

3. **Detailed quantitative risk assessments** use detailed, site-specific information to estimate risk (this stage also includes information for intrusive site investigations).

Land contamination risk assessments can only be completed a competent person. A technical approach to risk assessment must be followed for each tier of risk assessment, as follows:

- Identify the hazard – establish contaminant sources.

- Assess the hazard – use a source-pathway-receptor (S-P-R) linkage approach to find out if there is the potential for unacceptable risk.

- Estimate the risk – predict what degree of harm or pollution might result and how likely it is to occur by using the tiered approach to risk assessment.

- Evaluate the risk – decide whether a risk is unacceptable.

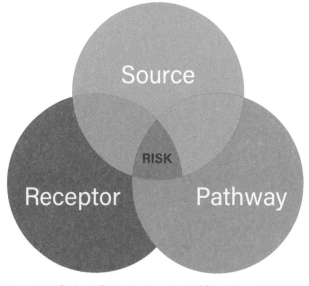

SOIL MANAGEMENT AND CONTAMINATION CONTROL

Pathways will be specific to the receptor type. For example:

- ingestion, inhalation or dermal contact for human health receptors
- infiltration and contaminant migration through permeable strata, such as the unsaturated zone for groundwater
- a secondary pathway from groundwater contamination to surface water
- migration of ground gases and vapours such as permanent gases, landfill gas and volatile hydrocarbons into buildings
- direct contact and uptake by plants.

You will develop an initial conceptual site model in the preliminary risk assessment that will need to be refined and updated as you progress through the LCRM.

Risk assessment evaluation criteria are the parameters used to judge whether particular harm or pollution needs further assessment or is unacceptable. Any evaluation criteria used must be:

- relevant to the site
- relate to the contaminants and receptors you are dealing with.

The exact choice of evaluation criteria will depend on:

- the reasons for doing the risk assessment and the regulatory context
- the conceptual site model and potential contaminant linkages
- any criteria set by regulators
- any advisory requirements such as from Public Health England
- the degree of confidence and precaution required to judge whether a risk is unacceptable
- how you have used or developed more detailed assessment criteria in further tiers of risk assessment
- the availability of robust scientific data
- how much is known – for example, about the pathway and how the contaminants affect receptors
- any practical reasons, such as being able to measure or predict against the criteria.

9.7.1.1   Evaluate the risks

For preliminary risk assessment, the risks need to be evaluated qualitatively. If you progress to a generic or detailed quantitative risk assessment, use evaluation criteria to judge whether particular harm or pollution needs further assessment or is unacceptable. You will need to collect detailed investigation data to support the use of evaluation criteria.

 For information on each of the risk assessment tiers, refer to the Government website.

9.7.2   Stage 2: Options appraisal

You must be a competent person to conduct an options appraisal. If this stage has been reached, then it has been decided that there is a need to remediate. Remediation is the action required to prevent, minimise, remedy, or mitigate the effects of the unacceptable risks.

This stage allows you to identify an appropriate remediation option, by following three steps:

1. Identify feasible remediation options.
2. Undertake a detailed evaluation of options.
3. Select the final remediation option.

9.7.2.1   Step 1: Identify feasible remediation options

To identify possible remediation options for further evaluation, the following needs to be considered:

- Is the information available sufficient?
- Formulating the appraisal objectives of options.
- Producing a shortlist of potential remediation options.
- Selecting the most feasible options, to assess in more detail.

When considering options, any required regulatory controls, such as permits, must be factored in. Regulatory controls covering most land contamination treatment activities will use one of the following:

- standard rules: SR2008 No 27: *Mobile plant for the treatment of waste soils and contaminated material, substances or products* and Form MPP2: *deployment form for land and groundwater remediation*
- a bespoke mobile plant permit for the treatment of waste soils and contaminated material, substances, or products
- a site-based permit.

Ahead of remediation, plan for any requirements such as for planning and Part 2A. If you intend to use the CL:AIRE Definition of waste: development industry code of practice (DoW CoP) you can find further details on the CL:AIRE website.

 If you intend to use the CL:AIRE Definition of waste: development industry code of practice (DoW CoP) you can find further details on the CL:AIRE website.

At the end of step 1, the following will have been concluded:

- identification of options appraisal management and technical objectives
- specific remediation objectives and criteria
- consideration of the regulatory controls that may be required
- production of a shortlist of feasible remediation options that will be further evaluated during step 2.

 For more detailed information on step 1, visit the Government website.

9.7.2.2   Step 2: Do a detailed evaluation of options

This step decides which options will be the most suitable for dealing with each relevant contaminant linkage. To achieve this, you will need to:

- assess the limitations, advantages, and disadvantages of each option
- develop and use options appraisal evaluation criteria to assess the merits of each option
- establish which options are most suitable – individually or combined
- put forward proposals for combining options
- ensure that detailed information on the technical aspects of each option, including the cost, are sourced.

The level of detail required for the evaluation criteria will be dependent upon site circumstances. The evaluation used needs to take account of the best practicable environmental option. Examples of criteria that must be considered when selecting an option(s) include the following.

Regulatory and stakeholder requirements. The option selected must be acceptable to relevant stakeholders, such as the regulator, client, site purchaser and local residents.

Sustainability. To address sustainability, Stage B of the SuRF-UK Framework can be adopted. This can be used to differentiate the remediation options against environmental, social, and economic indicators considering any relevant climate change issues. You can also refer to BS ISO 18504: Soil quality. Sustainable remediation.

Cost. Affordability needs to be assessed in line with the available resources and the approximate cost of verification and remediation.

Timescales. Consideration of how long it will take to complete remediation, the need for any post remedial monitoring and any future obligations required such as post-remediation or long-term monitoring and maintenance.

Practicability. Is the option practical regarding the site location, layout, size, maintenance needs, operational needs, compatibility with other planned site works.

Effectiveness. This needs to address if the remediation will successfully reduce or control the unacceptable risks to a pre-determined level, that the timescales are realistic, the option is applicable to the relevant contaminant linkages and if effectiveness can be demonstrated throughout the verification process.

Durability. This needs to address if the remediation will successfully reduce or control the unacceptable risks over a certain time.

Environmental impact. Will the remediation deliver direct and indirect benefits and how will it affect the quality of the environment during and after completion.

Track record. Identify evidence of other successful remediation using your selected approach.

Availability. Are the methods or techniques available and is there a need for specialist contractors or specific reagents.

Health and safety requirements. What levels of health and safety are needed associated with each option.

 For more information on the technical basis of selected remediation methods, refer to:

- **INFO-OA2: detailed evaluation of remediation options on the CL:AIRE website**
- **Contaminated land guidance tool for references on the CIRIA website**

At the end of step 2, the following will have taken place:

- an assessment of which remediation options are the most feasible for each relevant contaminant linkage
- a decision will have been made on any options that can or need to be combined.

 For more detailed information on step 2, visit the Government website.

09

9.7.2.3   Step 3: Select the final remediation option

This stage focuses on which option is the most suitable, which could be a single or combined approach. The final option must meet the overall site objectives identified in the preliminary risk assessment, the options appraisal management and technical objectives and the options appraisal remediation objectives.

It may not be easy to identify a remediation option that meets some or all the remediation objectives completely. Some of the reasons for this could be due to uncertainty on reducing or controlling the risks, achievability within the requirement timeframe, not practical because of the sites size, location, access, or topography, or it is too expensive despite it being the most effective, practicable and robust solution.

Stakeholders could have varying views on what is required, for example:

- the regulator, to meet regulatory and legal requirements, so this is most likely to be an important consideration
- the site owners' views on what they consider sufficient
- neighbouring property owners' views.

It may be necessary to review the remediation objectives, or alternatively:

- agreeing a lower standard of remediation, an example of this would be changing the layout or use of the site
- adjusting in other areas, such as the provision of additional health and safety protection
- looking at alternative remediation options such as new technology or approaches and use
- carrying out longer term monitoring and then re-evaluating, particularly if the site has complex contamination.

At the end of step 3, the following will have been achieved:

- selection of the final remediation option
- assessment of how a combined or integrated approach will work in practice
- a decision on actions needed if feasible options could not be identified
- a decision and agreement on longer-term monitoring and maintenance, or monitored natural attenuation as a remediation option
- confirmation that the selected remediation option will manage the risk effectively, and be verifiable at stage 3 of LCRM
- recording and justification of the decision in options appraisal report.

 For more detailed information on step 3, visit the Government website.

9.7.3   Stage 3: remediation and verification

This stage has four steps that need to be followed:

1. Develop a remediation strategy.
2. Remediate.
3. Produce a verification report.
4. Do long-term monitoring and maintenance, if required.

Only a competent person with training, knowledge and experience in remediation can complete stage 3.

9.7.3.1   Step 1: Develop a remediation strategy

A remediation plan will need to be developed and agreed. Monitoring objectives and criteria to track performance of the remediation will need to be established. This strategy will provide a record of how the remediation objectives will be met and conducted.

As part of the remediation strategy, a verification plan will need to be produced. This will contain all of the data requirements, including compliance criteria and monitoring details. This will establish an audit trail to verify remediation is working or has worked.

Once the remediation strategy has been agreed, and the correct regulatory controls are in place, the remediation can commence. A key part of this process will be remediation progress reporting and monitoring/maintenance reporting.

Once remediation is complete, a verification report is produced that demonstrates that the risk has been reduced and that the remediation objectives and criteria have been met. The verification report will detail a complete record of all remediation activities and evidence that it has been a success.

The remediation strategy and verification report are an integral part of the final record of the land quality.

 For more detailed information on the remediation strategy, see INFO-OA3: developing the remediation strategy on the CL:AIRE Water and Land Library.

9.8　Occupational health considerations

The health of workers on contaminated sites can be affected through one or more of the following ways.

- Asphyxiation.
- Gassing.
- Ingestion.

- Inhalation.
- Skin absorption.
- Skin penetration.

Under the Personal Protective Equipment at Work (Amendment) Regulations 2022, employers must carry out an assessment to ensure that the correct personal protective (PPE) clothing and respiratory protective equipment (RPE) are issued and worn at all times when work is carried out on contaminated sites.

Continuous assessments of the risk to health by exposure to any contaminated material or land must be carried out, and the control measures or precautions constantly monitored.

9.8.1　Personal hygiene

The level of risk to health by any contaminants will determine the need and scale of hygiene facilities, but certain consideration should always be borne in mind when working on a contaminated site.

A dirty area is required for workers to discard dirty or contaminated clothing. Such clothing should be bagged and identified within this area before being dispatched to specialist cleaners.

Washing and toilet areas. Toilets, showers and washing facilities should be positioned between the dirty and clean areas, so that workers may wash or shower in order to remove any contaminant from their bodies.

A clean area is required for workers to put on clean and non-contaminated clothing. Access to and exit from this area must only be to the clean part of the site. It is essential that the entry and exit point of the clean area is in the clean part of the site.

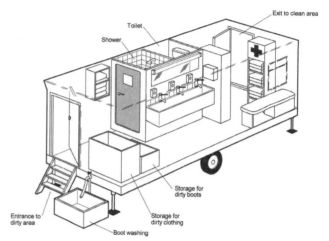

Typical layout of a hygiene unit, divided into three areas, with the dirty entrance remote from the clean exit

Daily cleaning of the toilet facilities and the decontamination of all facilities must be carried out.

9.8.2　Asbestos

Asbestos was widely used in construction and insulation materials and poor management and waste practices have led to asbestos contaminating brownfield sites. In addition, many unprotected sites have suffered from the indiscriminate fly-tipping of asbestos waste.

Asbestos is a highly dangerous material and presents substantial risks to the health of those who work with it and those who may come into contact with it. Asbestos-related diseases are responsible for around 5,000 deaths a year in Great Britain. Works dealing with asbestos come within the requirements of the Control of Asbestos Regulations.

Before the commencement of works, the site assessment should identify any risks posed by asbestos and the appropriate mitigation actions for dealing with it, which may range from physical containment to disposal.

 For further information on the management of asbestos waste refer to Chapter E10 Waste and material management.

CL:AIRE published the Joint Industry Working Group Asbestos in Soil and Construction & Demolition (C&D) materials guidance *Control of Asbestos Regulations 2012: Interpretation for Managing and Working with Asbestos in Soil and Construction* and *Demolition Materials: Industry Guidance*. Generally referred to as CAR-SOIL, this guidance document highlights the definitive explanation of how the legal requirements of the Control of Asbestos Regulations 2012 have been interpreted to apply to work with asbestos-contaminated soil, and construction and demolition materials. The aims of CAR-SOIL are listed below and overleaf.

- Bring together the asbestos management, occupational hygiene and brownfield management sectors with the aim of promoting the development of a consistent and harmonised approach to the regulation, investigation, analysis, assessment and management of asbestos in soil.

- Develop practical practitioner guidance on asbestos in soil that provides a consistent approach for UK industry, stakeholders and regulators.

09

SOIL MANAGEMENT AND CONTAMINATION CONTROL

- Promote the development of the relevant industry professional qualification framework for asbestos in soils for the brownfield and asbestos management sectors, building on the existing professional qualification framework for the management of asbestos in buildings, and relevant statutory requirements.

- Engage with the principal regulatory bodies for asbestos (the Health and Safety Executive (HSE), Environment Agency and representatives of Local Authority contaminated land officers) with the aim of promoting a consistent, unified and transparent regime for the regulation of all aspects relating to the remediation of land contaminated by asbestos.

- Promote and develop an improvement in public and stakeholder awareness of relevant issues, including health and safety, public health, technical, legal and insurance, related to the occurrence of and investigation and remediation of asbestos in soil.

- Promote the work of the Asbestos in soil JIWG to ensure all organisations are fully informed of its activities.

 For further information about CAR-SOIL, visit the CL:AIRE website.

9.8.3 Explosives

Extreme care must be taken on sites where explosives are known to have been stored or used. This includes old mine workings, coal mines, former explosives factories and Ministry of Defence establishments. Furthermore, unexploded bombs are occasionally unearthed when construction work takes place in areas that were subjected to bombing during World War II. Disturbing any explosives could have sudden and disastrous consequences, especially if they are old and starting to decay.

Once it is agreed that excavation work should proceed, this should be done with utmost caution. Any areas of soil discolouration, unusual objects or unusual cable presence should be taken as an indication that explosives are present. Work should be stopped immediately and the police informed.

Well-established procedures already exist for competent military personnel to deal with unexploded devices.

9.8.4 Anthrax

Anthrax spores may lie dormant within soil, or in horse or cow hair binders in old lath and plaster, for many decades.

When such spores are disturbed, they still have the capacity to cause severe environmental problems. You should regard all premises (such as old tanneries, wool sorting stations and premises used in connection with animal carcasses, hides, bones, offal, or for the production of gelatine and old lath and plaster walls or ceilings) as high-risk areas where anthrax spores may be present.

Defra will be able to supply advice as to whether contaminated carcasses have been buried on old farm sites.

Where it is suspected that anthrax spores may be present, it is essential for everyone on the site to exercise good personal hygiene and use impervious personal protective clothing, including gloves. Any cuts and scratches must be adequately covered. As an additional safeguard, advice on immunisation and general health procedures should be sought from a doctor.

9.8.5 Radiation

Before starting work on a site where any work involving radioactive materials has previously taken place (such as hospitals) or where radioactive contamination (whether natural or artificial) may be present, consult the HSE and the relevant environment agency.

It will be necessary to use specialist contractors for all aspects of both the removal of substances and decontamination where radioactive materials are being dealt with.

9.8.6 Persistent organic pollutants

Persistent organic pollutants (POPs) are poisonous chemical substances that break down slowly in the environment, bioaccumulate (build up in the body or in organisms over time) through the food chain, and pose a risk of causing adverse effects to human health and the environment. POPs can be transported across international boundaries, far from their sources, even to regions where they have never been used or produced. The manufacturer, sale and use of products containing POPs is now banned.

The ecosystems and indigenous people of the Arctic are particularly at risk because of the long-range environmental transportation and bio-magnification of these substances. Consequently, POPs pose a threat to the environment and to human health all over the globe.

09

CONTENTS

Waste and material management

Supporting
INFORMATION

GT700 Toolbox talks / supporting checklists and forms

Toolbox talks on some of these topics are available in the GT700 publication. Supporting checklists and forms covering some of these topics are available on our companion website.

WASTE AND MATERIAL MANAGEMENT

Summary of waste and material management legislation and guidance

This list is not exhaustive and only includes legislation mentioned in this section of GE700.

Legislation and guidance	Enforcement agencies*				
	EA	LA	NIEA	NRW	SEPA
Acts (primary legislation)					
Environmental Protection Act	✓		✓	✓	✓
Waste and Contaminated Land Order			✓		
Regulations (secondary legislation)					
Controlled Waste (England and Wales) Regulations	✓	✓		✓	
Controlled Waste (Registration of Carriers and Seizure of Vehicles) Regulations		✓	✓		✓
Waste Batteries and Accumulators Regulations	✓		✓	✓	✓
Waste Regulations (Northern Ireland)		✓	✓		
Waste (England and Wales) Regulations	✓	✓		✓	
Waste (Scotland) Regulations		✓			✓
Hazardous Waste					
Hazardous Waste (Amendment No. 2) Regulations (Northern Ireland)		✓	✓		
Hazardous Waste (England and Wales) Regulations	✓	✓		✓	
Special Waste Regulations		✓			✓
Landfill					
Landfill Regulations (Northern Ireland)		✓	✓		
Landfill (England and Wales) Regulations	✓	✓		✓	
Landfill (Scotland) Regulations		✓			✓
Permits and Licences					
Environmental Permitting (England and Wales) Regulations	✓	✓		✓	
Waste Management Licencing (Amendment) Regulations (Northern Ireland)		✓	✓		
Waste Management Licencing (Scotland) Regulations		✓			✓
Guidance					
HSE publications and guidance					
Net Regs Environmental guidance					
SEPA guidance notes					
Waste Resource Action Programme (WRAP) hosted by CIRIA					
Organisations with information and guidance on their websites	✓	✓	✓	✓	✓

*Key

CIRIA	Construction Industry Research and Information Association
EA	Environment Agency
HSE	Health and Safety Executive
LA	Local Authorities
NIEA	Northern Ireland Environment Agency
NRW	Natural Resources Wales
SEPA	Scottish Environment Protection Agency

10

Overview

The most recent data from 2018 for non-hazardous and construction and demolition waste from the Department for the Environment, Farming and Rural Affairs (Defra) established that the UK produced 137.8 million tonnes of construction, demolition and excavation (CD&E) waste (in England, this was 119.4 million tonnes).

This chapter gives a general overview of the legal framework for the regulation of waste. It outlines how waste is defined and classified for the purpose of disposal and introduces the waste hierarchy. This chapter also gives you an overview of the permits that are required for the management of waste and the documentation required under the duty of care for its safe and environmentally-sound disposal. It provides an overview of various types of waste, including hazardous waste, Waste Electrical and Electronic Equipment (WEEE) and waste batteries.

10.1 Introduction

Of the over 100 million tonnes of waste produced by the CD&E sector per year, a proportion ends up in landfill sites. This waste has further environmental impacts after its disposal (such as the generation of greenhouse gases) that contribute to climate change.

Waste is a by-product of the inefficient use of valuable resources that could be reused on site or recycled. The simple operation of cutting a brick in half, or sawing the end off a piece of wood, is producing waste if that half brick or off-cut is not reused. Waste costs money to produce, in terms of the materials thrown away, and also money to dispose of, along with costs for the skip or lorry to remove it. Landfill tax rates will continue to rise to provide a financial incentive to reduce the amount of waste being sent to landfill.

Research carried out on housing projects has indicated that the true cost of disposing of the material is around ten times the cost of the skip. This includes the labour to fill the skip and the cost of purchasing the materials in the first place. Typically skips account for 0.5% of the build cost. Overall waste and its disposal can amount to around 5% of the project costs. This is valuable lost profit for the project. Making the best use of materials and resources is therefore essential in reducing waste costs.

The incorrect or inappropriate disposal of waste (such as fly-tipping) is illegal, unsightly and can damage the environment for many years. To tackle the problem of waste crime, Local Authorities (LAs) have the power to stop and search vehicles thought to be involved in illegal waste activity. The Environmental Improvement Plan (EIP), Goal 5, sets out targets and commitments to maximise resources and minimise waste, as follows.

- Eliminate avoidable waste by 2050 and double resource productivity by 2050.
- Explore options for the near elimination of biodegradable municipal waste to landfill from 2028.
- Eliminate avoidable plastic waste by 2042.
- Seek to eliminate waste crime by 2042.
- To halve 'residual' waste (excluding major mineral waste) produced per person by 2042 (waste that is sent to landfill, put through incineration or used in energy recovery in the UK, or that is sent overseas to be used in energy recovery).

The residual waste target is underpinned by the following interim targets, to be achieved by 31st January 2028:

- Reduce residual waste (excluding major mineral waste) produced per person by 24%, and in total tonnes by 21%.
- Reduce municipal residual waste per person by 29%.
- Reduce residual municipal food waste per person by 50%.
- Reduce residual municipal plastic waste per person by 45%.
- Reduce residual municipal paper and card waste per person by 26%.
- Reduce residual municipal metal waste per person by 42%.
- Reduce residual municipal glass waste per person by 48%.

Insufficient attention to the generation of waste at design stage, during procurement and poor control and supervision by site management, including improper or unsafe systems of work on site, increase the production of waste. Waste materials lying around on a construction site are a major safety hazard, increasing the fire risk and the potential for trips and slips, which can have a huge impact on both people's work and personal lives. Legislation imposes conditions and obligations on how contractors in the construction industry must plan, manage and dispose of any waste produced during work both on and off site.

10.1.1 Waste regulation authorities

The principal waste regulation authorities are the Environment Agency (EA) in England, the Northern Ireland Environment Agency (NIEA), the Scottish Environment Protection Agency (SEPA), and Natural Resources Wales (NRW). The agencies took over these functions from LAs, and their responsibilities include dealing with the application and enforcement of waste management licences, permits and exemptions, waste carriers' licences and the duty of care regime *(refer to 10.9)*. LAs are also responsible for dealing with local air pollution control (LAPC) matters related to waste (such as the issue of permits for crushing equipment).

WASTE AND MATERIAL MANAGEMENT

 The improper disposal of waste is illegal, and can lead to prosecution and even imprisonment. The maximum penalty for waste crime is a £50,000 fine and up to 12 months' imprisonment in the magistrates' court, or five years' imprisonment and an unlimited fine at the crown court.

If someone finds your waste flytipped, and you cannot prove that you have not dumped it and that you have complied with all the necessary requirements, you could be fined up to £50,000 and face up to five years in prison. Failure to produce waste transfer notes can result in a fixed penalty notice of £300.

10.2   Important points

● Producers of waste must correctly identify whether surplus materials are waste and classify it as non-hazardous or hazardous using a waste classification code, also referred to as LoW (List of Waste) or EWC (European Waste Catalogue) code.

● With reference to the standard industry classification (SIC) code, producers of waste must correctly identify the SIC and which area of construction the waste originates from (for example, construction of buildings, civil engineering or specialist construction activities).

● Producers of waste have a legal duty of care to ensure that it is passed on to an authorised person who has the correct technical competence and holds a relevant environmental permit or licence.

● All contractors who carry or collect construction and demolition waste must have a waste carrier's licence.

● All waste transfers must be supported by the correct document (a controlled waste transfer note) for non-hazardous waste. The transfer of hazardous waste requires a consignment note. Both of these documents must include a declaration that the producer of the waste has considered the waste hierarchy in deciding to dispose of the material.

● In Wales, producers of 500 kg or more of hazardous waste (such as oils or asbestos) must register their premises with the NRW. Failure to do so could result in a fine of up to £5,000.

● All waste treatment or disposal facilities should have an environmental permit (England and Wales) or waste management licence (Northern Ireland and Scotland) unless they have a registered exemption from the EA, NRW, NIEA or SEPA.

● Where materials are treated or processed on site before being suitable for putting back into the works, consideration must be given as to whether this activity requires an environmental permit or registered exemption. Compliance with schemes, including the Contaminated Land: Application In Real Environments (CL:AIRE) Code of Practice or the waste and resources action programme (WRAP) quality protocol for the production of aggregates from inert waste, could avoid the requirement of an environmental permit for reuse of the processed material.

10.3   Waste hierarchy

Article 4 of the revised Waste Framework Directive (WFD) (2008/98/EC) requires that all reasonable measures should be taken to prevent waste and consider the waste hierarchy when waste is transferred.

The waste hierarchy is a series of steps for dealing with waste in order of priority and signifies the relative environmental benefits that can be made at each stage.

The waste hierarchy shows that the highest priority is waste prevention or reduction so that the need for other options (such as reuse, recycling and energy recovery) would be dramatically reduced.

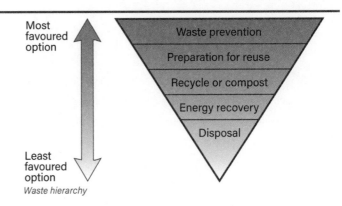

Waste hierarchy

 The Waste (England and Wales) Regulations now require that you declare on the waste transfer documentation that you have considered the waste hierarchy in the management of the waste.

Examples of applying the waste hierarchy on a construction project for waste reduction could include the following.

● Prevention or minimisation.
  – Designing the project to suit standard product sizes to avoid site cutting.
  – Designing the project's landscape levels to avoid excavation materials going off site.
  – Specification to allow the use of recycled materials.
  – Pre-assembling components off site or using pre-cast sections.
  – Not over-ordering materials.
  – Reducing the amount of packaging.
  – Ordering materials at the size required, to avoid off-cuts.
  – Promoting employee awareness of environmental matters.
  – Requiring sub-contractors to have a waste management policy.
  – Not over-excavating.

10

- Reuse.
  - Reusing soil for landscaping.
  - Using off-cuts of timber for alternative uses.
  - Using brick rubble as hardcore.
  - Investigating local environmental or construction work where other materials might be reused.

- Recycling.
  - Crushing waste concrete to use as hardcore.
  - Recycling asphalt planings as road sub-base or temporary surfacing.
  - Recycling scrap metal, glass and waste oil.
  - Segregating waste materials to a separate well-planned area.
  - Recycling timber by donation for educational use or social enterprise.
  - Recycling office waste (such as paper, cans and plastics).

- Recovery.
  - Sending waste for composting or for energy recovery (such as timber off site to be shredded for use as biomass fuel, or composting).

- Disposal.
  - Sending canteen or office waste for disposal to a local landfill site.

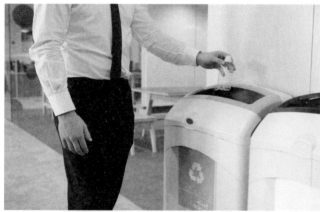

Office recycling

Plasterboard recycling

Segregated waste

Segregated waste streams

 The recycling or treatment of waste on or off site is likely to require a waste management permit (England and Wales) or licence (Northern Ireland and Scotland), or registered exemption *(for further details on waste management permitting refer to 10.12).*

 Social enterprise for waste – National Community Wood Recycling Project

The National Community Wood Recycling Project (NCWRP) was founded in 2003 to help set up and develop a nationwide network of wood recycling social enterprises.

The National Builders Collection Scheme was set up to market the service to building companies in 2010, allowing the NCWRP to become self-funding and offer support to enterprises without the need for grants or fundraising.

There are currently 30 enterprises operating across the country, collectively forming Community Wood recycling, and collecting around 20,000 tonnes of wood every year.

 The NCWRP website provides details of locations where wood can be recycled.

10.4   Site waste management plans

SWMPs on construction projects used to be a legal requirement under the Waste Management Plan Regulations. However, in line with the Government's Red Tape Challenge, designed to remove unnecessary legislation to free up businesses, **the regulations were repealed**.

The aim of an SWMP was to reduce the amount of waste produced on construction sites, by setting out how building materials and any resulting waste was managed during a project. The plan was updated during the construction stages, which recorded and confirmed how materials were reused, recycled or disposed of. The introduction of the regulations had aimed to:

1. improve resource efficiency and reduce waste

2. prevent fly-tipping.

SWMPs are often now referred to as resource management plans (RMPs). Whilst there is no legal requirement for an SWMP, implementing one helps manage materials more effectively and helps to reduce material waste and cost savings. Regardless of whether an SWMP (or RMP) is used, all construction companies have a duty of care towards managing their waste under section 34 of the Environmental Protection Act. An SWMP/RMP can raise the profile of waste planning, improve the environmental awareness of the workforce, and ensure compliance with the regulations.

10.5   The Environment Targets (Residual Waste) (England) Regulations

The government published new legislation, the Environmental Targets (Residual Waste) (England) Regulations 2023, which came into force on 30th January 2023 to address the residual waste volumes needing to be halved by 2042 in a target based on 2019 numbers.

The regulations, which extend to England and Wales but apply to England, come under the Environment Act 2021, which requires the setting of deliverable waste targets to help government improve the state of the environment on land and at sea. This includes having less waste alongside a more sustainable use of resources. These regulations are expected to have significant implications for waste policy and the development of recycling and residual waste facilities in years to come.

The waste target is for the reduction of residual waste (excluding major mineral wastes), on a kilogramme per capita basis, by 50% by 2042 from 2019 levels. This will be measured as a reduction from the 2019 level, which was updated to 574 kg per capita following updated evidence received by Defra following consultation. The residual waste long-term target is that by the end of 31st December 2042 the total mass of residual waste for 2042 does not exceed 287 kg per head of population in England.

10.6   Defining waste

Waste is defined in the Environmental Protection Act as: any substance which constitutes a scrap material, an effluent or other unwanted surplus arising from the application of any process or any substance or article, which requires to be disposed of, which has been broken, worn out, contaminated or otherwise spoiled.

In practice, however, this definition has been tested by case law; determining whether or not a substance is waste depends on applying the right legal tests. A substance can be classed as waste even if the producer still has a use for it or if other people are prepared to pay for it. This is important because whether or not a material is waste determines whether a complex body of legal rules and restrictions govern what can be done with it.

Surplus materials are generally not waste while they remain as the original manufactured product and do not need to be re-processed. However, construction or demolition waste that has been generated as part of the works could be classified as waste until it has been processed (for example, crushed and screened) and recovered back into the permanent works. In these cases there will be various requirements to demonstrate that the material has achieved an **end of waste** status.

Materials that meet the end of waste test must satisfy the following criteria.

- The material must be converted into a distinct and marketable product.

- It can be used in the same way as an ordinary soil or aggregate.

- It can be used without creating any negative environmental effects.

Aggregates manufactured from construction and demolition waste complying with the WRAP quality protocol, for example, can normally demonstrate that the material has achieved an end of waste status. Likewise, complying with the CL:AIRE Development Industry Definition of Waste Code of Practice (DoW CoP) will also help you to achieve end of waste status for the treatment and use of contaminated excavated materials *(for more on the CL:AIRE DoW CoP, refer to 10.13 and to Chapter E08 Resource efficiency, 8.5.2.)*

10.7   Describing and classifying waste

Wastes will always fall into one of four categories.

- Always non-hazardous, known as **absolute non-hazardous** (for example, clean bricks or glass).

- Always hazardous known as **absolute hazardous** (for example, insulating materials containing asbestos).

- May, or may not, be hazardous and need to be assessed known as **mirror hazardous** and **mirror non-hazardous** (for example, contaminated soils).

10

What makes a waste hazardous is whether it contains any hazardous substances above certain thresholds that make it display a certain hazardous property. Fifteen different hazardous properties exist, from HP1 to HP15, together with persistent organic pollutant (POP) criteria (for example, HP1 is explosive and HP6 is acute toxicity). The threshold concentration levels for the relevant hazardous properties are defined within the guidance on the classification and assessment of waste (WM3). Waste can be referred to as **active**, for hazardous waste, or **inactive**, for inert waste (such as rocks and bricks).

 For further information refer to the joint agency technical guidance *Waste classification – Guidance on the classification and assessment of waste* **(WM3).**

Where there is doubt over the presence or levels of hazardous materials the waste must first be classified as both mirror hazardous and mirror non-hazardous. Further testing then has to take place to confirm the presence and levels of hazardous content to ensure the final classification is accurate.

The most appropriate method of classifying waste, where it needs to be assessed, is to identify the hazardous constituents or chemicals in the waste, determine the hazard statement codes and hazardous properties of these substances and then to use their concentrations to identify whether they exceed the threshold levels of any of the hazardous properties. The safety documentation supplied with any product should provide sufficient information to make this assessment. For contaminated soils, however, detailed testing would need to be carried out by competent staff.

The waste classification code, also referred to as **LoW (List of Waste)** or **EWC (European Waste Catalogue)** codes, are classification codes for common types of waste. Arranged in 20 sections, Section 17 contains the codes for construction and demolition waste.

 Appendix A includes the full Section 17 list of wastes codes relating to construction and demolition waste.

The list of wastes refers to hazardous and non-hazardous entries. Where an entry is marked with an asterisk it is classified as **hazardous waste** if it meets one of the following criteria.

- The hazardous entry makes no reference to hazardous substances (for example, 17 06 05* construction materials containing asbestos). These types of entries are always hazardous and are called **absolute hazardous entries (AH)**.

- The hazardous entry refers to a waste containing hazardous substances where the concentration levels of these hazardous substances exceed the threshold limits (for example, 17 05 03* soil and stones containing hazardous substances). These entries are called **mirror hazardous entries (MH)** as it depends on the concentration of hazardous substances to determine whether they are hazardous or not. Wastes containing hazardous substances below the threshold limits are non-hazardous.

- The lists of wastes also contain **mirror non-hazardous entries (MN)**. The mirror non-hazardous usually (but not always) has a defined link to its mirror using the words 'other than those mentioned in....' (for example, 07-01-12 sludges from on-site effluent treatment other than those mentioned in 07-01-11 MN).

e.g. Typical construction wastes from Section 17 of the list of wastes

- Bricks – 17 01 02 Non-hazardous.
- Concrete – 17 01 01 Non-hazardous.
- Wood – 17 02 01 Non-hazardous.
- Plasterboard – 17 08 02 Non-hazardous (but must be segregated from other wastes).
- Insulation containing asbestos – 17 06 01* Mirror hazardous. (Will be hazardous if concentrations exceed thresholds.)
- Contaminated soil – 17 05 03* Mirror hazardous. (Will be hazardous if concentrations exceed thresholds.)

Other types of construction wastes not covered in Section 17

- Waste hydraulic oil – 13 01 13* Absolute hazardous.
- Mixed canteen waste – 20 03 01 Non-hazardous.

10

The disposal of hazardous waste arising from construction operations, or from contaminated land, is dealt with under the Hazardous Waste Regulations (in England, Northern Ireland and Wales) or the Special Waste Regulations (in Scotland) *(for further information refer to 10.11)*.

 All waste transfer documentation must include the relevant EWC six-digit code that describes and categorises the waste, and the relevant SIC code describing the area of construction from where the waste originated.

For the purpose of disposal of **waste to landfill** there are three classes of waste.

Inert waste that will not decompose to produce greenhouse gases (such as rubble, concrete and glass).

Non-hazardous waste that will rot and decompose (such as timber, food and paper) and does not contain hazardous substances.

WASTE AND MATERIAL MANAGEMENT

Hazardous waste that has substances in sufficient concentration to make it possess one or more of the 15 hazardous properties (such as explosive (HP1) or acute toxicity (HP6)) and is hazardous to human health or the environment (such as asbestos or oil).

There are strict criteria for the acceptance of waste at each of these three types of landfill site. Certain types of waste, particularly contaminated soil, would have to be tested in order to demonstrate that it meets the relevant waste acceptance criteria. The Landfill Directive introduces a hierarchy of waste characterisation and testing known as the **waste acceptance procedures**. The levels are shown below.

Level 1. Basic characterisation. A thorough determination, according to standardised analysis and behaviour-testing methods, of the leaching behaviour and/or characteristic properties of the waste.

Level 2. Compliance testing. A periodic testing of regularly arising wastes by simpler standardised analysis and behaviour-testing methods to determine whether a waste complies with permit conditions, and whether a waste with known properties has changed significantly. The tests focus on the main variables and behaviour identified by basic characterisation.

Level 3. On-site verification. This constitutes checking methods to confirm that a waste is the same as that which has been subjected to compliance testing and that which is described in the accompanying documents. It may merely consist of a visual inspection of a load of waste before and after unloading at the landfill site.

 Before sending waste to landfill, waste producers and landfill operators must ensure that they know all of the properties of the waste, relevant to its potential for pollution or harm to health, and the options for the management of the waste.

There are certain types of waste that are banned from disposal to landfill (shown below). These must either be recovered, recycled or disposed of in other ways (for example, incineration).

- Any liquid waste.

- Infectious medical or veterinary waste.

- Whole or shredded used tyres.

- Waste that might cause a problem in the landfill (such as hot or chemically active waste).

- Any waste that does not meet the waste acceptance criteria for that class of landfill.

The term **difficult waste** has come into common use, and applies to wastes that require handling in a particular way. It is not used in legislation, but is used to cover a grey area of wastes. Although not classed as hazardous by reference to the Hazardous Waste Regulations, this type of waste is nevertheless difficult to dispose of. Examples of difficult waste are shown below.

- **Invasive plants** that are waste materials, both soil and plant matter (contaminated, for example, with Japanese knotweed or giant hogweed), which can only be disposed of at sites that are specifically licensed to receive them.

- **Contaminated soil** that is a mixture of soils, stones, rubble and polluting substances, which could be hazardous depending on thresholds, and could be a range of things left over from former use of the site.

- **Gypsum and plasterboard wastes** that, when mixed with biodegradable waste, can produce hydrogen sulphide gas in landfill, which is both toxic and odorous.

 Gypsum and plasterboard waste

The land filling of gypsum and other high sulphate-bearing wastes, together with biodegradable waste, has been prohibited. All gypsum waste should be segregated from biodegradable waste before being sent to landfill. It should be noted that plasterboard waste itself (unless contaminated) is not hazardous waste but must be segregated.

10.8 Treatment of waste

The Environmental Permitting Regulations (England and Wales), Landfill Regulations (Northern Ireland) and the Landfill Regulations (Scotland) state that non-hazardous waste must now be treated before being sent to landfill. In practical terms, *treatment* is applying the waste hierarchy to reduce the quantity of waste that ends up in landfill. Treatment must satisfy all three criteria of a three point test, as shown in the table on the right.

1.	Be a physical, thermal, chemical, or biological process (including sorting).
2.	Change the characteristics of the waste.
3.	Be carried out in order to: – reduce the volume of the waste – reduce the hazardous nature of the waste – facilitate handling of the waste – enhance recovery of the waste.

On construction sites, in practical terms, this can be achieved by setting up segregated skips and separating out **(sorting)** any wastes that can be reused or recycled, which will change the **characteristics of the original waste stream**. This in turn will aid in **reducing the volume** of the waste, **facilitating the handling** of the waste and **enhancing recovery** of the waste destined for landfill.

Hazardous wastes are required to be stored and disposed of separately from non-hazardous wastes. Sending your waste to a transfer station or recycling facility, for sorting and recovery prior to the residual waste being sent to landfill, will also satisfy these treatment requirements.

Excavated materials that are to be treated on or off site are generally considered to be waste and the treatment facility operator must have an appropriate environmental permit or register a waste exemption allowing that particular treatment of the excavated materials *(for further explanation of this issue refer to 10.11, 10.12 in this chapter, and to 8.5.2 and 8.5.3 in Chapter E08 Resource efficiency)*.

Persistent organic pollutants (POPs) are poisonous chemical substances that break down slowly and get into food chains as a result.

Hexabromocyclododecane (HBCD) has now been listed as a persistent organic pollutant (POP).

Waste containing POPs should be destroyed at end of life.

For polystyrene blocks used in buildings that use the flame retardant HBCD, the best way of ensuring destruction is by incineration.

In England, municipal waste incinerators are likely to be sufficient to destroy HBCD.

10.8.1   Waste (Scotland) Regulations

These Scottish Government regulations expand the duty of care requirements, over and above those required in England, Northern Ireland and Wales, and require all waste producers, including construction companies, to present dry recyclable material for separate collection. To ensure waste producers can comply with this requirement, the waste industry in Scotland has to provide services that enable the separate collection of dry recyclables such as glass, metals, plastics, paper and cardboard.

Across the UK, food businesses, in urban areas, producing large amounts of food waste (> 50 kg per week) are required to present that food waste for separate collection. Construction canteens come under the definition of a food business.

Segregated waste streams

In Scotland and Northern Ireland the regulation has been amended and this requirement now extends to smaller food businesses that produce between 5 kg and 50 kg per week. Only businesses producing very small amounts of food waste (< 5 kg per week) are exempt from the duty altogether. There is an expectation that this new requirement will be expanded to cover the whole of the UK in the near future.

The use of macerators to dispose of food waste in the sewer system has been banned from 1 January 2016, except for domestic premises and food producers in rural areas.

10.9   Duty of care and waste carrier registration

If you are involved in managing waste you have a legal duty of care. The duty of care applies to everyone involved in handling the waste, from the person who produces it to the person who finally recovers or disposes of it.

You have a legal responsibility to ensure that you produce, store, transport and dispose of your business waste without harming the environment. Duty of care is one of the main ways to avoid environmental harm and combat fly-tipping and means that:

● waste has to be stored in a secure location and measures taken to prevent its escape

● waste has to be passed to an authorised person holding a valid licence or permit

● any waste passed to an authorised person must be supported by the relevant documentation.

10.9.1   Registration of waste carriers, brokers and dealers (England and Wales)

The Waste Regulations (England and Wales) implement a system for the registration of:

● waste carriers (those who move waste)

● waste brokers (those who arrange the movement and/or disposal on behalf of others)

● waste dealers (those who use an agent to buy and sell waste).

It is possible for a single registration to cover all of this work.

There are two classes of registration, known as lower tier and upper tier.

10.9.1.1   Lower tier

Those registered in the lower tier are known as **specified persons**. This group includes all those who are currently registered as professionally exempt. In general this refers to waste authorities, charities, voluntary organisations and those who only manage wastes from agricultural premises, animal by-product wastes or wastes from mines or quarries.

10

WASTE AND MATERIAL MANAGEMENT

Lower tier registration is not an option for construction and demolition companies that move their own waste. The guidance states that: anyone who normally and regularly carries their own business waste (excluding construction and demolition waste) will need to register in the upper tier. There is currently no fee for lower tier registration; the registration will be valid until it is revoked or cancelled.

10.9.1.2 Upper tier

If you are a construction or demolition company and you move your own waste you must register in the upper tier. There will be a fee payable for upper tier registration. Upper tier registration will be valid for three years unless it is revoked or cancelled. If you are a waste carrier, broker or dealer but you are not a specified person, you will need to register in the upper tier.

10.9.2 Registration of waste carriers (Northern Ireland)

A similar system of registration, with slight differences, applies in Northern Ireland under the Controlled Waste (Registration of Carriers and Seizure of Vehicles) Regulations (Northern Ireland).

 An application for registration as a carrier, broker or dealer can be made on the Environment Agency, Natural Resources Wales or Northern Ireland Environment Agency websites or by downloading the appropriate form.

10.9.3 Registration of waste carriers (Scotland)

The Controlled Waste (Registration of Carriers and Seizure of Vehicles) Regulations in Scotland require that if you transport waste within the UK, in the course of your business or in any other way for profit, you must register as a carrier of waste with the local waste regulation authority. You must register even if you only carry your own company's waste or carry waste on an infrequent basis. This applies whether you are a self-employed contractor, part of a partnership or a company.

Registration only needs to be made in the area where your company has its head office. All other offices will be covered by this one registration. Application for registration as a waste carrier must be made on the prescribed form, which is obtainable from the local waste regulation authority office. If you have applied for registration but have not yet received the documentation, you will be deemed to be registered and may carry waste.

 The law demands that waste carriers keep a copy of their registration document on their vehicle. Do not accept photocopies of registration documents as proof of registration. If you have any doubt as to whether the carrier is registered or not, ask the appropriate waste regulation authority.

10.10 Controlled waste and transfer notes

All waste subject to the provisions of the Environmental Protection Act is known as controlled waste and includes waste from domestic, commercial and industrial premises as well as hazardous waste. Under the duty of care waste must be passed to an authorised person (a holder of a waste carrier or waste management permit or licence).

When non-hazardous waste is transferred to an authorised person this must be supported by a waste transfer note. This also applies even if you have produced and carry waste yourself. The transfer of hazardous waste must be supported by a consignment note *(refer to 10.11)*.

 Refer to Appendix B for a sample of a controlled waste transfer note.

Whenever you pass non-hazardous waste on to someone else, you will have to declare on the waste transfer note that you have applied all reasonable measures to apply the waste management hierarchy. The duty of care waste transfer note must:

- include a declaration that you have taken all measures to apply the waste management hierarchy
- include the appropriate SIC code, identifying the area of construction that generated the waste
- give a description of the waste, including the six-digit EWC code
- state the quantity
- state how the waste is contained, whether loose or in a container and, if in a container, the kind of container
- identify the carrier of the waste
- state the date, time and location of transfer
- identify the disposal site
- contain your signature and the signature of the authorised person receiving your waste.

A copy of the transfer note must be kept for a minimum of two years. A copy must also be given to the disposal site representative, who will sign the documents to say where, when and how the waste will or has been disposed of.

10

If you use a registered carrier to dispose of your waste for you, the transfer note must contain all the points described above and, in addition, state the following.

● Name and address of the carrier, their licence registration number and issuing authority.

● Place of transfer.

If you use a registered carrier to remove your waste, they will raise and distribute the necessary documentation and will:

● give you a copy to keep

● keep a copy for themselves

● deliver your waste and a copy of the document to the management at the disposal site.

 You must keep all controlled, non-hazardous waste transfer documentation (such as waste transfer notes and consignment notes) and records accessible for two years.

10.11   Hazardous waste and consignment notes

 Sites producing or storing less than 500 kg per year must comply with the Hazardous Waste Regulations (England and Wales). There is no requirement to register your site in England, Northern Ireland or Scotland.

 For further information visit the Government legislation website.

The Hazardous Waste Regulations in England, Northern Ireland and Wales, and the Special Waste Regulations in Scotland, require that all hazardous waste must be segregated from non-hazardous waste.

The following controls should be adopted to comply with the regulations.

● Different types of hazardous wastes should be segregated, to identify the quantities and types on the hazardous waste consignment note.

● Mixing of different types of hazardous waste should be avoided as this may inadvertently create an explosive or fire risk, particularly in warm weather.

● The mixing of hazardous waste with non-hazardous waste to dilute the material below the threshold concentration is banned.

● Packaging or containers contaminated with hazardous substances should be treated as hazardous waste unless it can be shown that the concentration (including the packaging) is below the threshold limits.

Segregated hazardous waste

Where individual products are combined to form a substance (such as adhesives and resins) then each component should be considered for its hazardous properties and disposed of accordingly. Resins are often inert when set, so leaving materials to dry before disposal may make them non-hazardous.

10.11.1   Removal of hazardous waste

When hazardous waste is removed from site, a document called a **hazardous waste consignment note** (special waste consignment note in Scotland) must be prepared. The consignment note must stay with the hazardous waste until it reaches its final destination, and must be filled in first by the producer of the waste. The remaining parts will be completed depending on your role in the waste process (see below table).

In Scotland, a special waste consignment note must be obtained from the local office of the Scottish Environment Protection Agency (SEPA).

Your role	Part(s) you must complete
Producer	A and B
Holder (stores the waste)	A and B
Carrier (collects and transports the waste)	C
Consignor (hands the waste to the carrier)	D
Consignee (receives the waste for recycling or disposal)	E

10

WASTE AND MATERIAL MANAGEMENT

The hazardous waste consignment note must be completed in the following way. The producer must complete parts A and B, including:

- the consignment note code
- the address the waste is being removed from
- the process that gave rise to the waste, including the SIC code
- waste details, including:

- description of the waste
- LoW or EWC code
- quantity
- physical form

- the address the waste is being taken to
- the details of who produced the waste

- chemical components
- hazard code
- container type
- UN identification number.

The carrier must check the waste and journey details entered by the producer, and complete section C, including:

- vehicle and carrier details
- multiple collection details, if relevant.

The consignor must check sections A, B and C, and complete D, in the form of a consignor's certificate. They must keep one copy, pass one to the producer or holder, and hand the other back to the carrier. The carrier must then promptly deliver the waste to the consignee. On arrival, the carrier gives the consignee two copies, and they must then check and either accept or reject the waste. After checking the waste and the note to ensure it's correct and complete, the consignee completes part E, and enters:

- the EWC code
- the quantity of each code received
- whether the EWC code is accepted or rejected
- the waste management operation details.

The consignment note coding system for England and Wales was changed on 1 April 2016. The consignment note code is a unique code for each consignment of hazardous waste and is always in the same format of the first six letters or numbers of the company name, followed by a forward slash, and then five further letters or numbers (for example CJTILE/A0001).

10.11.2 Coding format for hazardous waste consignment notes

The part that applies to you depends on your role in the waste process, as follows in the below table. A consignment note code must be created (in the format XXXXXX/YYYYY) and entered onto the consignment note. The table shows the coding format for hazardous waste consignment notes in England and Wales.

Coding format for hazardous waste consignment notes		
Code	**Explanation**	**Example**
XXXXXX/	First six letters and/or numbers (not symbols or spaces) of the name of the company entered in Part A2 of the consignment note. This must be followed by a forward slash '/'. **Note:** *if your company name has less than six letters and/or numbers you must assign the letter 'Q' to the remaining characters.*	CJTILE/A0001
YYYYY	Exactly five digits made up of numbers and/or letters (not symbols or spaces) of your choice. **Note:** *each code can only be used once from the address in Part A2. You must change the 'YYYYY' to create a different code each time waste is consigned from that premises.*	
Additional letters		
An additional letter must be assigned at the end of the consignment note code for certain types of consignment: 'V' to waste removed from ships 'XXXXXX/YYYYYV' 'F' to fly-tipped waste 'XXXXXX/YYYYYF' 'D' to waste moving under a consignee return derogation 'XXXXXX/YYYYYD' 'P' to continuous piped waste 'XXXXXX/YYYYYP' Additional letters must also be assigned to rejected loads. The consignment note form contains two extra grey boxes for these additional letters.		

In Northern Ireland and Scotland, a copy of completed consignment notes must be received by NIEA or SEPA at least 72 hours before the waste is due to leave site.

Completed consignment notes are valid for 28 days after the anticipated date of collection.

 You must keep records of all hazardous waste documentation in a register for three years after the waste is transferred.

 For an example of a hazardous waste consignment note refer to Appendix C.

10.12   Environmental permits and exemptions

10.12.1 Environmental permitting in England and Wales

The Environmental Permitting Regulations (England and Wales) (EPR) combine the system of waste management licensing previously regulated under the Waste Management Licensing Regulations, and the system of permitting installations in the Pollution Prevention and Control Regulations (England and Wales). The EPR also now include the provision of permits to deal with groundwater protection, water discharges and flood defence activities.

 For further information on environmental permits visit the Government website.

 For further information on water protection refer to Chapter E07 Water management and pollution control.

The EPR specify which waste activities require an environmental permit and allow some waste operations to be exempt from requiring a permit: certain operations covered by other legislation are excluded from these permitting arrangements. An environmental permit is required for seven different classes of regulated facility, five of which relate to waste (the other two cover groundwater and water discharges).

Installations. Generally these are facilities at which industrial, waste and intensive farming, falling (mainly) under the Integrated Pollution Prevention and Control Directive, are carried out. These include landfill sites, asphalt plants and concrete batching plants.

Waste operation. Any other waste activity that is not defined as an installation will be classed as a waste operation. This includes the depositing, treatment or recycling of waste that is not exempt under the Environmental Permitting Regulations (such as waste transfer stations) including the treatment of contaminated land.

Mobile plant. Mobile equipment carrying out an activity listed in Schedule 1 of the EPR or a waste operation (such as crushers).

Mining waste operation. The management of mining extraction waste that may include the mining waste facility.

Radioactive substances. The keeping and management of radioactive material (including radioactive apparatus) or the storage and disposal of radioactive waste.

 It is an offence to operate a regulated facility without the relevant permit, or breach permit conditions. You could be fined up to £50,000 and imprisoned for up to five years for this offence.

Two types of permit can be applied for.

Standard permits for certain standard types of waste operation (such as a waste transfer station or mobile treatment plant for the treatment of waste soils). Each type of standard permit has standard rules and risk criteria that have to be met to comply with the permit.

Bespoke permits for more complex operations, which are specifically relevant to the waste facility or operation but cannot meet the criteria required in a standard permit.

If you can't meet the requirements of a standard permit then you may need to apply for a bespoke permit.

Exemptions are for works considered to be too trivial or below the threshold limit for a permit. Many need to be registered *(refer to 10.12.1.3)*.

10.12.1.1 Environmental permit applications

The starting point is to understand what type of waste activity will be carried out and who regulates it, and then to complete an application to the appropriate regulator. Part 2 of Schedule 1 to the EPR lists regulated facilities that are installations and mobile plant. They include Part A(1) work regulated by the EA (England) or NRW (Wales) and Part A(2) and Part B work regulated by LAs. The EA or NRW generally regulate higher-risk work that can pollute more than one media (such as water and air), whereas LAs regulate work that contributes to air pollution. The table below defines which authority is responsible for issuing permits for regulated facilities associated with construction.

10

Type of regulated facility	Regulator and where to send permit applications
Installations	
Landfill sites	EA or NRW
Asphalt plant	EA or NRW
Concrete batching plants	Local Authority
Waste operation	
Waste transfer stations	EA or NRW
Use of waste in construction	EA or NRW
Mobile plant	
Mobile plant for the treatment of contaminated soils	EA or NRW
Mobile plant for crushing and screening demolition waste	Local Authority

WASTE AND MATERIAL MANAGEMENT

Mobile plant for the treatment of waste soils and contaminated material is a waste operation regulated under a standard permit SR2008 No. 27 by the EA or NRW. In addition to holding the permit the operator is required to prepare a site-specific deployment form, which sets out in detail the type of technology used and specified work at the site. The treatment of contaminated soil and/or contaminated waters requires a mobile treatment permit (MTP).

A MTP is used to regulate a mobile plant activity that involves treatment either in situ or off site. The permit sets out the type and extent of work that can be carried out. A site-based permit has to be used where a mobile plant permit is not applicable. The environmental permit can be either a standard rules permit or a bespoke permit, depending upon the type of treatment and site location.

Operators who want to treat contaminated soil and/or contaminated waters using their mobile plant permit at a particular site must submit a site-specific deployment application (the deployment form and supporting information). The deployment application details site-specific information and potential impacts arising from the proposed use of the mobile plant. The operator must demonstrate that the activity will not cause pollution of the environment, harm to human health or serious detriment to local amenities.

Following treatment under a MTP the material would normally cease to be waste, providing it was excavated and treated on the site where it will be used or is part of a remediation cluster. Where this is not the case then an environmental permit or registered exemption would be required.

 For flowcharts providing further guidance on permitting the use or reuse of soils or aggregates refer to Appendix D.

The regulator has four months from receipt of the permit application and all supporting information to make a determination. You have the right of appeal to the Secretary of State should your permit not be granted, or the permit is granted but you are not happy with the conditions that have been imposed. Pre-application discussions with the regulator can help in improving the quality of permit applications so early contact with them is advisable. The Waste (England and Wales) Regulations cover a new permit condition to require waste to be managed in accordance with the waste hierarchy.

Only a person who is in control of a regulated facility may obtain or hold an environmental permit. This person is called the operator. To obtain an environmental permit you may have to prove that you have the appropriate technical competence *(refer to 10.12.1.2)* to be able to carry out the relevant work and fulfil the obligations of an operator.

The regulator will consider the following.

- Whether your management systems are adequate.
- If your site is run by someone who is technically competent.
- Any convictions that you, or other persons in your business, may have for pollution offences.
- If you have taken steps to meet the possible costs of the duties of the permit.

10.12.1.2 Technical competence

Certain types of waste management activity require the operator to demonstrate technical competence. They are called relevant waste operations. These include, for example, landfill sites, transfer stations and certain work involving hazardous waste.

You will be able to show that you are a technically competent operator if you can satisfy one of the following.

- Compliance with an approved industry scheme. There are currently two approved schemes for operators of relevant waste operations, the:
    1. Chartered Institution of Wastes Management (CIWM) or Waste Management Industry Training and Advisory Board (WAMITAB) scheme
    2. Environmentally Sensitive Areas/EU scheme.
- Holding an appropriate certificate of technical competence (CoTC) from the WAMITAB, which issues a range of certificates for the managers of most types of waste management site. This can be checked on the WAMITAB CoTC database.
- You have previously completed an environmental assessment for non-CoTC work.

10.12.1.3 Exemptions from environmental permitting in England and Wales

There are a number of exemptions from environmental permitting for certain waste activities that are not seen as a threat to the environment. The general requirements and descriptions of these exemptions are set out in Schedule 3 of the Environmental Permitting Regulations.

The Environmental Permitting Regulations have significantly changed the descriptions and references for exemptions, which are now grouped into four categories.

Use of waste. This includes the recovery or reuse of waste for a purpose. These exemptions will have a 'U' reference (for example, *U1 – Use of waste in construction*).

Treatment of waste. This includes the treatment of material for the purpose of recovery. These exemptions will have a 'T' reference (for example, *T5 – Screening and blending of waste for the purposes of producing an aggregate or soil and associated prior treatment*). Note that some wastes produced under this exemption may then be used under another exemption (such as the production of aggregates) that is then used under a *U1 – Use of waste in construction exemption*.

Disposal of waste. This includes the disposal of certain types of waste onto land. These exemptions will have a 'D' reference (for example, *D1 – Deposit of waste from dredging of inland waters*).

Storage of waste. This includes the storage of waste at a location other than where it was produced pending its recovery or disposal. These exemptions will have an 'S' reference (for example, *S2 – Storage of waste in a secure place*).

 Refer to Appendix E for materials and quantity thresholds for U1 or T5 exemptions.

These exemptions generally exclude hazardous waste and there will be conditions on most exemptions granted. Some examples of the conditions included in the exemption are shown below.

- Limits on the quantities and time periods for the temporary storage of waste produced on site for reuse on that site.
- Limits on the quantities for the spreading, on land, of waste soil.
- Certain other precautions that must be taken.

You may deal with waste under an exemption subject to the conditions imposed, but you must make sure that you do not pollute the environment or cause harm to anyone's health. To obtain a waste management exemption under Schedule 3 of the Environmental Permitting Regulations, an application must be made, together with the appropriate fee, to the correct waste regulation authority. In most cases this is the EA or NRW.

However, if you want to crush bricks, tiles and concrete you may need to register a *T7 – Treatment of waste bricks, tiles and concrete by crushing, grinding or reducing in size* exemption with your Local Authority. Also note that the equipment will need to have a valid mobile plant permit, which must be obtained from the Local Authority in which the business is situated. The information required varies considerably depending on the relevant exemption applied for. Notifications for more complex exemptions will generally require a form to be completed and must be supported by the following type of information.

- Name and address of applicant for the exemption.
- Location of the site where the waste activity is being carried out.
- Details of relevant planning permissions.
- Description, type and analysis of the waste.
- Intended use for the waste.
- The relevant fee.

A number of exemptions also have time constraints and cannot be renewed before the expiry date. For example, under a *U1 – Use of waste in construction* exemption, you cannot register more than once at any one place during the three-year period from first registration.

 For flowcharts providing further guidance on exemptions from permitting for the use or reuse of soils or aggregates refer to Appendix D.

10.12.2 Waste management licensing in Northern Ireland and Scotland

In Northern Ireland the waste licensing system is created under Part II of the Waste and Contaminated Land Order (Northern Ireland) and controlled through the Waste Management Licensing Regulations (Northern Ireland). In Scotland, the existing waste management licensing system is controlled under Section 33 of Part II of the Environmental Protection Act and the Waste Management Licensing Regulations (Scotland).

A waste management licence is required if you deposit, recover, treat or dispose of controlled waste. If you do any of these things without a licence, or a licence exemption, you could be fined and/or sent to prison. Obtaining a full waste management licence can be a lengthy and costly exercise. To obtain a waste management licence you have to prove that you are a fit and proper person. Applications for waste management licences should be made to NIEA or SEPA, who will consider the following.

- Any convictions that you, or other persons in your business, may have for pollution offences.
- If your site is run by someone who is technically competent.
- If you have taken steps to meet the possible costs of the duties of the licence.

10.12.2.1 Technical competence

In Northern Ireland the certificate of technical competence (CoTC) remains the primary means for managers of appropriate waste management facilities to demonstrate technical competence, in accordance with the Waste Management Licensing Regulations (Northern Ireland). In Scotland, under the Waste Management Licensing Regulations (Scotland) there is no longer a legal requirement for a technically-competent person to hold a CoTC. These were previously regulated by the WAMITAB under Waste Management Licensing Regulations.

CoTCs remain an appropriate qualification to demonstrate competence in Scotland and can be used on a voluntary basis. Operators in Scotland should contact their SEPA regulatory officer in the first instance to check other competence arrangements.

 For further details of competence requirements visit the WAMITAB website.

WASTE AND MATERIAL MANAGEMENT

10.12.2.2 Waste management licence applications

An application for a waste management licence can only be made if planning permission has been granted. To obtain a waste management licence, you should apply to the waste licensing office of NIEA or SEPA and ask the following questions.

> **? Questions for NIEA or SEPA**
>
> - How do you apply for the licence?
> - What information do they require?
> - How can you show that you are a fit and proper person, including technical competence?
> - How much is the application fee for the type of site you wish to run?

NIEA and SEPA have four months from when all information was received to consider the application. You have the right of appeal to the Secretary of State should your licence not be granted, or the licence is granted but you are not happy with the conditions imposed.

10.12.2.3 Exemptions from waste management licensing in Northern Ireland and Scotland

There are a number of waste management exemptions set out in Schedule 2 of the Waste Management Licensing Regulations (Northern Ireland) 2003 and Schedule 1 of the Waste Management Licensing (Scotland) Regulations 2011. These exemptions generally exclude hazardous waste and there will be conditions (examples below) on most exemptions granted.

- Limits on the quantities and time periods for the temporary storage of waste produced on site for reuse on that site.
- Limits on the quantities for the spreading, on land, of waste soil.
- Certain other precautions that must be taken.

You may deal with waste under an exemption subject to the conditions imposed, but you must make sure that you do not pollute the environment or cause harm to anyone's health.

To obtain a waste management exemption, an application must be made, together with the appropriate fee, if appropriate, to NIEA or SEPA. The information required varies considerably depending on the relevant exemption being applied for. NIEA and SEPA make a distinction between simple and complex exemptions and the notification process is different for each type. Notifications for complex exemptions will generally require a form to be completed and must be supported by the following type of information.

- Name and address of applicant for the exemption.
- Location of the site where the waste activity is being carried out.
- Details of relevant planning permissions.
- Description, type and analysis of the waste.
- Intended use for the waste.
- The relevant fee.

A number of the exemptions are also required to be renewed on an annual basis. Further advice should be sought from NIEA or SEPA.

10.13 Waste avoidance protocols

10.13.1 CL:AIRE Development industry Code of Practice (CoP)

The CL:AIRE (Contaminated Land: Applications in Real Environments) Code of Practice (CoP) has implications for waste management of contaminated land, but is essentially intended to avoid waste creation through treatments that convert materials for alternative uses to reduce landfill.

 For detailed information on the CL:AIRE CoP refer to Chapter E08 Resource efficiency.

10.13.2 WRAP quality protocol for the production of aggregates from inert waste

This protocol provides a formalised quality control procedure for the production of aggregates from recovered inert waste.

 For detailed information on the recycled aggregates quality protocol refer to Chapter E08 Resource efficiency.

10.14   Asbestos waste

There are slight differences in the respective legislation for England and Wales, Northern Ireland and Scotland. Contractors who work in any of these areas must comply with the relevant national legislation.

In essence, there is a duty of care placed on everyone in the waste disposal chain. Clients, whether they are commercial or domestic, have a responsibility to ensure that the waste is handled by competent and, as appropriate, registered contractors and is disposed of correctly. You can be prosecuted if waste is fly-tipped.

Where asbestos has been removed as part of a project, a prudent contractor would ensure that proof of disposal formed part of the information that was given to the client. In England, where a site waste management plan or demolition audit is utilised it should include details of the disposal of the asbestos waste and the waste carrier.

The principal contractor should ensure that disposal records are passed to the principal designer to ensure that this information is placed in the health and safety file to confirm that the asbestos has been transported and disposed of legally.

10.14.1 Classification

Asbestos waste is almost always hazardous waste (special waste in Scotland). There are two main scenarios to consider.

1. A single type of waste that has been separated.

2. A mixed waste.

For a single type of waste that has been separated, the hazardous waste concentration limit for asbestos in a waste is 0.1%, or more asbestos (weight for weight). All asbestos-containing materials (ACMs) used in building materials will contain asbestos at or above this concentration, and will be classed as hazardous waste.

For mixed waste, where more than one type of waste is present, mixing is prohibited. Dilution caused by mixing cannot be used to justify a non-hazardous classification. The waste containing the asbestos that is mixed with other waste should be assessed separately and would retain its hazardous status.

Examples of hazardous waste include the following.

● Another waste, such as soil, crushed secondary aggregate, or mixed construction or demolition waste containing one or more piece(s) of ACM, of a size visible to the naked eye.

● The mixing of a soil from a contaminated area of a site, containing 0.1% or more asbestos fibres, with other soil from the same site in a stockpile; on a gravimetric (weight for weight) basis.

Note: asbestos waste also includes contaminated building materials and tools that cannot be decontaminated; personal protective equipment; and damp rags used for cleaning. If in doubt, always treat waste as 'hazardous' or 'special'.

The below table shows the levels of asbestos, and what level is required to class it as hazardous across the UK nations.

England and Wales	● Asbestos waste is 'hazardous waste' when it contains more than 0.1% asbestos.
	● The Hazardous Waste (England and Wales) Regulations (HWR) apply.
	● You must complete a hazardous waste consignment note.
	● Contact the EA for more information in England, and the NRW in Wales.
Scotland	● Asbestos waste is 'special waste' when it contains more than 0.1% asbestos.
	● The Special Waste Amendment (Scotland) Regulations (SWAR) apply.
	● Complete a hazardous waste consignment note.
	● Contact the SEPA for more information.
England, Scotland and Wales	● All asbestos waste is subject to Schedule 2 of the Control of Asbestos Regulations, and most waste is subject to the Carriage of Dangerous Goods and Use of Transportable Pressure Equipment Regulations (CDG).
	● CDG does not apply to firmly-bound asbestos, asbestos cement, or articles with asbestos reinforcement which do not release hazardous or respirable fibres easily. However, HWR and SWAR still apply. CDG applies for all other asbestos waste.

  For further guidance on the classification and assessment of waste visit the Government website.

  For further information on asbestos refer to Chapter B09 Asbestos.

10.14.2 Management on the site of production

A refurbishment and demolition asbestos survey is required when any premises, or part of it, needs refurbishment or demolition. Where asbestos waste has been identified, details of the type, estimated quantities and disposal options should be included in the project site waste management plan (or alternative document if such a plan is not in place).

Asbestos cement sheets or other asbestos cement products should be double bagged in UN-approved packaging, with a Carriage of Dangerous Goods and Use of Transportable Pressure Equipment Regulations (CDG) hazard label and asbestos code information visible, or double-wrapped in 1,000-gauge polythene sheeting and labelled accordingly if they are being taken directly from the place of production to landfill (for example, not being taken to and stored temporarily at a contractor's premises or a transfer station). Alternatively, waste can be placed in a lockable skip, but it must be easily cleanable: it is unacceptable to throw sheeting over a standard skip.

Where a skip is used on site it must not be used for consolidating asbestos waste from other sites, as this would introduce more complex hazardous waste requirements. The site would then be recognised as a hazardous waste transfer station requiring an environmental permit.

Skips containing asbestos should be lockable and secured at all times. It is considered good practice to double bag or wrap waste from internal work to ensure that no asbestos is dropped when the waste is carried outside.

Labelling requirement of asbestos waste

If a van is being used to carry small volumes of asbestos waste, it must be double bagged and the bags secured (for example, by putting them in a bin with a lid). This must only be transported in a segregated compartment just for asbestos, and the vehicle must be easily cleanable.

Any fibrous asbestos removed from an enclosure must be double bagged. Bagged waste should consist of an inner red bag and an outer clear bag. These should be correctly marked. The packaging (bagging) and labelling must satisfy the requirements of current legislation and, where asbestos waste is to be transported by road, there is further legislation controlling its safe movement (International Carriage of Dangerous Goods by Road (ADR) Regulations). Containers should be designed and constructed so as to retain the asbestos without any spillage or loss during normal handling.

Where the asbestos removal contractor uses labels on waste or removed asbestos, the label must be clearly and indelibly printed so that the words in the lower half can be easily read. These words must be printed as specified in the diagram above. The label must be firmly affixed to the packaging using an adhesive type label, or directly printed onto the packaging (plastic bag).

10.14.3 Removal from the site of production

Contractors must ensure the following for hazardous waste.

- It is consigned from the place where the waste was produced, using a hazardous waste consignment note.

- The waste must be transported by a registered waste carrier.

- In Wales, the hazardous waste producer must also register, with NRW, the place where the hazardous waste was produced (unless they are exempt from registration). This requirement does not apply to England or Scotland.

- The waste is taken directly from the site of production to a suitably authorised facility within 24 hours. The facility should hold either a relevant environmental permit or an exemption from a permit.

- In Scotland and Northern Ireland the 72 hour pre-notification will apply.

10.14.4 Suitable authorised facilities

Any place where asbestos waste is taken must hold an environmental permit that authorises the acceptance of asbestos waste. This will normally be one of the following.

- A landfill with a separate cell set aside for asbestos.

- A temporary storage facility (operated by the asbestos contractor, or a waste contractor) that stores waste before transfer to landfill.

An asbestos contractor that takes asbestos waste back to their own premises must also hold an environmental permit. Although there is an exemption for storage at a temporary collection point controlled by the producer, this is restricted to bonded asbestos only, and excludes businesses providing a waste management service to customers (such as those contracted to remove asbestos).

- Asbestos waste must not be put into bays or transferred between different skips or containers.

- Keep all handling to a minimum (either manual or mechanical). Loading shovels must not be used to move asbestos waste.

- Keep designated skips secure and locked when asbestos waste is not being deposited into them.

- Operators must have emergency procedures to deal with delivered, non-conforming asbestos waste. This could include waste that is not properly contained in bags or skips (for example, unwrapped asbestos sheets in open skips). Sites should also have the capability to deal with appropriate non-conforming waste and spillages (for example, broken bags). Records should be kept of non-conforming waste.

● Do not use a skip that has been used to store asbestos for non-asbestos use, unless it has been verified that the skip has been fully decontaminated.

Any place that receives hazardous waste, including exempt facilities in England and Wales, is a consignee and required to send quarterly returns to the EA or NRW.

10.14.5 Crushed secondary aggregate

Companies that produce crushed secondary aggregate from construction or demolition waste are not authorised to accept and process waste containing asbestos. They should have effective waste acceptance and screening procedures to prevent this from happening. The secondary aggregates they produce should not contain asbestos.

A secondary aggregate containing the following is likely to remain hazardous waste, and will be subject to waste controls, which would prevent its use in construction:

● one or more piece of ACM (as detailed in Classification of waste), or

● any concentration of asbestos resulting from the processing of pieces of ACM or a waste containing asbestos fibres at a hazardous concentration.

10.15   Waste electrical and electronic equipment (WEEE)

The Waste Electrical and Electronic Equipment Regulations (WEEE Regulations) apply to England, Northern Ireland, Scotland and Wales, and designates safe and responsible collection, recycling and recovery procedures for all types of electrical and electronic waste (whether whole or broken) that is destined for disposal. This is widely known as WEEE or e-waste.

There are 10 broad categories of WEEE currently covered in the regulations, and the scope now extends to further categories of electric and electronic equipment (EEE).

 To discover the 10 broad categories currently covered within the WEEE Regulations, refer to Schedules 1 and 2; for a detailed list of the EEE, refer to Schedules 3 and 4.

A producer selling electrical equipment for non-household use (such as equipment used by a construction company) is obliged to finance the collection, treatment and recycling in an environmentally sound manner of:

● any waste electrical equipment replaced (with equivalent or similar function) by the electrical equipment sold, if it was originally purchased before 13 August 2005, whether supplied by this or another producer

● the electrical equipment the producer sold on or after 13 August 2005 when it is eventually discarded as WEEE.

The collection, treatment and recovery may be undertaken either by the producer, or by their producer compliance scheme (PCS), which they must register with. The PCS should be registered with the appropriate waste regulation authority (EA, NRW, NIEA or SEPA).

Equipment distributors (retailers, wholesalers, mail order or internet dealers) do not have any specific obligations for non-household electrical equipment. However, the PCS registration information should be passed on so that the end user (such as a construction company) can properly dispose of the item at the end of its life.

 Every year an estimated two million tonnes of WEEE items are discarded by householders and companies in the UK. This includes most products that have a plug, or need a battery.

10.15.1 End-user responsibilities for WEEE

A construction company's role in the WEEE Regulations means that, to dispose of WEEE, the following actions must be taken.

● It must be segregated from other types of waste for disposal.

● If the waste electrical equipment was purchased before 13 August 2005, and is being replaced with new equivalent equipment, then ask the producer for details of its PCS and collection arrangements.

● If the waste equipment is not being replaced with new equivalent equipment, or the PCS cannot be traced, then you must pay to transfer the waste equipment to an approved authorised treatment facility that can accept waste electrical equipment (such as a licensed transfer station).

● Any waste transferred to an authorised collector or waste carrier must meet all of the normal requirements for duty of care (such as waste carrier's licence, transfer notes and licensed treatment facilities, for example waste transfer station) approved by the waste regulation authority.

Waste electrical equipment

10.16   Waste batteries

The construction industry is a large user of batteries in many types of vehicles, plant and equipment. Currently the recycling rate for portable batteries is around 44%. The Waste Batteries and Accumulators Regulations apply to the UK and Northern Ireland. They set out requirements for waste battery collection, treatment, recycling and disposal for all types of battery, and aim to reduce the impact of waste batteries on the environment and increase recycling. The regulations define three types of batteries (listed below) and by chemistry as lead-acid, nickel-cadmium or other.

Portable batteries that are sealed, can be hand carried and are neither an automotive battery or accumulator nor an industrial battery. Examples of a portable battery include AA or AAA-type battery or the battery used to power a laptop, mobile phone, calculator and car remote-locking or alarm controls. The UK currently uses around 30,000 tonnes of portable batteries each year, which come in various sizes and chemistries.

Waste portable batteries

Industrial batteries used for industrial or professional purposes, such as the battery used as a source of power and propulsion to drive the motor in an electric forklift, batteries used to power hybrid motor vehicles, and batteries in solar-powered road signs. These batteries comes in a wide range of chemistries, and are subject to producer take-back.

Automotive batteries used for starting or the ignition of a vehicle engine, or for powering the lights of a vehicle. Due to the high levels of lead in these batteries, there has traditionally been a high recycling rate, currently of around 95%.

10.16.1   Take-back of waste batteries

These regulations require that distributors of **portable batteries** (for example, retail stores) have a duty to take back waste portable batteries through facilities such as in-store waste-battery bins. This requirement does not apply to distributors who supply less than 32 kg of batteries per year. A producer of **industrial batteries** is obliged to provide for the take-back of waste industrial batteries free of charge from the end user in the following circumstances.

● If the producer has supplied new industrial batteries to that end user.

● Where, for any reason, the end user is not able to return waste industrial batteries to the supplier who supplied the batteries, providing the waste batteries are the same chemistry as the batteries the producer places on the market.

● If the end user is not purchasing new batteries, and a battery with the same chemistry as the one being returned has not been placed on the market for a number of years, then the end user's entitlement is to be able to contact any producer to request take-back.

10.16.2   Guidance for battery users

An important aim of the regulations is to enable end users of industrial batteries to have them treated and recycled at no cost to themselves. As with any waste, the final holders must comply with the duty of care for waste by ensuring that all waste transfers are passed to authorised persons, together with the correct waste transfer documentation. Waste should only be carried by a licensed waste carrier.

 For further information on the Waste Batteries and Accumulators Regulations visit the Government legislation website.

10.16.3   Lithium-ion batteries

Lithium-ion (Li-ion) batteries come in a variety of shapes, sizes and chemistries. There are two basic categories: non-rechargeable batteries containing lithium metal, and rechargeable batteries containing salts of lithium. They are used for electric vehicles, but many smaller batteries are used in everyday devices, such as mobile phones, vaping devices, laptops, digital cameras, electric scooters and e-bikes.

While these batteries are designed to align with sustainability, they pose some serious safety risks. They are highly flammable, and if damaged or not fully sealed, or if they come into contact with water, they can quickly catch fire. Li-ion batteries should never be incinerated due to the risk of explosion.

Explosion of a Lithium-ion battery installed in a mobile Bluetooth speaker

They can be recycled, but it is essential that this is done safely, and they must go to a specialist recycling centre. The fire risk is particularly dangerous during waste transportation or the recycling process. If a fire occurs in a vehicle or at the facility, it could cause extensive damage, and even be life-threatening. Li-ion batteries need to be disposed of at a hazardous waste collection site: if disposed of in general waste or a recycling container, they could easily come into contact with water. This could happen if it is raining, if a crushed bottle of liquid leaks, or if condensation forms within the container.

Appendix A - European Waste Catalogue six-digit list of wastes codes

Section 17 - Construction and demolition waste

A six-figure list of wastes code for the type of waste being removed MUST be written on every waste transfer note (for example, skip/muck away tickets).

17 01 Concrete, bricks, tiles and ceramics

17 01 01	Concrete.
17 01 02	Bricks.
17 01 03	Tiles and ceramics.
17 01 06*	Mixtures of, or separate fractions of concrete, bricks, tiles and ceramics containing hazardous substances.
17 01 07	Mixtures of concrete, bricks, tiles and ceramics other than those mentioned in 17 01 06.

17 02 Wood, glass and plastic

17 02 01	Wood.
17 02 02	Glass.
17 02 03	Plastic.
17 02 04*	Glass, plastic and wood containing or contaminated with hazardous substances.

17 03 Bituminous mixtures, coal tar and tarred products

17 03 01*	Bituminous mixtures containing coal tar.
17 03 02	Bituminous mixtures other than those mentioned in 17 03 01.
17 03 03*	Coal tar and tarred products.

17 04 Metals (including their alloys)

17 04 01	Copper, bronze, brass.
17 04 02	Aluminium.
17 04 03	Lead.
17 04 04	Zinc.
17 04 05	Iron and steel.
17 04 06	Tin.
17 04 07	Mixed metals.
17 04 09*	Metal waste contaminated with hazardous substances.
17 04 10*	Cables containing oil, coal tar and other hazardous substances.
17 04 11	Cables other than those mentioned in 17 04 10.

17 05 Soil (including excavated soil from contaminated sites), stones and dredging spoil

17 05 03*	Soil and stones containing hazardous substances.
17 05 04	Soil and stones other than those mentioned in 17 05 03.
17 05 05*	Dredging spoil containing hazardous substances.
17 05 06	Dredging spoil other than those mentioned in 17 05 05.
17 05 07*	Track ballast containing hazardous substances.
17 05 08	Track ballast other than those mentioned in 17 05 07.

17 06 Insulation materials and asbestos-containing construction materials

17 06 01*	Insulation materials containing asbestos.
17 06 03*	Other insulation materials consisting of or containing hazardous substances.
17 06 04	Insulation materials other than those mentioned in 17 06 01 and 17 06 03.
17 06 05*	Construction materials containing asbestos.

17 08 Gypsum-based construction material

17 08 01*	Gypsum-based construction materials contaminated with hazardous substances.
17 08 02	Gypsum-based construction materials other than those mentioned in 17 08 01.

17 09 Other construction and demolition wastes

17 09 01*	Construction and demolition wastes containing mercury.
17 09 02*	Construction and demolition wastes containing PCB (for example, PCB containing sealants, PCB-containing resin-based floorings and PCB-containing sealed glazing units).
17 09 03*	Other construction and demolition wastes (including mixed wastes) containing hazardous substances.
17 09 04	Mixed construction and demolition wastes other than those mentioned in 17 09 01.

 Entries marked with * are either potentially hazardous (hazardous mirror entry) and will require testing to determine if hazardous properties are present or definitely hazardous (absolute) and must be disposed of as hazardous waste.

10

Appendix B – Example of a controlled waste transfer note

Duty of care: waste transfer note
Keep this page and copy it for future use. Please write as clearly as possible.

Section A – Description of waste

A1 Description of the waste being transferred

List of Waste Regulations code(s)

A2 How is the waste contained?

Loose ☐ Sacks ☐ Skip ☐ Drum ☐ ☐

Other ☐

A3 How much waste? For example, number of sacks, weight

Section B – Current holder of the waste – Transferor

By signing in Section D below I confirm that I have fulfilled my duty to apply the waste hierarchy as required by Regulation 12 of the Waste (England and Wales) Regulations 2011   Yes ☐

B1 Full name

Company name and address

Postcode _____ SIC code (2007) _____

B2 Name of your unitary authority or council

B3 Are you:

The producer of the waste? ☐

The importer of the waste? ☐

The local authority? ☐

The holder of an environmental permit? ☐

Permit number

Issued by

Registered waste exemption? ☐

Details, including registration number

A registered waste carrier, broker or dealer? ☐

Registration number

Details (are you a carrier, broker or dealer?)

Section C – Person collecting the waste – Transferee

C1 Full name

Company name and address

Postcode _____

C2 Are you:

The local authority? ☐

C3 Are you:

The holder of an environmental permit? ☐

Permit number

Issued by

Registered waste exemption? ☐

Details, including registration number

A registered waste carrier, broker or dealer? ☐

Registration number

Details (are you a carrier, broker or dealer?)

Section D – The transfer

D1 Address of transfer or collection point

Postcode _____

Date of transfer (DD/MM/YYYY) _____

D2 Broker or dealer who arranged this transfer (if applicable)

Postcode _____

Registration number _____

Time(s) _____

Transferor's signature _____

Name _____

Representing _____

Transferee's signature _____

Name _____

Representing _____

 You must keep all controlled, non-hazardous waste transfer documentation for two years.

10

Appendix C – Example of a hazardous waste consignment note

Form HWCN01v112

The Hazardous Waste Regulations 2005: Consignment Note

Environment Agency

PRODUCER'S/HOLDER'S/CONSIGNOR'S COPY (Delete as appropriate)

PART A Notification details

1 Consignment note code: ▢▢▢▢▢▢ / ▢▢▢▢▢ ▢

3 The waste will be taken to (name, address and postcode):

2 The waste described below is to be removed from (name, address, postcode, telephone, e-mail, facsimile):

4 The waste producer was (if different from 2) (name, address, postcode, telephone, e-mail, facsimile):

PART B Description of the waste   If continuation sheet used, tick here ▢

1 The process giving rise to the waste(s) was:

2 SIC (2007) for the process giving rise to the waste: ▢▢ . ▢▢ / ▢▢

3 WASTE DETAILS (where more than one waste type is collected all of the information given below must be completed for each EWC identified)

Description of waste	List of wastes (EWC code)(6 digits)	Quantity (kg)	The chemical/biological components in the waste and their concentrations are:		Physical form (gas, liquid, solid, powder, sludge or mixed)	Hazard code(s)	Container type, number and size
			Component	Concentration (% or mg/kg)			

The information given below is to be completed for each EWC identified

EWC code	UN identification number(s)	Proper shipping name(s)	UN class(es)	Packing group(s)	Special handling requirements

---

PART C Carrier's certificate

(If more than one carrier is used, please attach schedule for subsequent carriers. If schedule of carriers is attached tick here. ▢)

I certify that I today collected the consignment and that the details in A2, A3 and B3 are correct and I have been advised of any specific handling requirements.

Where this note comprises part of a multiple collection the round number and collection number are:

▢▢▢ / ▢▢▢

1 Carrier name:

On behalf of (name, address, postcode, telephone, e-mail, facsimile):

2 Carrier registration no./reason for exemption:

3 Vehicle registration no. (or mode of transport, if not road):

Signature

Date D D M M Y Y Y Y   Time H H M M

PART D Consignor's certificate

I certify that the information in A, B and C has been completed and is correct, that the carrier is registered or exempt and was advised of the appropriate precautionary measures. All of the waste is packaged and labelled correctly and the carrier has been advised of any special handling requirements.

I confirm that I have fulfilled my duty to apply the waste hierarchy as required by Regulation 12 of the Waste (England and Wales) Regulations 2011.

1 Consignor name:

On behalf of (name, address, postcode, telephone, e-mail, facsimile):

Signature

Date D D M M Y Y Y Y   Time H H M M

PART E Consignee's certificate (where more than one waste type is collected all of the information given below must be completed for each EWC)

Individual EWC code(s) received	Quantity of each EWC code received (kg)	EWC code accepted/rejected	Waste management operation (R or D code)

1 I received this waste at the address given in A3 on: Date D D M M Y Y Y Y   Time H H M M

2 Vehicle registration no. (or mode of transport if not road):

Name:

On behalf of (name, address, postcode, telephone, e-mail, facsimile):

3 Where waste is rejected please provide details:

I certify that waste permit/exempt waste operation number:

▢▢▢▢▢▢

authorises the management of the waste described in B at the address given in A3.

Where the consignment forms part of a multiple collection, as identified in Part C, I certify that the total number of consignments forming the collection are: ▢▢▢

Signature

Date D D M M Y Y Y Y   Time H H M M

You must keep all hazardous waste documentation for three years.

10

Appendix D – Waste flowcharts for the reuse of construction materials (soils and aggregates)

The following three flowcharts will help you to decide whether use and reuse of soil and aggregate materials in construction works is a waste activity or not and what you need to do to ensure legal compliance whilst minimising the regulatory burden. These flowcharts may also assist you in completion of a SWMP when assessing reuse or recycling options during design and construction phases. These flowcharts are applicable in England and Wales.

These flowcharts are not intended to cover exhaustive criteria of waste; however they do cover the typical scenarios that are commonly faced on construction and civil engineering projects.

For simplicity, these flowcharts have been split up into three priority operations (*see below and on the following pages*).

 EA refers to the Environment Agency in England, and NRW refers to Natural Resources Wales in Wales.

Materials arising from work to be reused on site

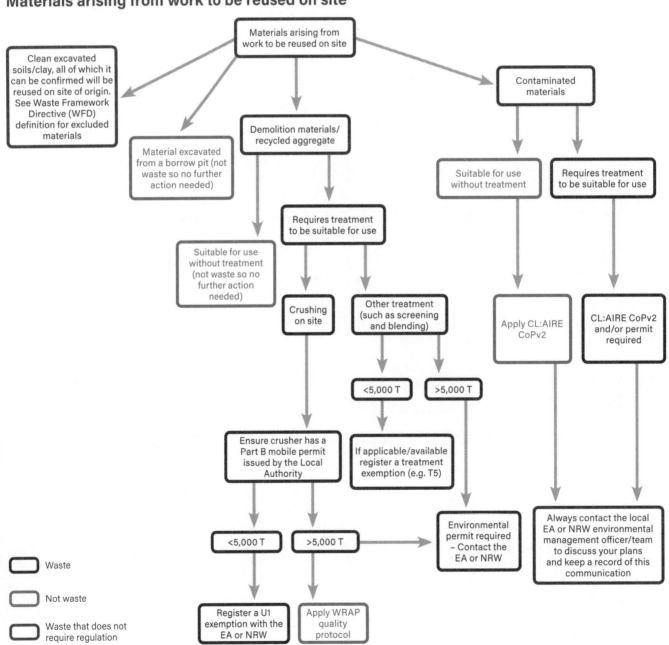

Materials to be brought onto site

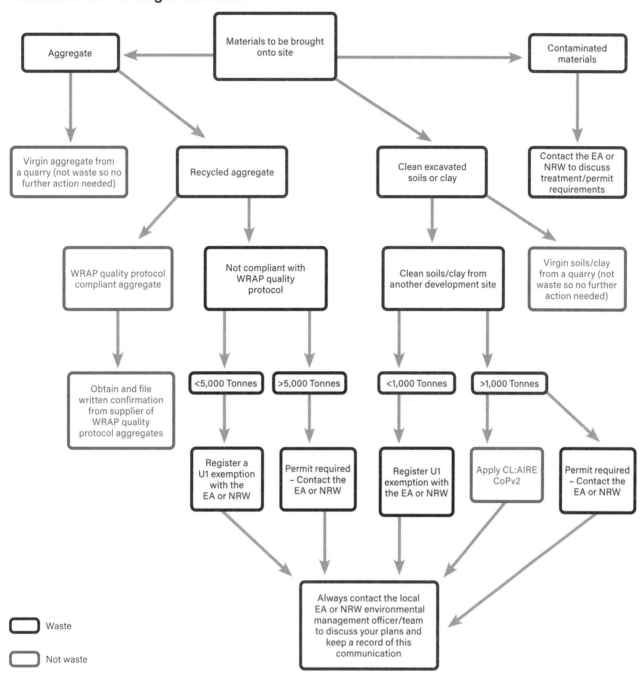

Waste

Not waste

Materials to be sent off site

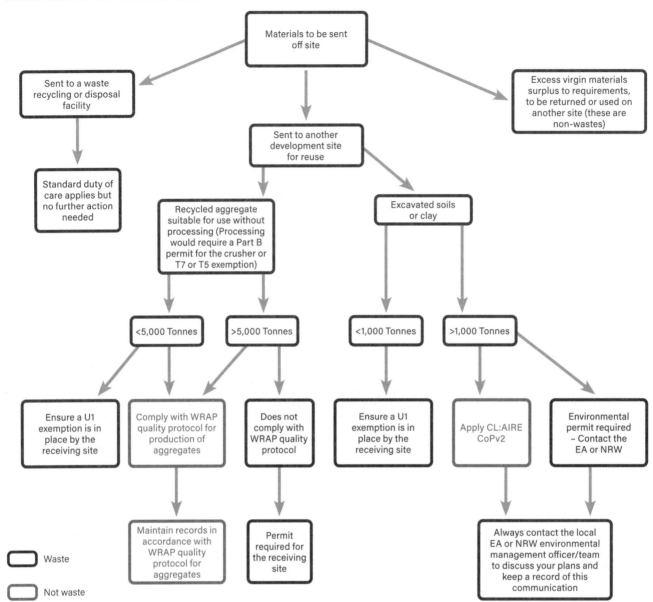

Waste

Not waste

Appendix E - Waste exemption materials and thresholds

Exemption U1 - Use of waste in construction

This exemption is referenced in the Environmental Permitting Regulations and allows the use of suitable wastes for small-scale construction instead of using virgin raw materials.

Construction for the purposes of this activity means:

 any building or engineering work, which includes the repair, alteration, maintenance or improvement of an existing work and preparatory or landscaping works.

Land reclamation is only permissible under this exemption when it's an integral part of a construction activity.

What type of work can you do?

Example work includes:

- using crushed bricks, concrete, rocks and aggregate to create a noise bund around a new development and then using soil to landscape it to enable grass to grow
- using road planings and rubble to build a track, road or car park
- using wood chip to construct a track, path or bridleway
- bringing in some soil from another place for use in landscaping at a housing development.

Where can you carry out this activity?

This can be done at any place that can comply with the environmental controls listed in the main limits and conditions.

What can't you do?

You **can't**:

- treat waste under this exemption to make it suitable for use
- dispose of waste under this exemption (you can only use waste types that are suitable for use and you should be able to justify the amount of waste that you use)
- use this exemption for land reclamation or disposal in a landfill (you must read the guidance on disposal vs. recovery RGN13: *Defining waste recovery: Permanent deposit of waste on land* and make sure that you are using the waste for recovery only)
- register this exemption more than once at any one place during the three-year period from first registration
- de-register this exemption and then re-register it at the same place within a three-year period
- store the waste for more than 12 months prior to use.

What are the significant limits?

Each table *(on the following pages)* lists the waste types and quantities that can be used over a three-year period from the date of registering the exemption.

You can use up to:

- 5,000 tonnes of any single waste stream or any combination of wastes in Table 1
- 1,000 tonnes of any single waste stream or any combination of wastes in Table 2
- 50,000 tonnes of any single waste stream or any combination of wastes in Table 3.

What are the significant conditions?

You may use a combination of wastes from Tables 1, 2 and 3 provided you do not exceed the limits for each table. Waste can't be stored for longer than 12 months prior to use.

There are three specific conditions to this exemption relating to certain wastes. These are outlined below and also in the relevant section of *What waste can be used under this exemption?*

1. Any person or company can use up to 1,000 tonnes of dredging spoil for any construction (within the 1,000 tonnes total for wastes from Table 2). Exception is made for the Environment Agency and other statutory authorities carrying out land drainage functions under the Land Drainage Act, the Water Resources Act or the Environment Act. These organisations may use up to 5,000 tonnes of dredging spoil for drainage work (within the 5,000 tonnes total for wastes from Table 1).

2. You can use 1,000 tonnes of wood chip (or similar waste) or road planings to construct tracks, paths, bridleways or car parks only (within the 1,000 tonnes total for wastes from Table 2). The waste must be processed into chipped form prior to use.

3. If you are constructing a road you can use 50,000 tonnes of road planings and road sub-base. The road should be constructed to a specific engineering standard and have a sealed surface in order to qualify for the higher limit.

WASTE AND MATERIAL MANAGEMENT – APPENDIX E

What waste can be used under this exemption?

Table 1

You can use up to 5,000 tonnes in total of the wastes below for any construction activity.

Codes	Waste types
01 01 02	Waste from mineral non-metalliferous excavation.
01 04 08	Waste gravel and crushed rock other than those mentioned in 01 04 07*.
01 04 09	Waste sand and clays.
02 02 02	Shellfish shells from which the soft tissue or flesh has been removed only.
10 12 08	Waste ceramics, bricks, tiles and construction products (after thermal processing).
10 13 14	Waste concrete and concrete sludge.
17 01 01	Concrete.
17 01 02	Bricks.
17 01 03	Tiles and ceramics.
17 01 07	Mixtures of concrete, bricks, tiles and ceramics other than those mentioned in 17 01 06*.
17 05 08	Track ballast other than those mentioned in 17 05 07*.
19 12 05	Glass.
19 12 09	Minerals (for example sand and stones).
19 12 12	Aggregates only.

Within the 5,000 tonnes total for use of wastes in Table 1, you can only use the waste below for drainage work carried out for the purposes of the Land Drainage Act 1991(1), the Water Resources Act 1991 or the Environment Act 1995. This is work that can only be carried out by drainage authorities (such as Inland Drainage Boards, Local Authorities or environment agencies).

Codes	Waste types
17 05 06	Dredging spoil other than those mentioned in 17 05 05*.

Table 2

You can use up to 1,000 tonnes in total of the wastes below for construction purposes.

Codes	Waste types
02 03 99, 02 04 01	Soil from cleaning and washing fruit and vegetables only.
17 05 04	Soil and stones other than those mentioned in 17 05 03*.
17 05 06	Dredging spoil other than those mentioned in 17 05 05*.
19 13 02	Solid wastes from soil remediation other than those mentioned in 19 13 01*.
20 02 02	Soil and stones.

Within the 1,000 tonnes total for use of wastes from Table 2, you can only use the waste below for the construction of tracks, paths, bridleways or car parks. The waste must be processed into chipped form prior to use.

Codes	Waste types
17 03 02	Bituminous mixtures other than those mentioned in 17 03 01*.
02 01 03	Plant tissue waste.
03 01 01, 03 03 01	Untreated waste bark, cork and wood only.
03 01 05	Untreated wood including sawdust, shavings and cuttings from untreated wood only.
17 02 01	Untreated wood only.
19 12 07	Untreated wood other than those mentioned in 19 12 06* only.
20 01 38	Untreated wood other than those mentioned in 20 01 37* only.

For waste codes beginning with 17 refer to Appendix A; for all other codes refer directly to the European Waste Catalogue.

Table 3

You can use up to 50,000 tonnes in total of the wastes below only for the construction of roads. The roads should be constructed to a specific engineering standard and have a sealed surface in order to qualify for this larger limit.

Codes	Waste types
17 03 02	Bituminous mixtures other than those mentioned in 17 03 01*.
17 05 04	Road sub-base only.

* Refer to Appendix A.

Exemption T5 – Screening and blending of waste

This exemption allows temporary small-scale treatment of wastes to produce an aggregate or a soil at a place (such as a construction or demolition site).

What type of work does this cover?

Example work includes:

- screening of soils on a demolition site to remove wood and rubble before sending the soils to a construction site for reuse

- blending of soils and compost that has been produced under an exemption on a construction site to produce a better soil for landscaping works on that site

- crushing wastes (except bricks, tiles and concrete) prior to screening or blending

- grading of waste concrete after crushing to produce a required type of aggregate.

Where can this activity be carried out?

You can treat waste on the site where it is:

- to be used (for example, on a construction site)

- produced (for example, on a demolition site).

What can't you do?

You **can't**:

- import waste, treat it and then export it elsewhere*

- treat waste where the main purpose is disposal to landfill or incineration

- crush waste tiles, bricks or concrete (this comes under a T7 exemption, which must be registered with the Local Authority)

- treat hazardous waste.

* This applies even if the treated aggregate meets the quality protocol standard and will no longer be considered as waste.

What are the significant limits?

- You can store or treat up to 50,000 tonnes of bituminous mixtures for making road stone over a three-year period from the date of registering the exemption.

- You can store or treat up to 5,000 tonnes of other wastes *(listed on the following page)* over a three-year period from the date of registering the exemption.

- Waste can only be stored for up to 12 months.

What are the significant conditions?

Treatment can only be carried out at the place where the waste is to be used or where the waste is produced. This applies even if the resultant material is no longer considered to be waste.

What else do you need to know?

When you have treated the waste the options available are:

- if the treated waste meets the requirements of a waste quality protocol (the quality protocols – WRAP) then it will no longer be considered a waste

- use the treated waste, subject to the significant conditions above, under a use exemption or environmental permit.

10

WASTE AND MATERIAL MANAGEMENT – APPENDIX E

What waste can be treated under this exemption?

Codes	Waste types
01 04 08	Waste gravel and crushed rocks other than those mentioned in 01 04 07.*
01 04 09	Waste sand and clays.
02 02 02	Shellfish shells from which the soft tissue or flesh have been removed only.
03 01 01	Untreated waste bark and cork only.
03 03 01	Untreated waste bark and wood.
10 01 01	Bottom ash, slag and boiler dust (excluding boiler dust mentioned in 10 01 04*).
10 01 15	Bottom ash, slag and boiler dust from co-incineration other than those mentioned in 10 01 14.*
17 01 01	Concrete.
17 01 02	Bricks.
17 01 03	Tiles and ceramics.
17 01 07	Mixtures of concrete, bricks, tiles and ceramics other than those mentioned in 17 01 06.*
17 02 01	Untreated wood only.
17 03 02	Bituminous mixtures other than those mentioned in 17 03 01.*
17 05 04	Soil and stones other than those mentioned in 17 05 03.*
17 05 06	Dredging spoil other than those mentioned in 17 05 05.*
17 05 08	Track ballast other than those mentioned in 17 05 07.*
19 05 99	Compost produced pursuant to a treatment described in the paragraphs numbered T23 or T26 of Chapter 2 only.
19 12 05	Glass.
19 12 09	Aggregates only.
19 12 12	Gypsum recovered from construction materials only.
19 13 02	Solid wastes from soil remediation other than those mentioned in 19 13 01.*
19 13 04	Sludges from remediation other than those mentioned in 19 13 03.*
20 02 02	Soil and stones.

For waste codes beginning with 17 refer to Appendix A; for all other codes refer directly to the European Waste Catalogue.

10

Index

INDEX

INDEX

INDEX

timber 95
Town and Country Planning Acts 46, 54
Town and Country Planning (Churches, Places of Religious Worship and Burial Grounds) Regulations 42, 54
Town and Country (Environmental Impact Assessment) Regulations 46
Town and Country Planning (Historic Environment Scotland) Amendment Regulations 38
Town and Country Planning (Trees) Regulations 54
traffic management plan 69-70
transport 69-70
treasure 43
treatment of waste 118-9, 124
tree and hedgerow protection 54-6
tree preservation orders (TPOs) 11, 54, 61

UK Green Building Council (UKGBC) 5
UNESCO World Heritage sites 40
US Green Building Council (GBC) 14

vapours 6, 68
    see also fumes; gases
vibration 6, 45, 70, 71, 72, 73
voluntary partnership agreements (VPA) 95

Waste (England and Wales) Regulations 112, 114, 124, 132
Waste (Scotland) Regulations 112, 119
waste
    acceptance procedures 118
    and litter 6
    avoidance protocols 126
    batteries 130
    carrier registration 119-20
    codes 138-9, 140
    controls, and local authorities 11
    defining 116
    describing and classifying 116-8
    duty of care 119-20
    exemption materials and thresholds 137-40
    flowcharts for reuse of construction materials 134-6
    hierarchy 114-5
    management licensing (Northern Ireland and Scotland) 125-6
    policy targets 12
    regulation authorities 113-4
    transfer documentation 21, 23, 117, 120-1, 129, 130, 133, 134
Waste and Contaminated Land (Amendment) Act 100
Waste and Contaminated Land Order 104, 112, 125
Waste Batteries and Accumulators Regulations 112, 130
waste electrical and electronic equipment 129
Waste Electrical and Electronic Equipment Regulations 129
Waste Framework Directive (WFD) 114, 134
waste management
    exemptions 114-5, 119, 124, 125, 126, 128, 134, 135, 136, 138-140
    legislation and guidance 112
    overview 113
    permits 112, 113-4, 123-6
    recycling 12, 92-3, 96-8, 130, 134-6
    standard industry classification (SIC) 114, 117, 120, 122
    technical competence 124, 125
    see also Definition of Waste Code of Practice (DoW CoP)

Waste Regulations (England and Wales) 119
Waste Regulations (Northern Ireland) 112
Water (Northern Ireland) Order 76, 81
Water Abstraction and Impounding (Exemptions) Regulations 76
Water Act 76
Water and Sewerage Services (Northern Ireland) Order 76

water
    companies 11, 103
    efficiency 93
    policy targets 12
Water Environment and Water Services (Scotland) Act 76
Water Environment (Controlled Activities) (Scotland) Regulations 76, 81
Water Environment (Miscellaneous) Regulations 76
Water Industry Act 76, 80
water management and pollution control
    abstraction 80
    consents 80-2
    disposal 82-3
    groundwater 79
    legislation and guidance 76
    overview 77-8
    pollution incident response plans 86-7
    pollution prevention 83-6
    run-off 6
water pollution 6
    discharge consents 82-3
    and disposal 82-3
    overview 77-8
    records of 84
Water Resources Act 76, 77, 79, 80, 137, 138
water scarcity 93
water use and conservation 93-4
water voles 51, 58
Weeds Act 46, 57
Weybridge 24-hour mooring (carbon reduction case study) 33-4
wildlife
    adverse effects of construction work 61
    avoidance of damage to 47-8
    biodiversity 49
    designated sites 48-9
    endangered species 50-1
    invasive species 56-7
    protected species and habitats 51-6
    refuges 48
    trees and hedgerows 54-6
    year planner 58-9
Wildlife (Amendment) (Northern Ireland) Order 46, 51, 52, 56
Wildlife and Countryside (Amendment) Act 46, 48, 51, 52, 56, 60
Wildlife and Natural Environment Act 46
workmanship 30
World Commission on Environment and Development 3, 6
WRAP (Waste Resources Action Programme) 2, 5, 8, 17, 96, 98, 102, 112, 114, 116, 126, 134, 135, 136, 139

Zero Carbon Hub 31
Zero Waste Scotland 96

CONTENTS

Specialist activities

Street works and road works

Supporting INFORMATION

GT700 Toolbox talks / supporting checklists and forms

Toolbox talks on some of these topics are available in the GT700 publication. Supporting checklists and forms covering some of these topics are available on our companion website.

STREET WORKS AND ROAD WORKS

Overview

In recent years the Health and Safety Executive (HSE) has expressed concern at the number of workers and members of the public killed or seriously injured through accidents related to road works. The New Roads and Street Works Act (NRSWA) provides a legislative framework for street works (including work carried out by public utility companies).

The NRSWA is supported by the *Safety at street works and road works* (SSWRW) Code of Practice (CoP). This chapter is an introduction to the comprehensive Code of Practice, with the content being provided as an overview to the legal requirements and guidance on a range of topics and issues that need to be considered when setting up temporary traffic controls.

1.1 Introduction

Road works will almost always bring the workers carrying out construction work into close proximity with vehicles (both construction plant and passing traffic). The safety of the workers and vehicle drivers or operators will depend upon the works being properly planned, carried out by trained and qualified workers and the behaviour of drivers in passing vehicles.

 Highways England data revealed that there were around 330 incidents of abuse reported from September 2019 to October 2020, an average of nearly one every day.

There are around 38.6 million registered vehicles in Britain, making our roads some of the busiest in the world. They are also some of the safest. In terms of overall road safety, current national figures show casualties are at their lowest level for 40 years. Although this is promising, overall injuries to road workers on the UK's roads have risen.

In today's traffic conditions, the live carriageway of any highway is a dangerous place to work.

Drivers ignoring temporary speed limits is commonplace, leaving road workers even more vulnerable and with little to protect them from approaching vehicles.

 80% of road workers have been physically or verbally abused by motorists and 40% of workers are abused on either a daily or weekly basis.

To help improve safety for workers on the highways, Highways England brought around an initiative to look at the health and safety for major road schemes. *Raising the Bar* was to identify best practice, raise standards and improve supply chain engagement within major projects.

Raising the Bar covers the following areas via support documents and guidance available on the Government website.

● Defining the minimum requirement and standards to be implemented on all major projects.

● Setting out 'desirable' elements, for consideration and implementation if deemed appropriate.

● Giving further guidance and supporting information on areas to be considered and applied where practicable.

● Continually reviewing working practices to reduce the risk to road workers, including the introduction of local targets, investigating layout changes and trialling new technologies.

● Reducing speed and improving compliance throughout road works, including the use of average speed detection.

 Visit the Government website for more information on this initiative, as well as safe working guidance on working on roads and highways.

1.2 Important points

● Works include any placement, connection or maintenance of temporary or permanent services, pipes, cables, sewers or drains that are laid or located within the carriageway or footway. This also includes forming new or temporary entrances and roads where they join an existing highway or footpath.

● All work should be carried out in accordance with the *Safety at street works and road works – A Code of Practice*.

● The Code of Practice (CoP), often referred to as the *Red book*, that supports the legislation must be complied with. The CoP is for works on all highways and roads, except motorways and dual carriageways with a speed limit of 50 mph or more. The CoP specifies minimum safety requirements for:

– signage, lighting and guarding   – controlling the speed of passing traffic

– methods of traffic control   – works near to tramways and railways, equipment and vehicles.

- Site-specific risk assessments must be carried out.

- Road users, whether in a vehicle or on foot, approaching the works on the road or footway, from any direction, must be able to understand exactly what route they must follow, when to stop or wait, when to give way and at what speed they should be travelling.

- Operatives who carry out work on the highway must be competent to do so, particularly anyone involved with setting up the traffic management layout on site, including positioning signage, lighting, cones, fences and barriers, and traffic control measures.

1.3 Legislative requirements

Three pieces of legislation specific to streets, roads and highways have an impact upon the way that works are carried out. The main relevant requirements are outlined below.

 Copies of all legislation can be found online.

1.3.1 New Roads and Street Works Act

- Applies to works carried out in a street by an undertaker exercising a statutory right to inspect, place and maintain pipes, cables, sewers or drains, which are laid in the carriageway or footway. The term *undertaker* also covers holders of street works licences.

- Provides a legislative framework for street works by undertakers (including public utilities).

- Created a number of criminal offences that are triable in Magistrates' Courts (Sheriffs' Courts in Scotland). Amongst the 20 possible offences are:
    - failing to carry out works safely (such as signing, lighting and guarding)
    - not having the works controlled by supervisors and/or operatives with the relevant prescribed qualifications
    - failing to complete the contracted works within a reasonable timescale.

When a Local Authority acts as an agent to an undertaker or contractor to carry out work for an undertaker, the execution of the works is governed by the Act. The efficient co-ordination of street works is one of the most important aspects of street works legislation, benefitting street authorities, undertakers and road users alike.

The main objectives of the New Roads and Street Works Act (NRSWA) are shown below.

- Ensure safety.

- Protect the structure of the street and the apparatus in it.

- Minimise inconvenience to people using a street, including a specific reference to people with a disability.

The Act comprises of the following parts.

- Part 1. New Roads in England and Wales.

- Part 2. New Roads in Scotland.

- Part 3. Street Works in England and Wales.

- Part 4. Road Works in Scotland.

- Part 5. General.

- Schedules.

1.3.2 Highways Act (England and Wales), the Roads (Northern Ireland) Order and the Roads (Scotland) Act

- Was introduced to tackle congestion and deal with the management and operation of the road network.

- Places a duty on local traffic authorities to ensure the efficient movement of traffic on their road network and the networks of surrounding authorities.

- Gives authorities additional tools to better manage parking policies, moving traffic enforcement and the co-ordination of street works.

- Empowers the Highway Authorities to impose conditions on those working on the highway. It makes provision for licences for skips and scaffolds, and places responsibility for safety with the Highway Authority. Contractors **must** obtain permission before working on the highway.

- Applies to all work on the highway. The Highway Authority (or Roads Authority in Scotland) must be consulted and grant permission for works to be carried out. This applies to any works for road construction or maintenance purposes.

1.3.3 Traffic Management Act

- Places a duty on Local Authorities to make sure traffic moves freely on their roads and the roads of nearby authorities.

- Places a duty on street authorities (such as County Councils) to secure more efficient use of their networks, to avoid or reduce traffic congestion and disruption and to regulate the use of the network.

- Requires a contractor who intends to work on the road to provide notice in advance of all works that directly or indirectly affect the highway network, effectively booking the road space. Minimum notice periods for different categories of work are contained within the NRSWA.

STREET WORKS AND ROAD WORKS

● Empowers Local Authorities to introduce a permitting scheme, which is designed to control the carrying out of specified works, in specified streets, in a specified area. In doing this it replaces the notice system under the NRSWA, whereby utility companies informed Highway Authorities of their intentions to carry out works in their areas.

 For further information on the Traffic Management Act visit the website.

1.4 Non-statutory guidance

There are two main documents (outlined below) that support temporary traffic management control.

1.4.1 Traffic signs manual

Published by the Department for Transport, the *Traffic signs manual* contents are instructional for roads, parking, road management and traffic signs.

The manual gives guidance on the use of traffic signs and road markings prescribed by the Traffic Signs Regulations and covers England, Wales, Scotland and Northern Ireland.

 The chapters can be downloaded from the GOV.UK website.

Chapters 1 to 7 outline and include details of permanent road signs and road markings.

The most relevant chapter for this section is Chapter 8, which gives guidance on road works and temporary situations where signage is required.

Chapter 1. Introduction. Introduction and an outline of the historical, functional and design aspects of signs.

The chapter includes sections dealing with the positioning and mounting of signs, and their removal with supports along with the specification on sign design and illumination requirements.

Chapter 2. Primary routes. Contains primary route destinations in England by region.

Chapter 3. Regulatory signs. Gives guidelines on the correct use of signs prescribed by the Traffic Signs Regulations. These include prohibited turns, waiting and loading restrictions, bus and cycle lanes, and so on.

There is also a comprehensive section dealing with the signing of speed limits.

Chapter 4. Warning signs. Warning signs are used to alert drivers to potential danger ahead. They indicate a need for special caution by road users and may require a reduction in speed or some other manoeuvre.

Chapter 5. Road markings. Road markings serve an important function in conveying to road users information and requirements that might not be possible using upright signs.

They have the advantage that they can often be seen when a verge-mounted sign is obscured, and, unlike such signs, they can provide a continuing message.

Chapter 7. The design of traffic signs. How sign faces are designed. Dealing with signs that are designed for a specific requirement or location (such as directional information signs and signs relating to the control of on-street waiting, loading and parking).

Chapter 8 (Part 1). Road works and temporary situations – Design. Guidance for the design of temporary traffic management arrangements, which should be implemented to facilitate maintenance work or in response to temporary situations.

Chapter 8 (Part 2). Road works and temporary situations – Operations. Guidance for planning, managing and participating in operations to implement, maintain and remove temporary traffic management arrangements.

Chapter 8 (Part 3). Road works and temporary situations – Operations. Guidance for traffic safety measures and signs for road works and temporary situations.

Traffic control signage

1.4.2 Safety at street works and road works – A Code of Practice (CoP)

This updated CoP (commonly referred to as the *Red book*) came into force on 1 October 2014. The first printing (2013) contained a list of amendments for users to update manually. Readers are strongly advised to ensure they use the second printing, which incorporates all of the additional amendments: the version annotated '2nd impression (with amendments), June 2014'.

This CoP is a pocket-size reference book, intended to be used at the place of work. Its content is aimed at all workers on site, but it does not attempt to cover every situation.

Authorities with responsibility for road maintenance in England, Wales and Northern Ireland **must** comply with the CoP for their own works. In Scotland, the roads authority **should** comply with the CoP for their works, as recommended by Scottish ministers. Wherever the term *Highway Authorities* appears, it should be taken

Check inside the cover to ensure you have the latest edition (the version annotated '2nd impression (with amendments), June 2014')

to refer to road authorities in Scotland and Northern Ireland, as well as in England and Wales. Failure to comply with the CoP is a criminal offence, potentially leading to prosecution and civil proceedings.

 The CoP is applicable to all highways and roads, except motorways and dual carriageways with a speed limit of 50 mph or more. It does not apply to skips or scaffolding located in the highway.

Anyone planning to work on the highway must obtain and refer to the CoP as necessary. It is easy to use and should be incorporated into your own systems of work. It should form part of the safety management system for whoever is planning traffic management. Checking site set-up against the layout drawing is a quick and simple way to audit procedures. Whilst a supervisor qualified under the NRSWA will know what to do in most situations, it is the employer's responsibility to ensure that safe procedures are in place, followed and controlled under supervision.

 Road users, including pedestrians, cyclists and horse riders, should not be put at risk and should be able to see the extent and nature of any risk before they reach it.

 The Code of Practice can be freely downloaded from the GOV.UK website, or it can be purchased from TSO. For more detailed advice on subjects not covered in the Code of Practice refer to Chapter 8 of the *Traffic signs manual*, which can be freely downloaded.

1.5 Carrying out road works

1.5.1 Before starting work

As with other construction projects, all road works fall within the Construction (Design and Management) Regulations 2015 (CDM) and, As such, require a construction phase plan. Additionally, where more than one contractor is involved, a principal designer and principal contractor

must be appointed, and the latter (or contractor, if only one) must actively manage site health and safety. Before starting work on the carriageway or footway, there are specific notice periods for informing the Highway/Streets Authority (or, in Scotland, the Roads Authority) that you intend to start, and three categories.

Minor. Three days' advance notice commencing with a duration of up to three days.

Standard. 10 days' advance notice commencing with a duration of four to 10 days.

Major. Three months' advance notice commencing with a duration of 10 days or more.

Depending on where the work is taking place, the Streets Authority may be the Local Authority, the County Council, the Department for Transport, or even the County Council on behalf of the Department for Transport, local Government and regions. The principal contractor or contractor should give notice to the recognised authority, taking into account any relevant lead-in period.

Notify before starting work

Lane rental schemes

The Department of Transport (DfT) has issued guidance to allow English local highways authorities to develop lane rental schemes. This gives local authorities the option to charge utility companies and highway authorities for digging up the very busiest streets at the busiest of times. The Government considers that charges must be applied only when works occupy the highway at peak periods, with exemptions from charges at other times, so as to provide a real financial incentive to carry out works at less disruptive times. After all initial costs have been covered, the remainder of the rental money is put back in road and future infrastructure investment,

1.5.2   Co-ordination of road works

When notice is given to the Highway Authority that the work is planned, they will inform the other utility undertakers in an attempt to co-ordinate works during a single excavation in order to avoid the same piece of roadway being continually excavated.

1.5.3   Major works

The term *major works* covers works carried out by the Highway Authority, which could include the following.

- The reconstruction or widening of the highway.
- Works on dual carriageways and at roundabouts.
- The construction of vehicle crossings over footways and verges.

1.5.4   Road widths

For two-way traffic, minimum road widths are shown below.

- 6.75 m on bus and HGV routes.
- 5.5 m on other roads for cars and light vehicles.

Any width less than 5.5 m is too narrow for two-way traffic and so the width must be reduced to a maximum of 3.7 m and a traffic control system introduced.

For shuttle working, minimum road widths are shown below.

Buses and HGV routes:

- 3.25 m desirable minimum width
- 3 m absolute minimum width.

Cars and light vehicles:

- 2.75 m desirable minimum width
- 2.5 m absolute minimum width.

1.5.5   Works on footways

An alternative safe route for pedestrians must meet the following requirements.

- Be provided before any footway or part of a footway is closed.
- Never be less than 1 m wide and ideally be 1.5 m or more in width.
- Be equipped with kerb ramps or a raised footway, as may be necessary, to take account of the needs of children, the elderly, people with disabilities (particularly visual impairment) or those with prams or wheelchairs.
- Be a non-slip surface and free of trip hazards (raised edges or overlaps on boarding may trip the elderly or infirm).
- Provide access to adjacent premises and public areas.

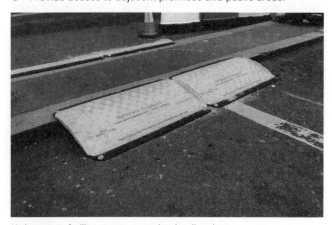

Kerb ramps to facilitate temporary pedestrian diversions

Footpath diversion showing the safe route for pedestrians

 For further information refer to Appendix C and the CoP.

1.5.6 Excavations

In many cases the excavation of trenches will form a part of road works. It is essential that a safe working area is established before excavations begin and the following requirements are met for the duration of the works.

● Be adequately guarded, where necessary, to prevent the public or construction workers being put at risk of falls.

● Be supported where the risk assessment shows that it would be unsafe not to do so.

● Be inspected before every shift where people are entering the excavation to work.

● Be fitted with lights at night where otherwise construction workers or the public would be put at risk of falling.

● Be equipped with dewatering equipment where necessary.

● Be equipped with forced ventilation where a build-up of hazardous gases or vapours could occur.

Excavations must be adequately guarded

There may be occasions where trenchless technology (such as pipe-jacking or thrust-boring) would be more suitable for the work, although the use of such methods must first be cleared with the client and designers of the scheme.

 For further details on safe working in or near to excavations refer to Chapter D06 Excavations.

1.6 Diversion and safety of apparatus

 For further information refer to Chapter D07 Underground and overhead services.

1.6.1 Diversionary works

The term *diversionary works* covers works to:

● protect apparatus on site

● relocate apparatus elsewhere.

The *Safety at street works and road works* CoP contains comprehensive information on the responsibilities of the various utility undertakers and Highway Authorities relating to major road works that may affect the safety of apparatus and the need to divert apparatus.

The CoP includes guiding principles and outlines considerations that should be taken into account and the procedures to be followed.

 Apparatus

Any pipe or ducting buried within the highway or pavement that is owned by one of the utilities. (Examples of apparatus are gas pipes, water mains, sewers, electricity cables, telephone cables and fibre optic communications cables.)

 Unexpected damage to, or disconnection of, any apparatus could have serious implications for many people who are unassociated with the work taking place.

Construction work, which may put apparatus at risk, includes the following.

● The removal or construction of the footway or carriageway.

● Construction plant crossing or working in the vicinity of apparatus.

● The undermining or removal of side support to apparatus.

● Any deep excavation adjacent to apparatus.

● Piling or ground consolidation operations.

These risks can be minimised by providing suitable and safe vehicle crossing and access points, as outlined below.

● Temporarily moving or diverting apparatus to a safe location during the construction work.

● Protecting or temporarily supporting apparatus in situ.

Methods of supporting apparatus during excavation form part of the assessment process incorporated within the relevant operative and supervisor qualifications.

The correct construction of permanent or temporary vehicle crossings for site access or new road junctions is important to avoid putting apparatus at risk. The following issues need to be considered.

● The majority of service apparatus is located in footways.

● Footway construction layers must normally be excavated to accommodate thicker construction layers.

● The new construction may no longer provide adequate cover to apparatus.

● The vehicular loading may be greater than the apparatus can withstand.

● Vibrations from vehicles may weaken joints over a period of time.

1.6.2   Safety of gas apparatus

1.6.2.1   Depth of cover

The normal minimum depth of cover for gas mains operating in the low and medium pressure ranges is:

● 600 mm in footways or verges

● 750 mm in carriageways.

However, in practice these depths may vary, as each area gas distribution network operator can have its own standards.

In certain circumstances, depending upon the mains material, operating pressure and depth of cover, it may be acceptable for the mains to remain in situ when only subjected to light traffic (for example, a vehicle layby or crossing). It is not generally permissible to allow cast iron mains previously in the footway or verge to be subjected to vehicular traffic.

1.6.2.2   Risks during construction

Liaison with the gas undertaker during the planning stage is essential because existing mains, specifically older materials (such as cast iron), cannot be raised, lowered or moved laterally even by a few millimetres without risk. Gas apparatus must not be undermined and certain apparatus is particularly vulnerable when adjacent to deep excavations.

Any proposals to excavate near live gas apparatus should be discussed with the gas undertaker. Mechanical excavation must not take place within 0.5 m of low pressure gas supplies and distances should be agreed with the gas undertaker for medium and high pressure mains.

1.6.3   Safety of water apparatus

Water mains may be protected or diverted. Requirements will be determined by the work taking place.

1.6.3.1   Depth of cover

The standard minimum cover for water mains is 900 mm. However, there are three types of mains (trunk mains, distributor mains and service pipes) and the depth of cover may vary according to the type and installation.

Further information can be found in the CoP and by consulting the water company in whose area you are working.

1.6.3.2   Risks during construction

Some water mains are under higher pressures and are liable to rupture with a reduction in cover. If water mains are medium or high pressure, the Water Authority must be contacted and any work must be supervised by the Water Authority representative. The distance is usually between 3-5 m either side of the pressured main.

Construction plant and heavy vehicles travelling over water apparatus with temporarily reduced cover can be an unacceptable risk. Therefore, diversions may be necessary unless protective measures are utilised.

Factors influencing the decision to divert water apparatus must include the following.

● The maintenance of the continuity of supply and the water quality.

● Material types and condition.

● The inability to raise, lower or slew pipes.

● The possible loss of ground support to pipes with the consequential risk of damage.

1.6.4   Safety of telecommunications apparatus

The need to exclude moisture from telecommunications cables and joints places constraints on the extent to which older cables can be moved during works.

For maintenance purposes there is the added need for vehicles to have access and be located at or near jointing chambers.

1.6.4.1 Preferred depth of cover

Varying depths of cover may be found with this type of equipment, depending on the types and design of the cables. As a rough guide, telecommunications cabling can be found at depths from 350 mm and television cabling at depths from 250 mm below a verge or footway and up to 900 mm in a carriageway.

1.6.4.2 Risks during construction

According to circumstances, the apparatus may be left in situ if ducts are adequately protected from construction plant and vehicles by the use of metal plates or tracks.

In some cases, it may be possible to accommodate small, temporary or permanent alterations in the line of a duct track by bodily slewing, raising or lowering a nest of ducts with the cables in situ.

1.6.4.3 Overhead telecommunications lines

Poles must be positioned to:

- minimise the risk of damage to overhead lines by vehicles
- be of minimum inconvenience to pedestrians
- avoid obstructing access to premises.

Road alterations may necessitate the replacement of poles if the clearance under the cables becomes inadequate.

Minimum heights above ground for overhead telecommunications lines are typically:

- 5.5 m at any point over a street
- 6.1 m on bus routes
- 6.5 m on designated roads.

1.6.5 Safety of electrical apparatus

The following factors should be considered when protecting cables in situ or diverting apparatus.

1.6.5.1 Underground cables

- The need to protect and support potentially hazardous services from mechanical impact, damage, strain and vibration during and after road works.
- A requirement to maintain the security of supply if alternative circuits are not available.
- The operating voltage of the apparatus.

The depth at which electricity cables or ducts are usually laid in the ground is determined by the need to avoid undue interference or damage.

Dependent on the type of cable and the power that it may be carrying, the depth of cover may vary from 450 mm up to 900 mm.

It is common to find electrical cables at much shallower depths of cover than these, particularly over bridges or culverts, and extreme caution must be exercised.

Plan – Locate – Dig (example of a shallow service)

In all cases, where the depth of cover is likely to increase or decrease, the apparatus owner must be consulted.

1.6.5.2 Overhead power lines

- The supports and stays of overhead power lines may have to be relocated.
- Earth wires from supports may have to be re-sited.
- Underground pilot wires may be associated with the route of overhead power lines (particularly where tramways are located).

The minimum height of overhead power lines above ground varies according to the voltage of the cable and as directed by the service supplier. The minimum height for lines carrying 33 kV is 5.2 m, 132 kV is 6.7 m, 275 kV is 7 m and 400 kV is 7.3 m.

Any temporary increase in ground level could affect the safe clearance between an overhead power line and the machinery.

Example of temporary goalposts to prevent contact with overhead power lines

 Further information can be found in *Guidance Note GS6* on the HSE website.

1.6.5.3   Risks during construction

● Additional protection or temporary diversion may be necessary to prevent damage to any apparatus during the construction stage.

● The hazards of accidental contact with electrical services by persons or machinery on site must be fully assessed. The installation of temporary goalposts may be required to prevent access by machinery with high reach attachments to areas where overhead power lines are located.

● Damage to overhead and underground cables can, in certain circumstances, cause widespread loss of electrical supplies for a long period.

1.7   Site layout definitions

Works area is the excavation, chamber, opening, reinstatement, or wherever work is taking place.

Working space is the space around the works area used to store tools, excavated material, equipment and plant.

It is also the space needed to move around the site without encroaching into live traffic or other hazards. Sufficient working space must be provided to ensure that the movement and operation of the plant (for example, swinging of jibs and excavator arms) is clear of passing traffic and is not encroaching into the safety zone.

Safety zone is the zone provided to protect site personnel from the traffic. No-one must enter the safety zone in the normal course of work.

It is only permissible to enter the zone to maintain cones and other road signs. Materials and equipment must not be placed in the safety zone.

The safety zone consists of the following.

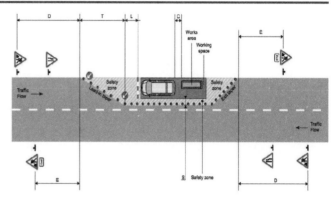

Basic layout with a works vehicle

Notes

1. For numbers and minimum size of cones, and dimensions D, T, C, L, S and E, refer to Appendix F.

2. An information board (omitted here for clarity) must be displayed.

For a larger version of this image, please see Appendix B and Safety at street works and road works: a Code of Practice (2013).

Lead-in taper of cones (T). The length will vary with the speed limit and the width of the works.

Longways clearance (L). This is the distance between the lead-in taper of cones (T) and the working space. It will vary with the speed limit.

Sideways clearance (S). This is the width between the working space and moving traffic. It will vary with the speed limit.

 For a chart showing the longways and sideways clearance dimensions required for works on roads with various speed limits refer to Appendix F.

 ## Prosecution by the HSE following injury to a road worker

A utilities contractor was fined £12,000 after a worker was injured when they were hit by a bus passing through the contractor's roadworks.

The court was told that the safety zone was not being maintained and no other control measures were in place. The worker had to manoeuvre into the live traffic lane briefly to position some equipment as the bus was passing.

If an advisory speed limit is in operation the chart at Appendix F must be used to determine minimum longways and sideways clearances. Wherever traffic speeds are to be reduced, the method must be agreed in advance with the Highway Authority.

For safety reasons, it may be necessary to advise the emergency services of the location and duration of the works.

Working spaces and safety zones must be provided when personnel are present. If pedestrians are diverted into the carriageway, a safety zone must be provided between the outer pedestrian barrier and the traffic.

 For further information refer to the CoP and also Appendix C.

Where the highway width is so restricted as to prohibit the provision of the appropriate sideways clearance and diversion of traffic would be impractical, traffic speeds must be reduced to less than 10 mph and a mandatory speed limit imposed.

There must also be an agreed safe method of working imposed on the site.

The safe system of work should be developed in advance and recorded in writing. It should prohibit working in the safety zone other than to maintain cones or road signs.

1.8   Signage and other site equipment

Traffic signs and other apparatus for the control of traffic must comply with the **Traffic Signs Regulations and General Directions**.

Compliance is achieved by the use of equipment conforming to the relevant British Standards. Equipment must also meet any requirements set out in the code as to size or performance.

All street works, irrespective of site and whether taking place at ground level or overhead, require adequate warning and information to be given to pedestrians and drivers.

 For a selection of signs and equipment refer to Appendix A.

1.8.1   Temporary traffic management works

Consideration must always be given to operatives who are setting up, altering or removing temporary traffic management.

Clients and employers must ensure that operatives carrying out these operations are appropriately trained, supplied with the correct equipment and follow a safe system of work.

1.8.1.1   Crossing high-speed roads on foot

The HSE was so concerned about this aspect of temporary traffic management works that it published specific guidance on it, which applies to motorways and dual carriageways with a speed limit of 50 mph and above.

 For further information refer to the HSE publication *Reducing risk in temporary traffic management operations* (CIS53).

The guidance puts the initial responsibility on the designers of road works to ensure that the risks arising from the installation, alteration and removal of temporary traffic management controls are, where reasonably practicable, eliminated or reduced.

Any remaining significant risks should be highlighted and subsequently controlled by the careful planning and management of the works.

Systems of work should not rely on workers crossing the carriageway unless there are:

- adequate, unobstructed lines of sight
- traffic flows in which there are suitable gaps
- no more than four continuous lanes to cross (including slip roads)
- safe points to start and finish crossing.

When crossing the live carriageway, make sure that workers:

- are wearing appropriate personal protective equipment (PPE)
- can see and be seen by oncoming traffic
- can estimate appropriate safe gaps in the traffic
- stand back from the edge of the live carriageway before setting off
- set off only when a safe gap is present in the traffic
- walk straight across the carriageway
- carry equipment in a way that does not obstruct their view of oncoming traffic
- avoid running or zig-zagging between lanes
- avoid cat's eyes and other trip hazards
- carry signs and equipment in a way that minimises the risk of dropping them and reduces their resistance to wind
- avoid displaying the front of signs to oncoming traffic
- do not obscure their hi-vis clothing
- move to a position of safety after crossing (where possible, protected by safety fences or cones), at least 1.2 m from the live carriageway on high-speed roads and 0.5 m on all other roads
- take care when moving equipment so as not to endanger themselves or road users.

Managers and supervisors should judge whether to start work when poor weather conditions are forecast. If weather conditions deteriorate whilst work is in progress, the supervisor on site should decide whether or not to stop working.

Traffic management workers require high standards of physical fitness, eyesight and hearing. Operatives' health, fitness and suitability should be assessed before they are assigned to traffic management work.

STREET WORKS AND ROAD WORKS

Assessment should ensure that workers:

- have full, unrestricted use of their neck, trunk and legs

- have at least 6/12 distance vision when wearing glasses or contact lenses

- have good hearing

- are suitable for this work if they suffer from specific conditions (such as vertigo, balance disorders, gastrointestinal conditions and sleep disorders)

- are not taking inappropriate medication, illegal drugs or excessive amounts of alcohol.

 Having 6/12 vision means you can see at 6 m what a person with perfect vision can see from a distance of 12 m.

1.8.2   Advance signs

A 'Road works ahead' sign must be placed where it can be easily seen, well before the works.

Its size and minimum distance from the start of the lead-in taper is governed by road type and traffic speed.

 For further information refer to *Safety at street works and road works: a Code of Practice* (2013).

A 'Road narrows ahead' sign, indicating which side of the carriageway is obstructed, should be placed between the 'Road works ahead' sign and commencement of the taper of cones.

1.8.3   Cones and lights

Traffic cones are placed to guide the traffic past the works.

The length of coned area and size of cones is governed by the speed limit and the type of road.

 For further information refer to Appendix A.

Road warning lights are added at night, in poor daytime visibility and in bad weather. They must not be positioned higher than 1.2 m above the road surface.

 For further information refer to *Safety at street works and road works: a Code of Practice* (2013).

Cones and lights control road use during work

Road warning lights are used as shown in the table below.

Warning lights	Lights can be used		Lights must be used		
Speed limit	20 mph	30 mph	40 mph	50 mph	60 mph
Maximum height	1.5 m	1.5 m	1.5 m	1.2 m	1.2 m
Flashing option permitted (on street lit roads only)	Yes	Yes	Yes	No	No

1.8.4   Keep left and Keep right signs

Place 'Keep left' or 'Keep right' signs as appropriate at the beginning and end of the lead-in taper of cones.

1.8.5   Traffic barrier or Lane closed sign

A traffic barrier is positioned within the coned-off area facing oncoming traffic to indicate the width of the works site.

Lane closure signs are positioned ahead of the works area to warn drivers of the upcoming lane closure.

If a conspicuous works vehicle is present, a barrier may not be necessary.

(For further information refer to 1.5.5 Works on footways.)

Managing closed lanes using good, clear signage

1.8.6 Pedestrian and traffic barriers

Pedestrian barriers should be used to mark out temporary footways, with a rigid barrier to protect pedestrians from traffic, excavation, plant or materials.

Handrails should be between 1 m and 1.2 m above ground level, with tapping rails (for blind or partially-sighted people) 150 mm deep, set with the lower edge up to 200 mm above ground level.

Road warning lights should be placed at the ends of the barriers at night. Barriers may be separate portable post and plank systems, gate frames linked together, or semi-permanent constructions built to enclose the site.

There are several different requirements for the barrier planks associated with post and plank systems.

The following section explains the requirements and how they may be met using barrier planks, which are red and white and manufactured in fully retro-reflective materials.

Barrier planks are required to carry out three functions, shown in the table below.

Sign showing right hand lane closure

1.	As a **traffic barrier**	When a traffic lane is closed, the regulations require this closure to be made using a retro-reflective* red and white barrier plank placed across the lane. This is illustrated as a traffic barrier in the top image, above. Advanced warning is shown by a 'Lane closed' sign (above).
2.	As a **pedestrian barrier**	Pedestrians must be separated from the works by barriers, which are conspicuous and mounted as part of a portable fencing system. Pedestrian barrier planks may be of several different contrasting colours; yellow, white or orange colours are best detected by partially-sighted people, but red and white is one of the acceptable combinations.
3.	As a **tapping rail** for blind and partially-sighted people	Tapping rails are placed as the bottom rail in a pedestrian fencing system. A red and white barrier plank may be used.

Note: *Since 1 April 2015 there has been an additional requirement that where a site is unattended for a period of 24 hours or more (including weekends), individual barriers or groups of barriers must be capable of withstanding winds of Class B (17.6 m/s) blowing from any direction.*

* *Retro-reflective means that at night the material reflects light back to the light source.*

All barriers facing oncoming traffic should be of the fully retro-reflective red and white form. Red and white barrier planks do not have to be used for pedestrian barriers or tapping rails but, if they are, they must be retro-reflective. Other planks used for these purposes do not need to be retro-reflective. There are other points to note about the use of barrier planks in portable fencing systems.

- The traffic barrier ('Lane closed' sign) is not needed if the works are protected by a conspicuous vehicle.

- Pedestrian barrier systems must be rigid enough to guard pedestrians from traffic, excavations, plant or materials. They must be placed with sufficient clearance to prevent pedestrians falling into the excavation and, when placed to create a temporary footway in the carriageway parallel to the traffic stream, must be protected by a row of traffic cones between the barrier and the traffic stream. If the excavation is deep, or positioned close to pedestrians, stronger barriers may be needed and/or other safety measures may be required (such as covering or temporarily refilling the excavation).

    Where a work site may be approached by pedestrians crossing the road from the opposite side, you should place barriers, including tapping rails, all around the excavation, even when pedestrians are not diverted into the carriageway.

- Where long excavations are sited in situations where pedestrians are not expected to cross from the opposite side, barriers on the traffic stream side of the works area do not need the tapping rail. In these circumstances, on an unrestricted road, the barrier on the traffic stream side can be replaced with an additional row of cones. These cones should be linked with a suitably supported traffic tape to attract attention to the boundary of the safety zone.

All sides of an excavation where a pedestrian may gain access must be fenced off

Use pedestrian barriers to mark out any temporary footway. You must always use a rigid barrier to protect pedestrians from traffic, excavations, plant or materials. Place road warning lights at the ends of the barriers at night so that they may be clearly seen by pedestrians.

 For further information refer to *Safety at street works and road works: a Code of Practice* **(2013).**

STREET WORKS AND ROAD WORKS

1.8.7 Information board

An information board **must** be displayed at all sites, except mobile sites, short duration works and minor works that do not involve excavation. On sites where it is not a mandatory requirement, it is still desirable that a board is displayed.

As a minimum, the following information must be provided on the board.

- The name of the organisation undertaking the works.

- A telephone number for emergencies.

- The name of the principal contractor.

Wherever practical, the board should also contain other useful information, such as a description of the work that is being carried out, how long the work will take and a message apologising for any delay or inconvenience.

1.8.8 End sign

Road works that are 50 m or more in length (excluding the length of the tapers) must have a 'Road works ahead' sign and an 'End' plate, beyond the end of the works, to indicate the end of the work and any associated restrictions.

Where there is a series of two or more sites close together, the 'End' sign should only be placed after the last site (remember to cater to traffic travelling in both directions).

There is no need for an 'End' sign at the following locations.

- Where works are less than 50 m in length, unless there are two or more such sites close together.

- At road works on minor roads, with a speed limit of 30 mph or less, that do not carry a heavy volume of traffic or many large vehicles.

Where the permanent speed limit changes within the section of a road covered by the temporary speed restriction, any signs indicating the permanent speed limit must be obscured.

At the end of the temporary speed restriction, signs indicating the return to the permanent speed limit must be positioned on both sides of the carriageway, to indicate the speed limit from that point on.

 For further information refer to *Safety at street works and road works: a Code of Practice* (2013).

1.8.9 Sign lighting and reflectorisation

Signs and any plates used with them must be directly lit when all of the following conditions apply.

- There is a permanent speed limit of 50 mph or above.
- The street lighting is on.

- There is general street lighting.
- The sign is within 50 m of a street light.

All signs, including cones and red and white barrier planks, must be reflectorised to BS EN 12899-1:2007 Class 1 or Class 2. The only exception is the information board and pedestrian signs.

 For further information refer to *Safety at street works and road works: a Code of Practice* (2013).

1.8.10 Security and stability of signs

Only use signs that are approved and in accordance with the relevant British Standard, and ensure that they are placed correctly. All signs and guarding equipment should be properly secured so that they cannot be blown over by the wind or dislodged by passing traffic.

Built-in weights or sacks containing sand or other fine granular materials should be used, not kerbstones or similar weights, as they could be dangerous if hit by moving traffic.

Signs or guarding equipment should not be pushed into the ground as there may be unidentified services positioned below the surface. Make sure that the signs are correctly positioned and are of adequate size to give early warning of the hazard, in accordance with the table in the CoP.

Check signs regularly for position, stability and cleanliness as they may have fallen over, been moved, or become damaged or dirty.

Signs should be properly secured and checked regularly

1.8.11 Visibility of signs

All signs must be reflectorised, regularly cleaned to remove dust and dirt thrown up from passing vehicles and adequately lit after dark in accordance with the CoP. Signs must be placed so as to give the required forward visibility to approaching vehicles.

 For sizing and siting distances of signage and cones refer to Appendix F.

1.8.12 Two-way roads

On a two-way road, the signs should be set out for traffic in both directions.

1.8.13 Surplus signs

It is illegal to leave any signage or guarding equipment in position when it is no longer required. Signage and guarding that is no longer required should be removed immediately.

A fallen sign means that drivers will be unaware of the hazard they are approaching and the actions they need to take

1.9 Traffic control

Select the method of traffic control from the table within the CoP. The CoP gives precise details of these methods.

 You will also need to refer to the table in the inside back cover of the CoP (also included at Appendix F).

 For example diagrams on how to manage traffic control refer to Appendix B.

1.9.1 Traffic control by give and take system

Only use the give and take system when **all** of the following apply.

- The length of the works from the start of the lead-in taper to the end of the exit taper is 50 m or less.
- Two-way traffic is less than 20 vehicles counted over three minutes (400 vehicles per hour).
- Fewer than 20 heavy goods vehicles pass the site per hour.
- The speed limit is 30 mph or under.
- Drivers approaching from either direction can see 50 m beyond the end of the works.

Parking near the works, especially in front and opposite, is controlled or prohibited, unless visibility or lane width is unaffected.

1.9.2 Traffic control by priority signs

Only use priority signs when **all** of the following apply.

- The speed limit is 60 mph or less.
- Two-way traffic is less than 42 vehicles, counted over three minutes (840 vehicles per hour).
- The length of the works, including tapers, is no more than 80 m.
- Drivers approaching from either direction can see through the length of works from a specified distance before the works to a similar distance beyond the works. Distances vary according to speed restrictions, as follows:
  - 60 m on 30 mph roads
  - 70 m on 40 mph roads
  - 80 m on 50 mph roads
  - 100 m on 60 mph roads.

Priority over oncoming vehicles

Priority over vehicles from opposite direction

1.9.3 Traffic control by stop/go boards

Remotely controlled stop/go boards should be used where possible. **All** of the following conditions must be met.

- The distance between stop/go boards is no more than 200 m.
- Use of the boards is restricted to daylight hours.
- An unobstructed view of both approaches is maintained.
- The operative is less than 100 m from both boards.
- Traffic flow is less than 840 vehicles per hour.

STREET WORKS AND ROAD WORKS

Where the shuttle lane with this type of system is more than 20 m, or it continues round a bend, stop/go boards will be needed at both ends of that lane. Manually-rotated stop/go boards can be used under the following circumstances.

Coned length (metres)	Maximum two-way traffic flow	
	Vehicles per three minutes	Vehicles per hour
Up to 100	70	1,400
101 to 200	63	1,250
201 to 300	53	1,050
301 to 400	47	950
401 to 500	42	850

1.9.4   Traffic control by portable traffic signals

Two-way portable traffic signals may only be used when all of the following requirements are met.

- The speed limit is a maximum of 60 mph.

- The length of the site is 300 m or less.

- The site does not straddle a railway level crossing.

- Traffic control is at least 50 m away from a level crossing equipped with twin red light signals.

- The Highway Authority has been informed and authorisation has been obtained.

- The signals are vehicle actuated (unless otherwise instructed by the Highway Authority).

- The signals are of a type approved for use on the highway.

- Stop/go boards are available in case the portable traffic signals cease to function correctly.

Traffic control in operation

 Worker dies as a result of inadequate traffic control

A Magistrates' Court heard that workers from a sub-contractor were using a road planer to remove the old tar from the south bound side of the road, while the north bound side had traffic lights to control the direction of the traffic. During the activity one of the workers was hit by a passing vehicle. The man, aged 37, was taken to hospital, but died of his extensive injuries.

The HSE prosecuted both companies after an investigation found they had failed to ensure the road planing operation was carried out in a manner that allowed vehicles and pedestrians to move safely around the roadworks, without exposing persons to risks to their health and safety.

Speaking after the prosecution the HSE inspector said: 'In this instance the only control measures in place were cones along the centre of the road, and traffic was allowed to pass at 60 mph, close to the workers who were not provided with a safety zone because of the lack of space. Had adequate controls and a safe system of work been in place this terrible incident could have been prevented'. *(Source: HSE)*

1.10   Personal protective equipment

1.10.1   High-visibility clothing

Given the nature of road works and the proximity of moving traffic, the importance of workers being clearly seen by colleagues and the travelling public cannot be overstated.

Whether working on site or just visiting, everyone must wear a high-visibility jacket or waistcoat at all times, manufactured to EN ISO 20471 standard requirements.

High-visibility clothing must conform to the relevant, current British or European standards and be worn as listed below.

- Correctly fastened.

- In a clean and usable condition.

Workers wearing PPE to Class 3 standard

- Where necessary, within the working space, as directed by the employer.
- When operating outside of the working space (such as when setting out, maintaining or removing signing, lighting, guarding and temporary traffic control).

The table below gives an indication of the requirements.

Class	Description	Colour
Class 1	Defines the lowest visibility level. The minimum level of protection required for any person working on a private road, or to be used in conjunction with high class garments. Minimum 0.10 m^2 of reflective material. Example: high-visibility trousers with two 5 cm reflective bands around each leg. These become Class 3 when worn with a Class 3 jacket.	The colour of the background should normally be fluorescent yellow or orange and the reflective material should comply with EN ISO 20471.
Class 2	Defines an intermediary visibility level. Required when working on or near to A or B class roads, and for delivery drivers. Minimum 0.13 m^2 of reflective material. Example: vest with two 5 cm bands of reflective tape around body or one 5 cm band around body and braces over both shoulders.	Colour scheme as Class 1.
Class 3	Defines the highest visibility level. Used when working near to or on motorways, dual carriageways or airports. Must be worn on dual carriageway roads with a speed limit of 50 mph or above. Minimum 0.20 m^2 of reflective material. Example: long-sleeved jacket and trouser suit with two 5 cm bands of reflective tape around the body and arms, and braces over both shoulders.	Colour scheme as Class 1.

 High-visibility garments and jackets with sleeves must comply with Class 3 and be worn when working on or near live high-speed roads.

1.10.1.1 England and Northern Ireland

A risk assessment must determine the standard of high-visibility clothing required. In most cases, for work outside the working area, the likely minimum requirement is for a jacket with the maximum area of visible material, as specified in current British and European standards.

1.10.1.2 Scotland and Wales

In Scotland and Wales the general requirement is for a jacket to have full length sleeves and comply with current British and European standards. However, where a risk assessment indicates that full length sleeves would increase the risk of harm, due to the activity being carried out, three-quarter length sleeves may be worn.

1.10.2 Other personal protective equipment

The wearing of other personal protective equipment (PPE) will invariably include safety footwear, which must have non-slip soles. Other PPE (such as head, hearing, eye and skin protection) must be worn, when required, depending on the nature of the work being carried out.

Hearing protection is not a requirement when crossing live carriageways. Hearing damage from passing traffic is considered to be less of a risk than a person being struck by a vehicle because they were not fully aware of what was going on around them. A risk assessment would be required in these circumstances.

 For further information refer to Chapter B06 Personal protective equipment.

1.11　Training

Although the NRSWA refers to a trained operative, there is no specific requirement in the Act for operatives or supervisors to undergo training or produce evidence of prior training. However, it is a requirement of the New Roads and Street Works Act that at least one person on site at all times has a prescribed qualification as an operative for the task being carried out.

If the works involve breaking up or tunnelling under the street, an operative and a supervisor with prescribed qualifications for the task being carried out must be on site at all times. The Act also requires that the site is under the supervision of a qualified supervisor. The supervisor does not have to be on site at all times, allowing them to control more than one site at a time.

Furthermore, attention should be paid to the employer's duties regarding training as laid down in the Health and Safety at Work etc. Act, the Management of Health and Safety at Work Regulations (as amended) and other relevant legislation. All Local Authorities will require evidence of the competence of operatives and supervisors prior to issuing a road opening or closure licence on the public highway.

Evidence of competence is achieved through the ownership of a street works card. Many contractors and individuals are registered on the street works qualification register (SWQR). To obtain the street works card individuals have to achieve one or more recognised qualification for the tasks they wish to carry out on site. These qualifications can be gained either through training and assessment or assessment only.

On achievement the body who award the qualification will contact the SWQR who, in turn, will register the individual and issue a street works card with the appropriate qualification endorsements. Each qualification is valid for five years. Two types of card are available, one at operative level and the other at supervisor level.

1.11.1   National Highways Sector Scheme 12

National Highways Sector Schemes (NHSS) are bespoke, quality management systems for organisations working on the UK road network. There are currently more than 20 individual schemes, covering a range of highways-related activities (such as fencing, landscaping, road surfacing and marking).

There are several parts to NHSS 12, which covers temporary traffic management. Each part relates to different road types *(shown right)*.

Any company that supplies services to the Highways Agency under the Specification for Highways Works (SHW) must be

12A/B	High-speed motorways and dual carriageways.
12C	Mobile lane closures on motorways and other dual carriageways.
12D	Works on rural and urban roads.

certified under all the relevant schemes for the work they will carry out. The schemes aim to make sure that work is carried out to the highest standards of professionalism, using properly trained staff. The scheme places a strong emphasis on health and safety qualifications under the various schemes, which are awarded by Lantra Awards.

 For the latest information, please visit *NHSS: certification for contractors and subcontractors* on the National Highways website.

Appendix A – Signs and equipment

Basic signs and equipment

Road works ahead

Road narrows on left-hand side ahead

Road narrows on right-hand side ahead

Keep right

Keep left

End of road works

Traffic cone

Warning light

Typical pedestrian barrier with tapping rail

Typical traffic barrier

Information board

High visibility clothing

Other signs and plates

Road narrows on both sides ahead

Traffic signals ahead

Traffic control ahead

Where vehicles should stop at temporary traffic signals

Where vehicles should stop at temporary stop sign

Stop/Go boards

Give way to oncoming vehicles
Priority to vehicles from opposite direction

Priority over oncoming vehicles
Priority over vehicles from opposite direction

Stop Works

Ramp ahead
Ramp

Traffic signals not in use

Zebra or signal controlled crossing is not in use

Direction of temporary pedestrian route

Workforce in road slow

Other danger ahead (use only with a supplementary plate)

Slippery road

Loose chippings

Temporary road surface

Cyclists dismount

Or variations of these signs

Left-hand lane of a dual two-lane carriageway road closed

Left-hand lane of a dual three-lane carriageway road closed

Centre lane of a three-lane two-way road closed

Examples of supplementary plates for use with other signs

Single file traffic
Grass cutting
Gully emptying
Line painting

For 1 mile
Distance over which hazard or prohibition extends

1 mile
800 yds
Distance to hazard or obstruction

250 yds
Distance and direction to hazard or obstruction

Max speed 20
Maximum speed advised

Note: this shows some of the more common signs in use. It does not show every sign that might be required.

Based on © Crown copyright diagrams from *Safety at street works and road works: a Code of Practice* (2013). For further information visit the HSE website.

Appendix B – Traffic control

Traffic control by give and take for roads with a speed limit of 30 mph or less

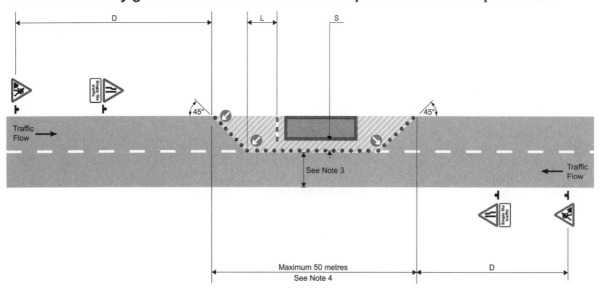

Notes

1. For numbers and minimum size of cones, and dimensions D, L and S, refer to Appendix F.

2. An information board (omitted here for clarity) must be displayed.

3. Refer to page 52 of the CoP for guidance on unobstructed width past the works.

4. 50 m maximum applies only where two-way flow cannot be maintained past the works.

Traffic control by priority signs

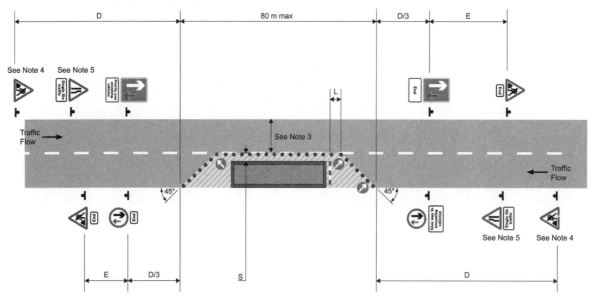

Notes

1. For numbers and minimum size of cones, and dimensions D, L, S and E, refer to Appendix F.

2. An information board (omitted here for clarity) must be displayed.

3. Refer to page 52 of the CoP for guidance on unobstructed width past the works.

4. A supplementary distance plate is required for roads with a speed limit of 50 mph or more.

5. For roads with a speed limit of 50 mph or more an assessment should be made as to whether 'for' and a distance should be included on a supplementary plate.

 Based on © Crown copyright diagrams from *Safety at street works and road works: a Code of Practice* (2013). For further information visit the HSE website.

Traffic control by stop/go boards

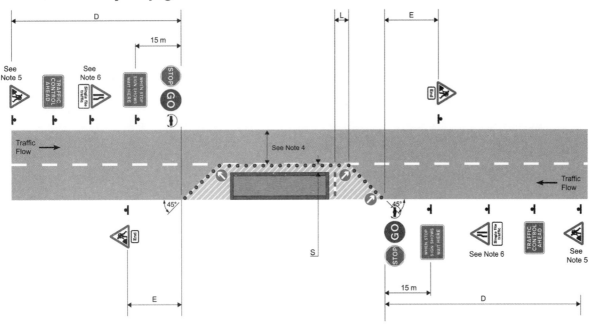

Notes

1. For numbers and minimum size of cones, and dimensions D, L, S and E, refer to Appendix F.

2. An information board (omitted here for clarity) must be displayed.

3. Stop/go boards should be placed where they will be in full view of approaching drivers. They may be located on either side of the carriageway.

4. Refer to page 52 of the CoP for guidance on unobstructed width past the works.

5. A supplementary distance plate is required for roads with a speed limit of 50 mph or more.

6. For roads with a speed limit of 50 mph or more an assessment should be made as to whether 'for' and a distance should be included on a supplementary plate.

Traffic control by portable traffic signals

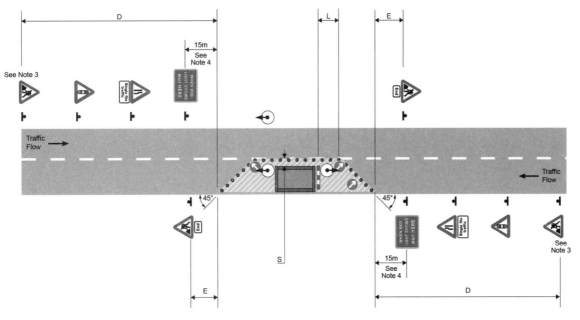

Notes

1. For numbers and minimum size of cones, and dimensions D, L, S and E, refer to Appendix F.

2. An information board (omitted here for clarity) must be displayed.

3. A supplementary distance plate is required for roads with a permanent speed limit of 50 mph or more.

4. This distance may have to be increased in some cases to allow larger vehicles to pass the works.

 Based on © Crown copyright diagrams from *Safety at street works and road works: a Code of Practice* (2013). For further information visit the HSE website.

Appendix C – Works on footways

01

Works entirely on the footway

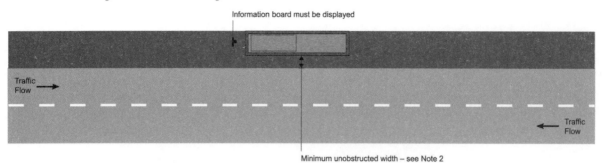

Notes

1. Advance signs are not required when the works, signing, lighting and guidance are entirely on the footway.

2. 1.5 m preferred minimum unobstructed width, 1 m absolute minimum.

Works on footway with pedestrian diversion into carriageway

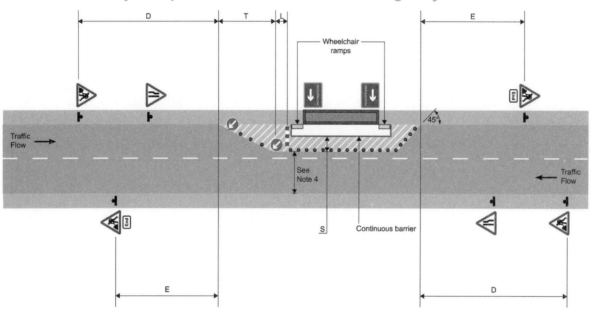

Notes

1. For numbers and minimum size of cones, and dimensions D, T, L, S and E, refer to Appendix F.

2. An information board (omitted here for clarity) must be displayed.

3. Wheelchair ramps must be provided at the transition from footway to carriageway.

4. Refer to page 52 of the CoP for guidance on unobstructed width past the works.

5. Additional pedestrian barriers may be provided parallel or at right angles to the kerb, as site conditions require, to guide pedestrians past the works.

 Based on © Crown copyright diagrams from *Safety at street works and road works: a Code of Practice* (2013). For further information visit the HSE website.

Appendix D – Carriageway works

Works between parked vehicles with a speed limit of 30 mph or less

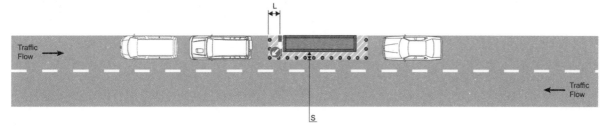

Notes

1. No advance signing, lead-in taper or exit taper required provided that the whole works, including the safety zone, do not extend beyond the line of vehicles.

2. An information board (omitted here for clarity) must be displayed.

3. If parked vehicles move away, tapers and advance signing should be provided.

Works obstructing a signal controlled pedestrian crossing

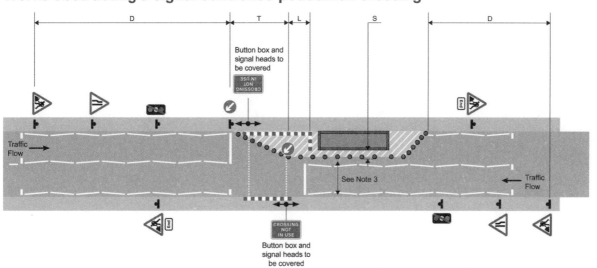

Notes

1. For numbers and minimum size of cones, and dimensions D, T, L and S, refer to Appendix F.

2. An information board (omitted here for clarity) must be displayed.

3. Refer to page 52 of the CoP for further guidance on unobstructed width past the works.

 Based on © Crown copyright diagrams from *Safety at street works and road works: a Code of Practice* (2013). For further information visit the HSE website.

Appendix E – Mobile works

Mobile works on a single carriageway road

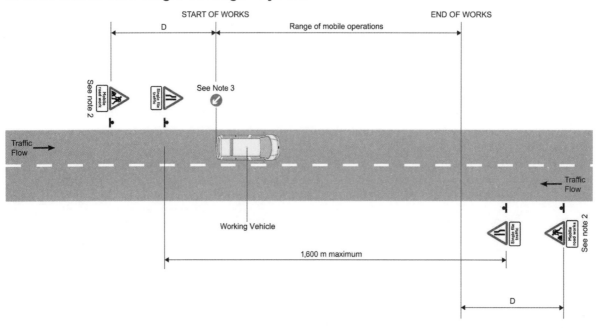

Notes

1. For dimension D refer to Appendix F.

2. Or permitted variants.

3. Where a risk assessment determines that it is necessary to display signs on the working vehicle, they must comply with TSRGD (TSR (NI) in Northern Ireland).

 Based on © Crown copyright diagrams from *Safety at street works and road works: a Code of Practice* (2013). For further information visit the HSE website.

Appendix F – Setting out the site

(Distances in metres unless stated otherwise. Numbers are minimum numbers.)

Type of road	Minimum visibility distance to first sign	D Distance from first sign to start of lead-in taper		Lead-in taper Width of works including sideways safety zone							S Minimum width of sideways safety zone	E Distance from last cone to End of works sign	Minimum size of signs (mm)
				1m	2m	3m	4m	5m	6m	7m			
Single carriageway – speed limit 30 mph or less	60	20 to 45	**T** Taper length	13	26	39	52	65	78	91	0.5	10 to 30	600
			No of cones	4	4	6	7	9	10	12			
			No of lights	–	–	–	–	–	–	–			
Single carriageway – speed limit 40 mph	60	45 to 110	**T** Taper length	20	40	60	80	100	120	140	0.5	30 to 45	750
			No of cones	4	6	8	10	13	15	17			
			No of lights	3	5	7	9	12	14	16			
Single carriageway – speed limit 50 mph or more	75	275 to 450	**T** Taper length	25	50	75	100	125	150	175	1.2	30 to 45	750
			No of cones	4	7	10	13	15	18	21			
			No of llights	3	6	9	12	14	17	20			
All-purpose dual carriageway – speed limit 40 mph or less	60	110 to 275	**T** Taper length	25	50	75	100	125	150	175	0.5	30 to 45	750
			No of cones	4	7	10	13	15	18	21			
			No of lights	3	6	9	12	14	17	20			

Speed limit mph	20	30	40	50	60
L Longways clearance	0.5	0.5	15	30	60

Speed limit mph	30 or less	40 or more
C Clearance to works vehicle	2	5

Notes

1. For roads covered by this Code, the minimum height of cones is 450 mm where the speed limit is 40 mph or less, and 750 mm where the speed limit is 50 mph or more.

2. The maximum spacing between cones in longitudinal lengths shall be 9 m, but no fewer than two cones shall be used in any length between tapers.

3. Lead-in tapers where two-way traffic control is used, and all exit tapers shall be at about 45° to the kerb line with cones spaced 1.2 m apart maximum.

4. In certain circumstances on congested roads with speed limits of 30 mph or less, the lead-in taper may be reduced to 45° (see page 19 of the CoP).

5. The longways clearance (L) is the distance between the end of the lead-in taper and the first traffic barrier placed across the lane.

 Based on © Crown copyright diagrams from *Safety at street works and road works: a Code of Practice* (2013). For further information visit the HSE website.

STREET WORKS AND ROAD WORKS

Trackside safety

GT700 Toolbox talks / supporting checklists and forms

Toolbox talks on some of these topics are available in the GT700 publication. Supporting checklists and forms covering some of these topics are available on our companion website.

Supporting
INFORMATION

02

Overview

Working on a railway is a high-risk activity. Not only are there the normal problems of construction work to contend with, there is also the hazard of trains moving at high speed and close proximity. High Speed 1 was introduced for the Eurostar trains, which are capable of speeds of up to 186 mph. Domestic passenger services may run at 140 mph on this route. High Speed 2 (HS2) will enable line speeds of up to 250 mph. There could also be rail traction current supplied via overhead electricity lines at 25,000 volts AC or third and fourth rails carrying up to 750 volts DC.

Despite the UK having one of the safest railways in Europe, there has still been an increase of around 21% in workforce injuries. Some of these avoidable injuries were due to insufficient planning, failure to follow the safe system of work and worker competence.

It is important to understand that this chapter is intended as a brief guide for site managers to provide awareness only. For those who may be required to work, or put people to work, on the rail network, further information can be found in the Network Rail Standards and the *Rule book*.

 Supporting information to complement this section can be found in the Rail Safety and Standards Board (RSSB) standards catalogue or the Network Rail Safety Central website.

2.1 Introduction

Competence plays an important role in controlling health and safety risks when working on an operational railway system. It depends upon managing a complex mix of infrastructure, railway-specific rules, safety management systems and human factors.

Network Rail (which manages the railway infrastructure) has laid down standards and procedures that have to be strictly followed by all people working on railways. While the following information will contribute to working safely on railways, it can only be a summary of this complex subject and it is recommended that readers contact Network Rail directly for more detailed information relating to individual projects.

With the decentralised management of the railways, the fear was that the safety of the railway would be jeopardised by the introduction of independent railway operators. To prevent this happening the Office of Rail and Road (ORR) took overall responsibility for rail industry health and safety regulations in April 2006. At the same time new regulations were introduced in the form of the Railways and Other Guided Transport Systems (Safety) (ROGS) Regulations.

The ROGS Regulations and the Health and Safety at Work etc. Act are administered and enforced by the ORR.

 An explanation of how the ROGS Regulations apply to safety critical work is contained in the ORR publication *Safety critical tasks – Clarification of ROGS Regulations requirements* (Railways safety publication 4).

The Rail Safety and Standards Board (RSSB) is a not-for-profit company, owned and funded by major stakeholders in the railway industry. A part of RSSB's remit is to publish and update Railway Group Standards, which govern the way that work is carried out on the railways, including the management of health and safety. Under the leadership of RSSB the industry has developed a series of *Rule book* handbooks, which are task based and cover a wide range of subjects, such as duties of the controller of site safety (COSS) or the safe work leader (SWL) and the practicalities, logistics and 'people' aspects of railway operations. The *Rule book* is also available as an app.

The primary purpose of the change to the handbook format was to rationalise the content and structure of the document so that it is more accurately targeted at the skill sets of end-users and clearly aligned with operational principles. The objectives of rationalisation and restructuring are explained below.

● Reduce rule-based errors, violations and misapplication.

● Enable end-users to exercise greater judgement and discretion in resolving operational issues.

● Reduce the need for, and the costs of, future rule changes.

● Support industry goals for competence management and performance improvement.

The onus is on organisations who work on the railways to make sure that they are referring to the most recent edition of any reference material.

Persons who work on the railways must achieve additional competencies beyond the requirements for those employed in conventional construction work.

For further details on the RSSB guide on developing the competence of staff at all levels to work on the rail network refer to Appendix C.

2.2   Important points

- There are two important terms you need to be aware of: 'Lineside' and 'On or near the line'. It is important that any work taking place on the lineside must not encroach or affect the area known as 'on or near the line'. Where any work is likely to affect the 'on or near the line' area, there must be a COSS or SWL present and operatives will require additional training.

- Means of access to the work site must be stated in the safe system of work (work package plan (WPP), task briefing sheet (TBS) or safe work package (SWP)). The access point may consist of a cabin, which may be staffed for the duration of the work.

- In order to ensure that members of the public do not gain access to rail sites, all sites must be secured at all times and any security or safety-related incident must be reported through the safety management information system (SMIS), as detailed in the Railway Group Standard GE/RT8047 – *Reporting of safety related information*.

- The site rules must be displayed in the access point; each member of staff is required to sign in and out of the site.

- The work area must be scanned using a Network Rail approved cable avoidance tool (CAT) for underground services by a competent, authorised person prior to the work commencing. Any services identified must be marked and, if possible, temporarily removed (signalling cables).

- The COSS or SWL must brief the workforce on the site safety rules prior to the work starting, and brief the incoming COSS or SWL at the shift changeover.

- Following the briefing, each member of staff must sign the COSS or SWL briefing form to confirm they have understood the brief.

- Personal protective equipment (PPE) must comply with relevant legislation, British Standards and Railway Group Standards; the requirements are different to those for general non-railway construction work.

 PPE requirements must comply with Network Rail's PPE policy.

Network Rail is constantly committed to eliminating all injuries and fatalities within the rail network industry. They run frequent safety campaigns to highlight specific areas of safety awareness. Visit their website to find out more about the latest campaign.

 For further information visit the Network Rail Safety Central website.

2.3   Network Rail licensing

 If making enquiries about becoming a supplier of construction services to Network Rail, a list of the main contacts can be found on the Network Rail website, or you can contact them directly.

All principal contractors who tender for work with Network Rail must maintain a principal contractor licence (PCL), which is subject to ongoing scrutiny by Network Rail.

When a contract is awarded, the principal contractor must produce a construction phase plan (CPP) for the contract. The principal contractor, their workforce and sub-contractors are then measured against the arrangements described in the plan.

A contractor will require sponsorship from Network Rail to enable them to enter the licensing system. The contractor applying for a licence will need to be able to demonstrate a significant level of knowledge of working in the railway environment.

The application process may, where appropriate, involve the requirement for specialist support.

However, it is important that everyone involved understands that the main aim is to check the contractor's existing systems, either against the Network Rail Standards or to align the contractor's systems with those of Network Rail (not to invent new ones).

Where a licence has been submitted, but is being reviewed, Network Rail may issue a provisional licence, which will allow the contractor to bid for rail work.

Acceptance of a licence by Network Rail should lead to training for the staff responsible for its implementation.

This is important because, whilst the document will contain the company's normal management systems, there will be a number of areas that are specific to rail work (such as drug and alcohol procedures, competence management, accident reporting and medical requirements).

Managers working on rail contracts must understand and implement these requirements.

2.3.1   Railway contractors certificate

The railway contractors certificate (RCC) will be required by companies who do not hold a principal contractor's licence but wish to employ and appoint a safe work leader (SWL) to act as the person in charge.

Holders of the RCC will be contracted directly to Network Rail, **not** the principal contractor.

2.4   General safety management

2.4.1   Safety management systems

Rail operators must obtain a safety certificate for operating trains, or a safety authorisation for infrastructure managers (which includes station managers).

The status of a safety certificate and a safety authorisation is the same, in that they allow access to the railway; however, their scope will be different. Safety certificates and safety authorisations have a maximum period of validity of five years.

There are various exemptions for the requirement to have either a safety certificate or authorisation. Some of these are shown below.

- Those operating only in engineering possessions.
- Those operating on non-mainline transport systems where the maximum permitted speed is 40 kph or less.
- Tramways.
- Railways in factories and most harbours.
- Railways within maintenance or goods depots or military establishments.

In order to obtain a safety certificate or safety authorisation the operator must implement a safety management system that includes the following.

- A statement of the safety policy.
- Targets for the maintenance and enhancement of safety, and plans and procedures for reaching those targets.
- Procedures to meet relevant technical and operational standards or other requirements set out in national safety rules, for example:
  - procedures and methods for carrying out risk assessments and implementing risk control measures
  - provisions for employee training and maintenance of competency
  - arrangements for the provision of information relevant to safety
  - procedures and formats for the documentation of safety information
  - procedures to control the layout of and changes to vital safety information
  - procedures to ensure that accidents, incidents, near misses and other dangerous occurrences are reported, investigated and analysed and that necessary preventative measures are taken
  - provision of plans for action, alerts and information in the case of an emergency
  - provisions for internal auditing of the safety management system.

In practice, a train operating company, as a vehicle operator, or Network Rail, as an infrastructure manager, will stipulate safety conditions in accordance with their safety management systems that need to be complied with for a particular contract. These will be incorporated into the licensing arrangements *(refer to 2.3)* and the construction phase plan for the project.

However, if contractors operate trains or carry out infrastructure maintenance outside of possessions then the requirements for the safety certificate, authorisation and safety management system will apply.

2.4.2   Sentinel scheme

If work on a railway entails working on or near the line, workers must have completed appropriate track safety training, including industry common induction (ICI) and a personal track safety (PTS) course, and be issued with, and be in possession of, a sentinel smartcard. This smartcard must be presented for authentication each time the worker goes on or near the line.

Card authentication can be achieved by a number of means including swiping the card with a smartcard reader, iPhone or Android check, QR code scanning, web check and interactive voice recognition (IVR).

Before undergoing training for personal track safety, workers must be certified medically fit for work in a railway environment, and undergo screening for drugs and alcohol. The standards of medical fitness are laid down in Railway Group and Network Rail Standards.

Any workers who do not meet the full medical standards may still be permitted to work on the railway subject to risk assessment and work restrictions being applied.

 Workers who successfully undergo PTS training receive a *Keypoints – Personal track safety* (PTS) health and safety booklet outlining safe working procedures and their responsibilities when working on the railways. A PDF copy of the booklet is available online.

2.4.3   Competency and training in track safety supervision

The Office of Rail and Road (ORR), having taken over responsibility for health and safety on the railways (from the Health and Safety Executive (HSE) in 2006), introduced a competence management system (CMS), the structure of which is explained in the ORR publication *Developing and maintaining staff competence (Railway safety publication 1)*.

The publication is a guide for people who are responsible for ensuring and maintaining the competency of operatives whose work could have an impact on the rail network. Managers responsible for maintaining the CMS should be familiar with the detail within the ORR publication.

2.4.4 Personal track safety card

This competency allows qualified workers to walk on or near the line alone, to access or egress the site only, without the requirement to have either a COSS or SWL present. PTS card carriers at the most basic level cannot carry out **any** work on or near to a line. The PTS cards are also endorsed with more detailed information specific to working on tracks that use conductor rail equipment (CRE) and overhead line equipment (OLE). The person in charge will have to ensure that operatives' cards are endorsed appropriately before allowing them near the tracks.

The competency card allows qualified workers to work on alternating current (AC)/direct current (DC) line areas under the control of a COSS or SWL, providing the staff hold AC/DCCR competence and PTS on the sentinel database.

This competency is valid for two years. Upon successful completion of a new course and any additional modules, the online sentinel database will be updated. However, another card will not be issued. (The new sentinel smartcards replace the previous cards, which are no longer valid for access to Network Rail infrastructure.)

2.4.5 Lookout or site warden

This competency allows a qualified person to have the following.

- Lookout duties to provide enough warning to allow everyone involved in the work to reach a position of safety at least ten seconds before any train or vehicle arrives at the site of work (formerly known as the *red zone*).
- Site warden duties to maintain the safe limits of a protected area (formerly known as the *separated green zone*).

2.4.6 Person in charge of possession

This competency enables a person to carry out person in charge of possession (PICOP). This role is specific to Network Rail. To be a PICOP (or engineering supervisor), the person's details demonstrating COSS experience within the last 24 months must be held in the employer's competence management system. The PICOP will also be required to meet in full certain experience criteria. PICOP competence itself does not qualify anyone to do COSS work, which requires a separate COSS qualification.

 For information on developing and maintaining staff competence refer to Appendix C.

2.4.7 Safety critical work

The ROGS Regulations lay down a procedure to ensure that those engaged on a transport system in a work situation do so in a manner that will not affect the health and safety of people using that transport system. All workers must be competent and physically fit to carry out their allotted tasks. They must also work in such a way that the number of hours worked, combined with the rest periods taken between work, does not increase the risk of fatigue to operatives.

It is obvious that any work carried out on the railway (whether to the track, the signalling system or the trains themselves) could have disastrous effects if it is not carried out correctly. The whole reasoning behind the ROGS Regulations is to ensure that only healthy, physically fit and competent persons carry out work on the railways. These regulations should ensure that the work will be carried out to such a high standard that the risk of disaster will be negligible.

2.4.8 Working alone

People must never work alone unless they are qualified to carry out the duties of the:

- controller of site safety (COSS)
- individual working alone (IWA)
- safe work leader (SWL).

In addition, workers must have permission from and be in communication with the:

- protection controller (PC)
- engineering supervisor (ES).

2.4.8.1 Going on or near the line alone

In most instances individuals should never work alone on or near trackside. The only time when they can be alone is when they are walking and only if they comply with these requirements.

- Have a valid certificate of competence in personal track safety issued by the employer.
- Wear the correct high-visibility clothing issued by the employer.
- Have a suitable lamp if they will be on or near the line during darkness, poor visibility or if they will enter a tunnel.

 The only occasion when a worker can go on or near the line without a COSS or SWL is when they are walking alone.

2.4.9 Train movements

A train travelling at 80 mph will cover nearly 36 m (120 feet) per second.

If it takes 10 seconds to realise that a train is approaching and move off the track to a place of safety, in that time the train will have covered nearly 360 m (1,200 feet).

When anyone is working on or near a railway line, the driver of an approaching train should blow the train whistle or horn to warn of the train's approach, although this must not be relied upon.

The worker, in return, must acknowledge that they have heard the whistle, and have moved to a position of safety, by raising one arm straight in the air above their head.

All work on or near the line must be pre-planned. If lookout protection is to be utilised, then the COSS or SWL needs to assess the position and number of lookouts to ensure that warnings are provided.

The time required is decided by the COSS or SWL by conducting a risk assessment, and will depend on the speed of the approaching train and the length of time necessary to remove staff and place tools away from the running lines to enable the whole group to be standing in a position of safety for at least 10 seconds before the train passes the worksite.

The speed of the train is always taken as the maximum permissible speed at that location.

When setting up a safe system of work, a COSS or SWL needs to determine the distance at which they must be able to see a train approaching. The *Rule book* (GE/RT8000) defines safety distances according to the following factors.

If the **maximum speed** is:

- 100 mph or less, a person is in a position of safety if they are at least 1.25 m (4 feet) from the nearest line on which a train can approach;

- over 100 mph, the distance increases to 2 m (6 feet 6 inches).

A train sighting chart and an explanation of how it is used is included at Appendix A.

2.4.10 Communications protocol

You must make sure you properly understand the meaning of all messages, whether they are communicated by phone, radio or face-to-face.

- Make sure you are talking to the right person.

- Give your location, if using a phone or radio.

- Give your name and the name of your employer.

- State what task you are performing.

- If necessary, let the person know how you can be contacted.

- Use the phonetic alphabet to make sure names and locations that are difficult to pronounce are fully understood.

- Never use the words 'not clear' to describe a line that is obstructed; always use 'line blocked'.

- You must say numbers one at a time (for example, you should say 8107 as 'eight, one, zero, seven'). There are exceptions to this (such as when giving the time or when referring to a rule book module or handbook).

If you are receiving a message, make sure you fully understand it. You must repeat the message back so that the other person knows you correctly understand it.

Ensure the following to help make sure your message is fully understood when using a telephone or radio.

- Speak with the mouthpiece close to your mouth and speak directly into the mouthpiece.

- Talk slightly slower than normal using a natural rhythm.

- Use your normal level of volume when speaking.

- Avoid using hesitation sounds (for example 'um' and 'er').

- Use clear sentences.

- Get the person to repeat your message back to you.

During any conversation, one person must always take **lead responsibility**.

The person who must take lead responsibility depends on the task being carried out.

Examples are shown in the table on the next page.

Lead responsibility	When communicating with
Electrical control operator (ECO)	Anyone
Signaller	Anyone except the ECO
PICOP (person in charge of the possession)	Anyone except the ECO or signaller
Engineering supervisor	Each COSS/PC
Route-setting agent	Points operator
Protection controller (PC)	Each COSS
COSS	Members of the work group
COSS	Each lookout/site warden

If it is not clear who has lead responsibility, or if two people carrying out the same task are communicating with each other, the person who begins the conversation must always take lead responsibility.

Phrases to use when using a radio or telephone	
Phrase	**Meaning**
This is an emergency call	This message provides information that needs immediate action to prevent death, serious injury or damage
Repeat back	Repeat all of the message back to me
Correction	I have made a mistake and will now correct the word or phrase just said

Other phrases to use when using a radio and only one person can be heard at a time	
Phrase	**Meaning**
Over	I have finished my message and am expecting a reply
Out	I have finished my message, no reply is expected

The **phonetic alphabet** must be used:

- to identify letters of the alphabet
- to spell words and names that are hard to say, or misunderstood
- if there is interference on the radio or phone
- when quoting the identity of signals or points
- when quoting train descriptions.

The phonetic alphabet

A – Alpha	H – Hotel	O – Oscar	V – Victor
B – Bravo	I – India	P – Papa	W – Whisky
C – Charlie	J – Juliet	Q – Quebec	X – X-ray
D – Delta	K – Kilo	R – Romeo	Y – Yankee
E – Echo	L – Lima	S – Sierra	Z – Zulu
F – Foxtrot	M – Mike	T – Tango	
G – Golf	N – November	U – Uniform	

2.4.11   Confined spaces

There are work areas on a railway that may be classified as confined spaces. These include box girders, closed arches, culverts, station basements and inspection pits. Having identified a confined space, the following questions should be asked.

- Is there any way of carrying out the work task without entering that space?
- If there is a need to enter that area, how long is it going to take for the work to be completed?

Entry into confined spaces must be in accordance with the Confined Spaces Regulations and controlled by a permit to work system.

 For further information on working in a confined space refer to Chapter D08 Confined spaces.

2.4.12 Lineside fencing

The boundary of railway property is protected by the erection of lineside fencing. Any work on this fencing must be carried out in a controlled way to prevent inadvertent or unauthorised access to the railway.

Some sections of fencing, due to the close proximity of electrified lines, should be connected together by bonding to earth. This will avoid the risk of electric shock to people coming into contact with the fence.

Renewal of fencing should be carried out in such a manner that the access created can be controlled by use of personnel or temporary fencing during these periods.

 Whenever the site has to be left unattended, the fencing must be left in such a state that access cannot be gained.

2.4.13 Lineside vegetation

Removal of lineside vegetation can be hazardous for those involved. Some hazards are shown below.

- The close proximity of electrified lines.
- Fire.
- The types of tool used.
- Discarded rubbish.
- Injuries from sharps (such as discarded needles or broken glass).
- Vermin infestation.
- Injurious plants (such as giant hogweed).
- Insect stings (such as bees or wasps).

Removal of vegetation must be carried out in such a way that it does not come within 2.75 m of overhead electrified power lines and does not cause an obstruction of the track. Consideration also needs to be given to the presence of sub-surface cables, as many of these have previously been cut during the removal of vegetation.

Vegetation must not be burnt, because of the risk of smoke obstructing a train driver's vision.

Tools used for vegetation clearance can present hazards of their own. Safe systems of work should include the setting up of exclusion zones around hazardous operations, where tools such as chainsaws and flails are being used. To control the risk of hand-arm vibration syndrome (HAVS) it is important that you understand trigger times, use of job rotation, taking regular breaks and reporting any symptoms to your manager immediately.

Rubbish attracts vermin, which in turn can create the hazard of Weil's disease. There is also the hazard of discarded hypodermic syringes. These should be removed while taking every precaution against wounds from contaminated sharps. If you come into contact with an unprotected syringe, you should seek immediate medical advice.

 For further information on HAVS refer to Chapter B12 Vibration.

2.4.14 Working on stations and platforms

Although passengers use station platforms regularly and feel safe doing so, when work is being carried out a platform can be just as dangerous as the open track. Work on platforms and the station infrastructure can be in various guises, such as painting, billboard erection, maintenance work and installation work.

Whatever the work being carried out, the inherent risks are the same.

- Passage of trains.
- Presence of electrified tracks and overhead cables.
- Movement of station staff.
- Movement of passengers and their luggage.
- Risk of fire.

Work on stations and platforms should be planned in the same way as work on any other part of the railway system. This will ensure the health and safety of all concerned. All work will require approval by the station manager.

Consideration must be given to the following points whenever work is undertaken on stations or their platforms.

- Work must not be allowed to interfere with the normal operation of trains.
- Work must not be allowed to interfere with the normal operation of the station.
- Work must be carried out safely, bearing in mind the presence of electrified tracks and overhead cables.
- The use of flammable substances may create additional hazards.
- The way in which materials to be used on site will be transported and stored.

Over the years, work being carried out on stations and their platforms has resulted in several fatal accidents. This has been due to the lack of proper planning, failure to isolate power supplies and lack of proper control.

A safety-conscious approach is now being adopted in the way that contracts are drawn up for tendering. It involves bringing into the contract the requirements of the Construction (Design and Management) Regulations 2015 (CDM), the ROGS Regulations and the various Railway Group Standards that govern the way in which people work in a railway environment.

Below are the golden rules to remember when working on station platforms.

- Beware of passing trains.
- Beware of electrified tracks and overhead cables.
- Do not obstruct a train driver's vision of signalling equipment.
- Do not obstruct passenger routes.
- Know the fire and other emergency procedures.

Working on platforms within four feet of the platform edge, when carrying out engineering or technical work, is classed as working on or near the line. People working there are required to hold a valid personal track safety certificate.

A system of creating a 'high street environment' can be accomplished if the work is not on or near the line.

This can be done by erecting a physical barrier or by appointing a site keeper who is responsible for preventing the work encroaching on the railway infrastructure.

If you are creating a high street environment within the station, this system must be agreed with the station manager to ensure that there is no conflict with the travelling public or with station operations. You may still need a safe work pack (SWP) to enable you to access the area known as 'on or near the line' in order to access your high street environment working area.

2.4.15 Work sites

Work sites are categorised depending upon the level of protection required.

2.4.16 Possession of the line

When major engineering work is to be undertaken, a possession will be required.

This is an agreement with the signaller to give over control of the line, but control must be returned to the signaller when requested.

Possession of the line is taken by the person in charge of possession (PICOP) from the signaller, and the PICOP is the only one who can allow trains in or out of the line(s) under possession. This procedure must be planned well in advance of the possession being required, otherwise it will not be granted.

Extra care is needed if one line is under possession and the line next to it is still open to train movements. Steps have to be taken to prevent people straying from the line under possession onto the open line *(refer to Figure 1 in Appendix B)*.

2.4.17 Blockages of the line

Under this arrangement, trains are not permitted to run. The line block is established by a controller of site safety (COSS) or safe work leader (SWL) in order to protect staff from train movements but not traction current. Signals are set to danger in advance of the works.

This arrangement may require additional protection (for example, in the form of placing detonators (railway fog signals) on the line on the approach to the work site).

Extra care is needed if one line is blocked and the line next to it is still open to train movements. Steps have to be taken to prevent people straying from the line that is blocked onto the open line.

2.4.18 Considerations when undertaking track work

2.4.18.1 Fencing and separation

To prevent people at a work site straying onto lines that are open to train movements, physical reminders can take the form of blue, 1 m high fencing, or black and yellow tape extending beyond the length of the work site. The fencing must be supported to prevent it being dragged under passing trains. An alternative type of fence is a magnetic rigid barrier.

Fencing acts as a continual reminder to people on site that, beyond the fencing, the track is open to movement of trains. Therefore, a safe system of work exists, providing no-one strays beyond the fencing *(refer to Figures 2 and 3 in Appendix B)*.

An alternative to fencing is to use site wardens to prevent people straying onto lines that are open to train movements.

The wardens are positioned by the COSS at least 2 m away from the nearest rail of any line on which a train may run, to warn anyone who moves towards that 2 m point *(refer to Figure 4 in Appendix B)*.

Employing this system as a means of warning depends upon the alertness of the site wardens ensuring their colleagues do not stray beyond the limits set by the COSS, within 2 m of the open line.

2.4.18.2 Prohibition of work

At some locations, as detailed in Network Rail's hazard directory, it is not permitted to carry out works with trains running (formerly known as the *red zone*). An alternative safe system of work must be established at these locations.

2.4.18.3 Work planning

All work on or near the line must be planned by a safe system of work planner (SSOWP). The planner provides a safe system of work pack, which is issued to the COSS at least one shift prior to the planned work item. The COSS must verify the proposed SSOW with the planner in advance of the work. Then the COSS must implement the SSOW, as planned. Any changes thereafter must be formally agreed by a responsible manager before work can be allowed to continue. SSOWP is a sentinel competence.

The protection arrangements chosen must be the best available from the following list.

Best	Safeguarded.
2nd	Fenced.
3rd	Separated.
4th	Equipment warning – Permanent.

5th	Equipment warning – Human activated.
6th	Equipment warning – Portable.
Last resort	Lookout warning.

Together, these will lead to work that is better planned and co-ordinated to provide a higher level of safety. They will also help to drive further improvements through the introduction of systems that offer better protection and are simpler to use.

These include track circuit operating devices (T-CODs), automatic track warning systems (ATWS) and plans for a simplified version of protection arrangements to make it easier to obtain the separation of people from train movements.

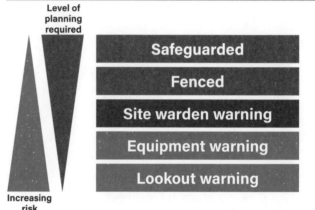

Level of planning required

Safeguarded

Fenced

Site warden warning

Equipment warning

Lookout warning

Increasing risk

2.5 Plant and equipment

2.5.1 Mobile plant

Any mobile plant used on the railways must not create a danger to the passage of trains or fixed rail infrastructure. This entails the COSS setting up a safe system of work for the use of that plant within the designated work area.

A work package plan and task briefing sheets should identify how plant will be brought to site, used on site and taken off site.

Some mobile plant is capable of being driven on both the road and on rails *(refer to illustration on right)* and such plant must conform to the appropriate Railway Group Standard. Contractors using plant that can move on rails must be a plant operating scheme (POS) provider.

The method of getting the plant to and from site must be carefully planned. Contractors should ensure that the plant does not damage other vital equipment (such as structures, signalling equipment (including cables) and communications equipment).

Plant and machinery must conform to the appropriate Railway Group Standard

Ways of protecting the various items of equipment must be clearly outlined in the work package plan and task briefing sheets for the work. When working on site with mobile plant, various factors have to be taken into consideration, such as the following.

- The presence of electrified lines.
- The presence of underground services.
- The presence of signalling equipment.
- Working on embankments.

- Obstructing train drivers' vision and sighting of signals.
- The use of lights on road vehicles.
- The distance from running lines open to traffic (any line open (ALO)).

These are in addition to the normal precautions that have to be taken by plant operators in any working environment.

Where items of plant are used in relation to railway infrastructure, they must be used and controlled only by competent persons.

Certificates of competence to operate items of plant must be carried, along with means of identification. These credentials can be asked for at any time. Failure to provide them when requested will result in the person being removed from site.

2.5.2 Cranes and mobile lifting equipment

Tower cranes, mobile cranes and other mobile lifting equipment present risks to railways during rigging, use, maintenance and de-rigging. The risk of a crane collapsing or failure of loads during lifting operations could lead to fatalities; damage to the tracks, power lines or rolling stock; or injury to passengers and/or railway staff.

 In recognition of these serious risks the Construction Plant-hire Association and Network Rail have developed guidance for tower cranes and mobile cranes alongside railways, which are free to download from the CPA website.

The guidance provides detailed information on early planning and liaison with the rail authorities, site set up and foundation requirements for rigging and de-rigging of cranes and the lines of communication through planning, operation and requirements for supervision, maintenance and thorough examination of cranes.

In essence, the guidance is a guide to the good practice that must be followed to protect people and property from harm or damage.

 For general information on lifting operations and lifting equipment refer to Chapter C07 and Chapter C08.

2.5.3 Scaffolding and mobile access towers

Scaffolding work in a railway environment is a specialist activity, requiring the scaffolders to be competent not only in scaffolding but also in railway work.

A train requires clearance between itself and any structure that it passes. These clearances vary according to the train speed, the type of rolling stock, the presence or non-presence of curves and the cant of the track.

The required clearances need to be observed when erecting a scaffold or mobile access tower to ensure that it cannot be struck by passing trains, and that the movement of air caused by trains passing does not affect the structure.

A thorough survey of the site must be made prior to the erection of any scaffold or mobile access tower. The survey must consider the needs of railway personnel who need an unobstructed view of equipment in order to carry out their work safely.

Failure to carry out this survey correctly could have serious consequences.

Erection of scaffolds and mobile access towers on the railway must consider the following factors.

- Movement of trains.
- Movement of station staff and passengers.
- Proximity of electrified lines.
- Location of signals and other equipment used in rail operations.

 It is vital that scaffolds or mobile access towers are not erected in positions that will obstruct signals and other equipment that need to be seen by train drivers.

Particular standards exist and must be complied with for the erection and use of scaffolds or mobile access towers, adjacent to or over the tracks, and these must be carried out in such a way that train movements are not affected.

When scaffolding has to be erected where electrified lines are situated, the method of erection, working and dismantling must take account of the hazards presented by the presence of the electrified lines.

Some sections of scaffolding, due to the proximity of electrified lines, should be bonded to earth to avoid the risk of electric shock to people coming into contact with the scaffold. The erection or dismantling of a scaffold or mobile access tower must not commence until an isolation permit has been received to indicate that it is safe to work near the electrified lines.

The need for the isolation of electrified lines during scaffold erection and dismantling is of paramount importance to avoid contact with live lines when moving scaffold poles around.

The stoppage of trains during this process should also be considered, because of the possibility of the incomplete scaffold collapsing onto the track.

 Even if an electrical isolation permit has been received, it will not prevent the movement of non-electrified trains or runaway rolling stock.

Signalling systems operate when the wheels and axles of a train running along the rails create an electrical connection of one rail to the other. This allows a small current to flow, which completes the track circuit to operate signal lights, indicating that the train is in that section.

Extreme care must be taken when erecting or dismantling a scaffold or mobile access tower over tracks. If scaffold tubes fall, or are placed across rails, the signals may change. This will result in false signals being given to train drivers (for example, green lights instead of red or yellow ones), which could have serious results.

2.6   Electrified lines

A large amount of the railway network is electrified, creating a hazard to anyone working in the vicinity of these sections. There are three different types of electrified line.

- Alternating current (AC) overhead line systems.

- Direct current (DC) third rail systems.

- DC fourth rail systems.

2.6.1   AC overhead line system

> ❗ **You can only go on or near the line with overhead line equipment if your sentinel card is endorsed with PTS AC.**

An example of the typical components incorporated in an overhead line equipment system is shown in the following diagram.

Key

1	Contact wire	7	Insulators
2	Dropper	8	Headspan type structure
3	Contact wire	9	Structure number
4	Headspan wire	10	Return conductors
5	Cross span wires	11	Structure bond
6			

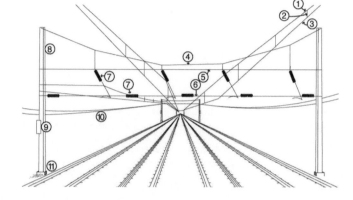

In addition to the wires shown, bare-feeder wires supply electricity from trackside cabins. The overhead line equipment and the attachments are electrified at up to 25,000 volts AC.

Current is taken from the suspended contact wire by a pantograph on top of the train and passed through the train equipment to power the motors.

2.6.1.1   Precautions to take when working on or near to overhead line equipment

- Assume that the overhead line equipment is live at all times.

- You must not use a crane, plant or similar equipment on or near the overhead line equipment unless the:
  – overhead line equipment has been isolated and earthed

– COSS or SWL has been issued within an overhead line permit.

- Keep people, clothing, tools and equipment at least 2.75 m from:
  – anything attached to, or hanging from, the overhead line equipment
  – any broken or displaced wire connected to the overhead line equipment, whether hanging or lying on the ground.

- Take extra care not to come within 2.75 m of overhead line equipment in cuttings, when working on embankments, structures or in vehicles.

- Keep paint, water and other liquids well away from where they could be thrown, splashed or fall onto live overhead line equipment.

- Keep tools and equipment or ropes, wires, tapes and surveying equipment clear of live overhead line equipment.

- Keep pipes, rods, poles, brooms, mops or ladders horizontal when carried.

- Take special care when standing on the floor or load of open wagons if the overhead line equipment is live on the next line.

- Make sure there is no possibility of branches or debris coming within 2.75 m of live overhead line equipment if trimming or felling trees.

- Use ladders made of wood or approved non-conducting material. Do not use steel or aluminium ladders, or wooden ladders reinforced by metal attachments.

- When cutting water, gas or other metal pipe or metallic cable sheathing you must:
  – first connect a temporary electrical continuity jumper cable across the point where you will make the cut
  – keep the jumper cable in position until the pipe is again complete.

> ❗ **You must immediately contact the electrical control officer (ECO) if a person is in contact, or is in danger of coming into contact, with the overhead line equipment.**

2.6.2   DC third rail system

 You can only go on or near the line with conductor rails if your sentinel card is endorsed with PTS DCCR.

Current passes through the third rail, which is raised **slightly above the height** of the running rails and is supported on insulators.

The third rail is referred to as the conductor rail, which is carrying 750 volts DC.

Current is picked up from the conductor rail by a pick-up shoe, situated on the outside of the train and passed through the train equipment down to the motors.

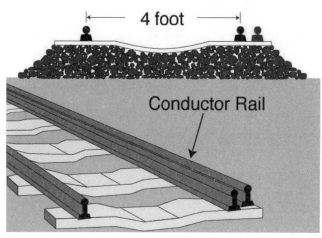

Third rail system

2.6.3   DC fourth rail system

On this system, current is returned to the supply by means of a fourth rail that is situated between the two running rails.

The fourth rail, like the third, is mounted upon insulators, and is slightly higher than the running rail. It is carrying 750 volts DC.

2.6.4   Precautions to take when working on or near to conductor rails

2.6.4.1   Precautions before working on or near DC electrified lines

Do not start work on, or close to, the conductor rail (or its connections) until it has been isolated.

The person requiring the isolation will be given a conductor rail permit. However, the issue of this permit does not mean that train movements are stopped on the lines concerned.

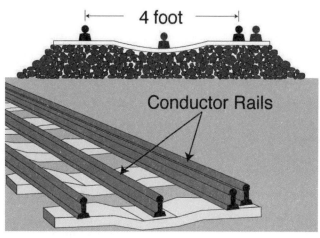

Fourth rail system

Do not work outside the limits shown in the conductor rail permit or those specified by your COSS or SWL.

The only exception is when special authority is given for certain types of work to be carried out without isolation.

In such instances, precautions are specified that may include the use of approved insulated tools, insulated troughing, approved rubber mats or gloves. These must be in good condition and dry.

2.6.4.2   Precautions when working or walking adjacent to live conductor rails

● Keep paint, water and other liquids away from where they could be thrown, splashed or fall onto live conductor rails.

● Keep all tools and equipment or ropes, wires and surveying equipment clear of live conductor rails.

● Keep pipes, rods, poles, brooms, mops or ladders horizontal when carried, to avoid accidentally touching the live conductor rails.

2.6.4.3   Precautions when working or walking near DC lines

● Assume that the conductor rails are live at all times.

● Avoid crossing the tracks unless it is absolutely necessary, and whenever possible cross at a gap in the conductor rail.

● Do not step on, touch or allow clothing, tools or equipment to come into contact with a conductor rail or any of its connections.

● Do not step on protection boarding or between a conductor rail and the adjacent running rail. Instead, step over in one movement.

● Do not touch the collector shoes or their connections on any traction unit, whether or not in contact with the conductor rail.

● Do not step into flood water, which may be in contact with the conductor rail.

● If using a track circuit operating clip or device, apply it first to the rail furthest from the conductor rail.

 You must immediately contact the electrical control officer (ECO) if a person is in contact, or is in danger of coming into contact, with the conductor rail.

2.7   Personnel

 As far as moving trains are concerned, the best form of personal safety is for every person in the workforce to keep a lookout for themselves and for everyone else.

2.7.1   Communication with the workforce

When working on or near the line the COSS or SWL will brief you on the following.

- The nature and location of the work.

- The approved access point and route to site.

- The limits of the site and how they are defined.

- The lines at site, including the maximum speed and direction of trains.

- If any lines are blocked.

- The best means of contacting the signaller and ECO if necessary.

- Information on any site hazards.

- Whether you will be working in an area where the line is blocked to trains or if the line remains open to trains.

- Any safe limits of the working area, the position of safety and method of warning, if applicable.

On electrified lines this will include the following additional requirements.

- The limits that it is safe to work within.

- Whether any nearby electrification equipment is still live and dangerous and its location.

- Whether any non-electric trains or on track plant (OTP) could still approach on the isolated lines.

When undertaking construction work a task briefing sheet must be used, which will provide the following information.

- An outline of the work to be undertaken.
- Access and egress arrangements.
- Activity risks.
- Resources.

- Site risks.
- Emergency arrangements.
- Contact information.

At the end of the briefing operatives should be asked to confirm their understanding. At this point the COSS or SWL should ask some questions to confirm understanding.

Operatives should be given the opportunity to ask any questions too.

 Operatives should be told not to sign the confirmation of the briefing unless they are clear on the safe system of work.

2.7.2   Personal protective equipment

The main priority is that workers are easily seen, particularly by train drivers. Therefore, wearing high-visibility clothing is an important requirement. The clothing must conform to the requirements laid down by Network Rail and must be clean and worn correctly.

However, train signals are in three colours: red, yellow and green, and so to reduce confusion to train drivers, there are colour restrictions for items of clothing worn by people working on or near a railway.

Red, green or yellow clothing must **not** be worn in case a train driver mistakes the item for a signal. Railway workers should wear fluorescent orange.

The minimum PPE for the work site is shown below.

- High-visibility upper body clothing with reflective tape, which complies with EN ISO 20471:2013 Class 2 and RIS-3279-TOM.

- High-visibility lower body clothing with reflective tape, which complies with EN ISO 20471 Class 1 and RIS-3279-TOM.

- A safety helmet, which complies with BS EN 397:2012.

- Safety footwear, which complies with BS EN ISO 20345:2011, provides support to the ankle, includes mid-sole protection and has a protective non-conductive toecap.

- Other items of PPE as may be required to safely carry out specific tasks.

All high-visibility clothing must conform to the requirements laid down by Network Rail

2.7.3   Working hours

At the Clapham Disaster Inquiry, Lord Justice Hidden made several recommendations regarding the causes of accidents. One of his recommendations was that the hours of work should be controlled to prevent excessive times on duty.

As a result of these recommendations, the contractor must now prohibit excessive overtime working and shift lengths. Accordingly, personnel should:

● not work more than 13 turns of duty within any 14 consecutive days

● not work more than 72 hours within seven consecutive days

● have a minimum rest period of 12 hours between consecutive shifts

● not work more than 12 hours in any one shift.

Where a contractor is employed to work on signal and control systems or the renewal or maintenance of track, the requirements are enhanced to not more than 13 turns of duty to be worked in any 14-day period, and no more than 23 turns of duty to be worked in any two consecutive 14-day periods.

A contractor is required to keep records of the working hours of all staff working on railways, and these records must be kept available for inspection and audit.

2.7.4   Drugs and alcohol

The Transport and Works Act stipulates the limits for alcohol consumption in the rail industry.

This legislation lays down the methods that must be adopted to ensure that anyone working on the railway is not under the influence of drugs or alcohol.

Personnel, both railway staff and contractors, working on a railway will be medically screened prior to employment for the presence of any of the following.

● Drugs, other than medication that does not affect their work performance.

● More than 29 milligrams of alcohol in 100 ml of blood.

● More than 13 micrograms of alcohol in 100 ml of breath.

● More than 39 milligrams of alcohol in 100 ml of urine.

Compare these figures to those laid down for driving a car.

● Not more than 80 milligrams of alcohol per 100 ml of blood.

● Not more than 35 micrograms of alcohol in 100 ml of breath.

● Not more than 107 milligrams of alcohol in 100 ml of urine.

It can be seen that far stricter controls are placed on those working on the railway infrastructure than on the ordinary car driver.

There is a 'for cause' screening system for screening after a safety-critical incident has taken place, where drugs or alcohol may be considered a contributory factor. All personnel working on the railway must comply with screening.

Personnel found to register positive in any screening will be dismissed and could face prosecution under the Transport and Works Act for working under the influence of drugs or alcohol in a safety-critical work post.

 All railway workers are subject to unannounced random screening in the workplace. This may take place at any time.

Appendix A – Train sighting chart

Required sighting distances are calculated from the following chart.

 The warning time must be sufficient to enable everyone to be in a position of safety at least 10 seconds before the arrival of a train.

Permissible speed	Sighting distances (metres) to provide minimum warning time of:						
(mph)	15 sec	20 sec	25 sec	30 sec	35 sec	40 sec	45 sec
125	900	1,200	1,400	1,700	2,000	2,300	2,600
120	900	1,100	1,400	1,550	1,900	2,200	2,500
115	800	1,100	1,300	1,550	1,800	2,100	2,400
110	800	1,000	1,300	1,500	1,800	2,000	2,300
105	800	1,000	1,200	1,450	1,700	1,900	2,200
100	700	900	1,200	1,350	1,600	1,800	2,050
95	650	850	1,100	1,300	1,500	1,700	1,950
90	650	850	1,050	1,250	1,450	1,700	1,850
85	600	800	950	1,150	1,350	1,600	1,750
80	550	750	900	1,100	1,300	1,500	1,650
75	550	700	850	1,050	1,200	1,400	1,550
70	500	650	800	950	1,100	1,300	1,450
65	450	600	750	900	1,050	1,200	1,350
60	450	550	700	850	950	1,100	1,250
55	400	500	650	750	900	1,000	1,150
50	340	500	600	680	800	900	1,050
45	320	420	520	620	720	820	920
40	280	360	460	540	640	720	820
35	240	320	400	480	560	640	720
30	220	280	340	420	480	540	620
25	180	240	280	340	400	460	520
20	140	180	240	280	320	360	420
15	120	160	180	220	240	280	320
10	80	100	120	140	160	180	220
5	40	60	60	80	80	100	120

 The permissible speed at a location is 75 mph, and the work is of such a nature that the minimum warning time required is 30 seconds. Therefore, the sighting distance required is 1,050 m.

However, not all lengths of track are straight and the view may be obstructed by bends, bridges or other structures. Therefore, it is essential for the COSS to assess these potential hazards as part of the risk assessment and by possibly appointing more than one lookout, or alternative mechanical means operated by competent users, in order to obtain the necessary sighting distance for an approaching train and to allow time for everyone to get into a position of safety at least 10 seconds before the arrival of the train. There will need to be a warning of the train's approach, which will be given by the site lookout.

If the work involves the use of noisy equipment, the noise produced may prevent the work team from being able to hear any warnings given by lookouts, a problem compounded by the requirement of wearing hearing protection.

In such situations, a system of alerting the workers by the use of a touch lookout should be implemented. This entails a lookout at the worksite to touch all the members of the work team to warn them of approaching trains.

02

Appendix B – Safe system of work hierarchy

Figure 1

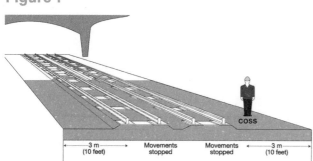

The diagram above shows a safeguarded safe system of work. This means train movements are stopped on all lines. Be aware that track plant may be used on any line.

Figure 2

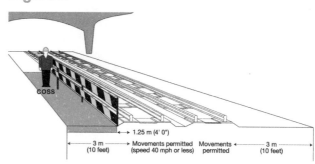

The diagram above shows a fenced safe system of work. This example is of a rigid safety barrier, which should be positioned no less than 1.25 m from the nearest open line.

Figure 3

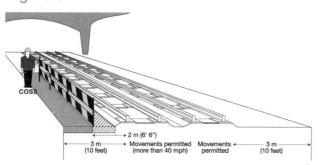

The diagram above shows a fenced safe system of work. This example is of a plastic netlon safety barrier, which should be positioned no less than 1.25 m from the nearest open line if trains are travelling no more than 40 mph. If trains are travelling more than 40 mph the distance must be increased to 2 m.

Figure 4

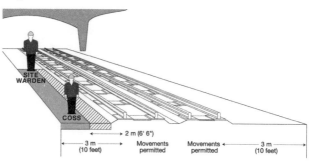

This diagram shows a safe system of work using site warden warning. The site warden warning area must be at least 2 m from the nearest open line. If you stray outside of the site warden warning area, the site warden will shout a warning: 'Get back'.

If none of the above safe systems of work can be employed then an equipment warning safe system of work may be used, which will warn you when a train is coming.

The final and last resort safe system of work is lookout warning. This safe system of work uses unassisted lookouts. The warning is given by a horn, whistle and touch (if there is noise or the group are wearing hearing protection).

In both of these instances, the COSS or SWL will make sure you get enough warning to enable you to reach a position of safety at least 10 seconds prior to the arrival of a train.

Appendix C – Good practice guide on competence development

Purpose

The *Good practice guide* (GPG) *on competence development* represents a collation of previous Rail Safety and Standards Board (RSSB) good practice guides relating to training and competence, and reflects the latest developments and thinking around how to ensure staff competence.

It is designed to be used as a reference guide and a source of inspiration to help people working in the area of competence, allowing them to pick and choose ideas that are useful and practical, depending on their own requirements.

The GPG aims to move its users past the minimum standard as required by legislation – it is about going beyond the basics and providing the tools needed to develop comprehensive competence management systems as per your business and individual needs.

As understanding in the field of competence is always evolving, this is a live document that will be periodically reviewed and updated to reflect the latest thinking and resources relating to competence development.

Target audience

Railway duty holders (infrastructure managers and railway undertakings) are required under the Railways and Other Guided Transport Systems (Safety) (ROGS) Regulations to make provisions within their safety management system (SMS) to ensure, so far as is reasonably practicable, that the competence of all safety-critical staff under their control is developed and maintained to a minimum safe standard.

This GPG has been developed to provide information and practical guidance to anyone who needs to understand, manage or contribute constructively to the analysis, design, delivery, review or assessment of training and other competence management activities.

The core text of this GPG is relevant to anyone with an interest in competence development (including the learners themselves), whereas the appendices are for more specific audiences (such as those with a more detailed interest in simulators, assessments, etc.).

Scope

This guide is designed to act as a reference manual. It pulls together:

- the **evidence-based findings** of recent research projects, highlighting **practical guidance** rather than focusing on the academic theory behind them

- the content of the **previous five RSSB good practice guides** in the area RS/220; *Good practice in training* (RS/220)*, *Good practice guide to train driver training* (RS/221)*, *Good practice on simulation as a tool for training and assessment* (RS/501)*, *Good practice guide on competence review and assessment* (RS/701) and *Good practice guide for driver assessment* (RS/702)

- **details of technology** or other relevant mediums that support the implementation of innovative concepts

- a variety of small and more in-depth **case studies** (these provide real-life demonstrations to highlight good practice in the various areas, illustrating how different companies have adopted approaches that suit their learners and business)

- **links and signposts** to practical tools and further information.

The advice in this GPG mainly pertains to the competence of safety-critical staff, though many of the principles are widely applicable in the field of learning and development and will have relevance to other roles. Although the overriding objective of competence management is mitigation of safety risk, it should be borne in mind that safety risk is one component of overall business risk.

*This good practice guide is not a mandated document, even though it sits in the suite of Railway Group Standards documents.

 For further details refer to the Rail Safety and Standards Board's *Good practice guide on competence development.*

(The above text is extracted from the Good practice guide on competence development, *Document no. RS/100, Issue 1, March 2013. This document is copyrighted and has been reproduced with the permission of the Rail Safety and Standards Board Ltd.)*

Demolition

Supporting INFORMATION

GT700 Toolbox talks / supporting checklists and forms

Toolbox talks on some of these topics are available in the GT700 publication. Supporting checklists and forms covering some of these topics are available on our companion website.

DEMOLITION

Overview

Demolition can be a hazardous activity. It is technical, can be high in complexity and should only be carried out by appropriately trained, competent and authorised personnel.

This chapter gives an understanding of the potential problems associated with demolition, the good practices that must be followed and the requirement and importance of appointing competent demolition contractors.

3.1   Introduction

Safe demolition is a process that requires technical skill and competence. It can be hazardous if carried out by contractors who are not experienced and competent in demolition planning, management and delivery.

The word *demolition* is often misinterpreted to only mean large-scale, or to involve the complete removal of a structure or building. However, the removal of a single element or the partial removal of a structure or building also constitutes demolition.

Information, planning, implementation of suitable and sufficient controls, and the provision of adequate and appropriate resources are essential elements for safe and successful demolition projects.

Whether demolition is required for a small building or structure, or for a complex industrial, commercial or residential site, you must be aware of the hazards and risks. These need to be identified, assessed and effectively controlled to avoid danger and remove or reduce the potential for injury to persons and damage to adjacent property and the environment, as far as is reasonably practicable.

A systematic approach to the demolition process starts with responsible clients making suitable arrangements for managing a project, including making sure duty holders are appointed and sufficient time and resources are allocated. Inexperienced clients may need to seek the assistance of a demolition engineer or consultant for guidance in the appointment of duty holders and management of the demolition process.

- Demolition works should be planned in such a way that they are undertaken using systems of work that take into consideration safety, health, the environment, cost and efficiency.

- All those involved, from concept, through tender, to contract delivery, should ensure effective planning and communication, through the provision of sufficient time and resources to facilitate effective planning and delivery of a safe, successful and efficient project.

- Time is required to acquire licences, permits and to disconnect utility services. Utility surveys should start in the pre-construction phase.

- After the contract has been awarded, and before work commences, the demolition contractor should determine the proposed safe sequence of operations on the basis of an assessment of the comparative risks, related specifically to the site and local conditions.

- Pre-construction information, the sequence of operations, programme and safe system of work should form the basis of the construction phase plan, which will include the arrangements for carrying out demolition or dismantling. These arrangements must be written down before the work starts.

- The methods of work should allow for demolition work and site clearance, as stipulated by the contract, taking account of any constraints imposed by the client or local conditions.

- Adequate time should be allowed for setting up the site, including the provision of welfare facilities, prior to work commencing.

- Waste management plans should also be developed.

3.2   Important points

- Demolition can be hazardous and should only be entrusted to experienced contractors who employ well-trained, competent personnel.

- Many demolition projects, particularly within buildings constructed prior to 1999 (especially between 1960 and 1990) may contain asbestos.

- Recognise that structural refurbishment may involve demolition work, which should be planned with the appointment of a competent contractor.

- Planning and supervision is vital to ensure a successful project.

- Demolition should be carried out with due regard to the British Standard (BS 6187:2011), good practice current at the time the works are being carried out, Health and Safety Executive (HSE) and industry guidance, and in full compliance with regulations.

- Ensure that prior to all demolition a site-specific demolition asbestos survey, as defined in the HSE publication *Asbestos: the survey guide* (HSG264), has been carried out by a competent person and that the information is available to those who need it.

- It should be noted that the HSE advises wherever paintwork or coatings are likely to be damaged or disturbed a lead (paint) survey should be carried out, regardless of the age of the building or the extent of the works.

- **The Construction (Design and Management) Regulations 2015 (CDM) apply to all demolition and dismantling projects**, regardless of size, but not all projects will be notifiable to the HSE.

- Ensure the works are properly planned, follow a safe system of work with written risk assessments and method statements developed, communicated to the personnel carrying out and supervising the work and understood by all concerned.

- Managers should ascertain the stability of the structure due for demolition. Where there are any doubts or concerns, the services of a demolition engineer and/or structural engineer should be engaged.

- The removal of non-structural fixtures, fittings and finishes, often referred to as soft stripping, must be planned and controlled to promote reuse or recycling and to avoid the risk of personal injury, uncontrolled release of asbestos, falling objects and so on.

- Demolition arisings should follow the hierarchy of waste minimisation (for example, reuse, recycle and recover) with waste being handled, managed and disposed of in accordance with current legislation and the waste duty of care Code of Practice.

- Demolition and refurbishment information datasheets (DRIDS) provide informative and practical guidance around reuse or recycling of the materials and products found on modern demolition sites.

- If processing and disposing of materials arising from the demolition (such as screening or crushing), ensure the relevant licences, permits or exemptions are in place.

- Ensure the necessary waste documentation is obtained, completed correctly and records kept.

- A waste management plan should be developed and kept up-to-date, including records of all demolition waste streams and the quantities. The plan will identify opportunities for materials to be reused, reclaimed and recycled, minimising the amount of waste being sent to landfill.

 ## Code of Practice for full and partial demolition (BS 6187:2011)

The Code of Practice gives good practice recommendations for the demolition (both full and partial) of facilities, including buildings and structures. This standard applies to demolition activities undertaken as part of structural refurbishment. It also covers decommissioning.

The standard gives recommendations for the following.

- The proper and effective management of demolition processes, including those forming part of structural refurbishment.

- Maintaining structural stability, including through the provision of temporary structural support, where necessary.

- Managing deliberate structural collapse.

- Identifying and establishing responsibilities during all phases of the demolition process.

- Acquiring a knowledge of the site, including its former uses.

- Managing environmental issues.

- Managing health and safety hazards.

- Carrying out risk assessments, developing safe systems of work and planning the work accordingly.

- Establishing and managing procedures effectively.

- Determining and managing safe exclusion zones.

It is essential that those carrying out demolition activities possess the necessary levels of competence. An important aspect of the Code of Practice is reference to exclusion zones and the safety of both people on site and others who may be affected by the work.

 For further information refer to guidance from the National Federation of Demolition Contractors (NFDC).

 For general definitions and terms used by the demolition industry refer to Appendix A.

3.3   Legislative requirements

3.3.1   The Building Act

Section 80 of the Act requires persons intending to carry out the demolition of a structure, or part-structure greater than 1,750 cubic feet (approximately 50 m³), to give six weeks' notice to the Local Authority Building Control department. This may incur an administration fee. A Section 81/82 counter notice is usually issued, providing conditions that apply to the works or a refusal with reasons. This is normally something that the client or design team should have carried out, but it frequently falls to the demolition contractor.

3.3.2 Construction (Design and Management) Regulations

Readers are advised:

- to refer to the industry guidance that supports CDM
- that under these regulations the definition of construction includes demolition and dismantling, and is to be regarded as such when used in the following text.

CDM applies to all construction, which includes demolition and dismantling work, as defined in BS 6187, regardless of the project's size or duration. A construction phase plan must be developed for all construction projects. A principal designer (PD) and principal contractor (PC) must be appointed where more than one contractor is engaged. Where there is only one contractor engaged a contractor and designer must be appointed by the client. This contractor (demolition contractor) will be responsible for health and safety on the site and for the development of the construction phase plan.

A project is notifiable if the construction work on a construction site is scheduled to last longer than 30 working days and have more than 20 workers working simultaneously at any point in the contract, or exceed 500 person days.

To ensure site safety during demolition the principal contractor or contractor must ensure that one or more competent person(s) are appointed to plan and supervise the work. The level of supervision required will depend upon the risks to health and safety and the skills, knowledge, training and experience of the workers (for example, workers will require closer supervision if they are young, inexperienced or starting a new work activity). Other factors to consider are the levels of the individuals' safety awareness, education, physical ability, literacy and attitude. Any duty holder who puts another person to work on a construction site (for example, a principal contractor engaging the services of a demolition contractor) must ensure that the person is competent to do what is required of them. Any person engaged must ensure that they have the competencies, skills and experience required for the work, otherwise they must refuse the work.

The NFDC and the Institute of Demolition Engineers (IDE) can provide information regarding the competence required for particular projects.

A construction phase plan is required for all projects.

3.3.2.1 Stability of structures

- All practicable steps shall be taken to prevent danger to any persons, to ensure that any new or existing structure or any part of such structure that may become unstable or in a temporary state of weakness or instability, due to carrying out of construction work, does not collapse.

- Any buttress, temporary support or temporary structure must be designed, installed and maintained so as to withstand any foreseeable loads that may be imposed on it, and must only be used for the purposes for which it is so designed, installed and maintained.

- No part of a structure shall be so loaded as to render it unsafe.

For further information refer to Chapter C04 Temporary works.

For further information refer to the *Code of Practice for temporary works procedures and the permissible stress design of falsework* (BS 5975).

3.3.2.2 Demolition or dismantling

The demolition or dismantling of a structure or part of a structure shall be planned and executed to reduce risk to as low a level as is reasonably practicable. The arrangements for carrying out demolition or dismantling work must be recorded in writing, prior to the commencement of the work.

3.3.2.3 CDM duty holders

The **client** is responsible for the provision of pre-construction information, which is already in their possession or is reasonably obtainable by them (such as the results of any refurbishment or demolition asbestos survey and the location and status of utility services). The client must also ensure the following.

- The project is notified to the HSE, if it meets the criteria defined in BS 6187.

- That adequate welfare facilities are provided.

- Relevant parts of the pre-construction information are distributed to contractors and designers to enable them to tender for, or prepare to carry out, the work.

- Suitable arrangements are made for managing the project so that health, safety and welfare are secured.

The client sets the tone for the intended demolition and, as such, care should be taken to ensure sufficient time and resources are made available to properly plan, procure and carry out the works.

03

The **principal designer** must plan, manage, monitor and co-ordinate the work of the pre-construction phase. They must liaise with the principal contractor in providing relevant information for the planning and monitoring of the construction phase.

Principal designers may also be designers. Design work may include any structural work and temporary works design.

The principal designer is responsible for the co-ordination of health and safety design and planning aspects, including those below.

● Co-ordinate matters relating to health and safety during the pre-construction phase.

● Estimate the period of time required to complete work stages.

● Take account of general principles of prevention.

● Identify, eliminate or control foreseeable risks to health and safety of any person carrying out construction work, maintaining or cleaning a structure and/or using a structure designed as a workplace.

● Ensure designers comply with their duties.

● Ensure all persons co-operate with the client, principal designer and each other.

● Assist the client in the provision of the pre-construction information.

● Provide pre-construction information promptly and in a convenient form to every designer or contractor.

● Liaise with the principal contractor and share information relevant to the planning, management and monitoring of the construction phase and the co-ordination of health and safety during construction.

The minimum lead times for the project must form part of the pre-construction information. Principal designers must themselves be competent; demolition and asbestos issues may be too specialist for many who normally perform the principal designer's role and they should be prepared to take specialist advice, if required.

Depending on the number of contractors on site, the **principal contractor** or the **contractor** is responsible for the overall construction phase, taking into account health and safety issues and the development of the construction phase plan.

Contractors and other workers must all work together as a team to achieve high standards in health, safety and welfare and protection of the site. The contractors, which normally include utility companies, must co-operate with the principal contractor by obeying site rules and complying with relevant parts of the construction phase plan.

Regardless of the size of the contract, the client has to ensure there are suitable management arrangements for the project welfare facilities and allow sufficient time and resource for all stages. A written **construction phase plan** will be required for all demolition projects. The plan should be written by the contractor and include training and information for workers.

The **demolition contractor** may be appointed as the principal contractor subject to having the necessary expertise, understanding and resources to undertake the role.

Irrespective of the size of the project, the demolition contractor must ensure the work is properly planned and carried out safely with the arrangements recorded (risk assessment, method statements, programme, construction phase plan and so on). They must also ensure these arrangements are communicated and clearly understood by those carrying out the work.

3.3.3   Provision and Use of Work Equipment Regulations

The Provision and Use of Work Equipment Regulations (PUWER) apply to work equipment used in demolition. They require that an employer supplies work equipment that is safe, correct and suitable for the job, the equipment is maintained and staff receive information, instruction and training in the use of the equipment.

Demolition can involve some work being carried out at height, particularly salvage and soft stripping (for example, the recovery of slates), which has in the past been the cause of deaths and injuries to demolition operatives. Due to advances in demolition techniques, and the increasing size and reach of the machines used, there is now a reduced need to work at height.

However, the presence of such machines on site brings about responsibilities for maintenance, inspection, thorough examination, operator competence and so on under these and other regulations.

Under the regulations, falling object protective structures (FOPS) are required for machinery. A demolition specification machine must have a FOPS-rated cab, as it is foreseeable when working overhead that material could fall onto the cab. Demolition attachments are common on a demolition site.

Quick hitch couplers requiring the fitting of a safety pin when changing attachments should never be operated without that pin being in place. The use of reinforcing bars as makeshift retaining pins for attachments is not acceptable and would be contrary to these regulations.

It is common to see mobile crushers employed during a demolition project to process the demolition arisings for reuse as part of ongoing works on site. These machines can pose a great risk to untrained or unaware operatives. Issues such as machinery guarding and clearing blockages, as well as dust, noise and vibration, must be considered.

Safe working practices dictate that operators should avoid standing on a crusher whilst it is running (for example, trying to remove foreign objects from the demolition arisings) or near the crushing jaws.

 For further information refer to the NFDC guidance on demolition attachments.

DEMOLITION

3.4 Project documents

3.4.1 Pre-construction information

Relevant pre-construction information, relating to the health, safety and environmental hazards associated with the work, should be provided by the client regardless of the size of the project. Where more than one contractor is engaged, the principal designer must carry out the tasks outlined previously, with regard to the collection and distribution of the pre-construction information.

In the context of this chapter, such information is likely to include:

- the location and physical condition of any asbestos where its presence has been identified by a refurbishment or demolition asbestos survey, as defined in HSG264
- the results of structural surveys
- notices, acknowledgements and disconnection certificates received for all services
- plans identifying the location of underground and overhead services
- the possible presence of contaminants, for example:
  - polychlorinated biphenyls (PCBs) in old electrical transformers
  - the residual contents of tanks and pipelines
  - the location and nature of contaminated ground
- environmental information on watercourses, wildlife, archaeology, and so on
- any other information that is required to ensure that the work can be planned safely and would not reasonably be expected to be known by a competent contractor.

After being appointed by the client, the principal contractor must use the pre-construction information provided by the client to develop the construction phase plan to the satisfaction of the client.

3.4.2 Construction phase plan

The construction phase plan provides a focus for the construction phase of a project.

 The arrangements for carrying out demolition, or partial demolition, should be recorded in writing (with a level of detail proportionate to the risks involved) before the demolition work begins. The demolition plan should form part of the construction phase plan.

The construction phase plan must be:

- sufficiently developed prior to any work commencing on site
- reviewed and amended as often as is necessary for the duration of the project
- communicated to those on the site insofar as it is necessary for any person to be aware of any part of it.

3.4.3 Health and safety file

The health and safety file is a record of information for the client or user of the premises. Its purpose is to inform anyone who might be responsible for the structure or site, now or in the future, of the risks that will have to be managed during any maintenance, repair or renovation. Generally, for demolition work, the health and safety file will contain information such as details of the following.

- Any services that have been capped or discovered and worked around.
- The presence of any voids and details of any areas that may have been filled.
- The actions taken to remove or treat contaminated land.
- Asbestos removal from retained structures, including copies of the clearance certificate and disposal records.

Such information may be useful to add to the asbestos management plan for a site, or to provide confirmation for future use that contaminants have been removed from the site. A health and safety file is only required for projects involving more than one contractor, although the client may insist on one being developed for future reference. Initially the health and safety file is the responsibility of the principal designer but if the duties of the principal designer finish before the end of the project then responsibility passes to the principal contractor.

3.4.4 Programme

The programme time allocated must be adequate to allow the demolition work to be planned and carried out safely. This should detail the mobilisation and planning, and correct sequence of the works with any hold and review points. Where the programme has unavoidable interfaces with other trades or contractors on site, this must be recognised as a potential area of risk. Good communications, planning and management are therefore essential to ensure high standards in health and safety. The operator of mobile crushing equipment must also give notice to the relevant Local Authority of their intention to carry out crushing work each time the equipment is moved.

3.5 Essential elements of a construction phase plan

When developing a construction phase plan that incorporates demolition work, the following elements must be included. (Also refer to *Chapter A03 Construction (Design and Management) Regulations, 3.8.2 Construction phase plan.*)

3.5.1 Project information

Names, addresses, contacts and telephone numbers should be detailed indicating the client, project managers, quantity surveyors, architects, structural engineers, the principal designer and principal contractor.

3.5.2 Scope of work

An explicit and concise opening paragraph should be included, outlining the extent of work, along with any other related work (such as asbestos removal), items or equipment to be recovered and set aside, façade retention, and so on.

3.5.3 Existing environmental information and drawings

Where available, construction drawings should have been supplied to the contractor, by the client, along with information on the former use of the site or buildings to be demolished. This information should include the health and safety file for the premises (if available), to determine what (if any) physical or chemical hazards are on the site or in the buildings (such as underground tanks and/or potential chemical or biological hazards or contaminated land).

The details of the building or structure should be checked to ensure that it is not a listed building. In addition, the locality of the site in relation to schools, roads, hospitals, protected wildlife, plants, watercourses and so on, which may be affected by the demolition activity, should be taken into account.

3.5.4 Risk assessment and special hazards

Having gathered all available information and visited the site to assess the work involved, along with identifying all known hazards and confined spaces, the contractor's appointed person on site should ensure that risk assessments (such as assessments for asbestos, lead, hazardous substances or noise) are made. Method statements should then be drawn up.

Information from these assessments should be included in the construction phase plan for the project, which must also take into consideration risks to health, and detail any safety precautions that are being taken to control and manage the risks.

Consideration must be given at an early stage to control the access for vehicles and pedestrians (including any visitors) and, where practicable, ensure separate access and egress for vehicles and pedestrians.

Finally, assess the impact that the site environment will have on any people who might be affected by the activity (such as neighbours or members of the public).

 For further information on method statements and risk assessments, including examples of both, refer to Chapter A05 Risk assessments, method statements and permits to work.

3.6 Selection and appointment of a demolition contractor

The client or principal contractor, in selecting a demolition contractor, should satisfy themselves of the contractor's competence, knowledge, ability and resources to carry out the work safely.

Expertise is vital. If there is more than one contractor on site, the client has to appoint a competent principal designer and principal contractor to co-ordinate and manage the health and safety issues during the demolition works.

The principal contractor's role can be taken by the demolition contractor. References must be sought, and relevant questions asked, to establish the credibility of the contractor involved. If there is only one contractor on site, there is no requirement to appoint a principal contractor or principal designer.

The contractor and designer(s) respectively will have to fulfil their duties in accordance with the CDM Regulations.

Care must be taken to ensure that the principal designer has the necessary level of competence in demolition work as it is a highly specialised field.

Alternatively, it may be wise to consider appointing an independent demolition engineer as an adviser.

 A useful source of information is the National Federation of Demolition Contractors (NFDC).

 When looking to appoint a competent demolition engineer, membership or fellowship of the Institute of Demolition Engineers (MIDE/FIDE) and/or the Construction Skills Certification Scheme (CSCS) professionally qualified person (PQP) in demolition is a good indicator of their competence.

DEMOLITION

3.6.1 Pre-qualification

If more than five people are employed by the demolition contractor, then that contractor should have a written health and safety policy.

 For further information refer to Chapter A04 Health and safety management systems.

The health and safety policy should be signed and dated by the director responsible and communicated to employees.

The client should also consider the following.

- Does the contractor employ a health and safety adviser, or do they purchase the services of a health and safety adviser or consultants?
- Does the contractor employ a demolition engineer, or do they purchase the services of demolition consultants?
- If consultants are used, how often will they visit the site?
- Are the consultants experienced in the health and safety management requirements of demolition sites?
- Are the consultants always available for advice, particularly if something goes wrong?

The safety record of the contractor should also be considered.

- Are safety statistics for injuries, lost time and dangerous occurrences kept and available?
- Has the HSE issued any improvement or prohibition notices against the contractor? If so, have the root causes of such been resolved?
- Are there any pending potential enforcement actions against the contractor?
- Is it the intention to use sub-contractors? If so, for what elements and how do they select and control sub-contractors?
- Is the contractor a member of the NFDC?

Membership of the NFDC is a useful competence indicator and will give the client the assurance of a minimum of five years' satisfactory trading experience, and a knowledge that certain recognised minimum standards have been and are being met (for example, insurance, training and supervision).

However, irrespective of membership of the NFDC, checks must be made regarding whether the organisation has the relevant experience to be deemed competent for the project in accordance with the requirements of CDM.

- Does the contractor have adequate public and employer's liability insurance that covers demolition?

Check for any restrictive covenants or other restrictions (for example, for work to be carried out above a height of 30 m).

- Do the company's employees hold the appropriate certification of competence for demolition operatives (CCDO) cards for operatives, supervisors and managers (Levels 1, 2 or 3)?
- Are references available? It is useful to speak to a client from a similar project size and complexity, as well as from their last project.

3.6.2 Appointing a contractor

A genuine and competent demolition contractor will not object to supplying the name of the client for whom the last contract was carried out. If that client is then contacted, they can be asked whether they were satisfied with the work.

They can be asked for information on the works, type, size, approximate value and so on, and asked the following questions.

- Were any problems experienced during the works?
- How did the contractor perform overall?
- Would they use the contractor again?

These are some examples of the kinds of question that should be asked to ensure satisfaction when considering the appointment of such a contractor. An interview with the potential contractor should be held to clarify matters. The client can also see if they would be prepared, or if they are qualified and competent, to take on the role of principal contractor.

3.7 Planning for demolition

 It cannot be emphasised too strongly that demolition is potentially hazardous and must be left to the experts (competent persons). Experience, knowledge, training, planning and supervision are of paramount importance.

Before any work starts, the implications of the demolition project to be carried out must be determined.

- What is the age of the building(s) and what was (were) the previous use(s)?
- What is the type of construction and what were the materials used?
- Where are the separation points, if any, and what are the perceived load paths?
- What is the scope and extent of the works?
- Is it full or partial demolition?
- Are floor slabs, foundations or piles to be removed?

- Are there any hazardous substances or invasive species in, around or under the building that is to be demolished (for example, asbestos, lead paints, flammable liquids, unidentified drums or packages, Japanese knotweed and so on)?

- Is asbestos suspected? (If so, a full invasive demolition survey must be carried out to form part of the pre-construction information.)

- Is the building on contaminated land?

- Are there any proximity hazards present (such as overhead or underground services, voids, tunnels, watercourses and so on)?

- Are there any site restrictions (such as access and egress)?

- Are there people and adjacent properties that may be affected by the proposed working hours?

- Will people be affected by noise or vibration emanating from the site? If so, a Section 61 noise notice may be required.

- Will there be a need to carry out a dilapidation survey of the adjacent buildings and/or highways?

- Will any waste management licences or permits be required to process or reuse the demolished material?

- Is the project likely to be notifiable?

- Who will notify the Local Authority under the Building Act, Section 80?

The information above would form the basis of the pre-construction information collected by the client, and assisted by the principal designer, under CDM. Once these things have been determined, decisions should be taken as to what are the acceptable or unacceptable methods to carry out the demolition.

Information on contaminated land must include details of the past and current uses of the site. Advice can be sought from the Environment Agency (EA), Northern Ireland Environment Agency (NIEA), Natural Resources Wales (NRW) or the Scottish Environment Protection Agency (SEPA), and the Local Authority Environmental Health Department. This may result in a requirement for a site survey, including the taking, observation and analysis of core samples.

Two important final questions remain.

- What is the timescale for the project and is it sufficient for the demolition to be carried out safely?

- How should the job and site be left safe?

The first point is particularly relevant as CDM place a duty on the client to indicate the minimum project mobilisation period.

3.7.1 Personnel and the appointed person

All persons on site are responsible for health, safety and the environment. The following have specific responsibility for health and safety and for supervision of the site.

- All designers.
- The principal contractor.
- The demolition contractor and specialist sub-contractors (for example, asbestos removal contractors).
- The director responsible for safety.
- The site safety adviser.
- The contracts manager.
- The environmental manager.
- The appointed person – a competent demolition supervisor.
- The person who has first-aid training or emergency first-aid training.
- All other contractors on site.

A method of recording who is on site must be rigorously maintained throughout the contract by signing in and out in the (daily) site register The principal contractor or contractor, with support from the appointed person and others, must ensure that the relevant sections of the construction phase plan are communicated to all people on site at appropriate intervals (such as site induction, task briefings and toolbox talks). These occasions should be recorded and signed for in order to indicate ownership by the recipients.

White card	NDTG approved trainer: five year renewable.
Yellow card	Demolition site visitor: five year renewable.
Green card	Demolition labourer L1 equivalent: five year renewable.
Red cards	Demolition apprentice: two year non-renewable.
	Demolition and refurbishment operative: three year non-renewable, NVQ required.
	Demolition topman: three year non-renewable, NVQ required.
	Demolition chargehand: three year non-renewable, NVQ required.
	Demolition supervisor: three year non-renewable, NVQ required.
	Demolition manager: three year non-renewable, NVQ required.
Blue cards	Demolition and refurbishment operative NVQ L2: five year renewable.
	Demolition topman NVQ L2: five year renewable.
Grey card	Demolition chargehand NVQ L3: five year renewable.
Gold card	Demolition supervisor NVQ L3+: five year renewable.
Black card	Demolition manager NVQ L6: five year renewable.

Company fined £100,000 and director given suspended prison sentence after worker dies

A property development company has been fined £100,000 and a building firm director handed a suspended prison sentence after a labourer was fatally crushed while demolishing a wall.

The self-employed labourer was hired as a sub-contractor by the building firm to work on a house refurbishment project for the property development company in Liverpool. The 41-year-old, who was originally from Czechia, was tasked with demolishing a rear yard wall dividing the property from the neighbouring house.

That same day, other workers on the job left the site at 3.30pm; however, when a neighbour returned home from work at around 5.40pm they saw the labourer trapped between an outer kitchen wall and a collapsed section of the yard wall. He was pronounced dead at the scene by emergency services.

An investigation by HSE found that the demolition work was not planned nor accounted for in the construction phase plan. No risk assessment or method statement was provided, and the labourer was not trained to carry out safe demolitions.

There was also a lack of supervision, as the system of work implemented by the property developer and the building company prohibited non-English-speaking workers from carrying out demolitions.

The development company from Liverpool pleaded guilty to breaching Regulation 4(1) of the Construction (Design and Management) Regulations 2015. They were fined £100,000 and ordered to pay £8,401.59 in costs at Wirral Magistrates' Court.

A director of the building company, from Holyhead, Anglesey, pleaded guilty to breaching Regulation 13(1) of the Construction (Design and Management) Regulations 2015, by virtue of 37(1) of the Act, and was given 26 weeks' imprisonment, suspended for two years, and ordered to pay £5,836 in costs at Wirral Magistrates' Court.

A HSE inspector said: 'HSE will not hesitate to consider the roles of not only organisations when investigating serious incidents, but also those individuals such as directors and managers who are the controlling minds and best placed to direct work and ensure that it is carried out without risks to health and safety.'

Source: HSE

 A card scheme for the certification of competence of demolition operatives (CCDO) is managed by the National Demolition Training Group.

3.7.2   Services

Before any work starts, all utility companies must be contacted by the client or, if agreed, by the principal contractor, and sent a site plan showing the footprint and extent of the planned demolition, with the proposed commencement date, requesting the disconnection or isolation of the appropriate service (for example, electricity, gas, water, telecommunications or other cables).

These requests should be made in good time and be acknowledged in writing by the relevant utility company, with confirmation that the services have or will be isolated or disconnected.

Prior to their arrival on site, utility companies should be sent any relevant sections of the pre-construction information to incorporate within their own safe systems of work (for example, details of ground contamination and/or unsafe conditions or structures prevailing on site).

Where such disconnection is not possible, any pipes or cables should be clearly identified, marked and protected to ensure that they are not disturbed during the works. Disconnection confirmation in writing must be received and be on site before any demolition work commences.

Finally, if in doubt over any services, the contractor should seek further advice from the utility provider, specialist services contractor or services consultants. If overhead power lines are present, care needs to be taken, particularly where lifting equipment, excavators or demolition machines with high reach are to be operated.

Adequate control measures should be put in place (such as warning goalposts) following advice from the relevant power supply company.

 For further guidance refer to the NFDC document *Disconnection of services for demolition and refurbishment work places*.

 For further information refer to Chapter D07 Underground and overhead services.

3.7.3   Lead

If proper precautions are not followed, there is a risk of exposure to lead paint through dust and fumes.

The risk of lead exposure is considered to be greater when working in pre-1970 buildings, especially during repair, maintenance, refurbishment and demolition.

It should be noted that, wherever paintwork/coatings are likely to be damaged or disturbed, the HSE advises lead (paint) surveys **regardless of the age of the building or the extent of the works**. Where lead exposure is likely to be significant an initial air monitoring survey to check how much lead is in the air may be required.

 Information on reducing the health risks of lead construction work can be found on the HSE website.

 For further information refer to Chapter B08 Lead.

3.7.4   Asbestos

Under Asbestos Regulations, there is a duty on building owners and/or the tenants to identify (via asbestos surveys) and manage the presence of asbestos in the non-domestic properties under their control. HSE publication HSG264 provides the following guidance.

● The types of survey.

● The circumstances in which either type of survey would be required.

● Appointing a competent asbestos surveyor.

● The exchange of information that is necessary between all interested parties.

● Avoiding caveats whereby some areas would not be surveyed.

● What should be expected by way of a survey report.

The regulations state that all asbestos-containing materials should be removed prior to demolition, so far as is reasonably practicable. They also require that the necessary planning actions and notifications are carried out.

The management process should be based on the information gained from a refurbishment or demolition asbestos survey, carried out before contractors are invited to tender for the demolition. This should include a drawing of the building footprint (all floors) and a list of the approximate amounts and locations of asbestos-containing materials found.

Simply writing 'throughout the building' is not acceptable and the client should be informed that the survey is inadequate. The survey should be checked for any exclusions (caveats) or areas not accessed and for any specific recommendations. However, it should be noted that such clauses are generally unacceptable, as detailed in HSG264.

If the survey identifies licensable asbestos materials (typically asbestos insulation, coatings and insulating board), which must be removed by a licensed contractor, then 14 days must be allowed for the notification process to the enforcing authority, usually the HSE. The licensed contractor will submit the notification online using the FODASB5 notification form.

Asbestos pipe lagging

All non-licensed work (for example, removal of asbestos cement sheets) needs to be carried out with the appropriate controls in place. However, for notifiable non-licensed work (NNLW) additional requirements have to be met, including notifying the relevant authority of the intention to work with or remove asbestos, ensuring medical examinations are carried out and maintaining registers of work. Some examples of NNLW are removal involving textured coatings, where the method of removal requires deterioration of the material, and removal of asbestos paper and cardboard products, if not firmly bonded in products.

 Notification of notifiable non-licensed work can be made online using form ASB NNLW 1.

 The client should ensure that appropriate surveys have been carried out and that the results are acted on accordingly.

From the survey, an inventory of asbestos-containing materials should be made and ticked off as they are removed. This should prevent creating risk during soft strip and demolition.

There are many occasions when asbestos-containing materials are only revealed during the demolition.

All operatives and machine drivers must receive mandatory annual asbestos awareness training so that they can recognise materials that could be, or contain, asbestos and stop work and take appropriate advice. This training does not prepare workers or self-employed contractors to carry out work with asbestos-containing materials. Training can be classroom based or offered as an e-learning course, provided it satisfies the requirements of Regulation 10 of the Control of Asbestos Regulations and the supporting Approved Code of Practice.

Workers who carry out work that will disturb asbestos (non-licensed work, notifiable non-licensed work and licensed work) must receive a higher level of training.

 Company fined for employee asbestos exposure

A construction company has been fined for safety breaches after employees were exposed to asbestos after removing false ceiling tiles during a shop conversion in Hull.

Beverley Magistrates' Court heard that the company had not commissioned a refurbishment asbestos survey prior to the work commencing. Employees removed over 1000m² of asbestos insulation board (AIB) ceiling tiles in an uncontrolled manner, exposing them to asbestos.

An investigation by the HSE found that the company's director, and the casual labourers they employed, spent approximately three to four weeks removing the suspended ceiling, along with the ceiling tiles which contained asbestos, to install new stud walls to divide the shop floor into separate units.

The labourers were unskilled and untrained. They were provided with a claw hammer to knock the tiles down. The asbestos-containing tile debris was then shovelled or collected into approximately 62 one tonne bags.

The company from Bradford, pleaded guilty to breaching Regulation 5 of the Control of Asbestos Regulations 2012. The company has been fined £16,000, ordered to pay £3,011.87 in costs and a victim surcharge of £190.

After the hearing, a HSE inspector commented: "If the company had identified any asbestos on the site through a refurbishment asbestos survey, carried out by a competent surveyor, and had it removed by licensed asbestos removal contractors prior to the refurbishment work commencing, then employees would not have been exposed to asbestos.

"No matter how small or large your company, there is a need to prevent exposing your employees and the public to asbestos by ensuring that it is identified on site prior to any work commencing."

Source: HSE

 For advice on suitable awareness training visit the HSE website.

Asbestos guidance note *Industry guidance for non-licensed work with asbestos containing materials within a demolition or refurbishment environment* is available from the NFDC.

 For further information refer to Chapter B09 Asbestos.

3.8   Methods of demolition

This section gives an outline of the types of demolition techniques commonly employed, with a view to giving the reader an appreciation of the demolition activity.

The key to a successful demolition project is to ensure that the appropriate risk assessments and method statements have been developed to identify the correct sequence of carrying out the work, together with the necessary tools, equipment and people required.

These must be recorded in writing, fit for purpose, site and task specific, and clearly communicated and understood by the persons using them.

3.8.1   Partial demolition

Partial demolition is often carried out where refurbishment is being undertaken and can include façade retention. In any demolition, daily or, where required, more frequent checks should be carried out to confirm the stability of the remaining structure.

If at any time during the demolition the structure appears or becomes unsafe, all workers should be withdrawn until actions have been taken to remove any danger. This may involve the use of mini machines (such as skid steers and/or mini excavators).

Therefore, an assessment of the floor-loading capacity should be undertaken by a competent person (such as a structural engineer) to take into account the dead and live loads, and any necessity for temporary works (such as propping, shoring and so on).

3.8.2   Progressive (top-down) demolition

Progressive demolition is generally carried out in the reverse order to construction, and often follows the soft strip-out phase. This is the most commonly used method of demolishing structures and should be detailed in the construction phase plan.

Demolition of high-rise building

In high-rise buildings where a floor-by-floor demolition is being carried out, the following danger points should be recognised and adequate precautions taken.

- Structural stability.
- On-floor loadings (machinery and arisings).
- Falling debris.
- Slips, trips and falls.

- Maintaining clear access and egress.
- Risk of fire.
- Open and unprotected edges, including shafts and voids.

 The NFDC has produced guidance on demolishing multistorey structures of 18 m and above, and in the use of high and ultra high-reach demolition machines, to improve procurer and user awareness, entitled *Guidance for deconstruction of tower blocks floor by floor/piecemeal.*

3.8.3   Demolition by designed collapse mechanism

Demolition by designed collapse can be achieved by pre-weakening the structure, followed by explosive displacement of important structural elements, remote mechanical demolition by a demolition machine, high-reach demolition rig or crawler crane or similar, or occasionally by pulling it down using a wire rope.

Explosive displacement requires a high level of expertise, planning, supervision and execution. Consequently only qualified explosive demolition engineers should be involved in this type of demolition (for example, members of the Institute of Explosives Engineers).

3.8.4   Manual demolition techniques

Manual demolition techniques are used when other methods of demolition are not suitable or possible (for example, city centre or confined sites, where there is insufficient space around the structure for mechanical demolition).

Some of the types of tools or operations that can be used in manual demolition are listed below.

- Hand tools.
- Breakers, compressors or hammers.
- Concrete nibblers or hydraulic pulverisers.
- Stitch drilling.
- Drilling and hydraulic bursting.
- Drilling and expansive pastes.
- Oxy-propane cutting equipment.
- Diamond cutting and sawing.

For brick or concrete structures:

- wherever practicable, carry out demolition in the reverse order to construction
- identify any pre-stressed or post-tensioned concrete beams, columns and trusses that may be present within the structure and determine a safe method of demolition
- use compressed air, battery-powered tools or those from a 110 volt supply
- maintain tools in good condition, and use them safely
- make operatives fully aware of the safe procedures
- recognise the potential health risks from exposure to high levels of noise and vibration requiring assessments and the associated control measures
- in addition to site induction, ensure task and toolbox talks are prepared, delivered and understood at key stages of the work.

As far as is reasonably practicable, employees should not work above each other and care must be taken to ensure that debris does not drop into working or otherwise occupied areas.

If lift or service shafts or other openings through floors are used for the removal of debris, the lift car, services and equipment must be cleared in advance to remove any snagging points. Openings must be adequately protected by either suitable guard-rails and toe-boards (with no gap between guard-rails and toe-boards exceeding 470 mm) or by other substantial, effective barriers.

It may not be possible to guard an opening where plant (such as a skid steer) is being used to bulldoze arisings into a shaft or chute. In such cases a safe system of work must be developed, which is sufficiently robust to:

- protect other workers from falling down the shaft
- stop the item of plant falling into the chute or shaft
- control when materials will be loaded and unloaded to stop materials being tipped onto someone below.

It is still acceptable to use window openings as a means of removing debris from upper floors under certain conditions. The opening would have to be protected to prevent operatives falling whilst throwing the debris out. Furthermore, the landing zone (that is, the area to receive the materials arising from the soft stripping or demolition operations) must be clearly identified and completely protected so that materials cannot fall on anyone. Typically the area (drop zone) will be fenced off with mobile fence panels and then the material loaded with an excavator into a hook bin container; this area should be controlled by a vehicle marshaller to ensure that no entry can be effected by unauthorised persons.

If the structure has more than two storeys, consideration should be given to the prevailing wind conditions, use of an enclosed scaffold chute and fitting the receiving skip with suitable dust covers or shrouds. With regard to falling materials and exposed edges, where necessary, hazard areas (personnel exclusion zones) must be created in accordance with the requirements of current regulations and good practice.

3.8.4.1   Oxy-propane cutting equipment

The use of oxy-propane cutting equipment requires the following.

- Operatives are trained and competent in the safe use of the equipment.

- Appropriate PPE is used (such as the correct respiratory protective equipment (RPE), goggles and hand or arm protection).

- The equipment is inspected and tested for leaks before use.

- Cylinders are secured in an upright position, at least 3 m from any party wall, boundary fence line or hoarding.

- Hoses are secured with crimped fittings, not jubilee clips.

- Flashback arresters are always fitted between cylinder gauges and hoses.

- Spare cylinder storage areas are recommended to be separated by a gap of at least 3 m between oxygen and propane bottles.

- A hot-work permit system is in place and is followed.

Do **not**:

- operate hot cutting equipment within an enclosed space, because of fumes, leakage of fuel and/or oxygen gases

- use oxygen or compressed air to blow dust off clothing

- carry or use petrol or gas lighters to ignite the cutting torch (use only approved flint guns)

- rely on existing site fire points (ensure additional fire extinguishers are in place prior to commencement of hot works).

Whenever oxy-propane cutting equipment is used, the correct fire-fighting equipment must always be available. All operatives involved in the work should be trained in the safe use of fire extinguishers.

Hot work should generally be stopped one or two hours before the site closes and be regularly monitored to avoid the potential of smouldering material developing into a fire unobserved.

 For further information refer to Chapter C02 Fire prevention and control.

3.8.5   Mechanical demolition techniques

Machinery should be fit for purpose (in line with PUWER), operated by authorised, competent persons (for example, those holding a CPCS card for the appropriate category of machine) and be used in safe working spaces.

Because of the danger of debris falling onto the demolition rig and its driver, the machine should be a safe distance from the structure and be fitted with roll-over protective structures (ROPS) and/or falling object protective structures (FOPS). As an added precaution, it should be fitted with shatterproof glass.

Before using the demolition equipment, steps must be taken to ensure that the building is completely empty and that all services are isolated with the appropriate written confirmation of disconnection on site.

ROPS and FOPS cab

3.8.5.1   Remote control demolition

Remote demolition is generally carried out by specialised equipment, often in hazardous or aggressive environments (for example, nuclear installations). The use of pedestrian operated machines is becoming more common and they offer possible solutions to the difficulties of complying with the problems of noise and vibration experienced during hand demolition.

These types of machine enable the operator to stand well clear of danger areas. They are particularly useful where the machine is breaking out the structure of the floor above, and/or when the operating surface is being progressively removed.

3.8.5.2 Using a 360° adapted demolition rig with multi-functional attachments

This type of demolition machine is commonly used to demolish relatively low level buildings, or is used after other height reduction techniques have been carried out.

The machine should always be positioned at a safe distance from the structure, taking into account the height of the structure and the build up of debris as it is reduced. In situations where the machine operator cannot see all elevations of the structure or in circumstances where external influences may dictate stopping the work until such distractions have been removed, a vehicle marshaller or lookout may be required to assist the operator. The vehicle marshaller or lookout should be positioned in a safe location, outside of the machine's operational exclusion zone, and preferably within sight of the operator (or in radio contact, where this is not possible).

Whereas the machine driver is isolated from noise and dust, the vehicle marshaller or lookout is not and may need to wear additional PPE, depending on the findings of the risk assessments for the work being done (for example, impact-resistant goggles if there is a possibility of debris being thrown off).

The height of the wall or building to be demolished should not normally be greater than the maximum reach of the machine; this maintains a safe distance between the machine and the structure being demolished.

In some circumstances, it is appropriate and practicable to create a ramp for the machine to sit on to increase the reach using rubble from previous demolition. Care must be taken to ensure the ramp and operating platform are properly designed and constructed and that there has been sufficient compaction to avoid the machine sitting on an unstable base.

It is not good practice to construct a ramp within a building, due to potentially overloading the floors or surcharging the outside walls.

It is not recommended to allow undermining or undercutting of structures when the machine cannot reach the top of the building. Any contractor suggesting this method should consider selecting a larger (higher reach) machine to avoid putting the operator at unnecessary risk from falling structures and debris.

3.8.5.3 Super high-reach 360° excavators

Typically these machines have a reach of between 15 and 65 m (or more), plus the length of the fitted attachments for shearing concrete or steel structural elements. To ensure a safe distance between the machine and the structure, a ratio of 2:1 height to distance must be maintained for machines up to 45 m reach. In some cases this may mean that the recommended maximum working height for the machine is restricted to 75% of its maximum reach. A useful visual indicator that the machine is working within safe limits is when the dipper (the last section of the excavator's arm) is horizontal or approximately 90° to the boom.

These sophisticated machines are fitted with variable width tracks and are heavier than standard machines, thus giving increased ground-bearing pressure and extended working envelopes. It is vital that ground conditions are known and any voids and ducts, located where the machine will track, are identified, clearly marked (fenced off) and, where possible, adequately filled and compacted. In terms of ground conditions, these machines should be considered more as a crane or piling frame in terms of stability, rather than an excavator.

Operator training is supported by a specialist CPCS category for high-reach machines with various endorsements for different reach machines (for example, up to 15 m, 30 m and 30 m+).

It is essential for operators to understand how to operate the machines safely and also have knowledge of good practice with regard to fitting and changing attachments. The manufacturer or the supplier of the machinery can provide advice on this. There are further CPCS card endorsements for this activity.

Ground conditions should be assessed before using super high-reach excavators

 High reach demolition rig guidance notes **can be downloaded free from the National Federation of Demolition Contractors.**

3.8.5.4 Hydraulic pusher arm

Demolition using a hydraulic pusher arm is occasionally used for removing masonry structures. However, with the advent of super high-reach machines with multi-functional attachments, it is almost obsolete now and its use should only be carried out by experts. It is therefore not covered within the scope of this chapter.

3.8.5.5 Demolition ball

Demolition using a ball is extremely rare due to the advent of super high-reach machines. When a ball is used, the lifting equipment must be heavy duty and only drop or pendulum (for example, in line with the jib) balling techniques should be employed. When a ball is employed, regular (for example, hourly) inspections of the equipment must take place, paying particular attention to the attachments and shackles. Arrangements for safely rectifying the situation should be in place in the event of the demolition ball becoming trapped within the structure. Further detail is not appropriate within the scope of this chapter.

3.8.6   Bridges or steel structure demolition

The demolition of bridges, pylons, masts, or similar, requires specialised planning and techniques. The information provided below can be used as a guide, but specific detail is not covered within the scope of this chapter. An assessment by a demolition engineer and/or a structural engineer should be undertaken. A comprehensive safe system of work must be developed providing a safe means of access, using a competent crane hire operator and experienced slingers and signallers to ensure compliance with the Lifting Operations and Lifting Equipment Regulations. For bridges that run over roads or cross railway lines, liaison must take place with the Highways Department of the Local Authority involved or Network Rail, as appropriate.

For further information refer to Chapter C07 Lifting operations.

3.9   Environmental and other considerations

Noise, dust, fumes, vibration and fire controls need to be properly addressed before and during the demolition operation. Consideration should be given to the following points.

3.9.1   Noise

Where demolition operations are carried out in locations likely to affect the general public, the Local Authority may request the principal contractor to submit an application under Section 61 of the Control of Pollution Act (COPA), specifying working methods, working hours and maximum noise levels (called prior consent). A Local Authority can issue an abatement notice (Section 60 notice) for failure to comply with Section 61 consent conditions, or where noise levels are creating a statutory nuisance. Checks should also be made for any constraints in site working hours (such as planning permission conditions or the Local Authority or council's own restrictions on working hours).

In accordance with regulations, where noise levels are above (or expected to be above) the lower exposure action value, the demolition contractor must ensure that a noise assessment has been carried out and that, where possible, people are kept out of the danger area.

A monitor to assess periodic noise

Any machinery that is to be used in the demolition process should, as far as possible, be fitted and used with soundproofing or noise reducing equipment (such as exhaust silencers). Where it is necessary for people to work within the area of noisy operations, adequate hearing protection must be provided and used as necessary. If the upper exposure action value, 85 dB(A), is exceeded, or is likely to be exceeded, hearing protection must be worn and hearing protection zones clearly indicated with mandatory signs.

Where the findings of a risk assessment indicate that the hearing of any employee is at risk due to noise exposure at work, health surveillance, including hearing checks, must be provided.

BS 5228 gives advice on the provisions for noise and vibration control on demolition sites. For further guidance refer to Chapter E06 Statutory nuisance.

3.9.2   Dust

Nearly all demolition work creates dust and requires a control of substances hazardous to health (COSHH) assessment (for example, respirable crystalline silica). Taking simple precautions (such as those listed below) can help to reduce dust generation and exposure.

● The use of light water sprays both before and during demolition are effective. However, consideration should be given to any potential run-off contaminants that may be produced and to the proximity of demolition work to electrical services, retained structures and drains.

● Where demolition is being carried out inside a building and water sprays are inappropriate, local ventilation, using air movers and filters, can help to alleviate dust levels. (It may also be possible to create voids in the structure by taking out, for instance, walls and partitions.)

● Consideration should be given to identifying the type of dust the operative is exposed to and measuring the actual dust levels to confirm whether or not the anticipated levels are being achieved and thereby whether the measures being taken (for example, personal and perimeter pumps) are effective.

● Respiratory protective equipment, as with any other PPE, should be used only as a last resort. Most forms of respiratory protective equipment require the wearer to be **face-fit tested** before use.

For further guidance refer to Chapter B10 Dust and fumes (Respiratory hazards) and Chapter E06 Statutory nuisance.

3.9.3 Fumes and gases

A cutting torch, used on steelwork, may produce toxic gases (such as nitrogen dioxide). If a phosphate coating is present, phosphine may be produced. If a chlorinated solvent has been used, sulphides may be formed, which have no smell until high toxic levels are present. Toxic metal fumes may additionally be given off.

Attention is drawn particularly to lead (lead-painted steelwork), cadmium (cadmium bolt heads) and zinc.

Before any hot work cutting is allowed, available information or paint samples may be required for analysis, a COSHH assessment must be undertaken, and the necessary control measures implemented.

Operatives undertaking hot work must be issued with the appropriate PPE, including appropriate respiratory protective equipment (RPE), as necessary.

 For further information refer to Chapter B07 Control of substances hazardous to health, Chapter B08 Lead, Chapter B10 Dust and fumes (Respiratory hazards) and Chapter E06 Statutory nuisance.

3.9.4 Vibration

Vibration from demolition operations can cause damage to adjacent property and injury to personnel working on site or to members of the public.

Exposure to vibration must be minimised and controlled in accordance with the requirements of the Control of Vibration at Work Regulations.

Using a machine-mounted breaker instead of a hand-held version will eliminate the risks associated with hand-arm vibration

- Where possible avoid exposing people and/or property to vibration by selecting appropriate demolition techniques.
- Attempts should be made to establish the presence of any existing sources of vibration and whether vibration monitors are needed in sensitive locations.
- Where buildings adjoining those to be demolished are being retained, separation should be carried out using hand tools rather than machinery.
- Necessary precautions should be taken or alternative equipment considered to alleviate the risk of permanent physical injury, such as hand-arm vibration syndrome (HAVS) (for example, vibration white finger, from continued use of vibrating tools) or whole-body vibration (WBV) from continued exposure to vibration from mobile plant operation.

With regard to the last point, the exposure time for most demolition hand tools is extremely short, and the contractor will need a robust policy that includes health surveillance to carry out hand demolition using pneumatic electric or hydraulic demolition picks.

 For further information refer to Chapter B12 Vibration and Chapter E06 Statutory nuisance.

 For further information refer to the *Code of Practice for noise and vibration control on construction and open sites* (BS 5228).

3.9.5 Fire and explosion risks

Where flammable liquids, gases or vapours have been used, or released in a building that is under demolition, any equipment, tank or pipes, which could have contained such substances, must be purged and tested for explosive gases prior to work taking place. Any such work should be done under a permit-to-work system.

General hot work, using oxygen and propane cutting equipment, should be carried out only by operatives trained in its safe and proper use, wearing the appropriate PPE, including goggles, gloves, overalls and respiratory protective equipment.

Before any burning of debris is undertaken, consideration needs to be given to waste management licensing, or any local byelaws, which may prohibit such actions taking place. Penalties for the contravention of such conditions can be severe in some circumstances.

If the occasional burning of debris (such as wood or paper) is allowed on site, the fire must be as small as possible, well away from buildings, roadways and fuel stores, and kept under constant supervision.

All fires must be completely extinguished at least one hour before work stops for the day and checked again, to ensure there are no glowing embers, before operatives leave the site. Adequate fire-fighting equipment must be available, with fire points containing extinguishers in prominent and well-marked areas adjacent to the demolition hot-work operations.

 For further information refer to Chapter C02 Fire prevention and control.

3.9.6 Recycling

Demolition works should always consider opportunities for reuse, reclamation and/or recycling of materials. A material survey of the site will identify what materials are on site and how they may be recovered, managed and removed to maximise recovery. Where relevant, the contractor can opt to use a site waste management plan to record such material.

 For further details refer to Chapter E10 Waste and material management.

In addition to removing recoverable items from demolition operations, it is common to crush the resultant brick and concrete into a sub-base (hard core) material for future construction purposes.

- Crushing on site will generally take place when environmental conditions permit such actions. Environmental emissions (noise, fumes and dust) are considered as statutory nuisances and should therefore be eliminated or reduced to the lowest possible level. Regular monitoring of all control measures are required daily and should be recorded on a check sheet. Operations should cease if there are excessive emissions, which lead to nuisance being caused to people outside of the site boundary.

- Mobile crushers must be registered with the supplier's own Local Authority, which must be notified in advance each time the equipment is moved.

- All materials to be recycled should be checked for contaminants and dealt with in the correct manner to the required specification. The reuse of construction and demolition waste may require an environmental permit or relevant exemption. Advice should be sought from the local environment agency waste licensing officer on a case-by-case basis where any doubt may arise.

- Operatives working on the crushers and screeners must be properly trained (both general training on the use of crushers and screeners and specific training in respect of the equipment being used).

- Serious consideration must be given to the need for machinery guarding. A daily check sheet should be completed by the operator, which confirms that all guards are in place and the emergency stops are working.

- Robust safe systems of work are required to deal with blockages. These often happen because the operator loading the crusher or screener overfeeds the belt or because lumps are too big for the machine to process. The machine operator feeding the crusher or screener should sort the materials prior to loading by removing the timber, metals, plastics and fabrics that have entered the stockpile.

- All crusher and screener operators are required to wear suitable and adequate hearing protection and may require hearing checks and monitoring as the noise levels can be high.

- Dust suppression systems can be an effective, operational, engineering control, if fitted and working correctly. Reusable half mask respirators are preferred to the use of disposable paper masks as these will offer a higher level of protection. A risk assessment will be required to determine the appropriate type of RPE. Face-fit testing will be required following this.

- Operators should not be allowed to stand on an operating crusher, and must never stand near the jaws where the feedstock is being crushed. The risks arising from this practice can be combatted at source by effective soft stripping and, if necessary, allowing picking from a product feed belt (in other words, before or after it has gone through the crusher).

3.9.7 Removal and disposal of materials

Before any materials are removed from site, both vehicular access to, and egress from, the site must be agreed with all concerned.

It is prudent and practicable to leave the floor slabs, roads and hard standings in place until the end of the project to avoid mud and other debris being carried out onto the highway. Where necessary, bog mats, to create mud free stable access routes, and wheel-washing facilities should be provided to ensure that mud and debris are not carried onto the highway.

Depending on the nature of the material being transported, covering lorries to stabilise the load and prevent dust and debris being released may be appropriate. Daily records (duty of care notes) must be kept of materials taken off site.

It is the responsibility of the demolition contractor to ensure that the carrier they are using is licensed and registered with the relevant agency and that non-hazardous waste is accompanied with a waste transfer note. These documents must be kept for a minimum of two years by the producer of the waste, the carrier and the treatment or disposal facility.

For hazardous waste (such as asbestos) the reception site must be registered with the relevant agency and a hazardous waste consignment note must accompany all such waste leaving site. You should retain the consignor's original. All such documentation should be kept for a minimum of three years.

 The demolition industry has developed DRIDS to help identify waste streams and explain how they can be reused or recycled. For more information, visit the NFDC DRIDS website.

03

3.10   Monitoring the work

The key to a successful and safe demolition project is to plan, implement, monitor and maintain a safe system of work.

 Daily inspection checklist for use by the site supervisor and/or client

- Provide daily briefings to the workforce on complex projects.

- Check for continuing safe working practices.

- Ensure access and egress routes are properly maintained.

- Ensure the site is kept secure, tidy and, as far as possible, free from any piles of combustible rubbish.

- Ensure that sufficient signs are available and clearly visible to warn of hazardous areas and activities.

- Check the contractor's operatives are continuing to wear suitable protective equipment.

- Check the progress and sequence of the job to ensure that it complies with the construction phase plan.

- Check that an approved safe system of work is written down and is being followed.

Make sure all signs are clearly visible

Appendix A – Definitions and terms used by the demolition industry

General

CCDO	Certificate of Competence for Demolition Operatives, partner of the CSCS scheme.
Competent person in demolition	Someone who has practical and theoretical knowledge, with actual experience, of the type of demolition that is taking place on the site. This person is generally accepted to be on site full time as the person responsible for the demolition activity.
Demolition	The deliberate pulling down, destruction or taking apart of a structure or a substantial part of a structure. It includes dismantling for re-erection or reuse.
Exclusion zone	An area where people are fully (sometimes partially) excluded during a demolition activity. This zone should be determined by a competent person, detailed in the construction phase plan, and may need to be defined by physical barriers on site.
Explosives demolition	This involves the designed collapse of a structure using controlled explosives. It is normally preceded by the removal of hazardous materials (for example, asbestos, soft stripping and pre-weakening of the structure).
Façade retention	Where the outer wall of a building or structure is retained in its original position during the demolition phase. The outer wall is usually supported by a façade retention system, internal or external.
Fan	A protective screen fixed to scaffolding to contain falling debris during demolition. Any fan must be designed to withstand the intended load.
Felling	The designed collapse of a structure in such a way that the debris falls in a predetermined area.
Hot work	The application of heat (including the use of tools that can produce an incendiary spark). It generally uses oxygen and propane gas cutting equipment.
Mechanical demolition	This normally involves the use of excavators, including high-reach machines fitted with attachments (see below) or, occasionally, a crawler crane with a demolition wrecking ball to create progressive controlled collapse of the structure.
Party wall structures	These are as defined under the Party Wall etc. Act and are typically where common structures (horizontal and vertical) exist between two or more parties. There are responsibilities to comply with when work affects a party wall structure.
Propping and shoring	A system of temporary supports to prevent movement.
Remote mechanical demolition	Where the machines mentioned in 'Mechanical demolition' are operated via a remote control process. This is used in highly dangerous conditions and removes the need for the operator to be seated within the machine, allowing them to control the machine from a safe location.
Safe working spaces	Areas where demolition work is taking place, often protected by physical barriers (for example, machines protected by ROPS and FOPS as applicable).
Top-down demolition	This generally involves demolition in a reverse sequence to the building's construction.

Machine-mounted attachments

Combination cutter	A tool that can crush concrete and also cut steel reinforcing bar.
Demolition ball	A cast steel ball (drops or pendulum swings in line with the jib) used to demolish a structure. (Slew balling, although rarely used now, may be unacceptable as it places high stresses on the crane.)
Grapple	A powered claw for handling waste and recycled material.
Impact hammer	A large breaker, mounted on an excavator, and usually powered by hydraulics (occasionally by compressed air).
Pedestrian operated	Pedestrian operated, boom equipped, tracked machine.
Pulveriser	Hydraulically powered jaws for crushing concrete. It may be hand-, machine- or crane-mounted.
Pusher arm	An extension to an excavator, which enables it to carry out high-reach demolition.
Quick hitch coupler	A device fitted to the dipper arm of an excavator for a quick and efficient mechanical change of attachments.
Rotator	A part of an attachment fitted between the tool and the end of the dipper arm of the excavator, which allows the tool to be turned. Essential for most work in restricted sites.
Shear	Powered jaws for cutting metal or concrete.

Reproduced with permission from NFDC (National Federation of Demolition Contractors).

03

CONTENTS

Shopfitting and interior contracting

04

SHOPFITTING AND INTERIOR CONTRACTING

Overview

The nature of shopfitting and interior contracting can give rise to additional challenges, including working in and around live retail environments, difficult site logistics, out-of-hours working and congested sites.

This chapter highlights some of the main issues. However, most topics encountered on site are common issues and are addressed in other sections of this GE700 publication.

4.1 Introduction

Shopfitting refers to the sector of the construction industry requiring the manufacture and installation of equipment and fittings, including the installation of bespoke furniture for interior environments.

It should always be remembered that health and safety in all such projects begins at the moment that the specific enquiry lands on the estimator's desk.

A shopfitter executes planning, designs, shop layouts and installation of equipment and services. Under the Construction (Design and Management) Regulations 2015 (CDM) shopfitting is regarded as construction work and as such will require a construction phase plan to be developed for each project.

The term **interior environment** incorporates retail (shops), non-retail (banks, building societies, museums and offices) and leisure (sports centres, restaurants, pubs and garden centres). This list is not exhaustive, but it does illustrate the range of places where shopfitting work is conducted.

This chapter will be relevant to any project that involves the creation of an interior environment.

Shopfitting and interior contracting is about managing risk and developing a strategy of **Safe place – Safe person.**

 Fine for high street retailer

Following a recent case where a high street retailer was fined £1 million for safety failings and the contractor was fined for failing to protect the general public, a Health and Safety Executive (HSE) spokesperson said: 'This outcome should act as a wake-up call that any shopfitting refurbishment programmes involving asbestos-containing materials must be properly resourced, both in terms of time and money – no matter what.

'Large retailers and other organisations that carry out major refurbishment works must give contractors enough time and space within the store to carry out the works safely. Where this is not done, and construction workers and the public are put at risk, HSE will not hesitate in taking robust enforcement action'.

Refurbishing interior environments brings a unique set of hazards, which clearly sets this sector apart from base build construction.

These environments can then be sub-divided into the following categories.

- Sheds (out of town).
- High street.
- Shopping centres.
- Existing buildings.

4.2 Important points

- Site set up is often only in one area of the building with a requirement to keep the rest of the building operational.
- If out of hours working is required there are additional security risks that need to be considered to keep the whole building secure.
- Delivery of materials into city centres can be restricted to certain times. Vehicles will have to contend with congestion and parking may be some distance from the site.
- Refurbishment work is known to create a higher risk of fire and the fire action plan and emergency planning will need to reflect this.
- Services will often be live in the site environment and where isolation is required it will often need to be arranged so as not to impact the ongoing operations around the remainder of the building.
- Nuisance will have additional complexity due to the often close proximity of the general public in city centres and live retail environments. Additional controls may be required to address nuisance from dust, noise, obtrusive lighting and vibration.
- Pay close attention to waste management. Location of skips in a tight site environment may require smaller skips with regular collection and exchange.
- Look for opportunities to reuse and recycle materials to support resource efficiency and reduce waste.

4.3 Identifying risk

From a health and safety point of view, **before the project commences** the fit-out team should give serious consideration to how they intend to manage the following.

- Difference between new build interior and refurbishment of an existing interior.
- Meccano job (removal of some fittings) or full refit (strip back to the original shell).
- Client-appointed contractors – managed by the principal contractor from the commencement of works.
- Third-party liability (general public/store staff).
- Merchandisers.
- Site logistics and waste management.
- Project team and retail team.
- Asbestos (a survey should be carried out before works commence).
- Fire safety and emergency escape routes for contractors, existing occupiers, employees of the building and members of the public when working on a live site.
- Possible vermin infestation.
- Carrying out the work whilst the premises continue to trade, if applicable.

 Fatal incident at a retail unit undergoing refurbishment

A fatal incident involving a shopfitting contractor highlighted the need for clients, designers and contractors to be aware of the structural condition of existing works. If in doubt a structural engineer should be employed on the project to assist in managing the risk of accidental collapse.

 Everyone involved in site work has health, safety and environmental responsibilities.

Checking that working conditions are healthy and safe before and during the work, and ensuring that the proposed work is not going to put others at risk or damage the environment, requires planning, organisation, communication and resources, whatever the size of the site.

4.4 Site-based issues

Site-based issues that need to be considered during shopfitting contracts are listed below.

Site induction – ensuring all workers attend a full, site-specific induction, especially during busy weekend and night-time shift working.

Hoardings and signage – phasing, safe erection and inspection and clear signage for mandatory protection, safe areas and hazards.

Structural design and temporary works following design.

Live services – identification and isolation, installation of temporary electrics, gas and water and maintaining services to other areas of a building that are still in operation.

Occupational health – physical (for example, vibration and noise, especially in internal spaces) and mental health and wellbeing (for example, stress).

Dust – controlling the movement and breathing in of construction dust, which is a high risk to health.

Welfare – providing suitable welfare facilities in restricted spaces to accommodate peak numbers of workers.

Waste management – managing space constraints to allow for waste segregation, the provision of chutes and to avoid build up of waste.

Fire – maintaining integrity of existing fire arrangements, managing additional risks posed by construction work and avoiding the build up of waste and stockpiling of materials. The current fire risk assessment should be reviewed by the responsible person, and ensure that it covers the changes whilst the works are being undertaken. This should be continually reviewed as the work progresses and the nature of the risk changes.

Working at height – avoiding, where possible, or preventing falls, and the selection and correct use of suitable access equipment.

Plant and equipment – using battery-powered or 110 volt equipment, providing access for equipment, managing cartridge tools and gas nail guns, and appropriately selecting to handle space constraints.

Logistics – planning the removal of waste, the delivery and distribution of materials and large prefabricated items and early or phased deliveries.

Manual handling – ensuring materials are distributed utilising mechanical means to minimise manual handling.

SHOPFITTING AND INTERIOR CONTRACTING

Personal protective equipment (PPE) – ensuring everybody has the correct PPE for the task and enforcing any protection zones.

Site deliveries – managing any shared delivery areas, planning phased deliveries and using vehicle marshallers.

Nuisance – considering neighbouring third-parties, disturbance, traffic, noise, dust, vibration and light levels.

 For further guidance refer to the corresponding GE700 chapters, where applicable.

Large shopfitting contract in a city

Pedestrian and vehicle segregation in front of hoarding to control access and deliveries

Temporary works behind hoarding complete with working platforms

Planned road closures for a crane and lifting in a public space

Pre-planned temporary scaffold removal to facilitate lifting and access for steelwork and fall arrest in use for slinger. Note: collective and personal fall prevention methods should be considered before personal fall arrest

Moving the steelwork into position

Removing the lifting equipment used to manoeuvre the steelwork into position

04

4.5   Working at height

Work at height is work in any place, including a place at, above, or below ground level, where a person could be injured if they fell from that place. Access to and egress from a place of work can also be deemed to be work at height. Below are some examples in a shopfitter's environment that would be classified as work at height.

- Working on any type of scaffolding.
- Working on a mobile elevating work platform.
- Being on the back of a lorry or raised loading bays.
- Working close to an excavation or a shaft opening (lift pit).
- Working off steps, hop-ups and mobile access towers.

- Mezzanine floors with no edge protection.
- Staircases with no handrails.
- Temporary wheelbarrow ramps onto the back of skips.
- Creating voids through floors or risers.

Full height barriers provide an internal safe zone by segregating the high-risk façade replacement works

Mobile access towers, stepladders and MEWPs providing a typical range of access solutions

The Work at Height Regulations cover all work where a fall that is likely to cause injury may occur. The scope of the regulations includes all locations, above or below ground, and all types of access and work platforms from which a person may fall and suffer injury, regardless of how long a worker is at height. The Work at Height Regulations require duty holders to ensure the following.

- All work at height is properly planned and organised.
- Those involved in work at height are competent.
- The risks from work at height are assessed and appropriate working procedures and equipment are selected and used.

- The risks from fragile surfaces are properly controlled.
- Equipment for work at height is properly inspected and maintained.

The shopfitting industry often includes the use of stepladders as a work platform for maintenance or other tasks.

Contrary to what some people believe, stepladders are not banned or illegal under the regulations. However, they should only be considered when the risk assessment, in accordance with the work at height hierarchy, shows that the task is of low risk and of short duration, and all safer alternatives for work at height have been ruled out.

It should also be noted that stepladders come in many forms, some of which are safer than others, and include features such as adjustable out-riggers, platforms, handrails, lightweight glass-reinforced plastic (GRP) construction and tool tray attachments.

Lift shafts, new openings, strip out and removal of partitions, windows, façade, handrails, escalators and staircases create open edges and voids that need to be controlled with suitable protection measures to prevent people from falling. The risk assessment must also consider how falls will be prevented while removing or reinstating these features.

Edge protection and fall prevention measures must be robust and secured into position, and again the method of installing these must include fall prevention. Plastic or free-standing barriers offer little resistance and a person can easily fall through them.

Falls from height are the most common accidents that lead to serious injury, accounting for around 50% of fatalities to construction workers.

Temporary edge protection fixed into position

 For further information on working at height refer to Chapters D01 to D05.

4.6 Fire

Fire is an ever-present threat throughout the majority of construction and demolition projects. As shopfitting progresses, the nature of the fire risk is likely to change as different work starts and finishes. Therefore, not only must the risk of fire be managed continuously but the management process must allow for the changing nature of the risk. A site-specific fire risk assessment must be completed for all construction projects, including shopfitting work, and should be continually reviewed as the work progresses and the nature of the risks changes.

The fire triangle

4.6.1 Common sources of fire risk

- Storage and use of flammable materials, including liquefied petroleum gas (LPG).
- Hot work (blow torches, welding and sparks from cutting).
- Arson.
- Smoking (discarded cigarettes and matches).

- Operating plant and equipment.
- Poor housekeeping.
- Electrical systems and equipment, including temporary lighting (some sites have banned halogen lights due to the high risk of fire).

 It is vital that the project fire strategy takes into account all existing third-party fire arrangements.

4.6.2 Specialist advice

The Fire Protection Association (FPA), in conjunction with the Construction Confederation, published *Fire prevention on construction sites*. This joint Code of Practice (CoP) deals with the protection from fire on construction sites and buildings undergoing renovation. The CoP does not have any legal status; however, it does outline good practice and many insurance companies now require that the authoritative guidelines (such as those detailed in the CoP) are properly implemented on construction projects before they will give full insurance. The FPA also publishes *Construction site fire prevention checklist – a guide for insurers, surveyors and construction industry professionals*.

 For further guidance refer to Chapter C02 Fire prevention and control.

 For further information refer to the HSE publication *Fire safety in construction* (HSG168).

4.7 Health risks

The following topics must be considered when shopfitting and interior contracting. These are also covered in detail in other chapters.

4.7.1 Construction dust

Many shopfitting activities will create dust, which is a high risk to health. Typical activities that create harmful levels of dust are shown below.

- Sweeping a dusty floor.
- Mechanically cutting, chasing or drilling concrete, bricks and blocks.

- Mixing plaster, sand and cement to make mortar.
- Sanding down MDF or timber.
- Rubbing down taped joints or plaster.

 All dusts are hazardous to health. The creation of dust, regardless of the amount, must be controlled. Risk assessments should identify how exposure to dust or fumes will be minimised.

 ## Rubbing down taped joints

Traditional methods of rubbing down taped joints create a lot of dust, which is hazardous to health, has to be cleaned up and is manually intensive.

This drywall sander with collection system minimises these issues, to the extent that the operative does not need RPE.

 For further guidance on how to manage dust and fumes, and to check if method statements and risk assessments adequately address respiratory risks, refer to Chapter B10 Dust and fumes (Respiratory hazards).

4.7.2   Asbestos

Asbestos was widely used in the UK until it was banned in 1999; disturbance of the fabric of any building built before this time has the potential to expose asbestos.

In the majority of cases, work with asbestos removal needs to be carried out by a licensed contractor.

This work includes all work with sprayed asbestos coatings and asbestos lagging, and most work with asbestos insulation and asbestos insulating board (AIB).

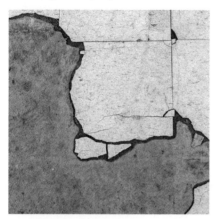

Damaged asbestos floor tiles

Asbestos (AIB) panels at high level

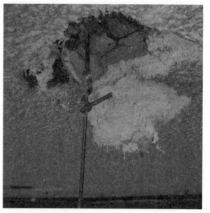

Damaged asbestos spray applied acoustical ceiling material

- All asbestos-containing material (ACM) has the potential to be hazardous. However, if the material is in good condition, or is not disturbed or damaged, there is negligible risk. The danger arises when the fibres become airborne and are inhaled into the lungs.

- The priority for any employer is to prevent the spread of and exposure to asbestos fibres.

- Before any work that has the potential to expose anyone to asbestos is carried out, an appropriate survey must be carried out and a written risk assessment completed.

- A written, site-specific plan (or register) of work must be kept on site and followed.

- Workers liable to disturb asbestos while carrying out their normal, everyday work, must be given asbestos awareness training.

- Anyone who carries out work where they will knowingly disturb asbestos must be specifically trained to do it, and this training must be repeated at least annually.

- If you are carrying out non-licensed asbestos work, this still requires effective controls.

- Some non-licensed work is notifiable to the relevant enforcing authority. This is known as notifiable non-licensed asbestos work. (For example, large scale removal of textured decorative coatings and removal of asbestos cement products where the removal process will involve substantial break-up of the product.)

- Written records should be kept of all notifiable non-licensed work (such as a copy of the notification with a list of workers on the job), plus the level of likely exposure of those workers to asbestos. This does not require air monitoring on every job, if an estimate of degree of exposure can be made based on experience of similar past tasks or published guidance.

- Contractors producing hazardous asbestos waste must check that the site receiving the asbestos waste is authorised to receive asbestos.

- Be aware of other hazards that may arise from working with or managing asbestos (such as working at height, in a confined space or where the presence of live services must be managed).

- The HSE must be notified of all work involving the disturbance of asbestos, apart from non-licensed work.

- The regulations require anyone who issues a site-clearance certificate to be accredited by an appropriate accreditation body as competent to carry out such work. In the UK the sole source of this accreditation is UKAS.

 For further information refer to Chapter B09 Asbestos and Chapter E10 Waste and material management.

The Control of Asbestos Regulations require all those who may be exposed to asbestos to have appropriate asbestos awareness training.

4.7.3   Lead and lead-based paint

Old, lead-based paint may still be present in UK buildings built before the early 1990s. It was completely removed from general sale by 1992. It is a hazardous material and therefore a survey should be undertaken in order to comply fully with the requirements of CDM. Survey results should form part of the pre-construction information for the structure. Where lead is present this residual risk should then be detailed in the health and safety file.

SHOPFITTING AND INTERIOR CONTRACTING

Where the previous use of lead-based paint is suspected, and it is likely that the work will involve the disturbance of coated surfaces, then a risk assessment must be carried out under the Control of Lead at Work Regulations.

Exposure to lead, lead dust and fumes constitutes a major hazard to the health of those who work with lead, lead products and lead-containing materials (LCMs) (such as lead-based paint).

Lead paint and dust exposure risks are greatest within pre-1970 buildings and structures, especially during repair, maintenance, refurbishment and demolition, if proper precautions are not followed.

 For an explanation on the risks and controls that are required when working with lead refer to Chapter B08 Lead.

4.8   Supporting information

Supporting information, training and guidance is available from the National Association of Shopfitters and Interior Contractors.

Training and supervision. By law, all workers must receive training and supervision that is appropriate to the equipment they will be using.

Competency cards. Shopfitting and interior contractors must be able to prove competency for the role they specialise in, and hold the relevant competency card. The Shopfitting and Interior Contractors Card Scheme (SICCS) is a mandatory requirement, managed by the National Association of Shopfitters (NAS), the only CSCS partners that issue this card. The SICCS cards are digital only, will bear the CSCS logo and are validated through the Smart Checker system on site.

Workplace management. Paying attention to layout, worker movement and keeping workshops and storage areas tidy can help reduce the risks. Workers have legal responsibilities with regard to health and safety and should be encouraged to become actively involved. Workers are often the best people to understand the risks and help find solutions to health and safety issues.

Through worker involvement you can act together to reduce accidents and ill health within your manufacturing environment.

 For further guidance visit the National Association of Shopfitters website.

04

Working over or near to water

05

Supporting INFORMATION

GT700 Toolbox talks / supporting checklists and forms

Toolbox talks on some of these topics are available in the GT700 publication. Supporting checklists and forms covering some of these topics are available on our companion website.

WORKING OVER OR NEAR TO WATER

Overview

Where construction or demolition work takes place over or near to water, steps must be taken, primarily to stop anyone from falling into it, but also to ensure that should someone fall in they will not come to harm and can be promptly rescued.

When planning for safe working over or near to water, in addition to looking after the health and safety of employees, it will also be necessary to take into consideration the safety of the public, including those using the waterway. Consideration should also be given to the environmental impact of the work activities and materials used and to dust, noise and vibration generated by the works, all of which could contaminate the water or create nuisance.

Tidal and fast flowing waters pose additional problems for anyone falling into them and their rescuers.

Whilst the word *water* will be used throughout this chapter, the dangers and precautions apply equally to work being carried out near to other liquids (such as slurries and chemicals in vats) and free-flowing solids (such as foodstuffs in silos).

5.1   Introduction

Managing and controlling the risks associated with working over or near to water is something that many managers will do only on rare occasions. This in itself could be a problem because they could be ill-prepared when the need arises. The dangers in doing such work are significant and must be proactively managed.

Where construction and/or temporary works will block or partially block a navigable waterway, even on a temporary basis, it will be necessary to gain the permission of the navigation authority responsible for that waterway during the planning stage.

The Health and Safety Executive (HSE) states that accidental drowning is often linked to one or more of the following factors.

- Failure to provide personal buoyancy equipment.

- Failure of personal buoyancy equipment to operate properly.

- Disregard for, or misjudgment of, the severity of the risk of getting it wrong.

- Lack of supervision, particularly of the young and inexperienced.

- Inability to cope once a problem arises.

- The absence of rescuers and rescue equipment.

- Failure to take account of weather forecasts.

Raising the awareness of managers, supervisors and workers to ensure effective control measures are always put in place and followed is fundamental to safe working over and near to water.

 Anyone who may accidentally fall into water should ideally be able to swim, have trust in their personal bouyancy equipment and be confident in the effectiveness of the rescue procedures, so that they remain calm and do not panic.

5.2   Important points

- Working over water will often involve working at height. The potential risks arising from both hazards must be managed.

- The risks must be assessed and a written method statement and rescue plan produced.

- As with any other work at height, options to eliminate the requirement to work at height should be considered first. Work must be carried out from a stable working platform that will prevent an accidental fall into the water; only as a last resort should fall-arrest equipment be relied upon.

- Where there is a risk of someone accidentally entering the water, appropriate rescue equipment and people who are competent to use it must be immediately available.

- Appropriate personal protective equipment (PPE), offering protection should a fall into water occur, must be made available. Suddenly falling fully clothed into cold, deep water may induce shock and an increased risk of drowning if appropriate PPE is not worn.

- Instruction and training must be given to the workforce in relation to PPE and the use of equipment.

- Rescue procedures must be planned and practised regularly to ensure quick and effective response times.

- Powered rescue boats must only be operated by someone trained in boat-handling and rescue procedures.

- If the use of a rescue boat is not appropriate, an established hierarchy of rescue methods must be in place and followed.

- Working near to deep water (for example, adjacent to canal locks) can be as dangerous as working over water if appropriate control measures are not put in place.

- Potential health risks, such as leptospirosis (Weil's disease), must also be controlled.

 Providing there was no immediate danger, would all members of your workforce be at ease if they were to fall into the water wearing a lifejacket, and how would a rescue be facilitated?

5.3   Risk management

5.3.1   Risk assessment

The risk assessment must investigate different methods of work that could reduce or eliminate the hazard of working over or near to water. An example of this is the removal of lock-gates for off-site repair rather than repairing the gates in situ. The number of people and the length of time they will be exposed to the hazard will both be significantly reduced.

 As for all work, the significant risks arising from a task must be communicated to the workforce and the workforce must understand their role in completing the work safely.

Where there is a risk of falling from height into water and/or where the water is fast flowing or tidal, the employer is advised to consider the selection of workers carefully.

The HSE does not make any recommendations regarding whether anyone who runs the risk of falling into water must be able to swim, although it is preferable that they can swim because they are more likely to be at ease in the water until they are rescued. A lifejacket will keep a non-swimmer afloat and automatically turn them face up.

The following points must be considered.

- Safe access to dry land, where people and materials are transported to site over the water.

- Site access by the emergency services and how an injured person is going to be removed from the water and transferred to an ambulance.

If the work involves the use of a mobile elevating work platform (MEWP), employers must assess whether the risk to the operator is greater from wearing a harness to prevent a fall or if the harness would increase the risk of drowning should the MEWP fall into the water and prevent the operator reaching the surface of the water.

A lifejacket should be worn instead of a harness where there is a higher risk of drowning.

Safe access for the arrival and departure of site staff by waterborne transport

 For safety precautions that need to be observed when working over or near to water using an articulated boom mobile elevating work platform, refer to the HSE information sheet *The selection, management and use of mobile elevating work platforms* (GEIS6).

5.3.2   Areas of risk

Hazardous work areas include the following.

- Quaysides, docks and wharfs.

- Locks.

- Canals and rivers, including bankside paths.

- Open sea (off-shore construction sites and installations).

- Lakes, lochs, reservoirs and ponds (natural and ornamental).

- Sewage and slurry ponds.

- Water-filled pits.

- Water-holding tanks, including those located underground.

- Culverts and other storm-drainage channels.

- Swimming pools and aquatic sports facilities.

- Water features (such as fountains and rock pools).

It is essential that fall prevention measures are taken, as for any other type of construction work

5.3.3   Hierarchy for working at height

There are six steps in the hierarchy for working at height *(refer to D01 Work at Height Regulations for further information)*.

In summary, the issues that must be considered when working over water are:

- avoid working at height (over water) if it is possible to do the job another way

- prevent falls, if it is necessary to work at height, and

- minimise the trauma of anyone who does fall.

To avoid duplication, familiarise yourself further with the content of Chapters D03 to D05, which are relevant to working over or near to water, in that they cover:

- scaffolds and other stable working platforms

- safe access using ladders

- use of MEWPs

- personal fall prevention by harness and restraint lanyard

- collective fall arrest by safety nets and soft-landing systems

- personal fall arrest by harness and shock-absorbing lanyard (the last resort).

When working over water, scaffolds will often be cantilevered off the structure, slung underneath or secured via other complex designs. People competent to do so must ensure scaffolds are:

A fully sheeted bridge scaffold, protecting the workforce and river users. (Note the rescue boat on the left bank)

- properly designed and fit for purpose

- erected, modified and struck (dismantled) appropriately

- regularly inspected.

5.3.4   Preventing accidental entry into water

Every effort must be made to eliminate the risk of accidental entry into water. This will involve protecting employees against the following.

- Falls from heights.

- Trips and slips from low level.

- Banks and edges crumbling away, causing people to enter the water.

- Persons being knocked over by moving objects (for example, crane loads).

- Loss of balance (for example, caused by high winds) particularly when handling sheet materials.

- Failure or absence of barriers.

- Failure of ropes or lines.

- Rising swell or swell from passing waterborne traffic.

- Failure to correctly use fall prevention or arrest measures provided.

- Messing around (horseplay).

- Being on site whilst under the influence of drink or drugs.

Collective fall prevention (such as barriers) should always be considered before the use of personal prevention methods

Site management must actively manage any of the above points that affect their project and others that may not be covered.

5.3.5 Dangers from falling into water

The greatest risk following accidental entry into water is drowning. Below are some possible causes or contributory factors.

● Shock of sudden immersion in cold water.

● Weight of waterlogged clothing.

● Fatigue or hypothermia where rescue is not immediate.

Other effects of falling, which importantly may render the victim incapable of assisting in their own rescue, include the following.

● Being knocked unconscious by hitting part of the structure during the fall.

● Suffering broken bones by hitting the structure during the fall.

● Suffering physical injury from an impact with the riverbed or rocks when falling into shallow water.

Risks to health include the following.

● Leptospirosis (Weil's disease) if infected rats are present.

● Digestive illnesses from swallowing water contaminated with natural organisms, chemicals used in the work process or other contaminants (such as diesel oil).

Dependent on the control measures that are in place, not all falls will result in the operative entering the water.

Consideration must be given to an operative suffering suspension syncope (fainting) by being left suspended in a harness (above the water) for too long.

5.4 Rescue equipment and procedures

Although every effort should be made to prevent people falling into the water, the risk of this happening may remain and you must have a rescue plan in place.

In the event of someone falling into water, three things are of paramount importance.

● The person must be kept afloat.

● Their location must be immediately obvious and continuously tracked, especially in flowing water.

● Rescue must be achieved as quickly as possible.

A process must be in place to call the emergency services immediately, so they can be on their way whilst others facilitate the rescue.

 Getting a rescue wrong could put the rescuers and the victim at risk.

Methods of rescuing a casualty, other than by using a rescue boat, could include the following.

Involving the emergency services. In many cases, the fire and rescue services (or coastguard in appropriate circumstances) will have the expertise and equipment to carry out rescue procedures. A judgement will have to be made as to whether it is advisable or practical to await their arrival. This must be balanced against the risks involved in attempting the following means of rescue.

Reaching out from the bank or edge. If the casualty is near enough to the bank or edge, it may be possible to grab their hand, or use a sturdy stick, boat-hook, oar, broom handle, or anything they can grab and hold on to, to be pulled in to safety. Rescuers should ensure that they have a secure foothold, sufficient grip and balance to counteract the weight of the casualty in the water.

Throwing out a means of personal buoyancy. When the casualty is some way out in the water, a lifebuoy and rescue line or any personal buoyancy aid with line attached should be thrown to them. This technique is preferable to entering the water to reach the casualty, especially if the depth of water and presence of currents are not known.

Wading out. A shelving bed or shore may enable rescuers to reach the person in the water by wading out to them, and to work with suitable onshore assistance (for example, the rescuer should be wearing suitable buoyancy equipment and a harness and line. The line must be anchored and attended by at least one other person). However, even with these precautions extreme care should be taken as currents, underwater obstacles and sudden changes in the depth of water may put the rescuers at risk.

Going out. Assistance should be summoned first when possible. A boat should preferably be used to reach the casualty. If a boat is not available, the rescuer should swim out with a lifeline secured to the shore or edge. The rescuer should also be wearing suitable personal buoyancy equipment.

All rescue work should be properly planned.

 Everyone on site must be familiar with the rescue procedure and understand the actions they must take in an emergency.

Avoid becoming a casualty. People who cannot swim should not enter the water, but must raise the alarm and wait for assistance.

WORKING OVER OR NEAR TO WATER

5.4.1   Personal buoyancy equipment

 Refer to the HSE information sheet *Personal buoyancy equipment on inland and inshore waters* **(AIS1).**

Anyone working over or near to water, and at risk of falling in, should wear some form of personal buoyancy equipment – generally a lifejacket or buoyancy aid. Lifejackets and personal buoyancy aids are designed to keep the wearer afloat. There are, however, important differences and it is recommended that lifejackets are used in preference to buoyancy aids.

Decisions on the type of equipment best suited to specific types of work should be based on an assessment of the factors involved by the employer. In some circumstances consultation with suppliers may be required.

These may include, for example, the length of time a person may be in the water, the risks of injury, water temperature, current and the proximity of assistance.

Lifejackets must be made to the relevant British Standard and must be obtained from a reputable supplier. Ideally, they should be fitted with crotch straps, which will stop the lifejacket riding up over the person's head. The lifejacket's primary aim is to support an unconscious person in the water by turning them face upwards.

Inflation of the lifejacket is by means of a CO_2 cartridge, activated manually or automatically, depending upon the item purchased. Lifejackets that inflate automatically are preferable because:

- on making contact with the water the lifejacket will inflate within seconds and an unconscious person will be turned face upwards in the water
- with manually inflated lifejackets, not only must the wearer be conscious and capable of locating and pulling the manual inflation toggle but the toggle can get caught on obstructions during work activities and accidentally inflate the lifejacket.

Manually inflated lifejackets, which are inflated by mouth after entry into the water, should not be used.

 For advice on the selection of lifejackets and personal buoyancy aids refer to Appendix A.

Buoyancy aids are intended to provide a conscious person with enough extra buoyancy to stay afloat and achieve a reasonable floating position. A basic buoyancy aid may not turn an unconscious person face up. The use of a buoyancy aid assumes that the wearer is able to help themselves to some degree by swimming to safety or by keeping themselves afloat while assistance arrives, if required.

Buoyancy is achieved by means of closed-cell foam pads sewn into the material of the buoyancy aid. Buoyancy aids are bulky and, in some people's view, hinder movement and may slow the progress of work, in comparison to lifejackets, which offer greater freedom of movement.

Where a **safety harness** is to be worn in addition to personal buoyancy equipment, it is important to ensure each of these items is compatible and will not interfere with the correct functioning of the other.

Safety harness and buoyancy aid combinations are available from some manufacturers, although professional advice should be sought on their suitability for wearing during construction work before committing to them.

The provision of whistles and lights as aids in the search to locate people in the water may be advisable in some circumstances.

Wearers should be fully trained in the use of safety harnesses, lifejackets and personal buoyancy aids. The functions of the equipment and, where appropriate, its limitations should be clearly understood by users.

 The selection and care of personal buoyancy equipment are covered in Appendices A and B respectively.

5.4.2   Lifebuoys

Lifebuoys should be available wherever people are working on, over or near to water. Standard 760 mm diameter lifebuoys with rope or cord lifelines (usually 30 m) attached should be placed where they can be clearly seen near the water's edge.

A lifebuoy can be thrown only a short distance, perhaps 6-8 m and then with little accuracy. Lifebuoys should be suspended from a suitable hook or bracket at a height where they can be clearly seen, with the lifeline coiled ready for use.

Handling 30 m of rope, to enable it to unravel as it is thrown, may also present problems to the inexperienced person (lifebuoys are available with the rope packed into plastic containers, from which it reels out when the lifebuoy is thrown).

Check the location of the lifebuoy in case of an emergency

5.4.3   Rescue lines

Drownings have occurred close to the bank or water's edge. Safety provision should take account of this, where it is the dominant risk.

Lightweight throwing lines or similar equipment should be provided to supplement lifebuoys, especially if workers are moving from place to place, adjacent to the water.

Various types of rescue line (sometimes referred to as throwing lines) are available. Typically they contain 20 or 30 m of rescue line enclosed within a canvas bag.

The free end of the line is fitted over the thrower's wrist and held, while the bag is thrown underarm towards the casualty. The line can be delivered accurately up to its full length, but underarm throwing may be hindered by guard-rails and other forms of edge protection.

Upon completion of the rescue, the line should be left extended to dry, and it can then be repacked into the canvas bag when that has also dried.

The image to the right shows a typical rescue line, with a loop tied in the free end to fit over the wrist. The bag, complete with the line, is then thrown to the person in the water, trailing the line as it goes into the water.

A typical rescue line showing the throw bag and wrist loop

This particular line shown is equipped with a padded handle on the outside of the bag, which the person in the water will hold on to whilst they are pulled ashore.

Another method of delivering the line is the capsule emergency lifeline. A light but strong line, 40 m in length, is packed into a small plastic capsule. The free end of the line is secured to a cord grip that is held while the capsule is thrown, the line paying out as it goes.

The capsule may be thrown or flicked to the full distance of 40 m using an extension rod that fits into the handle. Both line and capsule will float, allowing the casualty to grab the line and be hauled to safety. If the first throw misses, it can be quickly used again.

The ability to deliver the line up to 40 m may avoid the need to launch a boat or for somebody to enter the water.

The capsules are small enough to be carried in a belt or, alternatively, can be mounted in cabinets (with the extension rod) at convenient locations.

5.4.4   Stop nets or lines

As a pre-emptive measure stop nets or lines can be suspended across or in the water for a conscious person to hold on to whilst they are awaiting rescue, or to pull themselves to the bank.

For nets and lines to be used there must be no waterborne traffic and the water must be still or gently flowing.

These cannot be totally relied upon, because a casualty may be unconscious or otherwise unable to help themselves.

If there is a weir or sluice, stop nets or lines should not be relied upon unless they can be positioned well upstream.

5.4.5   Rescue nets

Recovering a fully dressed person from the water into a rescue boat can be difficult, particularly if there is a heavy swell and/or they are unconscious or injured and therefore unable to assist in their own rescue. Rescue nets, which clip to fittings along one side of a rescue boat, have been developed to assist in such rescues by holding the person horizontally parallel with the boat and enabling the crew to lift and roll the person into the boat.

Requirements for a rescue net are shown below.

- When not required, it should be clipped in a roll and stored in the boat.

- When required for a rescue it should be unravelled and one side clipped to the edge of the boat. The net should then be lowered into the water with the rescue boat crew keeping hold of the outer edge.

- Slight negative buoyancy, enabling the rescue boat crew to slide the person, supported by their lifejacket, from the water, over the net.

- Equipped with handles and loops to enable the person in the water to be gently hauled over the side of the rescue boat.

Rescue net extended over decking for illustrative purposes

05

5.4.6   Rescue boats

A risk assessment will identify if a rescue boat will be required. If the water is tidal or fast flowing, it will be more likely that a rescue boat will be required.

A rescue boat may also be required in situations where high, steep banks and the absence of self-rescue ladders prevent the person in the water effecting their own rescue.

Any rescue boat must comply with the regulations and byelaws of the navigation authority in whose waters it is operating.

The craft may be rigid (wooden or fibreglass) or inflatable. It must have a reliable engine and, depending on the findings of the risk assessment, carry the following.

- A radio, if they are being used on site, or a working mobile phone.
- A first-aid kit.
- Paddles, in case of engine failure.
- A boat-hook.
- A throwing line.
- Grab-lines around the hull.
- A rescue net.

A typical powered rescue boat, equipped with radio, throwing line, paddles, boat-hook and a first-aid kit

The boat crew should be experienced and competent at handling the rescue craft on appropriate waterways, particularly in rescue situations that involve specialist boat-handling skills.

 Where a powered rescue boat will be used it is strongly recommended that the operator is trained to a minimum standard of Royal Yachting Association (RYA) Power Boat Level 2 and also in rescue techniques. Rescuing a person from the water in a power boat with a rotating propeller demands skill and experience, particularly if there is a current flowing and/or strong winds. Ideally, there will be two people in the boat, the driver and a rescuer.

 The RYA runs courses throughout the United Kingdom.

Whether the rescue boat is to be permanently manned and constantly afloat or not will depend on the circumstances, as will its size and the equipment to be carried. If any work is to be done during the hours of darkness, the rescue boat will require high efficiency lighting.

Two-way radio communication between boat and shore may be necessary on large areas of water. Regular practice rescue drills should be held, so that the best method of rescuing, securing and landing a potential casualty is known in advance.

 It is advisable for practice drills to be carried out and people on site made aware of the emergency arrangements.

ⓘ Kill cords

It is essential that powered rescue boats are equipped with a kill cord, which will stop the engine if the driver falls overboard or otherwise moves from the driving position.

A driverless power boat is dangerous, particularly if on full lock so that it drives itself around in circles when people are still in the water. To make sure the kill cord is suitable and used safely, follow these recommendations.

- Test regularly to ensure the engine stops when the kill cord mechanism is operated.
- Check that the kill cord is in good condition.
- Always attach the kill cord securely to the driver, ideally before the engine is started, but definitely before the boat is put into gear.
- Stop the engine before transferring the kill cord to another driver.

05

5.5   Onshore facilities and procedures

First aid. Irrespective of the size of the operation, first-aid facilities must be provided, as indicated in the first-aid needs assessment. A trained and qualified first aider should be present at the site of all work adjacent to water.

Facilities should include provision for transferring casualties from the boat to shore and ambulance access.

Alarms. An effective means of raising the alarm should be provided. Gongs, bells, whistles, pressurised canister fog horns, klaxons or similar items of equipment could be used. All people on site should be trained in the correct use of the alarm and the actions to be taken when the alarm sounds.

Lighting. Water surfaces should be illuminated at night so that victims of falls can be seen and constantly watched while awaiting rescue.

Communications. The telephone number for the ambulance, coastguard and lifeboat services (999) should be stressed to operatives and adequate provision should be made for effective on-site communications (usually site radios).

Rescue equipment is for use in an emergency. It must be properly maintained, not misused and never relied upon as a primary safeguard against accidents.

Clothing. High-visibility vests or jackets should be worn. These will assist in keeping the casualty in view while the rescue operation is being mounted. High-visibility immersion suits will be appropriate in some circumstances.

Checking personnel. Periodic checks should be made to ensure nobody is missing. Personnel should work in pairs or in sight of each other to enable one person to raise the alarm in the event of an emergency.

Weather and tides. Details of weather and, where appropriate, tides should be obtained before each shift.

Safety ladders. Where there is a quay-heading to the bank, there is likely to be a significant height difference between the water level and the dry land, which can make it difficult or impossible for someone who is fully dressed in wet clothes to clamber out of the water.

Recovery of equipment from the water. In the event of tools, equipment or small plant falling into the water, no attempt should be made to recover those using improvised techniques.

Special regulations apply to all diving operations and expert advice should be sought where it is necessary to recover equipment.

5.6   Training

Safe working practices and rescue procedures must be covered during site induction, refresher training and any specialist training.

All personnel should be made aware of the location of emergency equipment and training should be given to the people involved in its use. Responsibility for co-ordinating and supervising rescue operations must be allocated to individuals sufficiently trained and competent to carry out emergency rescues, and who are quickly identifiable as such. Rescue procedures should be practised on a regular basis.

Locally employed site-based staff and the employees of sub-contractors should receive training in emergency procedures and the use of life-preserving and rescue equipment, and must be given such information as is necessary to enable them to act effectively in an emergency.

With regard to personal buoyancy equipment, all workers who are likely to use it must be trained in the following.

● Adjust the securing straps to make sure it will not come off over the head, upon impact with water.

● Check that the firing (inflation) mechanism of a lifejacket has not already been activated.

● Carry out pre-use and routine maintenance checks.

● Store the equipment correctly when not in use, particularly if it is wet.

● Appreciate any limitations in its use or performance.

● Report suspected or actual defects and obtain a replacement item if necessary.

 Training on how to use life-preserving equipment should be given to all involved, without exception.

05

Appendix A – Selection of personal buoyancy equipment

Equipment is divided into different categories of buoyancy. The criterion of each class is the support (personal buoyancy) provided by each category, which is expressed in Newtons (N).

The European Union standards that cover lifejackets also require a level of protection for the unconscious person in the water. This means that lifejackets must distribute the weight of the wearer in such a manner that the person is turned face up.

The standards require that automatic lifejackets must self-inflate within 10 seconds of contact with water.

The personal buoyancy level in the standards relates to a person weighing 70 kg, thus the amount of actual personal buoyancy provided by any lifejacket will depend upon the weight of the wearer.

Consider the following situations.

● Wearing a lifejacket with too little personal buoyancy poses obvious problems, as there may be too little support for a heavy person to keep their face out of the water or for the lifejacket to turn them face up if they are unconscious.

● Conversely, wearing a lifejacket with too much personal buoyancy could also pose problems; wearers who are not particularly heavy will be more buoyant and could find it difficult to escape from an air pocket if they have to fully immerse themselves and their lifejacket to duck under an obstruction.

The selection of the most appropriate equipment is therefore essential.

50 N personal buoyancy aid

For use by good swimmers in safe water only as long as assistance is at hand. Not safe for unconscious persons.

100 N lifejacket

Suitable for adults who are swimmers and for use in inland waters and safe areas, providing limited protection for unconscious persons depending upon the clothing worn.

150 N lifejacket

Suitable for swimmers and non-swimmers in all waters. This level is intended for general offshore and rough weather use where a high standard of performance is required.

It will turn an unconscious person into a safe position and requires no subsequent action by the user to maintain this position.

275 N lifejacket

For offshore use and extreme conditions. Offers immediate protection for unconscious persons. It is designed to ensure that the user is floating in the correct position with their mouth and nose clear of the surface.

Adequate personal buoyancy is provided even in heavy clothing.

A personal buoyancy aid should not be used if there is any likelihood of a person being rendered unconscious

Appendix B – Caring for personal buoyancy equipment

Pre-use checks

 These must be carried out each time an item of personal buoyancy equipment is used.

Inspecting personal buoyancy aids is relatively simple with regard to looking for defects in the securing straps, zips, seams and fabric.

Inspecting a lifejacket is slightly more complex and should be carried out in accordance with the manufacturer's instructions. It will normally include visual checks to ensure:

● the firing mechanism has not been activated (this is usually made obvious by the fact that the lifejacket is found inflated)

● the automatic firing capsule and gas cylinder are correctly screwed in place

● there are no signs of corrosion, cracks or dents in the gas cylinder or automatic firing capsule

● unwanted movement within the firing mechanism (creepage) has not occurred.

Some automatic inflation mechanisms have colour coded indicators to show when compression in the spring has been lost. Those that do not have such indicators will require careful inspection to judge whether the spring has lost any compression. Examination of the piston or other visible component may also show whether creepage has happened.

The user must make sure that the:

● whistle and light (when fitted) are in position

● oral inflation tube is capped

● straps and main body of the jacket are not worn or damaged

● inflatable bladder of the lifejacket is correctly packed in accordance with the manufacturer's instructions, ensuring that any Velcro is correctly fastened and the manual inflation lanyard is easy to get to.

Where damage to a personal buoyancy device is discovered, unless it is to be discarded and replaced, it must be returned to the manufacturer or its appointed agent for repair. Local repairs should not be attempted.

Routine maintenance

The routine maintenance of lifejackets must be carried out in accordance with the manufacturer's instructions, in addition to pre-wear checks. As a general guide, where lifejackets are used daily, it is recommended that inspections are carried out at least monthly. However, where lifejackets are used in more harsh conditions (for example, off shore) the periods between inspections may need to be more frequent.

Inspection and testing must be carried out by those competent in recognising defects and the remedial action to be taken. Records must be kept of all inspections and repairs carried out.

Testing the air-tightness of the lifejacket will involve orally inflating the lifejacket and leaving it overnight (or submerging it in water) to check for leaks. The automatic inflation mechanism must be dismantled to make a detailed examination of its condition.

As part of the maintenance inspection, further checks are shown below.

● All screw threads must be examined for signs of rust. Rust can lead to problems in locating the cocking cap or keeping the gas cylinder in the correct position.

● The gas cylinder must be examined for corrosion, cracks, dents and other defects. Particular attention must be paid to the cylinder cap as any indentations found could mean that the automatic firing mechanism has fired but failed to pierce the cylinder. If this is the case, the reason for activation and the cause of failure needs to be identified.

● The cylinder fitting and groove of the firing pin must be checked to ensure that they are free from dirt.

● The automatic inflation mechanism must be operated manually (with the gas cylinder removed) to ensure that it operates smoothly, and that there is no obstruction to the movement of the pin that prevents it piercing the cylinder. The firing pin must be checked to ensure that it is sharp.

● The salt or paper ring must be inspected for any cracking, dissolving or tearing that has taken place since the last inspection.

● Where fitted, the rubber 'O' ring must be inspected for damage and that it is correctly seated.

● The mechanism must be checked for signs of creepage.

Once the inspection is complete, the lifejacket should be reassembled according to the manufacturer's instructions.

Servicing

The servicing of each lifejacket should be carried out by the manufacturer or their appointed agents, every two years. However, where lifejackets are used regularly and in harsh conditions, an annual or more frequent service may be needed.

Management

A clear policy on the use, inspection and storage of automatically inflating lifejackets must be in place. This policy also addresses the training needs of the lifejacket users.

Lifejackets, if used regularly, should be allocated to individual users. Each individual, having been adequately trained, can then be responsible for carrying out pre-wear checks and inspections, and report defects according to company procedures. This will help ensure that correct inflation of the lifejackets is not jeopardised by the carelessness of others.

Management must enforce its policy on lifejackets. This can be achieved by spot checks of both the condition of the lifejackets in use and the records of inspection and servicing.

Storage

Personal buoyancy equipment must be stored in dry conditions when not in use. Exposure to damp, humid conditions can lead to deterioration in the automatic inflation mechanism, known as creepage. This has the potential to lead to failure of the pin to pierce the carbon dioxide gas cylinder. The following advice should be observed when storing lifejackets.

Personal buoyancy equipment should be stored in dry conditions with sufficient space to allow air to circulate

- Do not hang lifejackets in contact with wet oilskins or other damp clothing; make sure there is enough space around them to allow the air to circulate.

- If a lifejacket is wet, unpack it and leave it to dry on a hanger.

- Do not store lifejackets close to or directly above heat sources (such as convection heaters).

- To prevent water getting into the automatic inflation mechanism, do not store wet lifejackets upside down or flat.

05

House building

HOUSE BUILDING

Overview

The nature of house building can give rise to additional challenges, such as working in and around live residential environments, tight site logistics, fast-track programmes, changing workforce, trades working in close proximity to each other in small spaces, security and theft.

This chapter highlights some of the main issues specific to house building. However, most issues encountered on site are common to the construction industry and are addressed in other sections of GE700.

6.1   Introduction

House building is a major sector of the overall UK construction industry. Whilst much of the guidance provided in GE700 can be applied to the work carried out on housing developments, there are some subtle differences to take into account in house building.

The Home Builders Federation (HBF) is the representative body of the home building industry in England and Wales. Members of HBF account for 80% of all new homes built in England and Wales in any one year. Members are from companies of all sizes, ranging from multi-national, household names, through regionally-based businesses to small local companies.

The HBF supports and facilitates collaboration between home builders, companies committed to working together and with subcontractors to recruit and train more people to the highest industry-agreed standards, to deliver the supply of good quality new homes that the country needs. Furthermore, the HBF Skills Partnership team supports the following:

A typical house building project

- Collaboration and sharing. To share best practice across attraction, recruitment and skills development.

- Training to a standard. To train the workforce to a qualified and recognised standard.

- Engaging and supporting. To lead by example and train recruits to industry standards developed for their roles and support sub-contractors to do the same.

- Championing diversity and inclusion. To recruit a more diverse workforce and assist in improving the skills gap.

- Promoting careers. To promote home building as a primary career choice.

 For further information on the Home Building Skills Partnership (HBSP) visit the HBF website.

6.2   Important points

In general the requirements placed on house builders to assess risks in line with the Management Regulations and to work in accordance with other applicable regulations (such as CDM, Work at Height, PUWER, LOLER, Manual Handling and PPE) are no different to those covered in other sections of GE700. In accordance with the Construction (Design and Management) Regulations 2015 (CDM) many house builders take on the combined role of more than one duty holder (for example, a house builder with technical, commercial and construction departments will often act as the client, principal designer and principal contractor).

Whilst establishing duty holder competency through training and experience is a priority, it is the requirements in **Part 4** of CDM (general requirements for all construction sites) that set house building apart from large-scale one-off projects that can be more easily managed and controlled. This is because large housing developments are, by design, made up of many individual domestic dwellings, which require a greater degree of co-ordination (for example, vehicle movement, pedestrian segregation and public protection).

 For further information on CDM refer to Chapter A03 Construction (Design and Management) Regulations.

6.2.1   Home Builders Health and Safety Committee (HBHSC)

The HBF is committed to ensuring that all aspects of health and safety are a priority not only on sites, but in offices as well. It provides full support to the HBHSC, and in 2019 fully supported the revitalisation of the committee's health and safety charter to drive further improvement in the performance of the sector. The charter is backed by an annual action plan looking at key areas of safety improvements.

 For further information on the Charter, visit the HBF website.

6.3 Planning

The planning of any development, including compound set up, show-house area, car parking, welfare, and so on, at the outset is an important factor in the management of health and safety. Often, however, the progressive sale of new homes can dictate and alter the speed and direction of build, and ongoing changes to plans require careful management.

Any house building site manager therefore must employ effective, ongoing monitoring systems to ensure that neither the workforce nor members of the public are put at risk by the sequence of build. The major items for ongoing review are shown below.

Site security (out of hours). Ensure boundary fences are maintained to prevent access by unauthorised persons. Children and teenagers are inquisitive and reasonable attempts must be made to prevent entry and to protect them from any hazards that are on site (such as securing inspection chamber covers and blocking off ladders or access towers).

House building materials, fixtures and fittings are desirable to thieves and the risk of theft is high, particularly as the build enters the final stages. Measures should reflect the increased risk, especially as fencing and storage areas reduce.

Site security (during work hours). Ensure that site entrances and exits clearly indicate that unauthorised access is not permitted. This may, in some circumstances, require the need for security personnel to be located at these points.

Traffic management (pedestrian). Safe pedestrian routes should be introduced for site operatives within the work area and for members of the public on adjacent footpaths. Consideration should be given to how the public used the area before development started, to ensure they do not ignore signage and continue as before.

Traffic management (vehicles). Vehicle routes should be properly planned, constructed, clearly indicated and maintained. One-way systems should, wherever possible, be established and the reversing of vehicles should be kept to a minimum.

Traffic management (deliveries). Material delivery areas should be established taking into account turning points, use of marshals, and so on. Consideration should be given to routes that pass through residential areas, especially housing developments, taking into account public and home owners' vehicles and peak periods of traffic movement (such as commuting and school runs).

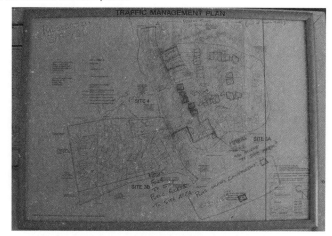

The traffic management plan should be displayed in the site office

The HSE has produced several before-and-after interactive case studies on vehicle safety in the workplace, which are based on events that inspectors have reported.

 A safety, health and environmental agreement is available for use by house builders intending to work together to ensure the safe development of the main infrastructure in respect of traffic and pedestrian management and public safety throughout the works.

 All the above points require ongoing evaluation to meet the changing site dynamics as new homes become occupied.

Phased construction work and completion of new homes within developments is generally carried out in the planning phase but progress can change dependent on sales and, therefore, site planning should be regularly reviewed as part of any house builder's site review process as plots are released for sale.

6.4 Common house building issues

6.4.1 Deliveries

The Building Products Delivery Working Group (BPDWG) has produced a leaflet *Delivering safely – Guidance for the delivery and receipt of building products,* and has acknowledged the support of the HSE in writing this. It represents good practice, which may go further than the minimum needed to comply with the law.

This guidance is designed to help delivery companies, drivers and site managers understand what is required to ensure the safe delivery of building products across the industry.

Delivering safely **can be downloaded from the British Precast website.**

 For detailed information refer to the Construction Plant-hire Association's *Work at height whilst loading and unloading transport* **(Best practice guide).**

This leaflet offers guidance on the safe delivery and receipt of building products

6.4.2 Roof trusses

The HSE have produced guidance, in the form of case studies, with reference to the unloading of roof trusses.

Refer to Appendix A for a case study example. For further information on lifting operations refer to C07 Lifting operations.

When planning any lift it is important to remember that this must be carried out by an appointed competent person, sometimes referred to as the lift planner.

Equipment selected to support roof truss installation must be suitable for carrying out the task safely. In most cases the safest choice will be a crane.

If a telehandler is being used for lifting and is travelling with roof trusses, it should be remembered that this is not the primary purpose of telehandlers.

The lifting of suspended loads with telehandlers and travelling with those loads is generally more hazardous than lifting unit loads on the forks of a telehandler.

All lifting operations should be properly planned by a competent person

Basic telehandler operator training does not include lifting or travelling with suspended loads

If these tasks are to be carried out the employer must ensure that the operator is suitably trained and assessed as competent. The majority of basic training courses deal only with fork-mounted unit loads. Only training providers who can demonstrate having appropriate expertise of suspended loads and lifting operations with telehanders or mobile cranes should be selected. Any training should also include an appropriate element of slinging and signalling.

Visit the Strategic Forum for Plant Safety website for guidance on safe use of telehandlers in construction and guidance on lifting suspended loads with telehandlers.

For further information on the safe use of vehicles on construction sites visit the HSE website.

In addition to this guidance the HBF Health and Safety Forum has produced accompanying guidance for the manoeuvring of roof trusses by telehandlers.

For further information and extracts refer to Appendix B.

6.5 Work at height

Almost every house building project will involve working at height. Statistics clearly illustrate that working at height is a major cause of accidents.

The Work at Height Regulations apply where a person could fall a distance liable to cause personal injury; this includes deliveries, roof work and working near excavations. The scope of the regulations includes all types of access equipment and work platforms, regardless of how long an employee is at height, or of the height at which the activity occurs.

Some examples in a house building environment that can be classified as working at height are shown below.

- Working on any type of scaffold.
- Accessing the back of a lorry or raised loading bays.
- Working close to an excavation or trench.
- Working off steps, hop-ups or mobile access towers.
- Mezzanine floors with no edge protection.

- Installing roof trusses or working above open joists.
- Open stairwells with no stairs or staircases with no handrails.
- Temporary wheelbarrow ramps onto the back of skips.
- Working off external scaffold, while there is no fall prevention or protection on the internal side of the wall or roof, and especially across window openings.

For further information on working at height refer to:

- **Chapter D01 Work at Height Regulations**
- **Chapter D05 Fall arrest and suspension equipment.**

👎 Examples of poor work at height practice

Poor use of soft-landing system

Missing midrails, toe-boards and loose boards

No stairwell edge protection or working access

Incorrect scaffold access, ramp and edge protection

06

👍 Examples of good work at height practice

Good standard of access scaffold

Birdcage scaffold system

Crash decking system

Soft-landing system

Stairwell access platform (viewed from ground floor)

Stairwell access platform (viewed from first floor)

6.6 Fire

Fire is an ever-present threat during construction and demolition projects. As house building progresses the nature of the fire risk is likely to change as different work starts and is completed. Therefore, not only must the risk of fire be managed continuously but the management process must allow for the changing nature of the risk. A site-specific fire risk assessment should be completed for all construction projects and continually reviewed as the work progresses.

 For further guidance refer to Chapter C02 Fire prevention and control.

6.6.1 Common sources of fire risk

- Storage and use of flammable materials, including liquefied petroleum gas (LPG).
- Hot work (soldering, welding and tasks that create sparks).
- Electrical systems and equipment, including temporary lighting (some sites have banned halogen lights due to the high risk of fire).
- Arson.
- Smoking (discarded cigarettes and matches).
- Operating plant and equipment.
- Poor housekeeping.
- Unacceptable fire performance of temporary protective coverings (not complying with the loss prevention standard (LPS 1207) and approval from the loss prevention certification board).

! **It is vital that the project fire strategy takes into account occupied homes, fire hydrant points and emergency fire and rescue vehicle access.**

6.6.2 Specialist advice

 The Fire Protection Association (FPA), in conjunction with the Construction Confederation (CC), publishes *Fire prevention on construction sites*.

This joint Code of Practice (CoP) deals with the protection from fire on construction sites and buildings undergoing renovation.

The CoP does not have any legal status; however, it does outline good practice and many insurance companies now require that the authoritative guidelines (such as those detailed in the CoP) are properly implemented on construction projects before they will offer full insurance cover.

The FPA also publishes *Construction site fire prevention checklist – a guide for insurers, surveyors and construction industry professionals*.

6.6.3 Timber frames

All timber-frame construction is deemed high risk and additional precautions must be taken.

 Guidance can be found in the HSE publication *Fire safety in construction* (HSG168), which can be downloaded free from its website.

 The Structural Timber Association (STA) publishes free guidance documents that can be downloaded from its website, including *16 steps to fire safety*, which promotes good fire safety practice on timber-frame construction sites.

The Structural Timber Association (STA), has produced a guidance document *Site safe*. *Site safe* policy is mandatory for building system supply members because it ensures that its members fulfil their CDM duties in relation to fire safety. It makes them aware of their legal obligations and provides support to their customers.

By following the *Site safe* policy members provide support for their insurance and engage with the customer to enable the opportunity for the best outcome for a project.

In line with CDM the *Site safe* policy is applicable for all projects, regardless of size and location. The scale and position of a project will influence the depth and scope of the outputs needed, but the processes are the same.

The *Site safe* strategy has many component parts. Together these form a comprehensive set of guidelines that are reliant on the collaborative working of the entire construction supply chain to reduce the risk of fire on timber-frame construction sites.

Site safe ensures STA manufacturing member companies that are working on large projects give clear, concise information and assistance to the principal contractor regarding fire safety on construction sites.

The guidelines should ensure that all contractors involved in timber-frame sites are fully briefed on identifying fire risks during the construction phase. While the responsibility for addressing the fire risk lies with the principal contractor, *Site safe* provides a framework through which any risk can be consistently communicated so that appropriate action can be taken.

The STA provides advice for a number of timber systems including the following.

- Glulam and cross-laminated timber (CLT).
- Structural insulated panels (SIPS).
- Timber frame.

- Roof systems.
- Floor systems.

Site safe follows the Royal Institute of British Architects (RIBA) plan of work stages, shown in the table below.

Stage	Plan of work
0	Strategic definition.
1	Preparation and brief.
2	Concept design.
3	Developed design.

Stage	Plan of work
4	Technical design.
5	Construction.
6	Handover and close out.
7	In use.

 The STA has produced a *Designers' guide to structural timber frame fire safety during construction* video.

6.7 Construction dust

Many house building works will give rise to dust. This is a high risk to people's health. Each year thousands of construction workers are diagnosed with respiratory diseases as a result of inhaling harmful dust and fumes.

In some situations, the amount of dust that workers inhale each day as they go from site to site can seem small or insignificant, and in some cases the effects of exposure may be immediate, but generally it can take years before the symptoms of ill health become apparent. Because of this, respiratory risks are often overlooked or underplayed.

Typical work that creates harmful levels of dust includes the following.

- Sweeping a dusty floor.
- Mechanically cutting, chasing or drilling, stone, concrete, bricks and blocks.
- Mixing sand and cement to make mortar.
- Sanding down MDF or timber.
- Rubbing down tape and jointing or plaster.

 All dusts are hazardous to health. The generation of dust, regardless of amount, must be minimised and controlled – all risk assessments should identify how exposure to dust or fumes will be controlled.

Cutting roof tiles can create a lot of silica dust, which is hazardous to health. The National Federation of Roofing Contractors (NFRC) has issued guidance that clearly identifies the controls, including separate cutting areas and suitable dust suppression.

 The National Federation of Roofing Contractors' (NFRC) guidance sheet *Controlling silica when disc cutting roof tiles* can be downloaded free from its website.

The Construction Dust Partnership provides information to industry to promote good practice and reduce dust-related diseases.

The cutting of other building materials that produce dust (such as using petrol cut-off saws on kerbs and paving slabs) must be carried out using methods to eliminate or minimise dust (such as water suppression, dust extraction systems or using a block splitter).

Operatives should be issued with appropriate respiratory protective equipment (RPE) with an FFP3 or P3 rating to protect against all construction dust (such as silica) that is created when mechanically cutting concrete, bricks, slabs, and so on – even when wet cutting (which only removes about 75% of airborne particles). FFP3/P3 offers maximum protection compared to FFP1/P1 or FFP2/P2.

 When using RPE ensure that each wearer has an up-to-date face-fit test.

 For further guidance on how to manage dust and fumes refer to Chapter B10 Dust and fumes (Respiratory hazards).

6.8   Environmental considerations

When planning and monitoring the works, environmental impacts must be assessed.

These are covered in Section E: *Environment*, together with practical guidance on how to identify and manage important risks.

Consideration should also be given to how work could impact the local community, especially the potential for creating nuisance.

6.8.1   Mud

Mud and dust can be difficult to manage, and be made worse by unexpectedly prolonged wet weather or dry spells.

Mud can be carried far along a road, with large lumps being a specific hazard to cyclists and motorcyclists. Wet mud will also make the road surface slippery, especially in wet, cold and dark weather.

Roads must be kept clear, using measures from a spade and broom to hiring a wheel wash or road sweeper.

Installing roads, footpaths and driveways early in a project can help to reduce mud and protect people from tripping over on uneven ground.

It also provides a better standard of housekeeping and safer storage.

Early installation of roads, footpaths and driveways on site reduces construction mud and dust on and off site

Road brush attachments are available, which can be fitted quickly to the forks of a telehandler. Having one on site means roads can be regularly cleaned as and when required.

6.8.2   Dust

Mud can quickly turn to dust, and in dry conditions dust can swirl and carry in the wind, covering neighbouring properties and vehicles. Environmental impacts include dust landing on plants, preventing photosynthesis, and in watercourses, creating silts that can harm fish and micro-organisms. Efforts must be made to dampen down and monitor site and road surfaces.

6.8.3   Local community

Proactively keeping local communities and residents informed of what is happening is far more productive than dealing with complaints, which can quickly escalate.

Taking the time and effort early on (such as attending parish meetings, knocking on doors and introducing the site manager, or regular letter drops) will pay off in the long-term.

Letters can contain information on items such as changes to delivery schedules or the increased number of vehicle movements, any weekend work and why the changes have become necessary, together with contact information.

Engaging with the community should be encouraged, wherever possible (such as carrying out safety talks or careers events at local schools or supporting local community projects).

Local school children get involved in designing their school play areas

Appendix A - Unloading roof trusses

 Reducing the likelihood of falls during the unloading of roof trusses

The challenge

During a manufacturer's delivery of roof trusses, it was identified that customers had problems when unloading trussed rafters from the lorry by crane.

Slingers were required to climb the trusses on the lorry to cut the securing ropes. They were then required to attach the sling or chains to the truss and connect them to the crane before sliding back down from the truss.

Finding a solution

Introduction of a colour coded banding system.

Blue bands are now used to secure the trusses into bundles.

White bands secure the trussed rafters to the vehicle frame.

This development reduced the risk of the wrong band being cut during the unloading process. The drivers, who have been issued with telescopic cutting poles, now have no need to climb onto the lorry.

The next development was the introduction of sacrificial slings attached at the factory. As these are easy for the slingers to get to from the ground, there is again no need to climb onto the vehicle.

Results

- The introduction of these measures has reduced the risk of falls from vehicles.
- In addition, as there is now no requirement for the use of fall-arrest systems, there have been savings in time and money.
- Customers are now able to unload vehicles more quickly and safely.

06

 Further information can be found on the vehicles at work and slips and trips sections of the HSE website.

Appendix B - Manoeuvring roof trusses

 The information below is based on *Manoeuvring roof trusses* guidance developed by members of the Home Builders Health and Safety Forum, which is available to download from the HBF website.

Transporting or manoeuvring trusses

The following options can be applied to the transport, manoeuvring and placement of trusses on site.

All roof trusses should be delivered on vehicles in such a manner that operatives do not need to access the rear of vehicles to remove straps or attach lifting strops.

Where practicable, trusses should be lifted directly from the delivery vehicle onto the roof (such as just-in-time delivery); this will require planning of both the site and delivery of trusses and should be the primary method of delivery and lifting.

Where just-in-time deliveries cannot be achieved (for example, if the plot is not ready) trusses should be lifted from the delivery vehicle via the telehandler onto truss racks designed on loading bays or gable end scaffolds. The delivery vehicle should be positioned as close as possible to the plot under construction and the distance to be travelled by the telehandler limited. The storage of trusses must not impede the safe operation of the telehandler or access to the loading bays.

If the above is not practicable and/or access to the construction area is restricted for the delivery vehicle, the trusses can be lifted from the vehicle onto an appropriately designed, freestanding storage rack. The rack should be positioned close to the plots under construction to limit the distance the trusses need to be moved when required. The truss rack should be continually re-sited as close to the work area, where possible, and be easy to get to by delivery vehicles.

Lifting of trusses onto the wall plate

In the majority of circumstances, lifting of roof trusses should be undertaken by a mobile crane where a full pack can be lifted directly onto the wall plate. A lifting plan completed by a competent appointed person will be required for the lift.

If an alternative method is utilised to lift roof trusses onto a roof, then this will need to be justified by the completion of a lifting plan for each plot, by an appropriately trained appointed person, which will take the following into consideration.

- Capabilities of the lifting appliance.
- Any restrictions to the lifting operation (such as scaffolding or other obstructions).
- Height of the structure.
- Handling the trusses by workers on the scaffold working platform.
- Method of lifting the trusses safely, including consideration of the pitch, size and weight of the truss.

Transporting of trusses via a telehandler

The following conditions apply if trusses are to be suspended via the forks of a telehandler and transported on a development.

- The route from the truss rack or delivery vehicle to the plot should be through unoccupied areas of the development where practicable. If this is not possible a traffic marshal(s) will be required to ensure occupants or others are not put at risk from the movement of the trusses.
- The route should be reviewed prior to transporting the trusses and an assessment made if any obstacles (such as lamp posts or scaffold) will affect the ability of the operator to manoeuvre the telehandler and load safely.
- The maximum load of trusses that can be transported via a telehandler from a truss rack or delivery vehicle to a plot is 600 kg. The weight of all trusses installed on site should be known by site management and detailed in the lifting plan. This is the maximum load, but this may need to be reduced depending on the span/pitch of the trusses, potential obstructions, gradients/cross slopes and capabilities of the machine.
- The tyre pressures should be within +/- 5% of the maximum stated by the manufacturers and be checked prior to moving the load.
- The telehandler should be driven at no more than 7 mph with no sharp turns or manoeuvres.
- The operator should have full vision from the driving position and the trusses suspended from the forks so that the lowest point of the truss (top chord overhang) is within 500 mm (+/- 150 mm) of the ground. A banksman should be available, where there are obstacles to full visibility, to provide appropriate signals to the operator and ensure no other persons are affected by the movement of the trusses.

Trusses should not be moved when wind speeds at ground level are forecast to be or exceed 7 m/s or 16 mph. This should be assessed by the use of an anemometer and/or weather reports for the area.

 All lifting operations must be properly planned by a competent person in accordance with the Lifting Operations and Lifting Equipment Regulations (LOLER).

Index

INDEX

INDEX

CONTENTS

Supporting information

Overview

Construction site health and safety – The comprehensive guide (GE700) covers all aspects of current health, safety and environment issues in the building and construction industry. It is designed to help managers, supervisors and small businesses understand how they should comply with, and put into practice, their legal, moral and social responsibilities.

GE700 is a leading publication within the construction industry and is based on current construction health, safety and environment legislation, guidance and good practice. It will assist in the crucial areas of:

● construction site set up and management
● management of occupational ill health
● accident prevention and investigation
● environmental good practice.

The content has been written with the site manager in mind, with a balance between outlining the requirements of relevant legislation and providing practical guidance on how to comply.

GE700 is divided into the standard structure that is used across all core CITB publications.

Section A: Legal and management   **Section D: High risk activities**

Section B: Health and welfare   **Section E: Environment**

Section C: General safety   **Section F: Specialist activities**

Each section is a separate book, which has been designed to provide simple navigation for the user. These sections are supported by **G: Checklists and forms**, available on the CITB website. The companion website contains interactive PDFs of all the checklists and forms that users will find useful on a daily basis.

The content of GE700, which is developed with construction industry experts, is constantly reviewed to take into account the latest changes in legislation and new or updated health, safety and environment industry guidance and good practice.

GE700 is supported by **companion content** that keeps users informed of legislation changes, content updates and links to further guidance *(refer to the 'Companion content' on the CITB website)*.

GE700 is also available to purchase as a download.

GE700 is the official supporting publication for the *Site management safety training scheme* (SMSTS), a five-day course for construction site managers, which covers the content of Sections A to D. Section A is the official supporting publication for the *Director's role for health and safety* (DRHS), a one-day course for company directors, and Section E is the official supporting publication for the *Site environmental awareness training scheme* (SEATS), a one-day course for supervisors.

The UK's departure from the European Union has no impact on the Health and Safety at Work etc. Act 1974. Equally, UK regulations that were implemented to align with EU Directives, both generally and in relation to the construction industry exclusively, still apply, as they have been transposed almost entirely into UK law. Nevertheless, changes to legislation do occur from time to time, and CITB strongly urges you to remain alert to possible future changes.

This publication contains public sector information published by the Health and Safety Executive and licensed under the Open Government Licence.

For the latest editions of the GE700 publications and for any further updates see the companion content on the CITB website.

Acknowledgements

CITB wishes to acknowledge the assistance offered by the following organisations in the preparation of this edition of GE700. Grateful thanks is also given to all those who kindly gave permission for the reproduction of their images.

● Glasgow Museum
● John Kees Photography
● Morgan Sindall
● Mount Anvil
● NASC

● The Scaffolding Association
● Sepsis Research FEAT
● Simian Risk Management Ltd
● Torsion Construction (Mark Owen, QESH Manager).

How to use GE700

There are different ways to find the information you require within the sections. You can use the:

- initial contents pages at the start of each section
- more detailed chapter contents list
- index at the end of each section
- quick reference guide within this supporting information guide.

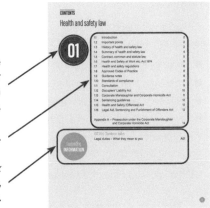

Chapter numbers have been included to help you find your way around the sections (for example, chapter one of Section A is 01 (pictured right), chapter three of Section E is 03, and so on). However, references to chapters within other sections are alpha-numeric (for example, A01, E03, and so on).

Each chapter contains a contents list at the beginning.

The chapter contents lists will discuss Section G: *Checklists and forms* or GT700 *Toolbox talks* supporting the chapter topic, which you may find a useful source of further reference, and can search for on the companion website.

Use of icons

A set of icons emphasises important points within the text and also directs readers to further information. The icons are explained below.

 Website/further info

 Example

 Question

 Ideas

 Notes

 Important

 Good practice

 Poor practice

 Caution

 Consultation

 Guidance

 Case study

 Quote

 Definition

 Interactive checklists and forms

 Video

 Additional content

GE700 companion content on the CITB website

The companion content (the 'Companion website') is a free resource that provides updates to the current GE700 publication, to keep it up-to-date. It also supports the reader in progressing from the GE700 book content to additional information available online.

The companion contains up-to-date information on:

- any amendments or updates to the current edition
- interactive PDF checklists and forms
- news (legislation changes, industry guidance and good practice)
- weblinks, phone numbers and addresses
- the current edition of each section (book).

 This icon indicates that further information (such as useful websites and links) can be found on the CITB website under GE700 companion content.

 The companion content is regularly updated to ensure that the information is current.

 Save the companion content website address to your favourites, so it is always available when you need it.

Steps to access a link

The content on the companion website is structured in the same way as the current edition of GE700. Accessing this or other weblinks in the book is achieved in the same way.

To access information from a link in a book use the following steps to navigate the structure. The example provided below is for the **legal (L) series guidance** referenced in **Chapter A03 – 3.2 Important points**.

Step 1	Open the companion content website	citb.co.uk/standards-and-delivering-training/health-and-safety-publications-and-support-materials/ge700-companion-content
Step 2	Open the weblinks section	**Weblinks**
Step 3	Open the relevant section for the content required	**A: Legal and management**
Step 4	Open the relevant chapter	**A03 Construction (Design and Management) Regulations**
Step 5	Select the relevant link	**3.2 The legal (L) series guidance**
Step 6	Access the third-party referenced site	HSE site opens

To access information from the download edition click on the GE700 **companion** link on the top left of each page, which will take you directly to the companion website.

Additional content

This additional content (AC) icon is used in our publications to direct you to complementary content such as videos, interactive scenarios and weblinks. To access this additional content use the following steps to navigate the structure. The example provided below is for the **needlestick injuries toolbox talk** referenced in **Chapter B01 - 1.9.4 Needlestick injuries**.

Step 1	Open the companion content website	citb.co.uk/standards-and-delivering-training/health-and-safety-publications-and-support-materials/ge700-companion-content
Step 2	Open the additional content section	**Additional content**
Step 3	Open the relevant section for the content required	**Supporting information**
Step 4	Select the relevant link	**Watch a needlestick injuries toolbox talk**
Step 5	Access the additional content	Video opens on YouTube

Where can I find additional content in this publication?

The table below identifies the pages in this publication where the AC icon appears, and the information that can be accessed via the companion website.

GE700 Section	Location	Content
I: Supporting information	Page 25	Buy related HS&E test products
B: Health and welfare	B01: page 10	Watch a needlestick injuries toolbox talk
	B01: page 13	Watch the BOHS *Breathe freely* film
	B04: page 43	Watch the ecstasy information film Watch the cocaine information film
	B04: page 44	Watch the heroin information film Watch the LSD information film
	B04: page 45	Watch the cannabis information film
	B06: page 87	Watch an eye protection toolbox talk
	B09: page 150	Watch Simon's story – living with an asbestos-related disease
	B11: page 188	Access the HSE noise exposure demonstration recordings
D: High risk activities	D02: page 25	Watch the fragile roofs film
	D04: page 55	Watch a working on scaffolds toolbox talk

INTRODUCTION

Interactive checklists and forms

 Interactive checklists and forms are available to download from the GE700 companion content part of the CITB website.

To access an interactive checklist or form use the following steps to navigate the structure.

The example provided is for the statutory nuisance checklist, referenced in **E06 Statutory nuisance**.

Step 1	Open the companion content website	**citb.co.uk/standards-and-delivering-training/health-and-safety-publications-and-support-materials/ge700-companion-content**
Step 2	Open the checklists and forms section	**Checklists and forms**
Step 3	Open the relevant section for the content required	**GE: Environment**
Step 4	Access the interactive PDF	**Download the GE06: Statutory nuisance checklist**

You can complete individual or multiple forms on your computer before saving or printing them to use, as required. The forms are compatible with both PC and Mac operating systems. You can also print off blank copies of the forms and fill them in manually, if required. We review these checklists and forms periodically to ensure that they are current and up to date.

The checklists and forms are user-friendly and quick to complete, making the recording of important information a simple process.

Further supporting information from CITB

CITB has a wide range of products, publications and courses that could help to improve your health, safety and environment knowledge.

After reading this publication or attending the CITB Site Safety Plus *Site management safety training scheme* (SMSTS) you may wish to consider the next step in expanding your health, safety and environment knowledge and competence.

 Details of course training providers can be found on the CITB website.

The Site Safety Plus scheme provides a number of courses that will enhance and develop your skills within the building, civil engineering and allied industries.

Courses give everyone, from operative to senior manager, the skills they need to progress.

 For further information on Site Safety Plus refer to their scheme rules.

Feedback

If you have any comments on the content within this product, or suggestions for improvement or extra topics, your feedback would be welcome. You can contact us by email or via the website.

 publications@citb.co.uk

Legislation

The following information shows some key legislation that relates to each section of GE700. This list is not exhaustive.

A: Legal and management

Construction (Design and Management) Regulations.

Corporate Manslaughter and Corporate Homicide Act.

Health and Safety at Work etc. Act 1974.

Health and Safety (Consultation with Employees) Regulations.

Health and Safety (Display Screen Equipment) Regulations.

Health and Safety (Enforcing Authority) Regulations.

Health and Safety (Fees) Regulations.

Health and Safety (Offences) Act.

Management of Health and Safety at Work Regulations.

Occupiers' Liability Act.

Reporting of Injuries, Diseases and Dangerous Occurrences Regulations.

Safety Representatives and Safety Committees Regulations.

Working Time Regulations.

B: Health and welfare

Classification, Labelling and Packaging of Substances and Mixtures (CLP) Regulations.

Control of Asbestos Regulations.

Control of Lead at Work Regulations.

Control of Noise at Work Regulations.

Control of Substances Hazardous to Health Regulations.

Control of Vibration at Work Regulations.

Food Safety and Hygiene (England) Regulations.

Health and Safety (First Aid) Regulations.

Manual Handling Operations Regulations.

Personal Protective Equipment at Work (Amendment) Regulations.

C: General safety

Electricity at Work Regulations.

Health and Safety (Safety Signs and Signals) Regulations.

Lifting Operations and Lifting Equipment Regulations.

Pressure Systems Safety Regulations.

Provision and Use of Work Equipment Regulations.

Regulatory Reform (Fire Safety) Order.

Supply of Machinery (Safety) Regulations.

D: High risk activities

Confined Spaces Regulations.

Dangerous Substances and Explosive Atmospheres Regulations.

Work at Height Regulations.

E: Environment

Building Regulations.

Climate Change Act.

Environment Act.

Environmental Permitting (England and Wales) Regulations.

Environmental Protection Act.

Hazardous Waste Regulations.

Landfill Regulations.

Special Waste Regulations.

Waste Batteries and Accumulators Regulations.

Waste Electrical and Electronic Equipment Regulations.

Waste Regulations.

Water Resources Act.

F: Specialist activities

Building Act.

Highways Act.

New Roads and Street Works Act.

Railways and Other Guided Transport Systems (Safety) Regulations.

Abbreviations and acronyms

The following list contains some of the abbreviations and acronyms that can be found in common use in the building and construction industry. The list should not be considered as exhaustive.

Abbreviation	Explanation
ACoP	Approved Code of Practice
BS	British Standards
BSI	British Standards Institution
CAA	Construction Awards Alliance
CAR	Control of Asbestos Regulations
CBH	Constructing Better Health
CDM	Construction (Design and Management) Regulations
CIOB	Chartered Institute of Building
CLAW	Control of Lead at Work Regulations
CMIOSH	Chartered Member of the Institution of Occupational Safety and Health
CONIAC	Construction Industry Advisory Committee
COSHH	Control of substances hazardous to health
CPCS	Construction Plant Competence Scheme
CSCS	Construction Skills Certification Scheme
Defra	Department for Environment, Food and Rural Affairs
DSEAR	Dangerous Substances and Explosive Atmospheres Regulations
EA	Environment Agency
EMAS	Employment Medical Advisory Service
FASET	Fall Arrest Safety Equipment Training
FMB	Federation of Master Builders
FPA	Fire Protection Association
FRS	Fire and Rescue Service
HASWA or HSWA	Health and Safety at Work etc. Act
HAVS	Hand-arm vibration syndrome
HFL	Highly flammable liquid(s)
HSE	Health and Safety Executive
IOSH	Institution of Occupational Safety and Health
ITB	Industry Training Board
ITO	Industry Training Organisation
JIB	Joint Industry Board
LA	Local Authority (ies)
LOLER	Lifting Operations and Lifting Equipment Regulations
LPG	Liquefied petroleum gas
LSC	Learning and Skills Council
MHSWR	Management of Health and Safety at Work Regulations
NEBOSH	National Examination Board in Occupational Safety and Health
NVQ	National Vocational Qualification

Abbreviation	Explanation
PPE	Personal protective equipment
PUWER	Provision and Use of Work Equipment Regulations
RIDDOR	Reporting of Injuries, Diseases and Dangerous Occurrences Regulations
RPE	Respiratory protective equipment
SSC	Sector Skills Council
SSP	Site Safety Plus
SVQ	Scottish Vocational Qualification
UKAS	United Kingdom Accreditation Service
WBV	Whole-body vibration
WEL	Workplace exposure limit
WWT	Working Well Together

A: Legal and management

B06 Personal protective equipment

B07 Control of substances hazardous to health

B08 Lead

B09 Asbestos

C: General safety

C01 Site organisation

C02 Fire prevention and control

C03 Electrical safety

C04 Temporary works

C05 Work equipment and hand-held tools

C06 Mobile work equipment

C07 Lifting operations

C08 Lifting equipment

C09 Frame erection

C10 Mobile workforce and driver safety

D: High risk activities

D01 Work at Height Regulations

D02 Working at height

D03 Common access equipment

D04 Scaffolding

D05 Fall arrest and suspension equipment

D06 Excavations

D07 Underground and overhead services

D08 Confined spaces

D09 Dangerous substances

E: Environment

F: Specialist activities

F01 Street works and road works

F02 Trackside safety

F03 Demolition

F04 Shopfitting and interior contracting

F05 Working over or near to water

F06 House building

Health, safety and environment publications

CITB is an established source of information and advice on health, safety and the environment within the construction industry. We produce a range of quality publications and resources that provide the construction industry with important and up-to-date information.

You'll find a format to suit you and your team, including printed books, CD-ROMs, apps and downloads.

Our essential publications are quick and easy-access sources of advice and guidance, providing you with the right tools to keep your site and workforce healthy and safe. We'll also help you to stay up-to-date with the latest legal obligations.

Our products are designed for:

● small, medium and large construction companies

● employees – from operatives to managers

● colleges and training providers.

We make sense of complicated legislation and advise you on how to manage your health, safety and environment responsibilities.

 For further information visit the CITB Shop for a list of our current publications and prices.

Work profitably

Well-trained staff working to safe practices are more productive. Let us help you to work profitably.

● We have competitively priced information for everyone, including managers, operatives, supervisors and trainees.

● We make sense of complex legislation – making it straightforward to understand and apply.

● Our training products are flexible to fit in with your business.

● Friendly and knowledgeable staff will help with your order.

How to order

Our competitively priced publications are easy to order.

 shop.citb.co.uk

 publications@citb.co.uk

CITB core publications

CITB offers a range of publications in various formats, a selection of which are shown below.

Construction site health and safety – The comprehensive guide

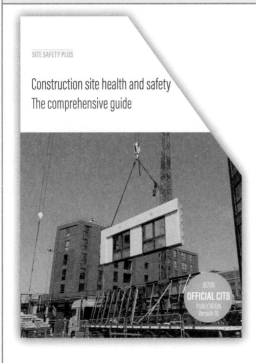
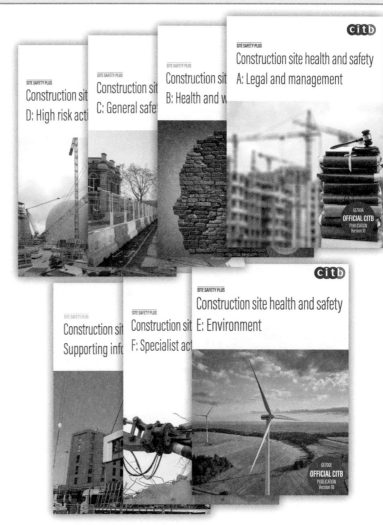

GE700 *Construction site health and safety – The comprehensive guide* is the only publication that brings together everything you need to know on current health, safety and environmental issues.

● Essential for managers who work on construction sites and *Site management safety training scheme* (SMSTS) candidates.

● GE700 contains all the guidance you need to stay safe and legal, with simplified legislation and a focus on providing practical guidance, photographs and real case studies.

● A supporting information section contains all the information you need to know on how to use GE700, including a contents and legislation reference guide and the special features contained within the publication.

● GE700 has a free-to-access complementary website (**citb.co.uk/standards-and-delivering-training/health-and-safety-publications-and-support-materials/ge700-companion-content**). This companion content provides updates, news, links to websites on related topics and interactive PDFs of checklists and forms, making GE700 a one-stop-shop for the latest information.

● Save yourself time, with all the information you need in one place.

The **eBook** edition offers the following additional features.

● User-friendly navigation with animated, page-turn design.

● Keyword search facility with highlighted results.

Order code: **GE700-V10**	Format: **Book/printed item**
Order code: **GE700-V10 eBook**	Format: **eBook**

Construction site supervision

GE706 *Construction site supervision* provides you with easy to understand information and practical guidance on supervising a site.

- Essential for site supervisors, front line managers and owners of small construction firms.

- GE706 is the official reference material for the CITB Site Safety Plus *Site supervision safety training scheme* (SSSTS), a two-day course for first line managers and supervisors.

- Each chapter starts with a summary of the employers' responsibilities, together with a corresponding list for supervisors, to help understand what they should be doing to protect their workforce.

- GE706 has a free-to-access complementary website (**citb.co.uk/standards-and-delivering-training/health-and-safety-publications-and-support-materials/ge706-companion-content**). This companion content provides updates and links to websites on related topics.

The **eBook** edition offers the following additional features.

- User-friendly navigation with animated, page-turn design.

- Keyword search facility with highlighted results.

Order code: **GE706-V20**	Format: **Book/printed item**
Order code: **GE706-V20 eBook**	Format: **eBook**

Toolbox talks

GT700 *Toolbox talks* is an important method of delivering advice on matters of health, safety and the environment, and engaging in discussions to obtain feedback, thus helping to maintain and improve standards. It has been designed to assist supervisors at all levels to prepare and deliver effective toolbox talks on building and construction sites.

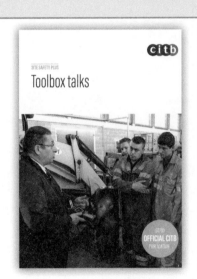

- Essential for supervisors and operatives.

- GT700 and GE706 are the official reference material for the CITB Site Safety Plus *Site supervision safety training scheme* (SSSTS), a two-day course for first line managers and supervisors.

- Full colour with photographs.

- Contains useful tips to help prepare a talk, a form to record all toolbox talks delivered, a feedback form and a briefing record sheet.

- Follows the GE706 structure, helping you to cross-reference and prepare for a toolbox talk.

The **eBook** edition offers the following additional features.

- Presentation for the trainer containing detailed prompt notes.

- Information for the trainer on how to make a good toolbox talk better.

- Films of three toolbox talks being delivered by real site personnel on a live site.

- User-friendly navigation with animated, page-turn design.

- Keyword search facility with highlighted results.

Order code: **GT700-V16**	Format: **Book/printed item**
Order code: **GT700-V16 eBook**	Format: **eBook**

Construction health and safety awareness

GE707 *Construction health and safety awareness* provides easy to understand health, safety and environmental information, and practical guidance for operatives.

- GE707 is the official supporting document for the CITB Site Safety Plus one-day *Health and safety awareness* (HSA) course.

- Each chapter starts with a list of key things that a site or employer should do, and a list of key things that operatives should do.

The **eBook** edition offers the following additional features.

- User-friendly navigation with animated, page-turn design.

- Keyword search facility with highlighted results.

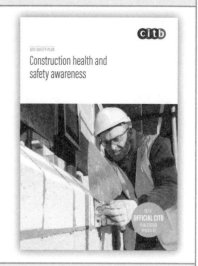

Order code: **GE707-V16**	Format: **Book/printed item**
Order code: **GE707-V16 eBook**	Format: **eBook**

Construction site management delegate workbook

This full colour delegate workbook contains information on the *Site management safety training scheme* (SMSTS) and scheme rules, aims and objectives, delegate exercises and self-study questions.

- Essential for delegates attending the SMSTS course.

- Can be used as an easy reference guide after the course.

- Designed so that delegates can take ownership of their workbook and use it to make notes.

- Includes exercises for general construction, house building, civil engineering, demolition, refurbishment and new road and street works.

- To be used in conjunction with the GE700 publication.

Order code: **XA6-V11**	Format: **Book/printed item**

Construction site health, safety and environment auditing system CD

This CD-ROM will provide you with the forms that you need to carry out compliant health and safety audits and evaluate your company's approach to health and safety step by step, identifying areas for improvement.

- It is essential for business owners, managers, supervisors and health and safety professionals.

This system helps you to:

- complete management systems audits and carry out site inspections

- carry out audits of health and safety procedures and the way they are put into practice

- customise the audit to your company's specific requirements

- identify areas for improvement

- complete action plans

- monitor improvements in health and safety standards

- demonstrate that you are fully committed to improving the health and safety of your workforce.

Order code: **SA03CD**	Format: **CD-ROM**

Safety critical communication – Toolbox talks

This pictorial *Toolbox talks* publication has been developed to assist with the communication of critical health and safety messages to operatives with limited understanding of English, keeping everyone safe on site. It complements the existing GT700 publication and GE700 Chapter A07 Communication with non-English speaking workers.

- Essential for training workers who have limited English.

- Laminated fold-out cards in two volumes covering hazard, risk and control measures.

- Can be used in inductions or via toolbox talks.

- Numbered for ease of use.

- Strong, long-lasting cards.

Order code: **GT701**   Format: **Book/printed item**

CITB Health, safety and environment test

The CITB *Health, safety and environment test* helps contribute towards a qualified workforce with the right skills, knowledge and training. For everyone working on UK construction sites the test helps to:

- raise health, safety and environmental standards

- support the prevention of incidents related to health, safety and the environment

- establish consistent standards.

Different tests have been developed to meet the demands of different trades and professions. The following tests are available.

- Operative test.

- Specialist test.

- Managers and professionals test.

 Visit the CITB website for more information about the tests and how to prepare for them.

Operatives and specialists	Managers and professionals

These revision books contain everything you need to know to prepare for and sit the *Health, safety and environment test*. Each book contains all of the content covered in the test.

Order code: **GT100**	Format: **Book/printed item**	Order code: **GT200**	Format: **Book/printed item**
Order code: **GT100 DL**	Format: **Download**	Order code: **GT200 DL**	Format: **Download**
Order code: **GT100 App**	Format: **App**	Order code: GT200 App	Format: **App**

Operatives and specialists digital editions	Managers and professionals digital editions

Practical revision apps provide you with the knowledge and information you need to prepare for and sit the *Health, safety and environment test* including:

- all of the content covered in the test.

- the *Setting out* film.

- options to revise for the full test or specific sections, and you can take the full test tutorial and practice tests, presenting a full test experience.

- Operatives and specialists apps and digital editions provide revision voice-overs in 14 different languages, including English and Welsh.

- Managers and professionals apps and digital editions provide revision voice-overs in English and Welsh only.

- the download versions provide revision voice-overs in English only.

Construction (Design and Management) Regulations supporting information

CDM guidance

Industry guidance documents, written by industry volunteers appointed by the Construction Industry Advisory Committee (CONIAC), have been produced with small businesses in mind.

This free industry guidance is available in the following six documents.

- Clients.
- Principal designers.
- Designers.
- Principal contractors.
- Contractors.
- Workers.

 These industry guidance notes are available on the CITB website.

CDM Wizard

A free app and desktop browser version of CDM Wizard has been produced by CITB, which will allow you to produce a construction phase plan. You can then print or save it to assist you in complying with the CDM Regulations.

 For further information on the CDM Wizard visit the CITB website.

CDM explainer video

 For further information watch the short CITB video, which explains the basics of CDM 2015.

CDM Wizard app